ANNUAL REPORT

OF THE

BOARD OF REGENTS

OF THE

SMITHSONIAN INSTITUTION,

SHOWING

THE OPERATIONS, EXPENDITURES, AND CONDITION
OF THE INSTITUTION

FOR THE

YEAR ENDING JUNE 30, 1887.

PART II.

WASHINGTON:
GOVERNMENT PRINTING OFFICE.
1889

FIFTIETH CONGRESS, FIRST SESSION.

Concurrent resolution adopted by the House of Representatives July 28, 1888, and by the Senate October 1, 1888.

Resolved by the House of Representatives (*the Senate concurring*), That there be printed of the Report of the Smithsonian Institution and of the National Museum for the years ending June 30, 1886 and 1887, in two octavo volumes for each year, 16,000 extra copies of each, of which 3,000 copies shall be for the use of the Senate, 6,000 copies for the use of the House of Representatives, and 7,000 copies for the use of the Smithsonian Institution.

II

REPORT

OF THE

UNITED STATES NATIONAL MUSEUM,

UNDER THE DIRECTION OF

THE SMITHSONIAN INSTITUTION.

1887.

REPORT OF THE UNITED STATES NATIONAL MUSEUM FOR THE YEAR ENDING JUNE 30, 1887.

SUBJECTS.

UNITED STATES NATIONAL MUSEUM,
UNDER DIRECTION OF THE SMITHSONIAN INSTITUTION,
Washington, August 1, 1887.

SIR: I have the honor to submit herewith a report upon the present condition of the U. S. National Museum, and upon the work accomplished in its various departments during the fiscal year ending June 30, 1887.

Very respectfully,

G. BROWN GOODE,
Assistant Secretary, in charge U. S. National Museum.

Professor S. P. LANGLEY,
Acting Secretary, Smithsonian Institution.

CONTENTS.

LIST OF ILLUSTRATIONS.*

REPORT ON SECTION OF TRANSPORTATION.

CRADLES OF THE AMERICAN ABORIGINES.

* The drawings from photographs and specimens in the Museum were made by
Messrs. W. H. Chandlee and W. H. Burger.

The reproductions of photographs in half-tone were made by the Reichenbach
process in the hands of the Photo-Engraving Company of New York City, by whom
the other photo-relief engravings were also made.

THE HUMAN BEAST OF BURDEN—continued.

* These nine plates are placed at the end of the article on Primitive Money.

THE EXTERMINATION OF THE AMERICAN BISON.

SECTION I.

REPORT UPON THE CONDITION AND PROGRESS OF THE U. S. NATIONAL MUSEUM DURING THE YEAR ENDING JUNE 30, 1887,

BY

G. BROWN GOODE,

Assistant Secretary of the Smithsonian Institution, in charge of U. S. National Museum.

REPORT UPON THE CONDITION AND PROGRESS OF THE U. S. NATIONAL MUSEUM DURING THE YEAR ENDING JUNE 30, 1887.

A.—GENERAL CONSIDERATIONS.

The report now presented relates to the period between June 30, 1886, and July 1, 1887. Before the completion of the report the Museum had suffered the loss of him who had been for ten years its official head, and who, from the very beginning of the Museum work of the Smithsonian Institution, had been its chief administrator and promoter. Although it is proper that any extended statement concerning Professor Baird and his relation to the Museum should be reserved for the report for the year in which his death occurred, it seems to be proper to refer in this place to the beginning of his protracted illness, in the fall of 1886, and to the year of sadness which followed, in which none of his assistants and associates could possibly feel the usual enthusiasm or interest in the work in which he had always been their leader as well as their director and counselor.

The work of the Museum was carried forward during the year in the customary way, and the amount of actual routine work accomplished has perhaps not been less than in previous years. There is, however, less of interest to chronicle in the way of new enterprises, and scarcely more will be attempted at this time than the customary statement of the progress of administrative routine.

One of the last official acts of the late Secretary was to request the Board of Regents, at its meeting on the 12th of January, 1887, to appoint two Assistant Secretaries of the Smithsonian Institution, who should relieve the Secretary of a portion of his official duties. By the appointment of Professor Langley to the position of Assistant Secretary in charge of Exchanges, Publications, and Library, and of myself as Assistant Secretary in charge of the National Museum, it was the definite purpose of the late Secretary to effect a return to the system of organization which existed at the time of his first connection with the Smithsonian Institution in 1850, when the senior Assistant Secretary was officially in charge of the Library, and the junior Assistant Secretary—himself—in charge of the Museum collections. It was Professor Baird's earnest desire that, so far as the Museum was concerned, the appointment of its executive officer to an assistant secretaryship

3

should lead to the strengthening of the bond of union between the Institution and the National Museum, a bond which, although nominally the same as it was twenty-eight years ago, had, as a matter of fact, become somewhat less definite and intimate.

The relations of the Museum to the Interior Department, as they now exist, are undefined and complicated, and it is important that early steps should be taken to secure that definite control over the Museum, on the part of the Regents of the Smithsonian Institution, which in later years it became more and more evident that it was the desire of Professor Baird to emphasize.

On the 10th of February, 1887, Professor Baird relinquished his active administrative control of the Institution and the Museum into the hands of the senior Assistant Secretary, who was at that time designated Acting Secretary, and from that time forward his failing strength prevented him from further efforts in its behalf. In the midst of his illness, however, he found time in July to arrange for a collecting expedition from Wood's Holl to Nantucket, for the purpose of obtaining a collection of sharks, and the letter which he wrote at that time shows that the Museum was in his mind to the last.

During the same summer he took advantage of a long-cherished plan for sending a Museum expedition to the islands in the Gulf of St. Lawrence to search for the remains of the long extinct Great Auk, by sending two collectors upon the Fish Commission schooner *Grampus*, which went to that region for the purpose of investigating the fisheries.[*]

B.—THE MUSEUM STAFF.

Few changes have been made during the year in the arrangement of the Museum staff. Prof. O. C. Marsh, of Yale College, whose high reputation as a paleontologist is familiar to all, and who has for many years been in charge of the vertebrate paleontological work of the U. S. Geological Survey, was early in the year appointed curator of the department of Vertebrate Fossils. Mr. S. R. Koehler, of Roxbury, a well-known authority upon the art of engraving, and custodian of the Gray Collection in the Boston Museum of Fine Arts, has undertaken to give a portion of his time to the arrangement of the collections of engravings, and has been appointed acting curator of the section of Graphic Arts.

Mr. A. Howard Clark has been requested to undertake the editorial work in connection with the Proceedings and Bulletin of the Museum, by this arrangement relieving Dr. Bean, who, since 1875, has performed this duty in addition to that of curator of Fishes.

The thirty-one departments and sections now recognized in the Museum are administrated by twenty-six curators and acting curators, of whom nine receive salaries from the Museum appropriation, while

---

[*] A report upon the results of this expedition will be published in the report for 1888.

four are "honorary" or unpaid officers, detailed from the U. S. Fish Commission, one from the U. S. Navy, five from the U. S. Geological Survey, one from the Bureau of Ethnology, and two are volunteers.

THE SCIENTIFIC STAFF.

The scientific departments are now arranged as follows:

DIVISION OF ANTHROPOLOGY.

I. Department of Arts and Industries, the Assistant Secretary acting as curator, with adjunct curatorships as follows:
Animal Products, R. Edward Earll, U. S. Fish Commission, acting curator.
Foods, Romyn Hitchcock, acting curator.
Fisheries, R. Edward Earll, acting curator.
Materia Medica, H. G. Beyer, M. D., U. S. Navy, honorary curator.
Textile Industries, Romyn Hitchcock, acting curator.
Historical Relics, A. Howard Clark, assistant curator.
Transportation, J. E. Watkins, honorary curator.
Graphic Arts, S. R. Koehler, acting curator.
Naval Architecture, J. W. Collins, U. S. Fish Commission, honorary curator.

II. Department of Ethnology, Otis T. Mason, curator.
Department of American Aboriginal Pottery, W. H. Holmes, Bureau of Ethnology, honorary curator.

III. Department of Archæology, Charles Rau, curator.

DIVISION OF ZOOLOGY.

IV. Department of Mammals, F. W. True, curator.
V. Department of Birds, Robert Ridgway, curator; Leonhard Stejneger, assistant curator.
Department of Birds Eggs, Charles E. Bendire, U. S. A., honorary curator.
VI. Department of Reptiles and Batrachians, H. C. Yarrow, M. D., U. S. A., honorary curator.
VII. Department of Fishes, Tarleton H. Bean, curator.
VIII. Department of Vertebrate Fossils, O. C. Marsh, honorary curator.
IX. Department of Mollusks, W. H. Dall, U. S. Geological Survey, honorary curator; R. E. C. Stearns, adjunct curator.
X. Department of Insects, C. V. Riley, entomologist of the Department of Agriculture, honorary curator; J. B. Smith, assistant curator.
XI. Department of Marine Invertebrates, Richard Rathbun, U. S. Fish Commission, honorary curator.
XII. Department of Comparative Anatomy, F. W. True, curator; F. A. Lucas, assistant curator.
XIII. Department of Invertebrate Fossils:
Paleozoic section, C. D. Walcott, U. S. Geological Survey, honorary curator.
Mesozoic section, C. A. White, U. S. Geological Survey, honorary curator.
Cenozoic section, W. H. Dall, U. S. Geological Survey, honorary curator.

DIVISION OF BOTANY.

XVI. Department of Fossil Plants, Lester F. Ward, U. S. Geological Survey, honorary curator; F. H. Knowlton, assistant curator.
XV. Department of Recent Plants, Lester F. Ward, U. S. Geological Survey, honorary curator; F. H. Knowlton, assistant curator.

DIVISION OF GEOLOGY.

XVI. Department of Mineralogy, F. W. Clarke, chief chemist U. S. Geological Survey, honorary curator; William S. Yeates, assistant curator.
XVII. Department of Lithology and Physical Geology, George P. Merrill, curator.
XVIII. Department of Metallurgy and Economic Geology, Fred. P. Dewey, curator.

C.—THE CONDITION OF THE COLLECTIONS.

The general condition of the collections is fairly satisfactory; for, although greatly hampered by lack of room, and impeded by the increasing amount of unproductive routine, such as the examination of material for correspondents and the preparations for participation in exhibitions in other cities, the curators have succeeded in bringing the material under their charge more fully under control than it had hitherto been and in preventing any deterioration in its condition.

CENSUS OF THE COLLECTIONS.

The recent extensions of the collections are indicated by the accompanying table. No enumeration was made in 1885, and the variation between the tables for 1884 and 1886 exhibits the increase during eighteen months, from December, 1884, to June, 1886.

Table showing yearly increase in the collections in the National Museum, 1882–1887.

Name of department.	1882.	1883.	1884.	[1]1885.	1885–'86.	1886–'87.
Arts and industries:						
Materia medica		4,000	4,442		4,850	5,516
Foods		[2]1,244	1,580		[3]822	[4]877
Textiles			2,000		3,064	3,144
Fisheries			5,000		[3]9,870	10,078
Animal products			1,000		2,792	2,822
Naval architecture			600			
Historical relics					1,002	
Coins, medals, paper money, etc					1,055	} 13,634
Musical instruments					400	417
Modern pottery, porcelain, and bronzes					2,278	2,238
Paints and dyes					[3]77	100
"The Catlin Gallery"					500	500
Physical apparatus					250	251
Oils and gums					[3]197	198
Chemical products					[3]659	661
Ethnology			200,000		[5]500,000	503,764
American aboriginal pottery			12,000		25,000	[5]26,022
Prehistoric anthropology	35,512	40,491	45,252		65,314	101,659
Mammals (skins and alcoholics)	4,660	[5]920	5,694		7,451	7,811
Birds	44,354	47,246	50,350		55,945	54,987
Birds' eggs			40,072		44,163	[6]48,173
Reptiles and batrachians			23,495		25,344	27,542
Fishes	50,000	65,000	68,000		75,000	100,000
Mollusks	[7]33,375		400,000		[8]460,000	425,000
Insects	1,000		[9]151,000		[5]500,000	[5]585,000
Marine invertebrates	[7]11,781	[7]14,825	[5]200,000		[5]350,000	[5]450,000
Comparative anatomy:						
Osteology	3,535	3,640	4,214	}	10,210	[5]11,022
Anatomy	70	103	3,000	}		
Palæozoic fossils		20,000	73,000		80,482	84,491
Mesozoic fossils			100,000		69,742	70,775
Cenozoic fossils	(Included with mollusks.)					

[1] No census of collection taken.
[2] Including paints, pigments, and oils.
[3] Duplicates not included.
[4] Foods only.
[5] Estimated.

[6] 2,235 are nests.
[7] Catalogue entries.
[8] Including Cenozoic fossils.
[9] Professor Riley's collection numbers 150,000 specimens.

Table showing yearly increase in the collections in the National Museum, etc.—Continued.

Name of department.	1882.	1883.	1884.	1885.	1885–'86.	1886–'87.
Fossil plants		4,624	[1]7,291		[2]7,429	8,462
Recent plants					30,000	[3]32,000
Minerals		14,550	16,610		18,401	18,601
Lithology and physical geology	[4]9,075	12,500	18,000		20,647	[3]21,500
Metallurgy and economic geology		30,000	40,000		48,000	[3]49,000
Living animals						
Total	193,362	263,143	1,472,600		2,420,944	2,666,335

[1] Fossil and recent.
[2] Exclusive of Professor Ward's collection.
[3] Estimated.
[4] In reserve series.

CATALOGUE ENTRIES.

The words "accession," "specimen," and "catalogue entry" are by no means synonymous. An *accession* may consist of several *classes* of objects, or may be a *single* specimen, or may include *several specimens of only one class*. A *specimen* is a single object. A *catalogue entry* represents one or more specimens of a class, and may include hundreds of individual objects. The number of catalogue entries during the year, as shown in the following table, is perhaps the best criterion of the importance of the accessions to the collections, since they represent the number of separate "lots" not only received but of sufficient value to be added to the collections. It frequently happens that material is received which is of no value and is therefore not entered on the catalogue.

Number and name of department.	Total number of entries.	Number and name of department.	Total number of entries.
I. Arts and industries:		IX. Mollusks	10,530
Materia medica	73	I. Insects	101
Textile industries	59	XI. Marine invertebrates	5,252
Foods	55	XII. Comparative anatomy:	
Animal products	425	Mammals	
Philosophical instruments	1	Birds	
Fisheries	324	Reptiles and batrachians	812
Chemical products	2	Fishes	
Musical instruments	17	XIII. Invertebrate fossils:	
Historical relics, coins, badges, etc	3,122	*a.* Paleozoic	1,036
II. Ethnology	2,308	*b.* Mesozoic	1,033
American aboriginal pottery	1,022	*c.* Cenozoic. *	
		XIV. Fossil plants	9
III. Archæology	3,863	XV. Recent plants	30
IV. Mammals	417	XVI. Minerals	875
V. *a.* Birds	2,393	XVII. Lithology and physical geology	442
b. Birds' eggs	355	XVIII. Metallurgy and economic geology	671
VI. Reptiles and batrachians	130		
VII. Fishes	1,225	Total	36,695
VIII. Vertebrate fossils	13		

* Included under "Mollusks,"

PROGRESS IN CLASSIFICATION AND ARRANGEMENT OF THE STUDY SERIES.

The final classification and arrangement of the material is a work of great moment, and the curator who makes progress in this direction is forwarding the legitimate objects of the Museum quite as much as if his whole time had been devoted to the acquirement of new material. Until a collection has been classified and arranged, it is of little or no use to visitors and students. Referring to the zoölogical collections, Professor Henry wrote in his report for 1856: "However valuable these collections may be in themselves, they are but the rough materials from which science is to be evolved, and so long as the specimens remain undescribed and their places undetermined in the system of organized beings, though they may serve to gratify an unenlightened curiosity, they are of no importance in the display of the laws of life."

The reports of the curators for the year give evidence of a steady forward movement in the work of classification and arrangement.

DEVELOPMENT OF THE EXHIBITION SERIES.

The general appearance of the exhibition halls has been somewhat improved during the year. The Grant relics have been placed in cases and have proved of much interest to the visitors. Considerable material has been gathered for the collection illustrating the graphic arts.

The east and west halls have been made attractive by the installation of the ethnological collection. The arrangement of Eskimo tools and implements is very satisfactory. The archæological collection is still exhibited in the upper floor of the Smithsonian building, and its arrangement is thorough and excellent. New cases have been constructed for the mammal collection, which is now being overhauled with a view to introducing a more satisfactory system of classification. The collection of birds still remains in the Smithsonian building, and although the hall, in which it is now, is entirely unfit for the purpose, no change for the better can be made until an additional building has been provided. There are now 7,000 specimens of birds on exhibition. The reptile collection is still stored away in the laboratory of the department on account of lack of room, a few casts of snakes and turtles, which are exhibited in the Smithsonian building, being the only representatives of this collection. The exhibition series of fishes, now numbering 34,000 specimens, is still unprovided with proper accommodations, and is installed temporarily in the Smithsonian building. The department of Mollusks has filled a few cases in the Smithsonian building with very interesting material, but nothing more can be done at present on account of lack of room. The same may be said in regard to the department of Insects, whose exhibit, when proper space can be provided, will probably become one of the most popular in the Museum. The osteological hall continues to present a very satisfactory appearance, which is enhanced by the effective method of labeling and installation which has been adopted. The curators of the several divisions of the department of Invertebrate Fossils are still unprovided with exhibition space. An immense quantity of material in each of these sections is ready for exhibition, and a special effort will be made during the autumn to provide in some measure for their exigencies. The collections of fossil and recent plants are provisionally arranged upon the south balcony, where they are at all times accessible to students. The curator of Minerals is giving much attention to building up the collection of meteorites. Several new cases have been constructed for the lithological hall, which will afford some relief to the unavoidably crowded condition of this collection. In this hall is being gathered together a valuable collection of relief maps and models showing the geological features of various parts of the United States.

D.—REVIEW OF THE YEAR'S WORK IN THE SCIENTIFIC DEPARTMENTS.

DIVISION OF ANTHROPOLOGY.

DEPARTMENT OF ARTS AND INDUSTRIES.

It has seemed desirable to continue the existence of the so-called department of Arts and Industries, as a convenient means of grouping together a number of special collections not elsewhere assigned, although the scope of this department is much less extensive than it was before the organization of the department of Ethnology, to which properly belongs a very large proportion of the objects formerly assigned to the department of Arts and Industries.

In this department, under the charge of a number of special curators, are included at present the various technological collections, which are for the most part made up of materials derived from the civilized races of mankind.

In the hall containing the Fisheries collection very little has been done since its formal opening to the public in April, 1884. Its arrangement had at that time been so thoroughly completed that this section was considered to be more nearly in a finished condition than any other in the Museum, and there was little left to be desired in the way of additional material. The collection is still under the charge of Mr. R. Edward Earll, one of the assistants in the Fish Commission, who has been so much occupied by his regular official duties that he has had little time to devote either to this or to the other collection of which he has voluntarily assumed the care, that of the Animal Products, which was thoroughly adjusted after its return from the New Orleans Exposition in the spring of 1885.

The section of Naval Architecture is also under the charge of an honorary curator attached to the Fish Commission, who has been constantly absent from the city, and there is little to report in the way of addition or change.

The section of Transportation, closely related to that of Naval Architecture, is under the charge of Mr. J. E. Watkins, of Philadelphia, who continues to act as honorary curator, and whose plans were described at length in his report presented last year. Owing to lack of space in the exhibition halls, no new steps have been taken in the development of the collection, although there are known to be numerous important objects which can be secured whenever arrangements shall have been made for their reception.

The absence in Japan of Mr. Romyn Hitchcock has necessitated a suspension of operations in the sections of Foods and Textile Industries.

The collections of Musical Instruments and Ceramics have received a number of important additions.

The Materia Medica collection is still under the charge of Dr. H. G. Beyer, U. S. Navy, who has been carrying forward with great industry the general plans adopted at the time of the establishment of this section in 1881, and who reports that up to the present time the arrangement and labeling of 1,970 specimens had been completed. Dr. Beyer has carried on a number of experiments in pharmaco-physiology and has published several papers. This work of investigation has been carried on chiefly at the laboratories of the Naval Museum of Hygiene in Washington, and of Johns Hopkins University. Incidentally Dr. Beyer had devoted a considerable amount of time to devising methods for preservation of the perishable animal and vegetable substances of which the bulk of the Materia Medica collection is composed, and reports that he has found bichloride of mercury to be the most satisfactory germicide. Seventy-three entries have been made in the catalogue during the year. The total number of specimens registered is 5,516, there being 3,488 in the exhibition series and 500 duplicates.

The collection of historical and personal relics, coins, medals, engraved portraits, and similar objects, is gradually increasing, though without direct effort, and Mr. A. Howard Clark, for some time attached to the Museum, has begun the work of cataloguing and arranging them. It would appear that no part of the work is more attractive to the visitor than that in which are displayed the personal relics of Washington, Franklin, Jefferson, and the other statesmen and soldiers identified with the early history of the nation, and its interest has been greatly increased during the year by the addition of the Grant collection of objects, including the swords and military and civil testimonials belonging to General U. S. Grant. These had been purchased by Mr. W. H. Vanderbilt, and by him given to Mrs. Grant in trust to hold during the lifetime of General Grant, and at his death, or sooner, at her option, to become the property of the United States Government. In accordance with Mrs. Grant's request, the transfer of this collection was made by

Mr. Vanderbilt in 1885, and a copy of his letter to the President of the United States transmitting the deed of trust is here given:

640 FIFTH AVENUE, *January* 20, 1885.

DEAR SIR: I purchased the articles of historical interest belonging to General Grant and gave them to Mrs. Grant in trust, to hold during the life-time of the general, and at his death, or sooner, at her option, they to become the property of the Government. They consist of his swords, memorials of his victories, from the United States and cities, and tributes to his fame and achievements from Governments all over the world. In their proper place at Washington they will always be secure, and will afford pleasure and instruction to succeeding generations. This trust has been accepted by Mrs. Grant, and the disposition of the articles is in conformity with the wishes of the general. I transmit to you herewith the deed of trust. Mrs. Grant informs me that she prefers to close the trust at once and send the memorials to Washington. May I ask, therefore, that you will designate some official representing the proper department to receive them, and direct him to notify Mrs. Grant of the arrangements necessary to perfect the transfer and deposit in such of the Government buildings as may be most suitable?

Yours, respectfully,

W. H. VANDERBILT.

His Excellency CHESTER A. ARTHUR,
President of the United States.

The matter was formally brought to the attention of Congress by the President of the United States in a message dated February 3, 1885, a copy of which follows:

To the House of Representatives:

I take especial pleasure in laying before Congress the generous offer made by Mrs. Grant to give to the Government, in perpetual trust, the swords and military and civil testimonials lately belonging to General Grant. A copy of the deed of trust, and of a letter addressed to me by Mr. W. H. Vanderbilt, which I transmit herewith, will explain the nature and motives of this offer.

Appreciation of General Grant's achievements and recognition of his just fame have in part taken the shape of numerous mementoes and gifts which, while dear to him, possess for the nation an exceptional interest. These relics, of great historical value, have passed into the hands of another, whose considerate action has restored the collection to Mrs. Grant as a life trust, on the condition that at the death of General Grant, or sooner, at Mrs. Grant's option, it should become the property of the Government. * * * In the exercise of the option thus given her Mrs. Grant elects that the trust shall forthwith determine, and asks that the Government designate a suitable place of deposit and a responsible custodian for the collection.

The nature of this gift and the value of the relics which the generosity of a private citizen, joined to the high sense of public regard which animates Mrs. Grant, has thus placed at the disposal of the Government, demand full and signal recognition on behalf of the nation at the hands of its representatives. I therefore ask Congress to take suitable action to accept the trust and to provide for its custody, at the same time recording the appreciative gratitude of the people of the United States to the donors. * * *

CHESTER A. ARTHUR.

EXECUTIVE MANSION, *February* 3, 1885.

In the mean time the collection was placed in charge of the War Department until definite action had been taken by Congress, and on August 5, 1886, the following resolution was adopted and became a law:

Whereas Julia Dent Grant and William H. Vanderbilt, by deed of trust executed on the tenth day of January, eighteen hundred and eighty-five, presented to the

United States certain swords, medals, paintings, bronzes, portraits, commissions, and addresses and objects of value and art presented by various Governments in the world to General Ulysses S. Grant as tokens of their high appreciation of his illustrious character as a soldier and a statesman : Therefore,

Resolved by the Senate and House of Representatives of the United States of America in Congress assembled, That the United States accept, with grateful acknowledgment, the said property and articles more fully described in the schedule attached to said deed of trust, to be held by the United States and preserved and protected in the city of Washington for the use and inspection of the people of the United States.

SEC. 2. That the said property and articles be placed under the custody of the Director of the National Museum, and he is hereby directed to receive the same for safe keeping therein.

Approved August 5, 1886.

The collection was transferred to the National Museum in November, 1886. A complete catalogue of the objects in this collection is given in the list of accessions, under No. 18528.

During the year has been commenced the formation of a collection of moneys of the world, exhibiting the metallic and paper currency in use at the present time, and the moneys of the ancient world. Several thousand specimens have been received by gift and loan, and a considerable number of them have been put on exhibition. In preparing the labels an attempt has been made to show the monetary standard of different nations and give the origin of each denomination.

The principal activity in this department has been in the promotion of the collection of Graphic Arts, for which provision was made in the general plan of classification proposed six years ago, and materials for which have since been accumulating so rapidly that it has become necessary to make some provision for their installation. In December, 1882, Mr. S. R. Koehler, of Boston, was invited to undertake the installation of an exhibition collection, illustrating the method of lithography, which had been presented to the National Museum by Mr. Louis Prang, and the preparation of a manual in connection with the same. At that time Mr. Peter Moran, of Philadelphia, was preparing for the Museum a series of plates illustrating the process of etching, and a set of etcher's tools. This was to form a basis for the etching collection. The Heliotype Company, the Photo-Engraving Company of New York, and several other firms and individuals, had tendered their co-operation. The Director of the United States Mint has offered to illustrate the art of die cutting, and Ringler & Co., of New York, have in hand the illustration of the process of electrotyping.

An excellent nucleus for a collection representing the graphic arts seemed to be available, but active steps towards its installation were materially retarded by the preparation of exhibits for the London Fisheries Exhibition in 1883, and for the New Orleans and other expositions in 1884. Matters did not take any definite shape until December 11, 1886, when Mr. Koehler was appointed acting curator of the section of Graphic Arts.

Offers of several collections additional to those already mentioned have recently been made. Hoen & Co., of Baltimore, are preparing an exhibit of the lithocaustic process. Mr. Charles Henry Hart, of Philadelphia, has given a number of specimens of work of the earlier American engravers. Messrs. Thomas Hovenden, Stephen Parrish, Peter Moran, James D. Smillie, Charles H. Miller, Alfred Kappes, Henry Farrer, and F. Juangling, of New York, have promised to contribute etchings and drawings. Mr. W. J. Linton, of New Haven, presents a collection of proofs, including both his own work and that of some English wood engravers. He has also promised a number of fac-similes of old work, collected by himself. The Century Company offers a technical collection—blocks, tools, etc.—drawings showing the various styles employed in designing for engravings, some of the process work done for them, and a series of proofs chronologically arranged. Harper & Brothers promise specimens of their work dating from the organization of their house, if possible. Mr. J. W. Osborne, of Washington, has a large and very interesting collection of early attempts in various processes, many of the specimens being undoubtedly unique, and this he wishes to present to the Museum if assured that it would be properly cared for. The Photogravure Company has offered to make a technical exhibit.

Arrangements have been made with the School of Drawing and Painting at the Museum of Fine Arts at Roxbury, Massachusetts, for a set of students' drawings illustrating various technical methods, and a selection of the best drawings will be made. The Art Students' League, in New York, will probably make a similar contribution. Among the latest accessions to this section is a machine said to have been invented and used by Joseph Saxton for engraving on copper plate.

DEPARTMENT OF ETHNOLOGY.

The additions to the ethnological collections have this year been of extraordinary value, and are described in the appended report of Professor Mason upon the work of his department. Nearly 2,500 entries have been made in the ethnological catalogue, and the work of classifying and arranging the great accumulations of the past has been actively continued. The results of the curator's labors in this direction will be more fully seen, as soon as certain proposed re-arrangements in the exhibition halls have made it possible to assign additional space and to construct more suitable exhibition cases. Special attention has been paid to the entire Eskimo collection, which is an exceedingly rich one, and probably unsurpassed even by the famous one of similar nature in the Ethnographic Museum at Copenhagen. In this work the curator has been assisted by Lieut. T. Dix Bolles, U. S. Navy, who, having been stationed for some years on the northwest coast, was familiar with the customs of the Eskimo race and especially well suited for this work. In this connection Lieutenant Bolles has prepared an exhaustive catalogue of the Eskimo collection in the National Museum, with indications of the localities in which the specimens were obtained. This geographical list is published in Section III of this report. It will be especially serviceable to collectors in the Arctic regions, who will be able at a glance to determine whether or not certain forms of implements are represented in the national collection.

Mr. L. M. Turner, formerly a Signal Service observer in Alaska and Labrador, has prepared for the use of this department an elaborate manuscript report relating to the Eskimo objects collected by himself and now in the Museum.

Paymaster E. B. Webster, U. S. Navy, also an experienced Alaskan traveler, was for six months detailed by the Navy Department for service in the National Museum, and rendered valuable assistance to the curator of ethnology.

Among the studies in progress in this department two have been brought to completion, and the results have been published in Section III of this report in the form of illustrated papers upon "The Human Beast of Burden" and "Cradles of the American Aborigines."

The methods of classification and arrangement now experimentally employed in the National Museum have given rise to much discussion, as it was but natural that they should, since they are so thoroughly unlike those employed in any of the other museums of the world. The conditions of growth and the character of the collections in the Museum have been from the start peculiar, and the adoption of novel means of administration was found to be necessary. In the first separate report upon Museum work, published in 1881, certain suggestions were made which became the subject of vigorous criticism on the part of some of the scientific journals. Passing reference has been made to this matter in previous reports, and it is probable that a full discussion of the subject may be undertaken hereafter. During the present year a very interesting debate has taken place in the columns of "Science" in regard to the proper method of arrangement of ethnological collections. The discussion was opened by Dr. Franz Boas, a German ethnologist, now a resident of New York, and was participated in by Professor Mason, Major J. W. Powell, and Mr. William H. Dall.

SECTION OF AMERICAN ABORIGINAL POTTERY.

Mr. W. H. Holmes, the curator of this department, has completed his studies of the wonderful pottery collection from Chiriqui, in Nicaragua. He reports that much valuable new material has been acquired, especially noteworthy having been that obtained through the agency of the Bureau of Ethnology, in the collections purchased from Dr. Edward Palmer and Mr. W. E. Curtis.

Col. James Stevenson, of the Geological Survey, has transferred to this department a series of Pueblo pottery, ancient and modern, collected by himself in 1881, and Dr. Cyrus Thomas, of the Bureau of

Ethnology, made some collections of pottery in the Mississippi Valley and the eastern states. A number of interesting pieces of Mexican and Peruvian work has been acquired by exchange.

The catalogue records show that 1,022 entries have been made during the year.

DEPARTMENT OF ARCHÆOLOGY.

The report of the curator, Dr. Charles Rau, consists chiefly of a geographical review of the principal accessions. Among these may be mentioned as especially valuable the collection of Mr. Thomas Wilson, made in Europe, embracing drift and cave relics of the paleolithic age, objects belonging to the neolithic age and the bronze period, and specimens of Etruscan and Roman origin.

The curator is writing a work upon North American antiquities, to be entitled, "The Typical Forms of North American Prehistoric Relics of Stone and Copper in the U. S. National Museum."

There have been 3,863 entries made in the catalogue during the year. The total number of specimens is 101,659, of which a large proportion has been received through Major J. W. Powell, director of the Bureau of Ethnology of the Smithsonian Institution.

The failing health of the curator has made it necessary for him to be absent during a portion of the year, and but little has been accomplished beyond the necessary routine work of the Department.

During the year the Museum was so fortunate as to secure a valuable accession from Easter Island, comprising two of the celebrated stone images, a large number of painted and carved slabs from the rock houses, and a choice collection of objects illustrating the ancient and modern history of the island. The last-named specimens have been lent to the Museum by Paymaster William J. Thomson, U. S. Navy.

Professor Baird made frequent attempts to secure specimens of the archæology of this island, and in 1885 received from Commodore John G. Walker, Chief of the Bureau of Navigation, the gratifying intelligence that the U. S. S. *Mohican* would be sent to Easter Island to relieve some American sailors who had been reported as castaways there. This expedition met with signal success. The *Mohican* anchored in Cook Bay in December, and spent twelve days there. A thorough survey of the island was made, and everything was secured which would enable the explorers to make a thorough report.

The specimens were brought to Panama by the *Mohican*. The Panama Railroad Company kindly forwarded the collections across the Isthmus to Aspinwall, and they were brought to Washington in the U. S. S. *Galena*.

Easter Island is a small volcanic projection, 12 miles long and 4 miles wide, isolated from all other habitable parts of the globe, the nearest land being about 2,000 miles away.

The Easter Island images are the most interesting of the archæological enigmas. There are over 600 of them on this island. Formerly they stood in groups of six to twelve on platforms of hewed stone facing the sea; but in later years they have been thrown down during the civil strife among the natives. Most of them are to be found on hill-sides at the eastern end of the island. They were hewn out of volcanic tufa in the center of an extinct volcano, and transported over its sides, sometimes 3 or 4 miles, to their destination. The island is almost treeless, and the wonder is how savages could remove objects fragile as these, weighing from 3 to 30 tons each, over a country so rugged. The images exhibited in the National Museum, together with many other objects of ethnological interest, were procured during a twelve-days' visit.

There are now about 400 people living on the island, and they are of pure Polynesian stock. They know nothing whatever of the erection of these images, and it is quite possible that they are the descendants of a later migration. The following brief description of the objects in this collection may be found interesting:

No. 1. Stone image, weighing about 3 tons and about 8 feet in height by 4 in width, showing head, shoulders, and bust, but only outline of arms, the latter not distinct from the body, but a slightly raised surface carved straight down the side, with the forearms placed across the stomach at right angles, fingers touching and slightly interlaced. Below this point the general shape of the monolith is square.

No. 2. Block of red tufa, or calcareous rock, porous and brittle, slightly oval shaped, square on top, with slightly convex base. Supposed to be a crown for image.

No. 3. Image (head and shoulders) composed of or cut from substance resembling sandstone, measuring about 26 inches across shoulders and about 40 in height. Mouth small, lips very thin, nose and ears well defined and abnormally large. Eyes are simply deep recesses.

Nos. 4 and 5. Stone slabs, with hieroglyphics in reddish-brown and white color traced upon them. Average thickness about 3 inches. Length and width about 4 feet by 2.

Nos. 6, 7, and 8. Stone slabs, similar to, but smaller than, the above, and hieroglyphics more indistinct.

No. 9. Stone slab slightly larger and heavier than Nos. 4 or 5, with diagonal and horizontal lines.

No. 10. Small, irregular-shaped porous stone, with an indistinct hieroglyphic cut into it. Weighs about 25 pounds.

No. 11. Stone about three times as large as No. 10, having numerous hieroglyphics cut into it. Weight about 60 pounds.

No. 12. Small stone of about the same size and weight as No. 10, on which is a rude carving representing a human head and features.

Nos. 13, 14, 15, and 16. Small slabs, seemingly of iron ore, very brittle. No tracings, carvings, or hieroglyphics anywhere visible.

DIVISION OF ZOOLOGY.

DEPARTMENT OF MAMMALS.

The most important work has been the commencement of a re-arrangement of the exhibition hall. The cases previously in use were found unsuitable, and others of a new model have been substituted. An exceedingly fine series of buffalo skins and skeletons from Montana has been added to the collection, as the result of the expedition sent out under the leadership of Mr. Hornaday.

Among the most valuable accessions may be mentioned the gifts of Dr. J. C. Merrill, U. S. Army; Mr. John Gundlach, Mr. C. B. Cory, and Mr. Anastasio Alfaro. The Zoological Society of Philadelphia and the Central Park Menagerie of New York have presented several animals in captivity. From the old world accessions have been received from Mr. E. Hargitt, and from the Fish Acclimatization Society of Ballarat. Among aquatic mammals obtained, may be mentioned a skeleton of an adult male West India monk seal, *Monachus tropicalis*, purchased from Mr. H. A. Ward. Capt. M. A. Healy, of the U. S. Revenue Marine, presented three skins of the ribbon seal, *Phoca fasciata*. The U. S. Fish Commission secured some harbor seals off Wood's Holl, Massachusetts. Specimens of porpoise were presented by Lieut. Commander H. E. Nichols, U. S. Navy, and skeletons of the common dolphin, pygmy sperm whale, and short-finned blackfish were received from Mr. Bayley T. Barco, keeper of the U. S. Life-Saving Station at Dam Neck Mills, North Carolina. In this connection reference should be made to the continuance by the Superintendent and officials of the U. S. Life-Saving Service of their courteous co-operation in notifying the Museum of the stranding of cetaceans and in attending to the shipment of specimens to Washington.

Specimens representing 27 species have been added to the exhibition series during the year. There are now 752 specimens in the exhibition series and 4,088 in the study series. The alcoholic series numbers 2,971.

The curator, Mr. F. W. True, has been occupied most of the time available for study in completing his "Review of the Species of the Family *Delphinidæ*." He has also made a special study of the color variations of the puma, *Felis concolor*.

DEPARTMENT OF BIRDS.

The accessions received by this department during the year have been numerous and important, and the curator, Mr. Robert Ridgway, has made in his report special mention of 59 as being of peculiar interest. The amount of literary work accomplished is exemplified by the fact that 92 papers, based upon the collection, have been published during the year. Of this number, 59 were written by the curator and assistant curator, Dr. Leonhard Stejneger.

Mr. Ridgway has completed his series of analytical keys to North American birds, which is being issued by a Philadelphia publisher under the title "A Manual of North American Birds." The assistant curator has continued his researches in Japanese ornithology, and reports upon several families have been already completed. These studies are of great importance, and are based on what is believed to be the richest collection of Japanese birds extant. The assistant curator has also worked up an interesting collection of birds from the island of Kanai, one of the Hawaiian group. That portion of the collection for which suitable provision has been made, is reported to be in excellent condition, and it is expected that during the next year it will be practicable to improve the condition of the exhibition series, which is suffering for want of insect-proof cases. The total number of specimens in this department is estimated to be 54,987, of which 40,875 belong to the reserve series, 7,000 are on exhibition, and 7,112 have been assigned to the duplicate series.

SECTION OF BIRDS' EGGS.

The collection of birds' eggs and nests was first properly arranged in 1884 by Capt. Charles E. Bendire, U. S. Army, who has since that year been acting as honorary curator. At that time the total number of eggs entered on the catalogue was 40,072, of which 8,000 beautifully prepared specimens have been contributed by Captain Bendire. There are now in the collection 45,938 specimens of eggs and 2,235 nests. An exhibition of birds' eggs would be of popular interest. Among the most generous contributors to the collection during the past year were Lieut. H. C. Benson, U. S. Army; Lieut. G. M. Stoney, U. S. Navy; Dr. A. K. Fisher, Department of Agriculture; Col. N. S. Goss; Capt. B. F. Goss; Mr. H. W. Henshaw; Mr. William Brewster; Mr. Loren W. Green, and Mr. J. Parker Norris.

The accessions for the year number 1,208 specimens, which have been classified and arranged. Measurements and records of 7,125 specimens have been made, and 235 nests have been mounted, labeled, and arranged for exhibition. A portion of the reserve series of eggs, which now includes 32,899 specimens, has also been relabeled and classified according to the nomenclature of the check-list recently published by the American Ornithologists' Union.

DEPARTMENT OF REPTILES AND BATRACHIANS.

Active work in this department, under the honorary curatorship of Dr. H. C. Yarrow, U. S. Army, has been confined chiefly to the preservation of new material and general routine work. The laboratory rooms have been closed during the fire-proofing of the west end of the Smithsonian building.

Some interesting accessions have been received during the year, notably of Corean serpents presented by Dr. N. McP. Ferebee, U. S. Navy; Mr. C. J. Herring; and Mr. D. Ridgway, of Wheatland, Indiana; and to this gentleman the Museum is indebted for previous co-operation,

Lieut. Commander H. E. Nichols, U. S. Navy; Ensign W. E. Safford, U. S. Navy, and Charles H. Townsend sent large collections. Hon. V. O. King, U. S. consul-general at Bogota, United States of Colombia, sent a large and valuable general collection, including some interesting species of snakes.

The curator has published a paper on the "Recurrence of Symptoms of Poisoning after Snake-bites." He has also prepared a paper entitled "Poisonous Reptiles of the United States." Prof. E. D. Cope, for several years a collaborator of the Smithsonian Institution, prepared a "Catalogue of the Reptiles and Batrachians of Central America and Mexico." This is now in the hands of the printer and will be published as Bulletin 32 of the U. S. National Museum.

Professor Cope has also prepared a monograph of the Batrachians of North America, the manuscript of which has been sent to the printer, and which will be published as Bulletin 34, U. S. National Museum.

The collection of reptiles is in good condition. and now includes 27,542 specimens.

DEPARTMENT OF FISHES.

The annual rate of increase of specimens in the collection of fishes continues to be exceedingly large. In 1882, Dr. T. H. Bean, the curator, reported that the collection contained not less than 50,000 specimens, and in the present year the total number is estimated at 100,000. The recent increase is largely due to the U. S. Fish Commission, which has contributed twelve of the most important accessions received during the year, while many other interesting contributions have been made by agents of the Fish Commission in various parts of the country. The officers of the Navy Department have, as usual, co-operated zealously with the interests of this department, and five very interesting collections have been received in this way. The curator has, during the year, been relieved of his duties as editor of the "Proceedings" and "Bulletins," a duty which he undertook many years ago.

The literary work of this department has been extensive, and in the bibliography there are noticed no less than thirty-six papers which have been published during the year, based upon the collection.

The curator is engaged in several investigations, one of the most important of which has for its object the publication of a synopsis of the Salmon family of North America, their study and identification.

There are now 34,000 specimens of fishes in the exhibition series, 41,000 in the reserve series, and 25,000 duplicates.

Dr. Bean, at the request of Professor Baird, accompanied the U. S. Fish Commission schooner *Grampus* in its cruise along the middle and southern Atlantic coast with a view to investigating the spring mackerel fishery, in the months of April and May. A report of this expedition will be published by the U. S. Fish Commission.

DEPARTMENT OF MOLLUSKS (INCLUDING CENOZOIC INVERTEBRATE FOSSILS).

From the report of Dr. W. H. Dall, curator of this department, it will be seen that seventy-five accessions were received during the year, including some 32,000 specimens. Some are of great extent and value, those perhaps most worthy of mention being the series of deep-sea mollusks dredged by the U. S. S. *Blake* and presented by Prof. Alexander Agassiz, the types of a report on the mollusks of the *Blake* expedition by Mr. Dall, and a valuable series of mollusks dredged in the Gulf of Mexico and the Bahamas, presented by Dr. W. H. Rush, U. S. Navy. The curator has made a special study of the mollusks of the *Blake* collection. The investigation of the mollusks from later Tertiary beds of South Florida is still in progress. Mr. Dall has also made studies upon a collection of mollusks obtained by the Jeannette Expedition at Bennett Island, has carried on his work upon the general Floridian and Gulf fauna, and on the geology of South Florida, besides working up several collections made by L. M. Turner in Labrador, by Nicholas Grebnitzki in Bering Sea, and by himself in several parts of northern Alaska.

Dr. R. E. C. Stearns, the adjunct curator, has been engaged, in addition to his regular work, in the study of the fossil *Tryonias*, of *Teredo*, and of the *Phoridæ*.

Very notable advances have been made in the arrangement and cataloguing of the mollusca, as is shown by the fact that 10,530 catalogue entries have been made, which represent the final classification of about 32,000 specimens.

DEPARTMENT OF INSECTS.

Progress has been made in the arrangement of the collections of insects. The curator, Prof. C. V. Riley, states in his report that the arrangement of the Lepidoptera from the *Rhopalocera* to the end of the *Arctiidæ* has been completed; the material embracing the order of *Diptera* has been separated into families. The collection of *Arachnidæ* has been re-arranged. The work of labeling and separating the duplicate material in the suborder *Heteroptera* has been completed.

Many important accessions have been received from the correspondents and agents of the entomological division of the Department of Agriculture, and conspicuous among them is the valuable collection made by Mr. Albert Koebele, in California, including several thousand specimens. Mr. E. A. Schwarz presented about 300 specimens of Coleoptera. In all, 102 accessions have been received during the year, representing, exclusive of the collection of the assistant curator, Mr. J. B. Smith (which has become the property of the Museum), at least 10,000 specimens. The exhibition series now includes 7,878 specimens (2,637 species), besides a large number of drawings. There have been made 101 entries in the catalogue of the department during the year.

Work has been continued by the curator and his assistant in the study of the *Noctuidæ*,* and the latter has investigated the Museum material in the lepidopterous family *Saturniidæ*, and also the genus *Callimorpha*.†

DEPARTMENT OF MARINE INVERTEBRATES.

Mr. Richard Rathbun, the curator of this department, reports that advances have been made in the permanent arrangement of the general reserve collection during the year, and that much material has been prepared for the display series. He has also during the year begun the preparation of a card catalogue of the identified material. This affords an excellent means of reference, and renders it possible to determine at a glance the presence or absence of a given species in the collection. During the summer of 1886 the curator completed, for the Fish Commission, a report upon the surface water temperatures of the Atlantic coast of the United States. The deep-water and littoral *Madreporaria* and *Hydracorallæ*, obtained by the U. S. Fish Commission steamer *Albatross* during 1884, 1885, and 1886, have been examined and identified. The determination of nearly all of the corals of the genera *Madrepora*, *Porites*, and *Synareœa* has been completed, and reports based thereupon have been prepared for publication in the Proceedings of the Museum. Mr. Rathbun is now engaged upon a revision of the star-fishes belonging to *Asterias* and the allied genera; and a description of the species *Heliaster*, with photographic plates of all the known forms, has been completed.

The accessions of the year number fifty-five, the largest and most important consisting of the material brought in by the Fish Commission steamer *Albatross* during the summer and fall of 1886, and the collection of 484 specimens of sponges and 266 specimens of corals, made by Dr. G. Brown Goode in Bermuda, in 1877, for the Wesleyan University at Middletown, Connecticut, and now sent to the National Museum in exchange.

There have been made 5,252 entries in the catalogue of this department, of which 996 represent Crustacea, 2,611 Worms, 130 Bryozoa and Ascidians, 1,412 Echinoderms and Cœlenterates, and 103 Sponges and Protozoans.

Thirty-one sets of duplicate series of marine invertebrates from the collections of the U. S. Fish Commission were sent to colleges and schools in various parts of the United States, and special sets were prepared for the Museum of Comparative Zoology at Harvard College and for the American Museum of Natural History in New York.

DEPARTMENT OF COMPARATIVE ANATOMY.

The collections in this department are under the care of Mr. F. W. True, assisted by Mr. F. A. Lucas, and are increasing very rapidly. The catalogue shows 468 entries of birds, 330 of mammals, 10 of reptiles

---

* See Proc. U. S. Nat. Museum, vol. 10, pp. 450–479.
† See Proc. U. S. Nat. Museum, vol. 10, pp. 338–352.

and batrachians, and 4 of fishes. The mammalian series is at present much the largest, and that of alcoholic birds, important for anatomical purposes, contains many forms.

Reference to the statement of work accomplished by the osteological preparator* will show the number of specimens which have been prepared or mounted. The Zoological Society of Philadelphia and the Central Park Menagerie in New York have generously continued to send specimens of animals which have died in captivity.

Among the principal accessions may be mentioned a gorilla, *Gorilla savagei*, obtained from the Museum d'Histoire Naturelle in Paris, a fine example of Caribbean seal, *Monachus tropicalis*, and a small whale, *Kogia breviceps*,† which was secured through the co-operation of Capt. B. T. Barco, of the life-saving station at Dam Neck Mills, in Virginia. Numerous skeletons and skulls of the American buffalo, *Bison americanus*, and of other mammals and of birds, were added to the collection as a result of the successful expedition sent out by the Institution to Montana under the charge of Mr. William T. Hornaday.

The exhibition series now includes nearly 500 specimens.

DEPARTMENT OF INVERTEBRATE FOSSILS (PALEOZOIC).

The work of this department, under the curatorship of Mr. C. D. Walcott, of the U. S. Geological Survey, has made marked progress. Thirty-six accessions, aggregating 4,009 specimens, have been received and, for the most part, identified. Many of these accessions consisted of materials gathered by officers of the U. S. Geological Survey during the summer of 1886, and duly transferred to the custody of the Museum by Major Powell, the Director of the Survey. Dr. R. R. Gurley has been designated to act as assistant, and the curator reports rapid progress in the classification and arrangement of the material. He further states that a very good representative collection for exhibition will be ready as soon as exhibition cases can be supplied. Mr. Walcott has continued his studies upon the Cambrian faunas of North America, and during the year has published in the American Journal of Science a memoir relating to the classification of this system.

DEPARTMENT OF INVERTEBRATE FOSSILS (MESOZOIC).

Dr. C. A. White, of the U. S. Geological Survey, continues his work upon the collection of mesozoic fossils. He states that during the year he has been enabled to complete the card catalogue of all the Museum materials in his custody. The entire collection is now ready for exhibition, and it is unfortunate that no space is at present available for this important and carefully identified material. The accessions during the year numbered twelve, and 1,033 entries were made in the catalogue.

---

* See page 40.
† See report of Department of Mammals.

DIVISION OF BOTANY.

FOSSIL AND RECENT PLANTS.

The collections of fossil and recent plants continue under the care of Mr. Lester F. Ward, of the U. S. Geological Survey, assisted by Mr. F. H. Knowlton. Much of the material in the collection of fossil plants is in the hands of Prof. Leo Lesquereux, of Columbus, Ohio, for determination, but nothing has recently been published by him. Mr. Knowlton has been carrying on an investigation of the microscopical structure of the wood and lignite of the Potomac formation. The results of his work are to be published in one of the bulletins of the U. S. Geological Survey.

The collection of fossil plants now contains 8,462 specimens.

The collection of recent plants has been greatly enriched during the year, notably by the addition of the material collected by Dr. Edward Palmer in southwestern Mexico. This includes about eight hundred species, of which one fifth are new to science. Mr. Pringle made valuable contributions to the fauna from Mexico, and from Mr. S. Applegate was received a small collection of Alaskan plants. Much interesting material which was exhibited at the New Orleans Exposition, has been added through the courtesy of the Government of Costa Rica.

The herbarium of the late Mr. O. E. Pearce has been received during the year. This includes over 600 finely mounted species, together with a large number of duplicates. Other collections of interest and value were received from Dr. J. C. McCormick, Mr. J. W. Johnson, and Prof. Alfred Dugès.

Active work in this department has been mainly confined to the determination of the material received. It is estimated that there are 32,000 specimens in the collection. Thirty entries have been made in the catalogue during the year.

DIVISION OF GEOLOGY.

DEPARTMENT OF MINERALS.

The honorary curator, Prof. F. W. Clarke, chief chemist of the U. S. Geological Survey, reports satisfactory growth in the collections under his charge.

The mineral collection received some remarkable specimens of quartz, stibnite, and amber from the Educational Museum at Tokio, Japan. A collection of 74 specimens of Swedish minerals collected by L. J. Igelström was purchased.

Among the important accessions to the series of gems were those from Mr. C. S. Bement, of Philadelphia, Mr. Thomas Wilson, of Washington, and Mrs. Spencer F. Baird. From the Treasury Department was received a collection of 133 small diamonds and 150 pearls, which were presented in 1840 to President Van Buren by the Imaum of Muscat.

The collection of meteorites now numbers about 301 " falls," of which 141 have been obtained during the year.

The celebrated collection of Prof. C. U. Shepard, jr., numbering 101 specimens, has been deposited during the year.

Researches have been made by Professor Clarke, and under his direction, upon the micas, the natural borates, and the tourmalines belonging to the Museum collection.

There are now 3,238 specimens on exhibition, 5,404 in the study series, and 8,530 duplicates, which, together with the Willcox collection of minerals and the Shepard collection of meteorites, make a total of 18,601 specimens in the care of this department.

DEPARTMENT OF LITHOLOGY AND PHYSICAL GEOLOGY.

Mr. George P. Merrill, curator, has devoted the greater part of his time to the arrangement of the exhibition and reserve series, both of which have been greatly extended during the year. Of the reserve series 5,687 specimens are on exhibition, 2,720 of which are examples of building stones, while 1,893 belong to the educational series of rocks and rock-forming minerals. Mr. Merrill has had permission to do a portion of his work in the petrographical laboratory of the Johns Hopkins University in Baltimore, and has there examined several hundred microscopical slides of the sections of rocks, and has thus been enabled to arrange a large mass of hitherto unclassified material which had been accumulating for several years. Mr. Merrill has, at his own cost, made expeditions to California and Montana, and has gathered much desirable material, described in the accession list accompanying this report (Section v). In his report he makes mention of 13 accessions received during the year, which are of special value. The total number of specimens in his department is estimated at 21,500.

DEPARTMENT OF METALLURGY AND ECONOMIC GEOLOGY.

The time of the curator, Mr. Fred. P. Dewey, has been in part devoted to the preparation of a preliminary descriptive catalogue of the collections.

The accessions of the year have consisted chiefly of material sent for examination and report, and 186 specimens have been examined. Six hundred and seventy-one entries have been made in the catalogue. There are now about 49,000 specimens in the collection, of which 18,000 are on exhibition.

E.—REVIEW OF THE ADMINISTRATIVE WORK.

PROGRESS OF GENERAL AND INCIDENTAL WORK.

TRANSPORTATION AND STORAGE.

Of the total number of boxes, packages, barrels, tanks, etc., received during the year, which was 38,367, no less than 3,798 contained material for the Museum.

The registrar, Mr. S. C. Brown, continues to act as transportation clerk for the Smithsonian Institution.

During the year 436 boxes and packages have been entered on the storage records. The temporary storing of material, it may be noted, is of very great convenience to the curators, who, upon the arrival of bulky accessions, may not be prepared to receive them immediately into their laboratories.

LIBRARY.

Mr. John Murdoch* has furnished the following statement concerning the operations of the library.

The work of the library has been carried on according to essentially the same methods as during the preceding years.

The total number of publications (exclusive of regular periodicals) added to the library during the year was 1,511—391 volumes of more than 100 pages, and 1,120 pamphlets. Of these, 237 volumes and 711 pamphlets were retained for the use of the Museum from the accessions of the Smithsonian Institution. The remainder were obtained as usual by gift, and less frequently by purchase. As in previous years, the chief donor to the library was Prof. S. F. Baird, to whom the library is indebted for 17 volumes and 109 pamphlets. Next in importance as contributors are Mr. Robert Ridgway, 49 pamphlets; Mr. W. H. Dall, 46 pamphlets; the Smithsonian Institution, 14 volumes, 18 pamphlets; Prof. J. O. Westwood, of Oxford, England, 27 pamphlets (a complete set of his shorter archæological writings); and the United States Fish Commission, 3 volumes and 19 pamphlets.

During the year 4,350 books were borrowed from the library, and 4,396 returned.

The card catalogue by authors has been continued, and 1,647 titles have been added to it during the year. A catalogue by subjects is a great desideratum, but it is impossible to begin it with the force now at command.

The condition of the sectional libraries remains practically unchanged since the last report.

The covering of pamphlets with the binders, described in the last report, has been continued, and 2,111 have been covered during the year. On June 24 we received a supply of Randolph pamphlet-boxes of the standard quarto and octavo sizes. It is intended to keep the covered pamphlets in these, grouping together, for instance, all the pamphlets by the same author in one of these boxes, which then forms practically a book, and can be put in its proper place on the shelf.

On the establishment of the Smithsonian reading-room, soon after April 1, the current volumes of nearly all the important periodicals not belonging to the sectional libraries, were transferred to it. This affords a long-desired opportunity for the display of the recent numbers of these publications, and as the periodicals in the reading-room are not allowed to circulate until the volume is complete, all readers have an opportunity of consulting them.

No changes were made in the force employed in the library until April 1. At this date, in consequence of the reorganization of the

* Appointed Librarian of the Smithsonian Institution April 1, 1887.

Smithsonian library, Mr. F. W. True resigned the position of librarian, and the assistant librarian, Mr. Murdoch, became librarian of the Smithsonian Institution, in charge also of the Museum library, with Mr. N. P. Scudder as assistant librarian.

The chief need of the library is more room for the storage of the files of periodicals. The room now available is scarcely sufficient to provide for the regular growth of the series now kept, and want of room is a serious hindrance to the acquisition of the files of important periodicals.

DISTRIBUTION OF DUPLICATES, AND EXCHANGES.

The policy of the Smithsonian Institution in reference to the distribution of its duplicate material has frequently been emphasized in its annual reports. It has always been the desire of the Institution to utilize this material by sending it to colleges, museums, and individuals, either as a gift or in exchange, and thus to extend as widely as possible the means of diffusing a knowledge of the natural history of this country. In the Smithsonian report for 1859* Professor Henry wrote: "The object of the Institution in obtaining so large a number of duplicates is that they may be distributed for the advancement of knowledge to persons who may be engaged in original investigations in natural history, and also to colleges for the purpose of education." In the same place he says: "Although the primary object of the Institution is not educational, yet the Museum is arranged with special reference to the study of the elements of different branches of science; and the distribution of the extra specimens will furnish the means of diffusing a knowledge of natural history more generally throughout the country."

During the last few years each department in the Museum has been under the care of a specialist, but in former years, when the Secretary of the Institution acted as the sole keeper of the Museum, the collections, as soon as they were received, were sent away to various specialists, who undertook to identify the specimens, which were duly returned, labeled, to the Institution.

Thus in the early days of the Museum the value of the collections depended in large part upon the willingness of specialists to co-operate, and to them distributions of material were of course most readily made. Professor Henry, in the annual report for 1861† states that up to that time 80,000 specimens had thus been distributed. He adds: "When it is considered that all these have been named and labeled by naturalists admitted to be of the highest authority in their respective departments, and that all have thereby the character and value of types, it will be readily understood how much their systematic and judicious distribution by the Institution all over the world must conduce to the advancement of science."

As a result, however, of the more thorough organization of the Museum at the present time, the determination of material is for the most part performed within the walls of the Museum, and therefore extraneous co operation is no longer so necessary a feature of the work of the establishment.

The applications for specimens this year numbered 83, most of which were filled, besides 46 which remained on file from previous years. The distributions for this year consist for the most part of material sent as gift to needy colleges and museums, or in exchange for material received. These amounted to 327 packages, among which were included 3,460 specimens of marine invertebrates (32 sets), 1,573 rocks, 1,462 birds, 1,168 minerals, 1,029 mollusks, 555 paleozoic fossils, 543 ethnological objects, 165 ores, 148 birds' eggs, 133 mammals, 106 reptiles, 94 fishing implements, and 84 fishes. Forty-nine boxes and one package, containing materia medica specimens, animal products, pottery, and fossil plants, were also included in the distribution. In addition to this, 13 sets of plans and drawings of Museum cases and bottles, 95 photographs of Museum specimens, and 9 musical instruments were also given or lent.

Among the most important distributions of the year have been those of the buffalo heads, skins, and skeletons which formed a part of the result of the Smithsonian exploration into Montana, and which were presented to corporations and individuals who had materially assisted in bringing the expedition to success. A large number of axolotls, for the most part presented to the Museum by Dr. R. W. Shufeldt, U. S. Army, were given away to various applicants for purposes of study.

FOREIGN EXCHANGES.

A collection of 112 specimens (105 species) of birds and 24 mammal skins was sent to the museum of the municipal library in Kurrachee, India, in exchange for collections of drugs, reptiles, and mammals received. A skull and 11 bones of *Rhytina* together with additional skeletons of mammals and birds and some insects, were sent to M. Beauregard, of the Museum of Natural History in Paris, in exchange for 18 mammal skeletons and a small series of insects received. Fourteen pieces of Chiriqui pottery were sent to M. Lauth, director of the establishment of Sèvres, France, in exchange for material received; and a bust of Osceola and a Sioux head-dress were transmitted to the minister of public instruction for the Trocadero Museum in Paris, in part exchange for a valuable collection of Sèvres porcelain received from the French Government. The negotiations which for some time have been pending with the Annecy Musée, Haute-Savoie, have been completed during this year by the transmission of a collection of ethnological objects and a series of fossils in exchange for a collection of minerals, rocks, etc., received last year. A buffalo-skin was sent to Dr. Tor Helliesen, curator of the zoological department of the Stavanger Museum in Norway. A sea-lion skin was sent to the Bergen Museum in Norway. A small and varied collection of fossils, moa bones, etc., was received from Mr. S. H. Drew, of Wanganui, New Zealand, and in exchange an equivalent in ethnological material has been sent. A series of the bones of *Rhytina* was sent to Mr. J. W. Clark, of the Museum of Zoology and Comparative Anatomy at Cambridge, England, in part exchange for some valuable skeletons received at the close of the London Fisheries Exhibition in 1883. An exchange of mammal skins has been made with Prof. Tycho Tullberg, of Upsala, Sweden.

In addition to these exchanges correspondence has been carried on with several museums with a view to arranging exchanges. Prof. S. Hertzenstein, of the Imperial Zoological Museum in St. Petersburg, Russia, has offered to send fishes and shells in exchange for American fishes. Dr. A. Strauch, director of that museum, has been invited to exchange Russian and Central Asiatic mammals for mammals from North, Central, and South America. An exchange of fishes is being arranged with Prof. T. Jeffery Parker, of the Otago University Museum, at Dunedin, New Zealand. Dr. Serrurier, director of the National Ethnological Museum of the Netherlands, in Leyden, has offered African ethnological material in exchange.

The arrival of specimens of tin-bearing material, together with systematic series representing the mode of occurrence and extraction, and of mammals, from L. Wray, esq., curator of the Perak Museum in the Straits Settlements, in exchange for mineralogical specimens, is awaited with much interest. Professor Bernardin, of the Commercial and Industrial Museum in the College of Melle, near Ghent, has been asked to send samples of commercial products. D. Morris, esq., assistant director of the Royal Gardens at Kew, in England, has made application for specimens of American woods. These will be put aside for that establishment as opportunity offers. Dr. Ernest Bayet, of Brussels, has requested an exchange of fossils, desiring quaternary and pliocene material. In behalf of the department of Mollusks this Museum has written to the director of the Cape Town Museum for a series of land, fresh-water, and marine shells of that region, offering in exchange any desired material. For the same department application for a series of Storms shells has been made to the director of the Brussels Museum. A letter has been addressed to Hon. St. John Larnack, minister of marine Wellington, New Zealand, asking for specimens in any department of zoology, an offer having been voluntarily made to send us any desiderata which could be supplied, in return for whitefish ova transmitted by the U. S. Fish Commission. M. Milne-Edwards, of the Museum of Natural History in Paris, has offered duplicate material from the dredgings of the *Travailleur*.

PUBLICATIONS.

The report on the operations of the Museum for 1884 was issued in October, 1886, as Smithsonian Report, Part II, and was the first bound volume published as a report on the Museum. This book consists of ix+458 pages. A new feature of this report was the inclusion of scientific papers based upon collections in the Museum. These are six in number and bear the following titles:

I. Throwing-sticks in the National Museum; by Otis T. Mason; 12 pages; 17 plates.
II. Basket-work of the North American Aborigines; by Otis T. Mason; 16 pages; 64 plates.
III. A study of the Eskimo bow in the U. S. National Museum; by John Murdoch; 10 pages; 12 plates.
IV. On a Spotted Dolphin, apparently identical with the *Prodelphinus doris*, Gray; by Frederick W. True; 8 pages; 6 plates.
V. The Florida Muskrat, *Neofiber Alleni*, True; by Frederick W. True; 6 pages; 3 plates.
VI. On the West Indian Seal, *Monachus tropicalis*, Gray; by Frederick W. True and F. A. Lucas; 5 pages; 3 plates.

The manuscript of the report for 1885–'86, the first report embracing an entire fiscal year, has been sent to the Printing Office.

Mr. A. Howard Clark has been appointed editor of Proceedings and Bulletins. This work has for many years been well performed by Dr. T. H. Bean, in addition to his regular duties as curator of fishes.

The eighth volume of the Proceedings of the U. S. National Museum, for the year 1885, appeared in October. It contains 78 contributions in 40 signatures by 36 authors, 14 of whom are officers of the Museum. Twenty-five of the papers related to fishes, 22 to birds, 12 to marine invertebrates, 6 to mammals, 3 to rocks and minerals, 3 to physiological subjects, 2 to botany, and 1 each to ethnology, entomology, paleontology, metallurgy, and materia medica. The report is illustrated by 25 plates and 15 cuts. The Appendix contains circulars 32 and 33 of the National Museum, the former being "A classification of the materia medica collection of the U. S. National Museum" previously published by Dr. James M. Flint, U. S. Navy, and extended by Dr. Henry G. Beyer, U. S. Navy, and the latter entitled "Notes on the Preparation of Rough Skeletons, by Frederic A. Lucas."

The ninth volume of the Proceedings of the U. S. National Museum, 1886, has been issued only in signatures, of which a list is published in Section iv of this report. The bound volume will soon be ready for distribution.

Of the tenth volume of Proceedings of the U. S. National Museum, for the year 1887, only six signatures (the sixth dated May 17) had appeared up to the close of the fiscal year now being reported upon.

Bulletin 31, SYNOPSIS OF THE NORTH AMERICAN SYRPHIDÆ, by Samuel W. Williston, M. D., Ph. D., was issued in May, 1887, and contains xxx+335 pages. It is illustrated by 12 plates. The subject is discussed in three parts, of which the first is devoted to classification, the second to descriptions, and the third to habits, structural characters, geographical and geological distribution, and chronological list of genera.

Bulletin 32, CATALOGUE OF BATRACHIANS AND REPTILES OF CENTRAL AMERICA AND MEXICO, by Prof. E. D. Cope, is in type and ready for printing.

The manuscript for Bulletin 33, entitled CATALOGUE OF MINERALS AND SYNONYMS, by Thomas Egleston, as well as that for Bulletin 34, CATALOGUE OF BATRACHIANS AND REPTILES OF NORTH AMERICA, by Prof. E. D. Cope, has been sent to the Printing Office.

In Section IV of the report will be found a list of the publications of the Museum, and also a bibliography of the papers by officers of the Museum and by others whose writings have a bearing upon Museum material. The authors of these papers number 84, 32 of whom are connected with the Museum, 10 being honorary officers. The papers number 345, and are thus distributed under the following subjects:

Subjects.	By Museum officers.	By other investigators.	Total.
Textiles	1	0	1
Foods	1	0	1
Materia medica	7	0	7
Naval architecture	1	0	1
Fisheries	9	5	14
Ethnology	37	6	43
Antiquities	5	0	5
Mammals	12	1	13
Birds	59	37	96
Reptiles and batrachians	2	1	3
Fishes	5	20	25
Mollusks (including crustaceans)	5	4	9
Insects	50	0	50
Invertebrates	5	3	8
Invertebrate fossils	11	1	12
Plants	12	0	12
Minerals	4	0	4
Lithology and physical geology	6	0	6
Exploration	2	0	2
Chemistry	3	0	3
Metallurgy	1	0	1
Physiology and histology	0	6	6
Taxidermy	2	1	3
Biography	5	0	5
General	15	0	15
Total	260	85	345

VISITORS.

The total number of visitors to the National Museum during the fiscal year ending June 30, 1887, was 216,562, giving a daily average of 691+, and to the Smithsonian building, 98,552, giving a daily average of nearly 315.

Table showing the number of visitors to the Museum and Smithsonian buildings since 1881.

Year.	New Museum building.	Smithsonian building.
1881	*150,000	
1882	†167,450	152,744
1883	202,188	104,823
1884	195,322	91,130
1885 (January–June)	107,365	60,428
1885–'86	174,225	88,960
1886–'87	216,562	98,552
Total number of visitors	1,213,117	596,637

* Estimated on basis of register.
† Estimated on basis of attendance from February 8 to December 31.

STUDENTS, LECTURES, AND MEETINGS OF SOCIETIES.

As in past years, the Museum has offered facilities to several students, who have in some instances rendered a partial equivalent by volunteer work upon the collections.

Mr. Walter H. Brown spent six weeks with the Department of Comparative Anatomy for the purpose of studying the methods of preparing and mounting osteological specimens.

In the Department of Insects volunteer service was rendered by Mr. S. Davis, of Washington, and Mr. W. H. Crane, of Cincinnati, whose assistance was utilized chiefly in the arrangement of the Diptera and in the synoptic collection of Coleoptera. Prof. P. R. Uhler, of Baltimore, having offered to arrange and name the insects of the family *Capsidæ*, the material was sent to him for that purpose.

Paul Pelseneer, of the museum at Brussels, applied for certain species of pteropod mollusks for study. Certain Pacific specimens and copies of colored drawings, made from life by Mr. Dall while in the North Pacific, were lent to him.

Mr. Delano Ames, of Washington, served as a volunteer in the department of Marine Invertebrates during the months of May and June. Prof. A. E. Verrill, of Yale College, assisted by Misses A. J. and C. E. Bush, and Mr. Sanderson Smith, Prof. J. Walter Fewkes, of the Museum of Comparative Zoology, Cambridge, Massachusetts; Prof. S. I. Smith, of Yale College, Prof. L. A. Lee, of Bowdoin College, Prof. E. Linton, of Washington and Jefferson College, Pennsylvania, and others have rendered valuable aid to this department by researches in special directions.

In the department of Minerals volunteer service was rendered from July to November, 1886, by Mr. H. H. James.

An examination of the entire collection of deer antlers, in connection with the question of bilateral asymmetry in the class Mammals, was made by Dr. Harrison Allen.

In the department of Ethnology Paymaster E. B. Webster, U. S. Navy, rendered valuable service.

Among the investigators who have utilized the ichthyological collections of the Museum in the preparation of papers, etc., were President David S. Jordan, of Indiana University, and his assistants, and Prof. John A. Ryder, of the University of Pennsylvania.

The gallery of the department of Birds was thrown open to the members of the American Ornithologists' Union, who held their annual meeting from November 16 to 18, and daily use was made of the library and collections by these gentlemen in connection with the objects of the meeting and their researches as ornithologists.

Mr. Anastasio Alfaro was sent to Washington by the Government of Costa Rica in October, 1886, to study the methods of the National Museum. This gentleman was shown every courtesy, especially by the department of Birds, in which he was particularly interested, and every possible facility was afforded him for familiarizing himself with the methods pursued by the Institution.

In the photographic laboratory instructions were given by Mr. T. W. Smillie to Lieutenants Schaefer, Rogers, Bolles, and Werlich, of the U. S. Navy; Messrs. Merrill and Hornaday, of the Museum; Mr. Thomas Lee, U. S. Fish Commission; the photographer of the U. S. Coast Survey, and to Dr. May King, a young Chinese lady who is preparing herself for a career as a medical missionary and scientific student in her native land.

Instructions in taxidermy were given by Mr. W. T. Hornaday to Prof. L. L. Dyche, of the University of Kansas, who served as an unsalaried volunteer in the department for the sake of the experience acquired.

Mr. L. M. McCormick asked for and obtained access to the collection of fishes and ichthyological literature, to aid him in the identification of a collection of fishes belonging to Oberlin College.

The use of the lecture hall has as usual been granted for a series of lectures delivered on Saturday afternoons, and in some cases on Wednesday evenings, under the joint auspices of the Biological and Anthropological Societies of Washington. These were largely attended. Some of the lectures had direct reference to the work of the Museum, and were illustrated by specimens.

The programmes of the two parts of this course are here given:

PART I.

March 12.—General A. W. GREELY, U. S. Army: Animals of the Arctic Regions.
March 19.—Capt. C. E. DUTTON, U. S. Army: Earthquakes.
March 23.—Mr. W J McGEE: The Charleston Earthquake.
March 26.—Prof. OTIS T. MASON: The Natural History of Human Arts.
April 2.—Dr. B. E. FERNOW: Our Forestry Problem.
April 6.—Mr. THOMAS WILSON: Prehistoric Man in Western Europe,

PART II.

April 16.—Dr. EDWARD M. HARTWELL: The Aim and Effects of Physical Training.
April 20.—Dr. FRANK BAKER: Facial Expression.
April 23.—Miss H. C. DE S. ABBOTT: The Chemistry of the Higher and Lower Plants.
April 30.—Prof. HARRISON ALLEN: Rights and Lefts.
May 4.—Prof. S. P. LANGLEY: Sunlight and the Earth's Atmosphere.
May 7.—Dr. J. H. BRYAN: The Mechanism of the Human Voice.

During the year the following-named societies have, by permission of the Secretary of the Smithsonian Institution, held their meetings in the Museum lecture hall: The National Dental Association, July 27 to 29, inclusive; The Biological Society of Washington,* annual meeting, January 22; National Convention of Superintendents of Schools, March 15 to 17, inclusive.

CURRENT ADMINISTRATIVE WORK.

FURNITURE, SUPPLIES, AND ACCOUNTS.

The following statement in regard to the cases and other furniture, supplies, and accounts of the Museum, covering the fiscal year 1886–'87, has been prepared by Mr. W. V. Cox, chief clerk.

The U. S. National Museum is supported by three appropriations annually voted by Congress; one being for preservation and increase of collections, one for furniture and fixtures, and one for heating, lighting, electrical, and telephonic service.

The principal appropriation made for the Museum is the one for the Preservation of Collections. The wording of the act of Congress making this appropriation for the year ending June 30, 1887, is as follows:

PRESERVATION OF COLLECTIONS OF THE NATIONAL MUSEUM: For the preservation, exhibition, and increase of the collections received from the surveying and exploring expeditions of the Government, and from other sources, including salaries or compensation of all necessary employés, one hundred and six thousand five hundred dollars.

Out of this appropriation, therefore, are paid the salaries of curators, scientific assistants, clerks, and other employés, the nature of whose work is properly chargeable to it. This service amounted during the year to $95,133.70.

The greatest number of employés on the roll in any one month was 126, in January, 1887; the smallest number was 106, in April of the same year.

The highest salary paid was $300 per month; the lowest was $20, paid to an attendant; the average salary being $65.

The further disbursements of this fiscal year were as follows: $1,768.69 was expended for stationery; $281.94 was expended for books; $4,847.63 for specimens; $2,619.61 for general supplies; $1,765.37 for freight and cartage; which, with the total of $95,133.70 paid for services, left a balance of 2 cents to be "covered into the Treasury."

---

* The regular meetings were held by this society every other Saturday evening until March 19, after which the society met in the Cosmos Club rooms.

The appropriation for Furniture and Fixtures for the year ending June 30, 1887, was $40,000.

Out of this sum there was expended $18,603.80 for exhibition cases of different designs, screens, wing-frames, insect-boxes, blocks, tablets, bird-stands, drawings for cases, furniture for offices, glass, brackets, locks, and other necessary fittings and appliances.

During the same time $2,139.04 was spent for lumber; $598.35 was spent for paints, oils, brushes, etc.; $161.40 was spent for glass vials and containers for specimens; $191.41 was spent for apparatus, appliances, etc., for laboratory, and exhibition halls; $941.28 was spent for miscellaneous purposes; making a total of $22,635.28.

The following fittings, appliances, etc., were made or furnished during the year by persons outside the Museum:

10 mahogany unit table cases	$750.00
36 mahogany table cases (sloping)	1,475.25
10 table cases with storage base	1,295.00
1 mahogany table case (special)	125.00
16 mahogany Kensington cases	1,040.00
20 mahogany Kensington cases	1,900.00
6 mahogany wall cases	1,489.00
20 pine unit tables	504.40
1 large walnut cabinet	250.00
2 cherry cabinets	250.00
4 white-pine herbarium cases	236.00
4 standard book-cases	64.00
5 white-pine wood cut cases	47.50
1 cherry case	15.00
4 mahogany table screens	288.00
1 half-unit ebonized table screen	45.00
102 oak frames	49.25
32 ebonized wing-frames	82.50
5 mahogany wing-frames	15.00
28,538 pasteboard trays, boxes, and covers	543.87
1,664 white-pine blocks, tablets, etc	124.80
180 wire bird-stands	14.58
222 insect-boxes	286.25
989 lights of glass—plate, crystal, and hammered	3,975.98
963 locks and rods	1,312.85
254 brackets	23.75
1,985 file-holders	223.91
Furniture, etc., for offices	743.63
Drawings for cases, etc	130.00
Traveling expenses to inspect cases, etc	11.86
Interior, and other fittings	1,266.42

There was also expended out of this appropriation for wages of mechanics and laborers, salaries of property clerk, copyists, and other necessary employés, $17,289.75, leaving an unexpended balance of $74.97.

The average monthly roll on furniture and fixtures was $1,440.81. The greatest number of employés in any month was 27, the smallest 20; the average number being 25.

The highest salary was $110, the lowest $30. The wages of carpenters, painters, and laborers were the same as paid for work of like nature in other departments of the Government, the average per individual on this rcll being $57.63.

The mechanics have been kept busy with the varied work of the Museum. When necessary to have cases of new design or of peculiar form made, it has often been found economy of both time and means, sometimes even with working drawings, to have a sample prepared in the Museum shop before finally awarding the contract. Our men have remodeled numerous old cases, and have built many new ones, as shown by the accompanying list.

The following cases, screens, etc., were made in the Museum shop between June 30, 1886, and July 1, 1887:

10 mahogany alcove cases.
4 mahogany pillar cases.
4 glass screen, sloping cases.
1 glass case, special form.
1 ebonized case, special form.
4 unit cases.
4 white-pine standard book-cases.
13 walnut bases.
7 pine bases.
1 water-tight base.
1 sample wall bracket.
2 diaphragms.
8 oak settees.

2 stationary screens with sliding doors.
2 large stationary screens.
4 poplar screens, between arches.
24 pine screens, between arches.
18 pedestals.
4 pyramids, pedestals.
4 gun-racks.
8 oak frames.
16 pine shelves and bases.
8 wall cases, remodeled.
2 storage cases, remodeled.
2 white-pine cases, remodeled.

The appropriation for heating, lighting, and electrical and telephonic service was $11,000.

Out of this sum there was expended for fuel, $2,923.87; for heating, supplies, and repairs, $852.58; for gas, $811.78; rental of telephones, $766.69; electric works and supplies, $748.42; rental of call-boxes, $120; salary of telephone clerk and telegraph operator, $1,080; wages of engineer and firemen, $3,678.12; leaving an unexpended balance of $18.54.

The methods described at length in report of 1885-'86 for purchasing supplies for the Museum have been followed, and have generally proved satisfactory. It is thought that by means of a few slight changes, which experience has suggested, still greater perfection in business methods may be attained.

Little has been accomplished towards the completion of the back records mentioned in the report of last year, for the entire time of the limited number of employés of the department of Property and Supplies has been taken up with necessary current work.

CORRESPONDENCE AND REPORTS.

The scope of the work of this department, under the charge of Mr. R. I. Geare, executive clerk, has been greatly enlarged during the year, owing to the fact that all letters bearing upon the work of the Museum are now referred from the Smithsonian Institution to the Assistant Secretary for final action. In previous years a considerable part of the Museum correspondence had been attended to by officers of the Smithsonian Institution.

The Museum correspondence may be grouped under the following headings:

(1) General Museum business, including matters connected with Museum administration, arrangement of foreign exchanges, etc.

(2) Replies to requests for information of a technical character.

(3) Acknowledgment of gifts, loans, and exchanges.

(4) Reports upon specimens sent for examination and report.

During the year, 1,406 letters were written relating to the general business of the Museum. The reports upon specimens sent for identification numbered 540, and 1,152 acknowledgments of accessions were made, a large number both of reports and of acknowledgments being in letter form. This gives a total of 3,098 official papers prepared for the signature of the Assistant Secretary in charge.

Reports upon specimens sent for examination.—The special researches which have been carried on by the curators during the year have been referred to at some length in the discussion of the work accomplished in the scientific departments. In addition to this a large quantity of laboratory work is necessitated by the receipt of specimens of all kinds which are sent to the Museum for examination and report. The examination of this material, of which a classified list is given below, occupies very much of the curators' time, elaborate reports being in many cases necessary. In each instance a copy of the report, or a letter embodying it, is mailed to the sender. The following table gives the number of requests of this kind received, and arranged by states, the state given being that in which the sender resides and not necessarily that from which the specimen originally came, this fact in many cases not being stated by the sender.

Alabama	10	Louisiana	4
Arizona	9	Maine	3
Arkansas	9	Maryland	5
California	11	Massachusetts	6
Colorado	5	Michigan	6
Connecticut	3	Minnesota	1
Dakota	5	Mississippi	10
Delaware	2	Missouri	3
District of Columbia	14	Montana	4
Florida	13	Nebraska	3
Georgia	5	Nevada	3
Idaho	1	New Jersey	6
Illinois	3	New Mexico	5
Indiana	5	New York	19
Iowa	4	North Carolina	12
Kansas	9	Ohio	16
Kentucky	4	Oregon	3

Pennsylvania	11	Wisconsin	4
Rhode Island	5	Wyoming	1
South Carolina	8	Bahamas	1
Tennessee	25	Canada	1
Texas	28	Costa Rica	1
Utah	1	Persia	1
Virginia	35		
Washington Territory	4	Total	347

LABELS.

There were received from the Government Printing Office 2,055 forms of labels, classified as follows:

Materia medica	83	Minerals	194
Metallurgical	14	Reptiles	70
Foods, textiles, etc	66	Coins	106
Mammals	471		
Ethnological	918	Total	2,055
Building-stones	133		

Each form contained 24 labels, 12 on board and 12 on paper.

BUILDINGS AND LABOR; POLICE AND PUBLIC COMFORT.

The staff employed for police and inspection under the charge of Henry Horan, superintendent of buildings, consisted of 20 watchmen and doorkeepers; for construction, care of buildings, and repairs, 8 carpenters, 2 painters; for labor and cleaning, 19 laborers, 6 cleaners, 2 attendants; for heating and lighting, 1 engineer and 4 firemen.

From the reports of the superintendent are quoted in brief the following statements, which will serve to show in part the character of the work accomplished by the laboring force during the year:

In July a large amount of mechanical work was done; eight large settees were completed and placed in the rotunda of the Museum building, and diaphragms made for the installation of photographs of fishery appliances, etc. The walls at the north entrance were wainscoted, and screens were placed at the west entrance. A sloping case was made for the department of Fishes for exhibiting relief maps. Sky-lights were placed in the east balcony. Tin trays were placed under the floor ventilators to catch the dust that would otherwise drift through. A number of boxes were received from the New Orleans Exposition, and were turned over to the superintendent for unpacking. Two mahogany pillar cases were completed for the department of Ethnology. The electrical clocks in the buildings were all overhauled and repaired. Screens were made for the different courts.

In August four mahogany pillar cases were completed for the department of Ethnology. Diaphragms were made for cases, and drawers fitted to them. A partition was put up on the north balcony separating the textile and label departments. Excavations were made at the east front and walled up for ventilation of trenches. Work was begun on eight mahogany upright floor cases and on a partition wall on the second floor in northwest pavilion, cutting off the larger portion of the room as a private office for the Assistant Secretary.

In September several large tubs were made for the reception of palm trees. A skylight was placed in one of the rooms on the north balcony. The wall cases were repaired. A large number of pedestals were made for the use of the taxidermist in mounting large animals. Book-cases were made for the Assistant Secretary's office. The large fur-seal case and pedestal of the kangaroo lizard were repaired.

In October a book-case was made for the property clerk's office, and work was continued in reconstructing the wall cases in the south hall of the Museum. Three pedestals were made for petrified logs, and others for use in the departments of Mammals and Comparative Anatomy. All the mahogany upright floor cases were completed. Screens were made to go over pier cases. The roof of the Museum building was painted. Slope cases for the building-stone department were made, and work was begun on a mahogany book-case for the chief clerk's office.

In November a plank walk was laid along the west front of the Museum building. The walls in the northwest court and the ladies' reception-room were painted. A mahogany slope case was completed, and work begun on mahogany upright floor cases. Work was begun on a small brick addition to the building at the east front.

In December partitions were erected in the Annex building for the purpose of making a larger number of rooms.

The collections of Paleozoic Fossils and the office of the curator of that department were removed to the first floor of the southwest pavilion, the curator of mammals removing his office to that vacated by Mr. Walcott. A large book-case in the office of the superintendent was remodeled. Cases for the department of Paleozoic Fossils were reconstructed and storage boxes made for the department of Fishes. The work on the walls of the ladies' room was completed and similar work begun on the gentlemen's lavatory. The taxidermist's outfits were moved from the Annex to the Armory building. Packing boxes were made for the Materia Medica department, and a book-case was repaired for the department of Mineralogy. The last of the lot of mahogany upright floor cases were completed, and work was begun on a mahogany slope case for Gobelin tapestries and carpets. Shelves were arranged in the cases in the anthropological hall.

During the last half of this fiscal year (January to June, inclusive, 1887) the following items relating to the most important work accomplished are given : Partitioning and fitting up room at Armory building; shelving cases in anthropological hall; repairing floors in pottery court; construction of pedestals for large models of pueblos; making bases for seals; construction of screen with sliding door at south entrance; making eight screens over wall cases; repairing eight cases for department of Metallurgy; shelving in wall cases for department of Building-Stones; construction of eight screens over pier case in east hall; three pedestals for Easter Island idols; fitting up cases and screens for the Grant relics.

THE WORK OF THE MUSEUM PREPARATORS.

The preparation of specimens for exhibition in the Museum or for the study series has been continued, and the character of the work of the preparators is indicated in the following statements:

TAXIDERMISTS.

During the present year the work of the department of taxidermy has been unusually extensive. The lack of satisfactory and fairly representative specimens of the American bison in the exhibition series made it imperatively necessary to send the chief taxidermist into the field to collect material for a proper representation of this most conspicuous and important quadruped of North America. During the months of October, November, and December, when the pelage was at its finest, an extremely rich and varied collection was made of fresh skins, skeletons, and skulls of animals of both sexes and all ages, from the fœtal young up to an enormous old bull which measured 5 feet 8 inches in height at the shoulders.*

Upon his return from the field Mr. Hornaday at once proceeded to mount a series of six of the finest skins to form a group, with natural surroundings. In view of the near extermination of the species the specimens are already of almost priceless value, and the group when finished will form a very important and attractive addition to the hall of mammals. The careful life studies made by the chief taxidermist in the field enabled him to produce specimens of unrivaled excellence.

Notwithstanding this very serious interruption to work in the laboratory by work in the field, and still further by a removal of the laboratory from the Annex building to the Armory, and the care of the Montana collection when it arrived, the amount of work accomplished in the laboratory has been very considerable. During the year thirty-one mammals were mounted and placed on exhibition, among which, after the group of buffaloes, the most commanding figure is that of a superb Bengal tigress. A very fine barren-ground caribou, an immense pronghorn antelope buck, and a family of coyotes are also noteworthy additions of the year, while the collection of marsupials is still further enriched by the addition of eleven more species.

During the months of April, May, and June, Mr. Joseph Palmer rendered the chief taxidermist very efficient and valuable assistance in the work of mounting some of the buffaloes, the caribou, antelope, and other mammals. Mr. A. H. Forney has continued to render satisfactory service as assistant taxidermist during the year, and remained at the Museum in charge of the laboratory during the absence of the chief taxidermist in Montana.

List of mammals mounted in the Museum workshops from July 1, 1886, to June 30, 1887.

15381. *Felis tigris.*	15694. *Bos americanus* (old bull).
15491. *Canis latrans,* juv.	15697. *Bos americanus* (old cow).
15707. *Canis latrans.*	15685. *Bos americanus* (young bull).
15708. *Canis latrans.*	15686. *Bos americanus* (young cow).
15575. *Vulpes fulvus,*	16703. *Bos americanus* (yearling).
Odobœnus obesus (remount).	15503. *Bos americanus* (young calf).
15478. *Sarcophilus ursinus.*	15502. *Bos americanus* (bull head).
15479. *Phalangista vulpina.*	15503. *Bos americanus* (bull head).
15477. *Thylacinus cynocephalus.*	15668. *Rangifertarandus grœnlandicus.*
15311. *Bettongia rufescens.*	15714. *Antilocapra americana.*
15303. *Halmaturus temporalis.*	15634. *Cariacus,* sp.
13600. *Halmaturus bennetti.*	15621. *Cariacus,* sp.
13606. *Halmaturus wilcoxi.*	15314. *Ornithorhynchus paradoxus.*
13602. *Halmaturus billardieri.*	13596. *Bettongia grayi.*
13598. *Halmaturus brachyurus.*	

Thirty mammals representing the following orders were skinned and preserved for mounting or for study: Pinnates, 2 specimens; Carnivora,

---

* See Section III, Paper 5.

19 specimens; Rodentia, 14 specimens; Ungulata, 4 specimens; Marsupialia, 1 specimen.

Three large fishes were cast and skinned for mounting.

One hundred and twenty large mammals were cleaned, retouched, and prepared for casing. Three large mammals were repaired. One large mammal was dismounted. Forty-three large mammal-skins were received (Montana field collection), cleaned, and preserved in bath.

Thirty-nine boxes of specimens were packed for shipment.

Moved furniture, materials, and specimens in the laboratory from the Annex building to new quarters in the Armory building.

Gave instructions in taxidermy to three persons.

Summary of specimens collected in the field† by Mr. Hornaday and his party.

EXPLORATION FOR AMERICAN BISON.‡

Bos americanus (Buffalo), 22 skins, 11 skeletons, 44 skulls.

Antilocapra americana (Prong-horn Antelope), 9 skins, 3 heads, 3 skeletons, 3 skulls.

Cariacus macrotis (Black-tail Deer), 5 skins.

Cariacus virginianus (Virginia Deer), 5 skins.

Canis latrans (Coyote), 4 skins, 43 skeletons.

Vulpes velox, 1 skin.

Taxidea americana (Badger), 1 skin.

Lepus callotis (Jack Rabbit), 2 skeletons.

Cynomys ludovicianus (Prairie Dog), 3 skeletons.

Aquila chrysœtus (Golden Eagle), 1 skeleton.

Nyctea scandiaca (Snowy Owl), 2 skins.

Centrocircus urophasianus (Sage Grouse), 22 skeletons.

Pediœcetes phasianellus (Sharp-tailed Grouse), 9 skeletons.

Ampelis garrulus (Bohemian Wax-wing), 3 skeletons.

Branta canadensis (Wild Goose), 2 skeletons.

Pica melanoleuca, var. *hudsonica* (Magpie), 1 skeleton.

Mr. Henry Marshall devoted his time, as usual, to mounting specimens for the department of Birds. During the year he has mounted about three hundred specimens for the exhibition series, and removed from old stands to new ones about five hundred specimens.

OSTEOLOGICAL PREPARATOR.

The following table shows the number of osteological specimens prepared or mounted during the year, as well as the number of animals received in the flesh whose rough preparation§ involved an outlay of considerable time and labor:

---

* This summary does not include any of the specimens collected during the spring operations in the field, which have been reported upon with the work of the previous year. See Smithsonian Report 1886, Part II. The spring collection, however, should be credited in summing up the total results of the expedition.

† Accession 18617.

‡ During October, November, and December, 1886.

§ Including the poisoning of the numerous specimens destined to be prepared as ligamentary skeletons.

Description.	Mammals.	Birds.	Reptiles.	Batrachians.	Fishes.	Total.
Received in the flesh :						
Entire skeletons....	17	96	....	1	2	116
Incomplete skeletons ..	4	3	....	....	3	10
Cleaned :						
Entire skeletons.......	40	26	1	3	1	71
Skulls........	16	....	....	....	1	17
Incomplete skeletons ..	7	....	....	....	....	7
Mounted :						
Entire skeletons.......	7	12	5	2	1	27
Skulls......	5	....	....	....	....	5
Limbs and other pieces.	2	1	....	....	....	3

These tables give a total of 256 specimens on which work was done during the year, and show that, while the entire number is much less than that of the year previous, the number of large pieces handled is very much greater. The necessary work of preparation has indeed interfered seriously with other work, and has increased to such an extent as to render it impossible with the present force to bestow upon it all the attention which could be desired.

The reflooring of the pedestals of the casts of *Megatherium* and *Hadrosaurus* has necessitated repairs, and in addtion the series of *Dinoceras* casts, numbering some twenty pieces, has been mounted and placed on exhibition. A number of skeletons have been transferred to new pedestals, leaving but little to be done in that direction.

The mounting of the skeleton of the Asiatic elephant "Albert" has been the most difficult and protracted work of the year. The skeleton forms a very important addition to the exhibition series. The labeling of the osteological collection, which has been done by Mr. Lucas, is in all respects satisfactory.

The transferring of the work-rooms to the Armory building caused a temporary interruption of work during the month of January.

Mr. Walter H. Brown, of the University of Kansas, spent six weeks in this department as a volunteer assistant, for the purpose of studying the methods of preparing and mounting osteological specimens.

MODELERS.

A portion of the time of Mr. Joseph Palmer has been devoted to making casts of fishes and reptiles received from time to time by the Museum, and to repairing casts already on exhibition, which have from handling at various expositions and from other reasons become damaged. Mr. Palmer has rendered much assistance to Mr. Hornaday in connection with the mounting of mammals.

Mr. J. W. Hendley has made casts of Eskimo heads, meteoric stones, various objects for the food collection, stone implements, etc. He also made a model of an Indian woman and several models of Eskimos, for use in the display of costumes.

PHOTOGRAPHER.

Mr. T. W. Smillie, in charge of the photographic work, states that 506 negatives have been added to the permanent files during the year, as follows:

Archæological and ethnological	36	Mammals	24
Lithological	8	For illustrations of lectures	86
Mineralogical	7	Miscellaneous	324
Ornithological	13		
Metallurgical	7	Total	506

In addition, 117 transparencies have been made, 110 being for use in connection with lectures given in the Museum. Seventy-two geological negatives have been stripped and developed. Three thousand seven hundred and six prints (silver) have been made, as follows:

Archæological and ethnological	183	Mammals	48
Lithological	49	Miscellaneous	3,268
Mineralogical	36		
Ornithological	28	Total	3,706
Metallurgical	94		

In addition, 506 cyanotypes of case drawings and 45 enlargements have been made. One hundred and fifteen miscellaneous photographs have been mounted. In connection with experimental work for the Institution upon solar and lunar spectrum, 5 negatives and 10 prints were made.

The following persons have been instructed in the methods of photography: Dr. May King (Kiu Yia Me), Mr. C. H. Townsend, Mr. G. P. Merrill, and W. T. Hornaday, of the Museum; Lieutenants Schaefer, Rogers, Bolles, and Werlich, of the U. S. Navy; Mr. Thomas Lee, U. S. Fish Commission, and the photographer of the U. S. Coast Survey. Every facility has been afforded them for acquiring sufficient knowledge of photography to be of practical use to them in the field. (See p. 32 *antea*.)

The usual routine work of numbering and filing negatives has been continued. Several photographic outfits for collectors have been prepared.

By order of the Secretary, a test of seven canceling inks and samples of paper for postal notes was made at the request of the Post-Office Department, and the contracts for the ensuing year were based upon the results of the test.

The large stereopticon has been transferred to the care of this department, and was very successfully employed during the last season of Saturday lectures.

COLORIST.

Mr. A. Zeno Shindler has, in addition to his regular work of coloring casts of fishes, reptiles, etc., for exhibition in the Museum, painted a large collection of similar objects for the American Museum of Natural History, New York, and has made a number of sketches in water color, among which are views of the Carp pond, a Pima Indian woman engaged in weaving, a Madagascar woman, and a sketch of a Mexican Indian. He also colored photographs of eleven Winnebago, thirty Apache, and twelve Sac and Fox Indians, and also a photograph of an Indian priestess.

Twelve life-size casts of Ute Indians were painted, and a pen-and-ink copy made of a painting of Japanese fishery. Six large casts of grinding stones were painted in oil, and a cast of an ancient plate painted in gold. He also made a chart of the spectrum, and sketches illustrating the mechanism of the voice for the lecture room.

PREPARATOR IN THE DEPARTMENT OF ARTS AND INDUSTRIES.

Mr. E. H. Hawley has devoted the greater portion of his time to the preparation of material for exhibition. Among the more important collections which he has installed during the year were the "Grant relics," and a large number of Japanese and Chinese objects received from Dr. D. B. McCartee, which have all been mounted and placed on exhibition. A considerable number of pictures for the section of Steam Transportation and the department of Lithology, as well as a large collection of photographs from the British Museum, were mounted in folding screens. In addition he has prepared for exhibition many smaller collections and detached objects and prepared manuscript for labels.

ACCESSIONS.

The total number of accessions to the Museum during the year was 1,646.

A table showing the number of accessions to the Museum each year, beginning with 1881, is here given:

Year.	Accession numbers (inclusive).	Accessions.
1881	9890–11000	1,111
1882	11001–12500	1,500
1883	12501–13900	1,400
1884	13901–15550	1,650
1885 (January to June)	15551–16208	658
1885–'86	16209–17704	1,496
1886–'87	17705–19350	1,646
Total since 1881		9,461

The first entry in the accession book bears the date of January 1, 1859, although considerable material had been received before that time. From these figures it will therefore be seen that the accessions of the past six years and a half nearly equal the total number received during the previous 22 years. An "accession" may include hundreds of specimens.

Mr. S. C. Brown, registrar, has completed an alphabetical index of all accessions to the Museum received up to January, 1887. The manuscript is included in fifteen quarto volumes, and contains 1,394 pages of type-written and printed matter. This is invaluable as a resource for reference.

Of the 1,646 accessions received during this year, no less than 369 consisted of material sent for examination and report. The quantity of this material is rapidly increasing each year, and a classified list may be found in the chapter on laboratory work.

A geographical statement has been prepared, showing the sources of the more important accessions.

GEOGRAPHICAL REVIEW OF THE MORE IMPORTANT ACCESSIONS.

AFRICA.

Comparatively few accessions were received from this continent, and these embraced but few specimens each, in some cases only a single object. The principal collection was that received in exchange from the Bureau of Arts, Paris. This included mammals, insects, ethnological material, and a series of casts of heads of various African tribes. The remaining accessions were the following: Fragments of garnet from Cape Colony; meteoric iron and a "tiger-eye" from Orange River; an ebony club, 2 bone-pointed arrows, a drum or tom-tom and a leather pouch, sent by Mr. Charles Heape, of Manchester, England, in exchange; an ibis (*Bubulcus ibis*) from Egypt. From Lieut. E. H. Taunt, of the U. S. Navy, was received a carved elephant's tusk, garment made of dyed native cloth embroidered, and a specimen of native cloth from the Baluba country, headwaters of Kassai River.

AMERICA.

BRITISH AMERICA.

From Newfoundland were received collections of marine invertebrates and of bird-skins. Col. Cecil Clay, of the Department of Justice, collected and presented moose-skins and skulls from Ontario. Skulls of a small quadruped, Richardson's Spermophile, obtained in Manitoba, were received from Mr. E. E. T. Seton. Mr. W. B. Anderson, of Fort Simpson, Northwest Territory, sent a collection of shells. Some fossils from the Chazy formation, Terrebonne, Quebec, and a few Canadian coins were also received.

CENTRAL AMERICA.

A few specimens illustrative of the natural history of Central America were acquired. Among them the following: An iguana from Big Swan Island, from which locality was also obtained a collection of twenty specimens representing five species of land shells, sent by Mr. Charles T. Simpson, and the skull of a Loggerhead turtle (*Thalassochelys caretta*); a series of the woods of Guatemala, and a collection of the fibers, fabrics, herbs, tallow, crude sulphur, etc., of the country were received from the Guatemalan Government through Enrique Toriello. Mr. Anastasio Alfaro, secretary of the National Museum of Costa Rica, sent three photographs of Costa Rican antiquities and a type of a species of rail, *Porzana alfaro.* Mr. José C. Zeledon sent from Costa Rica skins of *Cotinga ridgwayi*, Zeledon, a new species, and a female of *Carpodectes antoniæ*, Zeledon, hitherto undescribed. A peculiar woolen garment worn by Ixtatan Indians of Guatemala, and specimens of the foods used by that tribe, were sent by Prof. Miles Rock.

MEXICO.

Many contributions from this country were received, the most complete being that transmitted by Prof. A. Dugès, of Guanajuato, which embraced bird-skins, shells, fishes, plants, reptiles, insects, mammal skin, and polishing slate. The director of the Mexican Geographical Commission presented a collection of 324 specimens, representing seventy-six species of land, fresh-water, and marine shells. A collection of bird-skins was made at Simora by Lieut. H. C. Benson, U. S. Army. From Hon. John A. Sutter, U. S. consul at Acapulco, were received specimens of cotton, hand-spun yarn, quilt, dye, and shell-fish from which the dye is obtained, from the Indians of Acapulco. Gold and silver ores were sent by Hon. J. T. Morgan, and ores from the Piedras Negras mine were forwarded by the U. S. consul at Piedras Negras. A collection of Mexican pottery, including a clay head, thirty miniature clay heads, two clay toys, six obsidian arrow-heads, etc., was purchased from Rev. Ward Batchelor. A slab of meteoric iron weighing 850 grams, from Toluca, was forwarded by Messrs. Ward & Howell, of Rochester, New York, and a collection of twenty-seven specimens of the marine shells of the Gulf of Mexico, representing twenty species, was received.

SOUTH AMERICA.

Several countries of this continent are represented by small collections or single objects. Among them are the following: Barnacles found attached to a wreck at Payta, Peru, sent by Lieut. W. C. Babcock, U. S. Navy; a crystal from Brazil, sent by Lieut. Commander H. E. Nichols, U. S. Navy; fossil shells from the Pebas group of the valley of the Amazon; six humming-birds, contributed by F. S. Webster; a collection of vegetable fibers from Brazil; a reptile from British Guiana; a South American monkey received from the Zoological Garden of Philadelphia, where it died in captivity; specimens of a grub highly esteemed as food by the natives of Venezuela, found in the heart of palm trees along the Orinoco River. From Santarem, Brazil, were received three bird-skins. Mr. W. E. Curtis, of Chicago, Illinois, sent a small collection of ethnological material from Peru, Ecuador, Bolivia, Chili, Buenos Ayres, and Patagonia, and a specimen of moss from near the Pass of Chicta, Andes

Mountains, 15,000 feet above sea-level.   Mr. C. J. Hering, of Surinam, Dutch Guiana, sent a collection of lepidoptera, reptiles, bird-skins, ethnological objects, etc.   In addition to the above were received a few gourd-bowls, a young deer, and a Chilian coin.

UNITED STATES.

Alabama.—A large collection of archæological objects was gathered by Messrs. Henry J. Biddle and I. C. Russell of the U. S. Geological Survey.   This collection contained 222 specimens, among which were a human skull and bones, 2 bowls, beads, iron knife-blade, baked clay, 2 stone implements, flint chips, shells, and fragments of pottery, found on the bank of Coosa River, in Cherokee County.   A collection consisting of about 350 specimens of shells (*Unio*) from the same locality was sent by Mr. Russell.   A collection of 27 species (22 genera) of Clinton fossils and 2 species (2 genera) of Trenton fossils were sent by the U. S. Geological Survey.   Three specimens of pottery and 2 minerals were also received.

Alaska.—A number of large and valuable collections were received from Alaska, the principal ones being gathered by officers of the U. S. Navy stationed there.   Among these collectors were Lieut. G. M. Stoney, who sent a suit worn by himself while in Alaska, and a collection including ethnological material, and specimens of the different branches of natural history; Lieut. Commander H. E. Nichols, from whom was received a collection of reptiles, crustacea, echinoderms, porpoises and fishes; Capt. C. A. Abbey, U. S. Revenue Marine Steamer *Corwin*, who sent volcanic dust, found on a piece of board at Unga Island; Ensign A. P. Niblack, who sent a specimen each of mink and western porcupine, and also a series of twenty-three photographic negatives of scenes in Alaska; Capt. E. P. Herendeen, who forwarded Eskimo garments from Point Barrow.   Other contributors sent valuable material, among whom may be mentioned S. Applegate, who sent a very large collection of ethnological objects, crustacea, insects, fishes, echinoderms, a valuable series of grasses, etc.   J. W. Johnson forwarded a collection of bird-skins, plants, ethnological objects, etc., from Nushagak.   From W. J. Fisher was received a collection of one hundred and seventy-five ethnological objects, including stone axes, spear-heads, scrapers, snow-knives, pestles, etc.   A collection of Alaskan fossils was received from E. E. Howell, and two specimens of almandite in mica schist were sent by Messrs. Ward & Howell, of Rochester, New York.

Arizona.—The principal collections received from this Territory were those of Lieut. Harry C. Benson, U. S. Army, who was stationed at Fort Huachuca.   When not engaged in military duties he has collected diligently for the Museum, and has sent many interesting birds' nests and eggs.   Several specimens of minerals, insects, birds' nests, silver ore, rocks, and a decoy deer's head, used by the Apache Indians, were also received.

Arkansas.—A few ores and minerals were received from this State, principally those given by the Department of the Interior. A quartz crystal from Crystal Mountain, near Hot Springs, two rock crystals from Ozark Mountains, specimen of pyrolusite from the manganese mining district, and specimens of meteoric iron from Johnson County were contributed. Minerals, rocks, and fish were sent for examination and report.

California.—The collections though small were numerous. Among them may be noted an interesting collection of 98 pearls from California mollusks, sent by Mr. C. R. Orcutt, of San Diego; collections of bird-skins forwarded by Messrs. L. W. Green, L. Belding, John J. Snyder, E. W. Blake, jr., and H. W. Henshaw. F. Stephens sent a rare mammal, the Kangaroo rat (type), (*Dipodomys deserti*). Two blocks of calcite, from Siskiyou County, were given by Prof. J. S. Diller, of the Geological Survey. A mortar from the auriferous gravels on the north side of the American River was presented by H. W. Turner. A very valuable addition was a fossil fish, apparently a fresh-water sculpin, of the genus *Uranidea*, or an allied form of fresh-water Cottoids, found in the tunnel of the Monte Cristo mine on the summit of Spanish Peak, in the auriferous gravel, and sent by John G. Phelps. Chrome ores from Del Norte, Placer, and San Luis Obispo Counties, were presented by the Baltimore Chrome Works.

The State Mining Bureau of California sent shavings of the San Bernardino meteorite, with two photographs of the same object; also, twelve specimens of the mineral Colemanite, from San Bernardino County. Sugar-bearing oak leaves were received from Mr. Livingston Stone.

Colorado.—Of the birds from this State, Mr. Robert Ridgway gave two specimens of Richardson's Merlin, and two other specimens of this species were sent by Dr. Elliott Coues. Col. James Stevenson, of the U. S. Geological Survey, gave seven bird-skins, and C. W. Beckham presented ten specimens, representing six species. Birds' nests were received from H. W. Henshaw, and birds' eggs from A. W. Anthony and Mr. Dennis Gale, of Gold Hill (22 specimens). A few minerals came in, among which were a specimen of astrophyllite in quartz, from El Paso County, and two crystals of almandite in chlorite. A peculiarly colored specimen of the western brook-trout (*Salmo purpuratus*), was also received, through the Fish Commission.

Connecticut.—From Mr. G. Curtis Bishop was received a hawk (*Buteo latissimus*) for examination, and a small collection of birds' eggs was sent by Mr. M. Abbott Frazar in exchange. A specimen of Wall-eyed pike (*Stizostedium vitreum*), from the Connecticut River, was received from Prof. William North Rice, of the Wesleyan University, Middletown, Connecticut, the first of the genus ever found in this region. The Shell-Fish Commission of Connecticut sent 40 specimens of young shad (*Clupea sapidissima*).

Dakota.—Specimens of ore, and rocks stained by decomposition, were sent for examination. From A. T. Sherwood, two crystals of selenite, and from the Etta mine, Rapid City, specimens of tin ore were received.

Delaware.—Only two specimens were received from this State, one of them being a hair-worm, *Gordius* sp., sent by Dr. E. G. Shortlidge, and the other a fish for identification.

District of Columbia.—Among the materials received were a fossil oyster (*Ostrea sellæformis*), sent by John D. Bartlett; a Copper-head snake (*Ancistrodon contortrix*), a Red phalarope, from F. S. Webster; two specimens of lignite from the new reservoir of Washington, a cocoon of *Attacus crecopia* for examination, several Terns (*Sterna forsteri*) given by Thomas Marron, and 19 specimens, 13 species, of birds from H. W. Henshaw.

Florida.—W. H. Ashmead sent 38 specimens of insects. Specimens of Myriapoda were given by C. H. Bollman, also a cocoon of so-called "Electric worm" (*Telea polyphemus*). Several collections of insects (Diptera and Myriapoda) came from E. A. Schwarz. An ornamental gold disk from an Indian mound was sent by S. A. Robinson; an enamel bead, found in a mound, was sent for examination, by Mr. John E. Younglove. Commander L. A. Beardslee, U. S. Navy, presented a collection of fishes from Key West. W. H. Dall made a collection of fishes, mollusks, etc., which he gave to the Museum. Several bird-skins were obtained by exchange with A. P. Chadbourne, and at Key West some bird-skins were obtained by the naturalists on the U. S. Fish Commission steamer *Albatross.* Lieut. J. F. Moser, U. S. Coast Survey steamer *A. D. Bache,* sent a very interesting collection of marine invertebrates from the west coast of Florida. Skeletons and a cranium of a Blackfish (*Globiocephalus,* sp.) came from J. G. Webb, of Sarasota Bay. A young alligator, a Yellow-tailed fish, and six species of marine shells for examination, were also received.

Georgia.—The specimens sent were all for examination and report. Among these were insects, ores, decomposed rock, and stone implements.

Idaho.—The only object received was a specimen of bituminous coal sent for examination by S. D. Edwards.

Illinois.—R. S. Hodge presented some crayfishes, and a bird's nest and eggs were given by W. S. Adams. Plants were sent by H. G. Hodge, a bird by G. F. Morcom, and fresh-water shells by H. A. Pilsbry. Human skulls and bones from mounds and graves in Schuyler and Knox Counties were given by Mrs. Abner Foster.

Indiana.—A large collection of fishes was sent by Prof. O. P. Hay; a drift bowlder of quartz-porphyry was received from F. M. and C. O. Merica. The Hoosier Stone Company sent a specimen of building-stone. Insects were sent by C. H. Bollman and C. E. Rutherford.

Iowa.—Specimens of shells were received from C. R. Keys and H. E. Pilsbury. Sixteen specimens of quartz geodes containing calcite were given in exchange by W. T. Hornaday. J. F. Kemmerfield sent an arrow-head and a wedge-shaped Indian stone implement.

Kansas.—A collection of fishes sent by O. P. Hay, and a few birds' eggs and fishes comprised the gifts from this State. Numerous specimens were sent for examination and report; among them sulphides, quartz crystals, insects, magnesian limestone, zinc-blend, and a portion of the mandible of a fossil horse.

Kentucky.—Prof. J. S. Diller, of the U. S. Geological Survey, sent a specimen of peridotite from Elliott County, and C. U. Shepard, jr., a fragment of meteoric iron. A collection of birds was received from L. O. Pindar. From Ward and Howell came slices of meteoric iron in exchange. J. R. Proctor contributed a piece of rope with crystals of chalcedony clinging to it, found in a gas well.

Louisiana.—Among the objects received were land and fresh-water shells, polishing slate, an iron bullet—probably dropped by one of De Soto's soldiers—a stone ax, crystals of lignite, calcite, and selenite, a collection of rocks, a basket made by an Indian, minerals for examination, and miscellaneous specimens.

Maine.—E. C. Greenwood sent several specimens of birds. A collection of minerals came in from the U. S. Geological Survey, and another from N. H. Perry. In addition to these several minerals, a large quartz crystal, two large specimens of diaspore, and a specimen of green mica were given.

Maryland.—The material from this State was almost exclusively ornithological. Messrs. George and Henry Marshall sent a large number of birds, among them being skins of the Red tailed Hawk and the Red-shouldered Hawk, etc. From other contributors were received Albino robins, Ruffed grouse, Crow, Red crossbill, Cooper's hawk, Mourning dove, Whippoorwill, Screech owl, Short-eared owls, etc. O. N. Bryan gave a large collection of archæological objects from Charles County.

Massachusetts.—Minerals from this State were received from Amherst College, the U. S. Geological Survey, from H. H. Macia, who sent crystals of Diaspore, and Dr. O. J. Shepardson, from whom were received specimens of margarite and diaspore with corundophyllite. Seals were collected for the Museum by the U. S. Fish Commission. Isaac M. Jackson sent birds, and a collection of birds' nests was given by H. W. Henshaw. Eight Mandarin ducks and several fishes, etc., were also received.

Michigan.—Specimens of the Whitefish (*Coregonus clupeiformis*), the Lake Carp, and the Loon (*Colymbus torquatus*) were received. C. H. Bollman sent a collection of insects. Larvæ of *Eristalis* and of a small fly came in, and C. A. Whittmore sent some stalactites and stalagmites for examination.

Minnesota.—C. W. Hall sent four specimens of a fossil brachiopod mollusk (*Orthis*, sp.) from the Trenton formation at Minneapolis, and

J. Parker Norris sent three eggs of a gull, *Larus franklinii.* A collection of insects was sent by C. H. Bollman. A fragment of rock, supposed by the sender to be meteoric, came for examination.

Mississippi.—H. C. Medford sent specimens of a plant, *Hibiscus moscheutos* L., for identification. Ferruginous sandstone, quartz, sulphide of lead, iron, and insect larvæ were sent for examination. A. J. Rowland sent a specimen of meteoric zinc. A fossil from the Blue Rock Bluffs, of Metublie Creek, was received from G. V. Young.

Missouri.—Two collections were received from this State in exchange, one consisting of 53 specimens of quartz from F. P. Greaves, and the other of stone ax, arrow-heads, and flint chips, from Dr. A. D. Thomas.

Montana.—A collection of reptiles was sent by L. L. Kennedy. W. T. Hornaday, acting under the auspices of the Institution, made a collection of skins and skeletons of the buffalo and other mammals. The head of an Elk was deposited by Col. J. D. Wilkins. Specimens of fishes from the Gallatin River came from W. C. Harris. A collection of mammals, silver ore, rocks, wood-opal, minerals, reptiles, bird-skins, etc., was made by Mr. George P. Merrill, in Gallatin County, whilst in the field with the U. S. Geological Survey. C. S. Bement sent one cut sapphire.

Nebraska.—W. L. May sent some minnows, said to have fallen from the clouds in a shower. Rocks from lake beds were collected by George P. Merrill. A Kangaroo Gopher was sent by F. N. Sisk.

Nevada.—The specimens received from this State, were silver ore from John Ivey, minerals from L. C. Russell, cobalt and nickel ore, and other ores for examination.

New Hampshire.—A. P. Chadbourne and S. Albert Shaw sent bird-skins. John I. Legro and C. H. Hitchcock sent minerals.

New Jersey.—J. M. C. Eaton gave specimens of the Jumping Mouse. A Trumpet-fish from J. T. Havens, and a Lumpfish (*Cyclopterus lumpus*) from Joseph Reed were received.

New Mexico.—Dr. M. N. Van Fleet sent specimens of Hair-worms (*Gordius,* sp.); Dr. R. W. Shufeldt, U. S. Army, sent specimens of mice, and 250 specimens of a Salamander (*Amblystoma mavortium*); also birds, birds' eggs, and mammals. Dr. H. C. Yarrow gave a Green-tailed towhee (*Pipilo chlorurus*) from Zuñi. A specimen of cerargyrite was received from Dr. F. W. Taylor. By the Bureau of Ethnology a model of the ruin " Peñasco Blanco" was deposited.

New York.—From the American Museum of Natural History were received in exchange 17 mineral specimens. A large series, embracing 1,152 specimens of Taconic fossils, gathered by Mr. C. D. Walcott, was transferred to the Museum by the Geological Survey. In this series are represented 35 species of 23 genera. Mr. Walcott also obtained two slabs of Potsdam Quartz with ripple marks. A collection of archæological objects was given by W. W. Adams. From D. C. Beard was received a compound nest of the Red-wing blackbird (*Agelaius phœniceus*) and the Marsh wren (*Cistothorus palustris*), both occupied at the same time, and a double nest of the Summer Yellow-bird (*Dendroica œstiva*). G. H. Hudson sent a collection of 31 specimens, 26 species, of butterflies and moths. Among other objects were a Cramp-fish (*Torpedo*, sp.), decomposed tourmaline, larvæ of a Salamander (*Amblystoma*, sp.), apatite, iron ore, and 3 specimens of the Ausable granite.

North Carolina.—A collection of birds' nests and eggs was sent by M. Abbott Frazar in exchange. Minerals, among them a cut sapphire and two specimens of cassiterite, came from Dr. C. W. Dabney, from W. C. Poteat, who also sent some shells, and from T. J. Poyner. A. J. Austin, keeper of Poyner's Hill life-saving station, secured two Blackfish (*Globicephalus*) skeletons. A Bald eagle, several insects, birds' nests and eggs, and Indian stone implements were also contributed.

Ohio.—A collection of archæological objects was sent in exchange by W. C. Cone. H. W. Henshaw gave some birds' nests. A specimen of meteoric iron from a mound near Madisonville was received in exchange from the Peabody Museum, Cambridge, Massachusetts. Oberlin College sent in exchange 28 kinds of corals. A microscopical slide containing what was suppposed to be volcanic dust was sent by G. H. Curtis. This material upon examination proved to be the pollen of some plant. W. H. Crane sent ten specimens of an insect, a new species of *Cis*, from Cincinnati, and other insects were received for examination. The cast of a stone pipe found near Piqua, fossils and minerals for examination, a stone implement found in an ancient Indian camp in Hardin County, and four arrow-heads, were also received.

Oregon.—Among the contributors sending material from Oregon was Dr. J. C. Merrill, of the U. S. Army, who has rendered the Museum much valuable assistance in sending from time to time various specimens of natural history. From him this year come, among other things, five shrews, three gophers, two mice, and a chipmunk. A collection of fossils was received from Prof. T. Condon, and a collection of minerals from H. C. Durkee. W. B. Malleis sent skins of grouse and pheasants. The California State Mining Bureau sent ten specimens of priceite. A. W. Anthony sent a nest and five eggs of a Jay (*Perisoreus obscurus*). Specimens of obsidian were also received.

Pennsylvania.—A collection of plants numbering 269 specimens was purchased from Dr. J. F. Brunner. The Baltimore Chrome Works sent specimens of chrome ore. Robert Hare Powel's Sons gave a large collection of ores, minerals, etc., which had been exhibited in New Orleans in 1884. "Lead buckles" were sent by Harrison Bros. & Co., and a specimen of cassinite by Dr. Isaac Lea. Mr. Willard Nye, jr., gave three specimens of Pileated woodpecker (*Hylotomus pileatus*).

Rhode Island.—D. T. Church sent specimens of fishes.

South Carolina.—William Brewster sent a bird's nest and five eggs. A Barn-owl was given by Major T. B. Ferguson. A carved powder-horn, a relic of the French and Indian wars, was donated by Master C. McMichael Barton. A tortoise, an Indian ceremonial weapon, and a species of frog were given by Mr. Frank Burns, of the U. S. Geological Survey, who also sent mollusks. Mr. George H. Ingraham sent specimens of clay mixed with sand, thrown up out of the earth in Charleston during the earthquake.

Tennessee.—Dr. J. C. McCormick, of Strawberry Plains, sent several collections of human bones, teeth, fragments of flint, pottery, shells, etc. Four shells were received from Miss A. E. Law, and examples of meteoric iron from Prof. Ira Sayles. A carved stone pipe and small copper ax were lent for examination by J. B. Nicklin. A specimen of meteoric iron was received in exchange from Ward and Howell. A number of objects were received for examination, among them a Rhinoceros beetle, manganese ore, lithographic limestone, quartz, limonite, pyrite, pig-iron, etc.

Texas.—Among contributors sending ornithological material from this State were William Lloyd, who sent 40 specimens of birds, representing 22 species; L. C. Leith, who contributed 3 specimens of the Roseate spoon-bills (*Platalea ajaja*); and M. Abbott Frazar, from whom came 13 birds' eggs. Land and fresh-water shells were sent by H. A. Pilsbry, W. W. Westgate, Robert T. Hill, and Samuel Hammontree, who also sent the lower valve of an extinct species of the Rudistæ (*Radiolites austinensis*). A Virginia deer (*Cariacus virginianus*), plants, and minerals were sent for examination. A small collection of garnets was purchased from S. G. Maxwell. The hind feet of an ass, showing abnormal development, together with a photograph of the same, were sent by J. C. Baldwin. Dr. R. W. Noble gave a fossil fish-head, found embedded in blue slate rock 20 feet below the surface. Several species of fish were given by R. A: Golden, a fish-dealer of Washington.

Utah.—Only two contributions were received. Dr. F. W. Taylor sent specimens of silver from the Storm King mine, and Dr. A. S. Packard, of Brown University, gave a specimen of a peculiar snail (*Helix subrupicola*) from Clinton.

Vermont.—A beetle (*Adalia bipuncta*) was sent by Rev. J. W. Guernsey, and Prof. Henry M. Seely sent 31 specimens of *Nothozoa vermontana* and several specimens of *Olenellus.*

Virginia.—Collections of birds and nests were made by Robert Ridgway. A Great Horned owl, buzzard, Red-tailed hawk, Red tailed woodpecker, and several other birds were given. Prof. I. H. Morrison sent limonite crystals, pseudomorph after pyrite, and polished dufrenite; also, a slab of dendrites from the Lower Silurian formation. Two specimens of marble from Loudoun County, one cut moonstone, iron and manganese ore, limonite, iron pyrites, copper ore, black quartz, quartz with particles of mica, iron pyrites in quartz, meteoric iron, hematite containing a small amount of titanium were received, most of the specimens being sent for examination. From Mount Vernon were received several specimens of the Sand adder (*Heterodus*) and a "nest" of a hornet (*Vespa maculata*), containing a large number of insects, given by Mr. J. H. Kuehling. A few insects, among the number the larvæ of *Citheronia regalis*, were received. S. B. Hoopman sent a model of a "stone chair" found in a mountain near Hillsborough. Several small collections of Indian beads, pottery, and a rude chipping tool were received. J. McNamara sent a camphene chandelier, illustrating a method of house illumination prior to the use of gas. Several specimens of fishes and an Albino deer were also received.

Washington Territory.—Dr. W. E. Everett sent a Wood rat and birds' nests. A collection of ethnological objects was received from Charles Willoughby, U. S. Indian agent at Quinaielt.

West Virginia.—G. F. Kunz, of New York, sent eleven fragments of meteoric iron from Jenny's Creek. A "water bug" (*Belostoma americana*) was sent for examination. Dr. J. R. Mathers sent a Rattlesnake. A collection of 14 species, 13 genera, of Carboniferous fossils came from August D. Selby.

Wisconsin.—Capt. B. F. Goss sent a nest and eight eggs of a Wren (*Regulus satrapa*). C. H. Slayton sent a species of tape-worm taken from the white of an egg, and Andrew Oleson sent specimens of quartz and mica, both for examination.

Wyoming.—Col. James Stevenson, of the Bureau of Ethnology, sent eight garnet pebbles and garnet in quartz.

WEST INDIES.

The principal collection from these Islands was received from the Wesleyan University, of Middletown, Connecticut, and consisted of 484 specimens of sponges and 246 specimens of coral gathered in the Bermudas by Dr. G. Brown Goode, in 1876–1879, for the university, and now transferred to the National Museum in exchange. Prof. Alexander Agassiz, of Cambridge, Massachusetts, sent a collection of about 500 specimens of mollusks and brachiopods (representing 205 species), obtained by the Coast Survey steamer *Blake* in the West Indies and Gulf of Mexico, in the years 1876, 1877, and 1878. Mr. John Gundlach, of Termina, Cuba, sent 3 species of birds, one of which, a hawk (*Accipiter fringilloides*), was new to the collection. General D. E. Coombs, of Baracoa, Cuba, sent 2 specimens of Chromium ore. Eight specimens of Audubon's Shearwater (*Puffinus auduboni*) were received from C. J. Maynard & Co., and Mr. Charles B. Cory sent a collection of bird-skins.

ASIA.

Dr. D. Bethune McCartee made several additions to his already large Japanese and Chinese collections now in the Museum. Among the specimens received were mussel-shells with images of Buddha painted on the inside, a geomantic compass, a spoon made from the pearly nautilus-shell, such as is used by Buddhist priests in Siam for eating rice. He also deposited a Japanese stiletto.

Ethnological objects from Persia, India, and Japan were received from Mr. Charles Heape in exchange.

Dr. N. McP. Ferebee, of the U. S. S. *Trenton*, sent a collection of fishes, marine invertebrates, reptiles, etc., from China, Japan, and Corea.

Three trunks made of pig-skin, and two fragments of the "Great Wall," were received from China.

The Bureau of Education at Tokio, Japan, sent a large collection of ethnological objects, fishes, and minerals, and a valuable series of 104 bird-skins. Prof. R. Collett and Mr. Kneeland also made interesting contributions from Japan. P. L. Jouy presented some valuable objects from Japan and Corea. Dr. L. Stejneger contributed a collection of bird-skins, 40 specimens (17 species), from Kamschatka. This collection was an especially valuable addition, containing several species new to the Museum collection. He also contributed bird-skins from Japan.

From India specimens of meteoric iron were given by Ward & Howell, and a bird-skin by H. K. Coale. Mrs. Helen Tompkins sent from Lahore two tea-pots made of Cashmere lacquer.

AUSTRALIA.

Joseph S. Spinney forwarded some seed of the "Blue Bush" and "Salt Bush," collected by H. C. Mais.

A "Great kingfisher" (*Dacelo gigas*) was received from the Zoological Society of Philadelphia.

OCEANICA.

A collection of ethnological objects from Oceanica was received from the Musée de Trocadero in exchange.

Several Tasmanian mammals were received from the Ballarat Fish Acclimatization Society.

From Mr. Charles Heape, of Manchester, England, were received, in exchange, ethnological objects from New Guinea, Solomon Island, and New Hebrides.

Ethnological objects from New Britain, Savage Island, Admiralty Island, Tonga, New Ireland, Fiji Islands, and Navigator's Islands were received.

Valdemar Knudsen sent bird-skins from the Hawaiian Islands, whence also were obtained a bat, presented by C. N. Spencer, and a collection of mammals and 37 bird-skins. Most of the latter are new to the collection, while no less than 5 are new to science.

The U. S. S. *Mohican* was sent by the Secretary of the Navy to Easter Island, where a most interesting collection of archæological objects was obtained.

The Auckland Museum, in Auckland, New Zealand, sent a large collection of bird-skins, including 104 specimens.

A Fijian war club was received from Dr. Browers, and a collection of bird-skins was given in exchange by Oberlin College, Ohio.

EUROPE.

Mr. Thomas Wilson deposited a large archæological collection which he had gathered while residing in Nice, France, as United States consul. This includes specimens from Italy, France, England, Switzerland, and Sardinia.

B. Sturtz sent in exchange a collection of minerals from Germany, Switzerland, Norway, Sweden, and Austria. Minerals were also received from Germany, France, Italy, Norway, and Switzerland. F. W. True gave a collection of coins from Germany, France, and Switzerland.

A collection of shells from Northern Europe was sent by Rev. A. M. Norman, and 5 specimens (4 species) of European birds were given by Dr. L. Stejneger.

From France 4 specimens of cuprite altering to malachite were received from S. C. H. Bailey in exchange. Specimens of diptera were received.

A fossil cephalopod from Germany was sent by Prof. C. Schluter, of Bonn am Rhein.

From Italy was received a specimen of meteoric iron.

H. C. Hallowell sent in exchange minerals from Norway.

A spheroid of granite from Tonne, Sardinia, was sent by B. Sturtz.

From the Academy of Science at St. Petersburg, Russia, were received two specimens of a new Cyprinoid fish (*Phoxinus stagnalis*, sp. nov.).

A collection of rocks and minerals from Sweden was purchased for 200 francs from L. J. Igelström.

A collection of Irish archæological objects was sent by Mr. James F. Johnson, of Holywood.

CO-OPERATION OF THE DEPARTMENTS AND BUREAUS OF THE GOVERNMENT.

The courteous assistance rendered by the Departments of the Government has as usual been the means of adding much valuable material to the national collections, and has renewed the obligations of the Museum.

DEPARTMENT OF STATE.

Hon. S. S. Cox, United States minister to Turkey, sent a Turkish caique with oars and dresser from Constantinople, which unfortunately was destroyed by the carelessness of the transportation agents.

General A. C. Jones, United States consul at Chin Kiang, China, sent a brick from the " Great Wall."

John A. Sutter, United States consul at Acapulco, Mexico, contributed cotton, hand-spun yarn, quilt, purple dye, and shell from which the dye is made, used by Indians of Acapulco.

Jacob Schoenhof, United States consul at Tunstall, England, transmitted a case of scoured wools.

Charles P. Williams, United States consul at Rouen, France, forwarded specimens of flax, and consular report 67, containing a statement concerning the same; also specimens of ramie fiber in different stages of manufacture.

V. O. King, United States consul-general, Bogota, sent a collection illustrative of the natural history of the United States of Colombia.

TREASURY DEPARTMENT.

In 1840 the Imaum of Muscat presented to the United States Government a collection of 106 diamond brilliants, 27 diamond "chips," 148 perforated pearls, 2 large pear-shaped pearls, gold plate, inside lining of snuff-box, gold ornament, 2 lumps of gold, and bottle of "attar of roses." This collection has since the time of its presentation been kept in a vault at the United States Treasury, and was this year transferred to the custody of the Museum.

Life-Saving Service.—A. J. Austin, keeper Poyner's Hill life-saving station, North Carolina, sent two skeletons of a Blackfish (*Globicephalus melas*), and Joseph Reed, keeper life-saving station at Tom's River, New Jersey, sent a Lumpfish (*Cyclopterus lumpus*).

Light-House Board.—Herbert M. Knowles, keeper of light-house, Point Judith, Rhode Island, sent fishes in alcohol.

U. S. Revenue Marine.—A specimen of the rare Banded-seal (*Histriophoca equidens*) was presented by Capt. M. A. Healy, U. S. R. M. S. *Bear.* volcanic dust from Nuga Island was transmitted by Capt. C. A. Abbey, U. S. R. M. S. *Corwin.*

WAR DEPARTMENT.

Col. John D. Wilkins, U. S. Army, Fort Keogh, Montana, sent the head of a Deer (*Cervus canadensis*).

Maj. W. S. Beebe, U. S. Army, Brooklyn, New York, sent a cast of a carved stone of green serpentine.

Capt. H. Catley, U. S. Army, sent a Blue Spotted sunfish.

Capt. B. F. Goss, U. S. Army, contributed nest and eight eggs of *Regulus satrapa.*

Dr. J. C. Merrill, U. S. Army, sent several collections of mammal-skins and a collection of insects.

Dr. James Reagles, U. S. Army, sent a decoy (deer's head) used by an Apache Indian, found in a cave on the east fork of the Verde River.

Dr. R. W. Shufeldt, U. S. Army, sent 250 specimens of *Amblystoma,* 3 specimens of a striped snake (*Eutænia vagrans*), also several birdskins and birds' eggs.

Capt. Henry Romeyn, U. S. Army, Fort Keogh, Montana, sent specimens of a turbot (*Lota maculosa*) and of the blistering beetles (*Epicauta maculata*).

Lieut. H. C. Benson, U. S. Army, Fort Huachuca, Arizona, sent several collections of birds' eggs and bird-skins.

Dr. H. C. Yarrow, U. S. Army, sent samples of food used by the Indians of Venezuela, and reptiles from the Island of Trinidad.

Charles Ruby, U. S. Navy, sent some natural concretions, some fossils, and a Civet cat.

Sergt. S. Applegate, U. S. Signal Corps, sent from Unalaska, Alaska, a large collection of ethnological objects, crustacea, insects, and grasses.

Acknowledgment is here made for the continued service of Dr. H. C. Yarrow and Capt. C. E. Bendire as honorary curators, the former of the Department of Reptiles and the latter of the Department of Birds Eggs.

NAVY DEPARTMENT.

The Secretary of the Navy rendered a most important service to the National Museum and to science by detailing the U. S. S. *Mohican*, Commander Benjamin F. Day, to obtain a collection of stone images and archæological objects from Easter Island.

Lieut. Seth M. Ackley, U. S. Navy, sent a fragment from the "Great Wall" of China.

Lieut. W. C. Babcock, U. S. Navy, sent barnacles found attached to a wreck at Payta, Peru, and a fish.

Lieut. L. A. Beardslee sends a specimen of fungus.

A collection of silver and copper coins were given by Lieut. T. Dix Bolles.

Surgeon N. McP. Ferebee, U. S. S. *Trenton*, sent a large collection of fishes, marine invertebrates, reptiles, and insects from Japan, China, and Corea.

Capt. E. P. Henderson sent a collection of Eskimo clothing from Point Barrow, Alaska.

Lieut. J. F. Moser, U. S. Navy, of the Coast Survey steamer *A. D. Bache*, sent two collections of marine invertebrates from the west coast of Florida.

Lieut. H. E. Nichols, commanding U. S. S. *Pinta*, sent a collection of reptiles, crustacea, worms, echinoderms, and fishes.

Lieut. R. E. Peary, U. S. Navy, gave a collection of shells, minerals, volcanic rock, fish, mineral dust, etc.

Lieut. George M. Stoney, U. S. Navy, sent a large collection of nests, ethnological objects, mammals, insects, plants, bird-skins, birds' eggs, and a suit worn by the donor while in Alaska.

Lieut. E. H. Taunt, U. S. Navy, sent a collection of knives, spears, shields, etc.; native cloth, embroidered and dyed, from Central Africa.

Paymaster E. B. Webster, U. S. Navy, sent a Chilkaht drum, Tinné Indian snow-shoes, and a fishing catamaran, full rigged, from Pernambuco, Brazil.

Ensign A. P. Niblack, U. S. Navy, sent from Alaska the skin of a

Western porcupine, and 23 photographic negatives taken in Alaska and elsewhere.

Ensign W. E. Safford, U. S. Navy, U. S. S. *Mohican*, sent 5 bird-skins from the Isthmus of Panama; bird-skins, birds' nests and eggs, archæological and ethnological objects, marine shells, fresh-water and land shells, marine invertebrates, reptiles, etc., from various localities.

Dr. H. G. Beyer, U. S. Navy, has continued to act as honorary curator of the section of Materia Medica. Lieut. T. Dix Bolles, Paymaster E. B. Webster, and Dr. F. S. Nash have rendered valuable services in connection with the Department of Ethnology in the Museum.

POST-OFFICE DEPARTMENT.

A collection of United States postage-stamps, newspaper wrappers, stamped envelopes, and newspaper stamps, 170 specimens in all, was received from the Postmaster-General.

DEPARTMENT OF THE INTERIOR.

A collection of minerals from Arkansas and specimens of petrified wood from the Yellowstone National Park were received. From the Office of Indian Affairs was sent a set of bows and arrows. Charles Willoughby, United States Indian agent at Quinaielt, Washington Territory, sent a collection of ethnological objects.

U. S. GEOLOGICAL SURVEY.

As in previous years, a large amount of valuable material, including not less than 5,000 specimens, has been received from the U. S. Geological Survey, transferred by Major J. W. Powell, Director of the Survey. Among the collections received from this source were the following: Clinton fossils, 22 genera, 27 specimens, from Etowah and DeKalb Counties, Alabama; also, Trenton fossils, 2 species; Potsdam quartzite, with peculiar markings; Ausable granite, 3 specimens; Taconic fossils, 23 genera, 35 species, 1,152 specimens, collected by C. D. Walcott; Pogonip fossils, 31 genera, 68 species, 1,202 specimens, collected by Mr. Walcott; Trenton fossils, 19 genera, 26 species, from Nevada; a collection of fossils, rocks, sponges, etc., from Florida; Clinton and Oriskany fossils, 6 species; fossil bones from Mississippi and fossil wood from California and South Carolina; a mortar from the auriferous gravels at the north side of the American River at Folsom, California; gold in quartz, from Sky High mine, Plumas County, California; rocks, ores, etc., collected in Texas and Louisiana by L. C. Johnson; two slabs of marble from Loudoun County, Virginia; fragments of upper and lower molar teeth of a fossil horse, and fragments of mastodon molars, collection of fossil fishes, mammals, silver, ores, rocks, wood, opal, and minerals, collected in Gallatin County, Montana, by George P. Merrill, while in the field with the Geological Survey; collection of minerals from Arkansas and Yellowstone Park, and ferruginous concretions from Maryland.

Very valuable services have been rendered by the following gentlemen, who are acting as honorary curators in the Museum: Mr. W. H. Dall, Department of Mollusks; Mr. C. D. Walcott and Dr. C. A. White, Departments of Paleozoic and Mesozoic Invertebrate Fossils; Prof. Lester F. Ward, Departments of Fossil and Recent Plants, and Prof. F. W. Clarke, Department of Minerals.

DEPARTMENT OF JUSTICE.

Col. Cecil Clay, chief clerk of this Department, sent skins and a skull of a moose (*Alces machlis*) and photographs of cow-moose.

DEPARTMENT OF AGRICULTURE.

Dr. A. K. Fisher, of the Bureau of Economic Ornithology, sent Sparrow-hawk, Red-tailed hawks, Red-shouldered hawks, Red-breasted merganser, and birds' nests and eggs. The Museum still enjoys the co-operation of Prof. C. V. Riley, the entomologist of the Department, as honorary curator of insects.

U. S. FISH COMMISSION.

Several collections of marine invertebrates, fishes, birds, shells, reptiles, etc., have been received; also birds' nests and eggs, skulls of sailfish, birds, lice from seals, 3 worm-eaten planks taken from schooner *Melissa D. Robbins*, shark, fish, seals, fungi, etc. From Major T. B. Ferguson was received a specimen of Barn-owl, and from C. H. Townsend 15 specimens of *Menopoma* and eggs. Mr. Townsend made an exploration of Swan and Grand Cayman Islands, and has already forwarded a collection of birds, concerning which Mr. Ridgway, curator of birds, makes the following statement:

Swan Island.—The collection from this place embraces 31 species, of which 22 are land birds. Of the latter 17 are migrants from Eastern North America; *Coccyzus seniculus* is West Indian and Central American; *Columba leucocephala* belongs to the coast of Honduras and some of the Greater Antilles; *Mimocichla rubripes* (of which a good series was collected) is identical with the Cuban species, instead of being that found on Grand Cayman (*M. ravida* Cory); *Contopus albicollis* Lawr? (2 specimens) is probably identical with a Yucatan species, and *Dendroica vitellina* Cory, is identical with a species found elsewhere only on Grand Cayman. The only new form is a *Butorides*, allied to *B. virescens*, but altogether darker in coloration, and perhaps different enough to be considered specifically distinct.

The water-birds include five specimens of the following: *Tringa maculata, Ereunetes pusillus, Totanus flavipes, Porzana carolina, Sula cyanops, S. piscator, S. sula,* and *Fregetta aquila.*

Grand Cayman.—Mr. Townsend's collection from this island contains 12 species, including 5 of the 13 new species obtained by Mr. Cory's collector, viz: *Certhiola sharpei, Dendroica vitellina, Centurus cayman-*

ensis (good series), *Quiscalus caymanensis*, *Myiarchus denigratus*, and *Vireo caymanensis*. Mr. Townsend also collected a good series of the *Dendroica* which Mr. Cory identified (from a very poor specimen) as *D. petechis gundlachi*, which proves to be a very strongly characterized new race, not specially near to anything else.

Notwithstanding the very limited time spent on Grand Cayman Mr. Townsend did remarkably well, and the specimens secured by him are in fine plumage and beautifully prepared.

Although the results attained on Swan Island are disappointing, they show clearly that that island is, geologically, of very recent formation, and none of the birds (except the *Butorides*, which is a peculiarly "plastic" type) have yet had time to become differentiated into local forms. Additional collections are expected and will be referred to in the next report.

BUREAU OF ETHNOLOGY.

A series of 30 photographs of Apache Indians—10 of the Sacs and Foxes, and 39 of Winnebagoes, Utes, and Osages—was received. Models of the pueblos Bonito and Shemopavi, and ruin of Peñasco Blanco were also transferred. These numbered about 400 specimens in all. Dr. Washington Matthews sent a woolen blanket worn by a Navajo Indian. Prof. H. W. Henshaw sent birds' nests, eggs, and skeleton.

Mr. W. H. Holmes, of the Bureau, has continued to act as honorary curator of the Department of American Aboriginal Pottery.

EXPLORATIONS.

It is deemed appropriate to mention in this report certain explorations which have been made during the year, and which have redounded to the advantage of the Museum.

An expedition under the direction of Mr. William T. Hornaday was sent to Montana in May, 1886, in search of buffalo. The object of this undertaking was to secure a sufficient number of specimens for exhibition and for exchange with other museums. A subsequent expedition was sent out in the fall of the same year. The results have been highly gratifying. Special mention is made in this connection of the valued co-operation rendered to the Institution in this enterprise by the War Department, the Northern Pacific Railroad, and the Chicago, Milwaukee and St. Paul Railroad.

In addition to the collection of mammal skins and skeletons obtained by Mr. Hornaday on his first expedition, was a small collection of bird skeletons and skins.

The following is a complete list of the specimens obtained:

Antelope, *Antilocapra americana*, 2 skins and 3 skeletons.
Prairie Hare, *Lepus campestris*, skin and skeleton.
Wood Hare, *Lepus sylvaticus*, 2 skins.
Pale Chipmunk, *Tamias asiaticus pallidus*, skin.
Coyote, *Canis latrans*, skin.
Buffalo, *Bison americanus*, 3 skins, 7 skulls, and 5 skeletons.

* Accession 17750.

Eastern Striped Spermophile, *Spermophilus tridecim-lineatus* (skin.)
White-footed Mouse, *Hesperomys leucopus*, skin.
Muskrat, *Fiber zibethicus*, 3 skins.
Sage Cock, *Centrocercus urophasianus*, 2 skeletons.
Marsh Harrier, *Circus hudsonius*, skeleton.
Blue-winged Teal, *Querquedula discors*, skeleton.
Shoveller Duck, *Spatula clypeata*, skeleton.
Blue-headed Grackle, *Scolecophagus cyanocephalus*, skeleton.
Cliff Swallow, *Petrochelidon lunifrons*, 2 skeletons.
Red Thrasher, *Harporhynchus rufus*, 2 skeletons.
Lark Bunting, *Calamospiza melanocorys*, 3 skeletons.
Shore Lark, *Eremophila alpestris*, skeleton.
Lark Finch, *Chondestes grammacus*, skeleton.
Western Mourning Dove, *Zenaidura macroura*, skeleton.
Mountain Plover, *Ægialitis montana*, skeleton.

As the result of the second expedition quite a large collection of skins, skeletons, and skulls of buffalo, deer, antelopes, wolves, and smaller animals was received.* The collection included the following species: *Bison americanus, Canis latrans, Antilocapra americana, Cariacus macrotis, C. virginianus, Vulpes velox,* and *Taxidea americana.*

One of the buffaloes, an old bull, the most conspicuous of the group now being mounted by Mr. Hornaday for exhibition in the Museum, has attracted considerable attention. This specimen was examined by several gentlemen who from familiarity with the animal in its native condition were competent to express an opinion as to the accuracy of the taxidermist's work. Among the gentlemen who examined it were General Stewart Van Vliet, of the U. S. Army, and Col. James Stevenson, of the Bureau of Ethnology. Both of these gentlemen expressed their opinion in writing, and copies of their letters are herewith given:

WASHINGTON, D. C., *March* 10, 1887.

MY DEAR PROFESSOR BAIRD: On the receipt of your letter of the 6th instant I saw General Sheridan, and yesterday we called on your taxidermist and examined the buffalo bull he is setting up for the Museum. I don't think I have ever seen a more splendid specimen in my life. General Sheridan and I have seen millions of the buffalo on the plains in former times. I have killed hundreds, but I never killed a larger specimen than the one in the possession of your taxidermist.

General Sheridan thought the animal was too tall, but the taxidermist showed us, in his note-book, the measurements he made of the animal when he shot him, and they agreed with the stuffed animal. I thought that the left hind leg might be brought forward 6 inches. This would make the animal look a little shorter, but I doubt if I would do even this. It is a magnificent specimen as it is, and perfectly natural. You will have this consolation, anyhow, even if the animal is exaggerated—which he is not—and that is, not one in ten thousand who looks at him ever has or ever will see a live buffalo.

Yours, sincerely,

STEWART VAN VLIET,
Brevet Major-General U. S. Army.

Prof. SPENCER F. BAIRD,
Smithsonian Institution, Washington.

---

* Accession 18617.

SMITHSONIAN INSTITUTION, BUREAU OF ETHNOLOGY,
Washington, D. C., April 14, 1887.

DEAR SIR: After having made two visits especially to examine the buffalo bull which you recently secured from the West, and the mounting of which you have just about completed, I beg to freely express my opinion in regard to the same; that is, as to the general correctness of the attitude, shape, and appearance of the specimen. At first sight I would say that it appears too full about the rump; in the next place the specimen appeared somewhat lengthy, and the vertebral ridge does not seem quite prominent or sharp enough, especially to the rear of the loins. I think, however, as to the criticism first expressed, after a closer examination of the robe or coat, it is quite evident that the animal was in an unusually fleshy condition, as the coating of hair is the finest and heaviest I ever saw on a bull, either young or old, and this quite satisfactorily accounts for the fullness of the rump and the hind quarters. As to the second question, that is the length, I find upon examination of over two hundred measurements of buffalo bulls made by myself both before and subsequent to the war, when buffalo were counted by the millions, and the best specimens were available, that your specimen is as nearly correct in every respect as it is possible to make it. I find also upon examination that the profusion of wool along the back fully accounts for the apparent defect in the prominence of the backbone.

On general principles I would say from an extensive personal experience in skinning buffalo and preparing and mounting specimens during a period of many years, when the entire northern and western parts of our country were roamed over by vast herds of buffalo, that you have been most fortunate in securing one of the finest, if not the finest, specimen I ever saw, almost perfect in every respect, and in my opinion beyond criticism in the completeness of mounting, anatomical appearance, and naturalness of attitude.

I do not think that any one could safely venture to criticise any feature of the specimen referred to who has not killed, measured, and mounted specimens themselves.

Very respectfully, etc.,

JAMES STEVENSON.

WILLIAM T. HORNADAY, Esq.,
Taxidermist, U. S. National Museum.

A full account of these expeditions is given in a special paper prepared by Mr. Hornaday and published in Section III of this report.

Mr. C. G. Pringle, an accomplished botanist, went to northern Mexico under the auspices of Harvard University and the Smithsonian Institution for the purpose of securing botanical and general natural history collections.

Dr. T. H. Bean, on a cruise in the U. S. Fish Commission steamer *Albatross,* investigated the movements of the " southern mackerel."

A party sent out by the U. S. Geological Survey to make explorations in the Upper Mississippi Valley was accompanied by Dr. R. R. Gurley, of the Museum, who went for the purpose of securing additional material for the collection of Cambrian fossils in the Museum. This party left in June, and nothing has yet been heard as to the results of Dr. Gurley's work.

Through the courtesy of the Secretary of the Navy a valuable collection of stone objects was obtained from Easter Island. A full account of this collection is given on pages 15–16.

SECTION II.

REPORTS OF THE CURATORS OF THE NATIONAL MUSEUM UPON THE
PROGRESS OF THEIR WORK DURING THE YEAR
ENDING JUNE 30, 1887.

REPORT ON THE DEPARTMENT OF ETHNOLOGY IN THE NATIONAL MUSEUM, 1887.

By Otis T. Mason, *Curator.*

During the fiscal year 1886–'87 the Department of Ethnology has received many important additions. Chief among these may be mentioned a beautiful series of Greenland costumes, from Mrs. Lilla May Pavy; a collection of costumes and implements from northern Alaska, from Mr. E. P. Herendeen; many valuable articles from Kotzebue Sound, given by Lieut. George M. Stoney, U. S. Navy; Mr. S. Applegate's collection from Togiak River, Alaska; Mr. J. W. Johnson's collection from Fort Alexander, Alaska; Mr. William J. Fisher's collection from Ugashik, Alaska; Mr. Charles Willoughby's collection from the Quinaielt Indians, Washington Territory; an immense number of ethnological objects from the Zuñi and Moki pueblos, secured by Col. James Stevenson and the Bureau of Ethnology. A collection of rare and valuable specimens from the Congo region, brought by Lieut. E. H. Taunt, U. S. Navy; many precious objects from China and Japan, the gift of Dr. D. Bethune McCartee; and an exceedingly valuable series from the Department of Education in Japan, illustrating the common industries of that country.

The last-named series especially illustrates a method of collecting which the curator thinks should supersede, as far as possible, that which has formerly prevailed.

In following out this plan, the curator has sought to procure complete "outfits" of varied industries, with many pictures of steps in art processes, and minute detail of everything done and said from beginning to end. All of these furnish a polyorganic unit, to which desultory material may be referred.

In pursuance of the plan hitherto adopted of elaborating series of specimens on purely natural history principles, the cradles of the Museum, the scrapers of American savages, and the carrying apparatus pertaining to the human pack-animal have been arranged and described.

The chief labor of this department during the year, however, and the one of most lasting value, is the arrangement of the entire Eskimo collection according to our system, by Lieut. T. Dix Bolles, U. S. Navy.

65

An exhaustive statement concerning this work accompanies this report, and will enable scholars to know the riches and deficiencies of the National Museum.

As soon as our whole series can be worked out on the same plan, the Museum will furnish a type series of all savage apparatus.

During the first half of this fiscal year the curator was favored with the assistance of Paymaster Webster, U. S. Navy.

The following is a comprehensive list of accessions to the ethnological department, arranged by countries, and shows the chief source of supply to this department of the National Museum:

Lapland.—Dr. Emil Bessels (accession 17867): Pipe and case.

Greenland.—Mrs. Lilla May Pavy (accession 17854): Kayaks (2); umiak (1); dog-harness (1); sledge (1); long boots (1 pair); slippers (1 pair); belt (1); bag (1); hand-bag (1); mats (3); hassock (1); eider-skin cloak (1); cape (1); eider-skin muffs (2); wristlets (1 pair); eider foot-muff (1); eider-duck skins (3); beaded collar (1); ivory counters (95 pieces, 1 set); paper-knives (2); hand-bag (1). Dr. Emil Bessels (accession 17800): Model of child's sled (1); snow-knife (1); woman's knife (1); parka (1). R. E. Peary (accession 18485): Model of kayak and equipments. Capt. J. O. Spicer (accession 18669): Arctic cotton. Dr. R. M. Stone (accession 10127): Slippers (1 pair).

Cape Barrow, Alaska.—E. P. Herendeen (accession 19110): Boy's gloves (1 pair); infants' suits (2); infant's mitts (1 pair); man's coat (1); belt (1); tobacco-pouch (1); fire-bag (1); woman's coat (1); man's dancing coat (1); man's breeches (1 pair); man's winter boots (1 pair).

Kotzebue Sound, Alaska.—Lieut. George M. Stoney, U. S. Navy (accessions 18491 and 18616): Shaman's cup (1); dance paint (1); ivory carvings (4); ornament (1); doll-head (1); quoit pegs (2); top (1); belt-box (1); man's costume (1); woman's pants (1 pair); clothes-bag (1); combs (6); pipes (2); snuff-tube (1); dippers (2); snuff muller and pestle (1); fish-hooks (4); line eye (1); goose-snares (2); nets (7); seine needles (2); mesh-spacers (2); mesh weights (3); net-sinker (1); snow-shoe needle (1); snow-shoes (2 pairs); seal-hide line (1); harpoon lines (2); snow-goggles (1 pair); bow (1); arrows (9); quiver (1); arrow-pointer (1); flint-flaker (1); arrow wrench (1); knife-sharpener (1); spokeshave knives (2); handle of woman's knife (1); skin-scraper (1); fuller's earth (1); bark-peeler (1); baskets (3); box (1); spoons (2); pouches (4); sewing box (1); needle-case (1); model of snow-shovel (1); pickax (1); drill parts (2); buoy-mouth (1); raw sinew (1); picked sinew (1); suit of fur clothes (1).

St. Lawrence Island, Alaska.—E. W. Nelson (accession ——): Parts of harpoons (17); parts of bird tridents (2 sets); fish hooks and lines (20); sinkers (4); float (1); ice-creepers (7); arrows (3); bird bolas (2); parts of fox-trap (3); bird-arrow points (3); snares (14); bailers (3); oar-locks (1 pair); shovel-blades (2); bone wedge (1); thongs (4); toggles (3); jade adze-blade (1); drills (5); drill socket (1); slate knife-blades (2); woman's knives (6); carving tools (6); ivory charger (1); spacer (1); pipes (2); comb (1); armor plates (1 piece); ivory carvings (19); seal gut (1 roll); spoon (1).

Togiak River, Alaska.—S. Applegate (accession 18036): Masks (7); dance-house ornament (1); charm (1); labret (1); belt ornament (1); bead-spacer (1); chain of walrus whiskers (1); head-dresses (6); finger-masks (4 pairs); dolls (33); bull-roarer (1); combs (3); ear-rings (7 pairs); ivory carving (1); bird-arrow head (1); traps for ermine (20); sinker (1); fish-hooks (15); model of Kayak (1); harpoon points (3); beluga spears (4); harpoon fore-shafts (2); boat-book (1); snow-goggles (2 pairs); skin-scrapers (13); fat-scrapers (2); leather-crimper (1); clay pot (1); lamps (3); wooden boxes (3); wooden cup (1); grass-basket (1); bag-fasten-

Togiak River, Alaska—Continued.

ers (31); net-needles (2); mesh-measurer (1); piece of netting (1); fishing-line (1); awls (3); carving-knife (1); powder chargers (3); cap-boxes (3); toggles (3); needle-cases (12); thimbles (10); ivory rifle-bullets (7); chisels (4); daggers (10); berry-mashers (4); wooden tray (1); snow-knives (15); women's knives (12); adze (1); wedges (3); saw (1); spoons (9); fire-making sets (2 and 3 odd pieces); mittens (1 pair); grass-shoes (1 pair); skin bags (7); gut bags (10); bag-mender (1); bottle mouths (9); bone tubes (4); breast yoke (1).

Fort Alexander, Alaska.—J. W. Johnson (accession 18416): Necklace (1); mask-hoops (3); dance-wand (3); plumes (22); mask-frame (1); belts (2); water-proof coats (4); baskets (6); pouches (3); pail (1); dishes (4); snuff-boxes (2); scraper (1); spoons (9); knife (1); knife-sharpeners (2); women's knives (3); adze (1); fleshing-chisels (2); ivory mauls (2); needle (1); needle-cases (2); lamps (4); fire-making sets (2); bows (2); arrows (6); harpoons (3); throwing-sticks (3); harpoon heads (2); daggers (4); bird-dart (1); hook and line (1); ammunition belt (1).

Ugashik Region, Alaska Peninsula.—W. J. Fisher (accession 18490): Shaman's paraphenalia (7 articles); masks (2); ivory carvings of animals (55); ear-rings (4 pairs); comb (1); belt-hooks (2); belt (1); throwing-stick (1); beluga spear and throwing-stick (2); pike-gigs and decoy (3); goose-spear (1); fish-hooks (12); harpoon points (9); ivory fore-shafts (3); beluga spear, complete (1); walrus-spear (1); whale-spears (4); spear-heads (22); finger-rest for spear (1); sinker (1); snow-goggles (1 pair); spermophile nooses (20); goose-snares (8); drill (1); flesher (1); stone scrapers (5); woman's knives (35); spoons (5); tobacco-box (1); wooden box (1); paint mortar and pestle (1); snuff mortar and pestle (1); food dish and masher (1); braid-gauge (1); mesh-spacers (3); bobbins (8); needle-cases (2); clam-spades (2); bucket-clamps (1 pair); blubber-hooks (4); spokeshaves (2); hammer (1); stone axes (17); gut-scrapers (2); snow-knives (7); carving tools (2); polishers (2); wedge (1); bag-fasteners (9); fire-making sets (2); lancets (4).

Indians of Sitka and vicinity.—E. B. Webster (accessions 18409, 18397, 18028): Dance-wand (1); carved pipe (1); bent box (1); harpoon-head (1); slave-killer (1); charm (1); stone seal (1); drum (1); snow-shoes (1 pair).

Chilkat Indians, Alaska.—Mr. George M. Robeson (accession 19051): Blanket (1).

British Columbia.— State Department, New Orleans Exposition (accession 16550): Carved eagle and fish (1).

Quinaielt Indians, Washington Territory.—Charles Willoughby (accession 18615): Nets (3); salmon-spear (1); sleeping rug (1); baskets (2); baskets in process (3); braid (1); basket-grass (4); bag (1); rushes (1); cedar bark (1); stone maul and wedge (2); adze (1); wooden dishes (4); horn dishes (3); horn spoons (2); oil cup (1); shaman's wooden image (1); whale-rib chisel (1); fire-making set and slow-match (1); cedar-bark skirt (1); frame for bruising cedar bark (1); tool for bruising bark (1); rain coat (1); bowl (2); arrows (9); needle and creaser (2).

Hupa Indians, California.—Lieut. P. H. Ray, U. S. Army (accession 17688): Arrow tool (1); arrow-straightener (1); gambling sticks (2 sets); head pad (1); elk-skin armor (1); woven armor (1).

Baird, California.—Loren W. Green (accession 18608): Baskets (4); basket materials (3); pestle (1).

Naltunne Tunne Indians, Oregon.—Mrs. J. O. Dorsey (accession 18439: Model of a cradle.

Zuñi Indians, New Mexico.—Bureau Ethnology, Mrs. Col. Stevenson (accession 19294): Shrine idol (1); sacred sticks   ; plume sticks   ; sacred plumes   ; shells from shrine   ; sacred bow (1); spear-heads (3); belt-weaving outfit (4 objects); sword-swallower's blade (1); shrine objects   ; rattle (1); top (1); medicine (2); arrow-heads and flint chips   ; fragments of pottery   ; medicine-bag (1); spear-heads for dance (5); spindle whorl (1); shell breast ornament (1); fetishes (100); medicine-stones (4); concretions (8); ornaments for fetishes (1 lot); part of mask (1); sacred sashes (2); sacred belts (34).

Mokis, Arizona.—Bureau of Ethnology, Mrs. Col. Stevenson (accession 19294): Pipes (28); baskets (29); materials for making coiled trays (19 objects); ear-rings (1 pair); necklace (1); spindle whorls (6); apparatus for preparing cotton for sacred yarn (4 objects); weft combs (4); burling-pin (1); yarn (1); cotton seed (1); batten sticks (2); web stick (1); wool rope (1); knitting (1); embroidery sticks (2); flute (1); whistle (1); rattles (27); drums (4); music sticks (3); gourd bottles (4); rabbit sticks (8); cactus pickers (3); stone axes ; rubbing stones (7); reed mats (2); game of ball and sticks (3); gaming balls (2); children's bows and arrow (6 bows, 1 arrow); whirligigs (8); rotary drills (2); dolls (57); toy birds (4); boy's gun (1); dolls' cradles (5); game of darts (1); hat (1); gaming cups (6); fetishes (87); head-dresses (27); bangs (2); hair bows (3); plumes (2); arrow head and stones used as medicine charms ; sun bird (1); sacred mortars (4); medicine-boxes (2); snake charms (2); dance wands or sticks (101, mostly pairs); drills (5), mask (1); sacred fire-brands (2); shields (2); armlets (15 pairs); anklets (12 pairs); water jugs (4); bead-grinder (1); slate ax (1); powder-horn (1); plan of house (1); rake (1); lion skirt (1); women's blanket (1); men's sacred sashes (9); sacred kilts (5); breech-cloths (2); woman's belts (2); white sashes (2); white blanket (1); snow-shoes (1 pair); shoes (2 pairs); tassels (2); various pigments (6); meal (1).

Utes, White River.—E. B. Webster (accession 18351): Mummied head (1).

Navajos, Arizona.—W. M. Stephen (accession 18812): Awls (3); needles (2); unfinished shoes (3); finished shoe (1); dance shoes (1 pair). Dr. Washington Matthews (accession 18865): Woman's dress (1).

Navajos, New Mexico.—Cosmos Mindeleff (accession 18048): Model of cradle (1); string silver beads (1). R. W. Shufeldt (accession 18392): Cradle (1).

Arizona.—James Reagles (accession 17976): Deer decoy (1).

Yuma Indians, California.—A. B. Upshaw (accession 19212): Ceremonial bow (1); arrows (5).

Pawnee Indians.—Dr. J. O. Dorsey (accession 18438): War club (1). Nelson Rice, accession 19018): Head-dress (1).

Kaw Indians, Indian Territory.—Dr. J. O. Dorsey (accession 18438): War hatchet (1).

Omaha Indians, Nebraska.—Mrs. J. O. Dorsey (accession 18439): Moccasins (1 pair).

Poncas, Niobrara, Nebraska.—Dr. J. O. Dorsey (accession 18438): Catlinite pipe (1).

Winnebago Indians, Nebraska.—Mrs. J. O. Dorsey (accession 18439): Dolls (2).

Choctaws, Louisiana.—A. S. Gatchet (accession 18171): Basket (1).

Mexico.—S. L. M. Barlow (accession 18030): Votive offering (1). Dr. E. Palmer (accession 18723): Pottery figurettes (25); pot scourers (4); model of banana package (1); gourd dipper (1); prickly-pear knife, grooved (1); hammer (1); milk from mulberry tree; carved finger-ring (1). Bureau of Arts, Paris (accession 18694): Terra-cotta cup (1).

Central America.—Nicaragua, State Department, New Orleans Exposition (accessions 16658, 17048): Palmetto hats (5); pouches (2); saddle-bags (1 pair); halter (1); crupper (1); Belize fly-brush (1); calabash (1); bowl (1); baskets (3); native trunks (2); grater (1). Guatemala, Miles Rock (accession 18575): Black woolen coat (1). Yucatan, Bureau of Arts, Paris (accession 18694): Stone hatchets (4). V. O. King (accession 19112): Cane basket (1); sandals (1 pair).

South America.—Charles Heape (accession 18898): Gourd bowls (2); spoon (1).

Venezuela, Yaruros.—Bureau Arts, Paris (accession 18694): Tent (1).

French Guiana.—Bureau Arts, Paris (accession 18694): Hammock (1); cincture (1).

Ecuador.—W. E. Curtis (accession 18223): Carnival hat (1). Bureau Arts, Paris (accession 18694): Cincture (2); necklaces (2).

Bolivia.—W. E. Curtis (accession 18223): Leggings (1 pair).

Peru.—W. E. Curtis (accession 18223): Sandals (1 pair); head of baton (1). Bureau Arts, Paris (accession 18694): Necklace (1); feather pendant (1).

Chili.—W. E. Curtis (accession 18223): Knife.

Brazil.—E. B. Webster (accession 18364): Model of catamaran (1). Bureau Arts, Paris (accession 18694): Head ribbon (1); feather bracelets (1 pair).

Argentine Confederation.—W. E. Curtis (accession 18223): Horn cup (1); horn bottle (1); bone carvings (1).

Patagonia.—W. E. Curtis (accession 18223): Harpoon head (1). Museum Natural History, Paris: Busts of human races (55).

Russia.—State Department, New Orleans Exposition (accession 16550): Droshka yokes (2). Charles Heape (accession 18898): Spoon (1). Miscellaneous objects (15).

Congo Basin, Africa.—Lieut. E. H. Taunt, U. S. Navy (accession 17986): Wooden stools (2); spoons (2); ladle (1); muller (1); pipe (1); pestle (1); ivory pendant (1); armlet (1); legging (1); wristlet (1); pouches (5); belt (1); bark dresses (4); fly-flapper (1); mat (1); grass cloth (1); head-dress (1); feather pendant (1); daggers (6); shields (3); knife (1); swords (10); sword-blades (2); assagais (11); assagai-head (1); hippopotamus spear (1); paddle (1); war-horns (2); bell (1); "Sansa" music-box (1); carved elephant tusk (1); cloak of cloth (1).

Africa.—State Department, New Orleans Exposition (accession 16550): Hand loom (1). Bureau of Arts, Paris (accession 18694): Arrows (16), assagais (19); dippers (4); tray (1); spoons (2); powder cup (1); pots (4); comb (1): cinctures (2); plate (1); bracelet (1); model of a canoe (1); cloth (3); ceremonial hat (1); amulet (1); mat (1); bracelets (2). Charles Heape (accession 18898): Arrows (6); assagais (2); club (1); leggings (1 pair); pouch (1).

Madagascar.—Bureau of Arts, Paris (accession 18694): Horn spoons (2).

India, Cashmir.—Mrs. Helen Tompkins (accession 17866): Lacquer tea-tables (2).

Corea.—P. L. Jouy (accession 19276): Eating table. C. G. Talcott (accession 13867): Red stone ornament (1). Prof. G. B. Goode (accession 19010): Cloth armor (2 pieces).

China.—Dr. D. B. McCartee (accessions 17698, 17798, 17838, 17960, 18047, 18063, 18138, 18139, 18144, and 18900): Buddhist Sutras (2 volumes); books on tillage and weaving (2 volumes); Pekin Gazette (9 copies); visiting cards (10); envelope (1); geomantic compass (1); sun and moon dial (1); images in mussel-shell (1); carved frame (1); portrait of Liu Sin Yuen (1); autograph fans (3); scrolls of presentation (2 sets); traveler's case (1); silk and ivory fan (1); painting on silk (1); spoon (1); ethnographical photographs (10). Prof. G. B. Goode (accession 18994): Scroll picture. Mrs. W. P. Mangum (accessions 19079 and 19218): Charcoal birds (18); palm-leaf basket (1); student's bronze kettle (1). T. B. Ferguson (accession 17727): Lantern.

Japan.—Dr. D. B. McCartee (accessions 18047, 18138, 18144, 18283): Serrurier's Cyclopædia (1 volume); heraldic devices (1 volume); designs (5 volumes); painting on silk (2); stone spoon (1); stiletto (1); postal card (1). P. L. Jouy (accession 18348): Basket (1); photograph (1). G. L. Faucher (accession 18057): Image of Buddha. G. Goward (accession 19048): Original sketches by Japanese artists. Japanese Department of Education (accession 18415): Kindling wood (1); fire-wood (1); hard charcoal (1); best charcoal (1); soft charcoal (1); balls of charcoal (1); sulphur matches (3); flint and steel (2); warming box (1); fire-vessel (1); iron tongs (1 pair); kettle tripod (1); ash leveler (1); ash sieve (1); copper shovel (1); charcoal basket (1); fire-blower (1); smoker's box (1); sickle (1); hatchet (1); set carpenter's tools (58); set plasterer's tools (28); set metal-worker's tools (24); set ivory carver's tools (28); chest protector (1); rain coats (4); trousers (2); leggings (1 pair); socks (4 pairs); sandals (5 pairs); clogs (4 pairs); hats (5); hoods (3); women's collars (2); child's pouch (1); towels (4); hair pins (5); combs (7); hair ribbon (1); tinsel cord for hair (6); switch (1); rat (1); mirror (1); toilet case (1); razor (1); hair strings (2); face powder (1); powder cup (1); toilet brushes (2); pomatum (2); hair oil (2); rouge cup (1); bran bag (1); tooth-pick holder (1);

Japan—Continued.

tooth-picks (1 pack); tooth-powder (1); tooth-brushes (6); tooth-brush case (1); wash basin (1); hot-water kettle (1); fans (6); umbrellas (3); writing box (1); ink-holder (1); paper weight (1); stationery box (1); note paper (5 rolls); envelopes (2 packs); poem paper (7); pen-holder (1); ink and pen carrier (1); stone seal (1); ink paste (1); knife and awl (1); scissors (1 pair); night light (1); oil can (1); wick (1); lanterns (5); candlesticks (2); candles (14); smokers' sets (3); tobacco pouch and pipe case (2); pipe cleaner (1); pocket-books (2); money pouches (2); boiler (1); earthen plate (1); tile (1); water jar (1); tea-cup (1); tea-cloth (1), tea-stirrer (1); tea-spoon (1); tea-caddy (1); napkin (1); dipper (1); lid-rest (1); slop basin (1); charcoal basket (1); shaped charcoal (1); branch charcoal (1); iron tongs (1); boiler mat (1); incense box (1); duster (1); broom (1); linen cloth (1); powdered tea (1); pictures illustrating Japanese industries (30 sheets). W. H. Chandlee (accession 18315): Pipe.

Loo Choo.—Japanese Department of Education (accession 18415): Man's summer and winter robes (2); woman's summer and winter robes (2); woman's under trousers (1); man's ceremonial robes (2); girdle, under trousers and hat, in all (5); models showing coiffure of male and female (2); pipe (1); straw paper (3); hat (1); pouch and towel (1); towel rack (1); lantern (1); earthenware pan (1); earthenware furnace (1); rice bowl (1); soup bowl (1); dish (1); sake bottle (1); sake cups (3); flower vases (2); round fans (3); water-pail (1); tea-cups (4).

Fiji Islands.—Dr. Bowers (accession 17826): War club (1). Appleton Sturgis (accession 19186): Wooden pillow (1); wigs (2).

New Caledonia.—Bureau Arts, Paris (accession 18694): Assagais (4).

New Hebrides.—Charles Heape (accession 18898): Arrows (4).

New Ireland.—Appleton Sturgis (accession 19186): Paddles (2); ceremonial ax (1); carving (1).

Savage Island.—Appleton Sturgis (accession 19186): War ax (1).

Solomon Islands.—Charles Heape (accession 18898: Club (1); paddle (1); arrows (2).

New Britain.—Appleton Sturgis (accession 19185): Club with stone head (1).

New Guinea.—Charles Heape (accession 18898); Club and sago beater (1); lance (1).

Hawaii.—State Department, New Orleans Exposition (accession 17038): Seed-box (1); necklaces (6); tapa cloth (1). Mrs. J. C. Welling and Miss Dixon (accession 19116): Feather head-dress (1); feather cape (1).

South Pacific Islands.—Charles Heape (accession 18898): Cap (1).

Admiralty Islands.—Appleton Sturgis (accession 19186): Spear with obsidian head (1).

Tonga Islands (Friendly Group).—Appleton Sturgis (accession 19186). War club (1).

Samoa (Navigator's Group).—Appleton Sturgis (accession 19186): Paddle (1).

New Zealand.—Charles Heape (accession 18898): Chief's staff (1). Easter Island, U. S. S. *Mohican* (accession 19025): Stone images (2); tufa crown (1); stone slabs, decorated (6); carved stones (4); building slabs (4).

Malaysia.—Bureau of Arts, Paris (accession 18694): Poisoned arrows (1 case); cuirass (1); net (1); leather portmanteau (1); mat (1); lime tube (1); hats (4); baskets (9); dipper (1); brooms (3); vase (1).

JAPANESE ARTICLES USED CHIEFLY IN THE FORMER TIMES.

(Following mainly Dr. Klemm's classification, Smithsonian Report, 1873.)

FIRE AND FIRE IMPLEMENTS.

1. Takyi, fire-wood, chiefly used for kindling fire.
2. Maki, fire-wood.
3. Katadzumi, hard charcoal.
4. Kiridzumi, best charcoal.
5. Dogama, soft charcoal.
6. Tadon, ball made of charcoal powder and sea-weeds, paste generally used for keeping fire all night.
7. Tsukegi, match made of sticks tipped with sulphur.
8. Hinchibako, box for holding the instruments for striking fire.
9. Hinchibukuro, bag for holding the instruments for striking fire, carried in the pocket in traveling, etc.
10. Kuwairo, small metal box for holding fire, carried in the bosom to warm the chest, with a fragment of its burning charcoal inside.
11. Hibachi, vessel partly filled with fine ashes, containing when in use a few bits of burning charcoal.
12. Hebashi, a pair of iron rods, generally placed at the corners of hibachi for holding burning charcoal.
13. Gotoku, iron tripod. This is an iron ring on three feet projecting upward; half of it is buried in the ashes, and on the top of the feet the tea-kettle is placed.
14. Hainarashi, levelling ashes.
15. Haifurui, ash seive.
16. Juno, pan for holding burning charcoal.
17. Aumitoro, charcoal holder.
18. Hibukidake, a piece of bamboo used for blowing fire.
19. Tabakoton, a square wooden box containing a small earthen vessel for holding hot charcoal, and a segment of bamboo either with or without cover, used by smokers.

TOOLS AND IMPLEMENTS.

20. Kama, sickle.
21. Nata, hatchet.
22. Daiker Dogu, carpenter's tools (1 set, 59 articles).

TOOLS AND IMPLEMENTS—continued.

23. Sakuwan Dogu, plasterer's tools (1 set, 23 articles).
24. Kadzariya Dogu, metal worker's tools (1 set, 31 articles).
25. Ivory carver's tools and specimens of horn carving (1 set, 23 articles).
26. Tools and material used in making common lacquer.
27. Models illustrating process of making lacquered plate.
28. Tools and material used in making gold lacquer.
29. Specimens of gold lacquer.

CLOTHING.

Articles of clothing.

30. Harakake, cloth covering tied over the chest and abdomen, used by common laborers.
31. Amelapa, an oiled paper coat with square sleeves, used by common people in time of rain.
32a. Mino, a rain-coat made of *Barex*, sp., worn generally by Samurai in olden times.
32b. Mino, a rain-coat made of *Barex marrowii*, worn by farmers.
33. Kakegosa, a rain-coat made of *Juncus calticus*.

Foot covering.

34. Momohiki, tight trousers, used by common laborers.
35. Patchi, a kind of silk trousers.
36. Kiyahan, a pair of leggings, used by common travelers.
37. Tabi, a pair of socks.
38. Kokahe, a kind of socks without soles. These are only used when the people wear Waraji (No. 47).
39. Setta, a pair of leather sandals.
40. Ashida, wooden clog, used in wet weather; worn by males.
41. Ashida, wooden clogs, used in fair weather; worn by females.
42. Komageta, wooden clogs, used in fair weather; worn by males.
43. Komageta, wooden clogs, used in fair weather; worn by females.

CLOTHING—continued.

Foot covering—Continued.

44. Takekawa Zori, sandals of bamboo sheath.
45. Zori, sandals of straw.
46. Asaura Zori, sandals chiefly for indoor wear.
47. Waraji, pair of straw sandals, used in traveling.

HEAD GEAR.

48. Augegasa, a hat made of *Barex ditpalatha,* used by common laborers.
49. Amigasa, a hat of rattan, used by fishermen, etc.
50. Takinokogasa, a rain-hat made of bamboo sheath, used by common laborer.
51. Takenokogasa, a rain-hat made of bamboo sheath, used by Samurai in old times.
52. Nurigasa, a hat made of bamboo slips and lacquered paper on them.
53. Funazoko, a head covering of cotton cloth, worn in cold by common people.
54. Okoso, a head covering of crape for women.
55. Kappa Boshi, an oiled paper head covering.

ORNAMENTS.

Articles of ornament.

56. Hanyeri, collar for female.
57. Kinchaku, a pouch for child, suspended in the girdle.
58. Asetenogoi, summer towel for female.
59. Tenugui, a towel.

Head ornaments.

60. Kanzashi, hair-pin used by young girl.
61. Hanakushi, comb worn by young girl.
62. Hangake, crape for hair ornament.
63. Negake, paper cord for hair ornament.
64. Kamoji, false hair.
65. Marumagekata, mold for dressing women's hair, used as stuffing.
66. Tabodome, hair-pin.
67. Bindome, hair-pin.
68. Hariuchi, a kind of hair ornament, used the same as No. 63.
69. Nisebekko Kushi, hair ornament comb made of imitation tortoise shell.

ORNAMENTS—continued.

Head ornaments—Continued.

70. Nisebekko Kogai, hair ornament made of imitation tortoise shell.

TOILET ARTICLES.

71. Kushi, combs.
72. Kagami, mirror with case.
73. Kiodai, mirror-stand with drawers, for lady's toilet articles.
74. Kamisoribako, razor-case with a razor.
75. Motoyui, a bundle of paper cord for binding the hair into a bunch.
76. Oshiroi, white powder for powdering the face.
77. Oshiroi Tokashi, vessel for dissolving white powder.
78. Mayuhake, toilet brush.
79. Abura, pomatum for the hair.
80. Koyu, perfumed oil for the hair.
81. Gomanoabura, oil of *Sesamum orientalis.*
82. Benichoku, rouge-cup for painting lips by females.
83. Nukabukuro, small cotton bag to put rice bran in, used in place of soap.
84. Yojure, tooth-pick holder.
85. Yoji, bundle of tooth-picks.
86. Hamigakiko, tooth-powder.
87. Migakiyoji, tooth-brushes.
88. Migakiyoji bako, tooth-brush case.
89. Kanatarai, metal tub used for washing hands, etc.
90. Tuto, hot-water jar.

MISCELLANEOUS ARTICLES OF ORNAMENT.

91. Ogi, fan.
92. Uchiwa, round fan.
93. Amagasa, rain-umbrella.
94. Higasa, a parasol.
95. Biotengasa, umbrella used for sun or rain; 5 vessels, plates, and other objects for household use.

VESSELS, PLATES, ETC.

96. Kama, iron pot for boiling rice.
97. Kamashiki, stand for iron pot (Kama).
98. Meshiage, large wooden handle used for taking rice from iron pot.
99. Samoji, a wooden ladle used for filling cups with boiled rice.
100. Meshibitsu, a tub for holding boiled rice.

VESSELS, PLATES, ETC.—continued.

101. Meshibitsu, tub for holding boiled rice, with ladle.
102. Chatzubo, tea-jar.
103. Chagama, iron tea-pot.
104a. Chabukuro, tea-bag used for tea-straining.
104b. Chakoshi, tea-strainer for tea-powder.
104c. Chahoji, tea-roaster.
105. Chashaku, tea-dipper.
106. Nabe, iron pan for cooking.
107. Tukihira, earthen pan for cooking.
108. Tukihira, earthen pan for cooking.
109. Hotategai, a shell used for cooking food, etc.
110. Shakushi, a wooden ladle used for filling cups with soup, etc.
111. Kaishakushi, shell dipper.
112. Kaneshakushi, a copper ladle with numerous holes.
113. Saji, wooden spoon.
114. Renge, earthen spoon.
115. Dobin, tea-pot ordinary use.
116. Tetsubin, an iron kettle for boiling water.
117. Yuwakashi, kettle for boiling water quickly.
118. Hayanabe, a copper pan.
119. Midzusashi, water-jar.
120. Teoke, wooden pail.
121. Komeoke, a tub used for cleaning rice.
122. Hishaku, dipper.
123. Katateoke, a wooden pail with single handle.
124. Midzukoshi, a water-strainer.
125. Suribachi, a bowl for rubbing Miso, (fermented mixture of soy beans, wheat, and salt).
126. Surikogi, a rubbing-stick made of *Zamthoxylon piperitum* for the above.
127. Suino, a strainer.
128. Misokoshi, a sieve for filtering Miso.
129. Meyaru, a basket holding foods.
130. Komeagezaru, a basket for drying rice after cleaning in water.
131. Manaita, a chopping-block.
132. Debahocho, a kitchen knife, generally used for cutting fish, etc.
133. Nakiri hocho, a kitchen knife.
134. Sashimihocho, a knife for slicing fish (eaten uncooked).

VESSELS, PLATES, ETC.—continued.

135. Kogatana, a knife.
136. Kawamuki, peeling radish, etc.
137. Senninmai, chopping radish, etc.
138. Wasabioroshi, horse-radish grater.
139. Jago, a funnel.
140. Katakuchi, a pail with a lip.
141. Nomikuchi, faucet.
142. Katsuobako, box for shaving Katsuobushi (dried bonite for flavoring food).
143. Saibashi, chop-sticks for helping to food.
144. Uokushi, sticks of bamboo on which fishes are strung to dry or roast.
145. Kaneami, a gridiron for roasting food, etc.
146. Shibu uchiwa, a common fan used generally in kitchen.
147. Shakusashi, bamboo rack.
148. Hochosashi, knife-case.
149. Sasara, a small brush made of split bamboo for cleaning utensils.
150. Tawashi, mop for cleaning utensils.
151. Sudare, covering food.
152. Zen, a dining table (common quality).
153. Meshichawan, porcelain bowl for boiled rice.
154. Misoshiruwan, Miso soup bowl.
155. Hira, flat wooden bowl for fish and vegetables.
156. Sara, porcelain plate for fish.
157. Sara, porcelain plate.
158. Kozara, small saucer for dressed or salted vegetables, etc.
159. Osara, large porcelain plate.
160. Hashibako, box of chop-sticks.
162. Waribashi, chop-sticks made into tow by splitting.
163. Kobashi, short chop-sticks.
164. Konomano Hachi, porcelain dish for salted vegetables.
165. Donbuzi Hachi, porcelain bowl.
166. Choku, small cup for salad.
167. Shoyutsugi, Shoyu-pourer.
168. Kayoibon, small tray.
169. Tokuri, large bottle for sake.
170. Kan Dokuri, bottle for sake, with its stand.
171. Kan Dokuri, bottle for warming sake.
172. Saka dzuki, sake cup.
173. Chabon, tea-cup tray.
174. Chago, tea-measurer.

VESSELS, PLATES, ETC.—continued.

175. Kiusu, tea-pot.
176. Chawan, a set of tea-cups.
177. Chadai, tea-cup stand.
178. Kizara, wood plates.
179. Hegi, plates made of strips of bamboo for sweetmeats, etc.
180. Zen, dining table.
181. Meshiwan, lacquered wooden bowl for boiled rice.
182. Misoshiruwan (see No. 154).
183. Hira (see No. 155).
184. Tsubo, small pot for salad, etc.
185. Koshidaka, plate for salted vegetables.
186. Suimonozen, a table for soup bowl.
187. Suimonowan, a lacquered wooden bowl for soup.
188. Choshi, sake kettle.
189. Sakadzuki, sake cup.
190. Sakadzukidai, sake-cup stand.
191. Kuwashibon, confection tray.
192. Kuwashizara, confection dish generally placed on a tray.
193. Midzutsugi, water-jar.
194. Chaire, tea-caddy.
195. Chami, tea-measurer.
196. Chabon, tea-cup tray.
197. Yusamashi, vessel for cooling water.
198. Kiusu, tea-pot.
199. Chawan, tea-cup.
200. Chadai, tea-cup stand.
201. Koboshi, vessel for pouring out waste water.
202. Fukin, cloth used for wiping cup, etc.
203. Hatoki, feather duster.
204. Teboki, short broom, made of *Sorghum saccharatum.*
205. Hataki, paper duster.
206. Hoki, broom of the *Trachycarpus excelsa.*
207. Chiritori, dust-pan.
208. Zokin, house cloth used for cleaning floor.
209. Kamikudzukago, waste-basket.

LAMPS.

210. Andon, night-light with saucer, plate, etc.
211. Aburatsugi, oil-can for filling the saucer of Andon.
212. Toshin, *Juncus communis,* for the wicks of Andon.

LAMPS—continued.

213. Chiochiu (Umihar) lantern with bow-shaped bamboo handle.
214. Chiochin (Odawara) folding lantern with its bag.
215. Bajo, lantern used on horseback.
216. Gifu, ornamental lantern made of Gifu.
217. Shokudai, candle-stick.
218. Teshoku, hand candle-stick.
219. Bonbori, hand lantern.
220. Rosoku, candles.

PERSONAL ARTICLES.

221. Tobacco Ire (Koshisage), tobacco-pouch, which is fastened to the belt by means of the Netsuke (kind of button).
222. Tobacco Ire (Koshidzashi), tobacco-pouch with case for pipe.
223. Tobacco Ire (Kamasu), tobacco-pouch.
224. Tobacco Ire (Kawaichiu), pocket tobacco-pouch.
225. Tobacco Ire (Tamota-otoshi), pocket tobacco-pouch for female.
226. Kiserutostie, pipe-cleaners.
227. Kuwaichiumous, pocket-book for paper money, coins, papers, medicines, etc., when walking.
228. Kuwaichiumono, ditto for female.
229. Shiheuri, paper-money pouch.
230. Kuwa huire, coin pouch.

WRITING MATERIALS.

231. Sudzuribaki, writing-box for ink-stone, water-pot, etc.
232. Sumihasami, India-ink holder.
233. Bunchin, paper-weight.
234. Bunko, box for stationeries.
235. Makigami, note paper.
236. Fujibukuro, letter envelopes.
237. Tanzaku, tinted paper for writing verses.
238. Ihikishi, paper for writing verses.
239. Fudetate, pen-stand.
240. Yatate, portable inkstand, generally carried in belt.
241. In, stone stamp.
242. Nikuire, box of coloring stuff for stamping.
243. Kogatana, knife.
244. Hasami, pair of scissors.

WRITING MATERIALS—continued.

245. Hangi, engraved block for printing, with its printed paper.
246. Sumi, printing ink for 245.
247. Hake, brush for printing preparation.
248. Baren, rubber for printing.

A SET OF "POWDERED" TEA SERVICE.

249. Furo, furnace.
250. Kama, iron boiler.
251. Mayegawarake, earthen plate placed in front of Furo to keep off heat.
252. Marukoita, base on which the Furo is placed.
253. Hai, ashes produced by burning Sakura charcoal and then coloring them with tea. Such are the only ashes used in the Furo.
254. Midzusashi (water-jar) with lid. Its use is to hold water to fill the boiler.
255. Chawan, tea-cup used for a tea party.
256. Chakin, tea-cloth.
257. Chasen, tea-stirrer used for mixing the powdered tea with hot water.
258. Chashaku, tea-spoon.
259. Natsume, thin powdered-tea caddy for holding and presenting the powdered tea.
260. Fukusa, silk napkin.
261. Hishaku, dipper used for dipping up boiling water from the boiler.
262. Futaoki, rest for lid of iron boiler.
263. Koboshi, earthenware slop-basin.
264. Sumitori, charcoal basket.
265. Kiridzumi, shaped charcoal.
266. Yedadzumi, branch charcoal. This kind burns more readily than the above.
267. Kibashi.
268. Kuwan, small rings used when removing the boiler. These rings are attached to its handles.
269. Kamashiki, iron boiler rest. It is placed on the matting on which the kettle is put when taken off of furnace.
270. Kogo, incense case.

WRITING MATERIALS—continued.

271. Metsubaboki, eagle's feather duster.
272. Zatoki, hand broom.
273. Fukin, linen cloth; is used to wipe up water.
274. Kocha, powdered tea.

ARTICLES USED BY LOO CHEWUIN.

275. Male's garment for summer use.
276. Male's garment for winter use.
277. Female's garment for summer use.
278. Female's garment for winter use.
279. Under trousers for female.
280. Male's ceremonial garment for summer use.
281. Male's ceremonial garment for summer use.
282. Male's ceremonial girdle.
283. Male's ceremonial girdle under-trousers.
284. Red hat worn by male under twenty years of age on ceremonial occasions.
285. Model showing hair arrangement of male.
286. Model showing hair arrangement of female.
287. Tobacco-pipe.
288. Bundle of straw paper.
289. Bundle of paper made of Musobasjoo.
290. Hat.
291. Pocket and towel.
292. Towel hanger.
293. Lantern.
294. Earthenware pan.
295. Earthenware furnace.
296a. Porcelain bowl for boiled rice.
296b. Porcelain bowl for Miso soup.
297. Dish.
298. Bottle for warming sake.
299. Cup for Awamori (kind of brandy).
300. Pair of flower vases.
301. Round pans.
302. Pail for carrying water.
303. Tea-cup.
304. Oshiyekusa, pictures illustrating Japanese arts (30 sheets).

(Lined garments are almost unknown to the common people of the Loo Choo Islands, owing to the hot climate; and two thin garments are worn by them in winter when occasion requires.)

REPORT ON THE SECTION OF AMERICAN ABORIGINAL POTTERY IN THE U. S. NATIONAL MUSEUM, 1887.

By W. H. HOLMES, *Honorary Curator.*

The work of the Department of Aboriginal Pottery has been carried forward in the lines indicated in the report of the preceding year. A number of new cases have been constructed and series of representative groups of relics have been transferred to them from the Smithsonian hall.

Accessions have been numerous and important, but not equal in value to those of the years immediately preceding. The agencies through which the acquisitions were made are, first, those of the Smithsonian Institution and the National Museum, including donations, purchases, and the products of original researches; and second, those of the Bureau of Ethnology through corresponding channels. A series of pueblo pottery, ancient and modern, collected in 1886 by Mr. James Stevenson, of the Geological Survey, was turned over to this department during the year.

Amongst the 160 numbers are some extremely fine specimens of the white and the polychrome wares of ancient Tusayan. A small series of vessels of the ancient white ware were secured by purchase from Mr. C. M. Landar, of Lawrence, Kansas. Capt. J. G. Bourke, of the U. S. Army, presented a series of small plain and coiled vases obtained by him from cliff dwellings and caves in Arizona.

A few small collections were made in the Mississippi Valley and in the eastern States by Dr. Cyrus Thomas and his assistants.

From Mexico some interesting accessions have been made. Dr. Edward Palmer obtained from the State of Chihuahua a number of vases and fragments of ancient earthenware, besides a series of modern works and a most instructive set of pottery-making utensils. This collection was purchased for the Museum by the Bureau of Ethnology. A small number of interesting pieces of ancient ware, collected in the valley of Mexico, were acquired by purchase from Mr. Ward Batchelor.

By exchange with museums in France, through the agency of Mr. John Durand, we have acquired a number of interesting pieces of Mexican and Peruvian work.

A valuable collection of vases and other earthenware relics from the graves of ancient Peru, was purchased by the Bureau of Ethnology from Mr. W. E. Curtis, and is now exhibited in the pottery court.

Besides the above-mentioned accessions I may mention small series of earthen relics obtained through William J. Baker, C. J. Hering, A. A. Peling, J. K. Watson, J. N. McComb, jr., W. E. Safford, and E. M. Kirkby.

This enumeration includes only those acquisitions that were turned over directly to the curator of the department. Other accessions of objects of clay are included in series or sets intrusted to other departments.

The first catalogue number for the year is number 131934, and the last 132955. The total number of entries is 611.

The curator has been occupied during the year in completing his studies of the collections from Chiriqui and in taking initiatory steps looking toward the discussion of the ceramic art of Mexico.

A special paper upon a remarkable group of spurious antiquities from Mexico has been prepared and delivered to the Smithsonian Institution for publication. It is shown in this paper that for more than half a century the manufacture of pottery and certain other classes of objects has been extensively carried on and for no other purpose than to profit by sales to collectors of antiquities. It is also shown that museums in all parts of the world are well supplied with these spurious articles, and that a number of pieces have found their way into literature as genuine antiquities. Some twenty illustrations are given. They are taken from the most striking pieces in the National Museums of Mexico and of the United States, and from published illustrations.

The papers published during the year are referred to in Section IV of this report.

REPORT ON THE SECTION OF TRANSPORTATION IN THE U. S. NATIONAL MUSEUM, 1887.

By J. Elfreth Watkins, *Honorary Curator.*

During the year, work in the section of Steam Transportation has been conducted during such brief periods and irregular intervals that it has not been possible to make any systematic attempt to increase the collection or to install objects already obtained.

By correspondence I have been able to ascertain the whereabouts of considerable material which will naturally be deposited in the National Museum when the section shall be fully organized.

I have also succeeded in collecting a mass of information which I hope to make use of in preparing a series of models to illustrate the beginnings and the development of the English and American systems of track.

While illustrated histories of the steam-boat and locomotive are numerous, I am not aware that any systematic attempt has been made to preserve the history of the development of the systems of permanent way, which, after many years of experiment, are now being reduced to a series of standards depending on the traffic.

My connection with the Amboy division of the Pennsylvania Railroad Company, of which the famous old Camden and Amboy Railroad is a part, has made it possible for me to make a most interesting collection of rail sections, which I shall deposit in the Museum as soon as space for the purpose can be assigned.

A section of the first rail rolled with a base, which has ever since been known as the American rail, has been installed in the collection. This rail was designed by Robert L. Stevens, president of the Camden and Amboy Railroad Company, and was manufactured in Wales under his supervision in 1830–'31. A fac-simile of his letter (and draft of the cross-section first proposed)* to the English iron-masters soliciting pro-

---

*This fac-simile having been reduced, the section is not full size. The original rail was 3½ inches high; base 3 inches wide.

posals for manufacturing it, is reproduced in Plate I. It is a most interesting relic.

At the time that this rail was ordered, the section (Fig. 1) was in use on the best railroads in England, and modifications of it with the "fish-bellied" stem had been imported and laid on several American roads.

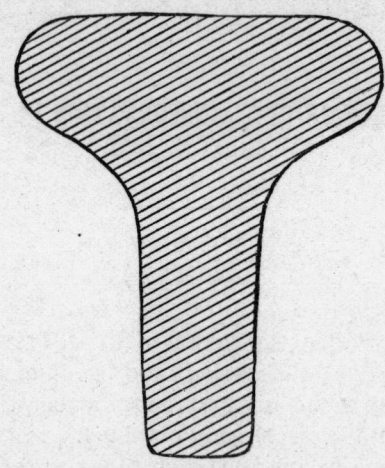

FIG. 1.—Birkenshaw's patent Malleable Rail, 1820.   (Full size).

Fig. 2 shows the shape of the wooden rail capped with strap-iron, which was in general use almost everywhere in the United States as late at least as 1839.

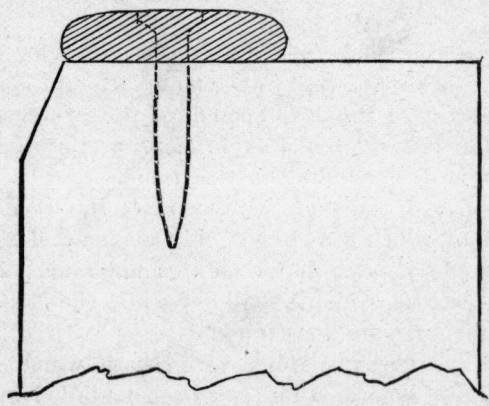

FIG. 2.—Strap-rail, ⅝ inches thick; laid on wooden stringers. In use on American Railroads, 1830–40.

I shall be glad if those interested in the matter and who have access to old rail piles will collect short sections, say 2 or 3 inches long, of the rails used on the roads in various States during early times and preserve them for future reference.

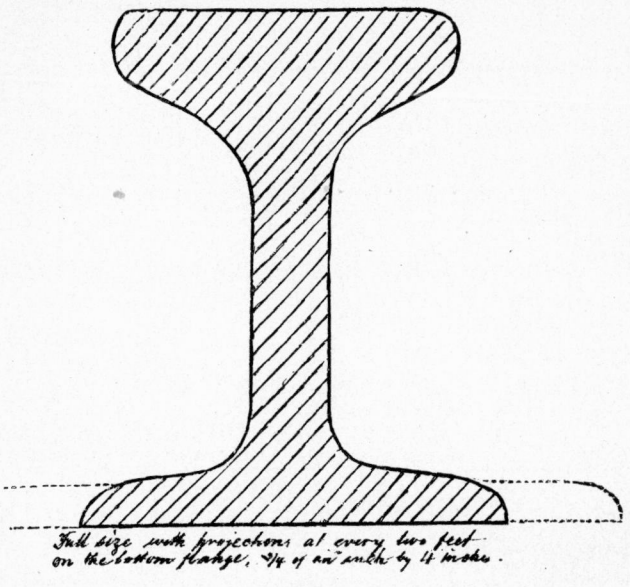

Full size with projections at every two feet on the bottom flange, 3/4 of an inch by 4 inches.

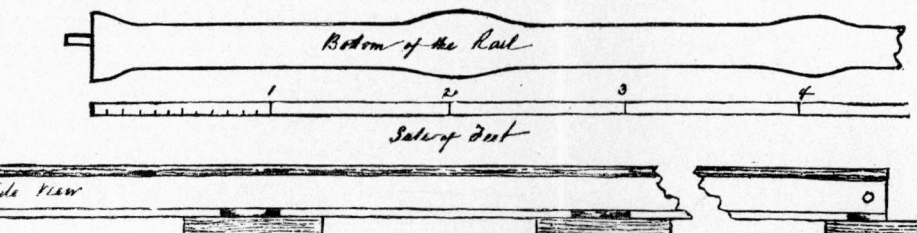

Bottom of the Rail

Scale of feet

Side View

Supports

Liverpool November 26 1830.

Gentlemen

At what rate will you contract to deliver at Liverpool; say from five to six hundred tons of Railway, of the best quality Iron rolled to the above pattern in twelve or sixteen feet lengths; to lap as shewn in the drawing, with one hole at each end, and the projections on the lower flange at every two feet. Cash on delivery —

How soon could you make the first delivery; and at what rate p[r] month, until the whole is complete — Should the terms suit and the work give satisfaction a more extended order is likely to follow, as this is but about one sixth part of the quantity required. Please to address your answer (as soon as convenient) to the care of Francis B Ogden, Consul of the United States at Liverpool ——

I am

Your obedient Servant

Rob[t] L Stevens

President & Engineer of the Camden & South Amboy Rail Road & Transportation Company

FAC-SIMILE OF LETTER SOLICITING PROPOSALS FOR ROLLING FIRST AMERICAN RAILS.

I am much gratified to find that the interest shown by many railroads officials and others when the work was first inaugurated still continues, notwithstanding the fact that it has been found necessary to delay the organization of the section upon a basis commensurate with its importance.

It is to be hoped that the affairs of the Museum will be in such a condition as to permit the inauguration of active work early during the coming fiscal year.

H. Mis. 600, pt. 2——6

REPORT ON THE DEPARTMENT OF ARCHÆOLOGY IN THE U. S. NATIONAL MUSEUM, 1887.

By CHARLES RAU, *Curator.*

REVIEW OF THE MOST IMPORTANT ACCESSIONS.

The following are the most important additions to the collection during the year:

Edward L. Hyde, of Middleborough, Massachusetts, sent six casts of depressions produced by grinding stone implements, taken from the rock on which they occur, at Middletown, Rhode Island.

W. W. Adams, of Mapleton, New York, sent a flint fish-hook from Cayuga County, and a copper dart-head found near the south end of Owasco Lake, in the same county.

From the Peabody Museum, Cambridge, Massachusetts (through Prof. F. W. Putnam), were obtained six argillite implements taken from the quaternary gravels at Trenton, New Jersey, by Dr. Charles C. Abbott, and two photographs, one showing the Abbott collection in the Peabody Museum, and the other a number of bone fish-hooks belonging to different collections in the same museum.

Dr. Charles C. Abbott, of Trenton, New Jersey, presented two argillite implements taken by the donor from the Trenton gravels, about 6 feet below the surface.

A. R. Roessler, of Liberty Hill, Texas, sent a cutting tool remarkable for unusual notching, from Fall Creek, San Saba County, Texas.

C. T. Wiltheiss, of Piqua, Oh o, gave a good cast of a stone pipe in the form of an animal's head. The original was found in Piqua.

T. L. Whitehead, of Dexter City, Missouri, sent a collection from a mound in Stoddard County: A quartzite celt, with expanding cutting-edge, chipped and afterwards polished, a large flint digging-tool, a large carved stone pipe (calumet pipe), eight clay vessels, and two fragments of pottery (birds' heads). A very good collection.

H. W. Turner, of the U. S. Geological Survey, gave a stone mortar from auriferous gravel on the north side of American River, near Folsom, Sacramento County, California. This mortar is of elegant form, and differs from any in the collection.

W. Cuppage, of Winfield, Kansas, gave a copper celt-gouge, found at Sunnidale, near Georgian Bay, Lake Huron, Ontario, Canada.

From W. W. Blake, of Kansas City, Missouri, was obtained the Fischer collection of Mexican antiquities, consisting of obsidian flakes and cores, arrow and spear heads of obsidian, flint, and chalcedony, a large cutlass-shaped weapon or implement of obsidian, polished celts and chisels, polishing-tools, pendants of chalcedony, obsidian, and other materials, some in the shape of human and animal figures and heads, labrets of obsidian, a large number of stone heads (partly of jade), mirrors of iron pyrites, a small skull carved in rock-crystal, stone carvings in human and animal forms (a number consisting of jade), face-marks (human) of serpentine, steatite, white marble, and obsidian, a carved box with lid (of volcanic stone), an ornamented stone cylinder 16 inches in diameter, probably part of a column, copper or bronze objects embracing celts, chisels, awls, needles, bells, T-shaped objects, and a small human head. Further, clay spindle-whorls, vess ls of various forms (plain and ornamented), a pipe, musical instruments, figures (human), and a number of stamps. This collection contains many rare and even unique specimens.

J. C. Zeledon, of San José, Costa Rica, gave a very large and fine metate from Costa Rica.

W. E. Safford, ensign, U. S. Navy, obtained and presented a collection from ancient graves near the beach at Arica, Peru. Eight flint dart-heads (four inserted in wooden stems and representing the detachable part of harpoons), a grooved stone sinker, two implements, a ladle, a small box with partitions, and five pin-shaped objects, all of wood ; a copper knife with wooden handle, four copper fish-hooks, one with line attached, a bone fish-hook with line and stone sinker, a fishing line, three spines of cactus (?), one with a head of plaited rushes, a spindle with whorl and cord attached, two wooden combs (?), two toy mattresses made of twigs, a Pandean pipe of small reeds, pulverized mineral substances taken from the blanket of a female mummy, and three fragments of pottery.

S. H. Drew, of Wanganui, New Zealand, sent seventy-five flakes of obsidian and chert from a Maori kitchen-midden, a fish-hook made of shell and bone, fragments of Moa bones, and a plaster cast of a nephrite idol.

James F. Johnson, of Holywood, Ireland, sent a collection of prehistoric antiquities from county Down: Rude stone celts or axes, pounding or crushing stones, rude implements more or less leaf-shaped, fragments of animal bones (split), ox-teeth and teeth of deer or elk from caves at Ballymenoch and Craigavad ; hammer-stones, polishing-stones, and rude axes and celts from an ancient manufactory at Ballymenoch; crushing-stones, a hammer stone, rude celts, arrow and spear-heads, scrapers, knives, harpoon-heads (?), sinkers, and sling-stones, all of flint, from second raised beach at Holywood.

Thomas Wilson, of Washington, recently United States consul at Nice, has deposited a large and valuable collection of prehistoric and, to some extent, historic antiquities, gathered by himself in Italy, Switzerland, France, England, and the Scandinavian countries, which was received and catalogued during the latter part of this year. The contribution embraces drift and cave relics (paleolithic age), objects belonging to the neolithic age and to the bronze period, and specimens of Etruscan and Roman origin. The whole collection, the value of which can hardly be over-estimated, contains 10,297 articles, and the entries nearly fill a volume of the catalogue. It would be impossible to give in the limited space of this report a statement in detail of the collection, but at the same time something more than the brief abstract above given is due both to the donor and to the collection. Where every specimen is of importance it is hard to discriminate, but worthy of special mention are the objects from the well-known caves of Southern France, the articles from the Dolmens in Brittany, and a fine series of implements of stone, bone, and horn, including a number of clay vessels (entire), from the Swiss lakes. Scandinavia is represented by a large number of chipped implements, and a series of perforated axes in different stages of manufacture, from the rude beginning to the finished specimen. Last, but not least, is the bronze collection, which numbers over seven hundred objects. In this we have an exhibit which can not be duplicated, except, perhaps, by some of the larger European museums. It contains specimens from Scandinavia, from the Swiss lakes, and a large number of Etruscan origin. Considering the fact that there were less than fifty articles of bronze in the collection previous to this accession, its importance will at once be seen,

The entering of specimens and their distribution, either for exhibition or for exchange, has been carried on in accordance with the plan indicated in the last annual report. This being the case, any further statement would be only a repetition.

Duplicates have been sent in exchange as follows:

To O. P. Rogers, Marengo, McHenry County, Illinois.—A grooved stone hammer.

To Dr. Alfred R. Wallace, Frith Hill, Godalming, England.—Collection of arrow-heads (114 specimens).

To Dr. Oskar Schneider, Dresden, Saxony.—Six small bottles of shell beads (California).

To Edward Lovett, West Burton House, Outram Road, Croydon, England.—Collection of archæological specimens (52).

The curator of this department has been engaged during the year in the composition of a work on North American antiquities, entitled "The Typical Forms of North American Prehistoric Relics of Stone and Copper in the U. S. National Museum."

The present state of the collection is shown by the following tabular statement:

Number of specimens entered in this department.

Brought forward from last year		48,763
Accessions during the year ending June 30, 1887:		
Exhibition series	12,869	
Duplicate series	764	
		13,633
Total		62,396
Received from the Bureau of Ethnology:		
Amount brought forward from report, January–June, 1885		16,551
For the year ending June 30, 1886	2,879	
For the year ending June 30, 1887	19,833	
		22,712
Total		39,263
Grand total		101,659

REPORT ON THE DEPARTMENT OF MAMMALS IN THE U. S. NATIONAL MUSEUM, 1887.

By Frederick W. True, *Curator.*

The most important work of the year has been the commencement of a re-arrangement of the exhibition hall. Of the movable cases which were in the hall at the close of the last year but one remains, and the wall cases have been remodeled and added to.

The new floor cases depart from the standard originally adopted for other departments of the Museum. Their size and proportions were determined upon after a careful study of the material to be exhibited, and the collection is, therefore, seen to a much greater advantage than formerly. The new wings added to the wall cases are designed for the reception of the longest specimens in the collection (the ruminants, seals, etc.), which have not hitherto been under cover, and have been subject to injury at the hands of visitors.

As a result of the expedition into Montana, under the charge of Mr. W. T. Hornaday, sent out by the Institution, the Museum has come into the possession of a very fine series of specimens of the Bison—a matter of great importance in view of the approaching extinction of that species.

The reference series has been enriched by purchases and donations of well-preserved skins of certain North American species of Mammals in which the collection was previously deficient.

In a region like North America, where, in many cases, the range of a species extends over thousands of square miles, and the species itself is differentiated into numerous geographical races, a large series of specimens will alone suffice to enable the student of zoogeography, or the systematist, to work out the problems with which he has to deal; and since the characters, which are chiefly relied upon for distinguishing subspecies, are external, it is necessary that the skins should be prepared in the very best manner. It is in this direction that the growth of the reference series of the National collection ought to tend, The work of the past year is but a beginning.

Six species and one subspecies have been added to the North American fauna during the year. These are—

Hesperomys taylori Thomas.   (Texas.)
Hesperomys anthonyi Merriam.   (New Mexico.)
Neotoma bryanti Merriam.   (Lower California.)
Dipodomys deserti Stephens.   (California.)
Vespertilio longicrus True.   (Puget Sound.)
Vespertilio ciliolabrum Merriam.   (Western States.)
Thomomys talpoides perpallidus Merriam.   (California.)

Of *H. taylori* the Museum possesses one specimen, a very defective skin, in alcohol, which was found soon after the species had been described by Mr. Thomas. *H. anthonyi* is represented by two specimens (apparently a subspecies) purchased from Mr. Stephens, who also presented the type of his *Dipodomys deserti*.

Several specimens of *Thomomys perpallidus* were purchased from Mr. Stephens. *Neotoma bryanti* is not in the collection. *Vespertilio ciliolabrum* is represented by several specimens, but of *V. longicrus* only the type (No. 15623) is known.

NOTES ON IMPORTANT ACCESSIONS.

The accessions of the past year compare favorably in point of interest with those of former periods. The sources from which they have been derived have been unusually varied.

The amount of material received from the different Bureaus of the Government has not been so great as in some previous years, while the number of private contributions has increased. For the first time in the history of the department a considerable number of specimens has been purchased.

TERRESTRIAL MAMMALS.

North America.—One of the most important accessions of the year was the series of skins and skeletons of the American Bison, obtained in Custer County, Montana, by the expedition sent out by the Smithsonian Institution (Mr. W. T. Hornaday in charge). A portion of this series, comprising individuals of both sexes and of different ages, has been mounted by Mr. Hornaday and his assistants and will soon be placed on exhibition. Good specimens of the Prong-horn Antelope, Coyote, etc., were also obtained by this expedition. The party sent out to reconnoiter in this region in the summer of 1886 found the Bison in poor condition and made no attempt to secure a series. They brought back a living Bison calf, which, however, survived but a few weeks.

Two collections of Mammals from southern California, purchased from Mr. F. Stephens, of San Bernardino, California, contain excellent specimens of numerous species occurring in that region, in which the Museum collections were previously deficient. Among these may be mentioned the Round-tailed Spermophile, *Spermophilus tereticaudus;* Anthony's Field Mouse, *Hesperomys anthonyi;* and the Desert Pocket-rat, *Dipodomys deserti,* of which the describer (Mr. Stephens) had previously presented the type to the Museum.

The Mammals collected by Mr. Charles H. Townsend in northern California, and described in the Proceedings of the Museum (Vol. x, pp. 159–241), were added to the study series during the year.

Dr. J. C. Merrill, U. S. Army, stationed at Fort Klamath, Oregon, has presented a considerable number of interesting specimens taken in the vicinity of the fort, including a series of *Sorex vagrans*.

Among the specimens of North American Ungulates received during the year was a very fine pair of antlers of the Wapiti, presented by the Hon. L. Q. C. Lamar. Col. Cecil Clay and Mr. R. A. Klock presented the skins of a female Moose and calf captured in Maine, together with photographs of the head of a Moose. An albino Virginia Deer from Clover Creek, Virginia, was purchased in the Washington market. Prof. George F. Atkinson, of Chapel Hill, North Carolina, prepared and presented a series of the southern variety of the common Chipmunk, *Tamias striatus*. A similar series of Richardson's Spermophile, *S. richardsoni*, was presented by Mr. E. E. Thompson, of Manitoba. The Museum is indebted to Mr. Daniel C. Beard for the storehouse and nest of a Field Mouse, *H. leucopus*. Good specimens of the rather rare Mountain Beaver, *Haplodon rufus*, and of the Dusky-footed Wood Rat, *N. fuscipes*, were purchased from Mr. A. Todd, of Elk Head, Oregon.

Central and South America (including West Indies).—By far the most interesting accession from the West Indies was a living specimen of the Almiqui, *Solenodon cubanas*, which was probably the first example of the species ever brought alive to the United States. It was obtained, together with two others, a female and a young individual, through Mr. John Gundlach, and was captured in the Sierra Maestra Mountains, Cuba. Mr. C. B. Cory presented about 56 specimens of the rare Bat known as *Natalus micropus*. These were obtained in Old Providence Island, Yucatan. Only the type-specimen was previously known. The authorities of the British Museum presented a specimen of the South American variety of the Horny Bat, *Atalapha cinerea grayi*, a variety not previously in the Museum collections. A specimen of the rare Ouakari Monkey, *Brachyurus rubicundus*, and three specimens of a South American Deer, believed to be *C. gymnotis*, were presented by the Zoological Society of Philadelphia. Mr. Anastasio Alfaro presented a series of skins of *Sciurus hypopyrrhus* and *S. rufoniger* prepared by himself.

Old World.—A number of mounted specimens of European Mammals were received from Mr. E. Hargitt, among which may be mentioned a specimen of the Wild Cat, *Felis catus*, and the European Badger, *Meles taxus*. In exchange for North American mammals, Dr. Tycho Tullberg, on the part of the Upsala Museum, sent a small collection of Swedish species. By a similar exchange the Museum received from the Museum d'Histoire Naturelle, Paris, a number of skeletons of Old World species, including the Gorilla, Bactrian Camel, Civet Cat, Entellus Monkey, etc. Among a number of Tasmanian mammals presented by the Fish Acclimatization Society of Ballarat, are a very fine native Wolf, *Thylacinus cynocephalus*, and two specimens of the so-called Tasmanian Devil,

Dasyurus ursinus. Specimens of the two species mentioned were also received from the authorities of the Australian Museum and have been mounted.

As in former years, the Philadelphia Zoological Society (through Mr. A. E. Brown) has presented to the Museum a number of valuable mammals which died in the gardens. The following species deserve special mention: *Capra ibex ♂, Hystrix cristata, Herpestes widdingtoni, Cercopithecus diana,* and *C. sabæus.*

Mr. W. A. Conklin, superintendent of the Central Park Menagerie in New York, presented a tiger cub; and Messrs. Barton and Logan, of Washington, a specimen of *Ateles arachnoides.*

AQUATIC MAMMALS.

Seals.—The most interesting representative of this order received during the year is a skeleton of an adult male West India Monk Seal, *Monachus tropicalis,* purchased from Mr. H. A. Ward, who obtained it in Los Triangulos Islands, off Yucatan. Capt. M. A. Healy, of the U. S. Revenue Marine, presented three skins of the Ribbon-seal, *P. fasciata,* obtained off the Alaska coast. During the winter of 1886–'87 a number of Harbor-seals were taken in the fish-nets off Wood's Holl, Massachusetts, and were forwarded to the Museum by the agent of the U. S. Fish Commission at that point.

Cetaceans.—A second skull of the interesting Porpoise described by the curator some time since, under the name of *Phocæna dalli,* was presented by Lieut. Commander H. E. Nichols, U. S. Navy, who obtained it, together with a skeleton of *P. communis,* on the coast of southern Alaska. The species is unquestionably valid. From the U. S. life-saving station at Dam Neck Mills, Virginia (Mr. Bayley T. Barco, keeper), were obtained skeletons of the common Dolphin, *D. delphis,* the Pygmy Sperm Whale, *Kogia breviceps,* and the short-finned Black-fish, *Globicephalus brachypterus.* Specimens of the latter species, which is quite distinct from the Blackfish of our northern coast, were also obtained from Osprey, Florida, through the efforts of Mr. Joseph Willcox.

DOMESTIC ANIMALS.

The series illustrative of the breeds of the domestic Dog has received several important accessions during the year. Among the races represented are a Blenheim Spaniel, an Irish Setter (Glenclaire), two Greyhounds, and a Bloodhound. A skull of a Pointer dog fourteen years old and the skull of a Newfoundland dog were also received.

Important changes in the arrangement of the exhibition hall have taken place during the year

The large special case for the group of Fur Seals, mentioned in the last report, was finished and the group was placed therein.

The new floor cases referred to in last year's report were received in February and the old cases were released and removed from the hall. The new cases are furnished with large glasses and are to be fitted with terraced bases instead of shelves. No diaphragms are employed. The specimens will be seen to a much better advantage in these cases than they could be while the old cases were in use, and the general appearance of the hall is likewise greatly improved by their introduction. None of the fittings have yet been completed, but it is expected that they will be finished early in the coming year.

The installation of the cetacean casts over the wall cases, which was contemplated last year, has been carried into effect. Finding that the glasses in the tops of the wall cases were constantly in danger of being broken, they were removed and wooden panels were substituted. At the same time the entire interior of the cases was painted afresh, and a partial re-arrangement of the specimens was effected.

After much deliberation it was deemed best to place the Seals and large Ungulates under glass to protect them from ruthless hands. A large wing has been added on the south end of each of the wall cases These wings (which practically form cases by themselves) are the highest and deepest cases which have thus far been erected. They are over 12 feet in height and are 7 feet deep in the deepest part. The Moose, Wapiti, Sea Lion, and other large mammals in the collection, will be arranged in them, the Ungulates occupying one wing while the other is given up to the Seals and Sea Lion. They will be furnished and in use early in the coming year.

There are at present in the hall thirty floor cases, including the two large cases containing the groups of Orangs and Fur Seals; and the two large wall cases referred to above. The principal addition during the ensuing year will be a large case for the group of Bison now in the hands of the taxidermists.

The mounted specimens added to the exhibition series during the year were chiefly Marsupials. The collection of representatives of that group is now large and very interesting. Of the placental Mammals added to the series may be mentioned as especially worthy of notice, the Tiger, Leopard, Cheetah, and Californian Sea Elephant.

The species represented by the specimens added to the exhibition series during the year were as follows:

Black Macaque, *Cynocephalus niger.*
Leopard, *Felis leopardus.*
Tiger, *Felis tigris.*
European Wild Cat, *Felis catus.*
Cheetah, *Cynælurus jubatus.*
Coyote, *Canis latrans.*
Red Fox, *Vulpes fulvus.*
European Ermine, *Putorius erminea.*
European Badger, *Meles taxus.*
Californian Sea Elephant, *Macrorhinus angustirostris.*
Hedgehog, *Erinaceus europæus.*
Black R   *Mus rattus.*
Rabbit, *Lepus cuniculus.*
Tasmanian Wolf, *Thylacinus cynocephalus.*

Ursine Dasyure, *Dasyurus ursinus.*
Great Rock Kangaroo, *Macropus robustus.*
Parry's Kangaroo, *Macropus parryi.*
Bennett's Wallaby, *Halmaturus bennetti.*
Red-legged Wallaby, *Halmaturus wilcoxi.*
Red-bellied Wallaby, *Halmaturus billiardii.*
Red-necked Wallaby, *Halmaturus ruficollis.*
Pademelon Wallaby, *Halmaturus thetidis.*
Crescent-marked Wallaby, *Onychogalea lunatus.*
Rufous Rat-Kangaroo, *Bettongia rufescens.*
Vulpine Phalanger, *Phalangista vulpina*
Wombat, *Phascolomys ursinus.*

The work of preparing specimens was considerably retarded by the absence of the chief taxidermist, who, as already stated, spent about three months in collecting specimens of Bison in Montana. As an offset, however, the exhibition hall will soon be graced by a very fine group of Bison.

Nearly all the larger mounted specimens were cleaned and repaired while the wall cases were being painted, and they are, therefore, in excellent condition. It is confidently hoped that when the new cases are completed the hall will present a much more attractive appearance than ever before.

The laboratory and office of the department were moved to a section of the Museum building in which the accumulation of dust, complained of in the last report, is less troublesome. The office now adjoins the exhibition hall, a matter of great convenience.

The laboratory had previously been fitted with racks, and the drawers containing the "study" series of skins were, therefore, simply transferred from the old racks to the new ones. The alcoholic series was temporarily placed in the south gate-way, where they have remained during the year. The erection of shelves in this space for the accommodation of the alcoholic series is contemplated, since it is very desirable that this series should be separated from the collection of skins.

The card catalogue has not yet been copied, but the first draft has been brought up to date. All specimens received during the year have been entered in the registers upon receipt and assigned to their proper places.

The rather large labels attached to the Rodents and other small species have been replaced by a smaller form, which renders the specimens less liable to injury when handled. The metal tags have also been discarded in the case of the smallest species, since they tend to endanger the integrity of the specimens by their weight.

The curator has had the assistance of a clerk and a copyist during the greater part of the year. He has been relieved of the care of the library.

The curator has spent the greater part of the time available for study during the year in completing the review of the species of the family *Delphinidæ*. The papers of Mr. McKay's Alaskan collection, on the Canada Lynx, on a new Mole from Japan, and on the genus *Dipodomys*, referred to in the report of last year, have been published.

Mr. Nelson's report on his Alaskan collection was ordered printed by act of Congress, and the proof of the portion of the same referring to the Mammals has passed through the curator's hands. The small collection of Mammals forwarded to Washington by the Geographical and Exploring Commission of Mexico was identified by request of Mr. Ferrari-Perez, chief of the natural history section.

The curator described, under the name *Vespertilio longicrus*, a new Bat received from Puget Sound. He also published a few notes on the living specimens of the Almiqui, *Solenodon cubanus*, which was obtained from Mr. J. Gundlach, and on a remarkable malformation of the hoofs of an ass received from Texas.

A considerable number of inquiries regarding North American Mammals have been responded to. A number of Texan species were identified for Mr. G. H. Ragsdale, of Gainesville, in that State, who also received information regarding methods of preparation. Dr. D. D. Slade, of Cambridge, applied for information regarding the metacarpals of the Auroch and Bison. A controversy between this observer and Mr. F. A. Lucas on the value of the character drawn from the differences in the metacarpals of the two species will be found in " Science."

At the request of the Director, the curator spent some time in investigating the question of the color variation of the Puma, *Felis concolor*.

Dr. Harrison Allen examined the entire collection of deers' antlers in connection with the question of bilateral asymmetry in the class Mammalia.

The collections are in nearly the same condition as at the close of last year; it is, on the whole, quite satisfactory. The entire series is under control, though a final division of material remains to be made, and appliances for keeping out dust are still needed. Very few of the specimens, either in the exhibition or study series of skins, are without written or printed labels. The alcoholic series is arranged by species in preserve jars, and the specimens themselves, in most cases, have only simple metallic labels bearing the catalogue numbers.

The number of specimens in the different series at the present date and at the close of the last fiscal year is shown in the following table:

	June 30, 1886.	June 30, 1887.
Number of specimens in the exhibition series of skins	735	752
Number of specimens in the duplicate-study series of skins	3,862	4,088
Number of specimens in the alcoholic series....................	2,854	2,971
Total	7,451	7,811

The number of skins and specimens in alcohol added and distributed during the year is as follows:

Number of specimens added during the year ending June 30, 1887 401
Number of specimens distributed during the year ending June 30, 1887 42

Among the skins and alcoholic specimens added were represented 17 species and subspecies not previously in the collection. The type of *Dipodomys deserti*, Stephens, was added, and Bat No. 15623 was made the type of a new species, *Vespertilio longicrus*, True.

The last entry in the register for skins and alcoholics on June 30, 1886, was No. 15482 ; on June 30, 1887, No. 15899.

Although the condition of the collection as regards preservation may be considered as generally satisfactory, its condition as regards completeness is quite otherwise. The need of larger series representing geographical races has already been referred to, and we now add some statistics as to the number of species represented.

Murray, in his *Geographical Distribution of Mammals* (1866), recognizes 378 genera of Mammals. The National Museum possesses skins of representatives of about 207 of these, or somewhat less than three-fifths. Again, in Troussart's *Catalogue des Mammifères* (1880), 112 genera of recent Rodents are given. Of these, the Museum possesses representatives of only 50 genera; while of the 791 species recognized as belonging in the order, the Museum possesses skins of about 160.

When it is remembered that the collection is chiefly made up of North American skins, it becomes evident that the exotic forms are but poorly represented. Though probably surpassing every other collection in the world in the amount of material representing a small number of species, it will not bear comparison in general richness with those of some other Museums of the first class, such as the British Museum, the Museum d'Histoire Naturelle, at Paris, and the Royal Zoological Museum of the Netherlands, at Leyden. Thus, in the latter institution, in the genus *Sciurus* (Squirrels), 59 species are represented, or about six-sevenths of all known species. These 59 species are represented by 638 mounted skins, an average of 11 specimens for each species. In the National Museum but 18 species of the same genus are represented. Again, the Leyden Museum has 26 mounted skins of the genus *Manis* (Pangolins), representing all of the seven known species; while the National Museum has but *two specimens*, representing two species.[*]

The same scarcity of material obtains in the case of the Monkeys, Lemurs, Antelopes, and other groups.

The desirability of securing more specimens of the larger Mamalia at the earliest day can not be too strongly set forth. The larger forms on every continent are rapidly diminishing in numbers, and some which were abundant half a century ago are now practically extinct.

The danger that the National Museum will never be able to exhibit some of the largest and most striking forms is real.

A list of the papers published during the year by the curator, and by co-operators, based upon Museum material. is included in the bibliography in Section IV of this report.

---

[*] See Notes from the Leyden Museum, V p. 142; IV, p. 209.

REPORT ON THE DEPARTMENT OF BIRDS IN THE U. S. NATIONAL MUSEUM, 1887.

By Robert Ridgway, *Curator.*

The character of work accomplished during the year has not differed materially from that of preceding years.

During the fourth annual meeting of the American Ornithologists' Union, held November 16 to 18, inclusive, in the lecture hall of the National Museum, the gallery of the Department of Birds was thrown open to the assembled members of the union, who daily made profitable use of the library and collections in connection with the objects of the meeting and their researches as ornithologists.

In October, 1886, the Government of Costa Rica sent to Washington Mr. Anastasio Alfaro as their accredited representative, to study the business methods and arrangement of collections in the U. S. National Museum. Being particularly interested in ornithology, Mr. Alfaro spent a very considerable part of his time in the Department of Birds, where he was shown every courtesy and extended every facility for familiarizing himself with the methods of the department. Since his return to Costa Rica that Government has formally established a national museum at the capital, San José, of which Mr. Alfaro was made secretary.

CLASSIFICATION AND PREPARATION OF SPECIMENS.

In regard to the character of routine work in connection with the arrangement and classification of the collection and in the preparation of the exhibition and study series there has been no change from the work of preceding years, there being no opportunity, in the absence of many facilities which are deemed desirable, for inaugurating any improvements in the condition or arrangement of the collection.

The taxidermist has performed the work here indicated:

Birds mounted for exhibition series 262
Mounted birds put on new stands 455
New stands put together 451
Birds skinned (including mounted specimens made over into skins) 103

REVIEW OF SPECIAL RESEARCHES PROSECUTED UPON MATERIAL BELONGING TO THE DEPARTMENT.

During the year Mr. Leonhard Stejneger has prosecuted actively his very important researches in Japanese ornithology, and the following families have been thoroughly worked up (put in shape for printing) during the year: Woodpeckers, Wrynecks, Rails, Tits, Thrushes (part), Pigeons, Auks; also the order Herodiones (Herons, Storks, Spoonbills, and Ibises), and some smaller groups, as the genera *Acanthis* and *Pyrrhula*. Mr. Stejneger's researches are based on what is believed to be by far the richest collection of Japanese birds extant, and are of very great importance, his methods being characterized by a peculiar degree of care and exactness. The published results include 100 pages referring exclusively to Japanese ornithology, in which are described 11 new species. In addition to his investigation of Japanese ornithology Mr. Stejneger has worked up an interesting collection of birds from the island of Kauai, Hawaiian group, said collection embracing no less than 7 new species (out of a total of only 15 species) and 1 new genus.

The curator has during the year completed his series of analytical keys to North American birds, soon to be published by the J. B. Lippincott Company, Philadelphia, under the title, "A Manual of North American Birds," a book of royal octavo size, consisting of 631 pages and 464 illustrations of the generic details.

ACCESSIONS.

The number of additions to the collection of birds has been large, and the following statement will show the sources of the more important contributions:

From W. B. Anderson, of Fort Simpson, British Columbia: 4 specimens, 4 species, from Fort Simpson.

From A. W. Anthony, of Denver, Colorado: 8 specimens, 3 species, from Denver, Colorado.

From the Auckland Museum, Auckland, New Zealand, were received in exchange 104 specimens, 59 species, all from New Zealand. An elegantly prepared collection, of unusual interest, containing many species new to the collection of the Museum. There are fine specimens of 2 species of *Ocydromus*, *Strigops*, 2 species of *Nestor*, *Apteryx mantelli*, *Anarhynchus* (4 specimens), *Larus*, *Hæmatopus unicolor*, etc.

From C. W. Beckham, of Bardstown, Kentucky: 10 specimens, 6 species, Passerine birds, from Pueblo, Colorado.

From James Bell, of Gainesville, Florida: A fresh skin of wild turkey, *Meleagris gallopavo*.

From Lieut. H. C. Benson, U. S. Army, Fort Huachuca, Arizona: 11 specimens, 6 species, of which may be mentioned 6 adults and young *Sialia azurea*, a young *Trogon ambiguus* in the first plumage, all from Arizona, and the head of a female Imperial Woodpecker (*Campephilus imperialis*), from Sonora, Mexico, a species of which the Museum as yet possesses no complete specimen, the above head being the first fragment of this magnificent bird to reach the Museum; 170 specimens, 70 species, chiefly from southern Arizona, and a few from Sonora, Mexico. This collection is one of unusual interest and value as containing a number of rare species excellently prepared. This is an exceedingly important accession, consisting as it does of a fine series of 7 beautifully prepared specimens of *Colinus ridgwayi* hitherto not represented in the Museum collection, and 4 equally fine specimens of a new subspecies of *Callipepla elegans*, named *C. elegans bensoni* by the curator in honor of its discoverer. A special interest arises from the fact that this collection was made about 150 miles from the United States and Mexican border lines.

From E. W. Blake, jr.: 2 Horned Larks from Santa Cruz Island, California.

From A. P. Chadbourne, of Boston, Massachusetts: 9 specimens, 6 species, of North American birds were received in exchange.

From H. K. Coale, of Chicago, Illinois: 90 specimens, 85 species, from different parts of the world, but chiefly from South America and India. A very valuable collection, containing several species new to the collection; 34 specimens, 34 species, mostly Old World birds, several new to the collection; 14 specimens, 14 species, of extra-limital birds, received in exchange; 46 specimens, 43 species, mostly Old World birds, some of them mounted. The collection is valuable and interesting, contains several species new to the Museum.

From E. A. Colby, of Chicago, Illinois: An Evening Grosbeak, *Hesperiphona respertina*, in the flesh.

From W. A. Conklin, of New York: A Black Swan, *Chenopis atrata*, in the flesh.

From C. B. Cory, of Boston, Massachusetts; 19 specimens, 10 species, West Indian birds. An interesting and valuable accession, containing as it does specimens of the recently described *Centurus caymanensis* and *Certhiola sharpei* from Grand Cayman Islands; *Calyptophilus frugivorus, Hirundo sclateri, Picumnis lawrencei*, and *Todus subulatus* from Santo Domingo, besides two fine pairs of *Chrysotis sallæi* and *Conurus chloropterus* from the same island, and two male *Geothlypis rostrata* from the Bahamas.

From Prof. A. Dùges, of Guanajuato, Mexico: 24 specimens, 20 species, of Mexican birds, among which may be mentioned two specimens of *Buteo albicaudatus*, and one of *Megascops trichopsis*.

From Vinal Edwards, of Wood's Holl, Massachusetts: Several lots of birds in the flesh, from Wood's Holl, mostly Bronzed Grackles, *Quiscalus æneus*.

From W. O. Emerson, of Haywards, California: 8 specimens, 2 species, six *Passerculus alaudinus* and two "hybrid" Flickers.

From Dr. W. H. Fox, of New York City: 10 specimens, 9 species of birds from New Hampshire.

From Dennis Gale, of Colorado: 12 specimens, 10 species from Colorado.

From Dr. John Gundlach, of Fermina, Cuba, West Indies: 9 specimens, 3 species, from Cuba.

From Edward Hargitt, of London, England: 91 specimens, 63 species, chiefly water birds and birds of prey, all from the Old World. This collection is very valuable and contains some species new to the collection.

From H. W. Henshaw, of Washington, D. C.: 19 specimens, 13 species, from the District of Columbia.

From W. T. Hornaday, of Washington, D. C.: 6 specimens, 5 species, from Montana.

From J. W. Johnson, of Port Huron, Alaska: 71 specimens, 48 species, from Alaska; a collection especially valuable for the good preparation of the specimens.

From P. L. Jouy, of Washington, D. C.: 13 specimens, 8 species, from Japan. A very valuable accession, containing a beautiful hybrid between the Copper Pheasant and the Green Pheasant; a fine specimen of *Spizaëtus nipalensis*, and a good series of the Japan Bullfinch, purchased; 6 specimens, 5 species, from Japan and Australia.

From Valdemar Knudsen, of Kauai, Hawaiian Islands: 37 specimens, 16 species, from Kauai. A most interesting collection, most of the species being rare and new to the collection, while no less than five are new to science, and will be described by L. Stejneger as *Himantopus knudseni, Chasiempis dolei, Phæornis myadestina, Himatione parva*, and *Oreomyza bairdi*, the latter being a type of a new genus.

From Dr. F. W. Langdon, of Cincinnati, Ohio: A specimen of *Vireo solitarius alticola*, the first one of this North American bird the Museum has ever possessed.

From L. C. Leith, of Texas: 3 specimens of the Roseate Spoonbill, *Ajaja ajaja*.

From J. A. Loomis: A specimen of *Buteo swainsoni*, from Texas.

From L. M. Loomis, of Chester County, South Carolina: A specimen of *Scolecophagus cyanocephalus*, from Chester County, South Carolina, the easternmost occurrence of this species.

From William Lloyd, of Paint Rock, Texas: 19 specimens, 9 species, mostly Vireos and Flycatchers, from Texas. Seven specimens, ten species, of Texan birds, among which are five species of *Spizella* and a series of *Thryothorus bairdi;* two specimens of *Spizella pusilla arenacea*.

From George Marshall, of Laurel, Maryland: 2 Crossbills, *Loxia curvirostra minor*.

From Fred. Mather, of Wood's Holl, Massachusetts: 2 chicks, in alcohol, of the Mandarin duck, *Aix galericulata*, bred in captivity.

From C. J. Maynard, of Boston, Massachusetts: 8 specimens of *Puffinus auduboni*, from the Bahamas; purchased

From G. Frean Morcom, of Chicago, Illinois: An adult Little Brown Crane, *Grus canadensis*, in the flesh.

From the National Museum of Costa Rica (through Mr. Anastasio Alfaro): 46 specimens, 23 species, of birds from Costa Rica were received in exchange.

From the Oberlin College, Oberlin, Ohio: 65 specimens, 51 species, from Africa (Natal and Gaboon), and from the Caroline Islands, were received in exchange. The collection is one of considerable importance, inasmuch as most of the species are new to the Museum, even a great number of interesting generic types being added to it; 22 specimens, 21 species, from Southern and Western Africa, nearly all new to the collection, among them no less than three different species of Hornbills.

From R. Ridgway, of Washington, D. C.: The type specimen of *Falco richardsoni*, from Colorado.

From C. D. Riker, of New York City: A specimen of a new species of *Picolaptes* from the Lower Amazon, named by the curator *P. rikeri*.

From Ernest E. T. Seton, of New York City: 6 specimens, 6 species, from Carberry, Manitoba.

From George B. Sennett, of New York City: A chick, *Buteo albicaudatus*, from Texas, and 6 specimens of Bronzed Cowbirds, from Texas.

From J. Schneck, of Mount Carmel, Illinois: A live Barred Owl, *Syrnium nebulosum*.

From R. B. Sharpe, of London, England: 38 specimens, 2 species. Extensive series of the British Redpoll, *Acanthis cabaret*, and the Linnet, *Linaria cannabina*, were received in exchange.

From L. Stejneger, of Washington, D. C.: 40 specimens, 17 species, from Kamtschatka. This is a very valuable addition to our coll ction of Kamtschatka birds, adding several species not hitherto possessed by the Museum. Among them is the type of *Picoides albidior* Stejneger; 5 specimens, 5 species, of European birds, chiefly interesting as being young birds in the first plumage; 4 specimens, 3 species, from North America and Europe. One immature Kamtschatkan Sea Eagle, *Thalassoœtus pelagicus*, was received in exchange.

From F. Stephens, of San Bernardino, California: 33 specimens, 21 species, from Arizona, Colorado, and California were purchased. This collection consists mostly of rare birds, excellently prepared, and all special desiderata of the Museum; also a specimen of *Junco cinereus palliatus*, from Arizona.

From Lieut. George M. Stoney, U. S. Navy, of Washington, D. C.: 142 specimens, 57 species, of birds from Putnam River, Alaska. This collection furnishes valuable information in regard to the geographical distribution of birds in Alaska. One of the most remarkable additions to the fauna of Northern Alaska is that of *Picicorvus columbianus*, of which there is only one previous record north of Sitka.

From R. C. Stuart, of Tampa, Florida: A pair of Wurdemann's Heron, *Ardea wuerdemanni*, from Cape Sable, Florida, was purchased. The type of this species (belonging to the Museum) was for a long time unique, and the acquisition of additional specimens is, therefore, of extreme interest. A mounted Wurdemann's Heron, *Ardea wuerdemanni*, from Cape Sable, Florida, and a fine specimen of the Great White Heron, *Ardea occidentalis*, from Southern Florida, were purchased.

From the Swan Island Club, Swan Island, North Carolina: A specimen of the Fulvous Tree Duck, *Dendrocygna fulva*, from Currituck Sound.

From Ernest E. Thompson, of Toronto, Canada: 3 specimens of Canadian Ruffled Grouse, *Bonasa umbellus togata*, and 2 Prairie Sharp-tailed Grouse, *Pediocætes phasianellus campestris*, were received in exchange; 35 specimens, 12 species, from Manitoba.

From the Tokio Educational Museum, Tokio, Japan: 155 specimens, 107 species, all from Japan. This collection is especially valuable on account of the care with which the specimens are prepared, sexed, and labeled. It also contains several species new to the collection of the Museum, besides three species new to science. Many of the species in this collection were not previously represented in our Museum by Japanese specimens. Altogether, it is a most interesting and valuable accession, which in many respects completes the collection of Blakiston and Jouy, making the collection of Japanese birds in the National Museum one of the best ones, if not the best one, in existence.

From the U. S. Fish Commission: 108 specimens, 10 species, of water birds from the coasts of Massachusetts and from the Newfoundland banks, collected by the naturalists at Wood's Holl and on board the "Albatross" and the "Grampus." The collection is very valuable and interesting, containing, as it does, a series of 44 specimens of *Puffinus borealis* (which was only described a few years ago, and up to date a very rare species in collections), besides very large series of Jaegers, *Stercorarius parasiticus* and *pomarinus*, illustrating the enormous individual color-variations in these birds. Nearly one-half of the collection was received in the flesh and was prepared by the taxidermist, who also mounted a great many of them in excellent style for the exhibition series. Only part of the collection was received during October, though, for reasons detailed in the report for September, were first entered in the Museum register during the former month. Also 11 specimens of Bonaparte's Gull, *Larus philadelphia*, from Wood's Holl, Massachusetts.

From F. S. Webster, of Washington, District of Columbia: 6 specimens, 4 species of Humming-Birds, from South America, and a *Crymophilus fulicarius*, shot on the Eastern Branch, District of Columbia, October 17, 1886, received in exchange.

From Hon. J. S. Wise, of Richmond, Virginia: A Loggerhead Shrike, *Lanius ludovicianus*.

From Henry D. Woolfe, Coal Station, Alaska: 27 specimens, 17 species, from Cape Lisbourne, Alaska.

From Don José C. Zeledon, of San José, Costa Rica: A specimen of a new species, *Cotinga ridgwayi* Zeledon, named in honor of the curator of this department, and one female *Carpodectes antoniæ* Zeled., a recently described and a very rare species, both from Costa Rica.

From Fred. Zeller, of Washington, District of Columbia: A specimen of *Quiscalus æneus* from Prince Charles County, Maryland.

From the Zoological Gardens, Philadelphia, Pennsylvania, through the superintendent, Arthur E. Brown: A Brush Turkey, *Talegalla lathami*, in the flesh, and a Parakeet skin, *Polyteles melanura*.

From the Zoological Museum, University of Christiania, Norway: 2 specimens, 2 species, of birds from Japan, one species new to the collection.

The present state of the collection is excellent so far as that portion included in suitable receptacles is concerned, except that the drawers are very much overcrowded. A considerable portion, however, yet remain in old drawers which are without lids or other fastenings, and therefore exposed to the attacks of insects. By a liberal use of naphthaline, and constant watchfulness, however, damage has been prevented to the reserve or study series, the few specimens which were injured belonging to the duplicate series.

The exhibition collection is still in decidedly the most unsatisfactory condition of any portion of the collection, it being impossible to prevent injury to the specimens from insects and dust, both of which have free ingress to the old and in every respect unsuitable cases in which the collection is arranged.

It has not been practicable to make an actual count of the specimens in the collection. In fact, it is the curator's opinion that this should only be done at intervals of several years (when it becomes necessary, on account of crowding, to re-arrange the collection) for the specimens suffer more or less deterioration from frequent handling. A careful estimate, however, based on the inventory of the preceding year and the accessions for the one just closed, gives the following as the approxi. mate numbers of specimens in the reserve, exhibition, and duplicate series, and the total number in the collection.*

Series.	1885–'86.	1886–'87.	Increase+ Decrease—
Reserve	38,875	40,875	+2,000
Exhibition	7,000	7,000	(none)
Duplicate	7,750	7,112	—638
Total	53,445	54,987	1,542

Last entry in catalogue, in June, 1886 109060
Last entry in catalogue, in June, 1887 111453

The papers published during the year by the curator and his official associates, and by collaborators upon Museum material, are noticed in the bibliography.

---

* Of the 2,393 total additions during the year it is estimated that 2,000 went into the reserve series and 393 into the duplicate series. This would increase the latter to 8,143, were it not that the specimens distributed during the year (1,031) were taken from that series.

REPORT ON THE SECTION OF BIRDS' EGGS IN THE U. S. NATIONAL MUSEUM, 1887.

By Captain Charles E. Bendire, U. S. Army, *Honorary Curator.*

My principal object during the year has been to fill as far as possible the existing gaps in the oölogical collection, and to increase the series of eggs, especially amongst the rarer species. In this I have been moderately successful.

The largest and most important collection received during the past year is that made by Lieut. Harry C. Benson, Fourth Cavalry, in the vicinity of Fort Huachuca, Arizona, consisting of 22 species and 630 specimens, a valuable gift, as all the specimens are nicely prepared, and the majority of them very rare, and scarcely known in collections. I mention a few of the rarer species: *Crvus coryptoleucus*, 57 sets, 275 specimens; *Aphelocoma sieberii arizonæ*, 33 sets, 137 specimens and nest; *Columba fasciata*, 3 specimens; *Buteo abbreviatus*, 1 specimen; *Psaltriparus plumbeus*, 9 sets, 41 specimens and nests.

With the exception of the first-mentioned species these eggs have been represented in the collection by but a single specimen, and the last-named species was till now unknown. In making this collection Lieutenant Benson has often ridden 40 miles a day, and he deserves a great deal of credit for the amount of work he has accomplished in a few weeks' collecting.

Dr. A. K. Fisher, Department of Agriculture, presented 18 specimens, representing 5 species, all of them rare, comprising the following: *Spinus pinus*, set of 4 eggs and nest; *Helminthophila pinus*, set of 5 eggs and nest; *Empidonax flaviventris*, set of 4 eggs. New to the collection.

Col. N. S. Goss, Topeka, Kansas, gave a set of 2 eggs of *Ictinia mississippiensis*.

From Capt. B. F. Goss, Pewaukee, Wisconsin, was received a set of 8 eggs and nest of *Regulus satrapa*.

Mr. H. W. Henshaw, Washington, District of Columbia, gave an egg of *Ammodramus beldingi*. New to the collection.

From William Brewster, Cambridge, Massachusetts, came a set of 4 eggs of *Junco hyemalis carolinensis*. New to collection. He also contributed one set of 2 eggs of *Pipilo erythrophthalmus alleni*, and one set of 3 eggs of *Helinaia swainsoni* with nests.

From Lieut. G. M. Stoney, U. S. Navy, were received: One set of 3 eggs and nest of *Seiurus noveboracensis notabilis*. New to the collection. One set of 4 eggs and nest of *Hesperocichla nævia*, and two sets of 4 eggs and nests of *Branta canadensis minima*.

Loren W. Green, of Baird, Shasta County, California, sent one set of 3 eggs of *Melanerpes formicivorus*, and two sets of 7 and 12 eggs of *Oreortyx pictus*.

J. Parker Norris, Philadelphia, Pennsylvania, gave one set of 2 eggs of *Syrnium nebulosum alleni*. New to the collection.

During the year 85 nests have also been received, of which some of the rarer ones have been mentioned.

The character of routine work for the fiscal year has been as follows: (a) The numbering, classifying, and arrangement of 1,208 new specimens; (b) taking the measurements and records of 7,125 specimens, and (c) mounting, labeling, and arranging 235 species of the nests for exhibition, and (d) relabeling and classifying part of the reserve series of eggs according to the nomenclature of the American Ornithologists' Union Check List.

NUMBER OF ENTRIES AND SPECIMENS.

Last entry in June, 1886, No. 22805; in June, 1887, No. 23160.

Total number of entries during the year (representing 1,208 specimens)	355
Number of eggs in reserve series	32,899
Number of eggs in duplicate	11,548
Number of eggs in exhibition	1,491
Total number of eggs (including 697 species)	45,938
Number of nests in reserve series	2,000
Number of nests on exhibition	235
Total number of nests	2,235

REPORT ON THE DEPARTMENT OF REPTILES AND BATRACHIANS IN THE U. S. NATIONAL MUSEUM, 1887.

By H. C. YARROW, M. D., *Honorary Curator.*

No special studies or investigations have been made by the curator or his assistant, their time having been taken up in attending to the general routine office work. The study of the Batrachia by Prof. E. D. Cope is elsewhere alluded to.

Among the accessions received during the year was quite a valuable collection, containing 23 specimens, from Prof. Alfred Dugès, of Mexico, comprising the principal forms of reptiles of that country. These specimens have not as yet been fully identified.

A small but interesting collection of Corean serpents, including 7 specimens, was received from Dr. N. M. Ferebee, U. S. Navy.

A collection from Surinam, made by C. J. Herring, was also received.

A large and valuable collection came from D. Ridgway, Wheatland, Indiana, containing most of the principal reptile forms of that locality.

A collection from Alaska, by Lieut. Commander H. E. Nichols, U. S. Navy; one from Ensign W. E. Safford, U. S. S. *Mohican*, collected at Montevideo; one from Charles H. Townsend, collected in the West Indies, and another from the United States of Colombia, South America, received from Consul-General V. O. King, comprise the largest contributions made during the year.

Valuable specimens have also been received from George Chandler, Georgetown, District of Columbia; F. W. Hayward, Oakley, South Carolina; L. Stone, McCloud River, California; Henry L. Barker, South Carolina; H. W. Turner, Butte County, California; Frank Burns, Darlington, South Carolina; Capt. E. S. Stone, coast of Nicaragua; Dr. J. R. Mathers, Upshur County, West Virginia; J. H. Kuehling, Virginia; H. J. Shaw, New Berlin, New Jersey; Dr. George H. Mitchell, Arizona; Dr. Robert W. Shufeldt, U. S. Army, Fort Wingate, New Mexico; Henry L. Barker, South Carolina; Dr. George W. Nelson, Panama; A. C. Peale, Montana; Dr. H. J. Bigelow, Massachusetts; U. S. Fish Commission; R. F. Hill, Texas; Otto Lugger, British Guiana; E. P. Alexander, Cuba; R. Ellsworth Call, Dent County, Missouri; W. H. Phillips (through Dr. H. C. Yarrow), Trinidad; L. W. Green, Shasta County, California; Dr. T. H. Bean, U. S. National Museum; S. D.

Karus, Deuel, Colorado; Dr. J. E. Nagle, St. Augustine, Florida; Mrs. Fannie Malone, Texas; G. M. Rhees, Mount Pleasant, District of Columbia; F. Stephens, San Bernardino, California; Mabel and Margaret Johnson, South Carolina; Anton Schott, Akanchee Lake, Wisconsin; Lieut. W. M. Wood, U. S. Navy, South America; Thomas Flynn, Arizona; and a new species of snake (*Tropidonotus bisectus* Cope) from the Central Station of the U. S. Fish Commission in Washington.

The routine work of the Reptile Department consists in entering in the record books all specimens on their arrival; in identifying and labeling them, when possible, and in placing them in the series to which they belong.

An order was received during the year to move temporarily the Department of Reptiles from the west basement of the Smithsonian building, so that that part of the building might be renovated. The specimens were all carefully removed, and stored in cases temporarily erected in the basement hall of the main portion of the Institution. The curator's office was removed to, and now occupies, the south-front room on the ground floor, in the brick building west of the Smithsonian.

The only paper published by the curator during the year is entitled "Recurrence of Symptoms of Poisoning after Snake-bites." This is noticed in Section IV of the report. He has prepared a paper for "Wood's Reference Hand-book of the Medical Sciences," entitled "Poisonous Reptiles of the United States." Prof. E. D. Cope has been specially employed by the Institution to prepare a report and description of the Batrachia of North America. The drawings and manuscript of the work are finished, and the work is nearly ready to go to press.

PRESENT STATE OF THE COLLECTION.

All of the reptile specimens are in excellent condition, but since they are stored away, as before mentioned, they are not as easy of access for study and comparison as formerly.

There have been 130 entries made in the catalogue, comprising 503 specimens.

Specimens received during the year ending June 30, 1886	1,705
Specimens received during the year ending June 30, 1887	503
Specimens in reserve series	9,631
Specimens in general series	8,819
Exhibition series, domestic (selected for)	600
Exhibition series, foreign (selected for)	150
Unclassified and exotic specimens, probably	6,134
Total	27,542

REPORT ON THE DEPARTMENT OF FISHES IN THE U. S. NATIONAL MUSEUM, 1887.

By TARLETON H. BEAN, M. D., *Curator.*

GENERAL REVIEW OF THE YEAR'S WORK.

Much time has been devoted to the identification of collections made in various parts of the world by correspondents of the Museum. This will be more particularly referred to in another part of this report.

Until the month of October I was much occupied with editorial work upon Museum publications and upon the reports of collectors in the service of other bureaus of the Government. After this time I was relieved of this duty by Mr. A. Howard Clark.

In preparing a sketch of the history of the collection of fishes it became desirable to prepare a geographical list of the principal sources from which fishes were received from 1851–1886, and to make a census of the collection now in the possession of the Museum. It was found that the Museum now has upwards of 24,000 jars of fishes, besides 208 tanks, 4 barrels, and a lot of stuffed skins, drawings, color sketches, and casts. The number of specimens in the collection must be not less than 100,000, which is probably the greatest number possessed by any museum in the world.

Messrs. B. A. Bean and Peter Parker, jr., besides attending to their usual routine work, have been employed in adding to the bibliography of ichthyology with particular reference to deep-sea species, and preparing copies of the original descriptions of species. In connection with this same work I have prepared a list of the deep-sea fishes, which is now almost completed. A comparison of the results of deep-sea explorations conducted by foreign Governments with those obtained by the United States Government reveals the fact that so far as the fishes are concerned we have brought to light more new forms than all the other Governments combined.

The curator has prepared descriptions of new fishes from Mexico, received from Prof. A. Dugès, and in connection with Mr. Goode has published a paper on new genera and species of deep-sea fishes collected by the steamer *Blake*. Work has also been continued upon other reports, which will be referred to under special researches.

Numerous important papers have been published by Prof. D. S. Jordan and his assistants, upon materials belonging to the Museum, and Prof. J. A. Ryder has published many valuable embryological papers, which will be found noticed in the bibliography.

The work has been continued upon the drawings of fishes by Mr. H. L. Todd and Mr. W. S. D. Haines. The character of the illustrations has been kept up to the high standard.

During the latter portion of the year almost the entire collection of fishes was moved out of the exhibition halls, the tank-room, the corridors, and the ichthyological laboratory at the expense of a considerable loss of time and the causing of more or less confusion.

ACCESSIONS.

The total number of accessions during the year was 110, of which the following are among the more important:

From S. Applegate, U. S. Signal Service, Unalashka, Alaska: 7 species of Alaskan fishes.

From Señor Don José Arechavaleta, Montevideo: *Geotria chilensis,Siphostoma, Halocypselus, Loricaria, Tetragonopterus, Curimatus, Acara,* and *Piratinga.*

From Commander L. A. Beardslee, U. S. Navy: 10 species of fishes from Key West, Florida, common to vicinity.

From R. E. Call, of Columbia, Missouri: A small box of fishes from the Ozark region in northern Missouri.

From A. F. Clapp, of Sunbury, Pennsylvania: A specimen of Lamprey, *Petromyzon marinus,* juv., from the Susquehanna River, at Sunbury.

From F. N. Clark, of Northville, Michigan: A specimen of *Coregonus clupeiformis,* 5 inches long, grown in railroad water-tank at Northville.

From Capt. J. W. Collins, Gloucester, Massachusetts: A specimen of an abnormal Cod-fish.

From Capt. J. W. Collins, U. S. Fish Commission schooner *Grampus:* Lower jaw of Ground Shark, *Somniosus microcephalus,* taken on Grand Bank, August, 1886, in 22) fathoms, by N. Day, of schooner *M. A. Baston;* also eggs of Slime Eel, *Myxine glutinosa,* from 122 fathoms on the trawl-line.

From the Connecticut Fish Commission, New Haven, Connecticut: About 40 species of young Shad, *Clupea sapidissima,* from 4 to 6 inches in length, from the canal at Birmingham, on the Housatonic.

From Alfred Dugès, of Guanajuato, Mexico: *Lampetra spadicea* Bu., *Characodon atripinnis, Characodon variatus,* Bn., *Limnurgus variegatus.*

From J. B. Edwards, of Amagansett, New York: A fresh specimen of *Torpedo occidentalis.* Sent to Mr. Hornaday to be stuffed.

From J. M. C. Eaton, of Irvington, New Jersey: 1 specimen of *Zoarces anguillaris.*

From C. H. Eigenmann, Indiana University, Bloomington, Indiana: Type of *Ophichthys retropinnis,* from Snapper Banks of Pensacola, Florida.

From N. M. Ferebee, surgeon U. S. Navy, U. S. S. *Trenton:* Alcoholic specimens of fishes from China, Japan, and Corea.

From C. H. Gilbert, of Cincinnati, Ohio: A specimen of *Etheostoma nianguœ spilotum* from Owsley County, Kentucky, and three specimens of *Etheostoma cragini,* Garden City, Kansas.

From R. A. Golden, of Washington, D. C. (through Henry Marshall, U. S. National Museum): A specimen of Chub Mackerel, *Scomber pneumatophorus.*

From R. A. Golden, of Washington, D. C., was purchased a specimen of Halibut, *Hippoglossus hippoglossus,* caught in the Potomac River, having in its stomach a partly-digested Cat-fish, *Amiurus albidus.*

From Loren W. Green, of Baird, Shasta County, California: 2 specimens of *Potamocottus gulosus* from the McCloud River. This fish is destructive to Salmon eggs.

From Gwynn Harris, of Washington, D. C.: A specimen of tench, *Tinca tinca*, from the Potomac River.

From William C. Harris, of New York: *Coregonus williamsoni*, *Thymallus tricolor* (*Montanus* form), and *Salmo purpuratus* (*virginalis* form), from the Gallatin River, Montana.

From William C. Harris, of New York: *Salvelinus malma*, *Coregonus williamsoni*, and *Ptychochilus oregonensis* from Clark's Fork of the Columbia.

From J. T. Havens, Fourth life-saving station, Point Pleasant, New Jersey: A fresh specimen of Trumpet-fish, *Fistularia tabaccaria*.

From O. P. Hay, of Irvington, Indiana: 16 species of fish from Kansas.

From William Herrick, Swan's Island, Hancock County, Maine: Specimens of food taken from mouth of Mackerel, *Onos cimbrius*, juv., *Gasterosteus gymnurus*, *Clupea harengus*, *Phycis*, juv., *Pollachius virens*, all very young.

From C. F. Hodge, Johns Hopkins University, Baltimore, Maryland: One jar of fishes for identification from Green Turtle Bay, Bahama Islands, out of which the Museum retains 3 specimens of *Querimana gyrans*, 2 of *Gambusia puncticulata*, and 1, 1½ inches long, *Sphyræna picuda*.

From E. B. Hodge, of Plymouth, New Hampshire: 8 fresh specimens of *Salvelinus agassizii* from Sunapee Lake.

From Prof. D. S. Jordan, of Bloomington, Indiana: *Prionotus roseus*, *Scarus evermanni*, *Steinegeria rubescens*, *Anthias vivanus*, *Scarus bollmani*, *Zygonectes escambiæ*, *Z. cingulatus*, *Gallechelys muræna*, *Serranus ocyurus*, and *Phycis floridanus*.

From Prof. D. S. Jordan, of Bloomington, Indiana: A specimen of *Thalassophryne dowi* from Punta Arenas, Gulf of California.

From Alfred Johnson, schooner *Mary S. Hontvet* (through W. A. Wilcox): A very large specimen of *Alepocephalus bairdi* and one specimen of *Pteraclis carolinus*.

From W. L. May, of Fremont, Nebraska: A small bottle of Fat-head Minnows, *Pimephales promelas*. Rained down at Harvard, Nebraska, June 14, 1886.

From H. C. Nichols, U. S. Navy, commanding U. S. S. *Pinta*, Sitka, Alaska: A tank of Alaskan fishes and a specimen of *Myxine australis* from the Straits of Magellan.

From Joseph F. Reed, keeper U. S. life-saving station, Island Beach, Tom's River, New Jersey: A specimen of Lump-fish, *Cyclopterus lumpus*.

From W. E. Safford, ensign, U. S. steamer *Mohican*: Seven bottles and nine vials of fishes from the Atlantic and Pacific Oceans and from Montevideo, Uruguay, South America; *Myxine australis* from Straits of Magellan, *Xiphorhamphus jenynsii*, and *Tetragonopterus*, besides some pelagic forms not yet identified.

From the Zoological Museum of the Academy of Sciences, St. Petersburg, Russia: 2 specimens *Phoxinus stagnalis;* new species.

From Miss Rosa Smith, of San Diego, Calfornia: A photograph of *Tetraodon setosus*. Picture of the type.

From Lieut. G. M. Stoney, U. S. Navy: 15 species of fishes from the Kowak River, Alaska. Large and well-preserved specimen of *Stenodus*, *Coregonus tullibee*, *Oncorhynchi*, *Salvelinus*, *Thymallus*, etc.

From Lieut. E. H. Taunt, U. S. Navy: Sketches of 10 species of fishes from the Congo River, Africa.

From Thomas Thompson, schooner *M. A. Baston* (through W. A. Wilcox, Gloucester, Massachusetts): 2 specimens of *Chimæra affinis*, and a specimen of *Haloporphyrus viola*.

From C. H. Townsend, Honduras, Central America: 17 species of fishes from Central America.

U. S. Fish Commission, Wood's Holl, Massachusetts: A fresh specimen of Amberfish or Yellow-tail, *Seriola lalandii*, from Menemshe, Martha's Vineyard.

U. S. Fish Commission, Wood's Holl, Massachusetts: A fresh specimen of *Histiophorus gladius*.

From the U. S. Fish Commission, Wood's Holl, Massachusetts : A fresh specimen of *Orcynus thynnus* and parts of a *Tetrapturus*.

From the U. S. Fish Commission, Wood's Holl, Massachusetts : A specimen of *Ophiognathus leci* Ryder.

From the U. S. Fish Commission schooner *Grampus : Somniosus microcephalus, Carcharias glaucus, Raia ocellata,* and *Raia lævis.* From Wood's Holl, Massachusetts.

From the U. S. Fish Commission, Wood's Holl, Massachusetts : 220 jars and bottles of fishes collected by the steamers *Albatross* and *Fish Hawk,* and by the schooner *Grampus,* during the summer of 1886.

From the U. S. Fish Commission schooner *Grampus,* Wood's Holl, Massachusetts : Eggs and milt of *Gadus morrhua,* of *Pollachius virens, Brosmius,* and *Phycis.* One specimen of *Maurolicus* and two of *Sebastoplus,* all taken near Gloucester, Massachusetts, November, 1886.

From the U. S. Fish Commission, Washington, D. C. : A fresh *Salmo purpuratus,* which was received at the Armory in December, 1885, from Colorado. It was kept at the Armory two months when it was sent to Wytheville, where it remained until April 1, 1887. Sent to Armory. Died April 21.

From the U. S. Fish Commission : Hybrid trout from Wytheville, Virginia, resulting from fertilizing eggs of *Salmo irideus* with milt of *Salvelinus fontinalis.* A beautiful fish, strongly resembling a similar cross between *Salmo fario* and *Salvelinus alpinus* in Norway.

From the U. S. Fish Commission schooner *Grampus :* 2 half-barrels and 3 boxes containing collections of fishes made on the southern mackerel grounds in April and May, 1887.

From F. L. Washburne, of Minneapolis, Minnesota : An 8-gallon tank containing 14 species of Minnesota fishes, principally from Lake Mille Lacs.

From W. A. Wilcox, of Gloucester, Massachusetts : An *Argyropelecus olfersi,* picked up alive at surface on Grand Banks.

From W. A. Wilcox, of Gloucester, Massachusetts : 4 specimens of *Chimæra affinis* (♂ and ♀).

From W. A. Wilcox, of Gloucester, Massachusetts : Sword of a Sword-fish, *Xiphias gladius,* that killed Capt. Franklin D. Langsford, of Lanesville, Massachusetts. Wounded August 9 and died August 12, 1886.

From Lieut. W. M. Wood, U. S. S. *Juniata :* A specimen of *Haplochiton zebra* from Puerto Bueno, South America. Taken from a small lake.

There have been made 1,225 additions to the Catalogue of Fishes. Collections received from the following sources have been identified :

Corea, China, and Japan, made by N. M. Ferebee, U. S. Navy.

Alaska, made by S. Applegate, U. S. Signal Service; Lieut. Commander H. E. Nichols, U. S. Navy; Lieut. G. M. Stoney, U. S. Navy, and C. H. Townsend.

Bering Island, made by N. Grebnitzki.

Pacific Ocean, made by Dr. W. H. Jones, U. S. Navy.

Mexico, made by Prof. A. Dugès.

Bahama Islands, made by a party from Johns Hopkins University.

West Indies and deep sea, by U. S. Fish Commission steamer *Albatross.*

Key West, Florida, made by Commander L. A. Beardslee.

Fishing Banks, made by U. S. Fish Commission schooner *Grampus.*

Prince Edward's Island, food of Mackerel (young fishes), made by Capt. William Herrick.

Montana and other Territories, *Salmonidæ,* sent by William C. Harris.

Minnesota (Lake Mille Lacs), made by Mr. F. L. Washburne.

New Hampshire, Trout of Sunapee Lake, by E. B. Hodge.

The usual work of labeling jars and changing alcohol has been continued at proper intervals. The card catalogue, also, has been kept up to date.

One hundred and eighteen drawings made by H. L. Todd and thirty-five drawings made by W. S. D. Haines were examined and accepted. An accurate census of the collection referred to elsewhere was made.

The preparation of reports upon specimens sent to the Museum or to the Fish Commission for examination has become an important feature of the work of this department.

SPECIAL RESEARCHES.

In connection with Dr. G. Brown Goode a partial report was prepared upon the fishes of the *Blake*. Thirteen species and two genera were described in the Bulletin of the Museum of Comparative Zoology, Vol. XII, July, 1886. The curator described some new fishes sent from Mexico by Professor Dugès. Other papers now in progress and well advanced are the following: (1) Report on the Fishes of Great South Bay, Long Island; (2) Report on the Fishes of Cozumel; (3) Synopsis of the Fishes of Alaska; (4) Synopsis of the Salmonidæ of North America; (5) in connection with Dr. Goode, Report on the Deep-sea Fishes; (6) with Dr. Goode, A Study of the Fishes of the Atlantic Basin.

The curator was detailed by Professor Baird to make an investigation of the spring mackerel fishery in the schooner *Grampus*. He accordingly left Washington April 20, joined the vessel at Fortress Monroe, and cruised with the mackerel fleet until May 31, when the spring mackerel fishing was practically ended. He published letters descriptive of this cruise in the Boston Herald of May 9 and 26 and June 6, and now has in preparation a more exhaustive report of the voyage for the Bulletin of the U. S. Fish Commission.

The collections of the Museum have been utilized to a very large extent by collaborators not belonging to the Museum force. Professor Jordan and his assistants have published many extensive papers, which are mentioned in the bibliography.[*]

Prof. J. A. Ryder has also published important embryological memoirs, which are likewise included in the bibliography.

A large number of specimens were at their request sent for study to collaborators of the Smithsonian Institution.

THE PRESENT STATE OF THE COLLECTION.

The present state of the collection is about the same as at the time of the last annual report, with the exception of some improvement in the condition of the specimens in jars and some additional deterioration in tanks. It will be found necessary for the safety of the tank specimens to transfer them as far as possible into large glass vessels. Requisitions have been made for preserving material from time to time, but so far we have not been able to obtain a sufficient quantity.

The first entry number in the catalogue in July, 1886, was 37894, and

---

[*]See Section IV of this report.

the last entry in June, 1887, was 39118, making the number of entries for the year 1,225.

NUMBER OF SPECIMENS IN THE COLLECTION.

Exhibition	34, 000
Reserve	41, 000
Duplicate	25, 000
Total	100, 000

In February, 1887, the total number of jars containing fishes, by actual count, was 24,069. This number has been increased by accessions since received. There were at that time 208 tanks and 4 barrels filled with fishes. There were exhibited in the fish hall 64 stuffed fishes. The total number of casts at that time was 1,086, of which 276 were exhibited, 315 duplicates and stored, and 190 moulds, which had not yet been utilized.

The number of drawings at that time was 1,354. There is also a large collection of photographs and color sketches, to which I have not yet obtained access. There is a large number of wood-cuts, 281 of which are stored in the fish hall and about twice as many in the wood-cut room.

A census of the types of species was made in February, when it was found that the Museum possesses 364 described in outside publications prior to the foundation of the Proceedings of the National Museum, and 549 which have been described in the Proceedings, 150 of these being deep-sea species and 399 fresh- and shoal-water species. To this number should be added a great many extra-limital species, principally described by Dr. Gill, and a large number of types of West Indian fishes described and contributed by Prof. Felipe Poey.

In 1871 the National Museum had more specimens in the collection of fishes than the British Museum, but they represented a smaller number of species. The British Museum at that time had 5,177 species, represented by 29,275 specimens.

REPORT ON THE DEPARTMENT OF MOLLUSKS (INCLUDING CENOZOIC INVERTEBRATE FOSSILS) IN THE U. S. NATIONAL MUSEUM, 1887.

By W. H. DALL, *Honorary Curator.*

The force of the Department of Mollusks beside the curator has consisted of Dr. R. E. C. Stearns, adjunct curator; Miss Agnes Nicholson, clerk (to February, 1887); Mr. Pierre Louis Jouy, aid (since February, 1887).

Assistance has also been rendered from time to time, by permission of the Director of the U. S. Geological Survey, by Messrs. R. Stuart, Frank Burns, and R. T. Hill, of the Geological Survey, chiefly in connection with the Tertiary fossils contributed by the Survey to the Museum.

The work, as during the past years, has chiefly consisted in the classification and preparation of material received during the year and left over from previous years. By the faithfulness and industry of those employed upon the work, good progress has been made, and with similar success during the next two or three years we may hope to see the last of eleven years' arrearages (to 1884) finally administered upon.

This once accomplished it will be a comparatively easy task to keep up with the annual accessions except in very unusual cases.

As there is no logical or biological reason for separating the Tertiary fossils from the recent shells in general administration (though the specimens may be kept in separate cases for convenience of reference), no separation has been made, and this report therefore is practically a report on the Department of Tertiary Invertebrate Fossils as well as of the Department of Mollusks.

A biological arrangement has been adopted in arranging the fossils, the distinctions of supposed age being retained only on the labels. The result of this is to bring together all the species of any one genus from the Eocene to the Post Pliocene, and, in the writer's opinion, a study of the collection thus arranged is likely to reduce by two-thirds the number of nominal species now on our lists of Tertiary fossils of the United States.

The general collection is divided into three principal geographical series with two subordinate groups, all being biologically arranged. Thus we have the species of West America from the Arctic province

111

to Cape Horn, the species of East America, and the general collection of exotic species. In the latter we have two subordinate divisions which are contained in one room with the East American series, but independently arranged. These are (1) the Jeffreys collection of North Atlantic, North European, and British shells, and (2) the collection of Arctic marine shells from all parts of the Polar basin and adjacent waters. Among the land shells of North America, a case is devoted to the types of Binney, and in the same way, when received and arranged, the Lea collection of Unionidæ and other fresh-water types will form a special series.

In this connection it is my sad duty to refer to the death, December 8, 1886, of Dr. Isaac Lea, for many years the oldest living American student of mollusks, and known all over the world for his researches on the Naiades, especially of North America. Dr. Lea had been a valued correspondent and friend of the Museum from its earliest stages, and had given large numbers of valuable specimens to the collection. In his will, subject to certain reasonable conditions, he left his entire collection of Mollusca to the Museum, which, when received and arranged, will put the Department of Mollusks, in the matter of Naiades, far in advance of any other existing biological museum.

The administration on our material is progressing so rapidly that it already exceeds our case room. I shall therefore be obliged to make requisition for some eight new cases with their accompanying drawers, etc., to accommodate the general exotic series.

The few persons available for work on the collection of mollusks, recent and fossil, have been engaged with the greatest assiduity in the labor above described, so that comparatively little work has been possible on the large and valuable collection of cephalopods and other mollusks in alcohol. They have been examined, however, to determine their safety, and a card catalogue of the collection begun, to be taken up as occasion serves. Though not available for certain sorts of work, the alcoholic specimens afford opportunity for determining with certainty many points of prime importance in classification; as in one case during the past year in the matter of the gills of *Neæra* (= *Cuspidaria*) this material enabled the remarkable fact to be determined that specialized gills of the ordinary form are entirely absent, thus rendering necessary the revision of the definition of the entire class and even the final rejection of one of the most commonly received class appellations. The impossibility of getting rare exotic material in a living condition will always give to a well-preserved alcoholic collection a certain importance.

The full list of accessions to this department will be found by reference to Section V of the report, and includes seventy-five numbers.

Among the more important of these are the series of deep-sea mollusks dredged by the Coast Survey steamer *Blake*, types of the report on the mollusks of the *Blake* expedition by the curator, presented by Prof. Alexander Agassiz; thirty-two species of *Scalaria* and allied groups from the Tertiary of France, obtained in exchange from M. E. de Boury; four hundred species of Pliocene fossils, and many species from older rocks, with a large collection of mollusks obtained by the curator during field-work in south Florida under the auspices of the U. S. Geological Survey; a small collection, representing eight species from Bennett Island in the Polar Sea, collected during the *Jeannette* expedition and presented by R. L. Newcomb, naturalist of the expedition; twenty specimens from Enoshima Island, Japan, presented by Mr. P. L. Jouy, containing some very acceptable rarities; seventy-six species of Mexican shells, presented by the Mexican Geological Commission; some interesting fresh-water shells, from H. A. Pilsbry; a valuable series of specimens dredged in the Gulf of Mexico and the Bahamas, partly in very deep water, and presented by Dr. W. H. Rush, U. S. Navy; a small but interesting collection of shells from South America, and pelagic mollusks, from W. E. Safford, U. S. Navy; a number of acceptable species from the southern coast of the United States and Honduras, presented by Charles T. Simpson; eleven boxes of fossils and rocks containing fossils, from the U. S. Geological Survey, through W. H. Dall; and eighty-four very beautifully preserved species of land and fresh-water shells of the Southern United States, by A. G. Wetherby, of Roan Mountain, North Carolina. Contrary to our usual experience, nothing of importance has been received from the U. S. Fish Commission during the year.

The work of the past year was chiefly devoted to the administration upon the marine forms of West America, the preliminary arrangement of which has been completed; to the unpacking and arrangement of the Indo-Pacific series of the Stearns collection; the selection and arrangement of the Floridian Tertiary and the general East American series; preparation of material for exchanges chiefly in favor of other departments of the Museum; and the assistance of students and correspondents desiring names of species or other information of use in their studies. A report was made and printed on the Blake brachiopods and pelecypods, which is more fully described in the list of publications appended to this report. A collection brought by the Mexican Geographical Commission was named for them, and will serve as a basis for future study to the conchologists of Mexico.

Information or assistance of more or less importance, involving the writing of letters to the number of some 350, was furnished by the Department of Mollusks to the following persons:

Agassiz, Prof. A., Cambridge, Mass.
Aldrich, T. H., Cincinnati, Ohio.
Beecher, C. E., Albany, New York.
Binney, W. G., Burlington, New Jersey.
Boury, E. de, Vigny, France.
Cooper, J. Y., Haywards, California.

Diller, J. S., U. S. Geological Survey.
Dominion Geological Survey, Ottawa, Canada.
Dugès, Prof. Alfred, Mexico.
Flint, Dr. Earl, Nicaragua.
Greegor, Isaiah, Jacksonville, Florida.

Greely, General A. W., U. S. Army.
Heilprin, Prof. A., Philadelphia, Penn.
Hemphill, H., San Diego, California.
Henshall, Mrs. James A., Cynthiana, Ky.
Hitchcock, Prof. C. H., Hanover, N. H.
Hodge, C. F., Baltimore, Maryland.
Jones, E. E., Sewanee, Tennessee.
Leidy, Prof. J., Philadelphia, Penn.
McCormick, Dr. J. L., Tennessee.
Mazyck, W. G., Charleston, S. C.
Merriam, Dr. C. H., Washington, D. C.
Mexican Geographical Commission, Puebla, Mexico.
Mills Seminary and College, Alameda, Cal.
Moser, Lieut. J. F., U. S. Navy, Cedar Keys, Florida.
Nash, Dr. F. S., U. S. Navy, Washington, District of Columbia.

Newlon, Dr. W. S., Oswego, Kansas.
Pilsbry, H. A., Des Moines, Iowa.
Redway, J. W., Philadelphia, Penn.
Rush, Dr. W. H., U. S. Navy, Philadelphia, Pennsylvania.
Ryder, W. P., Upper Marlborough, Md.
Sandberger, Prof. H., Würzburg, Bavaria.
Shaler, Prof. N. P., Cambridge, Mass.
Simpson, Charles T., Ogallala, Nebraska.
Sterki, Dr. V., New Philadelphia, Ohio.
Swan, J. G., Port Townsend, Wash.
Todd, Aurelius, Elkhead, Oregon.
Westgate, W. W., Houston, Texas.
Wetherby, A. G., Roan Mountain, N. C.
Whiteaves, J. F., Dominion Geological Survey, Ottawa, Canada.
Wilson, Thomas, Washington, D. C.

SPECIAL RESEARCHES.

In the flood of routine work an occasional rest was taken for study, and investigations prosecuted by the curator.

1. On the mollusks of the *Blake* collection, of which the brachiopods and pelecypods were completed and published; 2. On the fossils of the later Tertiary of south Florida, still in progress; 3. On a small collection of fragments, etc., obtained by the *Jeannette* expedition at Bennett Island in the Polar Sea; 4. On the general Floridian and Gulf fauna, still in progress; 5. On the geology of south Florida, in press; and on several Arctic or sub-Arctic collections made by Mr. L. M. Turner in Labrador, Mr. Nicholas Grebnitzki in Bering Sea, and by the curator in several parts of northern Alaska. The papers printed are enumerated in the list appended to this report. Dr. Stearns, the assistant curator, has devoted some time to the study of the fossil *Tryonia*, a small genus of the *Amnicola* group; of *Teredo;* and of the *Phoridæ*, or Carrier shells.

Mr. Paul Pelseneer, of the Museum at Brussels, having taken up the study of the pteropods, applied for certain material to be used in his studies. This, consisting chiefly of specimens of Pacific and other pteropods and copies of colored drawings made from life while in the North Pacific by the curator, was furnished to the Museum of Brussels for his use.

A preliminary paper describes a new genus found off the eastern coast of the United States by the U. S. Fish Commission steamer *Albatross*, and further publications may be expected.

In previous reports I have shown why it is impossible to state the exact number of specimens, species, duplicates, etc., contained in the collection. Two years ago the collection was estimated to contain 400,000 specimens. Since then not less than 25,000 specimens have been added to it. It will be several years before an exact statement can be made as to any of these details; certainly not before all arrearages are cleared up.

For the year 1885–'86 the number of entries in the Museum register, being the final culmination of some two years' preparatory work, was 18,638, representing between 50,000 and 60,000 individual specimens. A larger number of specimens has been handled during the past year, but owing to a deficiency of clerical assistance not so many of them have reached the final stage of registration.

The following table shows the state of the register, sundry gaps being due to the allotment of numbers to the Fish Commission for the use of Professor Verrill and his assistants:

STATE OF REGISTERS.

Volume.	From number.	To number, inclusive.	Total entries.
XIV	64,004	68,150	4,146
XV*			
XVI	73,050	77,876	4,826
XVII*	78,000	78,974	974
XVIII	82,950	83,534	584
Total			10,530

* Reserved for Fish Commission, and but partly filled.

The total number of entries for 1886–'87 is 10,530, equivalent to about 32,000 specimens, each lot registered averaging over 3 specimens. Adding this to the total for the preceding year, we get 29,168 entries, while in the twenty years previous to July, 1885, the whole number of entries was only 42,440, or less than one and one-half times as many as have been registered during the last two years. These figures show better than any lengthy explanation how the work has been pressed. It may also be observed that, whereas in former days many specimens were entered merely under the generic name or without any name, the present entries are nearly all identified and fully administered upon.

REPORT ON THE DEPARTMENT OF INSECTS IN THE U. S. NATIONAL MUSEUM, 1887.

By C. V. RILEY, *Honorary Curator.*

The general work of the year was mainly that of arrangement, as by far the greatest amount of time has been devoted to the separation of material, and its more or less complete arrangement either for exhibition or study.

First in order, the arrangement of the Lepidoptera from the *Rhopalocera* to the end of the *Arctiidæ* has been completed. This had been begun during the preceding year and nearly completed. The work this year embraced the addition of new material, the completion and partial re-arrangement of series, and such changes as experience suggested. A tolerably complete statement of this part of the work is contained in last year's report, and nothing more need be said here on the same subject.

A more tedious, and in many respects more important, work was the separation into families of the material in the order Diptera.

There was in the order the material of the Burgess collection, much of it without labels, and most all of it without arrangement of any kind; the material in the Belfrage collection in somewhat similar condition; the material of the Riley collection and that of the Department of Agriculture containing a vast lot of bred species; the Riley collection being the only one with any attempt at arrangement. The work of Dr. Williston, in the winter of 1885, on this collection included the separation and arrangement of some of the leading families, and these served as a guide and basis for the continuation of the work.

There are now 107 boxes of material arranged as to families, much of it determined generically or specifically; the boxes of all sizes, many of them large, double storage cases.

A series of eight unit boxes was prepared, containing a synoptic collection of North American Coleoptera, with labels defining and drawings illustrating the families of this order. A more detailed statement of this work is given further on.

The collection of *Arachnidæ* has been overhauled, partly remounted, and roughly separated for convenience of future study. The old material in adolescent stages has been similarly treated.

A lot of typical Myriapoda, received from Mr. Rathbun, the curator of Marine Invertebrates, has been carefully preserved and arranged.

A lot of slides containing parts of insects and many minute species, also from Mr. Rathbun, were carefully listed and arranged for ready reference.

The Heteroptera had been arranged by Prof. H. Osborn, as detailed in the last report, but the duplicate material had neither been labeled nor entirely separated; this unfinished work on the suborder was also done during the year.

The *Capsidæ*, one of the families of this order, was sent to Prof. P. R. Uhler, of Baltimore, for study, at his request.

The collection of Orthoptera had already been carefully arranged by Mr. Lawrence Bruner while associated with me at the Department of Agriculture, in 1884, in a series of single and double folding boxes; but in order to assist in the preparation of a monograph of the *Acrididæ*, which I have planned with Mr. Bruner, the whole order has been transferred to permanent cabinets. This re-arrangement has permitted the incorporation of the new material that has accumulated since 1884, and has placed the collection in far better condition both in regard to safety from breakage and to facility for study. In the re-arrangement a duplicate series was also prepared for the Department of Agriculture to facilitate reference work there.

Reports on accessions often require considerable study and time, and the correspondence of the department has been extensive.

A considerable amount of time was occupied in determinations for such entomologists as either sent specimens for the department or who had in some way deserved well of the Museum, and for institutions where the determinations would be valued and valuable.

Some twenty such lots were named in addition to those which were reported upon as accessions in the regular manner.

During the year two additional standard cabinets of the kind described in my previous report have been made. These are of cherry and mahogany, and superior to those previously received.

One hundred of the standard single folding boxes were also ordered and received.

The Smith collection is contained in one large walnut cabinet of sixty drawers; a small pine cabinet of nine drawers; 80 single folding boxes; 27 pine double folding boxes; 17 very large walnut double folding boxes, and a miscellaneous lot of over 100 boxes of all sizes and shapes. Two unit table cases were also assigned to the department.

A very fair proportion of the boxes received are already in use, and they are being rapidly filled as arrangement of material progresses.

The preparation of papers for publication, as a direct result of the Museum work, has occupied, compared with the other work, but a small part of the time. It is chiefly represented by the paper by Mr. Smith on the classification of some of the Bombycina in the Proceedings of the Museum, and hereafter more particularly mentioned, and of a few contributions by myself.

Based largely upon Museum material, and almost entirely upon material which will, I hope, ultimately become the property of the Museum, is the "Synopsis of the North American *Syrphidæ*," by Dr. S. W. Williston, published as Bulletin No. 31 of the U. S. National Museum.

This is the most valuable contribution to systematic dipterology in North America that has appeared in recent years.

NOTES.

In considering the more important accessions during the year, I have drawn attention to a few of those which have come through the ordinary channels with their accession numbers; but by far the greater number of important accessions to the collection have come (1) through the curator in the shape of material constantly received by him or collected during his travels, and which on account of their numbers and frequency are added to the general collection without accession numbers; (2) those received through the Department of Agriculture from the correspondents and agents of its entomological division. By far the most important of these last is the material that has been collected by Mr. Albert Koebele in California, which comprises many thousand specimens in all orders, much of which is exceedingly valuable material. Again, Mr. E. A. Schwarz, of said entomological division, very kindly donated some 300 specimens of the 108 species of Coleoptera which were required to complete the synoptic collection in that order which were either not represented in the collection or were represented in insufficient numbers.

Of the accessions by purchase, only one has been made during the year, but that is an important and valuable one, viz, the private collection of the assistant curator, Mr. J. B. Smith.

Of the numbered accessions direct to the Museum, the following may be mentioned as of special interest:

July, 1886.—Several specimens of *Epicauta maculata* from Capt. Henry Romeyn, Fifth U. S. Infantry, Fort Keogh, Montana. (17743.) These insects were said to have appeared suddenly in great numbers, and proved very destructive to vegetables, creating some alarm. Later Captain Romeyn wrote that *Pyrethrum* proved a complete remedy.

Specimen of the work of *Scolytus unispinosus* in *Abies douglassi* from L. E. Ricksecker, Sylvania, California, through J. B. Smith. (17767.) This specimen was interesting as presenting the first known instance of a true *Scolytus* boring in conifers.

August, 1886.—Twenty one specimens of fourteen species of Lepidoptera from Missouri, from Miss M. E. Murtfeldt, Kirkwood, Missouri. The species were undetermined, and many of them proved interesting. (17848.)

September, 1886.—Six packages of Lepidoptera and two vials of miscellaneous insects, from C. J. Herring, colony of Surinam, Dutch Guiana. (17929.)

The Lepidoptera were mostly fragmentary and so badly infested with *Anthreni* that they could not be saved and were destroyed. It was with great regret that this was done, for several of the species would have been desirable. The vials contained a few larvæ and some Orthoptera of much less value.

October, 1886.—One specimen, *Carabus truncaticollis*, from S. Applegate, sergeant, Signal Corps, Unalaska. (18036.) In point of value the most important accession of the month, as it is rather a rarity.

Thirty-one specimens of twenty-six species of Lepidoptera from northern New York, from George H. Hudson, Plattsburgh, New York. (18077.) This lot contained some good species, very useful to the Museum. A complete list was sent Mr. Hudson.

Nest of *Vespa maculata*, Mount Vernon, Virginia, from J. H. Kuehling, 419 Twelfth street northwest, Washington, D. C. (18081.) A very fine, large example, containing numerous inhabitants.

Thirty-one specimens of Lepidoptera in papers from Dr. J. C. Merrill, U. S. Army, Fort Klamath, Oregon. (18147.) A few of these were good species and of value to our collections. A complete list was sent Dr. Merrill at his request.

Twenty-eight species of Lepidoptera and three of Coleoptera from George H. Hudson, Plattsburgh, New York. (18148.) A list of determinations was sent to Mr. Hudson.

November, 1886.—Twenty-seven vials containing as many named species of Myripods, from C. H. Bollman, Indiana University, Bloomington, Indiana. (17905.) Contained a large proportion of forms heretofore unrepresented in the Museum collections.

A lot of named *Acrididæ*, four of them types of new species, from C. H. Bollman, Bloomington, Indiana. (18261.) These insects were badly damaged when they reached the department, but as they were of considerable value as typical of notes and descriptions by Mr. Bollman, they were carefully repaired and remounted in part.

January, 1887.—Two vials of insects in alcohol from the head of Usamasinta River, Mexico, from Richard M. Walker, Commision de limites con Mexico, Guatemala City, Central Mexico. (18478.) A mixed lot of species, some of them very bright and attractive. A desirable addition to a popular exhibition.

Smerinthus pallidulus, 1; *Pamphila*, sp. ?, 1; and an undetermined Geometrid, 1, from W. N. Tallant, 73 Jefferson avenue, Columbus, Ohio. (18507.) All of these specimens not in our collection and rare.

A lot of *Myriapoda* from Prof. L. M. Underwood, Syracuse, New York. (18494.) This is part of the material sent Professor Underwood for study and arrangement and now returned. It includes only the *Chilopoda* and the genera allied to *Scolopendra*.

A lot of named Coleoptera and Lepidoptera from James Fletcher, Ottawa, Canada. (18510.) Among the Lepidoptera were type specimens of *Chionobas macounii* and *Nemeophila selwynii*, as well as other good species. There were also a lot of Coleoptera, Lepidoptera, and Orthoptera for determination, and a list of these, so far as readily namable, was sent Mr. Fletcher.

Fifty specimens of thirty-nine species of Hemiptera, not in our collection, from William H. Ashmead, Jacksonville, Florida. (18550.) These were obtained from Mr. Ashmead in exchange for others to be sent him from the Museum.

Eleven type species of *Myriapoda*, Michigan–Indiana, from C. H. Bollman, Indiana University, Bloomington, Indiana. (18529.) These types accompanying a paper sent for publication in the Proceedings of the Museum.

February, 1887.—Three trap-door spiders and one nest of same from Prof. George F. Atkinson, Chapel Hill, North Carolina. (18678.) The species are typical specimens of *Pachylomerus carabivorus* Atk. and nest, *Myrmekiaphila foliata* Atk., and *Nidivalvata marxii* Atk.

March, 1887.—A lot of insects from Alaska, from Lieut. George M. Stoney, U. S. Navy, collected by Dr. Nash of the expedition. (18491.)

A list of the species contained in this collection was made and handed Dr. Nash. It contained: Coleoptera, 9 species, 30 specimens; Lepidoptera, 6 species, 18 specimens; Diptera, 4 species, numerous specimens; Orthoptera, 1 species, 1 specimen; Neuroptera, 4 species, numerous specimens; Arachnida, 12 species, 35 specimens; Myriapoda, 1 species, 1 specimen.

Ten specimens of a new species of *Cis* from William H. Crane, Cincinnati, Ohio. (18842.)

April, 1887.—Nest of *Vespa maculata* from Hon. Wade Hampton, United States Senate. (18886.) A fine specimen and one of the largest we have.

Pityophthorus rhois Sz. and sample of work; *Thysanoes ficus* Sz. in all stages and samples of work, and parasites; *Anisomorpha buprestoides; Penthetria* sp. and cocoon, and *Forficula* sp. and eggs from E. A. Schwarz, Washington, District of Columbia, collected in Key West, Florida. (18954.) These Coleoptera are types of manuscript species by Mr. Schwarz, and have been unknown as to life, history, etc., heretofore.

May, 1887.—Two boxes pinned Lepidoptera; specimen of twigs of fig, with *Pityophthorus ficus* Sz. in all stages; three small vials of Myriapods. (19040.)

Box of pinned Diptera and two vials of Myriapods. (19068.)

Box of specimens, all orders, pinned. (19113.)

All these are from Dade County, Florida, collected by Mr. Schwarz personally. They are mostly of great interest, many of them new species, and to some of them Mr. Schwarz has notes of interest and value.

A lot of butterflies in papers, and a mixed lot of several orders in alcohol, United States of Colombia, from V. O. King, consul-general of the United States at Bogota. (19112.) These have been mounted and are in very good condition throughout. They form a bright and sparkling addition to the collection, the butterflies and beetles being usually the most brilliant.

June, 1887.—A lot of dry Coleoptera in papers from Aurelius Todd, Elkhead, Oregon. (19015.)

A similar lot from Lewis L. Kennedy, Blackford, Custer County, Montana. (19227.) Two mixed lots containing considerable valuable material apparently.

1 box of White Mountain Coleoptera, from Rev. F. Gardiner, jr., Sioux Falls, Dakota. (18820.) Chiefly valuable because it has been worked over by Dr. Leconte; unfortunately in such poor condition that but a small fraction can be saved.

Two boxes of pinned insects (miscellaneous lot), from E. A. Schwarz, collected in Dade County, Florida. (19234.)

Altogether 102 accessions have been sent in to the department, comprising several thousands of specimens.

The mounting, labeling, and proper placing of these specimens occupied no inconsiderable time. Forty-eight of these accessions required reports of some kind, often taking up considerable time in making the necessary determinations; some sendings involving the determinations of from 50 to 75 species, or a few of them even a greater number.

In the first part of this report a general statement of the work done was given, and it needs but little amplification. In the Lepidoptera the chief work was the re-arrangement of the species of *Callimorpha*.

In the Diptera the work has been entirely in the way of temporary arrangement.

In the Coleoptera the principal work has been in the arrangement of the synoptic collection for exhibition. This has been most carefully arranged by Mr. Smith. Every family is defined, in almost every case there are drawings of structural peculiarities of the family, and wherever it was possible to obtain them, specimens of the leading genera in each family. In those cases where the species were very minute, figures of the species were either added or substituted. The eight unit cases in which this collection is arranged contain 571 species, 2,410 specimens, and 237 drawings, most of them made for this series, and many of them original.

The *Arachnida* were still mostly contained in jars and vials of all kinds and sizes, and the species were sadly mixed. They have all been assorted, and placed in the standard vials adopted by the curator. The material in the adolescent stages of insects was in somewhat similar condition and was similarly treated.

Several small lots of named Myriapods received, as noted in the list of accessions, were also mounted and temporarily arranged. In this class the Museum collection has an unusual number of types.

During a portion of the summer Mr. A. S. Davis, of Mount Pleasant, served as a volunteer in the department, and with his aid a large lot of material previously mounted was labeled and separated and the balance of the old material was mounted.

Mr. W. H. Crane, of Cincinnati, also served in the department for a short time this year, and his aid was effective in the arrangement of the Diptera and in the synoptic collection of Coleoptera.

The Orthoptera were arranged in two cabinets, occupying forty drawers in all. Of some groups drawings, illustrating specific distinctions, were made and pinned into the collection with the species.

Prof. P. R. Uhler has been for some time studying the Capsidæ (Hemiptera Heteroptera) of the United States, and offered to arrange and name the Museum material in the family.

The material was therefore carefully looked out and sent to Professor Uhler, who finds many new and interesting forms. Some of these he has referred to in describing new species in *Entomologica Americana*, but none have as yet been returned by him.

So far as the more pressing work would allow, progress has been made in the studies of the Noctuidæ in furtherance of the monograph in preparation by myself and Mr. J. B. Smith. The latter has also made a study of the material in the lepidopterous family Saturniidæ, and the results are published in the Proceedings of the U. S. National Museum, 1886. He has also studied the lepidopterous genus *Callimorpha*, and the results are embodied in a paper presented for publicaing in the Proceedings for 1887, but not yet issued. The genus *Euerythra* was also studied in the same way and a paper prepared and presented, but not yet published.

These papers contain many new facts of interest in structural Lepidopterology that have resulted from a careful study of the material; but the conclusions, especially in the *Callimorpha* and *Euerythra* papers, sometimes run counter to my own convictions and to the facts from the biologic side.

The curator's researches, so far as they are indicated by publication, have been as heretofore mostly in connection with his work for the Department of Agriculture, and are indicated in the bibliography.*

---

* See Section IV of this Report.

Dr. Williston's work of the *Syrphidæ* has been already referred to.

In the report for 1885–'86 a statement was presented giving as nearly as possible the state of the collection at that time. Its condition is more satisfactory at the present time, by virtue of the material that has been more carefully arranged and worked over during the year. Exclusive of the Smith collection at least 10,000 specimens have been added.

To the exhibition series has been added the synoptic collection of Coleoptera, contained in 8 unit cases, containing—species, 571; specimens, 2,410; drawings, 237, making a total in the exhibition series of—species, 2,637; specimens, 7,878; drawings not counted.

In the study series the arranged collection of Orthoptera now contains 542 species, comprising 4,442 specimens. The species are divided as follows:

Family.	Species.	Specimens.
Forficulidæ	17	66
Mantidæ	12	105
Phasmidæ	3	32
Blattidæ	25	165
Tettigidæ	30	190
Acrididæ	337	3,280
Locustidæ	85	464
Gryllidæ	33	140
Total	542	4,442

These numbers in regard to species may not prove exact, as so many are still either unnamed or entirely undescribed, and until they are carefully worked over the specific or other rank of some forms can not be defiinitely determined.

There are also twenty-seven double boxes, containing several thousands of duplicates for exchange.

In the parasitic Hymenoptera the Microgasters have all been rearranged so as to include all the new and many undescribed species, which I hope soon to find time to define; while in the biologic series, much of the alcoholic material has been brought together by families, especially that in the Noctuidæ, and all in the Rhopalocera has been brought together and classified. In the Coleoptera I have also begun, with Mr. E. A. Schwarz, the classification and study of the accumulated biologic specimens.

The last catalogue entry for June, 1886, was 242, and the last catalogue entry for June, 1887, is 343.

REPORT ON THE DEPARTMENT OF MARINE INVERTEBRATES IN THE U. S. NATIONAL MUSEUM, 1887.

By Richard Rathbun, *Curator.*

Most attention has been paid during the past year to the working up of the collection of Corals, Star-fishes, and parasitic Copepods, and to the sorting, cataloguing, and preservation of specimens. Several reports upon the groups mentioned, mainly of the nature of annotated catalogues, have been completed and submitted for publication in the Proceedings. No increase has been made in the number of specimens on exhibition, but much material has been prepared for the display series, and will be mounted as soon as opportunity offers.

The number of accessions has been rather above the average; and, as during many previous years, the Fish Commission has made the largest and most important contributions. Very valuable collections of Bermuda corals and sponges have been received from the Wesleyan University, and donations from the naval service have been numerous and interesting. The Fish Commission steamer *Albatross* was in active service only during the summer and fall, so that her regular southern cruises, which have always yielded very important results for this department, were omitted. Much progress has been made in the permanent arrangement of the general reserve collections, and many duplicates have been distributed to institutions of learning throughout the country. The card or reference catalogue of the identified specimens has been kept up to date, and now covers a large part of the collections.

The work-rooms of this department were closed from the first of July until the last of October, the curator and his assistants taking part in the investigations of the Fish Commission at Wood's Holl, Massachusetts, during that period.

Fifty-five accessions have been received by this department during the year. The largest and most important of these comprised the invertebrate collections made by the Fish Commission steamer *Albatross* during the summer and fall months, with headquarters at Wood's Holl, Massachusetts. Over 1,200 packages, many of which were of large size, and contained a great variety of specimens, were sent to Washington in October, as a partial result of the season's explorations, nearly as many more having been placed in the hands of naturalists elsewhere for special study. The regular winter and spring cruises of the *Albatross* were unfortunately omitted, for reasons explained below, and the Museum was thereby deprived of the source of revenue from southern waters, which had so greatly enriched its collections during the previous three years. A small amount of material was, however, obtained by this steamer from the shallow water off Fortress Monroe, Virginia, in April, while giving instructions in dredging to the officers of the U. S. S. *Thetis.*

The Fish Commission schooner *Grampus* has secured and transmitted to the Museum, in the course of its special fishery investigations in different regions, a large number of interesting specimens, including a fine series of surface towings taken on the southern mackerel grounds during April and May, to illustrate the food of that important econo- mic species. Several collections, made in the vicinity of Wood's Holl, Massachusetts, during the winter and spring, have been received from Mr. Vinal N. Edwards. They were especially rich in specimens of fish parasites. Mr. S. E. Meek, who was in the employ of the Commission in the summer and fall, has also supplied a number of interesting lots of specimens of the same character, obtained from the many varieties of fish that are brought to Fulton market in a fresh condition during those seasons. Mr. John Marshall, captain of the Gloucester fishing schooner *Landseer*, has presented, through the Fish Commission, a small but interesting series of Iceland crustaceans, mostly fish parasites, ob- tained from the shark fishermen of that region.

To officers of the United States Navy this department is indebted for several valuable contributions. Lieut. J. F. Moser, in command of the Coast Survey steamer *Blake*, has forwarded a large tank of alcoholic preparations, dredged in depths of 10 to 20 feet of water, in the neigh- borhood of Cedar Keys, Florida. Ensign W. E. Safford, formerly at- tached to the National Museum and Fish Commission, and now of the U. S. S. *Mohican*, has recently sent from San Francisco, California, an in- teresting assortment of specimens, mostly secured at the surface of the water by means of the tow-net, from off the Rio de la Plata, the South Pacific Ocean, and the western coast of America. Collections have also been received from Lieut. Commander H. E. Nichols, of the U. S. S. *Pinta*, obtained in southern Alaska ; from Dr. N. McP. Ferebee, of the U. S. S. *Trenton*, obtained in Corea and China ; and from Lieut. William C. Bab- cock, of the U. S. S. *Hartford*, obtained at Payta, Peru. Signal-Service observers Henry D. Woolfe and S. Applegate have supplied small col- lections from the northern and central Alaskan coasts.

The largest and most important accession of the year, next to that fur- nished by the Fish Commission, has been received from the Wesleyan University, Middletown, Connecticut. It comprises a portion of the ex- tensive collection made at the Bermudas in 1877 for that institution by Dr. G. Brown Goode, and consists of 484 specimens of sponges and 266 specimens of corals. They were sent in exchange for duplicates in the National Museum. The sponges include only the dried preparations of the larger and commoner species, identified by Prof. Alpheus Hyatt, of Boston, Massachusetts, who has not yet concluded his studies upon the rarer ones. Future installments of the same collection are promised at an early date. The following species are represented by numerous varieties: *Tuba vaginalis, Hircinia campana, Spongia tubulifera, Spongia punctata, Verongia fistularis.* The corals belong to the following genera: *Oculina, Madracis, Mycedium, Meandrina, Diploria, Isophyllia, Porites, Gorgonia,* and *Millepora.* A small lot of corals, comprising about 20 species, from the South Pacific Ocean and the West Indies, has also been received from Oberlin College, in exchange, and the Museum of Comparative Zoology, at Harvard College, has donated 5 species of *Stylaster* from the dredgings of the Coast Survey steamer *Blake.* to be used in the identification of *Albatross* collections.

Mr. P. L. Jouy, lately of Seoul, Corea, and now an assistant in the Museum, has contributed an interesting series of Crustaceans, Echinoderms, Corals, and Sponges, including several nearly perfect specimens of *Hyalonema,* from Corea and Japan. Mr. C. H. Townsend, who has been collecting for the Museum off Swan Island, in the Caribbean Sea, during the past spring, has already forwarded many finely preserved specimens of Crustaceans, Corals, and Echinoderms, and additional materials of the same character are expected from him. The following donations are also deserving of special mention: Mr. W. H. Dall, a small collection of Crustaceans, Radiates, Ascidians, and Sponges from Charlotte Harbor, Florida; Prof. A. Dugès, marine and fresh-water specimens from Mexico; Mr. S. F. Cheney, miscellaneous marine specimens from Grand Manan, New Brunswick; Mr. W. E. Curtis, through the Bureau of Ethnology, specimens of Echinoderms, Corals, and Barnacles from Peru; and Mr. S. Kneeland, also through the same Bureau, a fine specimen of *Hyalonema,* from Enoshima, Japan.

As in previous years, the curator and his assistants participated in the summer explorations of the Fish Commission at Wood's Holl, Massachusetts, leaving Washington July 4, and returning about the middle of October. During that period work was entirely suspended in this department in Washington, but was actively continued at Wood's Holl. The duties there comprised the sorting and working up of the zoological materials brought in by the steamer *Albatross,* and by the field parties collecting along the shore. Most of the specimens were at once entered in the catalogue books of the National Museum, whether they were to be sent directly to Washington or to the specialists engaged in studying them. By this method, which has now been practiced for several years, a careful record of all the specimens obtained by the Commission is kept under one series of catalogue numbers, by which they may always be recognized. The correcting of proof sheets of the writer's reports on ocean temperatures and the marine invertebrate fisheries for the quarto Fishery Report, and other Fish Commission duties, have greatly interfered with work upon collections, but many careful preparations of marine animals were made for the study and exhibition series of the Museum.

During the winter and spring much time was occupied in the care and preservation of collections. All of the accessions received during the year have been assorted, and the specimens catalogued and transferred to suitable receptacles where they are permanently safe. The record books show the following number of entries under each group: Crustaceans, 996; Worms, 2,611; Echinoderms and Cœlenterates, 1,412; Bryozoans and Ascidians, 130; Sponges and Protozoans, 103; a total of 5,252. The large number of entries made in the Worm catalogue resulted from the recording of the fine collection of annelids, turned over to the Museum by Mr. James E. Benedict, naturalist of the steamer *Albatross*, who resigned his position during the summer to engage in business. He had been making a special study of the group and had placed this collection in excellent condition.

Much progress has been made with the systematic or card catalogue of identified specimens in all the groups. This is used as the reference catalogue, and enables one to determine without delay the existence of any species in the collection, and the number and character of the specimens by which it is represented. Each " lot" of specimens of each species is entered upon a separate card, together with all the data known respecting it, including the catalogue number. These cards are then arranged in drawers in systematic order, after the manner of library catalogues, the principal divisions, down to genera, being indicated by taller cards appropriately inscribed. The main group to which these cards now serve as a convenient index are several divisions of the Crustacea, the Echini, Ophiurans, Asteridæ, and stony Corals.

The permanent arrangement of specimens has kept pace with the completion of studies in each group of animals. After all the material representing a species or genus has been determined, entered, and described, where necessary, the duplicates, if any, are selected and placed apart by themselves. Each "lot" of specimens is then boxed or bottled, according to its character, and given a conspicuous outer label, to facilitate arrangement in the cases and the subsequent reference to any desired species. The amount of material gone over in this manner has been very great, and a comparatively short time will suffice to place the bulk of the collection, and especially that portion composed mainly of the larger specimens, in similar good order.

As it was announced early in the year that extensive alterations would be made in the corridor connecting the west hall, containing the marine invertebrate display collections, with the main Smithsonian hall, thereby necessitating its being closed to the public for several months, very little attention has been paid to the exhibition series, and it remains in about the same condition as at the end of the previous year.

The same changes also required that all of the alcoholic collections be removed from the west basement, and they have been transferred to temporary storage elsewhere. The exhibition hall itself has been turned into a large store-room and work-room, where many of the alcoholic specimens are now safely stored for the summer. Advantage was taken of this opportunity to inspect all the alcoholic materials, in order to ascertain the condition of the specimens and to renew the preservative where necessary.

Mr. A. H. Baldwin and Miss M. J. Rathbun have acted as my assistants throughout the year, and Mr. Delano Ames served as a volunteer during May and June. Mr. Baldwin has had special charge of the sorting and care of collections, and has rendered valuable aid in the delineation of specimens for the Museum reports. Miss Rathbun has been occupied mainly with office work and cataloguing.

STATEMENT OF CATALOGUING DONE DURING THE FISCAL YEAR ENDING JUNE 30, 1887.

Invertebrates.	Entries to June 30, 1886.	Entries to June 30, 1887.	Number of entries made during year.
Crustacea	11,610	12,606	996
Worms	1,352	3,963	2,611
Bryozoa and Ascidians	829	959	130
Echinoderms and Cœlenterates	14,771	16,183	1,412
Sponges and Protozoans	5,328	5,431	103
Totals	33,890	39,142	5,252

The following institutions have been supplied with sets of duplicates belonging to Series IV during the fiscal year ending July 1, 1887. (These sets consist of about 105 species each, selected from the collections of marine invertebrates received from the U. S. Fish Commission): Berkshire Athenæum, Pittsfield, Massachusetts; Museum of Natural History of the State University of Iowa; Earlham College, Richmond, Indiana; Nebraska Fish Commission, Nebraska; Wilmington College, Wilmington, Ohio; Saint John's Ecclesiastical Seminary, Brighton, Massachusetts; Sherbrocke Library, Art, and Natural History Association, Sherbrooke, Canada; Moore's Hill College, Moore's Hill, Indiana; Chelsea High School, Chelsea, Massachusetts; Hyde Park High School, Hyde Park, Illinois; State Normal School, Emporia, Kansas; Massachusetts Institute of Technology, Boston, Massachusetts; Washburn College, Topeka, Kansas; Cairo Public Schools, Cairo, Illinois; Detroit High School, Detroit, Michigan; Northwestern College, Naperville, Illinois; State Agricultural and Mechanical College, College Station, Texas; Pennsylvania College, Gettysburgh, Pennsylvania; Western Normal College, Shenandoah, Iowa; Fremont College, Fremont, Nebraska; Eureka College, Eureka, Illinois; Bridgton Academy,

North Bridgton, Maine; High School, Syracuse, New York; Tulane University, New Orleans, Louisiana; Drake University, Des Moines, Iowa; Clyde High School, Clyde, New York; All Saints School, Sioux Falls, Dakota; Dana Natural History Society, Albany, New York; Public Schools, Carthage, New York; Fayetteville Public Cabinet, Fayetteville, New York; Miami University, Oxford, Ohio.

Special sets of duplicates were also furnished the Museum of Comparative Zoology at Harvard College and the American Museum of Natural History, New York. They were selected from the collections of the Fish Commission by Prof. A. E. Verrill and sent directly from New Haven.

RESEARCHES.

During the summer the curator completed for the Fish Commission a first report upon the surface-water temperatures of the Atlantic coast of the United States, based upon observations made at twenty-four of the more exposed light-houses and light-ships, beginning with Petit Manan, in eastern Maine, and ending with the Tortugas, in southern Florida. This report covers a period of five years, from January 1; 1881, to January 1, 1886, and includes 32 graphic charts, representing the yearly temperature at each station, by ten-day means, and the yearly and mean isotherms for the entire coast, plotted for every 5° F. The observations were taken specially for the Commission by the light-house keepers, whose services were kindly granted for that purpose by the Light-House Board. The reductions and original plottings were made by Miss M. J. Rathbun and the curator, and the final charts for engraving were prepared by Mr. C. E. Gorham. The report has been in type since last October, and will form a part of Section III of the quarto Fishery Report. Miss Rathbun also continued during the summer the work of reducing and mapping other series of temperature observations, mainly those taken at more enclosed stations of the Light-House and Signal Services. The object of this work has been to determine the bearing of temperature upon the migrations of such economic fishes as the mackerel and menhaden. The zoological studies of the curator, while at the Wood's Holl Station, were mainly limited to the parasitic copepods collected by the Fish Commission, and many drawings and descriptions were prepared.

During the winter and spring the writer examined and identified most of the species of deep-water and littoral *Madreporaria and Hydracorallæ* obtained by the steamer *Albatross* during the previous three years, on the Atlantic coast south of Cape Hatteras, and in the Gulf of Mexico and Caribbean Sea. Only a few species that are possibly new were discovered, but many of doubtful identity will be taken to Cambridge, Massachusetts, during the summer, for comparison with the *Blake* collections, described by the late Count Pourtales.

Nearly all of the corals of the genera *Madrepora*, *Porites*, and *Synaræa* have also been carefully determined, and reports upon the same have been submitted for publication in the Proceedings of the Museum That upon the *Madrepora* has already been issued; the second one, upon *Porites* and *Synarœa*, is accompanied by several figures of the exceedingly variable West Indian branching forms, *Porites furcata* and *P. clavaria*. The old coral collection of the Museum consisted mainly of the very valuable types described by Prof. James D. Dana, from the collections of the United States Exploring Expedition, 1838–'42, and by Prof. A. E. Verrill, from the smaller collections made by the North Pacific Exploring Expedition, 1853–'57. As explained in previous reports, the specimens received from the former expedition did not come into the possession of the Museum until some time after they had been returned to the Government, and in the interval many specimens were lost or badly injured, and numerous labels were displaced. About twenty years ago Professor Verrill made a partial revision of the collection, but the manner in which it was stored at the time did not permit of its being placed in satisfactory condition. Within the past few years, however, nearly all the specimens have been remounted and arranged in the exhibition cases, where they may be regarded as safe for all time, and are also convenient for reference. In view of this fact it becomes a labor of great satisfaction to undertake a second revision of the specimens in connection with the identification of similar materials more recently received; and as each group is gone over, it is proposed to publish catalogues of the species, like those above mentioned. This work has been rendered more easy by the discovery among Professor Verrill's papers during the past year of a copy of the coral catalogue of the National Museum, the original having been destroyed probably in the Smithsonian fire of 1865. Type specimens of all the species of *Madrepora* described by Dana and Verrill have been found in the collection, and of *Porites* the types of only one or two species are now missing. Work upon the family *Oculinidœ* had been nearly completed at the close of the year.

The collection of Star-fishes belonging to the genus *Asterias* and allied genera is also being revised in a similar manner, and a short paper descriptive of the species of *Heliaster*, with photographic plates of all the known forms, has already been offered for publication in the Proceedings. Stimpson's types of the species of *Asterias* are all preserved in good condition, and have recently been supplemented by very large collections from the western and northwestern coasts of North America.

The elaboration of collections belonging to the Museum, or soon to come into its possession, elsewhere than in Washington has been continued about as in former years. Professor Verrill, of Yale College, has retained general control of the Fish Commission invertebrates collected on the Atlantic coast north of Cape Hatteras, but has been occupied mainly with the study of the Mollusca, Echinodermata, Cœlenterata, and Annelidæ, assisted by Mr. Sanderson Smith, Miss A. J. Bush, and Miss C. E. Bush. Prof. S. I. Smith, of Yale College, has been at work upon the Crustacea of the Fish Commission, excepting the Copepoda; Mr. J. Walter Fewkes, of the Museum of Comparative Zoology, Cambridge, upon the Acalepha; Prof. L. A. Lee, of Bowdoin College, Maine, upon the Foraminifera; and Prof. E. Linton, of Washington and Jefferson College, Pennsylvania, and Mr. B. F. Koons, of the Storrs Agricultural School, Connecticut, upon the internal parasites of fishes.

The Hon. Theodore Lyman, of Brookline, Massachusetts, continued to give his kindly assistance in determining our collection of Ophiurans, until ill health obliged him to relinquish active work. He has, however, nearly completed the identification of the *Albatross* specimens collected south of Cape Hatteras, and has made considerable progress with the collections from western North America and Alaska.

EXPLORATIONS.

The Fish Commission steamer *Albatross*, Lieut. Commander Z. L. Tanner, U. S. Navy, commanding, was engaged in explorations from the beginning of the fiscal year until the latter part of October, when she returned to Washington and was laid up for the winter, pending the necessary changes to fit her for the contemplated expedition to the Pacific coast. The first cruise was made during July, and a line of dredging was carried across the inner edge of the Gulf Stream slope south of Martha's Vineyard, from a depth of 226 to a depth of 1,137 fathoms. The second cruise extended mainly to the eastward of New England, and was undertaken in the joint interests of the Fish Commission and Hydrographic Bureau. Sounding was begun August 3, in search of the mythical Hope Bank, about 200 miles south of Halifax, Nova Scotia, but during a three days' search no shallow water could be found, the depths on the reported position of the bank ranging from 1,930 to 2,900 fathoms. After leaving Hope Bank a line of soundings was run across the southern edge of the Grand Bank of Newfoundland, and a search was then instituted for another supposed bank, about 200 miles southeast of the Flemish Cap. The shoalest water discovered was 1,900 fathoms, the deepest 2,600 fathoms. Five dredge hauls were subsequently made on the Flemish Cap, in depths of 72 to 105 fathoms, and one between the Flemish Cap and the Grand Bank in a depth of 206 fathoms, after which the *Albatross* put into St. John's, Newfoundland, for supplies. On the homeward trip five dredgings were made on and south of St. Peter's Bank in depths of 59 to 215 fathoms, two east of Sable Island Bank in 110 to 140 fathoms, and one south of the same bank in 1,255 fathoms. Three days were again spent in sounding for Hope Bank, eighteen casts of the lead being made in depths of 1,587 to 1,943 fathoms. Just west of this locality the beam-trawl was hauled twice in 1,099 and 1,188 fathoms, and south of George's Bank three times in 866 to 984 fathoms.

From September 16 to 20 a second deep-water cruise was taken to the

Gulf Stream slope, about 200 miles south of New England, and twelve hauls obtained from depths of 594 to 1,867 fathoms. While returning to Washington, the latter part of October, a successful series of dredgings was carried along the same slope, off the Virginia coast, in depths of 679 to 1,685 fathoms. Early in April, when giving instructions in the use of the dredging apparatus to the officers of the U. S. S. *Thetis*, several hauls were made in about 15 fathoms of water, directly in front of Fortress Monroe, Virginia. The total number of dredgings made during the summer and fall was fifty-six (stations 2680–2735), in depths varying from 72 to 1,867 fathoms, and a large amount of valuable material was obtained. The large beam-trawl was almost exclusively employed, and with uniform success.

Mr. James E. Benedict, who had acted as chief naturalist of the *Albatross* since it first went into commission, resigned his position in August, to engage in business, and was succeeded by Mr. Thomas Lee, who had already served with the steamer about a year. Mr. Sanderson Smith also accompanied the steamer on all its cruises, taking special charge of the Mollusca.

The Fish Commission schooner *Grampus*, commanded by Capt. J. W. Collins, remained in active service during the entire year, and its explorations covered an exceedingly wide area. Collecting was done mostly by means of hooks and lines, but during April and May, while following the movements of the early school of mackerel, on the southern grounds, the towing-net was frequently employed at the surface in obtaining specimens of mackerel food. The results of this cruise, when fully worked up, will prove very instructive.

The Fish Commission station at Wood's Holl, Massachusetts, was open from early in July until the middle of October, and became for that period the headquarters of the steamer *Albatross*, where its collections were landed and studied. The Commissioner was present during the entire season, and retained general direction of the scientific work. Prof. A. E. Verrill took charge of the biological laboratory, while able to be present, or for about two months, the same duty being assigned to the curator at other times. The regular laboratory party was constituted as follows: Prof. S. I. Smith, of Yale College; Mr. Sanderson Smith, of New York; Mr. John A. Ryder, of Washington; Prof. L. A. Lee, of Bowdoin College, Maine; Prof. E. Linton, of Washington and Jefferson College, Pennsylvania; Prof. B. F. Koons, of the Storrs Agricultural College, Connecticut; Mr. Peter Parker, jr., of Washington, in charge of the fishes; Mr. J. Henry Blake, of Cambridge, Massachusetts, as artist; Mr. A. H. Baldwin and Miss M. J. Rathbun, the curator's assistants; and Miss A. J. Bush and Miss C. E. Bush, assistants of Professor Verrill. The chemical and physical laboratory was under Dr. J. H. Kidder, as in previous years; and Mr. W. P. Seal, of Philadelphia, had charge of the aquaria, which, under his arrangement, became very useful adjuncts to our work. Tables in the biological laboratory were also occupied by Prof. S. F. Clarke, of Williams College, Prof. E. B. Wilson, of Bryn Mawr College, and Mr. Bruce, of Johns Hopkins University. Mr. James E. Benedict and Mr. Thomas Lee rendered services on shore when the *Albatross* was in port, and Mr. Vinal N. Edwards, who is stationed at Wood's Holl the entire year, was always on hand for collecting and the preparation of large specimens. Mr. S. E. Meek was employed at Fulton Market, New York, during the summer and fall, in collecting the parasites of fish, which are now being studied by several specialists.

It is fitting that mention should be made in this connection of the death of one of the most valued members of our party. Capt. Hubbard C. Chester, well known as the executive officer of Hall's Polaris expedition to the Arctic regions, and the rescuer of the ship's crew, drifted from the land on the ice-floe bearing the ill-fated steamer, joined the Fish Commission in 1874, the year in which the writer first entered the same service. His duties were varied, and were always performed in the same thorough and conscientious manner, which brought success to all his undertakings. On the smaller steamers, before the *Albatross* was built, he was generally in charge of the dredging manipulations, and it was scarcely deemed auspicious to go to sea without him. After the completion of the new station at Wood's Holl, he became its superintendent, and so continued to the time of his death. He was thus brought again in intimate relations with the investigating party, but from that time on his attention was mainly directed toward improving the methods of marine fish culture, and the appliances of his invention are now exclusively employed in the hatching of cod and lobsters. He had been ailing more or less since the winter of 1878-'79, when he suffered from a severe attack of pneumonia, and died July 19, 1887, after a short but painful illness. His death brought sorrow to many friends.

No other branch of the Government besides the Fish Commission has such excellent opportunities for increasing the stores of this department of the Museum as the naval service, and scarcely a year passes without important contributions from that source. The U. S. S. *Thetis*, which left Norfolk, Virginia, for Alaska, in May last, in charge of Lieut. W. H. Emory, U. S. Navy, received a complete dredging oufit from the Fish Commission, at the solicitation of her commanding officer, who promises to devote much time to the collecting of marine specimens. The coast along which he will cruise has never been explored below a depth of about 50 fathoms, and as it is Lieutenant Emory's intention to work mainly between that depth and 200 fathoms, very valuable results may be expected, both for the fisheries and for science.

Lieut. J. F. Moser, U. S. Navy, in command of the Coast Survey steamer *Bache*, which has been sounding in the shallow waters of the Florida coast, in the neighborhood of Cedar Keys, and between Cape Roman and Cape Sable, found time, during the last spring, to do considerable dredging with very successful results. His outfit was furnished by the Museum and Fish Commission, both of which are benefited by his work. A portion of his collection, received before the close of the year, is acknowledged above. Ensign W. E. Safford, U. S. Navy, who was detailed in 1883 for instruction in natural history at the National Museum, arrived in San Francisco, California, during last spring from a long cruise on the U. S. S. *Mohican*, which sailed from the Atlantic coast about a year before. A collection received from him in June indicates that the many rare opportunities afforded him for obtaining specimens were not neglected, and the surface towings he obtained are very rich in interesting forms. Lieuts. W. M. Wood and A. Baker, U. S. Navy, who were also formerly in the service of the Commission, have made collections during their cruises of the past year, which have not yet been received. Lieut. Commader H. E. Nichols, U. S. Navy, of the steamer *Pinta*, has continued his collecting on the southern Alaskan coast, and Dr. Ferebee, U. S. Navy, of the U. S. S. *Trenton*, has sent in a number of specimens which he obtained in Corea and China.

REPORT ON THE DEPARTMENT OF COMPARATIVE ANATOMY IN THE U. S. NATIONAL MUSEUM, 1887.

By FREDERICK W. TRUE, *Acting Curator.*

For reasons already pointed out in the report for 1885, this department continues of necessity to be in fact a department of comparative osteology, and with the rapidly increasing amount of material it is difficult for the present force to do full justice to it, even as thus limited. Mammalian osteology still largely preponderates in the exhibition series, but representative forms of other classes are being added as fast as possible.

Among the more notable accessions of the year are a Gorilla (*Gorilla savagei*) obtained with other specimens in an exchange with the Paris Museum of Natural History; a fine example of the Caribbean Seal (*Monachus tropicalis*); and a Pygmy Sperm Whale (*Kogia breviceps*). This last was secured, with two other cetaceans, through Capt. B. T. Barco, keeper of the U. S. life-saving station at Dam Neck Mills, Virginia.

Mr. William T. Hornaday, chief taxidermist of the Museum, collected a large and valuable series of skeletons and skulls of the Bison (*Bison americanus*), besides many other very desirable skeletons of smaller mammals and of birds. By the continued courtesy of Mr. A. E. Brown, of the Philadelphia Zoological Society, and Mr. W. A. Conklin, of the Central Park Menagerie, many valuable specimens have been added to the collection.

The series of birds preserved in alcohol has very largely increased and contains many important forms.

Work upon the study and exhibition series has steadily progressed during the year, the number of specimens which have been prepared or mounted being shown in the report of the osteological preparator, who has been appointed assistant curator of this department.

As fast as possible the specimens on exhibition have been provided with printed labels, while to increase the educational value of this series many colored sketches of living animals have been placed alongside of the skeletons of the species to which they belong.

Much has been done in classifying and arranging the study series of bird-skeletons, but much still remains to be done.

It is impossible to state the number of specimens in the osteological collection other than in the exhibition series, but the following table gives the increase during the year as indicated by the catalogues:

Class.	Last entry number recorded in catalogue—		Increase.
	June 30, 1886.	June 30, 1887.	
Mammals	22,363	22,693	330
Birds	17,561	18,029	468
Reptiles and Batrachians	29,229	29,239	10
Fishes	26,063	26,067	4

On June 30, 1887, there were 425 specimens on exhibition:

Skeletons:
Mammals 168
Birds 55
Reptiles.......................... 33
Fishes 23
         ——
Total 279

Skulls:
Mammals 61
Birds 16
         ——
Total 77
Morphological and histiological series 69

Additional assistance is very greatly needed in this department, and the lack of it is being more and more severely felt. Much of the material received is of such a character as to require immediate attention, and this causes constant interruption of work already well under way, the assistant curator being compelled to devote to the work of preparation time which could be much more profitably employed.

The collection of alcoholic birds is in want of immediate attention, many specimens having lain untouched for ten or fifteen years, and to make this valuable mass of material thoroughly available a card catalogue is imperatively needed. A catalogue of the bird-skeletons, if available, would also be of much service.

REPORT ON THE DEPARTMENT OF INVERTEBRATE FOSSILS (PALEOZOIC) IN THE U. S. NATIONAL MUSEUM, 1887.

By CHARLES D. WALCOTT, *Honorary Curator.*

Two objects have been kept in view in conducting the work of the year: (1) The systematizing and recording of the old collections and accessions preparatory to classifying an exhibition, a study, and a duplicate series of specimens; (2) The obtaining by collection, exchange, and gift, of material to fill in gaps in the collection and to render it, in certain lines, more comprehensive and complete than any other American collection. And two events have taken place that have had and will continue to have a marked effect upon the first object. These are (1) the change from the small rooms in the south tower of the Museum to the larger laboratory and office in the southwest pavilion, and (2) the appointment of a Museum assistant in the person of Mr. R. R. Gurley, who began work December 1, 1886.

With better facilities for handling the collections, and with Mr. Gurley to do the routine work on them, I hope within another year to have the entire series properly classified and arranged. In order to advance this work more rapidly, during the winter, Mr. C. J. Akin, of the Geological Survey, was employed for three months in cataloguing and painting the record numbers on the specimens; and, with but slight exception, all the accessions have been recorded, numbered, and transferred to the main collection.

The additions to the collections, as given in the appendix to this report, show a satisfactory increase; yet there are over 6,000 specimens not therein included which will be transferred from the U. S. Geological Survey as soon as they shall have been studied.

In June, Mr. Gurley went into the field, accompanying one of the field parties of the Geological Survey, to collect fossils in East Tennessee, which are needed to give a fuller representation of the Upper Cambrian fauna of that region.

I respecfully repeat the recommendation made in my report for the last fiscal year, "that a sum be set aside each year for the increase of the collection, by purchase and by sending out collectors."

The following accessions have been received:

No. 17474,* from H. C. Powers, Beloit, Wisconsin, contains many fine

---

* Received prior to July 1, 1886.

specimens, and supplements the important accession given by him the previous year. With these additions the collection of Trenton fossils from Wisconsin is placed in a creditable condition.

No. 18532, from A. C. Benedict, Indianapolis, Indiana, is large and contains many interesting and valuable specimens, as also No. 18543, from John H. Lemon, New Albany, Indiana, and furnish corals which were very much needed in the Museum series.

No. 18642, collected by I. C. Russell, of the U. S. Geological Survey, although small, is of unusual interest; and Mr. Russell has indicated his intention of making a large addition to it during the ensuing field season.

No. 18991, collected and identified by N. H. Darton, of the U. S. Geological Survey, was received in good condition for exhibition and adds material to a weak spot in the collections.

Nos. 19043 and 19115, collected by myself, contain types of 26 new species and give a good series of the faunas they represent.

Altogether, 4,989 specimens were added during the year.

The first four months of the year I was engaged in field-work in connection with the Geological Survey. After returning in November and moving into the new office and laboratory, work was begun by Mr. Gurley on the accumulated accessions and pushed so vigorously that by June 1 all the accessions, with the exception of those I wished to study before identifying, were catalogued and the record numbers painted on the specimens. A large amount of material in the general collection was also cleaned, identified, and labeled. From the latter and other accessions the exhibition series will be selected.

From material collected by the U. S. Geological Survey not yet transferred to the Museum, and from material already in the Museum collections, I continued the study of the Cambrian faunas of North America. A large number of drawings were prepared, and the preliminary study of the Upper Cambrian fauna so far advanced that the work of another year will get the larger portion of it in readiness for publication.

A special study of the fauna of the Taconic rocks of New York was completed and a paper thereon prepared for publication. The specimens are recorded under accession number 19115. A paper was also prepared on the "Taconic System" of Emmons and read before the National Academy of Sciences April 22, 1887.

In my last report a summary was given of the material in the collection. To that must be added the accessions of the past year, 4,989 specimens.

The catalogue numbers taken up during the year were from 15461 to 16000 and from 17001 to 17496. The break in the numbering, from 16000 to 17001, represents the one thousand numbers assigned to Prof. Henry S. Williams, but not yet taken up.

Additions have been made to the material selected for exhibition, and by the time the exhibition cases are ready to receive the specimens a very good representative collection can be displayed. Until after the exhibition series is selected the collection will not be dismembered into exhibition, reserve, and duplicate series, as the work involved in the handling of over 80,000 specimens is too great to be undertaken until the entire collection shall have been labeled and systematized.

A list of the publications which appeared during the year and which were based on studies of the material contained in the collections, or on data obtained from field-work done by myself, will be found in Section IV of this volume.

RECAPITULATION.

Accession No.	No. of genera.	No. of species.	No. of varieties.	No. of specimens.
17713	1	1		1
17793	7	7		16
18012	1	1		3
18262	5	5		34
18341	1	1		6
18373	1	6		9
18440	2	2		34
18532	27	29	2	93
18539	(*)			
18543	21	65		351
18547	(†)			1
18558	6	6		15
18567	(*)			
18588	(*)			
18589	1	1		1
18641	9	11		69
18642	22	26		190
18661	20	22		84
18695	3	3		3
18735	6	6		22
18818	2	2		5
18860	4	4		7
18880	(†)			
18881	8	8		20
18882	1	1		4
18991	19	21		113
18997	1	1		1
18998	19	24		142
19013	7	7		107
19043	31	68		1,202
19094	1	1		4
19115	23	35	2	1,152
19206	44	77	5	893
19217	(‡)			2
19304	(‡)			4
19332	47	146	3	236
19334	(‡)			165
	340	587	12	4,989

* Identified and returned.
† Of no paleontologic value.
‡ Not examined.

Total accessions for the year 37
Identified and returned 3
Of no paleontologic value 2
Not examined.. 3
                             — 8

Passed into the Museum collections 29

REPORT ON THE DEPARTMENT OF INVERTEBRATE FOSSILS (MESOZOIC) IN THE U. S. NATIONAL MUSEUM, 1887.

By C. A. WHITE, *Honorary Curator.*

By far the greater portion of my time, and of my assistant, has been devoted to the performance of work connected with my duties as paleontologist of the U. S. Geological Survey, so that comparatively little has been accomplished in the way of Museum work. During the year, however, the card catalogue of all the material belonging to the Museum and now in the custody of the department was completed, and the entire collection is now identified, labeled, and ready for exhibition.

Only twelve accessions were received, among the most important of which were the following:

Four specimens of *Belemnitella quadrata*, from Prof. C. Schluter. A collection from the Pebas group of the Amazon, sent by Dr. O. Böttger. Seven specimens each of *Cyclostoma antiquus* and *C. tricarinata*, and two specimens of *Cyrena lirata*, from Prof. C. L. F. Sandberger, of Würzburg, Germany. A collection of 63 specimens from Prof. M. Neumayr, for which a collection was sent him in exchange. Eight specimens from Mr. Edward Crane, Brighton, England. A collection from the Laramie group, sent by C. R. Beiderman. Alaskan cretaceous fossils, from E. E. Howell. A collection of fossils from Oregon, sent by Prof. T. Condon. A collection of fossils, from Dr. J. S. Newberry, of Columbia College, New York City.

The number of the last entry for June, 1886, was 19970; that for June, 1887, 21003.

Five papers were published by the curator during the year, and are noticed in Section IV of the report.

REPORT ON THE DEPARTMENT OF FOSSIL PLANTS IN THE U. S. NATIONAL MUSEUM, 1887.

By LESTER F. WARD, *Honorary Curator.*

No very important accessions have been received. The additions have been mostly single specimens sent in by the various correspondents, either for scientific determination or as objects of interest, and are comparatively unimportant.

Prof. Leo Lesquereux, of Columbus, Ohio, has been engaged during a part of the year in determining the collection of fossil leaves made by Capt. Chas. Bendire, U. S. A., in the John Day River region, Oregon. Many new and interesting things have been reported by him from time to time, but the work was not finished at the end of June, nor was it in condition to admit of any systematic analysis. The specimens, with accompanying illustrations, will be returned to the Museum as soon as the work is completed.

Mr. F. H. Knowlton has devoted much time during the year to the investigation of the internal structure of fossil wood, a study which has been much neglected in this country, but in which there is manifested a great and constantly increasing activity in Europe.

A room in the west south balcony, before used only as a store-room, has been fitted up as a microscopical laboratory. A microscopical table, specially designed for this work, has been supplied by the Museum authorities, and a considerable number of microscopical appliances have been purchased by the U. S. Geological Survey. These, together with a good microscope, and other instruments which are the private property of Mr. Knowlton, make a fairly good working laboratory.

The special subject of investigation has been the wood and lignite of the Potomac formation, from which considerable material had been collected by the members of the U. S. Geological Survey and other parties. Microscopical sections of these specimens have been prepared, either by Mr. Knowlton or under his immediate direction, and carefully studied. The results reached have been very satisfactory indeed, and have helped to clear up several points that were before obscure. It was proved that all the fossil wood and lignite of this formation was coniferous, and includes types of structure that are very old. The ma-

H. Mis. 600, pt. 2——10

terial was found to contain five species, all new to science. These are, *Cupressinoxylon*, with four species, and *Araucarioxylon*, with one species. The results are embodied in a report which contains about 150 manuscript pages and is illustrated by 7 plates. It will be published as a bulletin by the U. S. Geological Survey in connection with reports by Mr. W J McGee and Prof. W. M. Fontaine on the geology and paleontology. In the preparation of this paper almost the entire literature of the subject was examined, and a brief *résumé*, from its first mention in literature down to the close of the year 1886, is included as an introduction to the paper.

A great amount of fossil wood is in the possession of the National Museum, which Mr. Knowlton proposes to investigate as opportunity may permit, since nothing is now known regarding its internal structure or botanical affinities.

PRESENT STATE OF COLLECTION.

Number of last catalogue entry, June 30, 18=6	240
Number of last catalogue entry, June 30, 1887	249
Total number of specimens of catalogued material (exclusive of my recent collections still in hand and not formally turned over to the Museum)	7,371
Number of specimens not specially identified (mostly wood)	1,757
Determined material	5,614
Duplicates, stored in the Armory building	1,091

Number of distinct species identified, catalogued, and installed:

Paleozoic	396
Mesozoic	203
Cenozoic	566
Total	1,165

REPORT ON THE DEPARTMENT OF RECENT PLANTS IN THE U. S. NATIONAL MUSEUM, 1887.

By LESTER F. WARD, *Honorary Curator.*

Probably the most valuable collection received during the year was that made by Dr. Edward Palmer in southwestern Mexico. It contained about 800 species, of which number about 20 per cent. were new to science. More than half the entire number proved to be new to the herbarium, which, through the activity of Dr. Palmer and Mr. C. G. Pringle, now contains a fairly good representation of the Mexican flora.

Mr. Pringle also made during this year a continuation of his "Plantæ Mexicanæ," which contained the usual number of new species.

Mr. S. Applegate contributed a small collection of Alaskan plants, a few of which were new to the herbarium.

Through the New Orleans Exposition the U. S. National Museum received a valuable collection of ferns from Costa Rica, which numbered 112 species. From lack of the necessary books and material for comparison these specimens were sent to Kew for determination, where they received the attention of Mr. J. G. Baker, the well-known authority on the Filices. He detected among them some species new to science. This collection, which is the largest ever received from Costa Rica, added 60 species to the list of ferns that were before known to grow in that locality. Two full sets were returned from Kew, one of which is deposited in the herbarium of the National Museum. The other was sent to the Gray herbarium at Cambridge, Massachusetts.

A very fine collection, numbering over 600 carefully mounted species and a large series of duplicates, was received from central New York. This comprised the entire herbarium of the late Mr. O. E. Pearce, whose death occurred September 11, 1886. The collection was made mostly in the vicinity of Ithaca, New York, and contains many interesting forms.

Other collections of smaller size were donated by Dr. J. C. McCormick, Mr. J. W. Johnson, and Prof. Alfred Dugès.

The routine work of the department has been largely a continuation of that outlined in several of my former reports. The herbarium was established so recently that the only thing to be done at first was to mount the specimens and arrange them in a suitable manner for reference and study. Consequently the routine work has been in this direction. Thousands of specimens have been poisoned and mounted on the regular herbarium paper and put in the commodious cases provided for them. They have been arranged according to the latest and best system of classification, and the compartments in which they are placed have also been labeled so that the contents of each is shown at a glance. There are now over 17,000 species arranged in the cases and ready for reference and study. The species index is kept up, and will continue to be made an important feature. The duplicates, of which there are probably from 8,000 to 10,000 specimens, representing about 4,000 species, have been arranged alphabetically and put away in the old herbarium cases. By this arrangement everything in hand can be readily found, and we are thus in position to begin exchanging with other herbaria, a matter that will receive early attention.

The new herbarium cases, four in number, were received during the month of December, and the entire collection expanded and placed in them. There is now probably ample spare room to accommodate the growth of several years.

No exhibition or study series has as yet been attempted; but it is hoped that something of the kind may soon be undertaken, as there is undoubtedly a great field for popular instruction open in this direction.

The active technical work has been confined mainly to the determination of such collections as have come unnamed to the Museum, or such specimens as have been sent in by the various correspondents of the Institution or Museum with the special request to have them identified. A little work has also been done on the collections of cultivated plants made about the District. Lack of books of reference and suitable material for comparison makes this work difficult. It will, however, be undertaken shortly in a more thorough manner, and then more satisfactory results may be looked for.

The following tabular statement shows the present condition of the collection:

Number of species in herbarium June 30, 1886	15, 538
Number of species added during the year	1, 709
Number of species in herbarium June 30, 1887	17, 247
Number of duplicate species June 30, 1887 (estimated)	4, 000
Number of duplicate specimens June 30, 1887 (estimated)	10, 000

REPORT ON THE DEPARTMENT OF MINERALS IN THE U. S. NATIONAL MUSEUM, 1887.

By F. W. CLARKE, *Honorary Curator.*

During the year the routine work of the department has been carried on under my direction by Mr. W. S. Yeates, assisted by Mr. H. H. James as clerk, and the growth of the mineral collection has been quite satisfactory. The following important accessions may be properly noted:

(1) The collection of meteorites has been enriched by the deposit of the private collection belonging to Prof. C. U. Shepard, jr. This collection numbers about 200 falls, some of them of extreme rarity. The meteorite collection has also been increased during the year by exchanges with the cabinets of Harvard, Yale, and Amherst Colleges, the British Museum, and Mr. B. Stürtz, of Bonn, Germany. About 40 falls were thus added, making our total number, exclusive of the Shepard collection, 101.

(2) There were obtained for the gem collection by purchase 154 cut specimens of agate, jasper, carnelian, bloodstone, etc. Additions have also been made by the special cutting of rough specimens previously in the Museum, and the collection has thereby gained several handsome gifts. Mr. C. S. Bement, of Philadelphia, gave some fine sapphires and zircons, and a large moonstone from Virginia. Mr. G. F. Kunz, of New York, gave 18 cut specimens of moss agate, bloodstone, onyx, sardonyx, etc. Mrs. S. F. Baird gave a brooch of Norwegian pegmatite, set in silver, and a fine bloodstone. Mr. Thomas Wilson deposited a large carved seal of yellow quartz and 10 antique intaglios of rock crystal, carnelian, agate, and plasma. From the Treasury Department was received a collection of 133 small diamonds and 150 pearls. These were presented by the Imaum of Muscat to President Van Buren. The gem collection has practically doubled during the year.

(3) The general collection of minerals has received important additions as follows: *By gift*—from H. H. Thorpe, of Liberty Hill, Texas, 40 specimens of celestite, garnet, aragonite, etc. *By exchange*—64 specimens of Maine minerals from N. H. Perry, of South Paris; 16 specimens of the Lake Valley vanadates, etc., from T. Kendall, of Reading, Pennslyvania; 37 specimens of Japanese minerals, including some remarkable quartz, stibnite, and amber, from the Educational Museum at Tokio; 30

specimens from the iron mine at Antwerp, New York, from Mr. R. S. Hodge, of Antwerp; 86 specimens, mainly of German minerals, from B. Stürtz, of Bonn. *By purchase*—74 specimens of Swedish minerals, collected by L. Igelström. The total growth of the collection during the year, though not remarkably rapid, has been satisfactory.

Concerning the routine work of the department little need be said. The usual amount of necessary cataloguing, labeling, mounting, etc., has been done, and the exchange system has been kept up so as to leave no outstanding obligations at the close of the year. In exchanges we sent out 28 packages, containing 753 specimens, and two collections, numbering 198 specimens, have been given to educational institutions. Seventeen specimens have been transferred to the chemical laboratory of the U. S. Geological Survey for use in current investigations. In field-work, under the Geological Survey, I visited a number of localities in Maine and Massachusetts, and sent in fair but not large collections.

A little scientific work upon minerals belonging to the Museum has been done by myself and my associates in the laboratory of the Geological Survey. This is covered by three researches, namely: One by myself upon the micas; one by Mr. J. E. Whitfield, on the natural borates; and one by Mr. R. B. Riggs, upon the tourmalines. None of these were published during the current year.

During the year 1,938 specimens have been added to the collection (comprising 875 entries in the catalogue). Of these, 1,283 have been assigned to the reserve and 649 to the duplicate series. Six were rejected. Of the 1,938 specimens above mentioned, 1,428 are derived from new accessions, 495 belonging to the old collection, and 15 being re-entered on account of polishing. Of the 1,428 specimens, 175 were acquired by gift, 589 through exchange, 241 by purchase, 12 were received on deposit, and 411 were collected by Government parties and transferred to the National Museum according to law.

In the above enumeration the Shepard meteorites are not included.

Number of specimens on exhibition, Museum series	3,238
Number of specimens on exhibition, study series, reserved	5,404
Duplicates	8,530
Total	17,172
In Willcox collection	1,229
In Shepard collection, say	300
Grand total	18,601

REPORT ON THE DEPARTMENT OF LITHOLOGY AND PHYSICAL GEOLOGY IN THE U. S. NATIONAL MUSEUM, 1887.

By GEORGE P. MERRILL, *Curator*.

The work of the year has been almost wholly in the line of preparing the exhibition and reserve series, and this necessitated the study with the microscope of a large number of thin sections of rocks. To facilitate this work the curator has passed three days of each week from December until March in the petrographical laboratory of the Johns Hopkins University at Baltimore. While there, several hundred slides were examined, and from the results obtained I have been enabled to classify and arrange a considerable amount of material which has been accumulating for many years, but which could not be utilized owing to a lack of proper identification.

No systematic collecting has been carried on during the year. In the course of a six weeks' outing in Montana during August and September, in company with Dr. A. C. Peale, of the U. S. Geological Survey, I obtained much material of interest and value, which will be noticed under the head of accessions. During a hurried trip to California in March I also obtained some valuable material and made arrangements for a series of exchanges by which I hope to gain much of interest.

Four new cases for the accommodation of relief maps have been constructed from designs furnished by myself, and have proved very satisfactory. In one instance the map—that of the Comstock Lode and Washoe district, Nevada, from surveys by Becker—is arranged to lie horizontally and is protected by a covering of plate-glass and a mahogany railing. In the other three instances the maps are inclined at a high angle, the bottoms being some 18 inches from the floor, and each case carrying two maps, one on each side. The cases are so constructed that when desired they can be separated vertically into two parts, each half constituting a case by itself. This arrangement is of especial convenience whenever it is desired to remove temporarily one or more of the maps to the lecture-room. A large wall case, consisting of three independent sections, has also been constructed for the west end of the exhibition hall. Owing to the two large doorways, gas-meter, and hose-pipe, no perfectly satisfactory case for purposes of exhibition could be constructed. All things considered, the present one is probably the best that can be designed.

The accessions of special interest are enumerated and annotated below:

John N. Atwood sent a collection of some 40 specimens of norite from Keeseville, New York.

Henry J. Biddle sent a fine series, comprising some 41 hard specimens, of olivine and bronzite-rocks from the vicinity of Webster, North Carolina.

Mrs. E. K. Huntington presented (through Prof. C. Chamberlain) one large slab glacial polished and fluted limestone from Kelly's Island, Lake Erie. This is a very fine and unique specimen, and the Museum was especially fortunate in being able to procure it before it was destroyed by the quarrying operations now being carried on in that vicinity.

W. J. McGee, of the U. S. Geological Survey, gave one large concretion of ferruginous sandstone from the glauconitic sand formations on Lloyd Creek, Sassafras River, Maryland.

George P. Merrill gave a small collection of serpentine and eruptive rocks from California and Arizona. Also a very beautiful vein of shodochrosite and quartz from Butte, Montana.

Dr. A. C. Peale and G. P. Merrill gave a beautiful series of wood opals from the bluffs on the Madison River. Also a fine lot of eruptive and sedimentary rocks from the region of the Gallatin Valley, Montana.

Pike Manufacturing Company, of Pike Station, New Hampshire, gave a large and carefully prepared series of hone whetstones, scythe stones, and grinding stones, both native and foreign.

Charles D. Walcott, of the U. S. Geological Survey, gave two large slabs of Potsdam quartzite with ripple marks. Extra fine specimens, both on account of size and the quality of the markings.

B. Sturtz, of Bonn, Prussia, sent in exchange for other material an interesting series of rocks, comprising 34 specimens, from Monte Vultari, Italy, Sardinia, Isle of Ponza, Transylvania, and other European localities.

Dr. George H. Williams sent a fine example of contorted gneiss.

Prof. W. O. Crosby gave specimens of contorted mica schist from Naragansett Bay.

E. Fritsch, New York, gave a series of 5 slabs African and German marbles.

J. S. Diller, of the U. S. Geological Survey, gave a collection of eruptive rocks from California and Kentucky.

A statement of the character of the routine work has been given in previous reports and needs no repetition here. A very considerable amount of time is being continually demanded in attending to correspondence and identifying materials sent in by outsiders. While this is a legitimate and necessary work, unfortunately for the curator it requires time which might otherwise be devoted to the preparation of his exhibition series, or other work in which he is more especially interested. The merely mechanical part of label writing also consumes much time. Some 825 labels have been written and sent to the printer during the year. In the preparation of these and in other clerical work, I was assisted from July until November 15 by Miss B. Frankland, and from November 30 to March 10 by Miss Carrie Rosenbusch.

The main points of growth in the exhibition series have been the lithological and stratigraphical collections. This, for the reason that proper cases are yet to be prepared for the other exhibits. The mechanical work of preparing the specimens both for exhibition and storage, has as heretofore been acceptably performed by Mr. Forney. About 50 samples of building-stone have been dressed and a large amount of material has been trimmed down into the form of hand specimens for storage exhibition, and exchange. Eleven lots of duplicates, comprising some 480 specimens, have been sent out during the year.

No researches of consequence have been carried on upon Museum material, excepting so far as was necessary for correct identification, and this has been already referred to. What papers have appeared have been wholly my own and are noticed in the bibliography.

The numbers given below regarding the present state of the collection are, so far as they refer to the duplicate collections, mere approximations. A large rock specimen which to-day counts as one, may to-morrow be a dozen or twenty, as it is the custom in many cases to bring in material in the mass, and cut it up or break it, as occasion demands.

Whole number of specimens in reserve series 18,000
Whole number of duplicates 3,500

Total... 21,500

Of the reserve series 5,687 are now on exhibition ; of these 2,720 are building-stones, and 1,893 belong to the educational series of rocks and rock-forming minerals.

REPORT ON THE DEPARTMENT OF METALLURGY AND ECONOMIC GEOLOGY IN THE U. S. NATIONAL MUSEUM, 1887.

By F. P. DEWEY, *Curator.*

The principal work of the department during the year was the preparation of a preliminary descriptive catalogue of the collections in economic geology and metallurgy.

Starting with the collections exhibited at the New Orleans exposition as a foundation, they were expanded, and as many systematic series as possible were constructed out of material in the Museum.

These systematic collections are designed to show the actual occurrence of each metal, and the processes used in their extraction. To these are added illustrations of the occurrences of non-metallic ores and their utilization.

The collections start, in the case of each metal, by showing the series of minerals in which the metal forms an important constituent; the specimens are selected to show each mineral in its best perfection, in order that it may be seen just how the metals occur in the ores.

The next step is a series of ores selected to show the actually occurring material that is mined, together with the associates of the ore. In the case of the base metal, there may not be much difference between the ore specimens and the mineral specimens, except the general purity and perfection of the latter, and that an ore may contain several minerals of the same, or even different, metals, especially alteration products, which do not have a definite composition.

In the case of the precious metals, however, there may be a wide difference between the two, depending upon the manner of occurrence of the valuable portion of the ore. In the case of silver, one part distributed through a thousand parts of foreign material, may constitute a paying ore; if now this one part be distributed through the remainder evenly it will not be possible to detect any silver mineral in the ore. If, however, the silver should be concentrated in separate portions through the mass, it may be possible to pick out distinct silver minerals.

The same observations apply to gold, but in a much greater degree, since gold is so much more valuable, and in some cases can be extracted at much less expense than silver; this is especially the case with the hydraulic gravels of California, where, in some instances, an average value of five or six cents worth of gold in a cubic yard of the gravel has yielded a profit.

The gangue or material carrying the valuable mineral varies greatly, and exercises much influence upon the processes to be followed in the extraction of the metal.

In many cases an ore contains more than one valuable metal, and, frequently, long and costly operations are required to separate the different metals, while in other cases their separation is quite easy, and in some cases a useful alloy can be smelted directly from ores containing more than one metal.

After the ore is mined it is frequently subjected to some kind of a concentrating process in preparation for smelting; these processes vary from simple sorting by hand, whereby much worthless material is removed, to very elaborate treatment by machinery, whereby the valuable portion of the ore is concentrated to a smaller volume and weight, generally with a loss of a small portion of the valuable constituents, and the waste material is rejected, and in some cases, ores of different metals occurring together are separated from each other. Illustrations of these processes form the next step in the series, and consist of the ores as mined, and the products of each step in the dressing operations, including both the valuable and the waste products.

The final step of the series represents the processes of extracting the metals from their ores and converting them into useful forms. These collections include the ores, the fuels, the fluxes, and all other materials entering into the operation. Where there are different stages in the operation, each stage is fully represented.

The non-metallic ores are treated in the same general way as the metallic ores.

The collections shown at the New Orleans exposition have been expanded to over 3,000 specimens, and the collections described are but a beginning. While generally complete in themselves, they will require many additions to even approach a full illustration of the subjects.

After this catalogue had been prepared 1,840 labels were written for the new material added to the collections.

During the year 139 accessions were received. Of these the most important were:

A large amount of tin ore and its associates from the Irish Creek locality in Rockbridge County, Virginia, presented by Mr. E. Willis, of Charleston, South Carolina.

A large collection representing the iron resources of Louisiana and Texas, containing many specimens of ore and pig-iron, and a few specimens of coal, presented by Prof. L. C. Johnson, U. S. Geological Survey.

A large amount of the nickel and cobalt ores from Lovelock, Nevada, containing both the sulphide ore, and ores consisting essentially of oxidized decomposition products, presented by George Lovelock, sr., Reno, Nevada.

A full series of chromium ores, presented by the Tyson Manufacturing Company, Baltimore, Maryland.

A full series illustrating the smelting of iron at the Pennsylvania furnaces of Robert Hare Powels' Sons & Co., Philadelphia, Pennsylvania.

A complete and very valuable collection illustrating the smelting of silver-lead or base bullion at the Colorado Smelter, South Pueblo, Colorado, presented by Mr. Anton Eilers, South Pueblo, Colorado.

This last collection is exceedingly full and complete, and is accompanied by a description of the process, with diagrams and many analyses, which render it especially valuable. It well illustrates the kind of collections that it is desirable for the department to gather in order to complete the systematic series.

The ores as received at the works are classified into oxidized and sulphureted; the oxidized ores are further divided into basic and silicious, that is, basic ores, the gangue of which is essentially a base, and silicious ores, the gangue of which is essentially acid or silica; these are sent directly to the shaft furnaces. The sulphureted ores are also divided into basic and silicious. In this case, however, it is the ores that are high in sulphur that are called basic, for the reason on roasting they furnish mainly oxides, which act as bases in the smelting operation. The silicious sulphureted ores consist essentially of quartz, with only a small amount of sulphides; they are generally very rich in silver and poor in lead, being more nearly true silver ores.

The basic sulphureted ores are separated into coarse and fine. The coarse are roasted in stalls and then go to the shaft furnaces; the fine are roasted in reverberatory furnaces, and are sometimes fused at the end of the roasting and sometimes not. From the roasting furnaces they go directly to the shaft furnaces.

The silicious sulphureted ores are sometimes roasted in the fusion furnace, but they are generally sent to the shaft furnaces, especially when they are very rich in silver.

The fluxes are all basic, and consist of iron ores and limestone, and go direct to the shaft furnaces.

The products of the smelting in the blast furnaces are:

Base Bullion, the valuable product which goes to market.

Slag, containing the earthy constituents of the furnace charge—divided into clean, or free from lead and silver, which is thrown over the dump; and impure, that is, containing lead and silver, which goes back to the shaft furnaces.

Matte, a by-product, essentially a sulphide of iron and copper, which goes to the roasting stalls and then back to the shaft furnaces.

Speiss, a by-product, essentially an arsenide of iron, which goes to the roasting stalls and then back to the shaft furnaces.

Flue dust, deposited in the flues of the furnaces, which is mixed with lime and ores low in lead, roasted in the fusion furnace, and then goes back to the shaft furnaces.

Accretions, which are deposits formed upon the walls of the furnaces; these are assorted according to their characteristics, and then go back to the shaft furnaces.

The bullion from these furnaces holds a high position with the refineries on account of its freedom from impurities, due to the purity of the ores of the Madonna mine, which form a large proportion of the charge in the shaft furnaces. It varies in richness, although it generally carries 300 ounces of silver per ton, and about an ounce of gold. It is cast into bars or pigs weighing 98 pounds, and is shipped from the furnace in car-loads of 300 bars.

By far the greater number of accessions are specimens sent in for examination and report, 80 reports, covering 186 specimens, having been made.

In cataloguing the collection, 671 entries, covering 1,266 specimens, having been made, and during the year 1,358 cards added to the catalogue; 1,840 labels have been written; 14 boxes of duplicates and reserve material have been sent to general storage; 242 specimens have been sent out in exchange.

The total number of specimens in the collection is about 49,000, of which 18,000 are on exhibition, 12,000 are duplicates, 7,000 reserves, the balance consisting of specimens as yet unadministered upon, and which are at present classed with the reserve series.

SECTION III.

PAPERS ILLUSTRATIVE OF THE COLLECTIONS IN THE U. S. NATIONAL MUSEUM, 1887.

---

1. Cradles of the American Aborigines. By OTIS T. MASON.
2. Notes on the artificial deformation of children among savage and civilized peoples. [With a bibliography.] By Dr. J. H. PORTER.
3. The Human Beast of Burden. By OTIS T. MASON.
4. Ethno-Conchology: A Study of Primitive Money. By ROBERT E. C. STEARNS.
5. A Preliminary Catalogue of the Eskimo Collection in the U. S. National Museum arranged geographically and by uses. By Lieut. T. DIX BOLLES, U. S. Navy.
6. The Extermination of the American Bison, with a sketch of its discovery and life history. By WILLIAM T. HORNADAY.
7. The Preservation of Museum Specimens from insects and the effects of dampness. By WALTER HOUGH.

CRADLES OF THE AMERICAN ABORIGINES.*

By OTIS T. MASON.

Many questions in anthropology depend for their answer upon a correct knowledge of the manner in which the child passes the first year of its life.

It is commonly believed that the shape of the head and, indeed, of the whole frame is modified by the cradle. From time to time the National Museum at Washington has come into possession of cradles and cradle-frames from the farthest north of their limit to the farthest south. A description of these with accurate drawings is herein given in order to throw further light upon the problem.

Deformation of the head, as is well known, is both designed and undesigned. Among the Chinuks and other tribes near the mouth of the Columbia River and northward, flattening of the head was intentionally practiced in a manner to be hereafter described.

Undesigned head-shaping is believed to have resulted among the Mound people as well as among our modern Indians, especially in the occipital region, from the contact of the soft and pliable head of the infant with the cradle-board or frame, even with the downy pillow.

In both Americas the majority of aboriginal children were confined in some sort of cradle from their birth until they were able to walk about. The cradle during this period serves many purposes:

(1) It is a mere nest for the helpless infant.

(2) It is a bed so constructed and manipulated as to enable the child to sleep either in a vertical or a horizontal position.

(3) It is a vehicle in which the child is to be transported, chiefly on the mother's back by means of a strap over the forehead, but frequently dangling like a bundle at the saddle-bow. This function, of course, always modifies the structure of the cradle, and, indeed, may have determined its very existence among nomadic tribes.

---

* I wish to express my sincere thanks to Dr. J. H. Porter for the valuable notes and references which accompany this paper.

(4) It is indeed a cradle, to be hung upon the limbs to rock, answering literally to the nursery rhyme:

> Rock a-bye baby upon the tree top,
> When the wind blows the cradle will rock,
> When the bough bends the cradle will fall,
> Down will come baby, and cradle, and all.

(5) It is also a play-house and baby-jumper. On many, nearly all, specimens may be seen dangling objects to evoke the senses, foot-rests by means of which the little one may exercise its legs, besides other conveniences anticipatory of the child's needs.

(6) The last set of functions to which the frame is devoted are those relating to what we may call the graduation of infancy, when the pappoose crawls out of its chrysalis little by little, and then abandons it altogether. The child is next seen standing partly on the mother's cincture and partly hanging to her neck or resting like a pig in a poke within the folds of her blanket.

An exhaustive treatment of this subject would include a careful study of the bed and especially of the pillow, in every instance. as well as of the frame. But collectors have been extremely careless in this regard. Very few cradles in the National Museum are accompanied with the beds and pillows. Were it not that here and there a traveler or a correspondent had made observations on the field, a hopeless lacuna would be in our way. Much remains to be done exactly at this point, and future investigators must turn their attention to this subject especially.

In this investigation much depends upon the age at which the child is placed in the cradle, the manner of bandaging and of suspending. Also there are a thousand old saws, superstitions, times and seasons, formularies, rites and customs hovering around the first year of every child's life in savagery that one should know, in order to comprehend many things attached to the cradle and its uses. Indeed, no one but an Indian mother could narrate the whole story in detail. Awaiting information from these sources, we shall describe as faithfully as possible the material now stored in the National Museum.

The method pursued in this description is that adopted in the series already begun in the report of 1884. The design is to apply the rules and methods of natural history to the inventions of mankind. We follow up the natural history of each human want or craving or occupation separately with a view to combining them into a comparative psychology as revealed in things.

Again, Bastian's study of "great areas" finds a beautiful illustration at this point in the fact that the cradle-board or frame is the child of geography and of meteorology. In the frozen North the Eskimo mother carries her infant in the hood of her parka whenever it is necessary to take it abroad. If she used a board or frame the child would perish with the cold. Indeed, the settled condition of the Eskimo does away with the necessity of such a device.

It is somewhat difficult to mark the southern limit of the cradle frame owing to the great elevations in Mexico and middle America. The National Museum does not possess a cradle frame of any tribe living south of the northern tier of Mexican States until we cross the equator. The most southern tribes of Mexico from which specimens have come, are the Pimas, Yumas, and Yaquis. It is not here denied, however, that tribes farther south use this device.

No attempt is here made to exhaust the study of child life in savagery. All who read this paper are doubtless familiar with the work of Dr. Ploss, entitled "Das Kind."*

The most exhaustive analysis of the subject will be found in the treatise of Dr. E. Pokrooski, of Moscow, published in the fourteenth volume of the Transactions of the Society of Friends of Natural Science, Anthropology, etc. The work is devoted especially to the different peoples of Russia. The table of contents is here appended because the volume is likely to be overlooked, and in order to show the ramifications of this interesting theme:

Chapter I. Attention paid to the protection and development of the embryo, heredity, relations of the sexes, condition of woman, consanguine marriages, polygamy and polyandry, marriage in classical antiquity, care taken of pregnant women among ancient and modern peoples.

Chapter II. Abortion and infanticide; motives: superstitions, fear of monsters, misery, etc.; legislation relative to abortion and infanticide.

Chapter III. Parturition and the condition of the new born.

Chapter IV. Care relative to the umbilical cord.

Chapter V. Dwelling of the infant in the family of the parents.

Chapter VI. Care of the skin.

Chapter VII. Bathing of infants.

Chapter VIII. Cold baths and baptism, in Europe, in Thibet, etc.

Chapter IX. Dressing of infants among ancient peoples and modern savages.

Chapter X. Dressing of Russian children.

Chapter XI. Enameling (emmaillotement).

Chapter XII. Kneading and rectification of the body of the infant.

Chapter XIII. Artificial deformation of the skull, ancient macrocephals, deformation among modern peoples, especially in Russia, Caucasia, Poland, Lapland, etc.

Chapter XIV. Influence of the infant's posture in its bed upon the deformation of the occiput, custom of bedding children among the Thracians, Macedonians, Germans, and Belgians of the sixteenth century, and among the modern Asiatics. The form of the occiput in Russians of the Kourgans, from the craniological collections of Moscow.

Chapter XV. The cradle among different peoples.

Chapter XVI. The cradles of the Russians.

Chapter XVII. Cradles among other peoples of Russia, Tsiganis, Fins, Esths, Livonians, Laps, Poles, Jews, Lithuanians, Tcheremis, Bashkirs, Nogaï, Sarts, Kirghiz, Kalmuks, Vakuts, Buriats, Tunguses, Soïotes, Woguls, Samoides, Goldoi, Koriaks, Kamchadales, Caucasians, etc.

Chapter XVIII. Methods of putting children in their beds, of carrying them and transporting them, dependence on climate, mode of life; bearing them on the arm, back, neck, head, hip; in bags, paniers, chests, skins, etc.; customs of the Chinese, Negroes, Hottentots, American Indians, Kamchadales, Japanese, etc., in this regard.

* Dr. H. Ploss. Das Kind in Brauch und Sitte der Völker. Anthropologische Studien. Leipzig (1884), Grieben, 2 vols., 8vo.

ESKIMO CRADLES.[*]

The Hyperboreans or Eskimos skirt the Arctic coast in Greenland, Labrador, the islands north of Canada, at the mouth of the Mackenzie River, all around Alaska to Mount St. Elias. In all of these areas the mother has the hood of her skin robe or parka made very large, so as to carry therein her babe, which nestles around the mother's neck secure from the cold. (Figs. 1 and 2.) The home life of the Hyperboreans is more permanent in its character than that of the southern Indians. There is provision made in the huts of the Eskimo for any babies that may be present.

The Indians contiguous to the Eskimo in Alaska and northeastern Canada belong to the great Tinnéan or Athapascan stock. They are called Kutchin in Alaska, and in the basin of the Mackenzie River have names ending with *tena* or *dene*, or an equivalent vocable. In the language of the Hudson Bay fur traders they bear various titles, most of

---

[*] Lyon, Capt. G. F. (Private Journal, *i. e.* of Parry's Arctic Ex., London, 1824, 8vo), remarks that the Eskimo women of Savage Islands had large hoods for the purpose of carrying their young children stark naked against the back (p. 20). Of the Eskimo in general he says that they have "slightly bowed" legs (p. 318). Their features of the face are diversified in an extraordinary manner (p. 309). About a sixth part * * * had high Roman noses (p. 310). Everywhere the hood answers the purpose of a child's cradle (p. 315).

Rink, Dr. Henry (Danish Greenland, London, 1877, 12mo) asserts that the external curvature of the legs is general among Eskimo women of middle age, and that it is due to the cramped position in which they sit on the ledge in the hut (p. 154).

Heriot, G. (Travels through the Canadas, London, 1807, 4to) describes the "Eskimaux" women of Newfoundland as having "their capuchins * * * much larger

them terms of derision.* The classification of the Tinné of Alaska is given by Dall.

Fig. 1.

ESKIMO WOMAN OF POINT BARROW, CARRYING CHILD.

(From photograph.)

Fig. 2.

ESKIMO WOMAN OF POINT BARROW, CARRYING SLEEPING CHILD.

(From photograph.)

The Tinnéan tribes use some sort of device in which to lash their children during the first year. One should expect, however, to find these Indians also copying the Eskimo cradle hood.† Strachan Jones,

towards their shoulders" than those of the men, "in order to cover their children when they wish to carry them on their backs" (p. 23).

Franklin, Capt. J. (Narrative of Second Expedition, London, 1828, 4to): The same kind of hood, for the same purpose as that among the Loucheux, was seen in use among the Eskimo women near the mouth of the Mackenzie, on the Arctic coast (p.

* Contributions to N. A. Ethnology, Bur. Ethnology, I, 24; also The Native Tribes of Alaska, A. A. A. S., Ann Arbor, 1885.

† Cradles (Dixon's Voyage, p. 239): It might be imagined that the children of these savages would enjoy the free and unrestrained use of their limbs from their earliest infancy. This, however, is not altogether the case. Three pieces of bark are fastened together, so as to form a kind of chair. The infant, after being wrapped in furs, is put into this chair, and lashed so close that it can not alter its posture, even with struggling, and the chair is so contrived that when a mother wants to feed her child, or give it the breast, there is no ocasion to release it from its shackles. Soft moss is used by the Indian nurse to keep her child clean; but little regard is paid to this article, and the poor infants are often terribly excoriated; nay, I have frequently seen boys of six or seven years old whose posteriors have borne evident marks of this neglect in their infancy.

Franklin, Capt. J. (Narrative of Second Expedition, London, 1828, 4to): The hood of the dress among the Lower Loucheux women is "made sufficiently wide to admit of their carrying a child on their back" (p. 28).

in his Notes on the Tinnê or Chippewyan Indians, gives the figure of an infant sitting on a diminutive " bedstead," having a soft fur seat. The body of the child is bandaged to the high back of the seat. (Fig. 3.)

Fig. 3.

CHIPPEWYAN CHILD-FRAME.

(From Notes on the Tinnê Indians. By Strachan Jones.)

The same observation just made concerning the Eskimo is true of the Indians on the Upper Yukon. Dr. Dall informs me that their homes are permanent, and that there therefore is no need of the cradle-frame. The infant, if lashed at all, is fastened in a kind of coal-scuttle-shaped cradle, and at night sleeps in a hammock or on the banquette.

E. W. Nelson has sent to the Smithsonian Institution, among the many thousands of specimens collected throughout the entire western Eskimo area, the model of a trough-shaped cradle of birch bark, made from three pieces, forming, respectively, the bottom, the top and hood, and the awning. (Fig. 4.) The two pieces forming the bottom and the hood overlap an inch and a half, and are sewed together with a single basting of pine root, with stitches half an inch long.   Around the bor-

118).   In Dr. Richardson's narrative of his expedition eastward from the mouth of the Mackenzie, he speaks of coast Eskimo women who "draw their children out of their wide boots, where they are accustomed to carry them naked" (I, p. 226). Franklin, Parry, Back, Richardson, and the more modern explorers, speak of the flat nose of the Eskimo. As in Oceanica this may be the result of compression, since Sir John Ross (Voyage to Baffin's Bay, London, 1819, 4to) found "small straight" noses and "large aquiline" noses among the Arctic Highlanders of Prince Regent's Bay (pp. 126, 127).

Holmberg says of the Koniagas (Eskimos), that the posterior part of the head is "not arched, but flat." The description of their huts and sleeping places suggests that this may be the effect of hard pillows or head-rests on an incompletely ossified skull. (Bancroft, Nat. Races of Pacific States, vol. I, p. 72.)

Ledyard, who accompanied the expedition of Captain Cook to the North Pacific, noticed the bowed legs of the Aleuts, and attributed it to their position in the boats, in which they spend so much of their time. (Bancroft, Nat. Races of Pacific States, vol. I, p. 88.)

Hall, C. F. (Life with the Eskimo, London, 1864, 12mo): Fac-simile of an Eskimo wood-cut showing mother and child, with position of latter in hood (vol. I, p. 53). Plate of child in what he calls (p. 98, vol. I) "the baby pouch" (vol. I, p. 159). "The infant is carried naked in the mother's hood, yet in close contact with the parent's skin" (vol. I, p. 189). Compression of head (vol. II, p. 313). This is lateral, made by the hands, and by a skin cap. But no cap could exert lateral pressure, and the words "a little skin cap placed lightly over the compressed head, which is to be kept there one year" (vol. II, p. 313), may not convey this idea.

Hearne, Samuel, in the narrative of his journey from Prince of Wales Fort, in Hudson Bay, to the Northern Ocean (London, 1795), informs us that no cradles are in use among the northern Indian tribes between 59° and 68° north. He says that the majority of the children are bow-legged from the way in which they are carried.

Portlock, in his Voyage Round the World (London, 1789), makes observations on the general distortion of the legs among Indians of Prince William's Sound (p. 248).

Kerr, Robert (Collection of Voyages and Travels, London, 1824, 8vo vol. XVI): In Cook's description of the natives of Nootka Sound, the same distortion of legs, from position in canoe, is noticed as has been before referred to. (Vid. notes, passim, p.

der of the body and just under the margin, continuing around the border of the hood and awning, lies a rod of osier. A strip of birch bark laid on the upper and inner side of the margin serves as a stiffener. It is sewed down by an ingenious basting, with stitches an inch or more long, which pass down through the two thicknesses of birch bark, around the osier twig that lies just below the margin, and up again through the two thicknesses of birch bark by another opening, to commence the next stitch. The hood is formed by puckering the birch bark after the manner of a grocer's bag. The bordering osier is neatly sewed to the edge of the hood and awning by a coil of split spruce root. Rows of beads of many colors adorn the awning piece. In a country intolerable by reason of mosquitoes it is not strange that provision for sustaining some sort of netting should have been devised. Playthings of various kinds are also hung to this awning for the hands and eyes and ears of the infant occupant, and it is quite sure that this bow or hood saves the face of the child many hurtful blows from a fall.*

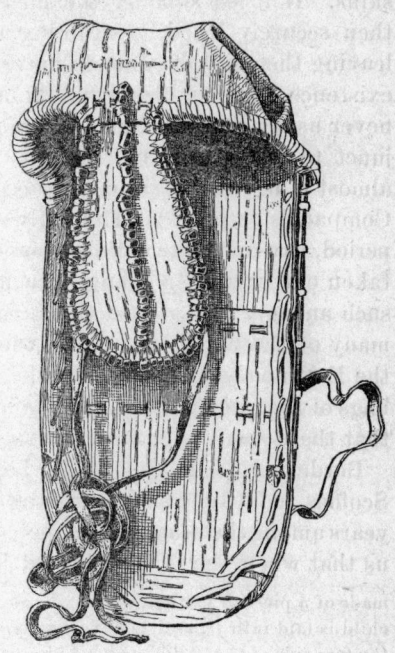

Fig. 4.

BIRCH-BARK CRADLE FROM YUKON RIVER, ALASKA.

(Cat. No. 32985, U. S. N. M. Norton Sound. Collected by E. W. Nelson.)

232.) (Voyages, etc.). Captain King states that he observed the custom of carrying children in the hood among the Chuckchees of the east coast (XVI, 364, note). On the other coast Captain Cook remarked of the dresses at Prince William's Sound that "some" only had hoods (XVI, 280).

* Long, J. (Voyages and Travels of an Indian Interpreter, London, 1791, 4to): He describes the cradle of the Chippewas, who range north to the Arctic Circle; describes also the position and mode of carrying the child, and its swathing; states that before the French occupation of Canada there were no swathings in use, failing material for them (pp. 60, 61). Before the French period the cradle was "a trough filled with dry rotten-wood dust," in which the baby, "covered with furs," was "kept until weaned" (p. 51). The head of the child in the Chippewa cradle is protected by a hoop (p. 60).

Back, Captain (Narrative of Arctic Land Expedition, Philadelphia, 1836, 8vo): On the shore of Great Slave Lake he saw infants "swaddled and unable to stir."

Harmon's Journal. (The title page of this work is lost. Harmon's expedition was made in 1800, and, under the auspices of the Northwest Company, he traveled through the same country as Mackenzie.) Speaking of the Sauteux, Crees, Assiniboines, Rapid Indians, Blackfeet, Bloods, Sussees, Cautonies, Muskagoes, Chipeways, Beavers, Sicaunies, Tâ-cullias, Ate-nâs, and Nâte-ote-tains, he says that they all use the cradle-board (p. 316). Harmon thus describes the cradle-board of the Indians of British America: "All Indian children, when young, are laced in a kind of bag * * *

Ross, in describing the Eastern Tinnêh, says:* "Among the Eastern Tinnêh, immediately after birth, without washing, the infant is laid naked on a layer of moss in a bag made of leather, and lined with hare-skins. If it be summer the latter are dispensed with. This bag is then securely laced, restraining the limbs in natural positions, and leaving the child freedom to move the head only. In this phase of its existence it resembles strongly an Egyptian mummy." Cradles are never used; but this machine, called a "moss bag," is an excellent adjunct to the rearing of children up to a certain age, and has become almost if not universally adopted in the families of the Hudson Bay Company's employés. The natives retain the use of the bag to a late period, say until the child passes a year, during which time it is never taken out except to change the moss. To this practice, continued to such an age, I attribute the turned toes and rather crooked legs of many of these Indians. One is somewhat reminded by this process of the Eskimo sleeping-bag. In the National collection are several small bags of the same pattern, but the label does not authorize the conclusion that these small bags were used as cradles for infants.

Bordering the Eskimo in the Labrador Peninsula live the Naskopi or Scoffies, in latitude as far north as 53 degrees. Lucien Turner spent two years among them, and has collected much precious information. He tells us that when the Naskopi child is born it is not washed or allowed to

---

made of a piece of leather. * * * Some moss is laid in the bottom of this bag, the child is laid into it, and moss is inserted between its legs. The bag is then laced to the fore side of the child as high as its neck. This bag is laid upon a board, to which it is fastened by means of a strip of leather" (p. 316). Further details of arrangement, ornamentation, and nursing (pp. 316, 317).

Mackenzie, Sir A. (Voyages from Montreal to the Frozen and Pacific Oceans, London, 1801, 4to): Descriptive of the "swaddling-board" used by the Beaver Indians (p. 149).

N. B.—This board, about 2 feet long, covered with a bed of moss, to which it (the child) is fastened by bandages "was in use in a sub-arctic climate"! Equally opposed to Hearne's statement concerning the absence of cradles in these regions is Mackenzie's full description of a board cradle "in which the child, after it had been swathed, is placed on a bed of moss." Head compression practiced here, i. e., near Northwest coast; tribe not named (p. 371). It is to be remarked that Mackenzie speaks of this last as a "new kind of cradle," the inference being that the Beaver "swaddling-board" was used by the Chippewa, Knisteneaux, Assiniboines, etc.

Fitz William (Northwest Passage by Land, p. 85) says that the cradle is "a board with two side flaps of cloth, which lace together up the center. The child is laid on its back on the board, packed with soft moss, and laced firmly down with its arms to its sides, and only the head at liberty. The cradle is slung on the back of the mother when traveling, or reared against a tree when resting in camp, the child being only occasionally released from bondage for a few moments. The little prisoners are remarkably good; no squalling disturbes an Indian camp."

Whymper (Alaska, p. 229): "The Tenan Kutchin (Tinneh) children are carried in small chairs made of birch bark." Richardson (Journal I, 384) makes the same statement. Bancroft (Nat. Races, etc. I, 131) says: "The women carry their infants in a sort of bark saddle, fastened to the back; they bandage their feet in order to make them small."

* Smithsonian Report, 1856, p. 302.

take the breast until three days have elapsed; it is considered to weaken
the infant if permitted to take the breast before that time.   The mother
prepares sphagnum moss by beating it until it becomes quite soft and
fluffy.   A portion of this moss is placed about the child, and it is then
wrapped in clothes or skins.   The swaddling process begins at the feet
and wraps the lower limbs close together; the trunk is also swathed as
far as the neck, until the child resembles a cocoon.   At earliest infancy
the arms are wrapped next the body, but when several months old those
limbs are free, except at night.   The reason of this is to make them
grow. straight and afford the mother convenience in handling them
when on a journey, or to prevent them from rolling about the tent and
into the fire.   The bandages are removed once a day and a clean
quantity of moss supplied.   Water is never given to the child to drink
until it is old enough to help itself—an occasion of remark among the
women—for it marks an event in the infant's life.

Figure 5 is from a sketch in the Century Magazine, taken at Cape
Breton, and gives us an excellent example of the combinations which

Fig. 5.

CHILD IN HAMMOCK.   CAPE BRETON.

(From sketch in *Century Magazine*.)

civilization entails.   The wigwam is to the manner born, the hammock
reminds one of the far south, while the baby, ensconced in fur and
blankets, without a pretense of lashing, points to Eskimo as well as
white man's methods.   Dr. Dall's remark about the Alaska Indian fash
ion of the hammock may be recalled here.

On the Pacific side of the Rocky Mountains appear in turn the Kolo
shan, the Haidan, Hailtzukan (Quackiool), Salishan, Wakashan, or
Nutkan stock.   All of these people are more or less the slaves in all

their arts to the splendid forests of pine and cedar which cover their lands. The Bellachoola or Bilkhula belong to the great Salishan stock. Their home is in the vicinity of Bentinck Arm. The cradle of this people is probably a fair sample of that used by the stocks north and south of the Bilkhulas (Fig. 6). It is a trough-shaped frame of cedar wood made in two pieces, as follows: The bottom and head-board are in one piece about one-half or three-quarters inch thick. The two sides and foot are also in one piece. The angles and the bends near the child's knees are effected by scarfing the wood almost through on the inside and boiling and bending it into shape. In this art these Indians are very expert, making great numbers of boxes for food and clothing, with

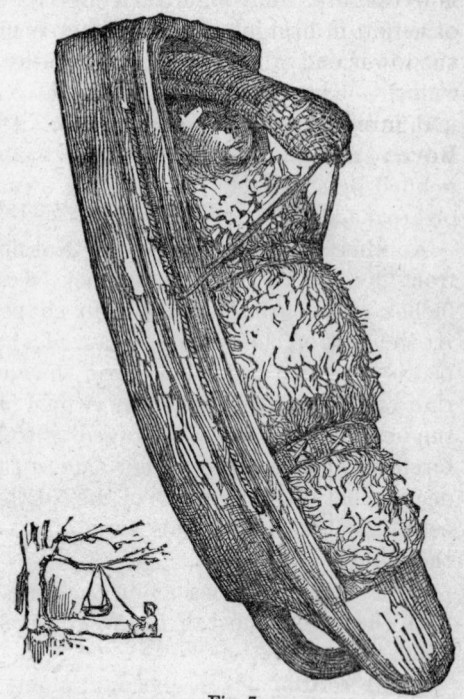

Fig. 7.
DUGOUT CRADLE, WITH HEAD-FLATTENING APPARATUS.
(Cat. No. 2574 B, U. S. N. M.   Chinuk Indians.   Collected by George Catlin.)

Fig. 6.
BELLA-COOLA TROUGH-CRADLE.
(Cat. No. 20556, U. S. N. M.   Bella Bella, B. C.   Collected by James G. Swan.)

joints invisible on the outside. The joints of this cradle are united by means of small withes of willow. The characteristic marks are a flat bottom; head-board, like a little grave-stone, painted in red and black with conventional symbol of a totem. Two streaks of red paint skirt the upper margin of the sides. The change in the angle of convergence of the sides near the child is effected by scarfing and bending. The bed consists of a mass of finely shredded cedar bark. This is overlaid with some kind of sheet of cloth or fur, and the lashing passes through holes in flaps of raw-hide, in place of the series of eyelet loops occurring on cradles farther south.

In the commencement of this article two kinds of deformation were mentioned, the designed and the undesigned. The first-mentioned method is found in British Columbia, on its western border, and in our domain along the coast of Washington and Oregon. On the extreme northwest corner of Washington live the Makahs, a people associated with the Ahts on Vancouver Island, and belonging to the Nutkan or Wakashan stock. Living as they do in the great cedar region, their cradle would naturally be similar to those of the Indians living farther north.

It is a trough rudely hewed out of cedar wood. (Fig. 7.) A low bridge is left across the trough to strengthen it. Slats are put across to level of height of bridge. The bedding consists of mats of cedar bark. On the lower end of the cradle is a handle. Around the sides are fastened strings. The compress is fastened to head of cradle. It curves over and is tightened by means of cords to the sides of the cradle. It is woven of, and stuffed tightly with, cedar bark. These cradles are suspended by strings to pliant poles, swung by the mother with her hand or great toe.

Another cradle-trough in the National Museum, said to have come from Oregon Territory, is a block of cedar wood 30 inches long and 12 inches square, roughly hewn in shape of a boat, with bulging sides. At the foot, on the outside, is carved a handle, function not known. The bed is shredded cedar bark, and the covering a quilt of the same material, roughly held together by twined weaving; a long pad is hinged to the head-board, and so arranged as to be drawn down over the child's forehead and lashed to either side of the trough. There is evident connection between the boats of the Northwest and the cradles. An interesting feature about this form of cradle is the appliances for lashing the child:

(1) A series of holes along the side, just below the margin, parallel with the border most of the way, but sloping quite away from it at the head.

(2) A cord of coarse root laid along over these holes on the outside of the cradles.

(3) On either side the standard series of loops for the lacing-string is formed by passing a twine through the first hole, around the root cord on the outside, back through the same hole up to the middle of the cradle to form a loop, back through the next hole in the same manner.

(4) The lacing-string runs through these loops alternately from bottom to top. The ornamentation of this type of cradle is chiefly by means of parti-colored basketry and furs. The Chinuks were an advanced people in art, and many of their cradles were very prettily adorned. Mr. Catlin figured one in which the process of head-flattening is going forward.

In Mayne's "British Columbia and Vancouver's Island" we read that the child lies at full length, and the sides of the cradle are sufficiently high to enable the mother to lace it in by a cord passed from side to side, a small block being put at one end as a pillow. When the mother is traveling she carries the cradle on her back in nearly an upright position, with the head appearing just above her shoulders. But if she is working she suspends the infant from the pliant branch of a tree, or, sticking the pole in the ground at a slight angle, hangs the cradle, sometimes upright, sometimes horizontally, on the end of it. They move pole and cradle so as to keep it near them, and every now and then give it a swing so that it rocks up and down. It is said that when children die they are put in some lake or pool, in their cradle, and left to float, the water being regarded as sacred ever after.

Swan, in his "Indians of Cape Flattery,"* says: "The practice of flattening the heads of infants, although not universal among the Makahs, is performed in a manner similar to that of the Chinuks and other tribes in the vicinity of the Columbia River. As soon as a child is born it is washed with warm urine, and then smeared with whale oil and placed in a cradle made of bark, woven basket fashion, or of wood, either cedar or alder, hollowed out for the purpose. Into the cradle a quantity of finely separated cedar bark of the softest texture is first thrown. At the foot is a board raised at an angle of about 25 degrees, which serves to keep the child's feet elevated, or when the cradle is raised to allow the child to nurse, to form a support for the body, or a sort of seat. This is also covered with bark (he-sé-yu). A pillow is formed of the same material, just high enough to keep the head in its natural position, with the spinal column neither elevated nor depressed. First the child is laid on its back, its legs properly extended, its arms put close to its sides, and a covering either of bark or cloth laid over it; and then, commencing at the feet, the whole body is firmly laced up, so that it has no chance to move in the least. When the body is well secured, a padding of he-sé-yu is placed on the child's forehead, over which is laid bark of a somewhat stiffer texture, and the head is firmly lashed down to the sides of the cradle; thus the infant remains, seldom taken out more than once a day while it is very young, and then only to wash it and dry its bedding. The male children have a small opening left in the covering, through which the penis protrudes, to enable them to void their urine. The same style of cradle appears to be used whether it is intended to compress the skull or not, and that deformity is accomplished by drawing the strings of the head-pad tightly and keeping up the pressure for a long time. Children are usually kept in these cradles till they are a year old, but as their growth advances they are not tied up quite so long as for the first few months. The mother, in washing her child, seldom takes the trouble to heat water; she simply fills her mouth with water, and when she thinks it warm enough spirts it on the child and rubs it with her hand."

---

*Smithsonian Cont. to Knowledge, No. 220, pp. 18–19.

Inhabiting the lower parts of the Columbia are a small tribe who correctly come under the name of Flat Heads, as they are almost the only people who strictly adhere to the custom of squeezing and flattening the head.

The process of flattening consists in placing the infant on a board, to which it is lashed by means of thongs to a position from which it can not escape, and the back of the head supported by a sort of pillow, made of moss or rabbit-skins, with an inclined piece (as seen in the drawing), resting on the forehead of the child, being every day drawn down a little tighter by means of a cord, which holds it in its place until it at length touches the nose, thus forming a straight line from the crown of the head to the end of the nose. This process is seemingly a very cruel one, though I doubt if it causes much pain, as it is done in earliest infancy, while the bones are soft and easily depressed into this distorted shape, by forcing the occipital up and the frontal down.

Fig. 8.
FLAT HEAD WOMAN AND CHILD.
(Showing the manner in which the heads of the children are flattened.)

The skull at the top in profile will show a breadth of not more than $1\frac{1}{2}$ or 2 inches, when in front view it exhibits a great expansion on the sides, making it at the top nearly the width of one and a half natural heads.

By this remarkable operation the brain is singularly changed from its natural shape, but in all probability not in the least diminished or injured in its natural functions. This belief is drawn from the testimony of many credible witnesses who have closely scrutinized them and ascertained that those who have the head flattened are in no way inferior in intellectual powers to those whose heads are in their natural shape.

In the process of flattening the head there is another form of crib or cradle into which the child is placed, much in the form of a small canoe, dug out of a log of wood, with a cavity just large enough to admit the body of the child and the head also, giving it room to expand in width, while from the head of the cradle there is a sort of lever, with an elastic spring, that comes down on the forehead of the child and produces the same effect as the one I have described. The child is wrapped in rabbit-skins and placed in this little coffin-like cradle, from which it is not in some instances taken out for several weeks.

The bandages over and about the lower limbs are loose and repeatedly taken off in the same day, as the child may require cleansing. But the head and shoulders are kept strictly in the same position, and the breast

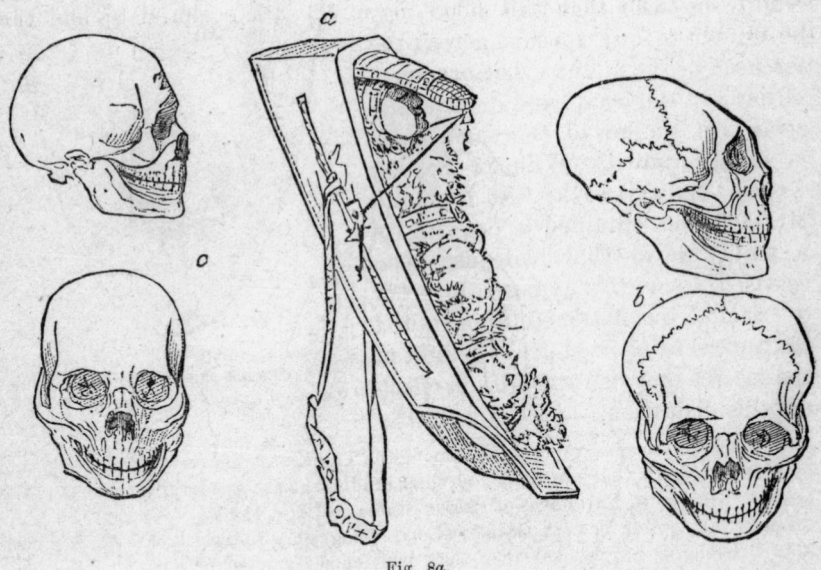

Fig. 8a.

THE CHINUK METHOD OE FLATTENING THE HEAD.

(Plate 210½, Vol. II, Catlin's Eight Years.)

given to the child by holding it up in the cradle, loosing the outer end of the lever that comes over the nose and raising it up or turning it aside so as to allow the child to come at the breast without moving its head. The length of time that the infants are carried in these cradles is three, five, or eight weeks, until the bones are so formed as to keep their shape.

This cradle has a strap that passes over the woman's forehead whilst the cradle rides upon her back, and if the child dies during its subjection to this rigid mode its cradle becomes its coffin, forming a little canoe, in which it lies floating on the water in some sacred pool. (Catlin, vol. II, p. 110.)

From the Oregon coast the Wilkes Expedition* brought a cradle which is shown in Fig. 9. The frame board is trowel or spade shape. The whole back and front are covered with buckskin. At a proper distance from the edges, the buckskin is sewed or lashed down, and the flaps form the inclosing wrappings of the child. A triangular " fly " covers the lower extremities. Compare this portion of the cradle with the Nez Percés (Sahaptian) cradle described further on. The hood is of rawhide, overlaid with a cover of beaded buckskin. It can readily be seen that this hood may be drawn to any tension across the forehead of the infant. The ornamentation and the head-band or carrying-strap are similar to the same parts in other cradles. Wilkes (Explor. Exped., IV, 388) says: "At Niculuita Mr. Drayton obtained a drawing of a child's head that had just been released from its bandages, in order to secure its flattened appearance. Both parents showed great delight at the success they had met with in effecting this distortion." (See Fig. 10.)

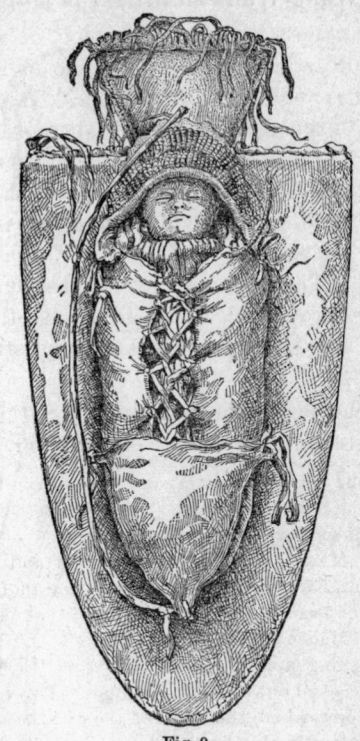

Fig. 9.
CRADLE OF OREGON INDIANS.
(Cat. No. 2575, U. S. N. M. Collected by Wilkes' Exploring Expedition.)

*Marchand (Voyages) reports that among the Thinkeets, infants are "so excoriated by fermented filth, and so scarred by their cradle, that they carry the marks to the grave." (Bancroft, Nat. Races of Pacific States, vol. I, p. 112.)

Lord (Nat., vol. II, p. 232), Scouler (Lond. Geog. Soc. Jour., vol. XI, pp. 218, 220, 223), Schoolcraft (Arch., vol. II, p. 325) mention the custom of flattening the head in infancy among the Haidahs (Columbians). (Bancroft, Nat. Races, etc., I, 158.) In their platform houses they slept on "cedar mats" (p. 161).

Bancroft (Native Races of the Pacific States, N. Y., 1875, vol. I): "The custom of flattening the head is practiced by the Nootkas in common with the Sound and Chinook families, but is not universal" (p. 180. See, also, note, p. 58).

Bancroft (Native Races of the Pacific States, N. Y., 1875, vol. I, note, p. 177) quotes the accounts of Cook, Meares, Mofras, Macfie, Poole, Sutil y Mexicana, Mayne, and Scouler, to the effect that the Nootka Indians are bow-legged and intoed from boat work, and have deformed limbs from the effect of garters.

Swan, J. G. (Indians of Cape Flattery, Smithsonian Contributions, No. 220): Description of the process of head-flattening among the Indians of Vancouver Island (pp. 18, 19).

Heriot, G. (Travels through the Canadas, London, 1807, 4to): "In the latitude of fifty-two degrees, on the northwest coast of America, there exists a tribe whose heads are molded into a wedge-like form" (p. 303).

Bancroft (Native Races of the Pacific States, N. Y., 1875, vol. I): The custom of head-flattening, apparently of sea-board origin and growth, extends * * * across

Governor Stevens (Ind. Aff. Rep., 1854, p. 227) says: "The women at Walla Walla sit astride in a saddle made with a very high pommel and

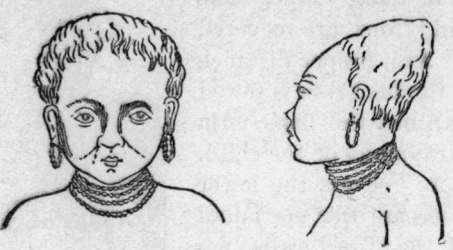

Fig. 10.

SHOWING THE EFFECT OF HEAD-FLATTENING.

(From drawing by Mr. Drayton, published in Wilkes' Exploring Expedition, IV, p. 388.)

cantle, and in traveling carry their infants either dangling by the cradle strap to the former or slung in a blanket over their shoulders." The

the Cascade barrier, and is practiced to a greater or less extent by all the tribes of the Sahaptian family." They merely depress slightly the forehead of infants, and this disappears at maturity" (p. 256).

Macfie, M. (Vancouver Island and British Columbia, London, 1865): Between lat. 53° 30' N. and lat. 46° N. the Indians of the northwest coast of America flatten the head, under the impression that the distortion is becoming (p. 441).

Macfie (idem., p. 441) gives the following account of the process of head-flattening among the coast tribes: "The child, as soon as born, is placed in a cradle scooped out of a log of timber. This rude ark is flat at the bottom, and raised at the point where the neck of the child rests. A flat stone is fastened to the head of the infant in this posture by thin strips of twisted bark. In the situation indicated the child is kept till able to walk, and its forehead has been molded into the required shape." In the Quatsino district the skulls of the women have "a tapering or conical form" * * * produced by artificial means. Only the families of chiefs (tenass) and "gentlemen commoners" (tyhees) are permitted to modify the form of the head.

Bancroft (Native Races of the Pacific States, N. Y., 1875, vol. I): The Sound Indians, among the Columbians, flatten the head, "but none carry the practice to such an extent as their neighbors on the south" (p. 210).

Bancroft (Native Races of the Pacific States, N. Y., 1875, vol. I): Among the Chinooks the "legs are bowed and otherwise deformed by a constant squatting position in and out of their canoes" (p. 224). Head-flattening "seems to have originated * * * about the mouth of the Columbia," and the Chinooks carry the custom to an excess of deformity (p. 226).

Bancroft remarks that "the Chinook ideal of facial beauty is a straight line from the end of the nose to the crown of the head. The flattening of the skull is effected by binding the infant to its cradle immediately after birth, and keeping it there from three months to a year. The simplest form of cradle is a piece of board or plank, on which the child is laid upon its back with its head slightly raised by a block of wood. Another piece of wood, or bark, or leather is then placed over the forehead and tied to the plank with strings, which are tightened more and more each day until the skull is shaped to the required pattern. Space is left for lateral expansion, and, under ordinary circumstances, the child's head is not allowed to leave its position until the process is complete. The body and limbs are also bound to the cradle, but more loosely, by bandages, which are sometimes removed for cleansing purposes." (Native Races, etc., vol. I, p. 227.)

same authority says that the Clallams, and in fact all the Sound Indians, flatten the head (243).*

Mr. William Meinold, in sending to the National Museum the skull of a Flathead Indian from northwest Montana, writes as follows: "When the child is about one week old it is put on a board and tied hand and foot. A small bag of sand is tied over the forehead and remains in this position eight or ten days. It is then taken off for a short rest and afterwards fastened to the board again. This continues from six weeks to six months. The head then has its shape and grows in the right direction. The skull mentioned belonged to Redgrass, a chief, who died about forty years ago. His body was deposited on posts 6 feet high. In his canoe were found beads, and a General Harrison badge of 1841.†

---

* Meares, J. (Voyages to the Northwest Coast of America, London, 1791, 8vo), describes the compression of head into the form of a "sugar loaf" among Indians of Nootka Sound by bandages. Says the process flattens the nose (vol. II, p. 37).

Wilkes, Commander (U. S. Exploring Expedition, Philadelphia, 1845, 4to, vol. IV): Two plates illustrating head-flattening among the Indians of Niculuita (Wallawalla), observed by Mr. Drayton (p. 415). Flower quotes Kane's description of the process of head-compression in Vancouver (p. 13). He refers to evident distortion in the case of an order of Chinese mendicants, as indicated by plate 131, vol. II, Picart, Histoire des Religions. He quotes Townsend's account of head-flattening among the Wallamets (p. 14).

† Catlin, George. (Illustrations of the Manners, etc., of the N. Amer. Indians. London, 1876, 8vo, vol. I.) Head of Crow chief distorted into semi-lunar shape, with compression of forehead (p. 50). Vol. II. Head-flattening among Chinooks. Description of cradle and process (pp. 110, 111). Statement concerning the former prevalence of this custom among Choctaws and Chickasaws (p. 112). The evidence afforded by this and other works dealing with the details of life points to the fact that head distortion is less practiced now than formerly. It exists at present sporadically.

Cox, R. (The Columbia River. London, 1832, 3d ed. 8vo.) On the Lower Columbia all heads were distorted; and there was a perfect uniformity in their shape (vol. I, pp. 105, 106). Speaking of "Flatheads," says, their "heads have their fair proportion of rotundity" (I, pp. 219–222). Gathlamahs, Killymucks, Clatsops, Chinooks, Chilts, at mouth of Columbia, flatten the head. Cradle oblong, with pillow. Pad and slab on forehead held by cords. Time, a year. No pain (vol. I, page 276). Among this group of tribes the body and limbs among the men well shaped, but the women's legs are "quite bandy," owing to the tight ligatures they wear on the lower part of the legs (vol I, p. 276).

Wood, J. G. (Uncivilized Races of Men. Hartford, 1871. 8vo.) Description of the process of head-flattening among the Columbia Indians (pp. 1319, 1320).

Lewis and Clark. (Expedition to the Sources of the Missouri, etc. Philadelphia, 1814. 8vo.) On the Kimooenim, an affluent of the Columbia, "the Sokulk *women*" had "their heads flattened in such a manner that the forehead is in a straight line from the nose to the crown of the head" (vol. II, p. 12). The *women* of the Pishquitpaws, on the Columbia, had "their heads flattened" (vol. II, p. 23). Among the Eneeshurs and Elcheloots "the heads of the males, as well as of the other sex," were flattened (vol. II, p. 45). The *women* of an unnamed tribe on the same river "universally have their heads flattened," and they saw "female children undergoing the operation" (vol. II, p. 57). Pressure of anklets and mode of sitting also distorted their legs (*id.*). "The Skilloots, both males and females, have the head flattened" (vol. II p. 64). The Wahkiacums "all have their heads flattened" (vol. II, p. 69). Head-flattening is general among the "Chinooks." Men's legs "small and crooked; women's tumefied

The Hupa Indians of northwestern California belong to the Tinnéan stock. They have been described in a paper entitled, "The Ray Collection in the U. S. National Museum."* The cradle-basket of the Hupas of northwestern California is a slipper shaped, open work basket of

osier warp, and twined weaving constitutes the body of the cradle. (Fig. 11.) It is woven as follows: Commencing at the upper end, the small ends of the twigs are held in place one eighth of an inch apart by three rows of twined weaving, followed by a row in which an extra strengthening twig is whipped or sewed in place, as in the Makah basketry. At intervals of 2½ to 3 inches are three rows of twined basketry, every alternate series having one of the strengthening twigs, increasing in thickness downward. The twigs constituting the true bottom of the so-called slipper continue to the end of the square toe, and are fastened off while those that form the sides are ingeniously bent to form the vamp of the slipper. This part of the frame is held together by rows of twined weaving (*boustrophedon*). When two rows of this kind of twining lie quite close it has the appearance of a four-ply plaiting, and has been taken for such by the superficial observer.

Fig. 11.
HUPA WICKER-CRADLE.
(Cat. No. 126519, U. S. N. M. Hupa Valley, California.
Collected by Lieut. P. H. Ray, U. S. A.)

The binding around the opening of the cradle is formed of a bundle of twigs seized with a strip of bast or tough root.

The awning is made of open wicker and twined basketry, bound with

by pressure of bead anklets (vol. II, p. 115). The Cookoooose, on the Pacific coast, do not flatten the head (vol. II, p. 119). It is stated that "the Killamucks, Clatsops, Chinnooks and Cathlamahs * * * have thick ankles and crooked legs" due to "the universal practice of squatting, * * * and also to the tight bandages of beads and strings worn around the ankles by the women," whose limbs are "particularly ill shaped and swollen." "The custom * * * of flattening the head by artificial pressure during infancy, prevails among all the nations we have seen west of the Rocky Mountains" (Snakes and Cookoooose they themselves except). "To the east of that barrier the fashion is * * * perfectly unknown." An error! "On the lower parts of the Columbia both sexes are universally flatheads; the custom diminishes in receding eastward, * * * till among the remoter tribes, near the mountains," the practice "is confined to a few females" (vol. II, pp. 130, 131).

* Smithsonian Report, 1886, i., pp. 205–239, pl. XXVI.

colored grass. This pretty, flat cone resembles the salmon-baskets figured and described in the Ray collection.*

There is in the National Museum a cradle for a new-born babe, from the McCloud River Indians of California, belonging to the basket-tray type. It is shaped very much like a large grain-scoop or the lower half of a moccasin inverted, and made of twigs in twined weaving. There are double rows of twining two inches or thereabouts apart, and nearly all of them are interlocked, which gives the appearance of a four-ply braid. The meshes form a diamond pattern by inclusion in the half turns of the twine quincuncially.

The general shoe-shape of the cradle is produced by commencing at the heel, which is here the bottom, and doubling the twigs by a continually sharper turn until along the bottom the rods simply lie parallel, that is, the rods that lie along the middle of the bottom terminate at the heel, while those that form the sides and upper end are continuous.

Around the edge and forming a brace across the upper end is a border made of a bundle of rods seized with tough bast or split root.† The twigs themselves project upwards an inch or two from this brace, and are not fastened off. (Figs. 11 and 12.)

The Modoc women make a very pretty baby-basket of fine willow-work, cylinder-shaped, with one-half of it cut away, except a few inches at the ends.‡ It is intended to be set up against the wall or carried on the back; hence the infant is lashed perpendicular in it, with his feet standing in one end and the other covering his head, like a small parasol. In one that I saw this canopy was supported by small standards, spirally wrapped with strips of gay-colored calico, with looped and scalloped hangings between. Let a mother black her whole face below the eyes, including the nose, shining black, thrust a goose quill 3 inches long through the septum of the nose, don her close-fitting skull cap and start to town with her baby-basket lashed to her back, and she feels the pride of maternity strong within her. The little fellow is wrapped all around like a mummy, with nothing visible but his head, and sometimes even that is bandaged back tight, so that he may sleep standing.

From the manner in which the tender skull is thus bandaged back it occasionally results that it grows backward and upward at an angle of about 45 degrees. Among the Klamath Lake Indians I have seen a man fifty years old, perhaps, whose forehead was all gone, the head sloping right

---

* Perouse, G. de la. (Voyage Round the World. London, 1799. 8vo. Vol. III.) Description by Dr. Rollin of the manner of swathing infants and of the cradles used by the California Indians (p. 209). Almost the same statement is made of the treatment of infants among the Tartars of the east coast, opposite Saghalien. Their cradles were of basket work, wood or birch bark (p. 237).

† Bancroft. (Native Races of the Pacific States. New York, 1873. Vol. I.) Among the central Californian tribes, "as soon as the child is born" it is washed "and then swaddled from head to foot in strips of soft skin and strapped to a board, which is carried on the mother's back" (p. 391).

‡ Powers, Cont. N. A. Ethnol., III, p. 257.

back on a line with the nose, yet his faculties seemed nowise impaired. The conspicuous painstaking which the Modoc squaw spends on her baby-basket is an index of her maternal love. Indeed the Modoc are strongly attached to their offspring. On the other hand a California squaw often carelessly sets her baby in a deep conical basket, the same in which she carried her household effects, leaving him loose and liable to fall out. If she makes a baby-basket it is totally devoid of ornament, and one tribe, the Mi-woh, contemptuously call it the dog's nest. It is among Indians like these that we hear of infanticide.

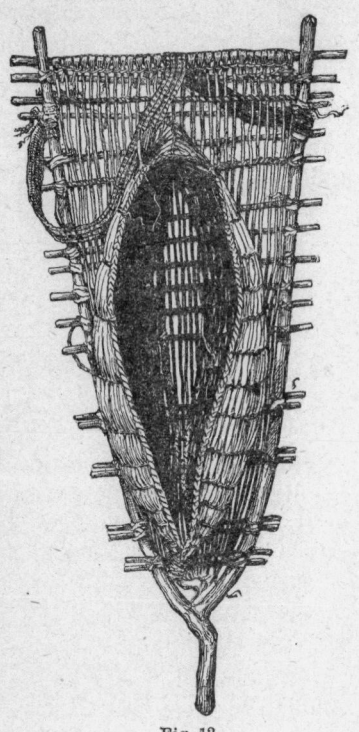

Fig. 12.

KLAMATH CRADLE OF WICKER AND RUSHES.

(Cat. No. 19698, U. S. N. M. Klamath Indians, Tule River, California. Collected by Stephen Powers.)

Fig. 13.

FRAME OF PITT RIVER CRADLE.

(Cat. No. 21411, Round Valley, California. U.S.N.M. Collected by Stephen Powers.)

The cradle of the Pitt River Indians is a transition between the forked stick and the ox-bow type. A pole of wood, with bark removed, is bent in the middle, the two ends crossed and lashed together. Across this primitive frame are laid broad laths, perforated at the corners, and lashed to the poles with buckskin strings (Fig. 13). The foot-rest is a block of wood 7 by 4 by $\frac{3}{4}$ inches, perforated, and through it are passed the two ends of the pole. The convergence of the ends prevents the slipping down of this little platform. Comparing this cradle with one from the vicinity, called a cradle of a new-born pappoose, it will be seen that we have before us two extremes of a series, commencing with a mere tray for an absolutely helpless creature to a standing place for a child just ready to learn to walk. Regarding the cradle in the light of a chrysalis, we discover not only the tiny creature within has passed through wonderful changes, but that the encapsulating cradle has passed from a horizontal to a vertical function. It was first a trough to be firmly lashed in; it ends with being a frame on which the juvenile Indian takes his stand prior to taking his flight into the realm of self-support. Compare this device with the practice of the Pimo and Yuma children of standing upon the mother's cincture and grasping her neck or shoulders. Another Pitt River example is a cradle net or bag, the warp of coarse twine of milkweed fiber laid close together and joined by twined weaving of finer twine, in double rows, an inch and a half apart. Some noteworthy features of this cradle are the following: The whole twining, from beginning to end, seems to be continuous, like plowing a series of double furrows. On the right edge the weaver simply turned and weaved back alongside of the former twine; at the left edge she laid her twine by the side of her warp for an inch and a half, and then turned in for another double row. Indeed, it seems as though the whole cradle were made of one pair of twines. The hood is made by puckering the ends of the warp together and tying them, as with a bag-string. The part over the forehead is formed of a separate set of warp strands. The sun-shade is a round, disk-like structure of twined weaving.

The Potter Valley cradle-trough is made of willow twigs laid closely together and held in place by an ingenious stitching, to be explained further on (Fig. 14).

The head of the cradle is a hoop of wood 1 foot in diameter, quite open. It is fastened to the wicker-work by a continuous coil of twine passing around it and between the willow rods consecutively, being caught over the curious braid that holds the twigs together. In the example described the lashing is cotton string, but in a more primitive form it would be sinew or grass cord. The ends of the twigs are cut off flush with the hoop. The sides and bottom of the cradle are scoop-shaped, with high perpendicular sides, the twigs forming it all terminating at the head hoop.

The rods of the cradle-frame are woven together by a series of braids about 2 inches apart. This braid is so constructed as to resemble two rows of coiled sewing on the inside and a close herring-bone on the outside, and is made as follows: Commence one edge and carry the twine along three osiers, bending to the left, bringing it back two and through to the front, forward two, crossing number one; through, back two, through to front, just over and over, forward three, back two, forward two, back two, ready to start again.

Long leather loops are attached to the bottom of the cradle where it joins the upright sides to receive the lacing-string which holds the baby in place.

The Tule and Tejon cradle-frame consists of three parts: the founda-

tion, which is a forked stick; the cross-bars, lashed beneath, and th
slat of twigs upon which the bed is laid. Some parts of this fram
demand minuter description. The fork is a common twig, not neces
sarily symmetrical, with short handle and prongs nearly 3 feet long
spreading about 16 inches at the distal end or top.

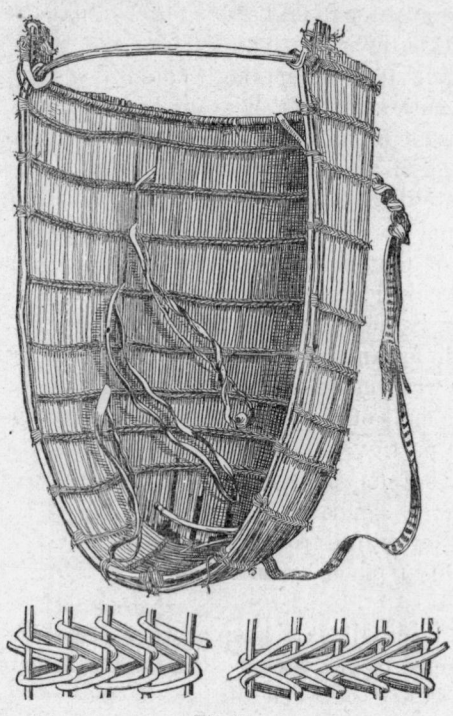

Fig. 14.

POMO CRADLE. THE CHILD SITS IN THE ROUNDED PORTION.

(Cat. No. 21398, U. S. N. M. Potter Valley, California. Collected by Stephen Powers.)

At the back of the fork are lashed seventeen rods of wood, projecting
at their ends an inch or more beyond the fork. The lashing of the rods
to the fork is by means of sinew skillfully crossed both in front and
rear, that is, the seizing is partly parallel and partly cross-laced to give
the strongest joint. These wooden rods seem to follow a rude plan of
pairs, but the design is not apparent. Between the upper pair is a
third rod, whose function is to hold in place the slats in front. The
slat-work or slats on the front consist of a separate transverse rod, to
which about forty twigs are attached by bending the large end of each
one around the rod and then holding the series in place by a row or
two of twined weaving with split twigs. To fasten this crib-work in
place the rod is put behind the two ends of the forked stick, and the
twigs laid in order on the front of the series of transverse rods so as to
fill neatly the space between the forks. These twigs are held in place
by lashing them here and there to the transverse rods and to the side

prongs. This lashing crosses the twigs diagonally in front and the rods behind vertically.

The Mohave cradle-frame is a prettily-made ladder or trellis, built up as follows (Fig. 15): A pole of hard wood about 7 feet long is bent

Fig. 15.

MOHAVE CRADLE, WITH BED OF SHREDDED BARK.

(Cat. No. 24146, U. S. N. M. Colorado River, Arizona. Collected by Edward Palmer.)

in the shape of an ox-bow, the sides 7 inches apart at top and $5\frac{1}{2}$ inches at bottom, so that the cradle is a little narrower at the foot. Eleven cross-bars, like ladder-rounds, connect and strengthen the frame, commencing at the bottom and ending near the bow. These rounds consist each of three elements: a rod or spreader between the two sides; a strap-like binding of two or three split twigs clasping the sides and laid along on the spreader; a seizing of tough twigs holding fast the straps and spreader. The drawing of the reverse side clearly sets forth the manner of administering the light but strong cross-bracing. Upon this ladder is laid the cradle-bed of willow or mezquite bast, made as follows: Three bundles of stripped bast, each about an inch in diameter, are lashed at their middle with bast. They are then doubled together concentrically and spread out to form a bed. On this is laid a little loose, finely-shredded bast like a nest, and the bed is ready for the baby.

A dainty quilt or counterpane of bast is made from strips 30 inches long, doubled and braided at the top like a cincture. This braiding is unique, and so very neatly done as to demand explanation. Two strips of bast are seized about their middle by a single twist of the two elements of twined weaving. Of course two halves will project above and two below the twist. Lay two more strips of bast in the second bight of the twist and draw down the first two upper ends, one to the right of and the other between the second pair of strips, seizing them in place by another half turn of the twines. Lay on a thin pair of bast strips and bring down the second pair of ends projecting upward, as at first. The weaving consists of four movements, namely: Laying in a pair of bast strips, grasping them with a half turn of the two twining wefts, bending down the two upward strips just preceding one between the other outside of the last two strips; and grasping them with a half turn of the twine. The lashing belts of this cradle are twelve to fifteen ply braids, made of red, green, white, and black woolen and cotton cords, braided after the manner of the peculiar type of ornamentation undesignedly originated by braiding with threads of different colors. On this belt of several colors the threads are so arranged as to produce a continuous series of similar triangles, filling the space between two parallel lines by having their bases above and below alternately. Now the gist of the ornamentation is the parallelism of the braiding threads, now to one side of the triangle, and in the next figure running in a direction exactly at right angles. One of the commonest ornaments on the pottery, rude stone, and carved wood is this distribution of lines in triangles.

Of the Pimos, neighbors of the Mohaves, Dr. Palmer says, that on long journeys they use the cradle-board; but as soon as a child is able to stand alone the Pimo mother allows it to mount upon the immense cincture of bark worn on her back and to grasp her around the neck.[*]

The floor of the Yaqui cradle is of the slatteded type, 30 inches long. A dozen or more reeds, such as arrow-shafts are made of, are fastened in the same plane by a dowel-pin. The reeds are not bored for the pins, but simply notched in a primitive fashion. (Fig. 16.)

There is no cradle-trough, but a bed of willow or other bast, shredded, is laid on longitudinally. The pillow consists of a bundle of little splints laid on transversely, at either end of which is a pad of rags. There is no awning; the lashing in this instance is a long cotton rag, taking the place of a leather strap, passing round and round baby and frame, and fastened off in a martingale arrangement, crossing the feet and tied to the lower corners of the cradle. Upon this cradle-rack or frame is fastened the true cradle, which, in this instance, is a strip of coarse mat,

---

[*] Bourke, Capt. J. G.: Speaking of the Umene of the Rio Helay, in 1824, who must have been the Yumas of the Rio Gila, Pattie says: "They contrive to inflict upon their children an artificial deformity. They flatten their heads by pressing a board upon their tender scalps, which they bind fast by a ligature. This board is so large and tight that I have seen women when swimming in the river with their children, towing them after them with a string which they held in their mouth. The little things neither suffered nor complained, but floated behind their mothers like ducks." (Pattie's Narrative, Cincinnati, Ohio, 1833, p. 92.)

made of soft flags, a foot wide, joined by cross-rows of twined weaving 2 inches apart. This mat is bordered by a braid of flags, and the two ends are puckered or drawn to a point. The cradle belongs to the open, unhooded type, and is made by doubling the matting at the head and drawing it together to a point at the foot. The two edges next to the cradle-frame are joined and fastened to the frame, while the outer edge is allowed to flare open. In this little ark of flags or rushes the baby is placed.*

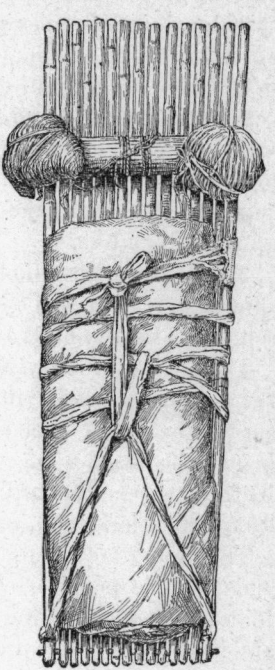

Fig. 16.

YAQUI CRADLE, MADE OF CANES.
SOFT BOSSES USED FOR PILLOWS.

(U. S. N. M.   Sonora, Mexico.   Collected by
Edward Palmer.)

The children of the California peninsula stand and walk before they are a year old. When they are born they are cradled in the shell of a turtle or on the ground. As soon as the child is a few months old, the mother places it perfectly naked astraddle on her shoulders, its legs hanging down on both sides in front. In this guise the mother roves about all day, exposing her helpless charge to the hot rays of the sun and the chilly winds that sweep over the inhospitable country.†

Like her white sister, the Indian mother (to be) in Montana and her friends make preparations for the coming event by collecting cloths, and the board that the child is to pass so many hours of its first year of life on, which, if richly ornamented with beads, otter-skin, and fringes, with bells on them, is worth a good horse, which is generally what is given for the child's board or cradle. This is usually the case when the boy or girl is given and adopted by another mother. So an Indian child has generally two mothers, and of course two fathers, but the father has but little to do with the child till it is old enough to run around.

When the child is born it is taken in charge by its adopted mother, or by a hired woman. It is washed, dried, then greased, and powdered with red ocher, then nursed by some Indian woman or its mother, and wrapped up, with its arms down by its side, in a buffalo-calf skin or shawl or small blanket, and placed in its board or cradle, to be taken

* Acosta, Padre José de. (The Natural and Moral History of the Indies. Ed. Hakluyt Soc. London. 1880. 8vo.) Of the "Chichimecas"—savage mountaineers—he says: "The wives likewise went a hunting with their husbands, leaving their young children in a little panier of reeds, tied to the boughs of a tree." (Vol. II, p. 450.) Head-flattening. (Mexico.) "Las parteras hacen que las criaturas no tengan colodrillos; y las madres las tienen echadas en cunas de tal suerte que no les crezca, porque se precian sin el." (Gómara, Mejico, p. 440.)

† Cradle of Turtle-shell, Low. Cal. Inds., 1773. Baegert, in Smithsonian Rep., 1863, p. 362.

around to its relations' lodges for inspection. Every evening it is taken from its confinement to be washed, painted, and dressed again, and greased. The first cloth over its posterior is laid with a coating of dry pulverized buffalo dung or chips, and this is used as a white woman uses a diaper.

As it grows older it is taken by its mother, placed up in the lodge or outside, while she goes about her work. If the child is restless it is nursed while on the board. After six to eight months of age the child is laid to sleep without the board, and it is generally discarded after a year old, though I have seen Indian boys and girls suckling at five and six years of age. An Indian child, like a white one, is pleased with toys, candy, etc., and their instincts are alike. They cry, laugh, are amused, frightened, and astonished, and as they are born and brought up so do they live.

The board upon which a child is laid is covered with a tanned elk-skin or deer skin, and beads worked on it. The place where the child reposes is loose, and is laced and tied up when the child is placed in it.[*]

The straps for carrying and suspending it are on the opposite side of the board, and in carrying, the strap is brought over the head and placed across the upper part of the breast and across the shoulders. This brings the board upon which the back of the child rests against the back of the mother. The board is one-quarter of an inch thick, from $2\frac{1}{2}$ to 3 feet in length, and $1\frac{1}{2}$ feet in bulge of board.

The Nez Percé Indians belong to the Sahaptian stock, and were once a noble people, dwelling on the Snake River and its affluents in Idaho. They have produced the historical character, Chief Joseph, but are now reduced to an enervated remnant dwelling on the Nez Percé Reservation. The basis of the cradle is a rough board, generally hewn out, 3 feet high, 15 inches wide at the top, and not more than an inch thick. It is shaped somewhat like a tailor's sleeveboard, but is more tapering (Fig. 17). This board is covered with buckskin, drawn perfectly tight upon the back and across the broad part of the front as far down as the hood, or about one-third the length. Below that the two edges of the buckskin form flaps, which meet nearly over the child. Along the edges of these flaps strings are looped, into which loops a lashing cord passes backward and forward to inclose the child tightly in its capsule. On the top of the back a fringe of buckskin strings is formed, either by slitting the buckskin covering itself or by a separate strip sewed on at this point. A little above the center is sewed the head-strap of buckskin, to enable the mother to transport her child or to suspend it when at rest. The hood of the cradle is based upon the flaps of buckskin, but these are entirely concealed by the covering of flannel or other substance. The most ornamented portion of the cradle is the

---

[*] Catlin, George. (Illustrations of the Manners, etc., of the N. American Indians. London. 1876. 8vo. Vol. I.) Head of Crow chief distorted into semi-lunar shape (p. 50).

part above the hood; a piece of flannel or buckskin is covered with bead-work, solid, or has figures wrought upon it in various patterns. To the hood are attached medicine-bags, bits of shell, haliotis perhaps, and the whole artistic genius of the mother is in play to adorn her offspring. After the child is lashed in the cradle, a triangular flap of buckskin, also adorned with bead-work, is tied over the child to the buckskin flaps on either side.

The Spokanes belong to the Salishan stock. They are described by Lewis and Clarke, by Governor Stevens (Rep. Ind. Aff., 1854), and by Winans. Living on the eastern border of the Salish area in Idaho and Washington Territory, their cradles are almost identical with those of the Nez Percés, just described.* Neither of the specimens contains a bed or a pillow, so that we are at a loss as to the effect of the cradle in occipital flattening. But we can be positive as to one thing, that in neither of these examples is there the least provision for intentionally deforming the forehead. The Salish are frequently called Flatheads, but from the example of cradle furnished it seems that they are the

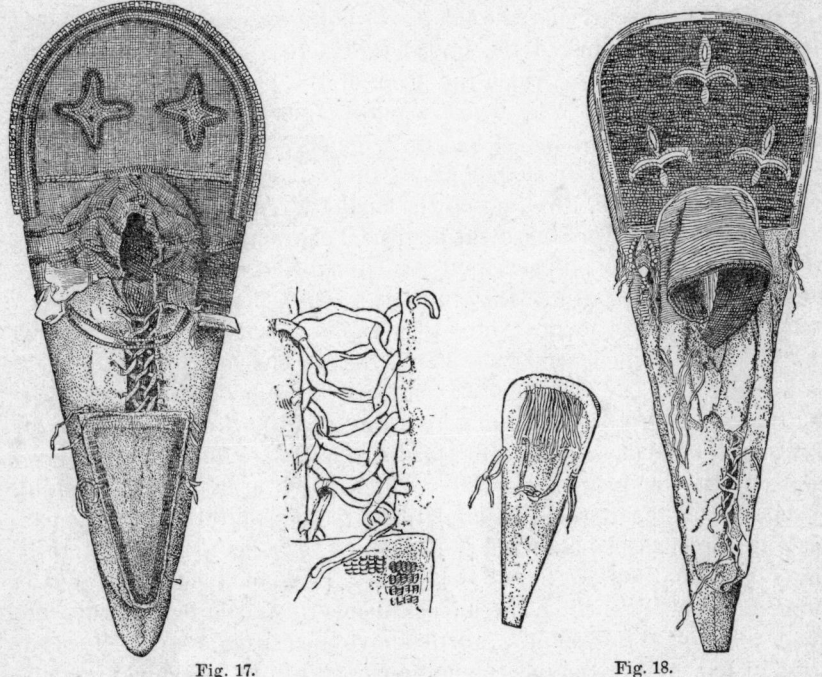

Fig. 17.   Fig. 18.

NEZ PERCÉ CRADLE-BOARD WITH BUCKSKIN SIDES.   SAHAPTIAN CRADLE-BOARD.

(Cat. No. 23845, U. S. N. M. Nez Percé Agency, Idaho. Collected by J. B. Monteith.)   (Cat. No. 129675, U. S. N. M. Spokane Indians, Washingtno. Collected by Mrs. A. C. McBean.)

only coast stock about the Columbia that does not practice intentional flattening. The Museum specimen from the Spokanes is an excellent example of aboriginal work. (Fig. 18.) Everything about it is complete.

* See Fig. 17.

On the back is a long ornamental fringe at top, and lower down both the head-strap and two extra straps at the margin to secure the cradle in other manipulations. The upper portion of the front is covered with bead-work, solid blue ground, with bird-shaped figures in amber and pink beads. On the right side of the hood hangs a long medicine-bag of buckskin, adorned with light-blue beads of large size. A newspaper correspondent from this region mentions a buckskin string upon these cradles in which a knot is tied for every moon of the child's life. There are little buckskin strings in the margin of this cradle near the hood, but no knots have been tied in either of the cradles here described.

In these two, as in many others mentioned in this paper, there is a charming combination of the old and the new. The slab, the buckskin, the medicine-bag, the fringe, the lashing are all pre-Columbian. The beads, the flannel, the cloth lining, etc., are evidently derived materially from the whites. There is no change of structure or function effected by any of these things. They simply replace other materials, such as quill-work, shell-work, native cloth, fur or buckskin, in use before the advent of the whites.

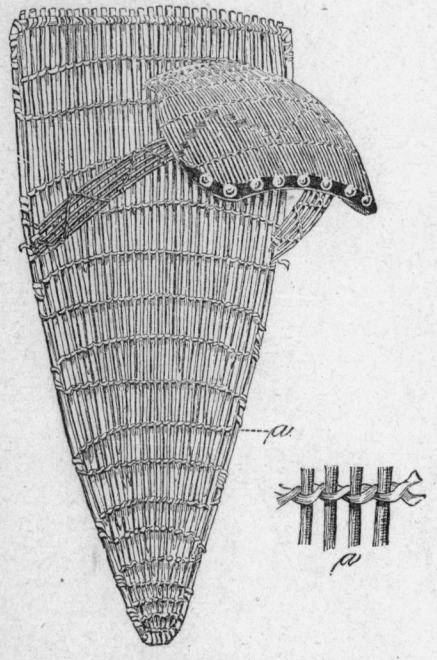

Fig. 19.

NEVADA UTE CRADLE-FRAME: OF RODS, WITH ADJUSTABLE AWNING.

(Cat. No 76734, U. S. N. M. Specimen obtained from the Nevada exhibit at the New Orleans Exposition)

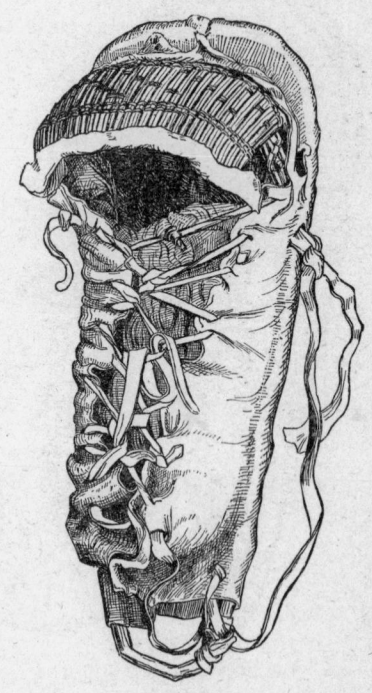

Fig. 20.

NEVADA UTE CRADLE; FULL RIGGED.

(Cat. No. 19040, U. S. N. M. Pyramid Lake, Nevada. Collected by Stephen Powers.)

One of the widest-spread stocks of Indians formerly were the Shoshonians, reaching down the Great Interior Basin throughout its whole extent, crossing the Rockies on the east under the name of Comanches, and in southern California extending quite to the Pacific Ocean. Spread over such a vast territory, the Shoshonian cradle was modified here and there by the nature of things, by the contact of dominant tribes, and by changed habits of life.

The Utes of Pyramid Lake, Nevada, make use of a flat wicker cradle-frame, kite-shaped or roughly triangular. The widening is effected by the intercalation of rods as they are wanted, At the top the rods are held in place by a cross-rod lashed to the ends of the parallel pieces. The twined weaving is characteristic of the Utes in all of their textiles. A pretty addition to the Ute cradle is the delicate awning of light wicker attached by its lower narrow border to the bed-frame and held at the proper angle by means of braces made of the same material (Figs. 19, 20).

Three specimens from this area are in the Museum, showing them as frame and as finished cradles. Indeed, we have only to cover the lattice with buckskin after the manner of those used by the Spokanes and the affair is complete.

In the eastern portion of Utah once dwelt various tribes of Ute Indians. In the National collection is a cradle from this region marked Uncompaghre Utes (Fig. 21). It is an old affair, showing scarcely a

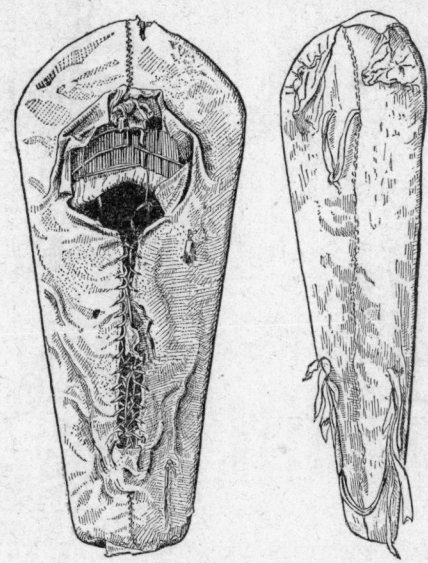

Fig. 21.
UNCOMPAGHRE UTE CRADLE; SHOWING FRONT AND BACK.
(Cat. No. 128342, U. S. N. M. Uncompaghre River, Colorado (?). Collected by Captain Beckwith, U. S. A.)

sign of white contact, excepting a bunch of blue rag over the hood. The cradle is built upon a thin board 4 feet high, 18 inches wide at top, and tapering to half that width at bottom. The covering is of buckskin, seamed on the back, and very clumsily put on. There are two suspension straps, one near the top and the other very low down. On the front the buckskin has loose flaps to inclose the child. The hood or awning is a very curious affair, and if closely drawn down would certainly give to the Uncompaghre child the forehead of a Flathead. It is a kind of tiara, made of little twigs lashed to stronger rods. The lower margin over the child's forehead is bound with soft buckskin The hard cradle-board allies it to the Northern type, where timber is larger, rather than to the pure Ute type, where a hurdle takes the place of the board.

The cradle-frame of the Southern Utes is so well shown in the three drawings presented as not to need very minute description (Figs. 22, 23, 24). The frame-work consists of three parts, the slats, the hoop,

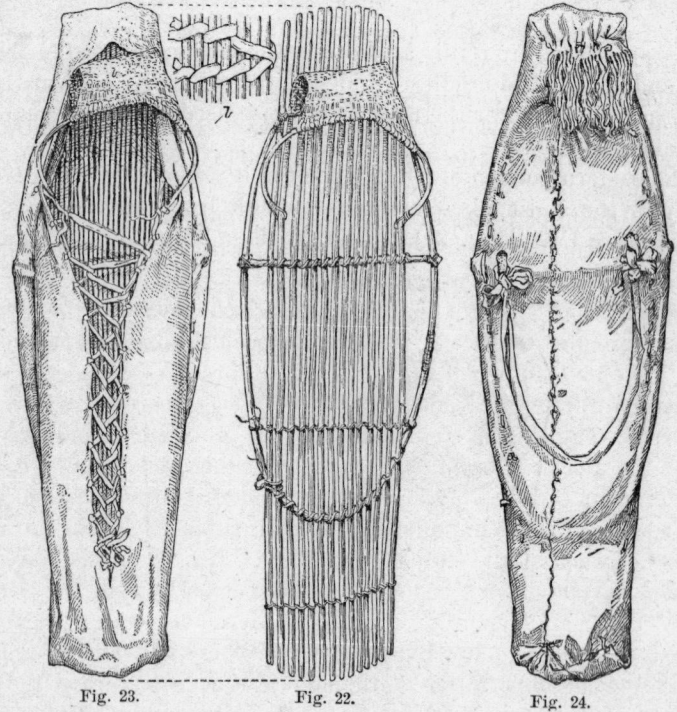

Fig. 23.   Fig. 22.   Fig. 24.

THREE VIEWS OF UTE CRADLE-FRAME, MADE OF RODS AND COVERED WITH DRESSED BUCK-SKIN.

(Cat. No. 14646, U. S. N. M.   Southern Utah.   Collected by Major J. W. Powell.)

and the hood. A dozen twigs like arrow-shafts, 4 feet long, are held in place by here and there a twine of basketry; across the portion to which the ends of the head-band are to be attached a rod is lashed to hold the lattice firmly in place. A hoop of twig, elliptical in form, is lashed to the frame wherever it touches and to the ends of the cross-rod. To the upper border of the hoop is sewed an irregular quadrangular piece of twined basketry weaving. Its outer border is sewed to a rod, which is bent and fastened at its ends to the slats. This forms the awning of the cradle.   We are now ready for the cover, which is formed by a wide piece of the whitest buckskin, wrapped on as in making a bundle, sewed on the back and slit open in front.   The upper portion is cut into the neatest possible fringe.   A broad head-band of soft buckskin completes the outfit.   A specimen from the same locality varies somewhat in detail.

This cradle has the ox-bow frame lathed along the back with twigs close together and held in place by a continuous seizing of sinew. Although a rude affair, this fact is evidently due to the lack of material in a desert country rather than to want of taste in the maker.   The awning for the face is a band of wicker, 4 inches wide, attached by its ends to the side frame of the cradle.   This band is of twined weaving, the weft running boustrophedon.   Notice especially that each half turn of the twine takes in two warp twigs, and that when the weaver turned backward she did not inclose the same pairs of warp twigs, but twined them in quincuncially, creating a mass of elongated rhomboidal openings, exactly as the Aleutian Islanders weave their marvelously fine grass wallets, while the Ute weaving is a model of coarseness in an identical technique.

The head-band of buckskin is not tied immediately to the bowed frame, but is knotted to a loop made of a narrow string, wound three times around the frame and knotted.*

The elements of the Moki cradle-frame are the floor and the awning. As a foundation a stout stick is bent in shape of the ox-yoke bow.   Rods of the size of a lead-pencil are attached to the curve of this bow and stretched parallel to the limbs of the bow.   Twigs are closely woven on this warp by regular basketry weaving.   The Moki are the only savages west of the Rocky Mountains who practice this real wicker weaving. The awning, as the drawing shows, is a band of the same kind of weaving on a warp of twigs in bunches of twos or threes, these last attached to blocks of wood at the ends of the fabric.   The awning is bowed upward and the end blocks lashed to the upper portions of the limbs of the bow.   A small aperture in the floor is for convenience in cleansing. The next figure shows how by using parti-colored and finer twigs, and by a different administration of the middle warp strands and the awning, pretty varieties of the same style of cradle may be effected (Figs. 25. 26).

The Zuñi cradle-board is worthy of our closest study (Fig. 27).   It is founded on a rough piece of board, hewn out to an inch in thickness, 3 feet long, and about a foot wide.   A pillow-rest of wood is fastened so as to steady the head.   This is pegged or nailed down to the board.

---

* Powell, Maj. J.W. (Exploration of the Colorado River. Washington, 1875. 4to).   In Grand Cañon the Indians "make a wicker board by plaiting willows, * * * sew a buckskin cloth to either edge, * * * fulled in the middle, * * * to form a sack," and place the child, wrapped in fur, within this.   There is a wicker shade at the head, and the cradle is slung on the mother's back by a strap passing over the forehead (p 127).

There is no buckskin covering, but a set of loops along the edges serve to accomplish the lashing. The most curious part of the apparatus is a series of four bows or half hoops of equal radius. These are woven to the side of the board, as indicated in the drawing. A string is tied to the top of the board and to each of the hoops at a certain distance, so that when the loose end of the string is pulled the hoops form a "buggy

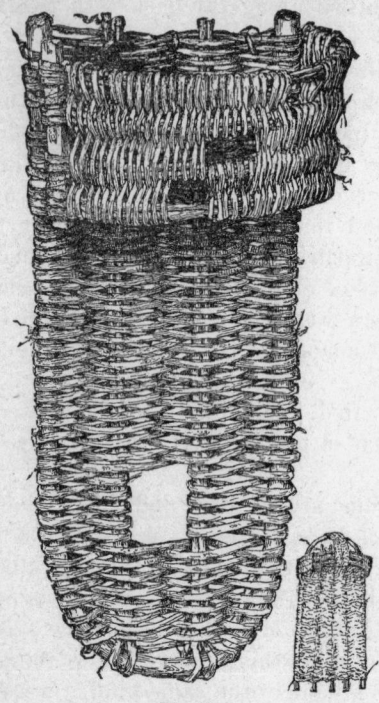

Fig. 25.

MOKI CRADLE-FRAME, OF COARSE WICKER, WITH
AWNING.

(Cat. No. 23154a. Moki Pueblos, Arizona. Collected by Maj.
J. W. Powell.)

Fig. 26.

MOKI CRADLE-FRAME, OF FINE WICKER, RE-
SEMBLING THE SACRED MEAL-TRAY. AWN-
IN : UNIQUE.

(Cat. No. 11789a, U. S. N. M. Moki Pueblos. Arizona.
Collected by Maj. J. W. Powell.)

top," or adjustable hood to the cradle. In no other cradle is the problem more delicate. It depends almost entirely upon the bed to nullify the effects of this cradle. Without examining the heads of Zuñi Indians at all we ought to find the occiput pushed in, flattened, and asymmetrical. Should they prove otherwise, it is right to assume a bed able to counteract this influence.

The Apache Indians of Arizona and New Mexico* make a very elaborate cradle, the substantial part consisting of the frame and the hood. (Fig. 28, *a b*) The frame is elliptical in form, the outline being formed by a pole of wood bent and the two ends spliced and lashed. Upon this ellipse are laid laths of white pine, planed. Over the child's

---

* Bancroft. (Native Races of the Pacific States. New York, 1873. Vol. I.) Among the Apaches of the Lower Colorado the great toe "is widely separated from the others, which arises probably from wading in marshy bottoms" (p. 479).

face is built the hood formed by bending two bows of supple wood to the required shape and overlaying them with transverse laths of pine laid close together and tied down. The upper edges of these laths are beveled, so as to give a pretty effect to the curved surface. The leather-work on the cradle consists of a gable of white buckskin to the hood, a binding of brown buckskin on to the bowed frame above the hood, variegated with narrow bands of white buckskin, and, finally, the true sides or capsule of the cradle, consisting of a strip of soft brown buckskin, say 10 inches wide, cut in a fringe along its lower border and edged with fringe of white buckskin along its upper outer edge. This strip is fastened to the cradle continuously, commencing at an upper margin of the awning, carried along this awning, fastened to its lower margin 4 inches above the junction of the awning and frame, passes on to the foot and around to the other side, as at first. Slits are made in the upper edge of the brown buckskin just below where the white

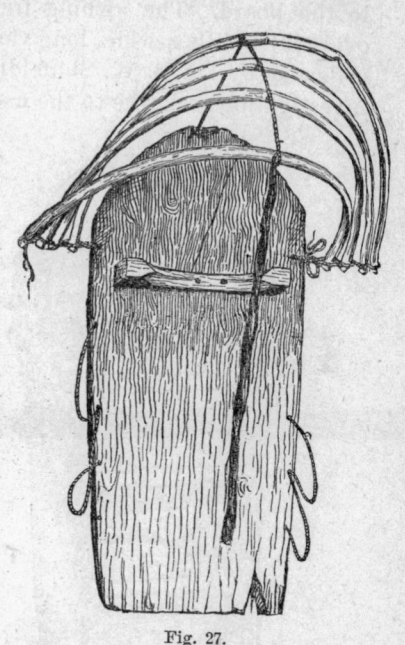

Fig. 27.

ZUÑI CRADLE-FRAME.

(Cat. No. 69015, U. S. N. M. Zuñi Pueblo, New Mexico. Collected by Col. James Stevenson.

buckskin fringe is sewed or run on, and back and forward through these slits a broad soft band of buckskin passes to form the cradle lashing. To perfect the ornamentation of this beautiful object, tassels of buckskin in two colors, and strings of red, white, and blue beads are disposed with great care. Thanks to the generosity of friends living on the frontier, it is possible to reproduce from photographs the method of fastening the child in the cradle. (Fig. 29.) A bed of fur lies between the back of the infant and the floor of the cradle. The head is perfectly loose and free during waking moments. Indeed, there is always free play to the child's head in all cradles except on the Pacific coast around the Columbia River and Puget Sound. Another drawing (Fig. 30) exhibits the method of nursing the babe without removing it from the cradle. Finally, Fig. 31 shows an infant and a small child that have been subjected to the cradle-board.

The cradle-frame of the Navajos is made of two pieces of wood lashed together so as to make the upper end or head in shape like a boot-jack. To the sides of these boards long loops of buckskin are attached to aid in the lashing (Fig. 32). A new feature in western cradles appears in the specimen figured. It is the foot-board, so common in all the Algonkin and Iroquois specimens. The pillow is to be noticed especially, consisting of soft furs and rags rolled up in soft buckskin and fastened to the board. The awning frame is a wide bow of thin, hard wood, over which falls a wide, long vail or flap of buckskin. This cradle was collected by Dr. R. W. Shufeldt, U. S. Army, who kindly made some investigations relative to the use and effect of the Navajo cradle.

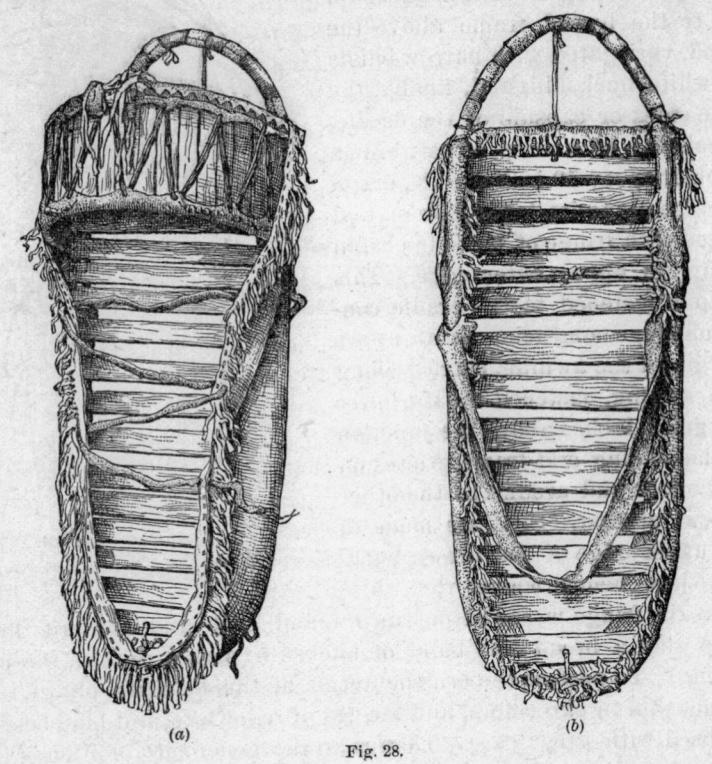

(a)   (b)

Fig. 28.

APACHE CRADLE. FRONT AND BACK VIEW.

(Cat. No. 21523, U. S. N. M. Arizona Territory. Collected by Dr. J. B. White, U. S. A.)

Of some two or three dozen children of all ages from the infant upwards that I have examined I have yet to find a case wherein the Navajo mother has not taken the special precaution to place a soft and ample pad in the cradle to protect the back of the child's head. Moreover, I have yet to see a case, except for a few days or more in the very youngest of babies, where the head is strapped at all. On the other hand, this part of the body is allowed all possible freedom. I am here enabled to present a picture, which shows exactly the method employed by these squaws in both carrying and strapping their babies in the cradle (Fig. 33.)

It will at once be observed that the head of the child is perfectly free, and that it has been supplied with a thick and soft pillow at the back of it, whereas the body and limbs have been strapped up almost to the last degree. This child has light, thin hair, through which the general form of the skull could be easily examined, but after the most careful measurements I failed to detect any flattening of the occipital region of the head.

In examining the full-blooded infants of different ages of this tribe of Indians I occasionally found one wherein I thought I could satisfactorily determine that the back of its head was unduly flattened, but it was by no means always the case.

Another thing must be remembered, and this is that these Navajo women do not always keep their infants thus strapped up in their cradles, and this fact goes to sustain the proposition that whatever pressure is brought to bear against the back of their heads, it is not a constant one. We often see here the little Navajo babies playing about for hours together at a time when they are scarcely able to walk. Among older children I have satisfied myself—as well as I could through their matted hair—that the hinder region of their

Fig. 29.
APACHE WOMAN CARRYING CHILD.
(From photograph.)

heads was flattened, but it never seemed to equal that of the Navajo girl, which I have illustrated in the October number of the Journal of Anatomy.

There can be, I think, no question but that Prof. Sir William Turner is correct in regard to its being not only a distortion but due to pressure, though it would appear from the examinations which I have been able to make that at some time or other the strapping must have been very differently applied. To produce posterior flattening of the skull alone the pressure must be applied only upon that side, and to do this, in order to produce anything like the extraordinarily distorted skull that I have figured in my second paper on this subject, the child would have to have its head against a hard board for a long time and continually kept there. If it were strapped it must be quite obvious that a certain amount of frontal flattening would also be produced, but I have never discovered such a distortion in any of the Navajo skulls.

Now, so far as I have seen, they do not treat their children in this way, but, as I have said, always give them a soft pillow and leave the head free.

Perhaps in former times the strapping of their babies in these cradles was very different from the methods now employed among this tribe, and again, the question of heredity may possibly enter into the subject, or more extended observations may prove that this flattening of the skull only occurs in a certain proportion of the representatives of this race, and not in every individual.

Fig. 30.
APACHE MOTHER NURSING CHILD.
(From photograph.)

Dr. R. W. Shufeldt, U. S. Army, sent to Prof. Sir William Turner, of Edinburgh, a Navajo skull, which is described in the Journal of Anatomy and Physiology, vol. XX, p. 430, as follows: The skull presented a well-marked parieto-occipital flattening, obviously due to artificial pressure, which had been applied so as to cause the suprasquamous part of the occipital bone and the posterior three-fourths of the parietal to slope upwards and forwards. The frontal region did not exhibit any flattening, so that in this individual, and it may be in his tribe of Indians, the pressure applied in infancy was apparently limited to the back of the head. Owing to this artificial distortion the longitudinal diameter of the head was diminished, and the cephalic index 94.6, computed from Dr. Shufeldt's measurements of the length and breadth, was therefore higher than it would have been in an undeformed skull. The cranium was hyperbrachycephalic.

The height of the skull was also very considerable and reached, as may be seen from the table, 115 millimeters; the vertical index was 89, so that the skull was hyperacrocephalic. In all probability the pressure during infancy, which shortened the skull in its antero-posterior direction, forced the vertex upwards and added to the height of the cranium, so that the high vertical index was occasioned both by diminished length and increased height. The skull was cryptozygous, for not only was the breadth in the parietal region great, but the stephanic diameter was 137 millimeters. The glabella was not very prominent, but the su-

Fig. 31.
APACHE MOTHER WITH CHILDREN.
(From photograph.)

praciliary ridges were thick and strong. The bridge of the nose was concave forward, so that the tip projected to the front. The basi-nasal diameter was 105 millimeters; the basi-alveolar 98 millimeters, the gnathic index was 93, and the skull was orthognathic. The nasal spine of the superior maxillæ was moderate. Where the side walls of the anterior nares joined the floor the margin of the opening was rounded. The transverse diameter of the orbit was 40 millimeters, the vertical diameter 36, the orbital index was 90, and the orbit was megaseme. The nasal was 48 millimeters, the nasal width 25, the nasal index was 52, and the nose was mesorhine. The palato-maxillary length was 56, the palato-maxillary width was 72 millimeters; the palato-maxillary index was 128, and the roof of the mouth was brachyuranic. The teeth were all erupted and not worn. The cranial sutures were all unossified.

Fig. 32.

NAVAJO CRADLE: FULL-RIGGED. OF
THE POORER SORT.

From Arizona.

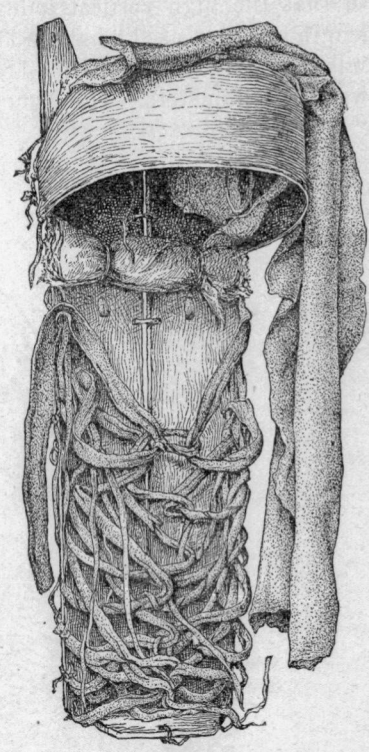

Fig. 33.

NAVAJO CRADLE, WITH WOODEN HOOD AND
AWNING OF DRESSED BUCKSKIN.

Cat. No. 127615, U. S. N. M. Fort Wingate, New Mexico
Collected by Dr. R. W. Shufeldt, U. S. A.)

The parieto-sphenoid suture in the pterion was 19 millimeters in antero-posterior diameter. There were no Wormian bones. The anterior end of the inferior turbinated bone was almost in the same plane as the anterior nares.

The Comanche cradle (6970) is the most primitive cradle in the National Museum (Fig. 34). It is a strip of black bear-skin 30 inches long and 20 wide, doubled together in form of a cradle-frame. Along the side edges loops of buckskin are made to receive the lacing. The loops are formed as follows: A buckskin string is passed through a hole in the bear-skin and the longer end passed through a slit or cut in the shorter end. The long end is then passed through the next hole and drawn until a loop of sufficient size is left; a slit is made in the string near the last hole passed through, and then the whole lashing is drawn through this slit. This serves the purpose of a knot at each hole, as in many other cradles. A foot-piece of bear-skin is sewed in with coarse leather string.*

Governor Stevens (Ind. Aff. Rept., 1854) says the Blackfeet women carry their children in their arms or in a robe behind their backs. When traveling, the children are placed in sacks of skin on the tent poles. I saw no cradle of any form. We have in this mention a parallel to the Comanche type. Note also the use of stiff rawhide as a substitute or antecedent of boards to secure stiffness. The subject will come up again in speaking of the Sioux and other Eastern cradles.

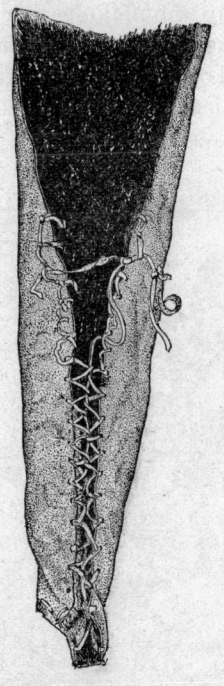 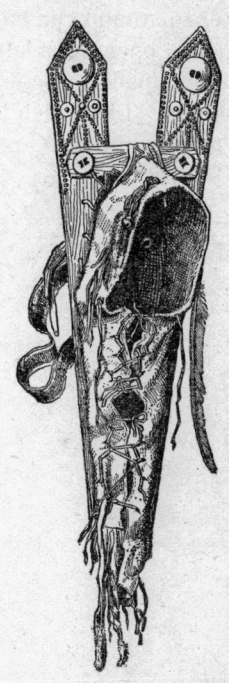

Fig. 34.

COMANCHE CRADLE OF THE RUDEST SORT, MADE OF A STIFF PIECE OF BLACK BEAR-SKIN.

(Cat. No. 6970, U. S. N. M. Texas. Collected by Edward Palmer.)

Fig. 35.

BLACKFEET CRADLE, MADE OF LATTICE-WORK AND LEATHER.

(Cat. No. 6918, U. S. N. M. Texas. Collected by Edward Palmer.)

The frame illustrated by Fig. 35 belongs to the latticed type, and is thus constructed: Two strips of narrow board, often native hewn, wider and further apart at the upper end, are held in place by cross-pieces lashed and apart just the length of the leather cradle sheath. This lashing is very ingeniously done; four holes an inch apart are bored through the frame board and cross-piece at the corners of a square, a string of buckskin is passed backward and forward from hole to hole

---

* Bancroft (Native Races of the Pacific States, N. Y., 1873, vol. I): As soon as a Comanche child is born "it is fastened to a small board by bandages, and so carried for several months on the back of the mother. Later the child rides on the mother's hip, or is carried on her back in a basket or blanket" (pp. 513, 514).

and the two ends tied, or one end is passed through a slit cut in the other. The lashing does not cross the square on either side diagonally. Above the upper cross-piece the frame pieces project a foot and are straightened atop like fence pickets. Disks of German silver and brass-headed nails are used in profusion to form various geometric ornaments; upon the front of the frame, between the cross-pieces, a strip of buffalo hide is sewn, with rawhide string passing through holes bored in with the hair side (the side pieces) towards the cradle-bed.

The inclosing case is a shoe-shaped bag made of a single piece of soft deer-skin lashed together half way on top in the usual manner, and kept open around the face by a stiffening of buffalo leather or rawhide. A small opening is left opposite the penis, and a stiffening piece keeps the bag open at the feet. This case is attached to the frame by thong lashings. Little sleigh bells, bits of leather, feathers, etc., complete the ornamentation (Fig. 36).

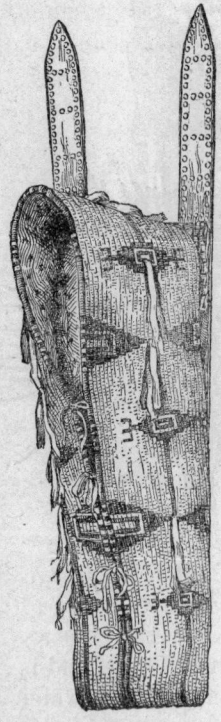

Fig. 36.

OGLALLA SIOUX CRADLE.
Similar to Fig. 35, with
addition of beading.

(Cat. No. 75472. Black Hills, Dakota.)

Fig. 36a.

OGLALLA SIOUX WOMAN.
(From photograph.)

The Sioux cradle is a frame of two diverging slats, painted yellow, held in place at the head and foot by cross-slats, lashed as in the Comanche cradle, with this difference, that the string crosses between the holes diagonally. This is true, but may have no significance. The tops of the side pieces project above the cradle sack at least 18 inches, and are studded with brass-headed nails in straight lines (Figs. 36, 36 *a*). As in the Comanche cradle there is a bottom or mattrass, and a quilt of calico, lined, supplants the buffalo hide. The baby-case is shoe-shaped, the part around the head and shoulders stiffened with a lining of buffalo leather. All over the outside of the baby-case bead-work is laid on in geometric patterns of blue, red, yellow, green, and blue-black on a white ground. The beads are strung on a fine sinew-thread in proper number and color to extend quite across the case. This string is then tacked down at intervals of three-fourths of an inch so regularly as to form continuous creased lines, extending from the foot longitudinally around the baby-case to the foot on the other side. Streamers of colored tape and ribbon take the place of old-fashioned strings, fur, and feathers. The edges of the lower half of the case are joined by four strings tied separately, instead of the universal lashing. There are about this cradle several marks of modification by contact with whites, which show at the same time the tenacity with which old forms remain and the readiness with which they yield to pressure at the points of least resistance, indicating also where the points of least resistance are.

Another specimen of Sioux cradle has the back-board square at top, carved and painted, barrow-shaped, like last, awning-frame bent and painted, covering-cloth decorated with beads. It is tacked around edge of side board, brought up and laced in the middle like a shoe. Model of doll with iron necklace. Length, 28¾ inches; width, 13 inches. Back-board carved on front above; back-brace has large rounded ends; foot-rest low, curved around at bottom; cradle covered over with quill-work in red, white, and black; pattern, lozenges, men, horses, etc.; decorated with iron bells; opening across cradle-cover in middle. (Fig. 37.)

Mr. Catlin thus describes the Sioux cradle, from a specimen in his collection, and the early life of the Sioux infant: "The back-board is wide; wedge-shaped opening made by cutting piece out of top; top is painted and decorated with beads; cradle has bent-wood sides, which make it like a barrow; the head-pad is over the lower part of the wedge-opening; ash awning-frame. The ends of this are fastened to a rod going across the back, by a device, which may be called an ear-mortise. It is held down over rod by an iron dog fastened to side of cradle. Cradle, 29½ inches long, 12 inches wide; length of side board, 2½ inches; height, 4½ inches; height of awning-frame, 14½ inches; width, 16½ inches.

"The custom of carrying the child, among the Mississippi Sioux, is not peculiar to this tribe, but belongs alike to all, as far as I have yet visited them, and also as far as I have been able to learn from travelers who have been amongst tribes that I have not yet seen. The child, in its earliest infancy, has its back lashed to a straight board, being fastened to it by bandages, which pass around it in front, and on the back of the board they are tightened to the necessary degree by lacing-strings, which hold it in a straight and healthy position, with its feet resting on a broad hoop, which passes around the foot of the cradle, and the child's position (as it rides on its mother's back, supported by a broad strap that passes across her forehead), that of standing erect, which, no doubt, has a tendency to produce straight limbs, sound lungs, and long life.

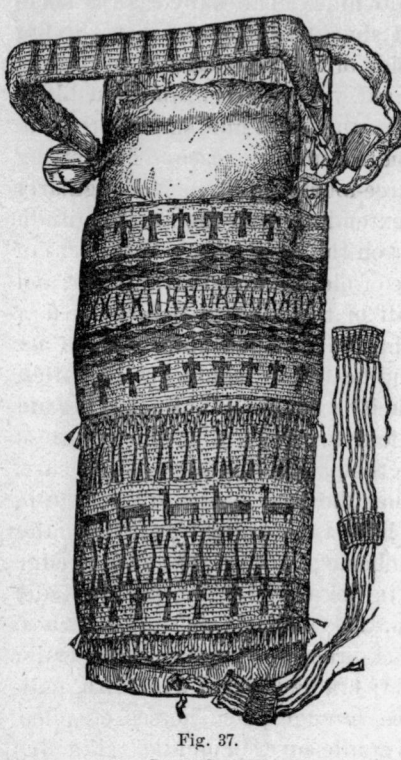

Fig. 37.
SIOUX CRADLE.
(Cat. No. 73311, U. S. N. M. Missouri River. Collected by George Catlin.)

"In plate 232, letter *d*, is a correct drawing of a Sioux cradle, which is in my collection, and was purchased from a Sioux woman's back, as she was carrying her infant in it, as is seen in letter *e* of the same plate.

"In this instance, as is often the case, the bandages that pass around the cradle, holding the child in, are all the way covered with a beautiful embroidery of porcupine quills, with ingenious figures of horses, men, etc. A broad hoop of elastic wood passes around in front of the child's face to protect it in case of a fall, from the front of which is suspended a little toy of exquisite embroidery for the child to handle and amuse itself with. To this and other little trinkets hanging in front of it there are attached many little tinseled and tinkling things of the brightest colors to amuse both the eyes and the ears of the child. While traveling on horseback the arms of the child are fastened under the bandages, so as not to be endangered if the cradle falls, and when at rest they are generally taken out, allowing the infant to reach and amuse itself with the little toys and trinkets that are placed before it and within its reach.

"The infant is carried in this manner until it is five, six, or seven months old, after which it is carried on the back in the manner represented in two of the figures of the same plate, and held within the folds of the robe or blanket.

"The modes of carrying the infant when riding are also here shown, and the manner in which the women ride, which, amongst all the tribes, is astride, in the same manner as that practiced by the men.

"Letter *b*, in the same plate, is a mourning cradle, and opens to the view of the reader another very curious and interesting custom. If the infant dies during the time that is allotted to it to be carried in this cradle, it is buried, and the disconsolate mother fills the cradle with black quills and feathers in the parts which the child's body had occupied, and in this way carries it around with her wherever she goes, for a year or more, with as much care as if her infant were alive and in it, and she often lays or stands it leaning against the side of the wigwam, where she is all day engaged in her needlework, and chatting and talking to it as familiarly and affectionately as if it were her loved infant, instead of its shell, that she was talking to. So lasting and so strong is the affection of these women for the lost child that it matters not how heavy or cruel their load or how rugged the route they have to pass over, they will faithfully carry this, and carefully, from day to day, and even more strictly perform their duties to it than if the child were alive and in it.

"In the little toy that I have mentioned, and which is suspended before the child's face, is carefully and superstitiously preserved the umbilicus, which is always secured at the time of its birth, and, being rolled up into a little wad of the size of a pea and dried, it is inclosed in the center of this little bag and placed before the child's face, as its protector and its security for " good luck " and long life.

"Letter *c*, same plate, exhibits a number of forms and different tastes of these little toys, which I have purchased from the women, which they were very willing to sell for a trifling present; but in every instance they cut them open and removed from within a bunch of cotton or moss, the little sacred medicine, which to part with would be to endanger the health of the child, a thing that no consideration would have induced them in any instance to have done."*   (Pages 130–132, vol. II, Catlin's Eight Years).

---

* Long, Maj. S. H. (Expedition to the Sources of the St. Peter's River. Philadelphia. 1824. 8vo.) Among the Pottawatomie great care is taken that the body shall be straight and well formed; no attempt   *   *   *   is made to change the shape of the head, "this being regarded as having a tribal significance" (vol. I, p. 100). On the Cottonwood River, Long saw an old Pottawatomie chief with "a child-board on his back, in which he carried his little grandson" (vol. I, p. 178). The child was naked (p. 179). Of the Dacotah, Long or Keating, who compiled and edited his notes, says: "The practice of shaping the heads of infants is unknown to them" (vol. I, p. 404).

Charlevoix, Pére de. (Journal of a Voyage to North America. London. 1761. 8vo.) The Têtes de Boule (Roundheads), an Algonquin tribe north of Montreal, "have their name from the roundness of their heads; they think there is a great beauty in this figure, and it is very probable the mothers give it to their children while in the cradle" (vol. I, Letter XI, p. 285). Speaking of the fine figures of the "Indians of Canada," Charlevoix says that one reason for this is, that "their bodies are not constrained in the cradle" (vol. II, Letter XXI, p. 79). Just after (p. 120) he describes the ornamentation of "their children's cradles" among the Hurons.

Lahontan, Baron. (New Voyages to North America. London. 1735, 2d ed. 8vo.) These observations were made upon the Algonkian and Iroquoian tribes of the St. Lawrence and the Lakes in the latter part of the seventeenth century. Like Hearne, he says: "There is no such thing as a cradle among the savages" (vol. II, p. 7); but he adds that "the mothers make use of certain little boards, stuffed with cotton, upon

East of the Mississippi River, north of the Tennessee and the North Carolina line, and south of Hudson Bay lived Algonkin and Iroquois stocks, and all of them used a flat cradle-board, not far from 2½ feet long, 10 inches wide, and one-half inch thick, tapering wider at the head. The St. Regis Iroquois, in the north of New York and near the Canada line, have for many years bought their cradle-boards from the whites or made them of material bought from a white man (Figs. 39, 40). The specimen illustrated has the back carved in flowers and birds, and painted blue, red, green, and yellow. The cleat at the upper end of the back is a modern chair-round. The foot-board is a small shelf or bracket. on which the child's feet rest.

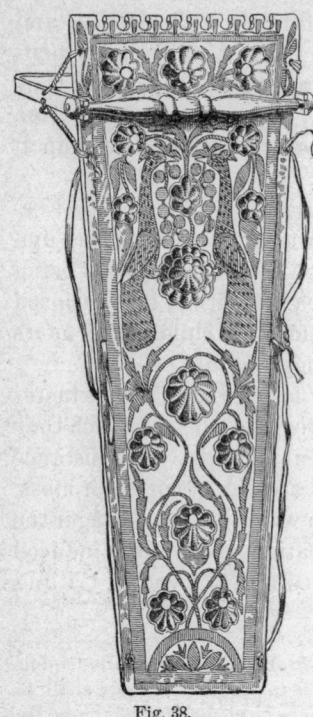

Fig. 38.

IROQUOIS CRADLE. BACK VIEW.

(Cat. No. 18006, U. S. N. M. St. Regis, New York. Collected by R. B. Hough.)

An interesting relic of savagery on this quite civilized cradle are the notches in the awning-bow, falling down over the ends of the cleat, extended and held in place by braces of leather thong. The hoop serves many functions, such as support for sunshade, rain protector, mosquito net, ornaments, dangling trinkets to please the child, etc.

18006. Cradle back-board, carved in peacocks, and painted bright colors. Square at top. Awning frame mortised at ends, which allow them to slide over awning-bar. Held down and guyed by stays on opposite side. Has a movable foot-rest at bottom. Thongs along sides for lashing baby in. Length, 29¼ inches; width, top, 10½ inches; bottom, 8⅝ inches. Foot-rest, height, 3½ inches; width, 6 inches. (Fig. 38.)

The following notes regarding the Indians east of the Mississippi River have been collected in the course of the author's reading, and are here appended to throw additional light upon the subject:

Heriot, G. (Travels through the Canadas. London, 1807. 4to.) "The use of a pillow is known to but a few" among the Iroquois tribes. Having seen that article in use, they imitate it "with a billet of wood, with a mat rolled up, or with skins stuffed with hair (p. 287).

---

which the children lie as if their backs were glued to them, being swaddled in linnen and kept on with swath bands run through the sides of the boards. To these boards they tie strings, by which they hang their children on the branches of trees" (vol. II, p. 7). "As soon as their children come into the world they dip them in warm water up to the chin." The Dacotahs, Aleutian Islanders, etc., use cold water. "After this they swathe them down upon little boards or planks, stuffed with cotton, where they lie upon their backs" (vol. II, p. 43).

Jefferys, T. (Nat. and Civil Hist. of French Dominions in North and South America, London, 1760, fol.), says of Algonkian Têtes de Boul: "The Round-Heads * * * take their name from the figure of their heads. * * * It is believed that the mothers * * * form the heads of the children into this shape when they are in the cradle" (part I, p. 47).

Liancourt, Duke de. (Travels through the United States, etc. London, 1799. 4to.) Very much the same account as that of Weld, etc., is given by this traveler of the cradle-board used by the Iroquois tribes. He says, however, that "suckling children are generally suspended in a basket fastened to the ceiling" (vol. I, p. 177).

Weld, I. (Travels through North America and Canada. London. 1799. 4to.) As the result of general observation of the tribes of Canada and the Lakes, he says that "an Indian child, soon after it is born, is swathed with cloths or *skins* (*vide* Long, Notes), laid on its back, and bound down on a piece of thick board, spread with soft moss." Hoops protect the face. The cradle-board is suspended on the mother's back when traveling, otherwise hung by the head-strap. Infants are also put in hammocks, and when able to crawl are released from the cradle-board (p. 387).

"Their infants are borne with haire on their heads, and are of complexion white as our nation, but their mothers in their infancy make a bath of Walnut leaves, huskes of Walnuts and such things as will stain their skinne for ever, wherein they did & washe them to make them tawny. The coloure of their haire is black & their eyes black."

· NOTE.—The idea that the Indian was born white was very commonly entertained in the first half of the seventeenth century. Lechford, in his " Plaine Dealing," p. 50, says: "They are of complexion swarthy & tawny. Their children are borne white, but they bedaube them with oyle & colours presently." Josselyn also speaks of the Indians "dying their children with a liquor of boiled Hemlock-Bark." (Two Voyages, p. 128.) Speaking of the Virginia women Smith says: " To make their children hardie in the coldest mornings they them wash in the rivers, & by paynting & oyntments so tanne their skinnes that after a year or two no weather will hurt them." (True, Travels, vol. I, p. 131.) Strachey gives a more particular account of the supposed process: "The Indians are generally of a cullour browne or rather tawny, which they cast themselves into with a kind of arsenic stone, & of the same hue are their women, howbeit yt is supposed neither of them naturally borne so discolored; for Capt. Smith (lyving somtymes amongst them) affirmeth how they are from the womb indifferent white, but as the men, so doe the women dye & disguise themselves into this tawny cowler, esteeming yt the best beauty to be neerest such a kynd of murrey as a sodden quince is of (to liken yt to the neerest coulor I can), for which they daily anoint both face & bodyes all over with such a kind of fucus or unguent as can cast them into that stayne." (Historie, 63.) ("New English Canaan." Prince Soc. Boston, 1883, p. 147.)

"These infants are carried at their mothers' backs by the help of a cradle made of a board forket at both ends whereon the childe is fast bound and wrapped in furres; his knees thrust up towards his bellie, because they may be the more usefull for them when he sitteth, which is as a dogge does on his bumme; and this cradle surely preserves them better than the cradles of our nation, for as much as we find them well proportioned, not any of them crooked backed or wry legged; and to give their charracter in a worde, they are as proper men and women for feature and limbs as can be found, for flesh and blood as active." ("New English Canaan." Prince Soc. Boston, 1883, p. 147.)

The Choktah flatten their foreheads with a bag of sand, which with great care they keep fastened on the skull of the infant while it is in its tender and imperfect state. Thus they quite deform their face and give themselves an appearance which is disagreeable to any but those of their own likeness.* (Adair's American Indians, p. 284.)

"The Indians flatten their heads in divers forms, but it is chiefly the crown of the head they depress in order to beautify themselves, as their wild fancy terms it, for they call us long heads by way of contempt. The Choktah Indians flatten their foreheads from the top of the head to the eye-brows with a small bag of sand, which gives them a hideous appearance, as the forehead naturally shoots upward, according as it is flattened, thus, the rising of the nose, instead of being equidistant from the beginning of the chin to that of the hair is, by their wild mechanism, placed a great deal nearer to the one and farther from the other. The Indian nations round South Carolina and all the way to New Mexico (properly called Mechiko), to effect this, fix the tender infant on a kind of cradle, where his feet are tilted above a foot higher than a horizontal position, his head bends back into a hole made on purpose to receive it, where he bears the chief part of his weight on the crown of the head upon a small bag of sand, without being in the least able to move himself. The skull, resembling a fine cartilaginous substance, in its infant state, is capable of taking any impression. By this pressure, and their thus flattening the crown of the head, they consequently make their heads thick and their faces broad, for when the smooth channel of

---

*Volney, C. F. (A View of the Soil and Climate of the United States of America. Philadelphia, 1804. 8 vo.) It is "the custom of the Choctaws to mould the skull of their new-born children to the shape of a truncated pyramid, by pressing them between boards. This method is so effectual that the tribe is known by the name of the Flat-Heads" (p. 365). Among the tribes near the head of the Wabash, "Weeaws, Payories, Sawkies, Pyankishaws, and Miamis, * * * the females * * * carry one or two children behind them in a sort of bag, the ends of which are tied upon their forehead. In this respect they have a strong resemblance to our [the French] gypsies" (p. 353).

Bartram, William. (Travels through North and South Carolina, Georgia, Florida, etc. London, 1794. 2d ed., 8vo.) "The Choctaws are called by the traders Flats or Flat-Heads, all the males having the fore and hind parts of their skulls artificially flattened or compressed" (p. 515). The infant is placed "in a wooden case," on its back, "a bag of sand being laid on the forehead, which, by continual gentle compression," causes the head to slope "off backwards * * * from the temples upwards." The occiput is received in a concavity "fashioned like a brick-mould" (p. 515).

Heriot, G. (Travels through the Canadas. London, 1807. 4to.) "Some of the tribes of Louisiana flatten the forehead of their children, and cause the summit to terminate in a point. * * * Beauty, in their conception, consists in moulding the head to a round form" (p. 348).

nature is stopped in one place, if a destruction of the whole system doth not thereby ensue, it breaks out in a proportional redundancy in another. May we not to this custom, and as a necessary effect of this cause, attribute their fickle, wild, and cruel tempers? Especially, when we connect therewith both a false education and great exercise to agitate their animal spirits. When the brain, in cooler people, is disturbed, it neither reasons nor determines with proper judgment. The Indians thus look on everything around them through their own false medium, and vilify our heads because they have given a wrong turn to their own." (Adair's American Indians, p. 8.)

Lafitau* speaks as follows concerning the Southern Indian cradle:

"The cradle for the savage children in New France is made throughout pretty and roomy. It consists of one or two very thin planks of light wood, 2½ feet long, ornamented on the edges and rounded at the foot, to give convenience of cradling. The child enveloped in fine fur is as though glued to the united planks, and is placed standing up in a way that it shall hang over a little ledge of wood where its feet are, the point turned under for fear lest they should get hurt, and in order that it should hold the fold by which it is necessary to carry the frame. The swaddling-clothes or furs are held up in front by large bands of painted skin, which does not stretch much, and which are passed and repassed in the small loops of tough skin which hang from the sides of the cradle, where they are firmly fastened. They let these swaddling-clothes hang considerably below the cradle, and they throw them behind when they wish to go walking with the child, or let them fall over a half circle, which is fastened to the planks near the head of the child, and which can be made to turn forwards in order that the child can breathe freely without being exposed to the cold of winter or to the stings of mosquitos or gnats in summer, and in order that it should not receive injury if the cradle fell. They put over that half circle little bracelets of porcelain and other little trifles that the Latins call *crepundia*, which serve as an ornament and as playthings to divert the child. Two large lengths of strong leather, which come out from the cradle at the head, enable the mother to carry it everywhere with her, and to fasten below all their other bundles, when they go to the fields, and to suspend to some branch of a tree, where cradled and soothed to sleep by the wind, while she works.

"The children are very warm in the cradle and very easy, for besides the furs, which are very soft, they put much down taken from the calamus (cat-tail, rush?), which they stuff in a wad, or perhaps the pounded bark of the peruche (birch?), with which the women scour their hair to invigorate it. They are also very careful so that it can not soil their furs; by means of a little skin or a rag which they pass between their thighs, which hangs out over the fore part, they can attend to their

---

*Moeurs des Sauvages Ameriquains, vol. I, p. 597.

natural needs without the inside being wet or soiled, except the down, which is easily replaced with new.

"Some nations in Louisiana, to whom the French have given the name of flat heads, * * * have a groove practically in their cradle, in which the mother puts the child's head; she applies on the front and back of the head a mass of clay which binds and bears down with all force. She cradles the child all the time until its head has taken its shape, and when the sutures of the head have taken consistency. The children suffer extremely, become almost black; a white and viscous liquor comes from the eyes, nose, and ears; they suffer much more from the uneasy situation, where they are forced to pass all the time during the first months of their infancy, but it is the cost of becoming beautiful by art and the suffering to get that charm which nature refuses.

"The Caribs and most of the Southern Indians have also flattened foreheads and pointed heads. Their mothers fasten the head down with little boards and pads of cotton bound stron_ ¹⁻ ʰᵃᵒᵏ of the head.

"The child has no other cradle but a hammock proportioneu ꝏ their height in which the mothers can suspend them and transport them very commodiously, and where the children are cradled all naked, without any pain from confinement.

"The Indians, which are called in Canada (le gens de Terres) *Garhagonronnon*, have a different taste from the Flatheads, for their beauty consists in having a round head; thence they are called 'Bullet Heads'" (pp. 593, 597).

"The first years the child is kept all naked in the cabin to keep its body from being injured by the air. When larger it works for the family. They carry water and little billets of wood; this they regard as sport. Up to puberty they neglect their person; no ornaments are worn until they are enrolled in the body of young men. They are educated like Spartans" (p. 597).

"Women strong and robust but are not prolific. The *enceinte* woman does not take care of herself; she carries heavy burdens and works harder as she approaches her time. They say this violent exercise facilitates their parturition and makes the child more robust. No one can deny that they do bring forth with surprising ease. If caught in labor away from the cabin they attend to themselves, and are apparently able to do their regular work the same day" (pp. 590, 591).

"They do suffer and die sometimes, but they bear their pain with such fortitude that they do not seem to suffer" (p. 592).

"Some Southern Indians think if the women do not bear their pain with fortitude the children will inherit their weakness, and they kill those children that are born of such a mother. They kill the mother of a still-born child, and also sacrifice one of twins, because one mother is not enough for two children" (p. 592).

"The Indians will not give their children to others to bring up. If it happens that the mother dies while the child is yet in the cradle, it is brought up in the family, and what appears strange, old grandmothers, who have passed the age of having children, have their milk return to them, and take the place of the mother. Indians love their children with an extreme passion, and although they do not show their affection by lively caresses, as do the Europeans, their tenderness is, however, not less real. They suckle their children as long as they are able, and do not wean them but from necessity. I have seen children three or four years old taking milk with their younger brothers" (p. 593).

In South America the same custom seems to obtain that we have seen in North America, namely, in the tropics the carrying of children in the shawl or sash, and bedding it in the hammock; while in the colder regions the cradle-frame appears. Frames corresponding to some in North America are found in Peru. Simon de Schryver, in his Royaume d'Araucanie-Patagonie (1887), figures at page 21 an Araucanian woman carrying a child in a frame (Fig. 39), which seems to be nothing more

Fig. 39.
ARAUCANIAN WOMAN CARRYING CHILD.
(From Simon de Schryver's "Royaume d'Araucanie-Patagonie.")

than a short ladder, with cross-bars. On this frame the child is lashed, the head being perfectly free, except that the lower part of the occiput rests against the top cross-bar, as in the case of the Polynesian pillow. In addition to her living freight the woman carries in front a bag of provisions suspended by a cord depending from the head-strap at its junction with the cradle-frame.

Fig. 40.
TURKISH GYPSY CARRYING A CHILD IN PEDDLER'S PACK.
(From photograph in U. S. N. M.)

A feature in the weaving of the Patagonian wallet is worthy of attention, although its description would be better in a paper on weaving. There is in the National Museum a game-bag from Mackenzie River, and another from Kodiak, made of exceedingly fine babbiche or buckskin cut into string. The weaving is effected by means of an endless chain of half-hitches, each loop caught into loop below. In Central America, everywhere, thousands of open net-work bags of all sizes are made from the pita fiber, the strings of which loop in the same manner. In Peru the same stitch occurs, and now from Patagonia and Tierra del Fuego we receive examples of the same method of weaving.

Fig. 41.

OSTJAK "BABY-JUMPER."

(From Seebohm's "Siberia in Asia.")

The insertion of a rod or a bundle of rushes serves to convert the open net-work bag into a water-tight wallet or a rigid basket.

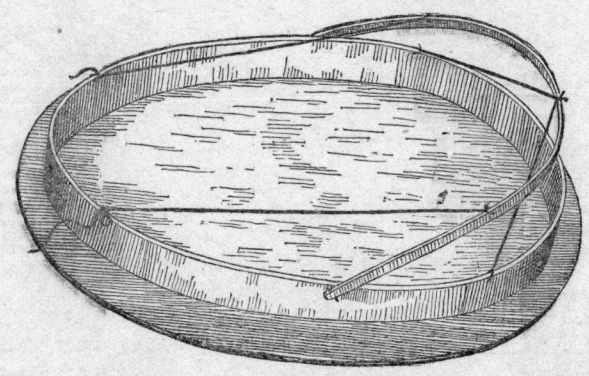

Fig. 42.

OSTJAK CRADLE.

(From Seebohm's "Siberia in Asia.")

Another method of carrying children is shown in Fig. 40. The woman the rerepresented is a Turkish Gypsy, and the child has been placed in a peddler's pack for convenience of carrying.

The resources of the Museum do not justify anything like an exhaustive treatment of the eastern continent. In the three figures shown (Figs. 43, 44, 45) we see the Northern device, in which the safety of the child from cold is the main source of anxiety. The Japanese mother is concerned partly with temperature and partly with transportation. The African mother consults transportation alone. There is nothing in the ordinary treatment of the child to occasion a deformity of the cranium. Any change of the shape of the head must be attributed to congenital causes or to custom.

Fig. 43.
APACHE SQUAW CARRYING A CHILD.
(From photograph in U. S. N. M.)

Fig. 44.
JAPANESE WOMAN CARRYING A CHILD.
(From Racinet's "Le Costume.")

Fig. 45.
AFRICAN WOMAN CARRYING A CHILD.
(From photograph in U. S. N. M.)

NOTES ON THE ARTIFICIAL DEFORMATION OF CHILDREN AMONG SAVAGE AND CIVILIZED PEOPLES.

[WITH A BIBLIOGRAPHY.]

By Dr. J. H. PORTER.

The accompanying notes are collected from various sources as a supplement to Professor Mason's paper on " The Cradles of the American Aborigines."* The time allotted did not permit the compiler to exhaust the subject, but enough is here given to show the practices concerning children in their first year throughout the world, and the varied beliefs obtaining as to the effects of such treatment. In the future the subject will receive more careful and systematic study.

The author embraces this opportunity to express his obligation to the librarians of the State, War, and Navy Departments at Washington for many courtesies.

Intentional modifications of the form of the head, although less general than other fashions by which conformity to an ideal of beauty has been attemped, have, nevertheless, been widely prevalent among races of men, but can not be said to include all the variations from an average cranial type actually existing in nature. The ethnical classification of M. Topinard (Éléments d'Anthropologie Générale) displays deformation with reference to race in a manner which fulfills all practical requirements. Deformity is, however, as real when slight as when excessive, and apart from those distortions he has described, from the many which are due to pathological causes, and the yet more numerous deviations from symmetry which unintentionally exerted pressure produces in the incompletely ossified skull, there still remain those variations in the processes of nutrition and growth through which assymetry becomes the rule not in the head and not in man only, but in the homologous parts of all axially developed animals.

As a matter of fact, and exclusive of the embryological identity of their elements, an ideal head is no more demonstrable than an ideal vertebra; and whatever may be hereafter accomplished, at present the anatomical and physiological constants of neither can be determined in detail. It therefore appears to be inexact to speak of the deformities of an organ whose conformation has not been distinctly ascertained. In addition to this, only a small portion of mankind have arrived at any common judgment on the subject of cranial contour, and wherever a standard is furnished by such a consensus of opinion, this is derived from art and not from science. Both empirical knowledge and physiological principles justify the general conclusion that the artistic form is that which is usually associated with superior brain power ; but it does not at all follow that an alteration of outline that would destroy the former would similarly affect the latter. Such facts undoubtedly dis-

---

* Most of the bigliography relating to the artificial deformation of children in North America is embodied in Professor Mason's work.

parage alike the methods and the results of anthropological research in certain directions, but they neither obviate the necessity of initiating further study from existing information, nor impugn its value as a whole.

In considering the natural history of the human head, account must be taken of the fact that man, while not alone in this respect, is nevertheless an execedingly aberrant form among the Mammalia. On any theory of life, however, except that of special creation, and independently of conflicting estimates of the systematic implications of structure, the organization of this most highly specialized being must be regarded as the outcome of descent, with modification, and should therefore be considered in connection with that of the groups to which man is affiliated.

As has been said, there is no absolute form for the head or for the vertebræ of which it is composed, and the fact that all classifications resting upon its features have failed, does not encourage the hope that the results sought through craniometry will be attained by means of its descriptive anatomy. All that can be properly affirmed is, that during the immemorial series of adjustments by which the mammals culminated in man, and in which evolutional changes of all orders are included, the human head assumed an incompletely distinctive form, which is, both in itself and in the causes which determine its variations, more or less clearly revealed in the tribal history of mankind. The statement that the anthropoid head becomes less human with development has been generally united with the assumption that this implies important generic differences between them, and if the observation were true in the sense in which it is for the most part understood, it would do so. Its special significance is, however, detracted from by the general truth that in zoology the rule is that, for obvious reasons, young creatures are less differentiated than those which are mature; while, on the other hand, the difficulty of discriminating between the adult brains of some of the higher apes and those of certain savages, may be considered as qualifying the former assertion to so great a degree as to suggest error, or at least inexactness, in the observation. No doubt the mistake is partially attributable to misconceptions arising from an idea of the fixity of species, but in itself, the error is involved in all comparisons between unlike things. To found a parallel upon the external tables of the skull, as if these were equally characteristic and similarly developed in a gorilla and a man, is to include in the terms dissimilar elements, and thereby vitiate the comparison. The contours of the head in these instances are differently related, and, considering the plates of the skull especially, the external table of the ape's cranium is much more prominently associated with the muscular apparatus than is the case with man, in whom the subordination of the entire head to the encephalon is exceptional. This is but a single illustration of the general fact that throughout the vertebrate class the cranium proper, amid innumerable subordinate variations, assumes the more specialized character of a brain-case as we ascend in the organic scale. In fishes, where the head contains other organs than those of the nervous system, its indefinite relations to the cerebro-spinal axis are conspicuous. Among the Reptilia, though containing only the brain, the extreme disproportion between the head and its contents indicates that its conformity with the cerebral ganglia is subsidiary to other conformities; while in birds the limited range of the cranial cavity, as contrasted with its range when compared with the bulk of the body, conveys in a modified form the implication of increasing specialization of the head. As might be expected, the anatomical evidence furnished by the Mammalia is corroborative of that derived from lower groups. No variation, however extreme, is competent to free a structure from the influence of heredity, and it might be argued *a priori* that the human head would have the outlines of its history delineated in the morphology of the primates.

The facts in this instance justify the anticipation. As in the developmental record of birds, among which the ornithic stamp, either general or special, is but gradually and indirectly evolved, so also with the more immediate congeners of man, where the more salient characteristics of his type, distributed throughout a group of anthropoids, do not admit of consecutive arrangement, and can not be attributed in their totality to any specific form. From the primates, as from the other mammalian sub-classes, a cranial figure involved in the metameric development of the encephalon, gradually disengages itself and becomes more regular and more definite in its cerebral relations as the grade of organization is elevated; so that the profiles associated with ganglionic mass increase in prominence, while those which are otherwise associated correspondingly diminish.

These anatomical traits link themselves naturally with physiological co-ordinates. Everywhere encephalic structure is related, though not directly, to function. Enhanced importance in the brain implicates increased solidarity in the entire organism. As the cerebral elements grow in multiplicity, variety, and complexity, this development is concomitant with cranial amalgamation, with progressive obliteration of the features attaching to lower forms, with condensation of the encephalic ganglia, with a more direct correspondence between the skull and brain, and finally with a greater conformity of the body with the head.

Whatever phylogenetic significance may be found in these facts, their morphological and physiological bearing is unmistakable. Through quite various structural gradations there appears, though not in linear sequence, "a series of forms," which ultimately display in modifications of cranial contour a more definite coaptation of the envelope to its contained viscus in developmental progress, and in the falling away and weakening of its muscular attachments, the paramount function of the skull as a brain-case, and the subordination of its structure to that of the organ which it incloses.

It is not necessary here to consider the elements which compose organic form or the conditions that determine their arrangement. The process, so far as the head is concerned, has been, to a great extent, masked among the vertebrates by adaptation to other than encephalic relations, while the part was carried through the cartilaginous, semiosseous, unamalgamated, and consolidated types of crania, to one which, as representative of the most important organ in the body, has been commonly selected by the anthropologists for investigation, and generally believed to promise results corresponding with its position and the function it sustains. Tried by the tests afforded by craniometry, however, it appears to have little or no taxinomical value, since the outcome of these measurements is to transpose races and fuse peoples otherwise known to be distinct.

At the same time, in man, cranial outlines are unquestionably preponderantly determined by the brain, while the features by which its action is obscured have been so frequently and completely described that they need not be recapitulated. But although this statement holds on the morphological side of the question, from the physiological standpoint the case is not the same. The brain limits the shape of the head and is itself limited by the laws of growth, heredity, and structural correlativity; but in the phenomenal series cerebral development is antecedent to cranial evolution, and the relation subsisting between these—a relation which is in its nature causal, so far as shape is concerned—places the factors upon different planes. In virtue of preponderant function and equivalent preponderance of structure in special ganglia, a general form of head has been attained; but from fluctuations in the energies by which it was produced in correspondence with variations in the conditions of life, this form varies both in human and prehuman history, and so widely as to have thus far prevented classification.

That the organ through which all adjustments to the environment are primarily made should vary among groups whose lowest aggregates are nearly as passive to the direct action of natural selection as beasts, and whose higher forms are but partially and incompletely adjusted, is not surprising; and while it must be assumed upon biological grounds that the plasticity of the brain has lessened since its deviation from the ancestral type, whence issued in divergent lines that of man and his congeners, still, the facts of descent suggest that to its organic variability, and to that expressed in specific adaptations, there must be added a strong inherited tendency in this direction.

The cerebral history of the primates seems to warrant the theoretical conclusion that among these great variability of the head exists.

In Lemuridæ, where the cranium relatively to the face is small, and the ethmoidal, tentorial, and occipital planes are greatly inclined towards the basi-cranial axis, the brain scarcely exceeds the base of the skull in length, whereas in Simiadæ the encephalon is more than twice as long. The anterior cerebral lobes in the Arctopithecini compare in mass with those of anthropoids, while the posterior lobes are more developed than in certain races of men. Among the Platyrrhini great cranial variations correspond with extreme contrasts in brain structure and mass. The low facial angle, inclined tentorial plane, and perpendicularity of the axis of the occipital foramen to that of the cranial base, belong, as in Mycetes, to a type in which the cerebellum is scarcely covered, while in Chrysothrix the posterior lobes of the cerebrum are of relatively greater proportions than in any of the Mammalia; and, moreover, the vertex is arched, the facial angle large, the basi-cranial axis short, as compared with its cavity, and the planes of the occipital foramen and tentorium are in correspondence. The surface of the brain in Cebus is nearly as much convoluted as that of the catarrhine apes, but the sulci fade almost to obliteration through Pithecia, Chrysothrix, and Nictipithecus. On the other hand, by the nearly total structural masking of the annectant gyri of the external perpendicular fissure, the brain in Ateles rises above the catarrhine type.

Diversities such as these, occurring within the limits of a single group, put craniological classification out of the question; but in Catarrhines and Anthropidæ differences obtain, which, though less extreme, are equally decisive, and without anatomical details, for which there is no space, it may be said that the heads and brains of Semnopitheci and Colobi vary from those of Macaci and Cynocephali as significantly as the same structures do in the man-like apes. Apparently, then, no typical cranium exists among the simians any more than among men, from whom an artistic preconception has to a great extent concealed its absence.

With regard to this standard of art, also, it must be remembered that it is primarily one of *form*, while, physiologically, form has no necessary connection with the constitution of a ganglion. Such expressions as "nervous arc" and "reflex action" emphasize as if essential, that which, except contingently, has nothing to do with either curves or angles. In "the building of a brain" the terminal elements of nervous tracts are cellular, and agglomeration therefore results in the composition of a mass attached to a pedicle. Nothing which is generally more exact than this can be advanced. Components like these make up the parts and wholes of all nervous systems, and how they have combined in man and his class, and with what degree of uniformity, has already been indicated.

Of course it is not meant that the human head has not an average shape, or that this or any other part whose conformation is due to actions and reactions between an ancestral group and its entire environment, could alter otherwise than infinitesimally under the incidence of discontinuous forces. Nor is it intended to say that the harmony which exists in other instances between an organ and its properties is here ignored. No more than in any other machine or structure can the skull be considered as unaffected by the laws which co-ordinate mechanical and functional fitness with functional and mechanical requirements. But resemblances of this kind are not those which are contemplated in anthropometry, where the relations of structure and function, and of those to the conditions of life, have been disregarded in a search for morphological constants, whose occurrence, under the circumstances, was biologically impossible. Much but not all has been done towards a science of man, when the divergent forms of his class have been united by forms that are intermediate, and when his pedigree has been reconstructed on the basis of kinship. The whole question of race is included in this generalization, although it is not thereby fully explained, neither is it likely to be elucidated by measurements.

Without pursuing the subject further it may be remarked that, abstractly, structure and function are determined in all organisms by the affinities of their units of composition; that complete homogeneity in a group of protoplasts is impossible, and that initial diversities will increase during evolution. The minuteness of these ultimates may not add to the difficulty of comprehension more than is the case with those dealt with by molecular physics and chemistry, but it is otherwise when the plasticity of life is added. That adaptation. is connected with changes in function and structure is obvious, but neither in an organism, an organ, nor in the plastidules which compose them, is adaptation a final term in the progress from homogeneity to heterogeneity, from simplicity to complexity, from indefiniteness to definiteness; since, without alteration of elementary composition, there are no conceivable circumstances under which re-adjustment can be effected.

As it is with these phenomena which lie at the foundation of life, so is it with all the vital phenomena to which natural and sexual selection, growth, survival, genesis, heredity apply. Amid all degrees of composition and recomposition, function constitutes the substance, adaptation the form of life. Every statical or dynamical distribution of organic energy by which incident forces are met is included in function; and though in large groups of organisms, correlative changes, structural and functional, occur slowly and within comparatively narrow limits, yet they are, in the nature of things, relatively indefinite, but contingently permanent, and do not afford on this subject the data which systematic ethnology requires. Not less than its co-ordinate, the evolution of form, does physiological development press for interpretation in every question relating to race, and the doctrine that all factors by which differences among men are worked out are resolvable into results of the intercourse between these and the conditions under which they are placed, is essentially a corollary from the persistence of force.

Space has permitted but the merest sketch of this subject, but there yet remains a question which sooner or later confronts the investigator of cranial deformities, and this is that of their transmission. Present opinion almost unanimously opposes the belief that these may, in any degree, be perpetuated when of artificial origin; nevertheless it may be maintained with reason that the grounds upon which unqualified denial rests, are theoretically as untenable, in the present state of anthropological science, as those upon which an unqualified assent could be founded. Future results in this direction will depend largely upon the possibility of connecting facts of observation with those furnished by the experimental physiology of the nervous system. The question is a biological one, and without adverting to what has been said concerning variation, it may be urged that in this, as in all such problems, the first necessity is to view them under biological conditions. This requirement has not in this instance been complied with. Teleological preconceptions seem to have been more or less obstructive of the view, and equally so, incorrect parallels between alterations apparently within the limits of health, and those which involve morbid consequences.

There is no doubt that modifications of development involve functional modifications, and that imperceptible molecular changes in the brain rest on precisely the same basis as perceptible ones in other parts of the body. The inconceivability of spontaneous variation, properly so called, the heredity of function as well as of structure, the certainty that if structure changed by function is transmitted, any alterations of structure which have physiologically altered function must be also inherited, appear to suggest an explanation of certain phenomena connected with this subject, which, except on the principle of descent, do not seem to be interpretable at all.

According to the statements of Mr. Spencer, there is reason to think that special structures of all varieties proceed from the special polarities of their organic units, and that any tissue or combination of tissues will impress the modifications it may have experienced upon its component elements, between which and the aggregate life implies perpetual action and reaction. If this process, as must be generally the case, takes place under normal conditions, the forces manifested tend towards equilibrium without reaching, practically, an exact physiological balance. During these adjustments and re-adjustments, however, one of two alternative results inevitably occurs. Either the structure will take the shape determined by the pre-existing tendencies of its elements, or the aggregate's altered form will mould these into harmony with itself. The question thus becomes one of affection of function, because, for every reason, it must be assumed that structural elements organically changed will, when acting as reproductive centers, engender similar changes.

To oppose to these statements the common assertion that mutilations do not become congenital, is to misconceive their character, and to confound pathological conditions with those which must be normal in order to be effective. It may readily be suspected that the impossibility of inheriting artificial alterations has been too hastily assumed, since this involves an additional assumption, which has not been demonstrated, viz, that such changes do not become organic because they may occur without implicating function. The profound alterations effected by artificial selection are, of course, due to functional modifications, but it has not been shown that these can not be artificially induced, or that deformation must be universally morbid in character because it is a departure from such standards of organic type as now exist in imagination.

On the morphological side the question seems equally uncertain. Given, however, any cause which will effectually modify function, and modification of structure is inevitable. No naturalist supposes that the digital variations recorded as inherited, or those of the teeth, skin, etc., are attributable to any other cause than physiological change; and the same with transmitted club-foot, harelip, amaurosis, deafness. Further, adjustments by involution take place in nature as well as those by evolution, and although there are no structures whose properties are not originally ascribable to predetermined structural traits, there are yet structures which have no discoverable physiological features; and while morphological species, or species whose specific forms have no biological value, are recognized in zoology, and which, whether permanently or not, are withdrawn from the action of natural selection, it is difficult to see why the production of variety by any means that would effectually change function should be disallowed.

As was stated, there are reasons for suspecting that some such process has occurred among mankind to a limited extent; but whether or not, when all accessible information on the subject is organized, this may not prove to be a misconception attributable to insufficient knowledge, remains to be determined.

GENERAL NOTES ON DEFORMATION.

Malte-Brun. (Géographie Universelle. Ed. of Lavallée. Paris, 1858. 4to, t. 1.) General remarks on the causes and modes of distortion of the head (p. 303).

Humboldt & Bonpland. (Voyage, etc. Paris, 1811. 4to, 3ᵉ partie, t. 1. "Essai Politique, etc.) Remarks on head-flattening, its character and cause among Indians of North and South America. (Note, pp. 89, 90.)

Jefferys remarks upon the fine forms of the Indians of North America, and says the fact is attributable to "their bodies not being swathed and straitened in the cradle" (part 1, p 96). The cradle-board was in use among all the tribes described by him; but this error is not surprising in an author who characterizes the Eskimaux as "tall of stature," and speaks of "their flaxen hair, their beards, the whiteness of their skin * * * quite as fair as that of Europeans" (part 1, p. 43). Certain blond tribes do occur among the Hyperborean races, but not where Jefferys places them; although the Eskimaux are not really dark-skinned. With regard to the fine forms so constantly noted among the American and other savages, most writers have ascribed it to their modes of life; Humboldt adding, in the case of the Americans, a certain racial implasticity. Most of the earlier authorities have evidently judged an assumed ethnological fact from the stand-point of a social theory. There does not appear to be any natural reason why a savage should be better shaped than a civilized man, and that this is the case remains to be shown. There is, however, an excellent reason why those who are physically defective should be eliminated from all aggregates in a state of savagery, both by the action of natural selection and by that of their fellow-creatures. A very large body of proof could be readily brought forward to support the view that Wrangell's statement concerning the Chukchees held true of most peoples in a similar social phase, viz: "La mort attend l'enfant qui a le malheur de naître avec quelque difformité." Le Nord de la Sibérie. Paris, 1843, vol. I, p. 267. Kennan and Bush made like observations in the same region, and Capt. John G. Bourke, U. S. Army, has pointed out that in the south this custom is mentioned by Padre Gumilla ("Orinosc." Madrid, 1741, p. 344), and by Clavigero (Historia de la Baja California. Mexico, 1852, p. 27). I do not recall any reference of the same kind in Hennepin, Le Clerc, Charlevoix, etc.; but though the custom may have existed among the northern tribes, despite Robertson's assertion that all the American Indians killed the children who "appeared feeble or defective" (Hist. Dis. & Set. of America. N. Y., 1856, p. 144), there is no doubt that in the literature of travel it is more frequently mentioned as occurring among the southern tribes; and this may have been one reason why the earlier discoverers, Columbus, Vespucci, Verrazzano, &c., have spoken only of the fine appearance of the natives. The same contrasts, however, are found in savage life in this as in other respects. Captain Bourke confirms from personal observation the statement make in Emory's "Reconnoissance" (p. 61), that among the Apaches the deformed are sometimes well cared for. He also refers to a like mention in Francis Parkman (The Jesuits in North America. Boston, 1867, Introductory, XL), and also to Peter Martyr's narrative (Hakluyt, Voyages, vol. 5, p. 357).

In connection with head-flattening in America, Humboldt (Political Essay on New Spain. London, 1814. 8vo, vol. I) asserts that the back-head is naturally flat (p. 155). Also that the American cranium is normally "depressed backwards * * * among nations to whom the means of artificially producing deformity are * * * unknown." The Aztecs "never disfigure the heads of their children." The Mexican, Peruvian, and Aturean heads—all flattened; those Bonpland and himself procured were natural. "Certain hordes do compress the heads of children" (pp. 154, 155).

Squier (The States of Central America. N. Y., 1858. 8vo) quotes Valenzuela to the effect that among the Indians found by the Spanish at Lacandon (Dolores), Guatemala, "the cradles for their children were made of reeds" (p. 567).

Under the heading Tête, Encyclopedie des Sciences, etc., Neufchatel, 1765, is the following: "Il est parlé dans les voyages et dans les geographies modernes, de certains peuples qui se rendent la tête plat que la main, et qui mettent la tête de leurs enfans, dès qu'ils sont nés, entre deux presses, ou planches, sur le front et le derrière de la tête pour l'applatir."

NOTES ON AMERICA.

Bancroft. (Native Races of the Pacific States, N. Y., 1873, vol. I.) Chichimec women carried their infants on the back, "wrapped in a coarse cotton cloth, leaving the head and arms free" (p. 633). The cradle was a wicker basket suspended from a beam or bough (p. 633).

Gomara (Con. Mex., fol. 318) states that the occiput was flattened among the Nahua nations by an arrangement of the cradle, this form being considered becoming. (Bancroft, Native Races, etc., vol. II, p. 281.)

Humboldt's statement that the Aztecs did not distort the head was, as Bancroft remarks (Native Races, vol. II, p. 281), too sweeping. That the custom "was practiced to a considerable extent in remote times by people inhabiting the country seems to be shown by the deformed skulls found in their graves, and by the sculptured figures upon the ruins." Klemm states that "the cradle consisted of a hard board to which the infant was bound in such a manner as to cause the malformation."

Sahagun, Torquemada, Clavigero, Brasseur de Bourbourg, Carbazal Espinosa say that when a Teochichimec child was born on a journey "the new-born babe was placed in a wicker basket and thrown over the back of the mother." (Bancroft, Native Races of the Pacific States. N. Y., 1875, vol. II, p. 271, note.)

"Torquemada (Book XIV, ch. 24) states that the Indians," in Mexico, "used to deform their heads with a view to appear more formidable." (Spencer, Des. Soc. Ancient Mexicans, Central Americans, etc., p. 27.)

Landa (§ XX). "The Indians of Yucatan are, * * * as a rule, * * * bow-legged, for in their infancy their mothers carry them about suspended at their haunch-bones. They were made 'squint-eyed,'" and their heads were flattened artificially. (Spencer, Des. Soc. Ancient Mexicans, Central Americans, etc., p. 27.)

Landa (§ XXX) describes the process: "Four or five days after birth the child was put on a small bed made of rods, and there, the face being underneath, the head was put between two boards, in front and behind. Between these they compressed it * * * until the head was flattened and shaped like their own." (*Idem*, p. 27.)

Brancroft. (Native Races of the Pacific States. N. Y., 1873, vol. I.) The Quiché woman (Central America) carries her baby on her back "in a cloth passed around her body" (p. 704).

Bancroft. (Native Races of the Pacific States. N. Y., 1875, vol. II, 8vo.) The Nicaragua and Yucatan infants' heads were compressed and permanently flattened between two boards as a sign of noble birth. Squier asserts that occipital flattening was effected by the cradle-board among the Quichés, Cakchiquels, and Zutugils (pp. 731, 732). Don Horatio Guzmán, minister from Nicaragua, informs me that no compression of the head and no swathing of the infant is now practiced in any part of that country.

Bancroft. (Native Races of the Pacific States. N. Y., 1873, vol. I.) The Smoos Indians of the Mosquito Group flatten the forehead by a process like that in use among the Columbians (p. 717).

Fuentes. (Palacio, p. 106.) In Guatemala children were fastened "to a board by means of straps wound round the body * * * from the feet to the shoulders, in consequence of which all the Indians have the backs of their heads smooth and flat." (Spencer, Des. Soc. Ancient Mexicans, Central Americans, etc., p. 28.)

Jefferys, T. (Nat. and Civil Hist. of French Dominions in North and South America. London, 1760, fol.) Among the aborigines of Hispaniola "the singular conformation of the head * * * is effected by art." Mothers pressed their infant's skull, either by hand or with boards, until it was distorted, "and in a manner bent back upon itself" (Part II, p. 8).

Oviedo. (Historia General y Natural de Indias, book 11, chap. 5.) His statement of head-flattening is rather vague. "Porque al tiempo que nacen los niños les aprietan las cabezas," etc. The width of the front head, which he remarks as the result of artificial interference, points to the same form, and like appliances, noticed by Porto-Seguro, and others, in Brazil. (*Idem*, book 42, chap. 3.) Gomara is cited as giving the same evidence concerning the natives of San Domingo. He says they flattened the head with cotton compresses for the purpose of enlarging the face. "Aprietan á los niños la cabeza muy blando, pero mucho entre dos almohadillas de algodon, para ensancharles la cara," etc.

There seems to have been some confusion in Gomara's mind on this subject—Bernal Diaz says there was on all subjects. At all events he gives another account of the manner in which the infant's head was distorted, which amounts to this: that it was done by the midwife at the moment of birth, or shortly after. In this case, a very common one among different tribes, the fact apparently indicates gradual extinction of the custom, since the effect of simple manipulation would be temporary, and where distortion implies as much as it sometimes does, its absence exposes the individual to the greatest misfortunes.

Topinard. (Éléments d'Anthropologie Générale. Paris, 1885. 8vo.) Remarks of forms of distortion by manipulation alone that they must be impermanent—"incapables de produire une déformation soutenue" (p. 756). Prof. William H. Flower holds the same views, and, indeed, the fact is physiologically self-evident unless the manipulation were of an unprecedented kind.

Las Casas (Apologética Historia. Madrid, 1875, chap. 34) remarks that in Peru head distortion was distinctive of the Inca family and of the highest nobility. "Privilegio grande concedian los del Perú á algunos señores y que ellos querían favorecer" (p. 396, *vide* Marcot, notes).

Major, R. H. (Select Letters of Christopher Columbus, etc. London, 1870. Second edition, Hakluyt So. Pub.) Dr. Chanca, fleet surgeon on Columbus's second voyage, says, of the native and Carib women in the West Indies, that the latter wore "on each leg two bands of woven cotton, the one fastened round the knee, the other round the ankle; by this means they make the calves of their legs large, and the above-mentioned parts very small. * * * By this peculiarity we distinguished them" (p. 30).

Dr. Chanca supposed this custom to depend upon an idea that the distortion was becoming—"que esto me parece que tienen ellos por cosa gentil" (p. 30).

De Rochefort, C. (Histoire Naturelle, etc., des Iles Antilles. Rotterdam, 1658. 4to.) Notice of head and nose flattening among the Caribs (p. 382).

Humboldt and Bonpland. (Voyage, etc. Paris, 1819. 4to, seconde partie, p. 11. Relation Historique.) Distortions practiced by the Caribs on the Orinoco (p. 235).

Squier, E. G. (Nicaragua, etc. New York, 1852. 8vo, Vol. II.) Head-flattening among aborigines. Process and local origin of custom (p. 345). *Vide* Relacion of Fray Bobadilla on the same points. (Archivo de Indias.) ?

Heriot, G. (Travels Through the Canadas. London, 1807. 4to.) "The Caraibs have their foreheads flattened. * * * The head of the infant is compressed into this shape by placing on its brow a piece of board tied with a bandage, which is allowed to remain until the bones have acquired consistence" (p. 348).

Heriot, G. (Travels Through the Canadas. London, 1807. 4to.) Carib girls have a cotton sock woven to the leg, and "so closely * * * that the calf thereby acquires more thickness and solidity than it would naturally possess" (p. 307).

Armas, Juan I. de. (Les Crânes dits Déformés. Havana, 1885.) This is a paper read before the Anthropological Society of Havana, November, 1885, to prove that mechanical deformation of the head was never practiced in the West Indies or on the continent.

Graells, Vilanova and Arcas. (Rapport présenté à Madrid, le 24 Mars, 1871.) This was to the effect that certain crania from Cuba, taken to be flattened Carib skulls, could not be identified as artificially deformed, but were probably natural heads. The text is, "having noticed that in the front and back part of the head the depression is not uniform, the commission is inclined to consider the flattening as natural, etc." These skulls seem to have been found by Don R. Ferrer, who very truly says that they can not be regarded as specimens of head-flattening among the Caribs, because there were never any Caribs in Cuba. (De Armas, Crânes dits Déformés, p. 7.)

De Armas (Les Crânes dits Déformés) says that no such practice could have been general in America for various reasons, viz, it was difficult, tedious, and painful, and would have been destructive to the intellect (?); also that the Indians, though savages, were men with natural feelings toward their offspring which would have prevented them from perpetrating a custom so destructive as distortion of the head (p. 14 *et seq.*). Having given this illustration of his knowledge of the literature of anthropology, he declares that neither among the Peruvian mummies nor in the existing race could von Tchudi and Rivero discover a justification of the theory of mechanical deformation. A fact, and a singular one, but no more decisive than Robertson's statement that the mound skulls of North America are all normal (pp. 14, 15). In conclusion he remarks that "there is no basis, scientific, historical, or rational, on which to rest the affirmation that there were * * * and are * * * parts of America in which the natural formation of the head was (or is) modified by mechanical means." And more particularly is this a self-evident truth with regard to the Caribs of the Lesser Antilles: first, because none of the earliest chroniclers speak of the custom; and second, because the crania of this people have not the form attributed to them. Of course it was not possible for de Armas to deny the unsymmetrical contour of certain skulls, but he asserted that this was natural, and if the statement could be relied on, none could be made of more importance. The weight of evidence is, however, overwhelmingly against him.

De Armas also asserts that Oviedo was the originator of the idea that distortion of the cranium was customary among the Indians of San Domingo, etc., but Gomara, Las Casas, De Leon, and Garcilasso de la Vega make like statements, and the evidence includes West Indian, Peruvian, Floridian tribes.

Walker (Colombia. London, 1822. 8vo) quotes Humboldt to the effect that among the Caribs of Panapana "the women * * * carried their infants on their backs." They also, for the sake of adornment, compress the thighs and legs by "broad strips of cotton cloth, by which" the flesh * * * was swelled in the interstices. * * * They attach great importance to certain forms of the body. (Vol. I, p. 545.)

Heriot, G. (Travels through the Canadas. London, 1807. 4to.) "The natives of South America generally make use of hammocks of cotton or of the interior bark of trees. * * * This they suspend in their cabins and sometimes on the boughs of trees" (p. 287).

Señor Mutis Duran, of the Colombian legation at Washington, states that no tribe of Indians known to him in New Granada or Colombia distorts the head, but that cranial compression may be practiced by other tribes of this area which he had not observed. Bandaging infants with the idea of preserving the symmetry of their forms is general among all classes. The cradles used by the wealthy are imported or made after European models. Among the poorer classes there are two forms of cradle in use—one a boat-shaped case of light wood or bamboo, which will rock on any plane surface, and another constructed of similar materials and of like form, which is suspended from the end of a crooked rod and swung in the air.

Hilhouse, William. (Warow Land of British Guiana. Jour. Roy. Geo. Soc. London, 1834. Vol. IV.) Dr. Hancock remarks (note, pp. 332, 333, on Hilhouse's account of the Indians seen here) that "these tribes have also," i. e., like the coast tribes of the Marañon, "the spread in the foot, or duck's foot. * * * Their feet and toes are spread out in the manner most suitable for walking on the muddy shores and marshes they inhabit."

Im Thurn, E. F. (Among the Indians of Guiana (i. e., British Guiana). London, 1883. 8vo.) Head-flattening customary among people of upper Essequibo River; formerly prevalent among chief tribes throughout Guiana and among all "true Caribs" (p. 191). Distortion of women's legs by Caribs (p. 192).

Ploss, Dr. H. (Das Kind im Brauch und Sitte der Völker. Leipzig, 1884. 2 Aufl., 2 Band.) Description of the treatment of infants in Peru under the Incas (Idem, p. 57). The same with respect to children in Asiatic Turkey and Chinese Turkestan (Idem, p. 60). Remarks on the effects of position at rest (Idem, pp. 81, 82). Statements concerning the cradle-board and head-flattening in America (Idem, pp. 101 102). Description of the suckling-board and swaddling of infants among the Maronites and Modern Germans (Idem, p. 113, 114).

Squier, E. G. (Peru, etc. New York, 1877. 8vo.) Distorted Aymara skull from Chulpas (p. 244).

Appendix B. Extract from Fourth Annual Report of Peabody Museum. Cambridge. Remarks of Professor Wyman "On crania. Two modes of distortion, their effects," etc. (pp. 580, 581). Vide Padre Arriaga on this custom.

Prichard, J. C. (Researches into the Physical History of Mankind. London, 1841. 4th ed. 8vo) quotes Spix and Martius on the separation of the great toe among the Puris, Coropos, and Coroados, South America.

Marcoy, P. (Travels in South America. London, 1875. 4to.) Head-flattening formerly practiced by Peruvian Conibos. Obsolete within two generations. All very old people seen by Marcoy had distorted crania; no young persons. (Vol. II, p. 40, and note.)

Acosta, Joaq. (p. 24). The Panches (Chibchas) compressed the skulls of infants between boards into a "pyramidal" shape. (Spencer, Des. Soc. Ancient Mexicans, Central Americans, etc., p. 28.)

Idem. Lengthening (apart from piercing) the lobe of the ear was a royal fashion of the first four Incas. After Mayta-Cupas it became designative of the Curacas (Caciques) of the body guard. Now prevalent among certain tribes of the Amazons, *e. g.*, the Orejones (Spanish), broad-ears. (Vol. II, p. 270.)

Piedrahita. (Book 1, ch. 2.) The Coyaimas and Natagaymas (Chibchas) "have the custom of putting the tender head of a new-born child between two boards * * * in such a way that it * * * gets flattened." The Pichaos and Panches of the same stock do this also. (Spencer, Des. Soc. Ancient Mexicans, etc., p. 28.)

Idem. Compression of the head into the shape of "a bishop's mitre." (*Vide* Porto-Seguro.) Now obsolete among the Omaguas or Flatheads—a Spanish corruption of the Quichua Omahuas. These are an emigrant stock—the Umaüas, called by the Tupinambas of Brazil Icanga-peña (flatheads), which was contracted and corrupted by the Portuguese into Cambebas, whence La Condamine's mistake. (*Vide* Ref.) He mistook a title for a race name. (Vol. II, 340–342.)

Cieza (ch. 100) says of the Peruvian Collas that "their heads are very long and flattened behind, because they are pressed and flattened into what shape they choose during childhood." (Spencer, Des. Soc. Ancient Mexicans, Central Americans, etc., p. 28.)

Owen, Prof. R. (Anatomy of the Vertebrates. London, 1866. 8vo.) In the Inca race the skull "is high behind, owing to the habit of carrying the infant with the back of the head resting on a flat board, the pressure usually producing unsymmetrical distortion of the occipital part of the skull." (Vol. II, p. 567.) The same statement is made concerning the Patagonians. (Vol. II, p. 568.)

Cieza (ch. 50). Among the Caraques of Peru the child's head was pressed between boards, so that it "was long and broad, but flat behind." The Indians said this was conducive to health and vigor. (Spencer, Des. Soc. Ancient Mexicans, Central Americans, etc., p. 28.)

Idem. Pls. Nos. 386, 387, and 388, vol. 11, p. 567, exhibit artificially distorted skulls of the ancient Peruvians from Titicaca.

Meyen (p. 36) mentions a decree of the Lima Synod of 1585 against flattening the head. Rivero and Tschudi say that the irregularities in crania from the coast of Peru "were undoubtedly produced by mechanical causes" (p. 32). Santa Cruz, Narratives, p. 78, states that Manco Capac introduced head-flattening to make the people silly and easily ruled. (Spencer, Des. Soc. Ancient Mexicans, etc., p. 28.)

Marcoy, P. (Travels in South America. London, 1875. 4to.) Notice of custom of distorting the head among the Aymaras. (Vol. I, pp. 67, 68.) Old Aymara sculptures showing vertical and antero-posterior flattening. (Vol. 1, p. 185.) This work contains many " typical portraits" (1, 103) "taken from life" (1, 518). If correct at all, the Quichuas on the west, and Antis and Chonlaquiro Indians east of the Andes, distort their heads *now*, though Marcoy does not say so. (*Vide* pls. Vol. I, pp. 103, 476, 515.)

Torquemada (Book XIV, ch. 25) affirms that permission to shape the heads of their children was a favor granted by the Inca to some nobles, *e. g.*, the artificial contour was that of the royal family. (Spencer, Des. Soc. Ancient Mexicans, Central Americans, etc., p. 28.)

In all these contemporary fac-similes, and in the portrait medallions (Vol. I, pp. 210, 216, sixteenth century) of Incas and Coyas—"The Imperial Tree "—it is noteworthy that, if the delineation is at all accurate, some heads are distorted and some not. It is not possible in this instance to reconcile the portraits with Las Casas' statement that after the fourth Inca the custom ceased.

Ulloa, Juan and Antonio de. (Voyage to South America. London, 1807. 8vo.) Among the Quito Indians, "their beds consist of two or three sheepskins, without pillows or anything else." (Vol. I, pp. 408, 409.) Children are carried on the mothers' shoulders. (Vol. I, p. 409.)

Miers, J. (Travels in Chili and La Plata. London, 1826. 8vo.) The Pampa Indians "never walk any distance * * * some use saddles, but not all; * * * they are ill made." (Vol. I, pp. 256, 257.) Dr. Leighton says of the "horse" Indians of Chili, that "their legs are generally bandy." (Vol. II, p. 473.)

Among the Indians of Chili, "the child is slung in a kind of basket, formed of wooden hoop having a net-work stretched across it; it is hung by thongs to the roof of the hut." (Vol. II, p. 462.)

De La Condamine. (Relation Abrégée d'un Voyage, etc. Maestricht, 1778. 12mo. Derivation of the tribal names, Omaguas and Camberas, from the custom of flattening the head; notice of the process (p. 70). Vide Porto-Seguro, Historia Geral Brazil. Vol. I, pp. 18, 19.

Porto-Seguro. (Historia Geral do Brazil. Rio de Janeiro, 1878. 8vo. Vol. Head-Flattening.) Etymological remarks on the derivation of the name of certain Tupi (Guaranie) tribes, from what appears to be antero-posterior compression "Parecidas a mitras de bispos." (Vol. I, pp. 18, 19.)

Southey remarks (History of Brazil. London, 1819. 4to. Vol. III, p. 703) that when Ribeiro encountered the remains of the Omagua at Olivença in 1774, "they had left off the apparatus for flattening the foreheads and elongating the heads their infants; still they admired the old standard of beauty so much that they moulded them by hand; but the custom is now wholly disused." In Note 32, Vol. III, p. 896, he adds that "several tribes of the Rio Negro flattened their heads like the Omaguas." Humboldt (Political Essay on New Spain. London, 1814. 8vo. Vol. I, p. 154) says, "the barbarous custom * * * of pressing the heads of children between two boards" in South America, "was, like the Greek exaggeration of the facial angle, the Kalmuck nose, the Hottentot lips, an attempt to conform to an ideal of beauty."

Spix and Martius. (Travels in Brazil. London, 1824. 8vo.) It is stated that the women of the Coroados of East Brazil "carry their children about on their backs" and from the context, as well as the fact that the sleeping-cradle is a hammock, seems probable that they are carried in a sling. (Vol. II, p. 247.)

Brown and Lidstone. (Fifteen Thousand Miles on the Amazon, etc. London 1878. 8vo.) They mention another exception to the use of the hammock. The Pamary Indians, on the Rio Negro, "have not the peculiarity of using hammocks, but sleep on the floor of their tents" on "mats of plaited palm leaves" (p. 433).

Heriot, G. (Travels Through the Canadas. London, 1807. 4to.) "The Brazilians, and several other nations in South America," plunge the new-born infant in water. It is then "swaddled to little boards lined with cotton, and more frequently with moss" (p. 343).

In connection with references to nose-flattening as a custom among Brazilian and other South American Indians, the following indicates both the variability of the facial type and that of the standard to which nasal contour conforms when artificially modified. De Moussy, V. M. (Description, etc., de la Confédération Argentine. Paris, 1860. 8vo.) quotes d'Orbigny's L'homme américain, etc., to the effect that in the Peruvian branch of the Ando-Peruvian race the nose is long and high-"nez long, très aquilin." In the Antisian branch of same race it varies—"nez variable." In the Araucanian branch of same race it is "très court." The Pampa branch of the Pampean race have the "nez très-court, très-épaté, à narines larges, ouvertes." Among the Chiquiteau branch of this race the nose is "court, un peu épaté." In the third or Moxcan branch of the Pampean race it is "court, peu large." Among the Guarani tribes of the Brazilio-Guaranian race, the feature is described as "nez cour étroit, narines étroites." Length is a natural characteristic; the rest may be natural or artificial, but no doubt are largely modifications. Vide references, passim. (Vol. II, pp. 145–147; note.)

Dobrizhoffer, M. (An Account of the Abipones. London, 1822. 8vo.) Father Dobrizhoffer was in Paraguay from 1749 to 1767, and his ethnological matter is ex ceptionally valuable. Of a certain tribe at Mbaevera he says: "The mothers put their babies in wicker baskets, and carry them on their shoulders." (Vol. I, p. 62.) This is the first notice of any cradle but a sling in this region.

Dobrizhoffer, M. (An Account of the Abipones, London, 1822. 8vo.) The mounted tribes—Indios bravos—of Paraguay "do not use stirrups, and most of them are unfurnished with saddles, even." This fact accounts for the excessive curvature of the legs noticed in previous references. (Vol. I, p. 236.)

Dobrizhoffer remarks of the Abipones of Chaco, also "an equestrian people," but who are provided with saddles, though "stirrups are not in general use," that "you never see an Abipone with * * * bandy legs." Like the Kirghiz, all these Indians ride more than they walk, and are placed on horseback at the earliest age. Father Dobrizhoffer's statement is not in accordance with the facts of common observation in this regard; but, taken with some reservation, the greater symmetry of limb among the tribes of Chaco is evidently due to the difference of position involved in the use of a saddle. (Vol. II, p. 113.)

King, Col. J. A. (Twenty-four Years in the Argentine Republic. London, 1846. 8vo.) The Chirivione Indians of Gran-Chaco would not eat mutton for fear " their noses would become flat" (p. 109).

Parrish, Sir W. (Buenos Ayres. London, 1852. 8vo.) Speaking of the Pehuenches—"Pine Trees"—a Pampa branch, he says: "I have seen some of these Indians who, from being so constantly on horseback, had become bow-legged to such an extent of deformity that the soles of their feet were turned inward, etc." (p. 173). This points to the absence of a saddle, such as used, at least, by their congeners, the Tehuelches-Patagonians.

Harris, J. (Navigantium atque Itinerantium Bibliotheca. London, 1744. Folio.) Sebald de Weert speaks of the "crooked legs" of a certain Indian woman found in the Straits of Magellan. (Vol. I, p. 42.) From what is said afterwards (*Idem.* p. 43) this was evidently a Fuegian.

There are several references to the distortion of limbs among the Fuegians, and to its cause. As an example of the uncertainty attaching to reports of the early voyagers, Harris', Navigantium, etc., quotes Jaques le Hermite, Voyage of Circumnavigation, 1623, to the effect that the inhabitants of Terra del Fuego were "as fair as any in Europe; * * * very strong and well proportioned, and generally about the height of the people in Europe." (Vol. I, p. 71.) Of the same kind is Captain Cowley's statement, made from personal observation, that the Hottentots "are born white, but make themselves black with soot." (Harris's Bibliotheca, Vol. I, p. 83.)

Cook, Captain. (Voyages, etc. London, 1773. 8vo.) Describing the beds of the natives of Terra del Fuego, says that "a little grass * * * served both for bed and chairs." (Vol. II, p. 55.)

NOTES ON EUROPE.

Rae, Ed. (The White Sea Peninsula. London, 1881. 8vo.) Bowed legs are mentioned as characteristic of the Norwegian Lapps. Not a pure race like those of South Finmark and Terski Lapland. Distortion probably due to the skin-bag cradle (p. 232).

Laing, S. (Journal of a Residence in Norway. London, 1836. 8vo.) He describes as a characteristic the bowed legs of the Norwegian Lapps. "They form a curve with the leg-bone down to the foot, so that in standing with their feet close together all above is far apart" (p. 247). Pressure in the hood, etc., during infancy probably causes this.

Panofka, T. (Manners and Customs of the Greeks. London, 1849. 4to.) Description of the Λίκνον, or wicker, shoe-shaped swinging cradle of Greece (Pt. II).

Guhl and Koner. (Life of the Greeks and Romans. London, ——. 8vo.) "The antique cradle," *i. e.*, the Λίκνον of the Heroic age, "consisted of a flat swing of basket-work." The child, enveloped in the σπάργανα, must necessarily have been bound to this. In the shoe-shaped basket-cradle the infant occupied a sitting position (*vide* pl., p. 195). The last-named cradle had handles, by which it could be carried or swung. Subsequently, when communication with Asia was constant, other forms of the cradle came into use, "cradles similar to our own modern ones" (pp. 195, 196). The σπάργανα, used everywhere in Greece, except in Sparta, were designed to prevent distortion. Besides the swaddling-clothes, however, there was in common use a sufficient variety of bed-clothes to make any kind of resting place for the child soft enough to insure safety against pressure, viz, the κλίνη of Homer was covered with hides (κώεα), and over this lay the ρήγεα, blankets or mattress, perhaps. At all events, the later κνέφαλον was a sack of some kind of stuff filled with feathers, picked wool, etc., and was laid across the straps of the δέμνια, or folding bed (cot). There were also linen sheets, the blankets before mentioned, and some kind of a heavier covering, presumably of wool, since it was rough on both sides—περιστρώματα, ἐπιβλήματα, etc.—together with stuffed pillows and bolsters.

Professor Becker (Charicles, London, 1880; Excursus, pp. 221, 222) gives much the same account of the Greek bed and bedding as Guhl and Koner, Life of the Greeks and Romans (p. 136, *et seq.*). Cradles, he says, are first mentioned by Plutarch. "Plato knew nothing of them." No author of his age can be said to have mentioned "a regular cradle." Mothers probably carried their children in their arms, and these "were not encouraged to walk very early." Wet-nurses were commonly employed, and among these the Spartan women were the most famous.

Potter, Dr. J. (Archæologia Græca. New York, 1825. 8vo.) It appears that observation had taught the Greeks the effects of pressure on immature bones, since everywhere, except in Sparta, where the end was otherwise secured, the infant was wrapped "in swaddling-bands * * * lest its limbs * * * should happen to be distorted" (p. 628).

De Perthes, B. (Voyage en Russie. Paris, 1859. 12mo.) Remarks on nose-flattening in Asiatic Russia, and probable cause of the custom (p. 288).

Burton and Drake. (Unexplored Syria. London, 1872. 8vo.) Cranium said to be Turanian, exhibiting "unilateral flattening * * * from use of the sucklingboard." (Appendix, vol. II, p. 277.)

Burton and Drake. (Unexplored Syria. London, 1872. 8vo. Vol. II, Appendix.) Distortion of cranial contour referred to "custom of swathing the child's head tightly after birth" (*vide* Foville on the process). This distortion of the calvaria was in the case of a Semitic (probably Jewish) skull (p. 346), (*ibid.*, Appendix, vol. II). Specimen of brachycephalous Græco-Roman cranium, exhibiting asymmetrical parietal and supra-occipital flattening, partially due to "suckling-board" (pp. 356, 357).

Seebohm, H. (Siberia in Asia, London, 1882. 8vo), describes an Ost'-yak cradle as "a wooden box, about 3 inches deep, with rounded ends, almost the shape of the child." The oval bottom covered with sawdust. Infant wrapped in flannel and furs, and lashed in the cradle. The child is nursed while in this position (pp. 62, 63).

Prichard, J. C. (Researches into the Physical History of Mankind. London, 1841. 4th ed. 8vo.) He quotes Pallas to the effect that the only deformity visible among Kalmuks is "an outward bending of the arms and legs, resulting from the practice of causing children to rest in their cradles on a kind of saddle" (vol. I, p. 263).

Prejvalsky, Col. N. (Mongolia. London, 1876. 8vo. Vol. I.) Chapter II, page 47 *et seq.*, "is especially devoted to the ethnology of Mongolia." He says of the Mongol, "his legs are bowed by constant equestrianism;" but nothing of any form of cradle, or mode of carrying infants, or of malformations other than the above, is said anywhere.

In Pumpelly's Across America and Asia, La Farge (p. 199) has given fac-similes of wood-cuts representing various deformities of the head, evidently artificial. Japanese art, and especially genre art, is of a high order, not relatively, but positively, and as it can not be supposed that such should be the case without a knowledge of the fact that all caricature depends for its effect upon an exaggeration of well-known characteristics to the degree of grotesqueness, it would be well to inquire if now or formerly any custom, etc., justified these contours.

From Dr. W. W. Rockhill the information is received that in China and Mongolia children are carried in the same way as described by Mr. Akabané in Japan, except that the crossed bands to secure the child on the mother's back are not made use of. Capt. John G. Bourke, U. S. Army, states that the Navajos use a cradle-board similar to that described by Major Powell on the Colorado, viz, a buckskin sack fastened to a board, into which the infant is put without being swathed. No cradles are used by the Japanese, Chinese, or in Mongolia.

NOTES ON ASIA.

The Emperor of China, Kien-hing (1736–1796), in his work *Mandchou-yuen-lion-kas*, says: "The ancient Mandchous some days after the birth of a child prepared for it a little hard bed, and laid it thereon face up. Little by little the back of the head was flattened and became larger. The Chinese have a custom opposite to this. They lay the new born upon its side, first right, then left, wherefore the head is made narrower." This would make the Mandchous brachycephals and the Chinese dolicocephals.

Busk, George (Jour. Anthrop. Inst. Great Britain and Ireland, Nov., 1878, "Notes on a skull termed Nabathæan") says that regarding the norma lateralis, its outlines "almost suggest that the skull has been constricted by a bandage."

Spencer, H. (Descriptive Sociology, N. Y. Asiatic Races among the Nomadic Arabs.) "Noble families used to alter the shape of children's heads." (Table XXXI.) This was done in the age of Abou-Zeyd. (Bastian. Mensch. II, 229. *Id.*, p. 21.)

Vambéry, A. (Sketches of Central Asia. London, 1868. 8vo.) The Turkoman head is "proportionally small" and oblong. This form "is ascribed to the circumstance" that infants are not cradled, but "placed * * * in a swing made of linen cloth" (p. 296). The Turkomans commonly have "their feet bent inwardly; probably the consequence of their continually riding on horseback" (p. 296).

Pallas. (I, 98, *et seq.*) The Kalmucks "are well made, with the exception of the legs, which are generally bent (arising from being so much on horseback), and slender, like the arms." (Spencer, Des. Sociol. Asiatic Races, p. 3.)

Featherman, A. (Social History of the Races of Mankind, 2d division. London, 18-7. 8vo.) The women among the Néasesa, "who are accustomed to bear heavy burdens, have their knees turned inward, and their hips are more or less deformed" (p. 347).

Featherman, A. (Social History of the Races of Mankind, 2d division. London, 1887. 8vo.) Among the Nicobar Islanders "the skull is depressed by art" (p. 239). "A block of wood answers the purpose of a pillow" (p. 240).

Langsdorf, G. H. von (Voyages and Travels, London, 1813. 4to) describes the Aïnos (Japan) as having "compressed noses" (vol. I, p. 328). He says the same of the people of Oonalashka (vol. II, p. 31). It is not stated that this peculiarity is produced by artificial means. In this, as in a great number of other instances, nothing is said of the appliances used; but the inference is that such must have existed in the case of infants. The following information, communicated by Mr. Shiro Akabané, secretary of the Japanese legation at Washington, exhibits a very simple mode of carrying infants on the back. No cradles of any kind are used in Japan. The child is never bandaged. It is wrapped loosely in a cloth of some kind, and placed on a soft mattress on the floor. There it remains, except when nursed, until it is old enough to clasp the body of its parent with its legs, when it is placed on the back beneath the outer garment, and supported by two bands passing over its back like cross-belts.

History of Kamtchatka (translated and abridged from official Russian account, based on all voyages and travels to Kamtchatka and Kurile Islands, by Dr. James Grieve. Glocester, 1764. 4to). The Koreki (Koriaks) "use neither cradle nor swaddling-cloths." No mention of any kind of bodily malformation (p. 233).

As Grieve says he only mentions facts concerning the Koriaks and Kurile Islanders, which are *not* true of Kamtchatdales, it may be true that in Kamtchatka and the Kuriles cradles *are* used.

Both among the Aïnos and Tartars, Rollin's descriptions point to distortions. The following are his cranial measurements in Saghalien and at the Baie de Castries: Island of Tchoka (Saghalien), circumference of head, 1 foot, 10 inches, 4 lines; long diameter, 9 inches, 8 lines; short diameter, 5 inches, 8 lines. Baie de Castries, circumference of head, 1 foot, 9 inches, 4 lines; long diameter, 9 inches; short diameter, 5 inches, 4 lines.

Bush, R. J. (Reindeer, Dogs, and Snow-Shoes. N. Y., 1871. 8vo.) In October Bush saw among the Gilaks, on the Amoor, "a babe tightly bandaged in a wooden box or cradle, something like that used by our American Indians, but with its legs from the knee downwards unfettered." This cradle was hung vertically to the "ridge-pole" of a "lean-to" shelter, and, the child's feet touching the ground, it "swung itself" (p. 123). In northeast Siberia in January, Bush saw "two little boys," belonging to the nomad Tungusians, "lashed together and thrown over a pack-saddle, the one balancing the other. * * * They were each sewed up in single garment * * * made of heavy reindeer fur." Only the eyes and nose were visible (pp. 240, 241).

A. E. Nordenskiöld (Voyage of the Vega, London, 1881, 8vo, Vol. II) describes "a wide skin covering with the legs and arms sewed together downwards" as the substitute for the cradle among the Chukchis. Similar devices used by most polar tribes apparently. No visible cause for distortion (p. 102).

NOTES ON AFRICA.

Wood, J. G. (Uncivilized Races of Men. Hartford, 1871. 8vo.) The Abyssinian midwives mold the features of infants "to make them handsome" (p. 658).

Wood, J. G. (Uncivilized Races of Men. Hartford, 1871. 8vo.) Among the Fans the child is carried astride of a bark belt (p. 530). The "paingkoont" or circular mat cloak of Australians serves to carry the child, vertically placed. The Australian form is exceptionally fine (p. 699). The cradle of the New Zealand infant is a mat wrap (p. 817). In New Guinea the child lies "in a sort of sling" of leaves or bark, and is so carried (p. 901).

Alexander, Captain (Jour. Royal Geogr. Soc., London, 1835, Vol. V, p. 318, note) says of the Fingoes (or Wanderers) of South Africa, that their "children are carried behind wrapped in the kaross."

Little, H. (Madagascar. Edinburgh and London, 1884. 12mo.) The Magalasy "mother carries her infant upon her back, and not in her arms" (p. 64). No description of the means used to support the child.

On page 193 of M. C. Buet's Madagascar la Reine des Iles Africaines, there is a plate of a woman carrying a child, placed in a sort of hood formed of a fold of the outer garment, which may explain Little's statement.

Wilkinson, Sir J. G. (Manners and Customs of the Ancient Egyptians, New York, 1879) states that the head-rest, or according to Porphyry "a half-cylinder of wood in lieu of a pillow," was in general use in Egypt. (Vol. I, pp. 185, 186.)

Wilkinson adds that the same kind of a pillow is found in China, Japan, and among the Ashantees and Kaffirs. This is a very incomplete statement of the peoples who use the head-rest; but there is a slight incongruity between his assertion of the universal use of this kind of pillow, and that made (Vol. I, p. 417) to the effect that the Egyptians commonly slept on couches, because many of those depicted in his plates would not have permitted the head-rest to be used on account of their form. He says also that the Egyptian bed was often a skin placed on the ground or a frame of palm wicker-work like the modern caffass, and in these cases a wooden pillow, cushioned as in Japan and China, for the rich, might have been employed.

The Madi women carry their infants in skins which have been dried in the sun and scraped clean and smooth with a stone and softened with butter. The skins of goats, gazelles, sheep, and calves are used, the legs being tied together and strung over the mother's shoulders. The baby is placed in the skin under the woman's arm, with its head behind. Sometimes a gourd is placed over the head to protect it from the sun. When older, the child is carried on the arm. (Proc. Roy. Soc., Edinburgh, 1883–'84, p. 325.)

NOTES ON OCEANICA.

Forbes, H. O. (A Naturalist's Wanderings in the Eastern Archipelago. New York, 1885. 8vo.) In Timor-Laut infants are laid "quite naked * * * on a hard palm spathe," which is spread in a siwela or "rough rattan basket" (pp. 315, 316). Every one sleeps on a banquette covered with bamboo mats, and they "rest their heads on a piece of squared bamboo with rounded edges" (p. 318).

Dr. J. G. Garson (Appendix to Part IV, p. 343), describing the Timor-Laut crania procured by Forbes, remarks that "all the brachycephalic skulls * * * exhibit more or less flattening in the occipital and parieto-occipital region, such as would be produced by laying an infant, without any soft material under its head, in a cradle like that described." Owing to race intermixture there are two types of cranial contour in Timor-Laut; but it is evident that the same conditions must be operative whether the head is short or long. The difference is one of degree, not of kind. Dr. Garson observes also that "the height of the skulls is in all instances less than the breadth," a fact which (although not mentioned as such) is of the same class as that of occipital flattening, and apparently due to the same cause, viz, the weight of a head incompletely ossified resting on an unyielding surface, and in which restitution during growth is prevented by the subsequent use of a wooden pillow. An isolated fact, and of course having only that value in this connection, is stated by Major Cambell (Geographical Memoir of Melville Island, north coast of Australia, in Jour. Royal Geogr. Soc. London, 1834, Vol. IV). He says that the pillows he saw were made of "pieces of soft silky bark, rolled up in several folds" (p. 157), and also that their cranial characteristic is that "the back of the head projects very much (p. 153). * * * The aborigines of Melville and Bathurst Islands are of the same race * * * as those throughout New Holland (p. 158). Hard or wooden pillows are not universal in warm countries. The Ovahs of Madagascar sit on cushions, lie on mats, and have a matted bolster." (Jour. Roy. Geogr. Soc., 1835, Vol. V, p. 332; Captain Lewis.)

Flower, William H. (Fashion in Deformity. Humboldt Library, New York. Vol. II, No. 28.) The author reports a statement made to himself by Mr. H. B. Law, to the effect that the Dyaks of Arawak practiced artificial flattening of the occiput (p. 12).

Featherman, A. (Social History of the Races of Mankind. 2d division. London, 1887. 8vo.) Among the Dyaks a mat like the Mexican petate, which serves the same purpose, is used for a bed. "A bag stuffed with grass answers the purpose of a pillow" (p. 258).

Reynolds, J. H. (voyage of the U. S. frigate Potomac, New York, 1835, 8vo) states that the heads of the Achenese "are somewhat flat or compressed," but gives no reason for this (p. 183).

Guillemard, Dr. F. H. H. (Cruise of the Marchesa, London. 1886. 8vo.) In the Sulu Archipelago the cradle used is a "little basket-woven cot" hung in the middle of a long bamboo supported at the ends. The vibrations of the bamboo when pulled rock the child. (Vol. II, p. 14.) Among the Hatam Papuans he saw a number of women "with babies strapped upon their backs." (Vol. II, p. 294.)

Featherman, A. (Social History of the Races of Mankind. 2d division. London. 1887. 8vo.) Among the Sumatras "the nose is flattened and the skull is compressed from early infancy as a mark of beauty" (p. 289).

Marsden (p. 44). "The Sumatrans flatten the noses, and compress the noses of children newly born. They likewise pull out the ears of infants to make them stand at an angle from the head." (Spencer, Des. Soc. Negritto and Malayo-Polynesian Races, pp. 20.)

Featherman, A. (Social History of the Races of Mankind. London, 1887. 8vo.) Among the Melville Island tribes "a roll of thin, silky bark serves as a pillow at night and as a seat in the day-time." (Papuo-Melanesians, 2d divis., p. 120.)

Featherman, A. (Social History of the Races of Mankind. London, 1887. 8vo.) The aboriginal Tasmanian women (Papuans) "throw over their shoulders the skin of an untanned kangaroo or opossum," in which they place their children "when carrying them on the back." (Papuo and Malayo Melanesians, 2d divis., p. 100.)

Cook, Captain. (Voyage towards the South Pole, etc., II, p. 34.) Natives of Mallicollo wear a belt which "they tie so tight over the belly that the shape of their bodies is not unlike that of an overgrown pismire." (Spencer, Des. Soc. Negritto and Malayo-Polynesian Races, p. 20.)

Busk, George (Jour. Anthrop. Inst. Great Britain and Ireland, Jan., 1877) speaks of the "extreme flattening * * * of the frontal region" in certain Mallicollo skulls as "artificial."

Cheever, H. T. "The unnatural flattening of the occiput" (in the Hawaiian head) "is thought to be owing to the way the mother holds her babe, which is by the left hand supporting the back of its head." (Spencer, Des. Soc. Negritto and Malayo-Polynesian Races; pp. 20, 21.) Occipital flattening also promoted by the use of a mat pillow or one of wood.

D'Albertis, L. M. (New Guinea. London, 1881. 8vo). On Yule Island "children were carried * * * in netted bags, resting on the backs of their mothers, suspended by a cord that passed round the women's heads. * * * Their legs were small in proportion to their bodies." (Vol. I, p. 262.) Both on the coast and in the interior of Yule Island the natives wear a tight, broad belt, "sometimes woven on the body." Compression from this results in distortion, giving the figure a "very peculiar appearance." (Vol. II, p. 302.)

Featherman, A. (Social History of the Races of Mankind. London, 1887. 8vo). State that the Riara women (Papuo-Melanesian group) carry their children "on their backs in a bag of net-work * * * suspended from the forehead by a band" (p. 51). Other Papuans carry their infants in the "flap" of a cloak made of cocoa-nut fiber (p. 21). The Tasmanians carried them "wrapped in a kangaroo-skin, which hung behind the back" (p. 21).

United States Exploring Expedition (Wilkes). (4to. Vol. VI. "Ethnography." Horatio Hale. Philadelphia, 1846.) General remarks on prevalent occipital flattening among Polynesians (p. 10).

In connection with the references to occipital flattening among the Polynesians (a fact variously explained), but not in any case, so far, referred to the general custom of laying infants on hard mats in warm countries, and especially so in Oceanica, thus undesignedly compressing the head by its own weight, the following statements are made: Sir J. Bowring (Philippine Islands, London, 1859, 8vo) quotes the ethnological tables of Buzeta to the effect that the "pure Indians" (Tagals) of the Philippines have this characteristic, whereas among the Mestizos and Negrittos it is not mentioned (p. 176). Wood (Uncivilized Races of Men; Hartford, 1871; 8vo) states that *in childhood* the Bushman skull exhibits excessive occipital *projection*, and this naturally (p. 249). Further, that the same is the case with the Ovambo at all ages (p. 316). Finally, that marked convexity of the front as well as the back head distinguishes the Wahuma (p. 400). These facts, *by themselves*, cancel any inferences from the exceptional contour of a *single* cranial bone unsupported by evidence of abnormal growth or mechanical interference. Hard mats and a wooden pillow explain the fact of occipital flattening, where a vertical occiput is not a decided race feature.

Wallace, A. R. (Australasia, London, 1879, 12mo) quotes Captain Erskine to the effect that among the Polynesian or Mahori race it is the custom to flatten the nose during infancy (p. 493). He remarks that the occipital flattening may be artificial

(p. 494). Throughout this work and the ethnological appendix by Keane, there are no notices of distortion other than the above. On page 476 is a portrait of a "chief of Vanitoro, Santa Cruz Islands," whose skull appears to have been compressed and elevated by circular bandages.

Pritchard W. T. (Polynesian Reminiscences. London, 1866. 8vo.) Without describing the process, he states the fact that the Tongans, Samoans, and Fiji Islanders have the custom "of squeezing the heads of infants into * * * a shape in conformity with their ideal of beauty" (p. 417). Remarks on contour of distorted skull (pp. 427, 428).

Martin, Dr. J. (An Account of the Natives of the Tonga Islands. London, 1818. 8vo). On Yule Island "children were carried in netted bags, resting on the backs of the mothers, suspended by a cord that passed round the women's heads." (Vol. I, p. 202.)

Buller, J. (Forty Years in New Zealand. London, 1878. 12mo.) Description of nose-flattening and modification of shape of limbs by manipulation (pp. 215,216).

Foster, Dr. J. R. (Observations made during a Voyage round the World. London, 1778. 4to). Notice of antero-posterior depression of skull in Mallicollo (pp. 242, 267, 268). People of Tierra del Fuego, constantly in canoes, have "the legs bent, the knees large, and the toes turned inwards" (pp. 251, 268). Remarks on nose-flattening in Tahiti (pp. 593, 594). Says Hottentots and natives of Macassar have same custom (p. 594).

Foster describes the process of flattening the nose in Tahiti, and quotes his description of the process used by the Hottentots and in Macassar from Gomara, Historia General de las Indias (pp. 593, 594).

Turnbull, John (Voyage Round the World, London, 1813, 8vo) remarks that the noses of the Otaheitans are "universally flat, occasioned by pressure during their infancy" (p. 344). Nothing further said.

Ellis, William. (Polynesian Researches. London, 1829. 8vo.) "During the period of infancy" in the Society and Caroline Islands "the children were seldom clothed, and were generally laid or carried in a horizontal position. They were never confined in bandages or wrapped in tight clothing." In Tahiti "the shape of the child's head" and its features were carefully observed, and parents and nurses "often pressed or spread out the nostrils of the females, as a flat nose was considered by them a mark of beauty." (Vol. I, p. 343.) In Tahiti "the forehead and the back of the head of the boys were pressed upwards, so that the upper part of the skull appeared in the shape of a wedge. This, they said, was done to add to the terror of their aspect." (Vol. I, p. 343.)

In general remarks on the "South Sea Islanders," i. e., natives of the Georgian, Society, Caroline, "and adjacent isles," Ellis says they "are generally above the middle stature," but their limbs are not correspondingly muscular, though " well formed." In mountainous parts they have inturned feet and an "exceedingly awkward" gait, from using the naked feet in climbing rocks and ravines. Except when distorted, "the facial angle is frequently as perpendicular as in the European." Nose-flattening is not so general as it was formerly, and the nose "is seldom flat," but "rectilinear or aquiline." (Vol. II, pp. 13–15.) The bed of the majority is a single mat. The chiefs have many. The pillow is wooden. (Vol. II, p. 67.)

On Carpentaria Gulf, Australia, the mothers flatten the nose of their young children by pressing it with the hand on the point and laying the child on its face.

Dr. Karl Scherzer. (Voyage of the *Novara*. London, 1863. 8vo. Vol. III.) Opinion that artificial flattening of occipital region prevails among women of Tahiti (p. 220). Remarks on artificial distortion of head on west coast of North and South America (*ibid.*, pp. 347, 348, 393).

Wood, J. G. (Uncivilized Races of Men. Hartford, 1871. 8vo.) Occipital flattening and nose-flattening among the Tahitans, with description of the process (p. 1059).

United States Exploring Expedition, i, 339. Method of carrying children illustrated.

Calvert, T. W. and J. (Fiji and the Fijians. N. Y., 1-59. 8vo.) The bed of a chief, made on the banquette, "is covered with mats, varying in number from two to ten, and spread over a thick layer of dried grass and elastic ferns, while on them are placed two or three neat wooden or bamboo pillows" (p. 108). There was an elaborate form of general bed. An infant is "anointed with oil and tumeric," but apparently not swathed in any way. The friends "plait small mats, measuring about 2 feet by 1, for the mother to nurse her babe upon." There is no notice that its bed is not like that described above (p. 138). "Natives nurse the child sitting quite naked astride the mother's hip, where it is kept from falling by her arm" (p. 139).

The Calverts also describe the nose as "well shaped, with full nostrils, yet distinct from the negro type." The "lower extremities" are "of the proportion generally found among white people." The "mold of the body is decidedly European" (p. 82). Dr. Pickering (Races of Men, p. 147) says the Fijian crania are unique, have "rather the negro outline," while "the profile" appears to be "as vertical, if not more so, than in the white race."

Nind, S. (Jour. Royal Geogr. Soc. London, 1832. 8vo. Vol. I.) Describing natives of King George's Sound (Swan River colony), Australia, he says: "For the first few weeks the child is carried on the left arm in a fold of the cloak, but subsequently is suspended on the shoulders" (p. 39).

Foville, A. (Influence des Vêtemens sur nos Organes, etc. Paris, 1834), describes cases of cranial deformity and mental incapacity produced by bandaging the head during infancy.

Foville quotes Blumenbach (Collectio Craniorum) with reference to cases of antero-posterior flattening accompanied by occipital protrusion, and to instances of the pyramidal form of the Peruvian skull. He states that Turkish crania grooved by ligatures have been found.

M. Virey (Art. "Enfant," Dic. des. Sci. Méd.) asserts that caps drawn tight by ribbons will "force the head into a sugar-loaf shape, and produce idiocy" in infants.

La Bret. (Compt. Rend. Soc. de Biologie. Paris, 1852, IV, et seq.) Sur la déformation artificielle du crâne en Amérique. The author gives a résumé of the opinions of well-known writers on the production of cranial deformity by artificial means in North and South America.

Guéniot (Bull. Soc. de Chir. de Paris, 1870, 2d Ser. X, 382 et seq.), "Obliquité par propulsion unilatérale," describes a case of flattening of the occipito-parietal region on one side, accompanied by corresponding projection of the other, due to constant position of the head on a hard surface during infancy.

Dr. J. Thurnam (On Synostosis of the Cranial Bones. London, 1865), describes a brachycephalous skull from the Round Barrows, with a broad, shallow depression passing behind the coronal suture, and over the occiput in the line of the transverse spine. This was evidently the effect of some kind of head-dress; probably, one such as MM. Foville and Lunier has described as now in use in France.

L. A. Gossei (Essai sur les déformations artificielles du crâne. Paris, 1855. Ackermann. Neues Magazin von Baldringer, Bd. 2, p. 5), says, "Hunc morem in Germania satis usitatum esse et Laurenberg; etiam Hamburgensis capita neonatorum vinculis artificiose compressisse." Schade, J. De Singulari cranii cujusdum deformitate. Gryphiæ, 1858, 11."

Idem. Lunier (Essai sur les déformations artificielles du crâne. Gosse. Paris, 1865), refers to this custom as prevailing in the Franco-Gallic Provinces, and adds, "Itague hand difficile intellectu videtur, forsitan etiam hujus cranii deformitatem ca causa affectam esse." 11.

Idem. Andry (Gosse's essai) reports the same in Flanders. Shadel recognizes the intra-uterine causes, and for the most part occupies himself with distortion due to affections of the sutures, following Hyrtl, Stahl, and Virchow.

Case of what Guéniot calls Obliquité par propulsion unilatérale, "reported by M. Mocquet. (Bull. Soc. Anat. de Paris, 1875, 1. 56.) Cause stated to be in all such cases, or most, prolonged pressure over occipito-parietal region from hard pillow, and position and weight of head.

Bourke, Capt. John G. (Snake-Dance of the Moquis, New York, 1884), describes "cradles of flat boards, with a semi-circular screen for the head. These differ among the Moquis in no essential from the ordinary cradle-board of the North American Indians. When the child is placed on it it is wrapped up tightly in blankets, with its arms pinioned tightly to its sides" (pp. 240, 241(.

Vambéry, A. (Sketches of Central Asia. London, 1868). Swaddling clothes are here in general use, and the kindik kesen, or cutter of the same, is a person of much consequence, because the act of cutting these out is accompanied by many ceremonial observances. Vambéry seems to indicate, however, that the child is not swathed for any length of time.

Harris, Maj. W. C. (Highlands of Ethiopia. London, 1844). The beaux of the Dankalis and Somalis, at Tajura, "employ in lieu of a pillow a small wooden bolster, shaped like a crutch-handle, which receives the neck * * * and preserves the periwig from derangement" (I, p. 58).

D'Albertis, L. M. (New Guinea). "Great varieties of type, in color, physiognomy, and in the shape of the skull," are found on Pangian Island. Here it is observed that parietal compression protrudes the supra-orbital arches (I, p. 29). The same statements may, he says, be made of the natives at Orangerie Bay (I, p. 97). Along the whole line, from Sorong to Dorey, the nose varied in form from flat to aquiline (I, p. 210). In his plate of the mummified head got from Darnley Island, Torres Straits, the type is macrocephalous.

Blake, Dr. Carter (Appendix Unexplored Syria, Burton & Drake. London, 1872), describes a female skull from the Dayr Már Músá el Habashi showing artificial "compression of the parietal bones," probably caused by use of the "suckling-board."

Davis. (Collection of Voyages and Travels, etc. London, 1745). "In Morria, a small, low island, lying in the river of the Amazons," children are thus carried· "They take a piece of the rind of a tree, and with one end thereof they fasten the child's head, and about the arm-pits and shoulders with the other, and so hang it on their backs like a tinker's budget" (II, p. 487).

Dawkins, W. Boyd. (Cave Hunting. London, 1874). Refers to Professor Busk's notes on the crania of Perthi-Chwaren, in which a skull with "a well-marked depression across the middle of the occipital bone" is described. This depression had the appearance of being "caused by the constriction of a bandage." Except this deformation the skull was "well-formed and symmetrical," not having any of the contours of the tête annulaire, due, according to MM. Foville and Gosse, to occipital compression (p. 170).

Professor Busk states, in his ethnological notes (Cave Hunting), that the Berber contingent of the Moorish invaders of Europe in the eighth, ninth, and tenth centuries "used to elongate the skull posteriorly and flatten the head" (pp. 170, 171).

In the same work Professor Dawkins suggests that the flattened occiput of the brachycephalous invaders of neolithic Britain "may have been caused by the use of an unyielding cradle-board in infancy" (p. 193). Evidently the flattened vertex of the Sclaigneaux cave was not natural (p. 219).

THE HUMAN BEAST OF BURDEN.

By OTIS T. MASON.

I never see a great passenger or express train approaching a station without thinking of the long and tiresome experiences through which the human mind has passed upward to this concrete climax of inventions.

I take my stand as near as safety will allow, that I may drink in the eddies of the boiling atmosphere with the aroma of civilization which it represents.

There is something wonderful in the iron horse—his glaring headlight, irresistible momentum, extreme docility. On the platform of the locomotive stands the controlling mind, the engineer, one hand upon a lever, which sets in motion all this ponderous mass at the rate of even a mile a minute, as Cicero says, "*quadam inclinatione corporis.*" His other hand rests upon the air-brake, by means of which he controls the momentum of 500 tons, reducing it at will to absolute rest. Who has not imagined, as he whirled along on one of these trains, that he could hear the measured hoof-beats of this horse of progress striking the ties or the iron rails? If we consider all the industries and motives involved in this man's activity, the myriad trades and occupations invoked in the manufacture of train and track, the multitudinous avocations accommodated by and stimulating his movements, the infinite variety of freight, animate and inanimate; bags of letters, the messengers of every want and emotion; an endless caravan of passengers of every class of humanity on every possible errand, representing all commercial designs, social and civil structures and functions, we shall have an example of the climax of human endeavor in its most highly organized condition relative to a long series of inventions, of which this is only the introductory chapter. Besides these there are thousands of other occupations, in which carrying is neither directly nor remotely interested, wherein man's handiwork has preceded, initiated, and kept up the higher utilization of animals and of natural forces.

But we are not concerned at the present moment so much with the tedious and varied manipulations by which the railway train has been manufactured from the forest and the mine (that would be its ontogeny) as with the millenniums of change through which a common human back-strap or head-band has passed upward through inventive creation into the train and track, the latest common carrier (which constitutes the phylogeny of the railway).

At the lower end of this line of inventions and experiences, neglecting all the mental burdens which often weigh heavier on us than our packs, as we pass downward ignoring wagon trains, mule trains, caravans, couriers, pack-horses, dog travois and sleds, reindeer sledges, donkeys, llamas, and other beasts of burden, we come at last to the primitive common carrier, the pack-man himself, and also the pack-woman, for men and women were the first beasts of burden.[*]

Primitive commerce and all the carrying and running involved in primeval arts connected with food, shelter, clothing, rest, enjoyment, and war were accomplished on the heads or foreheads, shoulders or backs, or in the hands of men and women; and civilization, while it has invented many ways of burden-bearing, finds also an endless variety of uses for the old methods. How many thousands of our fellow-creatures are still in this condition of mere beasts of burden? It is, for instance, only a few years since the invention of the passenger and freight elevator began to supplant that train of "hod-carriers," who have been since the beginning of architecture carrying upward to its completion every wooden and brick structure in the world.

To get something like an adequate conception of the enormous amount of labor performed by human backs, calculate the weight of every earth-work, mound, fort, canal, embankment, wooden, brick, metal, and stone structure and fabrication on earth. These have all been carried many times and elevated by human muscle. In the light of this contemplation, Atlas, son of Heaven and Earth, supporting on his shoulders the pillars of the sky, is the apotheosis of the human son of toil, and the gaping wonder of archæologists over the hand-made structures of Thebes, Palenque, Carnac, and Salisbury Plain subsides to the level of a mathematical problem. Indeed, the great majority of earth-works, mounds, menhirs, cairns, cromlechs, and dolmens now to be seen witnessed the exertions of no other artisan than the human carrier.[†]

In the Internationale Archiv für Ethnographie, Plate IX, is a street scene in Singapore. The first thing that arrests the attention is that everybody is carrying something or is harnessed to something. Commencing at the left hand occur the following:

(1) Two coolies carrying a lady in a hammock.

(2) Two coolies carrying a live pig in a bamboo cylinder suspended to a pole.

(3) A lady carrying a fan and a reticule.

---

[*] Innumerable examples of women as burden-bearers may be cited. See Schoolcraft, Archives, vol. VI, plate opp. p. 560; J. G. Wood, Unciv. Races, vol. I, p. 330, et seq.

[†] Cf. Lucien Carr, Mounds of the Mississippi Valley, p. 90, for a calculation of the time required to build an earth mound. Reference is made to the coal-carriers in St. Thomas, and to a paragraph by Isaac McCoy in the History of the Baptist Indian Missions, p. 27, for the capabilities in this line of a single tribe of Indians.

(4) A coolie carrying on his right shoulder a pole; from one end dangles a box, from the other a basket. Indeed, there are three men hitched in this fashion in the foreground.

(5) A man dragging a small truck loaded with bundles.

(6) A coolie carrying a furnace on the end of a stick resting on his shoulder, as a peddler does his pack.

(7) A coolie drawing a jinrickasha.

(8) A Chinese gentleman carrying a fan and a cane.

Considering the activity now displayed in transporting men and productions from one part of the earth to another, it will not be a valueless contribution to science if we trace the natural history of those early occupations and industries, the improvement of whose apparatus and methods stimulated the pristine inventors to make their burdens lighter, to enable the human carrier to bear the load with greater ease, to render his pack weight proportionate to the length of his journeys, and to adapt his occupation to the ever new exigencies of his environment.

It is a common saying that we must go to nature for our supplies. Equally true is it that we go in vain, unless we descend to the condition of the brutes, if we expect nature to supply us with aught else than that whereon we may exercise the inventive faculty. Indeed, there are innumerable examples of animals transporting materials to distant places in order to utilize them. The beaver, the bird, the lamprey eel, the bee, the ant are all carriers.* Many animals also modify natural objects for the purpose of using them. But the two ideas of modifying a natural object for the purpose of making a carrying tool seem to concur only in the human mind. We are the only animals that modify nature to produce a carrying device. Again, these creatures all carry their implements and weapons with them as part of their natural endowment; they do not have to invent them. But the farmer, the artisan, the professional man, even the laborers go about weighted down, with their tools, apparatus, books, or even their carrying implements as ponderous often as the trunk and tusks are to the elephant.

There are two sets of ideas involved in harnessing the human *jument*, which may be studied in part separately, in part together. They are *conveyance* and *transportation*, or the carrying of the man and the carrying of things. The former may be older, for devices in which to carry infants may have been the first in the order of invention. The passenger and the freight train express the two ideas exactly, because each, while encroaching on the function of the other, has modifications for its own ends. The subject of mere locomotion involving snow-shoes, canes, staves, alpenstocks, stilts, crutches, and the like will not be here considered, because they are only aids to locomotion and involve little that relates to the beast of burden.

The cradle-board and other devices for carrying infants will also be

---

* For comparison of the engineering skill of beavers and ants with that of the mound-builders, cf. Lucien Carr, "The Mounds of the Mississippi Valley," p. 66.

the theme of a separate chapter, inasmuch as other ideas are involved, but the methods of human conveyance on the backs of bearers among people not highly civilized will receive brief mention.

Many other industries have been created, stimulated and modified by the carrying trade. Every one will have a dozen suggested by the mere mention of the subject. One has lately come to the writer's notice, which will serve as a very primitive example. The crudest agriculture in the world is practiced by the Pimas and contiguous tribes in southern-most California to procure gourds for the transportation of seeds and water. The women, accompanied by a body-guard of men, go, in the spring time, to the bluffs or rocky slopes, where a little rich, moist earth fills the crevices, and therein, by the help of a sharpened stick, they insert their gourd seed. In the autumn the women return to these spots to gather the large gourds hanging from their natural trellis, and from them supply their households with a variety of utensils. So the carrier is patron to the farmer.

In the same way has the carrier stood friend to the potter. Among the Pueblos and other pottery-making peoples hundreds of jars are made to be carried on the head or to be swung from the shoulder in a yoke. The potter molds his vase at the order and convenience of the carrier.

Basketry has also lent its services largely to the carrying industry, and in turn has assumed a multitude of shapes and textures demanded by this occupation alone.

In the National Museum, at Washington, gathered from many parts of the world, are a great variety of devices designed exclusively to facilitate the carrying of burdens by mankind. There are many others in various parts of the world quite as important.

We may approach our task from different points of view, guided by a variety of ruling concepts. It is possible to consider the subject geographically. I was delighted to find this fact recognized by Plato :*

" CLEINIAS : Look at the character of our country. Crete is not like Thessaly, a large plain, and for this reason they have horses there and we have runners on foot here. The inequality of the ground in our country is more adapted to locomotion afoot."

The word " geography " as here used applies to all natural advantages, to materials used in constructing appliances, and to objects carried.

Or we may view the subject ethnically, in relation to tribal patterns, customs, and the prejudices of clan, class, or sex.

Or it may be regarded nationally, with reference to the regulations concerning carriers under the same government and treaties relating thereto between different political bodies.

A philogenetic method would lead us to scrutinize the various ways of carrying in relation to the influence of one invention in giving birth to another or in some way modifying the form of another, either in the same category or in other categories.

---

* Laws N. Y. (1873), Scribner, vol. IV, p. 156.

An interesting method of study would be by crafts, and it would enlist the co-operation of many searchers. For instance, we might ask the fur trader of Hudson Bay territory to tell us all the ways of carrying peltry that his land had seen, from packing up to the Red River cart. In like manner the emigrant over the earth, the peddler or merchant, the woodman, the miner, the fisherman, the farmer could each tell us a wonderful story, beginning with a very simple process and winding up with a story worthy of the Arabian Nights; or, finally, our thoughts could be arranged progressionally in relation to the phenomena, including both what some call natural evolution and also technical elaboration or design.

One of the most interesting chapters in the history is that which portrays the methods of hitching up this animal of burden, the parts of the body utilized, the harness adopted, and the adaptation of these to the burden, the country, and, in short, all the exigencies of the case. With this one idea in mind look carefully over the great works devoted to the ancient monuments of Egypt, Assyria, Greece, and Rome, or turn the leaves of pictorial journals and books of travel, and the variety of ways by which man has grown equal to his burden will be astonishing.

As the study of railroading includes the engine or motor, the train or burden, the road and the signal, no less does the consideration of the original freightman or pappoose-carrier involve the person, the load, the trail, and the primitive signal. Indeed, the germ of the latest passenger and freight train was in the first human burden-bearer.

The task of duly appreciating rude inventions is not easy, and some of the statements herein made may seem trivial. Living in the enjoyment of so many privileges in the matter of conveyance and transportation, we shall find it hard to realize the former condition of things unless we transport ourselves to savage and barbarous lands or out-of-the-way country places. In a thriving city one no longer thinks of walking. The cheapest hand laborers ride to their work in cars of palatial splendor drawn by horses, steam, or electricity. Men and women flit around on cycles. It is considered vulgar to carry a parcel. The servant girl buys a few cents' worth of tawdry stuff and has it brought to her in a parcel-dispatch wagon that is covered with forty coats of lacquer. Everywhere the old régime is changed in our civilization. We get an inadequate conception of the early history of human backs by contemplating the service that nature is at present rendering to the comfort and convenience of our race.

It would hardly be worth while to mention the clothing and adornment of mankind as a load to be carried, were it not for the fact that in some cases, such as the brass wire of the Africans and the mail of the mediæval knight,* as much as one hundred pounds are borne by a single individual. Counting all humanity, it is safe to say that two millions of tons of apparel and personal ornament are constantly worn to supply

---

* Cf. Meyrich, or Hewitt, or Demmin.

artificially what nature has given gratis to other animals, either in the way of hair or wool to keep them warm, or plumage to increase their attractions.

It is impossible to enumerate every form of burden-bearing, but to show the almost endless variety in which inventive genius has displayed itself in loading the human body, the following enumeration is introduced:

METHODS OF BEARING BURDENS.

1. *In the hand.*—This method is universal. In the house, at the station, on the street, wherever one turns, light parcels are flitting in every direction, which in the aggregate amounts to an enormous mass, carried principally in the right hand. At the other end of human history the act repeats itself. For we can scarcely frame a conception of man primeval without a club or stone weapon or rude spear in one hand, and here again the right hand has been selected to do the work.*

2. *In both hands.*—It is really easier to carry in both hands than in one, even though the load be larger. So it is a common sight to see a man or a woman dividing the luggage into two parcels, bearing two buckets or baskets, sometimes held apart with a hoop. In raising a load to the shoulders both hands are used. It is amusing to watch the potters on the Egyptian monuments—to see the multiplicity of attitudes they assume in the application of the two hands to burden-bearing.

3. *On the fingers.*—This is a kind of fine art in carrying. In the old descriptions and pictures of royal cup bearers the salver is delicately poised on three fingers. The climax of this plan is the summer-resort waiter's feat of bringing the food of half a dozen individuals borne aloft on the ends of his fingers in a huge tray.

4. *With a baldric.*—The modern tourist hangs his opera-glass, satchel, haversack, etc., to a strap passing over one shoulder and under the opposite arm. The hunter carries his game-bag in a similar manner. Among hurdy-gurdy players and fruit-peddlers the strap hangs on the back of the neck and the load rests against the stomach. The hands are then free to make music, handle the merchandise, or even to help in carrying the load. The baldric is now a military ornament especially, and may never have had extensive use among savages.

5. *Hung to a belt.*—Combining the belt with the baldric, the soldier carries his weapons. It is common to see small objects hung to a belt before, behind, or on either side. This is not an easy way to carry a heavy burden; yet among semi-civilized peoples it is the place for transporting treasures—in short, the first step in the insurance of carrying treasures. Also, the broad sash of many peoples serves admirably for holding children, victuals, weapons, papers, and things not to be exposed.

---

* The writer has examined a great many savage weapons and tools that will fit only one hand. The proportion of left-handed is not more than one in fifty for men, and he has never seen a left-handed woman's implement.

6. *On the arm.*—This might be called the retail method of carrying. One sees every moment about the farm boys and men using this method of carrying, and on the busy street multitudes of men, women, and children are ever flitting to and fro with loads. These vary from a few ounces to several pounds, and are borne under the arm, on the forearm, on both forearms. In the stores it is the same thing. The arm seems to be the vehicle for retail conveyance. To vary this style a little we must increase the load and basket and watch the market people as they trudge along with 50 pounds of food hung on the elbow, resting on the hip, and the body bent to get the center of gravity poised exactly. The writer has never seen in any book of travels a savage man with a load hung to his arm like a great hook and himself twisted around so as to throw a part of the weight upon his hip. This must be a product of civilization.

7. *Hung from the shoulders.*—This is the favorite device of farmers and others who carry small loads in a bag. One of the indelible recollections of country life is of the farm hand carrying grain, plaster, and other things about the premises in a sack suspended from his shoulders. The same man on Saturday afternoon trudges homeward from the mill and the store with the week's provisions for his family carried in the same manner. The peddler of small wares, the laborer moving with his little property, the hunter returning with his game, the woman of southern climes with her child, all are examples of the importance of the shoulder in the economy of transportation when used merely as an accessory to the back. The universal sack of the negro population of the rural districts in the Southern United States as a receptacle for everything, is a good example of this method of carrying, which has come down to us from the remotest antiquity. Travelers state that a Peruvian miner will ascend 100 or more feet of a rude ladder with 300 pounds of ore in a skin bag hung from his shoulder.

8. *On the shoulder.*—The shoulder alone plays a leading part in transportation. There is no lack of examples of women pursuing this method. The miller takes a sack of grain on his shoulder, places his palm on his hip, and moves on to his hopper, or he reverses the process with a sack of flour from the mill to the farmer's wagon.

In great shipping houses lines of porters carry sacks of grain to the ship in the same way.

Again, the hod-carrier, antecedent of all modern elevators, with 75 to 100 pounds of brick or mortar on his back, has been for ages all over the world transporting upward the material of the builder.

Look, moreover, at the coolies of the Orient. More than a million Chinese make their living as professional carriers. In the cities are the porters and others who carry rice, etc., on the shoulder in sacks or burdens upon a pole, half the weight at either end.

Writes a friend:

"The average load of a coolie is 100 pounds, and with this he travels

30 miles. Kinkiang is an important place for the export of tea. The tea districts are situated about 60 miles from the town, and the coolies bring in the chests in two days, each man carrying a load of 100 pounds. The weight of a load and the distance over which a coolie travels may be different in the north and south. I have not been able to make inquiries elsewhere but at this port."

In Shanghai 140 pounds is an ordinary burden. For long distances 100 pounds is the load and 20 miles the ordinary day's journey. The bearer has a staff in his hand and rests *ad libitum* by balancing his burden on top. One hundred pounds 20 miles equals a ton a mile per day. Now, if there are a million coolies, there are each day in China 1,000,000 tons of freight moved 1 mile on the backs of professional carriers. The ancient Egyptians practiced this mode of carrying extensively.

9. *On the scapulæ.*—The grain carriers or lumpers who load vessels with wheat or corn may frequently be seen with a full sack resting on top of their backs. They run up a plank to the hatch, toss the sack in the air, mouth downwards, and catch the lower corners so as to save the sack and dump the grain into the hold.

The English porters and furniture men have a knot, padded with something soft, which they place around the forehead and on the scapulæ. They are then ready to take on the largest pieces of furniture, such as bureaus, sideboards, etc. The higher form of this art of carrying on the scapulæ is the Holland yoke, a device which enables the bearer to bring the hands into play.

10. *On the back.*—The back is the natural resting place for the burden. The lowest savages know this, and inventive genius early began to devise apparatus for harnessing this part of the body. In Africa, on the Andes, in Mexico, throughout the civilized world, the peaceable carrier bears on his back the commerce of the race. The load is held in place either by the forehead strap, the breast strap, the shoulder strap, or by two or more of these combined. Bock, in his "Head-hunters of Borneo," represents a carrier using both the head band and the shoulder straps as in knapsack carrying. In war the soldier fastens his knapsack to his back and shoulders, leaving his arms free to do their work. There are many patent devices for distributing the soldier's load over the shoulders, breast, back, and hips. For obvious reasons his hips are left free. Children play at pick-a-pack, passengers are landed in shallow ports, persons of means pass over difficult places in the manner described by Cassius:

> I, as Æneas, our great ancestor,
> Did from the flames of Troy upon his shoulder
> The old Anchises bear, so from the waves of Tiber
> Did I the tired Cæsar.

The burdens of Kurdish women are thus graphically described:

"Soon we came to a place where the road was washed away, and we were obliged to go around. We saw a woman there with a loaded donkey which could not pass with its load; the woman took the load on her own back and carried it over, and then led the donkey over. She also carried a load of at least 100 pounds, and she had a spindle in her hands. Thus she went spinning and singing over the rugged way which I had passed with tears and pain. * * * In the evening they spin and make sandals; when they lie down, they place under their heads the ropes to bind the heavy loads of grass and wood which they bring down from the mountains. After midnight they go up to get loads. * * * In the early morning I often saw the women, looking like loaded beasts, coming down the precipitous mountain path, one after the other, singing and spinning as they came. * * * I saw women with great paniers on their backs and babies on top of these or in their arms, going four days over that fearful Ishtazin pass, carrying grapes for sale and bringing back grain. Men said the women must suffer much more before God could forgive Eve's sin.

"A few years ago a woman from Jeloo came to my home in Geogtapa. Her husband, who was almost a giant, sickened in Gawar, and she told me she had carried him on her back all the way, four days' journey. He died in our house. I did not believe her then; now I do, for my eyes have seen what loads these women carry."*

11. *On the head.*—This process is usually called toting, and is especially characteristic of women† of the lower classes and of negroes.‡ The traveler may see the dairy maids anywhere in Europe carrying 25 pounds of milk on the head, women in Iceland carrying loads of unsavory codfish on their heads, and Italian peddlers of all sorts use the head for a carriage. In the southern part of the United States 50 pounds is the "toter's" steady load. Men and women constantly bear that amount. A slater's assistant mounts a ladder with 50 pounds of slate on the head. The farm woman totes a tub of water holding 10 gallons, the whole weight being 100 pounds. The head-ring is seen among the Zuñi Indians as a means of keeping the load on the head and relieving the pressure. Pads of various kinds replace the ring where toting is for long distances.§

12. The forehead and the bregma are also parts on which to hang harness. In civilization the yoke has passed from the forehead of the ox to his scapulæ. Comparing the head-strap of all our Indian tribes with the neck-yoke of the Holland woman, it is permitted to see the same

---

* Woman's Work for Women, November, 1888, p. 296.

† See illustration of Kaffir women carrying fagots in Wood's "Unciv. Races, vol. I, p. 91.

‡ "All along the road we met numbers of men, women, and children going to the Badagry market, with palm-oil, corn, yams, fowls, fire-wood, etc., which they carried in heavy loads on their heads, according to the universal custom of this country, though the Golahs and others in that region carry burdens on their backs." (Bowen, Cent. Africa, p. 103.)

§ Wood mentions the Bechuana habit of "bogale," or drilling young girls in carrying loads of wood long distances and jars of water without spilling a drop. (Unciv. Races, I, p. 26.)

process of improvement antedating the domestication of the ox, and possibly suggesting his harness.

13. *In pockets.*—This method of conveyance is scarcely worth mentioning from the civilized point of view; yet, when we consider the endless variety of small merchandise carried in the pockets of men and women, and remember that all these pockets are for no other purpcse than to serve as instruments of transportation, we can not omit including it. We must remember also that the Oriental, especially the Corean, has pockets in his sleeves having the capacity of a half bushel. The Turk and the Arab stow away as much as this in the ample folds of their robes, and any boy who has stolen fruit can add his testimony.

14. *Men combined.*—Two men bearing a log or burden on their shoulders, four or six men carrying a bier or stretcher,[*] sailors hoisting to the rhythm of a song or "ōhyeā," two or more men with a palankin borne among them, a set of bearers in Madagascar and elsewhere with relays, a company or a regiment of men carrying an immense stone in India, as figured by Count Wurmbrand, a lot of men setting up a barn frame or telegraph pole, all illustrate the utility of combined effort to transport a heavy mass. There is no doubt that the great works of modern times, whose existence and utility depend entirely upon the co-working of thousands to make and to maintain them, were foreshadowed and completely outlined in the days when hand-work alone was the force employed. Herodotus ascribes the beginning of the first canal between the Nile and the Red Sea to Neku, and the completion to Darius, the Persian. A hundred and twenty thousand Egyptians lost their lives in Neku's reign.[†] Peons entering some Mexican city or slave trains from the heart of Africa often reveal a long row of men and women co-operating in carrying a great weight. The same is true of the pulley, answering to a compound hod, by means of which one man transports a single weight much too heavy for one.[‡] In an account of Cheops' causeway, "some were required to drag blocks of stone down to the Nile; others drew them to the range of hills called Libyan; a hundred thousand men eat bread constantly, and were relieved every three months by a fresh lot."[§] In Munich those who carry large sacks use an implement like **M** to grasp, as it hurts the hands to lock fingers under the end of the sack. They stand face to face and grasp the rounded sides of this wooden buckle, slide it under the sack, lift it up, and steady it with the free hand, which carries it along and gives it a toss in unloading.[||] In this country men carry pianos by means of a

---

[*] Rawlinson's Herodotus, II, 77, figure. The transportation of the disabled with reference to conveyance by human bearers. By James E. Pilcher, M. D., Ph. D. J. Mil. Serv. Inst., IX (1888), 222–242.

[†] Rawlinson's Herodotus, II, 158, with notes.

[‡] Rawlinson's Herodotus, II, 124.

[§] Rawlinson's Herodotus, II, 277; III, 377.

[||] Theo. A. Mills. See Prescott, Conquest of Mexico (Philad., 1874, I, 145) for the transportation of the calendar stone from the mountains beyond lake Chalco, a distance of many leagues, over a broken country intersected by water-courses and canals.

shoulder-strap and a peg that goes into the hole left by unscrewing the legs. Two men can carry a piano thus.

15. *Hauling.*—The simplest form of traction among men may be seen in the small boy dragging his wagon or sledge. With the arms alone for traces the primitive man dragged his game over the ground or ice to his distant home. Even two or more might co-operate in this primeval team. The next step would be the use of a line, perhaps of rawhide, perhaps of fiber. Along the edge of some quiet water they walked, those pristine tow-men, dragging their rafts or rude boats from the pebbly beach. Here began that immense industry now carried on in the canals of the world.

The ways of fastening one's self to this traction or tow line are many.* The simplest is the grasp of the hand. Others may be seen bending to their work with the line over the shoulder, around the waist, or tied to a becket or bricole. A curious variety of this tracking is seen on Russian rivers, where an anchor is carried up-stream in a small boat and dropped. The cable passes back to a windlass or a heavy barge, by which the great mass is moved up to the anchor. A delightful specimen of helpless modern invention is a picture in Baker's "Ismailia."† Steamer No. 10 has balked among the rank vegetation of a canal, and she is being hauled along by a hundred or more naked Africans dragging at a cable. In the Southern States formerly the great shad-nets were drawn ashore by a gang of fifty to one hundred negroes, who wore each a becket with a Turk's-head knot, which the seine-hauler knew how to attach or detach in a second.

A species of tracking practiced on the Upper Missouri and other northern rivers in the fur-trading period before steam-boat days, has been called to the writer's attention by Dr. Washington Matthews, U. S. Army. It is called cordeling.‡ The goods of the trader are loaded upon a boat and the craft dragged by a tow-line along the margin of the stream. These articles were traded for furs until the boat had gradually exchanged its freight of civilized wares for peltry. Then the craft was easily floated back to St. Louis, its starting point. Mention is made of this process by Lewis and Clarke, Prince of Wied, Brackenridge, and other travelers of the pre-steamboat days.

Before cordeling, even, there was a method of ferriage of the most primitive character practiced on the Missouri River. The bull-boat was a contrivance used as a primitive ferry. It was made as follows: A

---

* Hinds's Labrador, vol. 1, pp. 77, 94.

† New York, 1875, opp. p. 53.

‡ "The British fur companies held the trade of these Indians until 1807, when Manuel Lisa ascended the river in keel-boats to the Mandan villages and beyond. Until 1832 goods were brought up the Missouri River chiefly in keel-boats, or Mackinaw boats, which were *cordeled*, or towed by men with great labor against the rapid current of the river. Two summers at least were always occupied in dragging a boat from St. Louis to the head of navigation, the crew sustaining themselves chiefly by hunting." Ethnography of the Hidatsa, p. 30.

number of elastic poles were firmly inserted in the earth in a circle the size of the gunwale of the boat, and a horizontal pole was lashed to these a few inches from the ground. The tops of these poles were bent inward, each opposite pair being firmly and neatly lashed together at a height from the ground to correspond with the depth of the craft. This done, a buffalo-bull hide, depilated and thoroughly soaked, was drawn down and stretched over the frame, and the edges secured to the horizontal pole which served the purpose of a gunwale. The ends of the poles were then cut off, the vessel turned over, any little crevices were stopped, and the ferry-boat was ready to launch;[*] and this is the way the apparatus worked: Whenever an Indian wished to cross a river in his bull-boat he placed therein his luggage and babies, and fastening a rawhide line to his gunwale, he swam across the river with the other end attached to his body. Behind the craft swam his wife or daughters, pushing the boat as much as possible against the stream. Indians have told the writer that oblong bull-boats were formerly used, before the days of steam, whenever longer journeys were to be taken. The practice would be perfectly in keeping with the birch-bark canoe journeys of the tribes north and east, where the vessel was only an improved bull-boat, in which birch-bark took the place of rawhide.

According to Herodotus (I, § 1) Cleobis and Bito were honored by Solon with the second place of happiness among men. "There was a great festival in honor of the goddess Juno at Argos, to which their mother must needs be taken in a car. Now, the oxen did not come home from the field in time, so the youth, fearful of being too late, put the yoke on their own necks and themselves drew the car." Without dreaming of their distinguished company hundreds of rag-pickers, small-truckmen, and peddlers are pulling and pushing wagons and carts about the streets, sometimes alone and often hitched by the side of dog or donkey.[†]

16. *Throwing or tossing.*—An immense amount of material is moved by various methods of throwing, with or without tools. It is a process of rapid transit in which the material alone moves without the necessity of a track of any kind. Doubtless many will remember the old fashion of passing buckets of water at a fire before the invention of engines. The negroes in southern cities move many thousands of watermelons and other produce from the vessels to the warehouses or wagons, often hun-

---

[*] Cf. Lewis and Clarke's Travels, London, 1817, vol. 3, p. 348.

[†] The Egyptian sculptures abound in representations of human traction in every attitude in which it is possible for a man to be attached to a rope. See Rawlinson's Herodotus, II, 72. See also in Rawlinson's Five Monarchies, New York, 1871, p. 402, from Layard, a spirited picture of men moving a human-headed bull. We have here in one picture men drawing sledges, others drawing hand-carts filled with ropes, and others fixing rollers, working levers, holding props and guys, carrying rollers, relays coming to relieve their fellows, taskmasters with clubs, and the boss on the front of the sledge marking time for those at the ropes. All the draft-men have bricoles or beckets as individual harness.

dreds of feet, by tossing them from one to another, standing ten feet apart. It is a simple step from this to the shovel, the fork, the hoe, or the rake, used on every farm and in connection with almost every business in the world.* In the oldest forms of embankment the laborers doubtless carried the dirt in sacks or baskets. To this day the fellaheen of Egypt follow the primitive method.† But in all military operations, canal and railroad work, excavation in cities, the shovel is the vehicle of transportation, and the navvy, or his technical representative, is the beast of burden.

17. *Caravans.*—It is only a step from the single carrier to the organized train under the direction of a leader performing in common a task which would be dangerous to one, or in which mutual help is needed. No one supposes that the caravans of historic times were invented at a single effort. The caravansaries, the wells, the armed guard, the joining of forces at difficult places, are complicated affairs which are the resultants of many trials of much simpler character.

In the old slave-hunting days in Africa the same method was practiced with slaves. A lot of negroes would be captured and driven to the coast for sale, but to save freight each individual was loaded with ivory, gold-dust, and other commodities. On arriving at the coast the trader sold out the whole concern and returned to repeat the process.‡ In Southern Mexico and Central America the trade from the interior is brought to the coast on the backs of peons marching *en traine* under a leader.

18. In all the early accounts of settlements in our country trails are not only mentioned as the veritable war-path, but commercial trails were also known. This introduces us to the whole subject of roads, the series being paths marked by stakes or blazed trees, unkept roads, highways, turnpikes, plank roads, paved streets, tramways. In these rude trails or paths are many obstacles—declivities, streams, chasms. To overcome these, inventive genius has devised bridges, fords, steps, graded ways, tunnels, etc., part of the outcome of the packman's industry.§

---

* Dr. Samson reports a curious combination of the spade with traction. "In spading up the ground a fellah pressed the spade into the earth, while a woman on each side, by means of a rope attached to the handle, raised the spade with its load and turned it over."

† "I saw in the Delta of Egypt a common occurrence, young women and girls digging in the canals, shoveling the black, dripping mud with a bit of wood and their hands into palm-leaf baskets, putting the dripping baskets on their heads so that their hair and faces were all matted with slime, toiling up the sides of the canal to empty their loads, while a taskmaster with a whip would cut their bare legs as they passed if in weariness they loitered."—*Dr. G. W. Samson.*

‡ See reference to selling boat and cargo in Herodotus, vol. i, p. 194.

§ Mommsen's "Rome," New York, 1869, i, 177. For an excellent account of the swinging bridges of Peru, cf. Squier, Incidents of Travel, etc., New York, 1877, 544–547.

19. *Relaying.*—An important element in transportation is resting and relaying.* In most rude carrying-devices the greatest effort is put forth in rising from the ground or in getting the load in place. The organ-grinder and the coolie carry staves, on which they rest their load when they are fatigued. The Damara girl lifts her load from her head and holds it aloft on both hands while she proceeds on her journey. The soldier shifts his weapons; the Malagasy bearers replace one another under the poles of the *filanzana,* or carrying-chair, without interrupting their journey. The Montezumas had relays of runners between the sea and the city of Mexico, so as to receive fish and other lowland products in a fresh condition.

20. *Couriers.*—From this inquiry must not be omitted the courier, swift messenger of tidings, earthly prototype of Hermes, who was succeeded later by horses, dromedaries, carrier-pigeons, ships on the sea, steam-cars on land, and, last of all, the telegraph. His modern survival is the district and telegraph messenger boy. I have seen some-where the picture of a naked Kaffir running at full speed, bearing in one hand a pair of assegais and in the other a rod split at the upper end to receive a letter, carried thus to keep it from being soiled by contact with his naked body.

In ancient Mexico, says Prescott, "communication was maintained with the remotest parts of the country by means of couriers. Post-houses were established on great roads, about two leagues distant from each other. The courier, bearing his dispatches in the form of a hiero-glyphic painting, ran with them to the first station, where they were taken by another messenger and carried forward to the next, and so on until they reached the capital. These couriers, trained from childhood, traveled with incredible swiftness, not four or five leagues an hour, as an old chronicler would make us believe, but with such speed that dis-patches were carried from one to two hundred miles a day."†

There is no doubt that all of these various devices have had their in-fluence in shaping and deforming the human body. Students of crani-ology and anthropometry should have their attention called to the fact that among savages the use of carrying-pads, straps, and other devices about the head commences just as soon as the child can walk, with little loads at first in small baskets, wallets, nets, frames, or what not, when

---

* Hinds's "Labrador," vol. I, p. 43.

† Conquest of Mex., Phila., 1874, vol. I, p. 43. For an exciting account of couriers with lighted torches proclaiming the new cycle, *id.*, 130, compare C. A. Muray, Travels in North America, New York, 1839, vol. I, p. 193, who says that an Indian of his party traveled a hundred miles in four and twenty hours. Prescott also alludes to Plutarch's account of the Greek who brought the news of victory to Platæa, 125 miles, in a day; to pedestrian capabilities of man in a savage state collected by Buffon; to Marco Polo's account of couriers in China in the thirteenth century; to Anderson's account of Gov-ernment couriers in China in 1796. (Conq. of Mex., Phila., vol. I, p. 44, note.) "Noth-ing in the world is borne so swiftly as messages by the Persian couriers." (Herod., Urania, 98.) In this case horses were used as in the pony mail formerly in use across the plains, but the man or courier went on.

a forehead strap for the top of the head is employed. Even though these marks may not be hereditary, they can not escape the notice of the craniometer.

It should not be overlooked that this human pack animal possesses the greatest versatility. In the case of your train, hundreds of men load the cars, carrying burdens on back and trucks; men manipulate the senseless and purposeless thing looking so proud and capable; men unload the train, and, indeed, put the fiery steed to bed. Not so in primitive culture; the man-beast feeds, waters, and curries himself, gathers and adjusts his own load, changes himself into propeller, trackman, carrier *ad libitum*, besides adapting himself to a multitude of subsidiary occupations not here under consideration. Indeed, the man is engineer, engine, freight-car, truck, wheelbarrow, horse cart, dray, towpath, mule, etc., all combined.

The mean effect of the power of a man unaided by a machine, working to the best possible advantage and at a moderate estimation, is the raising of 70 pounds 1 foot high in a second for ten hours in a day.

Two men working at a windlass at right angles to each other can raise 70 pounds more easily than one man can raise 30 pounds.

Mr. Bevan's results with experiments upon human strength are for a short period:

	Pounds of force.
With a drawing-knife	100
With auger, both hands	100
With screw-driver, one hand	84
With bench-vise, handle	72
With chisel, vertical pressure	72
With windlass	60
With pincers, compression	60
With hand-plane	50
With hand-saw	36
With thumb-vise	45
With brace-bit, revolving	16
Twisting with the thumb and fingers only, and with a small screw-driver	14

By Mr. Field's experiments in 1838 the maximum power of a strong man exerted for two and one half minutes is 18,000 pounds raised 1 foot in a minute.

A man of ordinary strength exerts a force of 30 pounds for ten hours in a day with a velocity of $2\frac{1}{2}$ feet in a second, equal to 4,500 pounds raised 1 foot in a minute, equal to one-fifth of the work of a horse.

A foot soldier travels in one minute in common time ninety steps equal 70 yards; in quick time, one hundred steps equal 86 yards; in double-quick time, one hundred and forty steps equal 109 yards.

He occupies in the ranks a front of 20 inches and a depth of 13 inches without a knapsack; the interval between the ranks is 13 inches.

Average weight of men, 150 pounds each; five men can stand in a space of 1 square yard.

A man travels without a load on level ground during eight and one-half hours a day at the rate of 3.7 miles an hour or $31\frac{1}{4}$ miles a day. He can carry 111 pounds 11 miles in a day. Daily allowance of water for a man, one gallon for all purposes.

A porter going short distances and returning unloaded carries 135 pounds 7 miles a day. He can carry in a wheelbarrow 150 pounds 10 miles a day.

The muscles of the human jaw exert a force of 534 pounds.

Dr. Dwight observes: "Indians will travel with a facility, a celerity, and a freedom from fatigue unknown to the people of Europe. Their couriers or runners are said to go at the rate of 100 miles a day. Two Choctaws followed my father 500 miles to steal from him two valuable horses. When I asked how they could be willing to take so much trouble for such an object, he observed that they had no other business, and that roving was their favorite enjoyment." *

The number of pounds that a man is able to lift or carry a short distance hardly enters into this investigation, but rather belongs to feats of strength and agility. A naval officer tells of a Swede who, wishing to show his captain how nicely he had polished a brass cannon, took it on his shoulder and carried it upon the bridge. The weight could not have been less than a half ton. The following example of woman's strength, by Captain Healy, involves also the idea of ingenuity and the conquest of natural forces: A woman volunteered to bring in her boat a stone for an anchor to his launch which required two strong men to lift; weight guessed to be 800 pounds [that is too high]. She first filled her boat with small branches of spruce; then, choosing a part of the bank where her boat-rail would be on a level with the ground, rolled the stone over on the pliant boughs. Afterwards the spruce boughs were removed one by one, to allow the stone to slip to its place in the boat.† [From Capt. Healy's account I infer that she first filled her boat with water and used the buoyancy of the water to help her in moving the stone. He says that they understand this.]

As to the amount one man can carry, Prof. Asaph Hall, of the United States Naval Observatory, communicates the following :

" When I was nineteen years old I could carry a barrel of flour from the wagon into the house without putting it down, a distance of 3 rods, and up six stone steps; but I could not do this with a barrel of cider. If we put my carrying strength equal to x, we have therefore, barrel of cider 7×7, barrel of flour. It was the custom in Litchfield County, Connecticut, forty years ago, to use 112 pounds for a hundredweight. A common test of strength among the young men was to string ten half-hundredweights on the shanks of a fork for a lift. There were many men who could lift 560 pounds."

THE PROFESSIONAL CARRIER.

A new epoch in the history of the human beast of burden commences with the appointment of professional bearers or professional common

---

* Hodgson's North America, vol. I, p. 250.

† M. A. Healy, Cruise of the Corwin, 1887, p. 49.

carriers. It is brought about by the differentiating process of advancing society. As soon as a body or caste of men are allowed to give their whole time to a pursuit their efficiency is quadrupled; the unsuccessful drop out of line; advantages are handed down; powers of perception and skill are strengthened; all sorts of devices for packing, padding, shifting the load, resting, relieving, relaying, combining effort, are thought of as measures of self-protective necessity. The professional carrier is more likely to have been the inventor of the beast of burden, having to suffer more in his own back and legs by reason of his daily burden. The Bajuli of the Romans were professional porters: "Ferri proprie dicimus quae quis suo corpore bajulat; portari ea, quae quis in jumento secum ducit; agi ea, quae animalia sunt. Gaj. Dig., 50, 16, 235, etc. Bajulos dicebant antiqui, quos nunc dicimus operarios." Fest., p. 29. In late Latin, a bearer at a funeral. Ammian., 14, 7. The Greek equivalent is Βαύταχτής.

PEDDLERS.

This chapter would not be complete without a passing mention of the peddler as a beast of burden who enters on his work as a professional for the purpose of commerce. The coolie, for instance, is a carrier pure and simple. He takes up his burden at the instance of another and lays it down for the same reason. The peddler combines employer and employed, retail buyer and seller, with common carrier. Col. C. C. Jones says: "The primitive merchantmen engaged in this traffic were held in special repute, were generously treated, and had at all times safe conduct through the territories, even of those who were at war with each other."* The peddlers of the Middle Ages held a conspicuous place in the social order, special laws were enacted on their behalf, and they enjoyed immunities not accorded to warriors and statesmen. Julius Cæsar attributes the bravery of the Belgians to the absence of peddlers, "minimeque ad eos mercatores saepe commeant, atque ea, quae ad effeminandos animosi pertinent, important."

THE PREHISTORIC CARRIER.

Although we have no evidence in the remains of early prehistoric man that carrying apparatus of any kind was employed, yet the existence of mounds, earthworks, and walls of many sorts of material far from its original source, of relics in old camp sites, indicating that the former occupants lived very much as do those tribes from which the specimens hereafter to be described have been collected, attests the use of similar harness and methods of conveyance and transportation. Indeed, nothing is more probable than that the first men and women on earth bowed their backs and foreheads to those loads which their de-

---

* Cf. C. Rau. "Die Tauschverhältnisse der Eingebornen Nordamerika's." Archiv. f. Anthrop., v. (Antiq. So. Indians, 64, 243.)

scendants have borne unremittingly and will continue to carry in spite of, and forsooth because of, the progress of invention.

The whole world is covered with megalithic monuments in the erection of which it is extremely doubtful whether any living beings were used except men. In the Easter Island are immense platforms on which stand images weighing from three to twenty tons. These have been hewn out in the crater of a volcano and moved in some instances several miles over a region as rough as it can be. On the monuments of Egypt are exhibited teams of men hitched to long cables dragging a sledge on which sits an enormous statue. Rollers were used and greased tracks, but we look in vain for the pulley. The immense buildings on our own continent from Central Mexico to Southern Peru were the sole work of man. Without a draft animal he brought together the material for his splendid palaces and temples, and put every stone in place with his own hands. We may go further than this. Long after horses, camels, oxen, mules, and donkeys were used as beasts of burden the wagons and wheel conveyances were so clumsy as to be practically useless in transporting heavy loads. All over Asia, and indeed in many parts of Europe, the inconvenience of clumsy carriages kept rapid transport in the hands of human bearers.

To one who believes implicitly in the universal domination of invention throughout all human activities, the temptation is great to pass beyond the study of the human bearer to those intermediate stages between the same and the shifting of the load to vehicles and the backs of animals. As interesting to the technologist as to the naturalist are those intermediate forms that now and then appear to confirm his theories of creation.

The forces of nature, the wind, the water-fall, the expansion of steam, the electric current would form another series, the last in the climax, in which the wind acts directly like a hand ; the water, through machinery, as a hand turning a crank; the steam, through change of form and the element, like a hand winding a spring; the electricity, through chemical changes, like a hand discharging a gun.

THE ESKIMO CARRIER.

Let us commence the special application of our subject at the farthest north, the land of almost perpetual ice and snow. What time the Eskimo freight-man is not moving about in open waters moving chattels and merchandise from place to place in the lightest of all boats, the seal-skin pontoon or oomiak, he appears as a draft-man, dragging the dead seal or other game over the ice by means of a rawhide line. He has invented an infinite variety of toggles, made chiefly of walrus ivory in shape of seal, walrus, bear, and other game. These are grasped in the hand firmly, the rawhide line passing out between the ring and the middle finger. The short piece of rawhide attached thereto is a loop which is connected by an easily detachable arrangement to the drag-line of any length. It is rare to see an Eskimo carrying anything, except a mother bearing around a baby in her ample hood. It is a beautiful illustration of the play between environment and the industry to mark the absence of all carrying devices, and at the same time the greatest expenditure of invention and energy upon traction apparatus where the safety of the carrier would be endangered by the very medium which offers the greatest facility in the world to the draft-man. Nothing but this perfect harmony could have induced the Eskimo to expend so much time and energy. Parry, in his second voyage, gives a figure (plate opp. p. 274) of a man carrying a kyak by placing his head in the manhole and resting the gunwale on his shoulders. This is indeed the first step to the portages in the birch-bark country farther south.

In the study of the human burden-animal we must not forget that material had to be moved in very early times vertically as well as horizontally. For instance, a great walrus is killed out at sea or near the shore, and the carcass must be lifted out of the water. It has dawned on the mind of the Alaskan Eskimo that by cutting slits in the hide of the animal and placing paddles or other wooden bars between the rocks above, a very respectable tackle may be improvised with the aid of the ever present rawhide line (Fig. 1). Friction is overcome by means of

Fig. 1.

THE PRIMITIVE PULLEY. ESKIMO LANDING A WALRUS BY MEANS OF A RAWHIDE LINE (AFTER A DRAWING BY HENRY W. ELLIOTT).

abundant grease, and five or six sturdy fellows, by dint of surging and pulling, succeed in landing the monster, weighing many times as much as any one of the Eskimo hunters. This art may have been suggested by the tackle used by the Russians on their ships.

In many places along the sloping beaches and quiet waters the Eskimo has learned to track or tow his loaded oomiak. Again, on land he is often compelled to draw loads without the aid of a sledge. For these purposes he has invented a breast-board of wood. The specimens in the National Museum are from Nunivak Island and Oogashik, on the Alaskan peninsula. These localities have between them the shallows and inlets of Kuskokvim and Bristol Bays. The board is made of driftwood and has the curve to fit around the breast at the shoulders (Fig. 2). Unfortunately no description of the manner of use accompanies the spec-

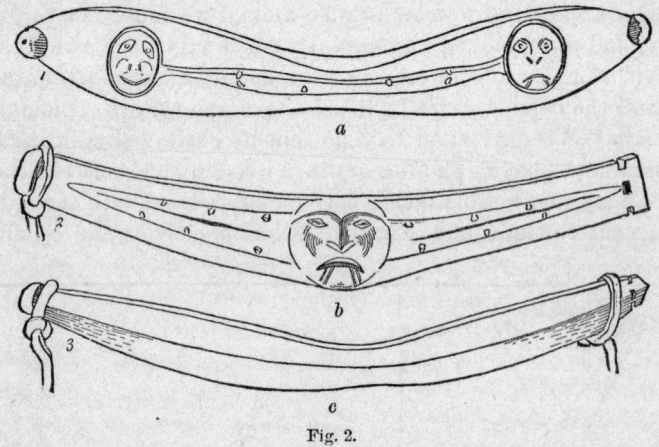

Fig. 2.

BREAST YOKES USED IN HITCHING THE ESKIMO TO HIS LOAD.

a. (Cat. No. 127326, U. S. N. M., from Oogashik, Alaska. Collected by S. Applegate. b and c. (Cat. Nos. 16251-2), from Nunivak Island. Collected by Dr. W. H. Dall.)

imens, so we must remain in doubt as to the way in which the primitive draft-man hitched himself up. In the northern regions traction of sledges is performed by dogs, either alone or assisted by men. There is no doubt, however, that the sledge was in use before the dog was domesticated. The material and style of the sledge vary much according to the region. Dr. E. R. Young, who spent many years in the Saskatchewan regions, says that a great deal of sledging is done by men. He has even seen dogs disabled riding on a sled drawn by men. In the east it is ruder than in the west. In Labrador, where timber can be procured, the sledge differs little from that of the school-boy. Only the uprights at the back enable the driver to steer. Farther north bits of old wrecks or sections of whale-jaw do duty for runners. The method of putting a coating of ice on the bottom of the runners is very ingenious and effective.

Parry's description of those in Igloolik is as follows:

"The Eskimo sledges vary in size, being from $6\frac{1}{2}$ to 9 feet in length and from 18 inches to 2 feet in breadth. Some of those at Igloolik were of larger dimensions, one being 11 feet in length and weighing 268 pounds, and two or three others above 200 pounds. The runners are sometimes made of the left jaw-bones of a whale, but more commonly of several pieces of wood or bone, scarfed and lashed together; the interstices being filled to make all smooth and firm, with moss stuffed in tight and then cemented by throwing water to freeze upon it. The lower part of the runner is shod with a plate of harder bone, coated with fresh-water ice to make it run smoothly and to avoid wear and tear. This coating is effected with a mixture of snow and fresh water, about a half inch thick, rubbed over until it is smooth and hard upon the surface. When the ice is only in part worn off, it is removed by taking some water in the mouth and spirting it over the former coating.

"We noticed a sledge which was curious on account of one of the runners, and a part of the other, being constructed without wood, iron, or bone of any kind. For this purpose a number of seal-skins were rolled up and disposed into the required shape, and an outer coat of the same kind was sewed tightly around them. This formed the upper half of the runner; the lower part consisted entirely of moss, molded while wet into the proper form, and being left to freeze, adhering firmly together to the skin. The usual shoeing of smooth ice completed the runner, which for six months of the year is as hard as wood. The cross-pieces which form the bottom of the sledge are made of bone, wood, or something they can muster. Over these is generally laid a seal-skin as a flooring, and in summer a pair of deer's horns are attached to the sledge as a back, which are removed in winter to enable them, when stopping, to turn the sledge up, to prevent the dogs running away with it. The whole is secured by lashings of thong, giving it a degree of strength, combined with flexibility, which no other mode of fastening could effect." (Parry's Expedition, 514, 515.)

Of the natives of Point Barrow, Lieutenant Ray says: "The sleds which they use for this purpose are made from drift-wood fastened with whalebone and rawhide lashing; they are about 10 feet long, 2 feet wide, and the runners 8 inches wide and $1\frac{1}{2}$ inches thick, straight on top, and have no rail; they are shod for ordinary use with strips of bone cut from the whale's jaw-bone, and sometimes with walrus ivory; but this would not do in hauling a heavy load over the snow, where there is no beaten trail, so they are shod with ice in the following manner: From the ice on a pond that is free from fracture, they cut the pieces the length of a sledrunner, 8 inches thick and 10 inches wide; into these they cut a groove deep enough to receive the sled-runner up to the beam; the sled is carefully fitted into the groove, and secured by pouring the water, a little at a time, and allowing it to freeze. Great care is taken in this part of the operation, for should the workmen apply more than a few drops at a time the slab of ice would be split and the work all to do over again; after the ice is firmly secured the sled is turned bottom up and the iceshoe is carefully rounded with a knife, and then smoothed by wetting the naked hand and passing it over the surface until it becomes perfectly glazed; the sled when ready for use will weigh over 300 pounds, and they load them with the carcasses of from seven to nine deer, weighing over 100 pounds each. Men, women, and children harness themselves in with the dogs to haul these loads to the coast, often the distance of 100 miles and over, seldom making more than 8 or 10 miles each day." (Report of the Expedition to Point Barrow, Alaska, Lieut. P. H. Ray, p. 28.)

The Eskimo sled is framed of spruce, birch, or whalebone, strongly bound with thongs, and the runners shod with smooth strips of whale's jaw-bone. This sled is heavy and fit only for traveling over ice and snow.

Indian sleds of the interior are lighter, the runners being of thin, flexible boards.

Sleds used by voyageurs of Hudson Bay are of different construction. Three boards, each about 1 foot in width and 12 feet in length, thinned and curved into a semicircle at one end, are placed side by side, and firmly lashed together with thongs. (Bancroft, I, 52.)

SLEDGE ISLAND.

This sledge is about 20 inches in breadth and 10 feet in length, a sort of rail-work on each side, and shod with bone, and put together with wooden pins or with thongs or lashings of whalebone. (Cook's Voy.)

KAMTSCHATKA.

The length of the body of this sledge is about 4½ feet and the breadth 1 foot. It is made in form of a crescent, of light, tough wood, fastened together with wicker-work, and, among the principal people, is stained with red and blue, the seat being covered with furs or bear-skins. It has four legs about 2 feet in height, resting on two long flat pieces of wood of the breadth of 5 or 6 inches, extending a foot beyond the body of the sledge at each end. These turn up before, somewhat like a skate, and are shod with the bone of some animal. The carriage is ornamented at the fore part with tassels of colored cloth and leather thongs. It has a cross-bar, to which the harness is jointed, and links of iron or small bells are hanging to it, which by the jingling are supposed to encourage the dogs. (Cook.)

YUKON RIVER.

The snow-shoes used in this district are about 4½ feet long, are rounded and bent upward in front and pointed behind. They are made of birch wood and covered at either end with a fine netting of gut. The lashings are strips of rawhide. (Whymper.)

The sledge consists of a plank, one end of which has been softened by steam and bent in prow-like form. The material does not exceed one-half an inch in thickness and the width varies from 10 to 14 inches. Thongs keep the curved ends in place. It is especially adapted to soft snow. Runners are occasionally added, the freight held in place by lashings.

When a canoe or other heavy burden requires to be transported over the land, the Indian has discovered that however much a piece of reindeer-skin may be used it will stretch a little more when again strained with the weight it is to support. The skin of a seal will not, when dry, sensibly lengthen after it has sustained a load for a length of time. This valuable quality renders the skin of the seal a matter of consequence to the people, who are unable to procure it for themselves, and must necessarily rely upon their Innuit neighbors to furnish it in exchange for other value.

The strap is employed to sustain the weight carried on the shoulders while the person may be traveling on snow-shoes, or when carrying a burden over a portage to the next landing place. It is generally placed over the forehead and shoulders, the muscles of the neck supporting the entire strain, while the hand carries the gun, spear, or staff.

Turner says that he has seen the Ungava natives place a barrel of flour on their shoulders and carry it up a hill-side so steep as to require one not burdened to pick his steps with care.

Day after day, with plenty of food or none at all, whether pack on back, trapping in the woods, treading out a path with snow-shoes in the deep snow for the sleigh dogs, or running after them at a racing pace from morning to night, when there is a well-beaten track, they will travel 50 or 60 miles a day for a week together without showing any sign of fatigue. (Northwest Passage, Fitzwilliam, p. 43.)

"The Indian packers over these mountain passes usually carry 100 pounds, although one I had walked along readily with 127 pounds, and a miner informed me that his party employed one that carried 160 pounds. The cost of carriage of a pack (100 pounds) over the Chilkoot trail for miners has been from $9 to $12, and the Indians were not inclined to see me over at any reduced rates, despite the large amount of material required to be transported, some two tons. By giving them two loads, or doubling the time over the portage, a slight reduction could be had, not worth the time lost in such an arrangement, and I made contracts with enough of them to carry my effects over at once. Mr. Spuhn was also very energetic in his efforts to secure for me better terms, but without avail, and after I had crossed the trail I in no way blamed the Indians for their stubbornness in maintaining what seemed at first sight to be exorbitant, and only wondered that they would do this extremely fatiguing labor so reasonably." (Lieutenant Schwatka, Reconnaissance in Alaska, 1883.)

Fig. 8 of the Reconnaissance is a view on Payer Portage, and represents a Chilkat Indian, with two ammunition boxes, going over the portage. The amount some of these packers will carry seems marvelous, and makes estimates for pack-mules or trails therefor seem superfluous. Their only packing gear is a couple of bands, one passing over the forehead, where it is flattened out into a broad strip, and the other over the arms and across the breast; the two meet behind on a level with the shoulder, and are there attached to lashings, more or less intricate, according to the nature of the material to be transported.

"If a box or stiff bag, the breast-band is so arranged in regard to length that when the elbow is placed against it (the box) the strip fits tightly over the extended forearm across the palm of the hand bent backwards. The head-band is then the width of the hand beyond this. At least I saw a few Indians arranging their packs and their harness according to this mode. The harness proper will not weigh over a pound and the lashing according to its length. The strip across the head and breast is of untanned deer-skin about 2 inches wide, with holes or slits in the ends protected from tearing out by spindles of bone or ivory." (Recon. in Alaska, p. 23.)

"It seemed marvelous beyond measure how these small Indians, not averaging I think over 140 pounds each, could carry 100 pounds up such a precipitous mountain, alternately on steeply inclined glacial snow and treacherous rounded bowlders, where a misstep in many places would have hurled them hundreds of feet down the slope or precipices." (Reconnaisance in Alaska, p. 18.)

"The Indian then chased the goat, almost keeping up with him, down into the valley where we camped, and up the steep mountain slopes of the eastern side, equally as high as those mentioned, and all this immediately after he had carried over 100 pounds across the trail." (Reconnaisance in Alaska, p. 17.)

"The things were then divided into bundles or packs of as even weight as possible, giving some 50 or 60 pounds to each man. Arranging these packs is a matter of no little difficulty, for the Indian has a great objection to altering his load after he has started, so that you have to give the men carrying the provisions, which grow lighter daily, a heavier load at starting than those who have the canteens or tent to carry. They generally stop for some five minutes' rest every half-hour. This they do with surprising regularity. They generally squat near a ledge of rock on which they can rest their burden without removing it. They carry everything the same way, viz, with a band over the forehead, the pack resting on their shoulder-blades or a little below." (Mayne's British Columbia and Vancouver Island, p. 100.)

Col. Cecil Clay says that the commonest methods used in carrying from the St. Lawrence to the jumping-off place northward and from Labrador to the Pacific is by a "tump-line," a long strap with a broad band in the center.

The Indians of the Ungrava district are often compelled, by particular conditions of weather, to travel afoot, and while on a journey of this description they must carry the articles necessary to their comfort or the articles they desire to barter and those they receive in return upon their backs. In order that the arms may be free and aid their progress, the bundles are made as compact as their nature will permit, and slung across the shoulders transversely or suspended over the neck, and the arms passed over the thong supporting the weight behind.

A piece of netting, made of deer-skin twisted and then netted, having thongs run through the outer meshes, draws the net tight over the bundle, which is slung as indicated above.

The method employed by the Makah Indians in carrying burdens when afoot is to strap or tie the load together, whenever practicable, in a compact form, and then, by means of straps or belts that they weave themselves from rags, the "pack" is carried resting on the back, the strap resting against the forehead. The packing strap is woven round, except when it is intended to rest against the forehead; then it is flat. In carrying a number of small parcels or berries, fish, clams, sea-urchins, small pieces of wood, and when haste in loading or unloading a canoe is desired, they use a basket, also woven by themselves, of different patterns, resting on the back and held by a strap around the forehead. They carry cord-wood in the same manner, the sticks lying transversely on the basket.

The baskets intended for heavier articles are woven of the twigs of a tree that resembles lignum-vitæ, the sides intended to rest against the back being flatter and broader than the others. For berries, dried fish, and lighter articles, the baskets are woven of the inner fiber of cedar bark. It may be needless to say that all this work is done by the women.

The native name for the heavier basket is "kah-ow-utz," and for the lighter "bu-hquee." Their name for the packing-strap is "de-de-quad-ut," derived from de-ahp (hanging) and quad-ut (handle), the combination or derivation meaning "hanging handle."

The Makahs do not "track," there being no rivers of any size in the country, and the nature of the country forbidding travel along the banks of such as there are for any distance, the timber being very dense and extending to the very edge of the stream. The canoeing is principally on salt water.

CARRYING LOADS.—INDIANS NEAR STILLWATER, MONTANA TERRITORY.

The men and women carry loads in a similar way. He or she takes a reata, or rope about the size of your finger, which is made out of buffalo-hair or braided elk-skin, three plait, lays it on the ground in the shape of an elongated U, placing the load across the legs of the letter. They generally get a little rise in the ground or a cut bank, but if on the level of a prairie they are helped to raise it by one of their number, or else work over on their side until they can get upon their knees, when they are all right. After placing their load of a hundred-pound sack of flour, or a quarter of a buffalo or steer, or a half cord of dry wood, they, with their back against it, take the curve of the rope over their head, down across their breast and across their shoulders, and then taking the tow ends in each hand bring them up behind their back, catch the rope on top of the load by running each end under, then pulling ends over each shoulder tighten the load if loose and then raise on one side, then the other, to make it more secure, and with a heave forward she or he comes to the knees before getting on their feet. The load or burden rests on the back and shoulders. When moving the body is bent forward and the heavier the load the more the body is inclined. Have seen them carrying wood over four miles in this way, resting whenever they found a suitable place like a cut bank or a washed gully so the load will be even with the place and can be taken again in a minute or so.

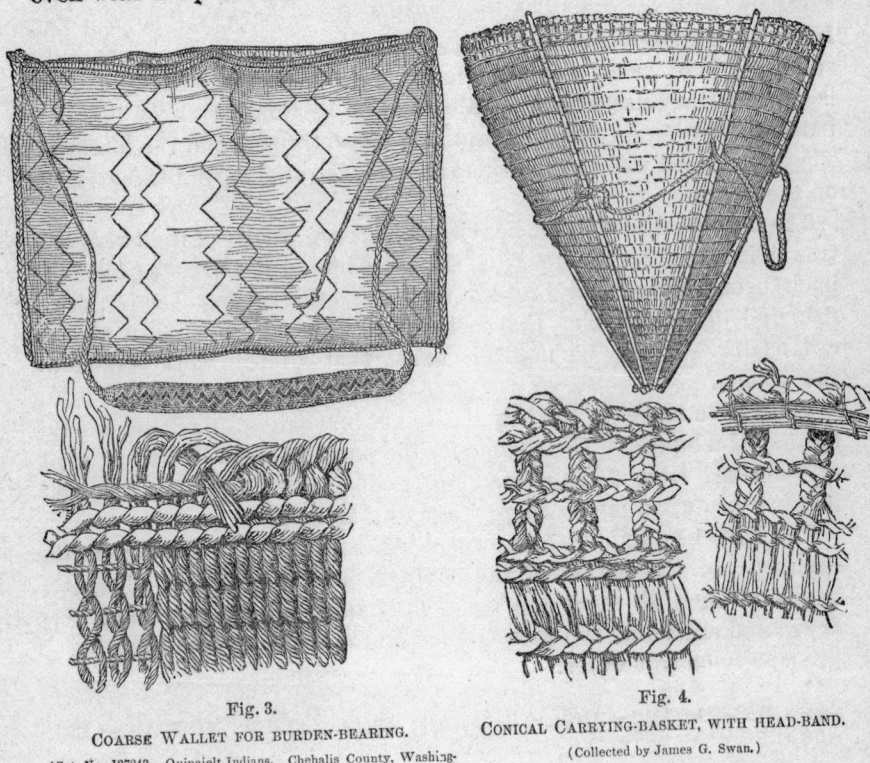

Fig. 3.

COARSE WALLET FOR BURDEN-BEARING.

(Cat. No. 127843. Quinaielt Indians. Chehalis County, Washington. Collected by Charles Willoughby.)

Fig. 4.

CONICAL CARRYING-BASKET, WITH HEAD-BAND.

(Collected by James G. Swan.)

Among the Salish tribes of Washington Territory, as well as those of British Columbia and southeast Alaska, twined weaving in pine root, cedar bark, rushes, and grasses is very common. These tribes all use the wallet for carrying, resting on the back, and prevented from falling as well as partly supported by the head-band resting on the forehead (Fig. 3). One specimen of wallet in the collection is a very interesting example of weaving. The warp threads are very far apart. The twine threads are coarse and loosely woven. At the top two rows of close twine run parallel with the warp. The loose ends of the weft are fastened off in true Indian style to imitate braiding.

A more elaborate example of carrying-basket from Washington Territory is cone-shaped, like those of the Utes. Strengthening rods are fastened to the outsides of the cone (Fig. 4). A braid of tough fiber passes quite around the basket and is loose enough to pass over the forehead of the bearer. The weaving is close enough to hold fine seeds, the rushes being held in place by twined weaving and by a species of braiding with one thread, which will be seen better in a cradle from northern California, in the article on Cradles in this volume. The top of the basket is explained in the enlarged drawing below the figure showing the outside and the inside of the margin.

Still further south are encountered the artistic tribes of northern California. Mr. Powers and the gentlemen of the Fish Commission have sent some beautiful examples of carrying-baskets from the McCloud fishing Indians. One here illustrated is in twined weaving, as close almost as the Sitka work. The bottom is protected frequently by a thimble of leather (Figs. 5 and 6). The ornamentation on the outside is

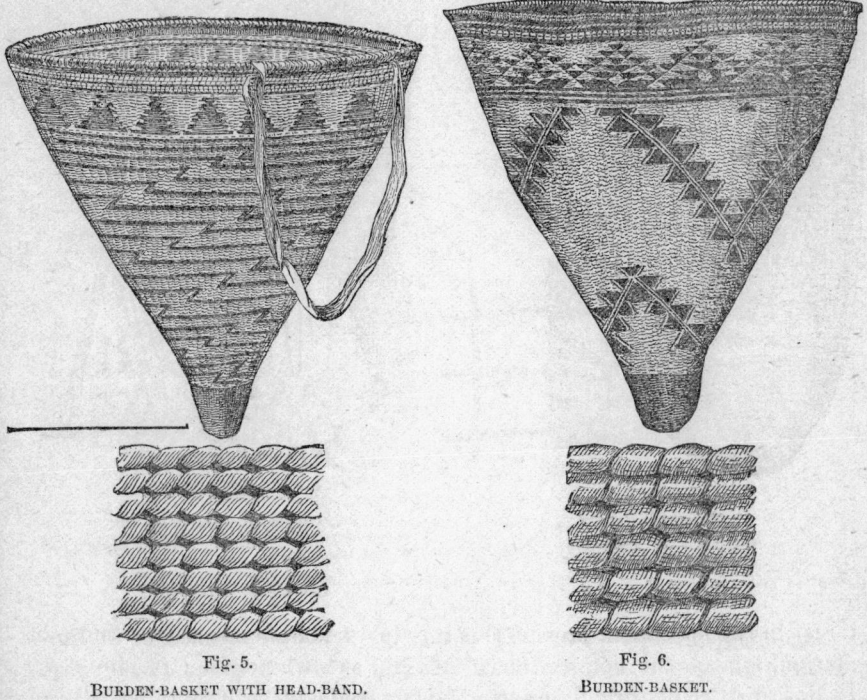

Fig. 5.

BURDEN-BASKET WITH HEAD-BAND.

(Cat. No. 19289, U .S. N. M. McCloud River Indians. Shasta County, California. Collected by Livingston Stone.)

Fig. 6.

BURDEN-BASKET.

(Cat. No. 19290, U. S. N. M. McCloud River Indians. Shasta County, California. Collected by Livingston Stone.)

produced by an overlaying of maiden-hair fern or dyed grass, and the figure may or may not appear on the inside of the weaving. This basket is bordered by a wooden hoop sewed on by coiled work.

One of the most noteworthy specimens of carrying appliances in the National collection was collected by Dr. Palmer from the Mohaves of the mouth of the Colorado River. The affair, as can be readily seen from the drawing, consists of two long bent poles, securely lashed together at their middles. The four ends are fastened to a hoop at equal distances (Fig. 7). Warp-threads are stretched from the intersection at the bottom to the hoop at the top. The weaving is done by a series of turns around the poles and the warp-threads in passing. This is the most interesting sample of aboriginal weaving the writer has ever seen. Collected many years ago from the Mohaves it is undoubtedly a genuine specimen of their work. Indeed, as no white man weaves in that manner, this could not possibly be an example of borrowing. The chief in-

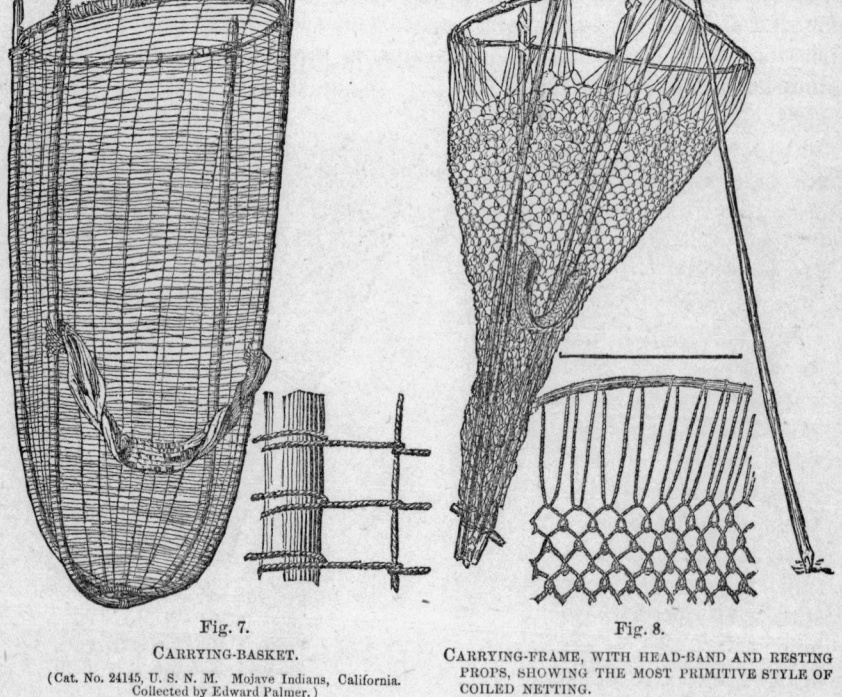

Fig. 7.

CARRYING-BASKET.

(Cat. No. 24145, U. S. N. M. Mojave Indians, California. Collected by Edward Palmer.)

Fig. 8.

CARRYING-FRAME, WITH HEAD-BAND AND RESTING PROPS, SHOWING THE MOST PRIMITIVE STYLE OF COILED NETTING.

(Cat. No. 126680, U. S. N. M. Pima Indians, Arizona. Collected by Edward Palmer.)

terest in the specimen, however, is not in its simple method of manipulation, but in the connection which it has with regions far remote. In Foster's Pre-historic Races (p. 225) is figured a piece of weaving, taken from the bottom of a mound in Ohio. There are three warp-threads, precisely as in our Mohave basket, and three weft-threads wrapped successively around each warp-thread in an orderly manner. Mr. Holmes, in speaking of impressions of textiles on pottery, draws attention to this interesting specimen from Foster. The writer has rolled out a large sheet of sculptor's clay and pressed it against the interior of this network and found that the threads held the clay in place perfectly until it dried. On the deserts of southern Arizona one has to go a long way for food and fuel. It is a common thing, says Dr. Palmer, to see a Mohave woman coming in with this great basket stacked full of mesquite-bean pods, to be broken up and ground into meal when they are dry. The head-band is made of coarse rags, made into a pad at the center for the forehead.

Contiguous to the Mohaves, and belonging to the same Yuman stock, are the Pimas. (By some writers the Pimas are relegated to a separate stock.) Their arts are similar to those of the Mohaves. In the example of carrying-basket figured four rude sticks form the uprights. The netting is formed by a continuous coil of yucca-fiber thread caught into the coil beneath it. When this material is pressed flat it has the appearance given by the drawing (Fig. 8). The head-band and the staff (which also serves to support the carrying-basket when the porter is resting) complete the outfit. The form of stitch here seen looks like the boundary between the hard coil of the California and interior basketry on the one side, and the more elaborate net-work of Mexico and Central America. From the same region Dr. Palmer has collected three specimens of a still more elaborate device for carrying. It consists of a frame-work of four sticks, two of which project downward for legs. These sticks are attached to a hoop, which holds them in place above, but they extend some distance above the hoop, like standards on a wagon, to hold a top load of all sorts of light material. There is a pad of cane fabric attached to the portion of the apparatus next to the back, and a broad head-band also, which can be used on occasion (Fig. 9). The net-work of these baskets is very delicately

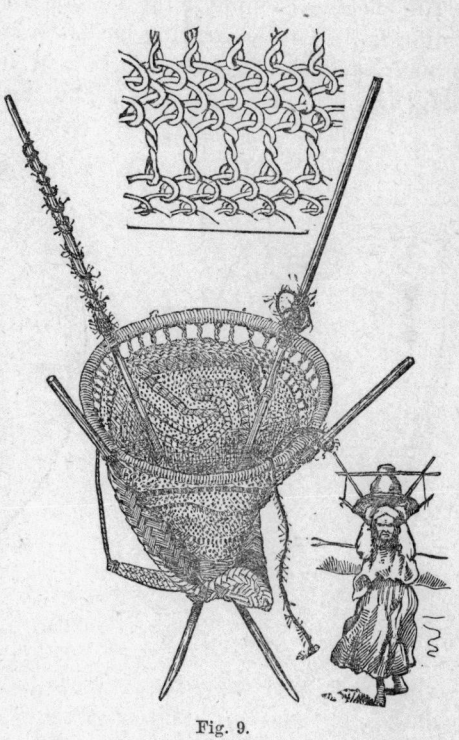

Fig. 9.

CARRYING OUTFIT.

(Cat. No. 76033, U. S. N. M. Pima Indians, California. Collected by Edward Palmer.

wrought. In reality the coarse yucca thread is coiled, as in the last example, but all sorts of straight or zigzag bands are produced by making a whole turn in the thread before passing downward through the next stitch of the underlying coil. This work is done with a needle and thread, as one may see the carrying nets and bags made in Central

America or the snow-shoes furnished with sinew among the Eskimos. The latter use a double-pointed needle, with the thread-hole in the middle, but the natives of Central America and Mexico employ a needle of wood or bone about 4 inches long and one-tenth inch in thickness. Around the uprights of this specimen are ropes for lashing on the load, and a staff, with a crutch at top, serves the double purpose of a cane and a rest.

In a former paragraph allusion was made to the correlation of primitive agriculture with transportation. At the borders of Mexico gourds raised by rude processes begin to appear as vessels. In the example here figured a long gourd, holding a gallon or more, is inclosed in a net-work of yucca twine, laid on in coils, with half hitches above, and with the standard open net-work below (Fig. 10). A bandolier of common rag furnishes the carrying-strap. This specimen was collected from the Pimas by Dr. Palmer.

The Diegenos belong to the Yuman stock, and dwell about San Diego, California. A rude carrying basket or wallet, collected by Dr. Palmer, is made of sticks in open work, held in place by a series of twined weft (Fig. 11). The handle is a common bale of string. There is noth-

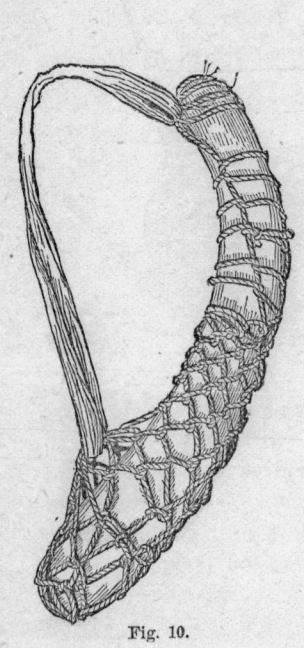

Fig. 10.

CARRYING-GOURD.

(Cat. No. 76047, U. S. N. M. Pima Indians. Colorado River, Arizona. Collected by Edward Palmer.)

Fig. 11.

BASKET FOR CACTUS-FRUIT, ETC.

(Cat. No. 19742, U. S. N. M. Diegenos Indians. San Diego, California. Collected by Edward Palmer.)

ing striking about the specimen, excepting the occurrence of twined weaving so far south. It will be remembered from former studies that this style of textile gives place to the coil in northern California. In the Great Interior Basin the Shoshonian stock have carried it much further southward, and even to the Pacific Ocean in southrn California.

The Shoshonian stock, especially the central tribes in Utah, are agriculturists in a crude fashion. The women gather the seeds of fifty or more plants, fan out the chaff in a basketry tray, elsewhere described, grind the seeds on a flat slab with a muller, and of the meal make cakes or mush. The gathering-basket in which this harvest is collected and transported is shown in the accompanying figures (12, 13). This

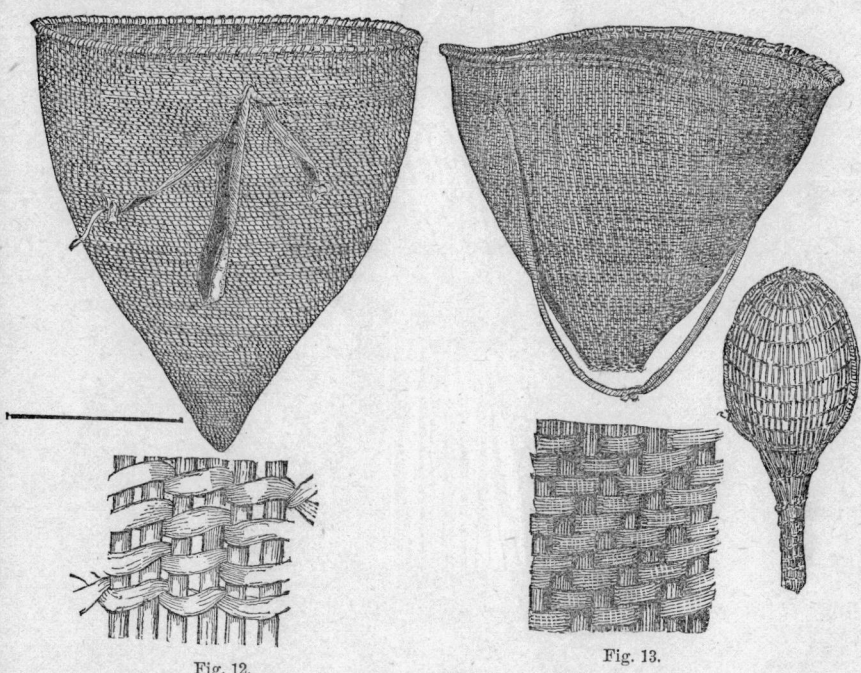

Fig. 12.

HARVESTING-BASKET, USED BY ALL TRIBES IN COLORADO, UTAH, AND NEVADA.

(Cat. No. 14664, U. S. N. M.)

Fig. 13.

UTE TYPE OF HARVESTING-BASKET AND FAN, USED BY ALL OTHER TRIBES; ALSO IN THE GREAT INTERIOR BASIN.

(Cat. No. 42155, U. S. N. M. Collected by James Stevenson.)

conical receptacle is held with the point on the ground and the rim close to the plants. The female harvester holds the gathering-basket with her left hand, and by means of a coarse fan held in the right hand beats the seed into the receptacle. The carrying-strap of soft buckskin is passed across the forehead to hold the basket high on the back. Thus burdened the Ute pack-woman trudges home to change her craft from the burden-bearer to the miller and the baker. The carrying-basket of the Utes is made in twined weaving. The pattern is varied according to the number of warp-sticks included within each turn. The simplest incloses each rod separately; another style takes in two, and the twines are always between the same pairs of warp twigs. A third style imitates diagonal or twill by including a different set of rods on each round. This has been described in another place. (Smithson. Rep. 1884, Pt. II.)

The Utes have no pottery except what they have borrowed. Not to be defeated, however, in a matter so necessary to their happiness, their ingenuity has been equal to the occasion. Both the Utes and the Apaches make bottles and jars of twigs (Fig. 14) holding from half a pint to many gallons. These they calk with hot pitch until they are perfectly water-tight. On the side of this primitive demijohn lugs or

Fig. 14.

SAN CARLOS APACHE WOMAN CARRYING WATER IN A WICKER JAR LINED WITH PITCH.

(From a photograph in the U. S. National Museum.)

loops are fastened, and a soft buckskin head-band served through these enables Aquaria to bring often from a great distance water, seeds, and other necessaries.

The use of the carrying-net is not common in America. Major Powell brought from Utah in 1874 a large collection to illustrate the life of the tribes there. The Utes, and indeed the tribes south of them, employ the net to catch rabbits and other small game. They know also how to turn the net into a carrying appliance. (Fig. 15.) One of the devices is here shown. The knot here used is the standard mesh-knot found all over the world, and it is interesting to find it here among the savages of Utah.

In northwestern Arizona are the Moki Pueblos. The westernmost of these, Oraibi, is celebrated for its basketry. In addition to the twined and coiled work, which they practice in common with their neighbors and blood kindred, the Utes, though with vastly greater taste and skill, they have somewhere learned the art of making true wicker-work. (Fig. 16.) This is indeed rare west of the Rocky Mountains. Two specimens are here figured, the one coarse and holding over a bushel, the other fine and having the capacity of a peck. Both of them are carried by means of a head-band. The wicker is based on a warp of rigid twigs, in bunches of twos or threes. The woof is made up of twigs passing alternately over and under the warp. In fact, it would be more correct to call the bent twigs the warp, because they are alternately raised and

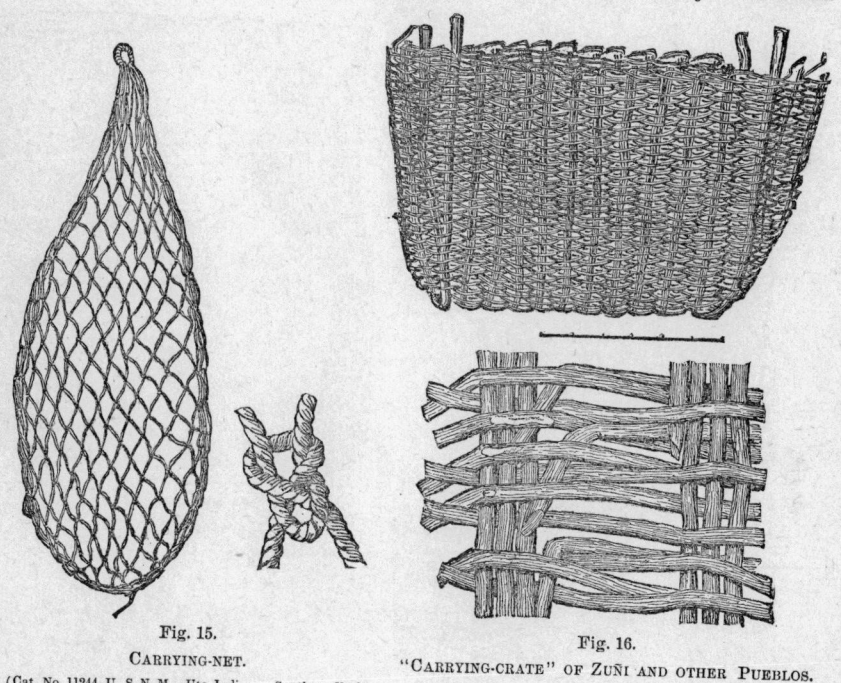

Fig. 15.
CARRYING-NET.
(Cat. No. 11244, U. S. N. M. Ute Indians. Southern Utah.
Collected by Major J. W. Powell.)

Fig. 16.
"CARRYING-CRATE" OF ZUÑI AND OTHER PUEBLOS.
(Cat. No. 22971, U. S. N. M. Collected by Major J. W. Powell.)

lowered as if with a weaver's harness, while the straight twigs pass along the openings just as the warp does in common weaving. The method of fastening off the wicker twigs is shown in the detail of the coarser pattern. (Figs. 17, 18.) Baskets of this very pattern are found at Zuñi, but the opinion obtains that the basketry of this region belongs especially to the Shoshonian and the Apache-Tinné stock. Barter is going on all the time, and it is difficult to follow tribal characteristics under such circumstances.

The Zuñi and most of the Rio Grande pueblos are famous for their pottery. The pack-men and the pack-women here distinguish themselves, especially for the ease and grace with which they carry water and other burdens on the head. Here comes in the head-ring or burden-pad, specimens of which are figured (Figs. 19, 20). They are made either by wrapping a bundle of soft bast or grass into a ring, as in the top figure, or by weaving a ring of yucca fiber neatly around a mass of the shredded fiber. This ring is placed upon the head and the round-bottomed jar upon that. When the jar is set down the ring still is made to support it and keep it in an upright position. Many jars have a concavity beneath, which really seems to be an afterthought. It is only a seeming, however, as there is no evidence either way. In comparison with the Zuñi water-carrier is shown an Italian girl in Palermo performing the same feat. It is only a short step from this figure to the caryatid, in which architecture glorifies in marble one of the humblest occupations of humanity. (Fig. 21.)

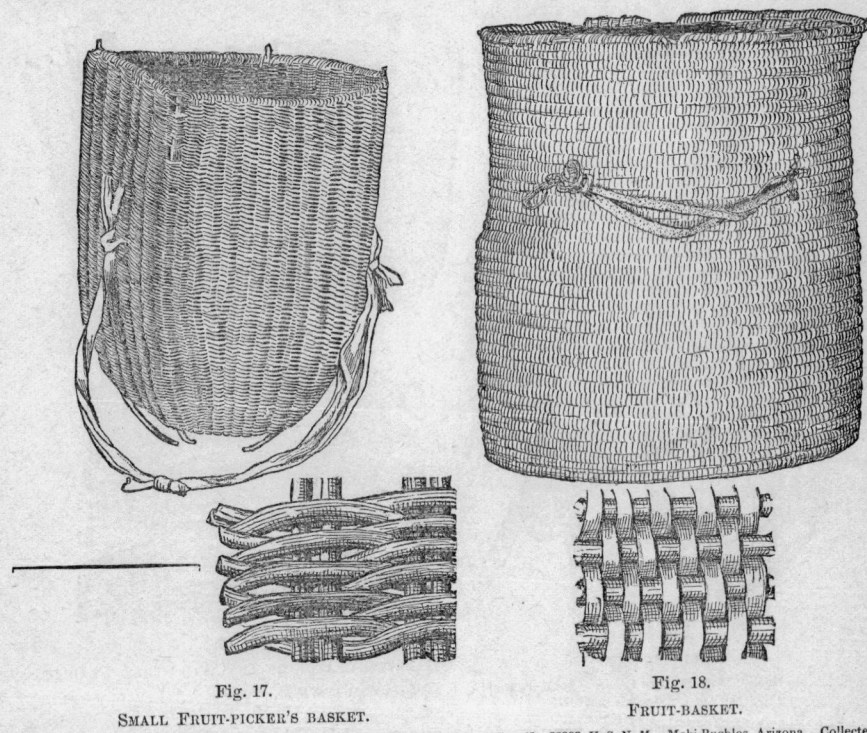

Fig. 17.

SMALL FRUIT-PICKER'S BASKET.

(Cat. No. 70937, U. S. N. M.   Moki Pueblos, Arizona.   Collected by James
Stevenson.)

Fig. 18.

FRUIT-BASKET.

(Cat. No. 22993, U. S. N. M.   Moki Pueblos, Arizona.   Collected
by Major J. W. Powell.)

The Pueblo Indians, like the Eskimo above described, use the breast-strap in dragging loads. They have the clumsy wooden Spanish cart and the diminutive burro, but there are occasions when the man or the woman is regularly hitched up to drag a load up the precipitous mesas, where even a burro could not climb. The breast-strap is made of yucca fiber woven in diagonal patterns, and forms a very efficient harness. This strap, however, is even more likely to be rested across the forehead than upon the breast. (Fig. 22.)

The Apaches are extremely artistic in their manufacture of appliances for burden-bearing. The carrying basket, here figured, is made of rods sewed together by the coiled process. Ornamentation is effected by the manner of stitching, by using different-colored material, and by sewing on strips of soft, white buckskin, to the lower end of which are attached the small hoofs of deer or bits of tin rolled up. (Fig. 23.) The method of carrying burdens among the Apaches is shown in the next figure, of a woman bearing the cradle frame hung to the top of her head. Note here the position of the strap high up on the head, as suggesting the inquiry whether various uses and abuses of the head may not have contributed to its deformation. (Fig. 24.)

Fig. 19.

ZUÑI WOMAN SUPPORTING A JAR OF WATER.

(From a photograph in the U. S. National Museum.)

Fig. 20.

HEAD OR MILKMAID'S PADS.

(Cat. No. 40466, U. S. N. M. Pueblo Indians, Arizona and New Mexico. Collected by James Stevenson.)

Before passing southward it is well to consider the habits of the Indians east of the Rocky Mountains. No less than their western neighbors were they formerly accustomed to carry heavy burdens. For this purpose they used baskets, hampers, wallets, par-flèche cases, skin bottles, skin wallets, and every other receptacle hitherto described. (Figs. 25, 26.) In some of the mounds that have been carefully examined little striæ showed that about a peck of earth constituted the separate loads of dirt which were doubtless scraped up near by and carried on the head or back in baskets to the mound. The first settlers found the aborigines carrying on a respectable commerce, and using inventions that were truly labor-saving machines.

Fig. 21.

ITALIAN WOMAN SUPPORTING EMPTY JAR.

(From a photograph in the U. S. National Museum.)

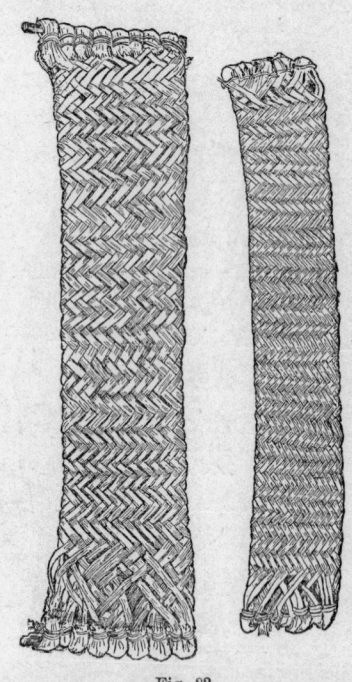

Fig. 22.

BREAST-STRAPS.

(Cat. No. 70962—4, U. S. N. M. Zuñi Indians. New Mexico. Collected by James Stevenson.)

Fortunately a beautiful example of a carrying apparatus was gathered forty years ago from the Arikara and Mandan area. (Fig. 26.) Its composition is worthy of our closest study. Four bent poles constitute the frame-work, two of them with a wide interspace, the other two narrow, like an ox-yoke bow. The two wide bows are placed nearly parallel and about 10 inches apart at top and 4 at bottom. The narrow ones cross these at right angles nearly, only they are spread a little at top. They are also as far apart as the length of the basket demands. These two narrow bows descend 6 inches to afford a rest for

the load. The carrying-strap is of rawhide. The weaving is allied
to that of the Columbia River natives and the tribes northward to the

Fig. 23.

DECORATED CARRYING-BASKET.

(Cat. No. 21489, U. S. N. M. Apache Indians of Arizona.
Collected by Dr. J. B. White, U. S. N.)

Fig. 24.

APACHE SQUAW CARRYING PAPPOOSE-FRAME BY MEANS
OF HEAD-BAND.

(From a photograph in the U. S. National Museum.)

Fig. 25.

THE UNIVERSAL "PAR FLESH" CASE OF RAWHIDE, USED BY ALL BUFFALO HUNTING INDIANS.

Peel River, in British Columbia. It is indeed weaving in diaper, the
warp and the weft equally important in width, flexibility, and manip-

ulation, narrow strips of birch or other tough bark, some of them having the dark, others the light side exposed. This gives a pretty figured effect to the surface.

Mexico is the land of carriers. The early chroniclers mention over and over the employment of professional bearers by the rulers of the ancient city. Indeed, the mountainous condition of the country has kept alive the practice of using men for beasts of burden up to the present time, when the very best substitute is the pack-mule. Travelers in modern Mexico refer to regular caravans of peons, who are to be seen entering the city from every direction, bringing to market every kind of commodity. Even the butchers send their meat around on the backs of men. The Mexican carrier is a student of attitudes, to the extent that there is not a position of his body adapted to burden-bearing with which he is not familiar.

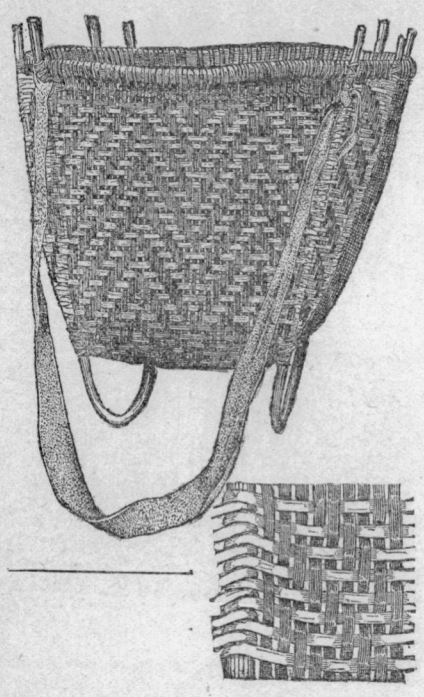

Fig. 26.

CARRYING-BASKET.

(Cat. No. 8430, U. S. N. M. Arikara Indians, Dakota. Collected by Drs. C. C. Gray and W. Matthews.)

One specimen of basket in the National Museum is made of split cane, woven in diaper. (Figs. 28, 29.) It holds about a bushel, but in some cases the top load is greater than the contents of the basket. The strap passes beneath the basket up to the two loops midway. It extends just around the shoulders to the breast-bone in front. The head-band is also used in Central America, but the breast-strap has not appeared since we left Alaska. In the figure of the carrier here presented, quite an elaborate back-pad is shown. In the Pima specimen a pad of this sort is attached to the basket, but in the Mexican example the pad is attached to the man. It consists of a large piece of soft leather, folded several times, hung to the neck above, and held down at the bottom by a belt around the waist. (Figs. 29, 30.) The Pima carrier, therefore, has but one basket, while the Mexican is detachable from his basket, and padded for any load whatever.

The human yoke is probably a foreign invention to Mexico. It is a common sight now to see a man with a stout strip of wood on his shoulder, from either end of which depends a jar by means of a strap, as shown in the figure. These jars hold about two gallons each of

Fig. 27.

PORTRAIT OF A WASHINGTON NEGRO, SHOWING A VERY COMMON
METHOD OF BURDEN-BEARING.

(From life, by W. H. Chandlee.)

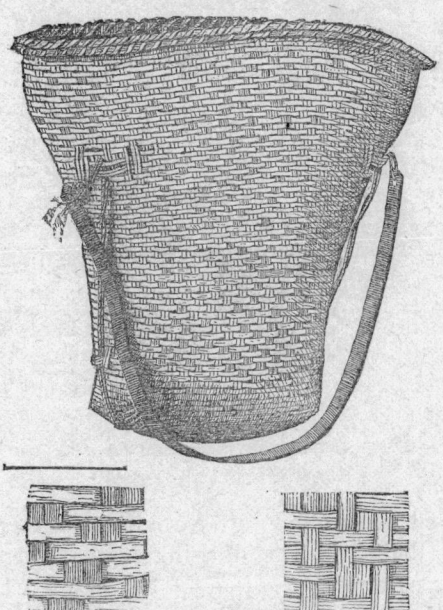

Fig. 28.

CARRYING-BASKET OF THE CARGADOR.

(Cat. No. 91508, U. S. N. M. Choctaw Indians, Mobile, Alabama. Collected
by Edward Palmer.)

water, pulque, flour, beans, etc. The frame at the bottom of the drawing holds two of these jars. Other frames hold three or more. One of these frames on either side of a burro makes up a pack, when the load is easily transferred from the pack-man to the pack-mule. The pottery is made in the mountainous districts, and one may frequently see mule-trains coming along, their packs filled with pottery of this kind. (Fig. 31.)

Fig. 29.

PORTRAIT OF A MEXICAN CARGADOR STANDING ON A TRACK, SHOWING THE TWO
EXTREMES OF TRANSPORTATION.

(Original drawing by W. H. Chandlee.)

Another method of hitching up mankind has crept into Mexico, namely, the wheelbarrow. The drawing here given is an exact copy of a Guadalajara potter's conception of the happy wheelbarrow man, his machine made entirely of wood, the shafts supported by a strap hung from one shoulder and passing under the right arm. (Fig. 32.)

Tylor (Anahuac, 120) says: "A crowd of women follow close in the rear of a Mexican army, almost every soldier having some woman who belongs to him, who carries a heavy load of Indian corn and babies, and cooks tortillas for her lord and master. The number of these poor creatures who perish in the wars is very great."

Fig. 30.
PORTRAIT OF A MEXICAN BUTCHER.
(After W. H. Holmes.)
Observe the parts of the body involved.

Mrs. Polhemus, in her "Woman's Work for Woman," speaks thus of the Mexican burden-bearers: "Who are these two men coming towards us, and what do they carry? The first is bearing to the city nothing less than a load of wash-tubs. Very primitive they are, as you may see, yet clothes will come from them as white and beautiful as any you may have washed in your stationary tubs at home, with all the modern improvements. Our next friend carries a bundle of wood, picked up outside the city, and how precious those crooked sticks are you would never guess till you tried to buy them. Here comes the baker's boy, with his great flat basket, nicely balanced on his head, and filled with fresh rolls and sweetened breads for your afternoon chocolate; then comes an Indian woman with a great bundle of charcoal strapped to her back, a baby tucked into her rebozo in front, and beyond walks another, bearing on her head an earthen jar. In Guatemala this is the way they carry milk, but here in Mexico City the jar is more likely to contain water, either for bathing or drinking. On the corner stands a porter, waiting and ready for a few cents to hoist to his back your heaviest Saratoga trunk and transport it whither you will. Here comes another Indian woman. A few peas, beans, and perhaps peppers are tied up in a blanket, which is knotted around her neck. She stops at doors, calls out her wares, and trots along till she is sold out and her blanket empty; and so, as we pass along, do you notice how much in Mexico is carried by men and still oftener by Indian women."

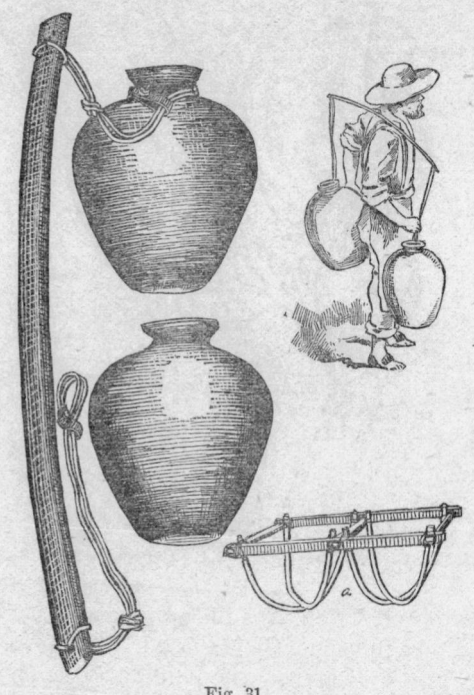

Fig. 31.

CARRYING-YOKE. A FRAME FOR SHIFTING THE JARS TO THE BACK OF A MULE.

(Cat. No. 126592, U. S. N M. Guadalajara, Mexico. Collected by Edward Palmer.)

It is well known that the ancient Mexicans worked in the silver mines. The art of mining is about as primitive now in Mexico as formerly. The ore is placed in rude bags or baskets. The carriers work their way to the surface by means of notched poles put across a part of the shaft in a zigzag fashion, and they then give their load to the breakers, who knock the ore into pieces exactly as if they were going to macadamize a road. (Mexico Illustrated, Mark Beaufoy, p. 268.)

Mr. W. A. Croffut speaks as follows about the remarkable carrying capacity of those ubiquitous porters of Mexico, the *cargadores*:

"In every part of the country have I observed them patiently following the trails and carrying immense loads on their backs. I recollect seeing, four years ago, near a railroad station, half a dozen of them squatting on the ground, resting. One had a sofa upon his shoulders, strapped on I could not see how; another bore a tower of chairs locked into each other and rising not less than 8 feet above his head; another carried a hen-coop with a dozen or twenty hens, and others were conveying laden barrels and various household goods. They had come, they said, from San Luîs Potósi, not less than 50 miles distant. These cargadores will cover 30 miles a day for a week or more, going from ocean to Gulf.

Fig. 32.

PEDDLER WITH RUDE BARROW. MEXICO.

(After a figure in the U. S. National Museum, by a Guadalajara potter.)

"During a ride which I made over the Andes, on the Mexican National Railroad, these persistent carriers were almost always in sight from the car windows, the peons and burros following each other up and down the slopes. The vice-president of the road, Thomas C. Purdy, whose guest I was, said, as we watched these animated trains advancing on parallel lines, 'There is our rival. That is the only transportation company we fear. If it were not for that line, this country would treble its railroads next year, and the roads would double their profits. We are combating the custom of centuries. Those fellows carry on their backs to Mexico the entire crops of great haciendas far over the mountains. I have been and sat down with a wealthy and enterprising haciendado, and explained to him that we could do his carrying in a quarter of the time and for half the cost, and have seen him refuse to change, and stubbornly stick to the old method. I was never before so impressed with the tremendous force of habit.'"

All the salt produced in Salinas is carried away on the backs and heads of men, who come for it (many from great distances) and sell it at home or in a suitable market. In Guatemala everything—with the exception of grain, vegetables, and sugar, which are transported on beasts of burden—is carried on the heads of men, there being no cart-road of any length except that from the port to the capital. The articles to be carried are adjusted into a package higher than wide, and secured by a net, called red. To the back part of this pack, near its base, is fastened a strap of rawhide, the two ends of which are attached to another strap, called tapal, of the size and form of a large hand. The burden is placed on a stone, or some other elevated object, and the man, stooping down, puts the tapal on the top of his head, and lifting his burden trots off with it. When a paterfamilias, going on a journey, has baggage to carry, either his wife or one of his children accompanies him to carry his provisions. A professional carrier dispenses with such company and secures his provisions on the top of the load. In most instances his food consists of tortillas and a few peppers as a condiment, to which, exceptionally, some boiled beans are added. Carriers always take with them, in a little bag, some meal of toasted maize mixed with scraped brown sugar (dulce). A handful of this mixture put in hot water forms their only beverage, for they never touch fresh water, and whatever they drink must be warm. For preparing this beverage every one carries with him a small iron pot. All these articles are put in a netted bag, called matate. There are, at certain intervals on the road, places where the carriers rest during the day or at night. Such places are generally near to a brook, if there is one by the road, or to a rancho, where there are always some sticks of wood left glimmering by the previous party for making a fire and preparing the drink (pinol). The usual weight of a man's load is from 4 to 5 arrobas, an arroba being fixed by law at 25 pounds. Occasionally a man will carry a great deal more for a short distance. To protect the load from rain every carrier takes with him a kind of cloak (soyacal) made of the leaflets of a palm, stitched together in such manner as to overlap each other and form a short cone with a broad base. This cloak is rolled up and secured to one side of the load, indicating the nationality of the bearer; for by this he is at once recognized as an inhabitant of Guatemala whenever he comes to the neighboring states. This mode of carrying loads is undoubtedly the cause of the fashion in which men wear their hair, which is clipped short in front and on the top of the head, but allowed to grow to some length on the back part. A similar fashion is observed by the Hanaks, the inhabitants of the fertile plain of Central Moravia. The hair on the top of the head of a professional carrier becomes much abraded.

A specimen of carrying frame from British Honduras begins to foreshadow the apparatus used in the Andes for transporting travelers. It consists of a stout wooden frame like the seat of a child's carriage elongated, and is fastened to the back as in the Mexican basket carrier. All sorts of luggage are brought within the lines of the British trading posts on the backs of men in frames of this sort. (Fig. 33.)

The far-famed coffee-carriers of Rio usually go in troops, numbering ten or twenty individuals, of whom one takes the lead and is called the captain. These are generally the largest and strongest men that can be found. While at work they seldom wear any other garment than a pair of short pantaloons; their shirt is thrown aside for the time as an incumbrance. Each one takes upon his head a bag of coffee, weighing 160 pounds, and when all are ready they start off upon a measured trot, which soon increases to a rapid run. (Fig. 34.) (Kidder and Fletcher, Brazil and the Brazilians, p. 29.)

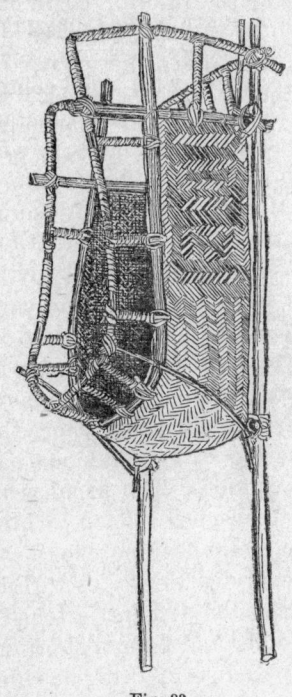

Fig. 33.
CARRYING-FRAME.
(Cat. No. 126805, U. S. N. M. British Honduras.
Collected by U. S. Consul A. E. Morlan.

Fig. 34.
COFFEE-CARRIER OF RIO.
(After Wilkes.)

Slaves are almost the only carriers of burdens in Rio Janeiro. They go almost naked and are exceedingly numerous. They appear to work with cheerfulness, and go together in gangs with a leader, who carries a rattle filled with stones, similar to a child's rattle. With this he keeps time, causing them all to move on in a dog-trot. Each one joins in the monotonous chorus, the notes seldom varying above a third from the key. The words they use are frequently relative to their own country, sometimes to what they heard from their master as they started with their load, but the sound is the same.

The coffee-carriers go in gangs of twenty or thirty. In singing, one-half take the air, with one or two keeping up a kind of hum on the common chord, and the remainder finish the bar. These slaves are required by their masters to obtain a certain sum, according to their ability, say from 25 to 50 cents a day, and pay it every evening. The surplus belongs to themselves. In default of not gaining the requisite sum, castigation is always inflicted. The usual load is about 200 pounds. (Wilkes.)

In Rio Janeiro as well as in the United States and the West Indies may be seen in perfection the African toting on the head. This practice does not seem to have been a favorite one among the American aborigines, if we except the water-carriers of the interior basin of the United States. In the coffee-carriers of Rio as well as among the stevedores of all our sea-ports and commercial towns, the load rests partly on the head and partly on the top of the scapulæ, there being local variations of the method running from support on the head alone to support on the scapulæ alone. The method is an exceedingly convenient one either for unloading or for emptying the sack.

Fig. 35.

NEGROES IN RIO JANEIRO, BRAZIL, ACTING AS DRAUGHT ANIMALS.

(From an old print.)

From Rio we have also an old sketch, after Wilkes, illustrating the use of man as a draft animal. (Fig. 35.) All over the world the "push-cart" is known. Nothing is commoner in Washington than the sight of a negro with his little two-wheeled cart, moving at a dog-trot, with a light load of everything conceivable. The freight of one of these carts rarely exceeds the quarter of a ton, but the draft-man moves much faster than a horse or a mule. The climax of this process of using men for draft is seen on the monuments of Egypt, where hundreds of them are hitched to a single sledge. The romantic survival presents itself everywhere in firemen's processions, the car of Juggernaut, the triumphal car.

A negro dray team in Rio consists of five stalwart Africans pushing, pulling, steering, and shouting as they make their way amid the serried throng. Now an omnibus thunders through the crowd, and a large

Fig. 35a.

NAPO INDIAN CARRIER, OF ECUADOR.

(After Stanford.)

four-wheeled wagon, belonging to some company for the transportation of "goods," crashes in its wake. Formerly all this labor was performed by human hands, and scarcely a cart or a dray was used in the city, unless, indeed, it was drawn by negroes. Carts and wagons propelled by horse-power are now quite common; but for the moving of light burdens and for the transportation of furniture, pianos, etc., the negro's head has not been superseded by any vehicle. (Kidder and Fletcher, Brazil and the Brazilians, page 29.)

The Napos Indians, of Ecuador, also use the head-band to support the basket; the staff is also introduced to throw a portion of the load upon the arms and turns the bearer into a veritable quadruped. (Fig. 35 A.)

In the island of Madeira is also seen the rudimentary form of loading up two or more men. The primitive palankin is simply a hammock swung on a pole, with ornamental awning and so forth to suit the rider. We will pause a moment to scrutinize this apparatus. (Fig. 36.) When-

Fig. 36.

HAMMOCK CARRIAGE, WITH TWO BEARERS. MADEIRA.

(From a photograph in the U S. National Museum.)

ever a man wishes to carry a stick of timber he finds the center of gravity and places that upon his shoulder. It is only a slight step forward to make the stick lighter and add weights on either end, as do the Mexican carrier and Chinese cooly. Revolve the pole ninety degrees so as to be perpendicular to the line of progression and we have the typical Holland yoke. We are proceeding here, as always, on the supposition that the human mind sets ever before itself the problem how to get the greatest result with the least effort. This involves in the case in hand a study of padding, fitting, resting, etc., all of which things have their local methods of treatment.

Again, suppose two men have a log or plank to carry between them, each rests one end of the load on his shoulder. This is the first step in that varied apparatus which becomes in different lands palankin, bier, filanzana, in which rank or circumstance make one set of men the carriers of another. Many of the peasantry are employed as carriers, and one is much struck by their numbers as they enter Funchal early in the morning with sheep-skins filled with wine upon their shoulders, looking at a distance more like a live animal than a filled skin. The skins are preserved entire, even the legs of the animal being retained. (Fig. 37.) These burdens are kept steady by a band that passes over the forehead, which supports a great part of the weight. About 25 gallons, weighing more than 200 pounds, is a load. They move rapidly and carry this load for a mere trifle. To us a remarkable feature in the population was to see a female not only thus employed, but a stout mountain lass trudging up a steep path with ease under a load that would have staggered one of our laborers even a short distance. (Wilkes.)

In the Madeira type two men

Fig. 37.
WINE-CARRIER IN MADEIRA.
(After Wilkes, in Report on the U. S. Exploring Expedition.)

are bearers, and they rest themselves by supporting the load on crutch-like staves, since they can not set it down. (Fig. 36.)

A sledge, about 6 feet in length, 20 inches wide, and 6 or 8 inches high, with two strips of hard wood fastened together for runners, used to transport pipes of wine, is the only vehicle employed in Madeira. Figured (Wilkes I, p. 10.)

A drawing of the Persian water-carrier is introduced here (Fig. 38) for the purpose of tracing the head-band and the skin bag in their distribution. The pulque-gatherer of Mexico uses the skin of a hog in collecting the crude juice of the plant; the Eskimo employs the closed skin for a water-carrier as well as for a float. All over the Orient and in Africa the goat skin is the accompaniment of

Fig. 38.
PERSIAN WATER-CARRIER.
(After H. Fenn, in Century Magazine.)

the water and the wine carrier. A load of this kind rests on no particular portion of the back, adjusting itself perfectly to head, neck, shoulders, and back.

The paternity of the modern knapsack appears in the carrying-basket of Holland represented in the figure. (Figs. 39, 40.) This method of

Fig. 39.

GERMAN WOMAN CARRYING-BASKET WITH SHOULDER-STRAPS.

(From a photograph in the U. S. National Museum.)

Fig. 40.

HOLLAND YOKE, SHOWING BOTH HANDS AND SCAPULAS USED IN CARRYING.

(From a photograph in the U. S. National Museum.)

hitching up the pack-woman can not be very ancient. It is not widely spread among the aborigines of America, where the woman is the bearer and the man goes on ahead to do the fighting or hunting. To all appearances this is a sacrifice of great weight to the labor-saving scheme of joining the bearer and the warrior in one individual. Hence the soldier discards the head-strap or the breast-strap, and adopts the knapsack. (Fig. 41.)

In an example of head-strap from Africa we have a repetition of one from Montana, in which the pack-man becomes, as it were, his own driver. He puts the sack, or bundle of fagots or what not, on the two lines about the middle. He then backs up to his load, inserts his forehead into the head-band, and seizing the lines by the outer ends rolls his load upon his back. In the same manner grocers roll barrels of goods up and down the cellar skids. (Fig. 42.)

A very neat and ingenious framework for burden-bearing comes from the Congo region. Two stout palm leaves are laid about a foot apart and the leaflets on their adjacent sides are braided together. The leaf-

Fig. 41.

PEASANT WOMEN OF RUSSIA CARRYING STONE ON A BIER.

(After George Kennan, in Century Magazine.)

lets on their outer margins are twisted into short cords and then braided into a continuous margin for the frame. (Fig. 43.) This apparatus is loaded with the greatest variety of merchandise, to be carried to and from the coast in trade.

"The Madis of Africa make admirable porters, being very careful of the loads intrusted to them, and display no little forethought and ingenuity in preserving them from injury. The rule is that no load should exceed 50 pounds in weight, and that it should be either square or oblong, the latter being preferred. They always carry the load on the head on a pad made of grass, very rarely steadying it with the hand unless going over very rough ground. They strongly object to carry loads over 50 pounds, but if pressed will take them up to 70 pounds, if the distance to be marched is not more than three days and extra food is given them. Loads of 100 or 120 pounds are carried by two men, hung on a pole, which they balance on their heads, but they do not like the work. If a very heavy load has to be carried, e. g., a man, they place him on a native bed and carry him, two at a time, changing relays of men at about each mile. This they prefer to carrying by four men at once. I can testify from personal experience that it is far better to be carried by two men than four, for they go much more easily and do not run against so many trees or overhanging branches. The relief men march before those who are bearers and cry out when obstacles occur.

As regards distance they carry loads of 50 pounds 20 miles a day, for eight or ten consecutive days, without showing signs of distress, but on the march they appear to require a great deal of water, and will sooner burden themselves with a gourd full than go without it for more than two hours at a time. If they go by a road where water is scarce, they generally take a few women or children with them to carry it. When they arrive at a stream all loads are put down, and they bathe, if the water is deep, or sit down and wash themselves, if it be shallow,

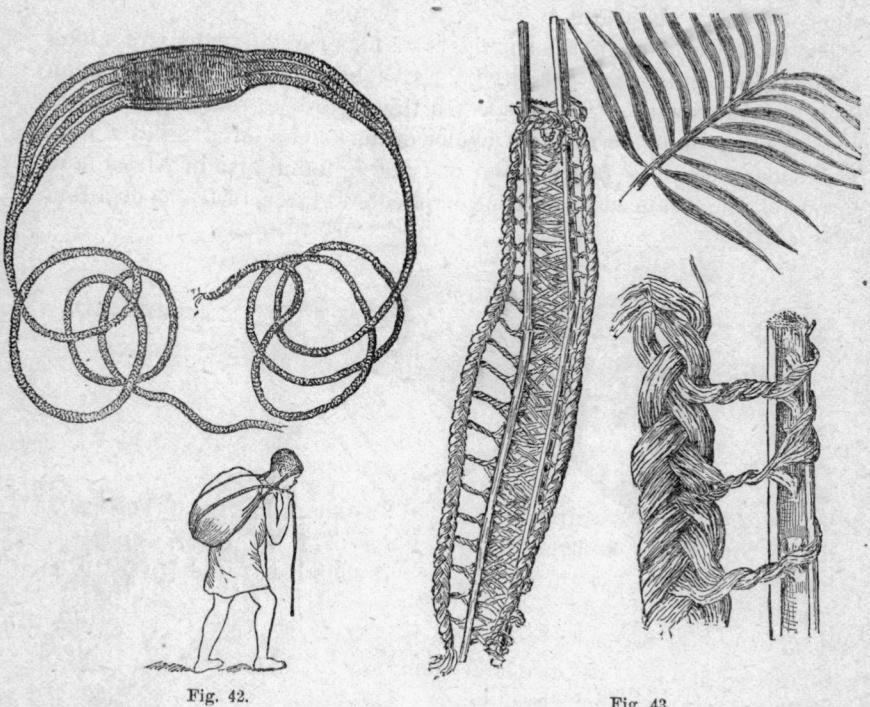

Fig. 42.

AFRICAN CARRYING-STRAP. THIS METHOD OF CARRYING ALSO PREVAILS IN NORTHWEST UNITED STATES.

(Cat. No. 4959 (?), U. S. N. M. Collected by Capt. Charles Wilkes, U. S. Navy.)

Fig. 43.

CARRYING-FRAME OF THE CONGO, MADE BY BRAID-ING THE LEAVES OF THE PALM.

Cat. No. 72708, U. S. N. M. Loango Coast, West Africa. Collected by Museum für Völkerkunde, Leipzig, Germany.

and then take a long drink. The Madis can scarcely be prevailed upon to march at night; even in bright moonlight, on account of bad roads, which is strange, as their eye-sight is remarkably good. Neither will they start until the dew is entirely off the grass, or if made to do so by promises of reward, they tie bunches of grass or skins before them to avoid as much as possible being wetted by the dew.

In crossing a river of 4 or 5 feet deep they stand in the water in a double row and hand the loads from one to the other. Should the stream be very strong, they break down branches which have broad forks, and placing one end firmly in the bed of the stream lean against the fork, and so get the needed support. They march at a quick pace, but generally halt for ten or twenty minutes after each 3 or 4 miles.

In carrying the Egyptian post these men make long and quick

marches, 60 or 70 miles often being accomplished in twenty-four hours. (Proc. Roy. Soc. Edinburgh, 1883–'84, Nos. 115–118, p. 316.)

The open palankin or chair has reached an excellent differentiation in Madagascar. A traveler sits in a leather seat, made to fit the body, attached to the two bearing poles and having a stirrup for the feet. To the poles are also attached the traveler's gun, haversack, assagais, and other necessary apparatus.

The frame rests upon the shoulders of four carriers, who trot along with the load until they get tired. Extra bearers shift the load upon their shoulders without stopping. In this method of relaying the bearers are enabled to carry the traveler oftimes a hundred miles a day. This same method of bearing and relaying is found also in Africa, and furnishes an advanced and quite complicated system of transportation. (Fig. 44.)

Fig 44.

FILANZANA OR CARRYING-FRAME OF MADAGASCAR.   (After Shufeldt.)

(Cat. No. of frame 75928, U. S. N. M. Madagascar. Collected by Lieut. M. A. Shufeldt, U. S. Navy.)

"The average load of a coolie," says Mr. Neumann, "is 100 pounds, and with this he travels 30 miles. Kinkiang is an important place for the export of tea. The tea districts are situated about 60 miles from the town, and the coolies bring in the chests in two days, each man carrying a load of 100 pounds.

"The weight of a load and the distance over which a cooly travels, may be different in the north or south. I have not been able to make inquiries elsewhere but at this port."

Any one who has looked at all into the subject will recall the thousand and one attitudes of Chinese carriers in all pictures of social life. The same is also true of Japan and the countries south of China. (Figs. 45, 46, 47.)

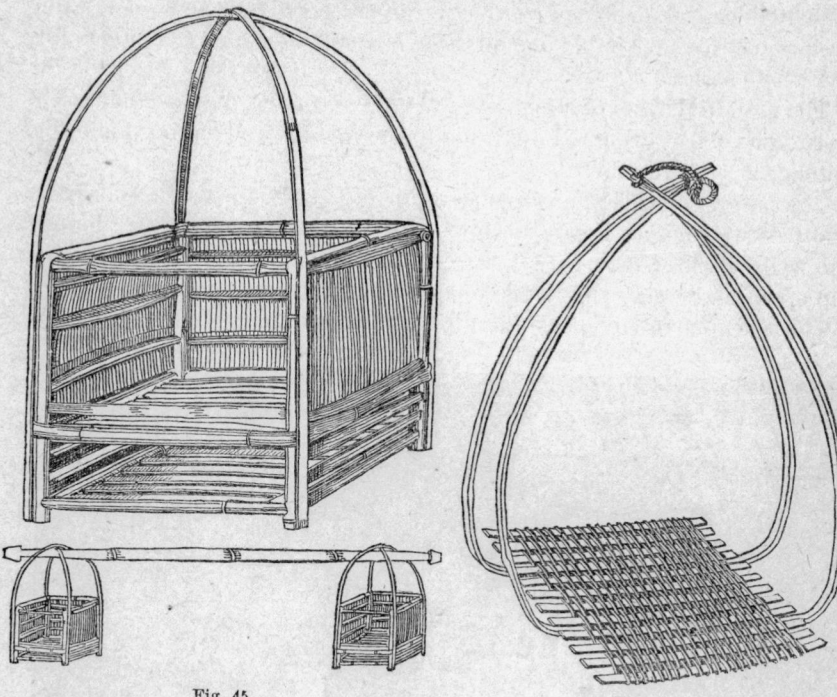

Fig. 45.

SHOULDER-YOKE AND CARRYING-BASKETS.

(Cat. No. 74506, U. S. N. M. China. Gift of the Chinese Centennial Commission, Philadelphia, 1876.

Fig. 46.

SIMPLEST FORM OF FRAME FOR SHOULDER-YOKE.

(Cat. No. 54174, U. S. N. M. China. Gift of the Chinese Centennial Commission, Philadelphia, 1876.)

Fig. 47.

JAPANESE PEDDLER AND SHOULDER-YOKE.

(From a photograph in the U. S. National Museum.)

The shoulder-pole, or carrying-pole, assumes as many forms in China and Japan as the ingenuity of one-fourth of the human race has been able to devise. Inasmuch as they all operate on the same plan, a description of a very simple one in the National Museum will suffice for the whole series.

The essential parts of a Chinese carrier's outfit are, first, a stout strip of bamboo, 6 feet or more long, wide in the middle, and having knobs or notches at either end.

The middle of this apparatus rests on either shoulder of the bearer, and from the notched ends, with or without suspending strings, hangs the well-balanced load. The bearer carries a staff in hand, upon the top of which he may support his load while resting.

The wheelbarrow reaches its highest perfection in China (Fig. 48).

Fig. 48.

CHINESE BARROW WITH TWO SIDES, FOR BURDENS OR PASSENGERS.
(From a photograph in the U. S. National Museum.)

The man of burden is harnessed by means of his hands acting as stirrups, and a rope or strap passing from the shafts over his neck. To his rope or band he gives the effect of a trace by fastening it to the shaft some distance behind the hand.

The wheel is, moreover, in the center of the barrow, so that the downward pressure on the shoulders is far less than in our European barrows.

The load of this apparatus is disposed around the wheel, with some attention to the center of gravity; and the disposing of men, pigs, merchandise, and household effects, with this sole object in view, gives to some of the Chinese loaded barrows rather a romantic effect.

The Japanese back is one of the best in the world, and the people have repeated many of the Chinese methods of burden bearing. The most frequent method of burden bearing is the bamboo basket, suspended from the shoulders in like manner to the knapsack. (Fig. 49.)

The palankin of Japan is also very similar to that of China. In both countries, especially in the latter, on ceremonial occasions, frames and other devices have been invented for hitching up a great number of men, and thus of securing the advantage of combined effort. This

Fig. 49.
COMMON CARRYING-BASKET OF JAPAN.
(From a photograph in the U. S. National Museum.)

should not be overlooked in studying the civilization of countries that became quite elevated without our modern appliances.

Any knowledge of Aino culture at this time is valuable, when a systematic effort is being made to discover the relationships of this primitive people. For carrying burdens the Ainos use a frame, like a small trellis or ladder, around which braided cord is wrapped to furnish a bed for the load. (Fig. 50.)

This frame is attached to the body by means of shoulder-ropes braided so as to be thick, and padded in the portions against the shoulders.

This is quite primitive as a carrying device, and has its counterpart only among the rude carriers of America and Africa.

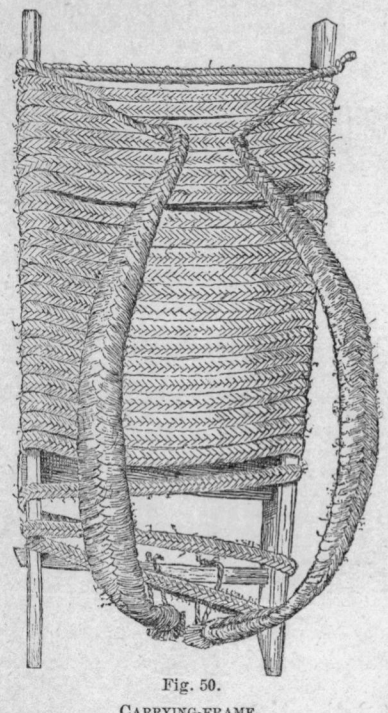

Fig. 50.
CARRYING-FRAME.
(Cat. No. 73093 U. S. N. M. Tate Yama, Japan. Collected by P. L. Jouy.)

The palankin of Corea is an empty cube 2½ feet each way. Little windows look out in front and on either side, each fitted with a pair of sliding screens. Into these are let tiny panes of glass 2 inches square. Two men carry this box and divide the burden by means of a yoke, with straps that fit over the ends of the poles to which the box is fastened, two other men accompaning as relief. Each man is armed with a stick, which is used to insert under the chair and lift it up to ease their fellows. (Percival Lowell, Chosön, p. 50.)

The same author informs us that there is not a single wheel in Corea, the palankin being the only means of conveyance.

One of the most primitive illustrations of carrying on the shoulder is furnished by a copy of a small photograph, taken in the Karen hill country by the Rev. R. M. Luther.

A boy is returning home with two bread-fruits attached to the stock by their natural stem. The pole on the shoulder, with a weight depending from either end, is the commonest device of the professional carrier throughout this whole region. And in this picture we have the ancestor of every Chinese coolie art, of the principal part of Japanese, Siamese, and Polynesian carrying on the shoulder.

Indeed the Karen bread-fruit picker is at a single view the primitive agriculturist, taking his load at once from nature and the primitive agent of transportation.

A very elaborate and highly artistic

Fig. 51.
KAREN BOY OF BURMA, CARRYING BREAD-FRUIT.
(From a photograph in the U. S. National Museum.)

offshoot of the Chinese coolie's double load is found in Siam. The pole rests on the shoulder, and on either end is suspended a long, daintily woven hamper. A wooden bottom protects the basket from injury, and the holes for the insertion of the pole are arranged like grommets by means of bamboo sewing. (Fig. 52.)

Cords are provided, both for the attachment of the top load and the convenience of the bearer. In all the Siamese carrying apparatus from Siam in the National Museum the workmanship is of the most delicate character. The baskets are woven of split rattan, and the stitching compares favorably with that of our best California weavers.

Compare the Siamese with the Sandwich Island pack, and the rude parentage of the Siamese method may be seen. (Fig. 53.) Captain Wilkes long ago said of the Hawaiian carriers: "One can not but be struck with seeing the natives winding their way along the different thoroughfares laden with all kinds of provisions, wood, charcoal, and milk, to supply the market and their regular customers.

Fig. 52.
CARRYING-BASKET.
(Cat. No. 27613, U. S. N. M. Siam. Presented by the King of Siam.)

Their mode of carrying burdens is to suspend them with cords from the ends of a stick; this is laid across the shoulders, and so accustomed are they to carry the load in this manner that they will sometimes increase the weight by adding a heavy stone in order to balance it. The stick on which they carry their load is made of the *Hibiscus tiliaceus*, which is light and tough. Instead of baskets they use a kind of gourd which grows to a large size. These are thin and brittle, but with the care the natives take of them are extremely serviceable. They are used for almost everything. It takes two gourds to make one of the baskets used for transporting articles, the smaller one being turned over the opening cut in the larger one, effectually protecting the contents from rain. Some of these gourds will contain upwards of two bushels. The gait of the Kanaka moving with his load is a quick trot, and he takes very short steps." (Wilkes.)

The carrying net of the Utes of Utah and Colorado re-appears in the Papuan area in the shape of a bow of wood, the space between being filled with a net-work. All sorts of loads are fastened within this frame and it is borne on the back in the most comfortable manner to the bearer. (Fig. 54.)

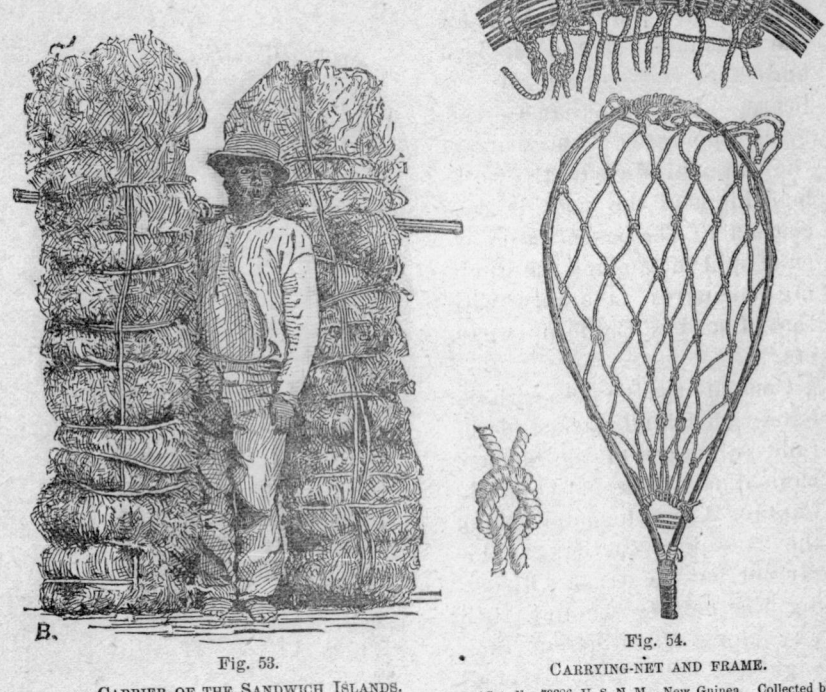

Fig. 53.

CARRIER OF THE SANDWICH ISLANDS.

(From a photograph in the U. S. National Museum.)

Fig. 54.

CARRYING-NET AND FRAME.

(Cat. No. 73386, U. S. N. M.   New Guinea.   Collected by A. P. Godwin.)

In the vast majority of the islands in the great oceanic area the human burden-bearer is transformed into the human propeller, most of the savage life here being passed on the water; but it is curious to notice that hand-work even here precedes machine work, in that men, women, and children are the most expert swimmers in the world.

"The women of New Britain," says Mr. W. Powell,* "carry their babies in net-work bags, the band or strap of which comes round the forehead, and the child in the bag rests on their shoulder blades, and in traveling to market and elsewhere, should the child require suckling, they do it over the shoulder.

"They will also carry on their backs two or three cocoanut-mat bags full of merchandise, as well as the baby; this gives them a stooping gait and makes them always walk in a doubled-up manner, even when not carrying anything."

---

* W. Powell, "Wanderings, etc.," London, 1884.

It would be a fascinating task to note the thousand and one devices by means of which mankind have shifted their burdens upon the backs of animals, upon the winds and the waters. The authorities of the U. S. National Museum have organized a section of Transportation and appointed to the curatorship Mr. J. E. Watkins, to whom I shall leave the task of working out the subsequent chapters in the history of this subject.

ETHNO-CONCHOLOGY—A STUDY OF PRIMITIVE MONEY.

By Robert E. C. Stearns.

The study of Nature leads through enchanted fields, full of new surprises and fresh delights. Whichever path we pursue, vistas open on either side equally inviting, with every charm of life and form and color, ever changing but never old.

" Who," wrote P. P. Carpenter, "has not admired the beauty of shells, the luster of the Cowries, the polish of the Olives, the painting of the Cones, the varied layers of the Cameos, the exquisite nacre of Mother-of-Pearl ? Who has not listened to the mysterious ' sound of the sea' in the Whelks and Helmets, or wondered at the many chambers of the Nautilus? What child ever went to the sea-shore without picking up shells; or what lady ever spurned them as ornaments of her parlor ? Shells are at once the attraction of the untutored savage, the delight of the refined artist, the wonder of the philosophic zoologist, and the most valued treasures of the geologist. They adorn the sands of sea-girt isles and continents now, and they form the earliest 'footprints on the sands of time' in the history of our globe. The astronomer wandering through boundless space with the grandest researches of his intellect and the most subtle workings of his analysis, may imagine indeed the history of past time and speculate on the formation of globes, but his science presents us with no records of the past; but the geologist, after watching the ebb of the ocean tide, examines into the soil on the surface of the earth and finds in it a book of chronicles, the letters of which are not unknown hieroglyphics but familiar shells."

Conchology, or the study of shells, in itself one of the most delightful studies, in its ethnological aspect is also full of interest.

Aside from the use of various species of mollusks as articles of human food all the world over, we find that several forms belonging to this division of the animal kingdom have in the past been curiously interwoven with the affairs of men, both in civilized and barbarous communities.

Some of these are still in use as of old, but to a comparatively limited extent.

As we follow the direction of ethno-conchological inquiry over the pathway of dead centuries, we catch glimpses of great events—events phenomenal, picturesque, and impressive; important in their time, characteristic of the period or epoch which they mark and in which they occurred, and it seems strange that forms of animal production so insignificant should have had any connection therewith.

PEARL-BEARING MUSSELS.

The fresh-water mussels are widely distributed over the surface of the globe; the rivers and minor water-courses of the northern hemisphere contain a great number of species, and individuals of these species are wonderfully abundant. The freshets which swell the streams and tear away their banks, and make their waters turbid with silt, carry into the soft parts of the mussels particles of sand which irritate the delicate tissues. This irritation causes a flow of nacreous lymph, which is deposited on and coats over the rough surface of the disturbing atoms, or it may be that a shriveled egg-case of the mollusk itself becomes similarly lodged and causes a similar annoyance and is coated with nacre in the same way. And so a pearl is commenced, and afterward receives coating upon coating until the accumulated deposits of nacre have reached a thickness that gives the pearl not only size but translucency and iridescence, and if the color is good and the shape symmetrical, a pearl of value, a precious pearl, is formed. And so in Nature's laboratory an aborted egg or a grain of sand is transformed into a thing of beauty.

THE INVASION OF BRITAIN BY THE ROMANS (B. C. 55).

The pearls of Great Britain were famous throughout Europe in the century before Christ. They were obtained from the fresh-water mussels (*Margaritana margaritifera*) of the mountain rivers and streams. Doubtless the extent of the fishery was exaggerated, and the value of the yield in pearls greatly overestimated. History has preserved the tradition that it was this source of wealth that tempted the Romans to the shores of that country in the year 55 B. C., and ancient writers refer to the shield studded with British pearls which Cæsar* suspended as an offering in the temple of Venus at Rome.†

It is highly probable that the invasion of Britain by this famous general was not for the single purpose of punishing the Britons for the assistance they had rendered to the Veniti of Brittany, with whom Cæsar was at war, but with an eye to the pearls, which in his time were far more highly prized than at the present day.

The invasion of Britain by the Romans, in daring and romance must yield the palm to the enterprise and expeditions of the Spanish conquistadores centuries later.

THE CONQUEST OF FLORIDA BY DE SOTO.

"Never was the spirit of wild adventure more universally diffused than at the dawn of the sixteenth century. The wondrous discoveries

* His journey in Britain was attributed by Suetonius to avarice, which had been kindled by the report of enormous pearls of fine quality to be found in that country.
† Simmonds.

of Columbus and his hardy companions and followers, the descriptions of the beautiful summer isles of the west, and the tales of unexplored regions of wealth locked up in unbounded wildernesses, had an effect upon the imaginations of the young and the adventurous not unlike the preaching of the chivalric crusades for the recovery of the Holy Sepulchre. The gallant knight, the servile retainer, the soldier of fortune, the hooded friar, the painstaking mechanic, the toilful husbandman, the loose profligate, and the hardy mariner, all were touched with the pervading passion; all left home, country, friends, wives, children, loves, to seek some imaginary Eldorado, confidently expecting to return with countless treasure."*

The glamour of wealth in gold and silver, the precious metals and precious pearls, the presents of these articles made by the kindly, hospitable, and unsuspecting natives to the Spanish captain, Diego Miruelo, and to the subsequent visitors to their country connected with de Ayllon's enterprise, was followed in 1539 "by the most splendid expedition that had yet set out for the New World," commanded by Hernando De Soto, and the conquest of Florida was soon an accomplished fact. The Portuguese and Spanish chroniclers of the exploits and adventures of De Soto and his men have given fabulous accounts of the quantities of pearls seen in the possession of the natives. One Portuguese narrator says "they obtained fourteen bushels of pearls" from a certain sepulchre, and at another place in the text it is stated that a common foot soldier, whose name is given as Juan Terron, had " a linen bag, in which were six pounds of pearls," and pearls are elsewhere spoken of that are "as large as filberts." Garcillasso de la Vega says " while De Soto sojourned in the province of Ichiaha the cacique visited him one day and gave him a string of pearls about two fathoms long. This present might have been a valuable one if the pearls had not been pierced, for they were all of equal size and as large as hazelnuts." That pearls were abundant and that great quantities were seen in the possession of the natives has been fairly corroborated in these later times. Within a few years a great number have been discovered in aboriginal graves.

Professor Putnam† has stated that in excavating the mounds near Madisonville, Indiana, not less than fifty thousand pearls were found, most of them pierced and injured by heat. Squier and Davis found them on the hearths of five distinct groups of mounds in Ohio, and sometimes in such abundance that they could be gathered by the hundred. Like the British pearls, these also were obtained from the freshwater mussels of the rivers and streams, from shells of various species, all different from the British form.

Before proceeding to the main theme of this paper mention may be made of the Pectens or scallop-shells, which have a place in history and in song. "In the days when Ossian sang, the flat valves were the plates, the hollow ones the drinking-cups of Fingal and his heroes."‡

---

* Irving's Conquest of Florida.　　　　† Proc. Am. Assn. Adv. Sci., 1884.
‡ The species referred to by the poet was most likely *Pecten* (*Vo a*) *maximus*.

THE CRUSADES AND PILGRIMAGES OF THE MIDDLE AGES.

The common Mediterranean shell (*Pecten jacobæus*) or St. James's shell was, during the Middle Ages, worn by pilgrims to the Holy Land, and became the badge of several orders of knighthood. "When the monks of the ninth century converted the fisherman of Genneseret into a Spanish warrior they assigned him the scallop-shell for his 'cognizance.'"[*]

Sir Walter Scott in his poem, "Marmion," refers to this badge or emblem, as follows:

> Here is a holy Palmer come
> From Salem first and last from Rome;
> One that hath kissed the blessed tomb,
> And visited each holy shrine
> In Araby and Palestine!
>
>   *   *   *   *   *   *
>
> In Sinai's wilderness he saw
> The Mount where Israel heard the law,
> 'Mid thunder-dint and flashing leven,
> And shadows, mists, and darkness given.
> He shows St. James's cockle-shell—
> Of fair Montserrat, too, can tell.
>
> The summoned Palmer came in place,
> His sable cowl o'erhung his face;
> In his black mantle was he clad,
> With Peter's keys, in cloth of red,
> On his broad shoulders wrought;
> The Scallop-shell his cap did deck.

From the romantic pages of the past which relate to Pearls and famous Pearl-hunters, from the Pilgrims and Pecten shells of the Middle Ages, let us turn over a few leaves and briefly review

THE USE OF SHELLS FOR THE PURPOSES OF MONEY.

It would be quite difficult to point out any natural production better adapted for use as money, or more convenient, when size, shape, and substance are considered, than the Money cowry, and no species of shell or form of shell money has had so wide-spread, so general and extended use as this species. With a few exceptions, other forms of shell money have been made from portions of shells of larger species, necessitating considerable labor in the process of manipulation, the natural form of the shells not being preserved, the form or shape of the money being altogether conventional.[†]

---

[*] Moule's Heraldry of Fish.

[†] When the division of labor was first introduced, commodities were directly bartered for each other. Those, for example, who had a surplus of corn and were in want of wine endeavored to find out those who were in the opposite circumstances, or who had a surplus of wine and wanted corn, and they exchanged one for the other. It is obvious, however, that the power of changing and, consequently, of dividing em-

The following extract from a paper on Early Hindoo Mathematics justifies the inference that the use of the *Cypræa moneta* for money has a very considerable antiquity, and quite likely extends back to a period many centuries earlier than the date of the treatise.

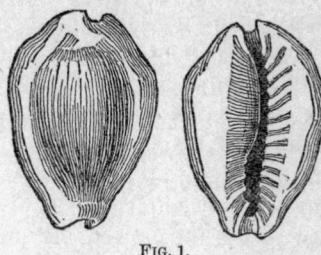

FIG. 1.

MONEY COWRY (*Cypræa moneta*).

(Pacific Islands. From specimens in the U. S. National Museum.)

This treatise, the Lilivati of Bhascara Acharya, is supposed to have been a compilation, and there are reasons for believing a portion of it to have been written about A. D. 628. However this may be, it is of the greatest interest, and its date is sufficiently remote to give to Hindoo mathematics a respectable antiquity.

"The treatise continues rapidly through the usual rules, but pauses at the reduction of fractions to hold up the avaricious man to scorn: 'The quarter of a sixteenth of the fifth of three-quarters of two-thirds of a moiety of a dramma was given to a beggar by a person from whom he asked alms. Tell me how many cowry shells the miser gave, if thou be conversant in arithmetic with the reduction termed subdivision of fractions.'"*

---

ployments, must have been subjected to perpetual interruptions, so long as it was restricted to mere barter. A carries produce to market, and B is desirous to purchase it; but the produce belonging to B is not suitable for A. C, again, would like to buy B's produce, but B is already fully supplied with the equivalent C has to offer. In such cases—and they must be of constant occurrence wherever money is not introduced—no direct exchange could take place between the parties; and it might be very difficult to bring it about indirectly.

The extreme inconvenience attending such situations must early have forced themselves on the attention of every one. Efforts would, in consequence, be made to avoid them; and it would speedily appear that the best, or rather the only way in which this could be effected, was to exchange either the whole or a part of one's surplus produce for some commodity of known value, and in general demand; and which, consequently, few persons would be inclined to refuse to accept as an equivalent for whatever they had to dispose of.

After this commodity had begun to be employed as a means for exchanging other commodities, individuals would become willing to purchase a greater quantity of it than might be required to pay for the products they were desirous of immediately obtaining, knowing that should they at any future period want a further supply of either of these or other articles they would be able readily to procure them in exchange for this universally desired commodity. Though at first circulating slowly and with difficulty, it would, as the advantages arising from its use were better appreciated, begin to pass freely from hand to hand. Its value, as compared with other things, would thus become to be universally known, and it would at last be used, not only as the common medium of exchange, but as a standard by which to measure the value of other things.

Now this commodity, whatever it may be, is *money*. McCulloch's Com'l Dict'y. Vol. II, p. 193. Phila. ed., 1851.

* Prof. E. S. Holden, Popular Science Monthly, July, 1873.

This well-known species, an inhabitant of the Indo-Pacific waters, is still "used as money in Hindostan and many parts of Africa. Many tons are imported to Great Britain and exported for barter with the native tribes of Africa."[*]

These shells are used both strung and unstrung.

Reeve mentions in the second volume of the Conchologia Systematica that "a gentleman residing at Cuttack is said to have paid for the erection of his bungalow entirely in these cowries (*C. moneta*). The building cost him about 4,000 rupees sicca (£400 sterling), and as sixty-four of these shells are equivalent in value to one pice, and sixty-four pice to a rupee sicca, he paid for it with over 16,000,000 of these shells."

Though the number above mentioned is very large, this is an exceedingly abundant form. We have received in a single box from the East Indies not less than ten thousand specimens at one time. "In the year 1848, sixty tons were imported into Liverpool, and in 1849 nearly three hundred tons were brought to the same port." "Their relative currency value varies in different localities. In British India about four thousand pass for a shilling, and the erection of a church, which cost £4,000, is said to have been paid for entirely with cowries. The ordinary gradation or value on the west coast of Africa is as follows:

40 cowries = 1 string.	10 heads = 1 bag.
2½ strings = 1 d.	2,000 cowries = 1 head.
100 cowries = 1 d.	3 heads = 1 dollar.
50 strings = 1 head of cowries.	20,000 cowries = 1 bag.

"In other places they are valued at 1s. 3d. the 1,000. Sometimes 60,000 to 100,000 (or from £3 15s. to £7 10s.) are given for a young wife, whilst a common or ordinary wife may be had for 20,000 cowries, or 25s. In Sudan, as much as the people trade, they have no other currency than the cowry, of which 2,000 shells, weighing seven pounds, are worth only one dollar. Although completely depreciated in the territory of the Upper Nile, cowries form among the Mittoo tribes, between 5° and 6° north latitude, a favorite ornament.

"The Dyaks stick small white money-cowry shells in the eye sockets of the skulls of their enemies, which they keep. In India these shells are much used to ornament the trappings of horses and elephants. * * * Cowry shells are also strung like beads or sewed like buttons on their dress by Brinjari women as personal ornaments, and are in circulation as money in the Hyderabad State, and in other parts of the country." Besides the true money cowry (*Cyprœa moneta*), the ring cowry (*Cyprœa annulus*) passes current in many parts of Africa as a medium of exchange. A Hamburg house, probably the late firm of Godeffroy & Co., sent annually fourteen vessels to Zanzibar for cargoes

---

[*] Baird's Dictionary of Natural History.

of cowries, with which they purchased cargoes of palm-oil and other kinds of produce on the west coast of Africa.

Simmonds gives the following as the imports of cowries into the port of Lagos alone in three years:

	Cwts.
1868	65,496
1869	56,040
1870	50,340
Total	171,876

Or nearly 8,594 tons.

The statistics of late years are not accessible. It is not unlikely that the trade interests involved have led to the suppression or non-publication of the extent of the transactions.

According to Pickering this species was formerly used as money in the Sandwich Islands. He says:* "An estimable and intelligent Hawaiian lady gave me the following particulars respecting former customs: * * * Money was certainly known, for with a string of cowries (*Cypræa moneta*) it was possible to buy any article wanted. Specimens of the same shell that were finer than usual, having a high polish and deep yellow color, were extravagantly valued, and could only be worn by the highest chiefs, who also exclusively possessed wooden calabashes."

Pickering further remarks: "On ascending the Nile I met with the first instances of mixed descent at Kenneh, the modern capital of the Thebaud, about thirty miles below the site of ancient Thebes. Market women of the Ethiopian race likewise made their appearance at Kinneh, where a change took place in the weights and measures, and cowries were seen used as money." The same author observed that "cowries were seen used as money at Poona, the species being *Cypræa annulus.*"

Cypræa moneta, also known as Guinea money, has been used as a financial medium in connection with the African slave trade, and doubtless many a poor negro has been kidnapped and sold, and lost his liberty for a greater or less number of these shells.

The main sources of supply of this species of shell are the Maldive and Laccadive Islands, two groups in the Arabian Sea.

Cypræa annulus, or the ringed cowry, so called, the back or upper side of the shell being ornamented with a bright orange-colored ring, aside from its use as money, as before mentioned, is also used by the Asiatic islanders to adorn their dress and to weight their fishing nets. Specimens of it were found by Dr. Layard in the ruins of Nimroud.†

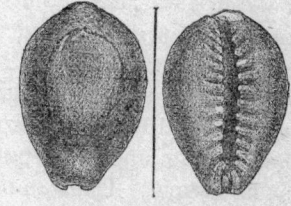

Fig. 2.

RINGED COWRY (*Cypræa annulus*).

(Pacific Islands. From specimens in the U. S. National Museum.)

---

* Races of Man, Bohn's ed., 1863.   † Woodward's Manual, 2d ed., p. 233.

ACHATINA MONETARIA, ETC.

The shell of the land-snail, *Achatina monetaria*, cut into circles, with an open center, is the monetary sign employed in commerce and in payment of a part of tribute in Benguella.*

Another Indo-Pacific species, *Nerita polita*, described by Linnæus, a very abundant form in the general region of the Viti or Fiji Islands and the Navigator or Samoan group, and at certain localities in the Australasian seas, sometimes (once in a thousand) exhibits a banded or striped variety; this, it is said, passes as money and is used in trade.

DIWÁRA, TAMBU, LIDERAN, AND PELE.

In the islands of New Britain and New Ireland and those of the Duke of York group, situated about 10° south latitude and 150° west longitude, shell money is used by the natives. The name of this money in the Duke of York group and New Ireland is *Diwára*. In New Britain it is called *Tambu*. There are other kinds of money in the group made of shells broken into flakes and ground down to a circular form; this is called *Lideran*. In New Ireland 1 fathom of *Lideran* will purchase more than one fathom of *Diwára*. Still another kind of money is made at a place called Mioko, in the Duke of York group; the name of this last is *Pele*. Some forms of this native money are exceedingly special and restricted as a tender, being used only in the purchase of swine. The author* does not give the names of the species or genera of shells from which the money he refers to is made, but some forms of it, impliedly, are made from bivalves and others from gasteropod shells.

It is noteworthy that some of it is in the disk form, in this respect like the *hawock* and *tocalli* of the California aborigines.

WAMPUM AND SHELL MONEY OF THE NORTH AMERICAN INDIANS.

The early settlers of New England found a form of shell money in use among the aborigines of that region. In the Historical Collections of Massachusetts, and from other sources, as recorded by Governor Winthrop and Roger Williams, we are informed as to its character and the purposes for which it was used. This shell money, to which the Indian name *Wampum* was given, consisted of beads made from certain species of shells, and unlike the cowry money of India and Africa, before described, required a considerable degree of manipulation in its manufacture. The cowry money, it will be borne in mind, was used in the natural state, except when strung, and to prepare it for stringing only a simple perforation was necessary. The wampum or shell-bead money of the New England Indians involved much labor and no small degree of skill. It consisted of *two principal colors of beads*, of cylindrical form, a quarter of an inch, more or less, in length, the diameter or thickness being usually about

---

* Tryon's Conchology, vol. I, p. 149.
† Rev. B. Danks, in Jour. Anthrop. Inst., May, 1888.

half the length. The color of the wampum determined its value. The term *Wampum, Wampon,* or *Wampom,* and *Wampam-peege* was apparently applied to these beads when strung or otherwise connected, fastened, or woven together,* as in Fig. 3; also shown in Plate I.

Outside of New England it was otherwise known. By the Dutch settlers of New York it was called *Seawan,*† *Seawant,* or *Zeewand,* and *Roenoke*‡ in Virginia, and perhaps further south, for shell money was also known in the Carolinas, but whether the roenoke of the Virginia Indians was made from the same species of shells as the wampum beads of the more northern tribes is not definitely shown, as the common names given to "shellfish" were then, as now, quite confusing.

Beverly§ says of Virginia wampum: "Peak is of two sorts, or rather of two colors, for both are made of one shell,‖ though or diffeent parts; one is a dark-purple cylinder, and the other a white; they are both made in size and figure alike, and commonly much resembling the English bugles, but not so transparent nor so brittle. They are wrought as smooth as glass, being one-third of an inch long, and about a quarter diameter, strung by a hole drilled through the center.

"The dark color is the dearest,¶ and distinguished by the name Wampum peak. The Englishmen, that are called Indian traders, value the wampum peak at eighteen

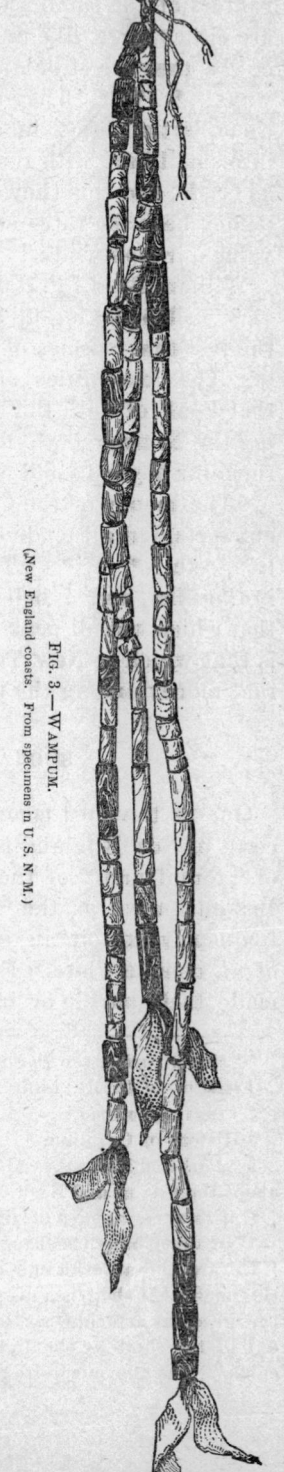

FIG. 3.—WAMPUM.
(New England coasts. From specimens in U. S. N. M.)

---

* Cylindrical shell beads similar to the wampampeege of the Atlantic coast Indians were made to some extent by the red men of the west coast, as is proven by examples in the National Museum from ancient graves, *vide* specimens as follows: Santa Rosa Island, California, 23698, 29123; San Miguel Island, 29122; San Luis Obispo, 21173; Santa Cruz, 18235; Santa Barbara, 15203. These are a modification of the *hawock* of the California tribes, and were made from the dark-purple shells of the mussel, *Mytilus californianus,* which abounds on the west coast.

† Weeden.

‡ Lawson.

§ History of Virginia, 1705.

‖ This certainly applies to the quahaug, *Venus mercenaria.*

¶ This difference in values is the same as among the New Englanders, whites and Indians.

pence per yard, and the white peak at nine pence. They also make runtees of the small shells, and grind them as smooth as peak; these are either large, like an oval bead, and drilled the length of the oval, or else they are circular and flat, almost an inch over, and drilled edgeways. * * * They also have another sort, which is current among them, but of less value; and this is made of the cockle-shell,* broken into small bits, with rough edges, drilled through in the same manner as beads, and this they call roenoke, and use it as peak. These sorts of money bear the rates set upon them as unalterably and current as the value our money are."

William Byrd,[†] F. R. S., wrote: "A vertuoso might divert himself here very well in picking up Shells of various Hue and Figure, and amongst the rest that species of Conque shells which the Indian Peak is made of. The extremities of them shells are Blue and the rest White, so that Peak of both these colors are drilled out of the same shell,[‡] serving the Natives both for Ornament and Money, and are esteemed by them far beyond Gold and Silver."

"The money of the Carolina Indians," says Lawson,[§] "is of different sorts, but all made of shells which are found on the coast of Carolina," etc. * * * "The general and current species of all the Indians in Carolina, and I believe * * * as far as the bay of Mexico, is that which we call peak || and roenoak; but peak more especially. This is that which at New York they call wampum, and have used it as current money among the inhabitants for a great many years," etc.

SUCKAUHOCK OR BLACK WAMPUM.

One of the most common bivalve shell-fish or clams of the southern coast of New England is the *Venus mercenaria*,[¶] the "hard-shell clam" or "round clam" of the New York market, and in the market-stalls of Boston known as the "quahog." The valves or shells of this species frequently exhibit an interior purple edge, the rest of the shell being of an opaque white. From the darker-colored portion ** the Indians made their purple or black money or beads, while from the axis of a

---

* ? *Fulgur carica*, the *Pyrula* elsewhere so called.

† History of the Dividing Line between Virginia and North Carolinia, 1728, p. 24.

‡ *Venus mercenaria*.

§ History of Carolina.

|| "*Peak* and *Roenoak* beads and white shells, with Holes, which they wear in strings about their Arms and Neck." (Jones, Present State of Virginia, 1724.)

¶ *Mercenaria violacea* of authors.

** In describing the hard clam or quahaug (*Venus mercenaria*), Ingersoll says: "Toward the anterior end of the otherwise white interior of each of the valves of this mollusk's shell is a deep purple or brownish black scar, indicating the point of the muscular attachment; the fishermen call it the eye. This dark spot was broken out of the shell by the Indians, and formed the material of their more valuable coins." The above is quite misleading; the term "eye," often applied to the *mono-*

species of *Pyrula*,* or conch, and from other shells, as we are led to infer, they made their "white *wampum*." In reference to the first, and its use as a substance from which the *wampum* was made, we have the following: "The quahaug (*Venus mercenaria*), called by Roger Williams the *poquau* and the *hen*, is a round, thick shell-fish, or, to speak more properly, worm. It does not bury itself but a little in the sand; is generally found lying on it, in deep water, and is gathered by rakes made for the purpose. After the tide ebbs away a few are picked up on the shore below high-

Fig. 4.

THE QUAHAUG (*Venus mercenaria*).

Atlantic Coast of North America.   From specimen in U. S. N. M.

water mark.   The quahaug is not much inferior in relish to the oyster, but is less digestible.   It is not eaten raw, but is cooked in various modes being roasted in the shell or opened and broiled, fried, or made into soups and pies.   About half an inch of the inside of the shell is of a purple color.   This the Indians broke off and converted into beads, named by them *suckauhock*, or black money, which was twice the value of their *wompom*, or white money, made of the *metauhock* or periwinkle (*Pyrula*).*

---

myarian oysters, where the muscular scar is in a general way central, does not apply to the *dimyarian quahaug* with *two* muscular scars—one anterior, the other posterior. In such shells as have a purple interior both of these scars are often more or less merged in that color, which is principally seen on the ventral or lower portion of the valves.   Mr. Ingersoll refers to the periwinkle shells, "Meteaûhock" or Pyrula, from which the "white wampum" was made, thus: "It was only necessary to take out one or two small sections of the central column of the spire and smooth the edges; the hollow core made them natural beads."   I am somewhat familiar with these shells, but have never observed a specimen with a perforated columella.   (See "Wampum and its History.")

*Mass. Historical Society Collections, VIII, 192 (1802).

"As to the derivation of the word 'quahog,' Governor Winthrop refers to it as *'Poquahauges*, a rare shell and dainty food with the Indians. The flesh eats like veal; the English make pyes thereof; and of the

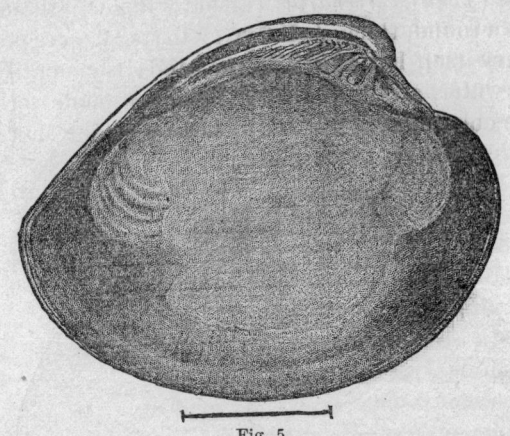

Fig. 5.

Quahaug (*Venus mercenaria*). Inside view of left valve, showing the dark ventral margin.

(Atlantic coast of North America. From specimen in U. S. N. M.)

shells the Indians make money.' He says of the money, 'it is called *wampampeege*.'* Also called by some English *hens-po-qua-hock*. Three are equal to a penny; a fathom is worth 5 shillings.†

"*Poquahock*, corrupted into *quahaug* or *quahog*."

WHITE WAMPUM, OR WAMPUM-PEAGE.

In Cadwallader Colden's History of the Five Indian Nations, he says that wampum is made of the large whelk-shell *Buccinum*, and shaped like long beads; it is the current money of the Indians. Whether the shells of the true *Buccinum* (*B. undatum*, Linn.) or those of *Pyrula canaliculata*‡ and *Pyrula carica* were used is not satisfactorily explained. Probably all of these were used, the long columella of the two latter species causing them to be specially desirable for the purpose of bead-making, particularly the latter for the white beads.

These shells are frequently referred to by the old colonial writers as "cunk" or "conch" shells; and the names "periwinkle," "winkle,"

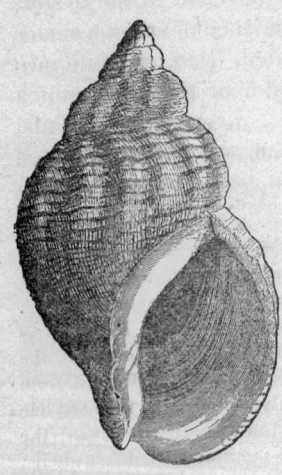

Fig. 6.

Common Whelk (*Buccinum undatum*).

(Atlantic coast of North America. From specimen in U. S. N. M.)

* Journal Royal Society, June 27, 1634.

† *Vide* Invertebrata of Massachusetts, Binney's edition, p. 134. Specimens of wampum are contained in the National Museum from Newport, Rhode Island, No. 17975; Cuyahoga, New York, 17157; Georgia mounds, 10027; Franklin, Tennessee, 19974.

‡ *Fulgur* (*Sycotypus*) *canaliculatus*, the grooved whelk. (*See* Plate II.)

"coccle," "oyster," etc., were confusingly applied to the various species of shells out of which the wampum beads were made.

In the inevitable intercourse and early traffic between the white settlers and the Indians, the wampum or shell money of the latter, in the place of the ordinary money of civilization, naturally came into use as a medium in bartering and exchange, or in adjusting the differences arising in trade between buyer and seller; at first only to a limited extent, afterwards growing into such general use that its value was fixed by legal enactment.

Col. T. W. Higginson, of Massachusetts, in one of his Atlantic essays, "The Puritan Minister," says: "In coming to the private affairs of the Puritan divines, it is humiliating to find that anxieties about salary are of no modern origin. The highest compensation I can find recorded is that of John Higginson, in 1671, who had £160 voted him in country produce, which he was glad, however, to exchange for £120 in solid cash. 'Solid cash' included beaver-skins, black and white wampum, beads, and musket balls, value one farthing."

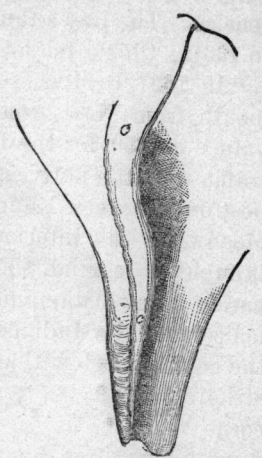

Fig. 7.

Fulgur carica: Portion of basal whorl, showing axis, *c c,* from which the white peage was made; ⅓ natural size.

(See, also, Plate III.)

The value of wampum, as heretofore given on the authority of Governor Winthrop, was for that known as hens-po-qua-hock, three to a penny; and five shillings as the value of a fathom.

"The fathom was a name for a count, an enumeration of beads. * * * Sixty pence, the fathom of beads, was more or less, according to the number of beads allowed by the statute to be equivalent to a penny. If the number was six, then the fathom was 360; but if it was four, as under the Massachusetts standard of 1640, then the fathom numbered 240 beads. We are not to forget that this was a fluctuating standard of value. The tributes of the Indian tribes to the colonists were usually payable in fathoms. Contracts for the sale of land were made by the Indians for considerations of all kinds—wampum, coats, guns, bullets, and wares of all sorts. The island of Conanicut, in Narragansett Bay, was sold to Coddington and his associates in 1657 for 'one hundred pounds in wampum-peage.'

"The unit of the fathom of wampum brought it into correlation with the other currencies used in the colonies. The beads were at first worth more than five shillings a fathom, the price at which they passed current when Williams wrote in 1643. A few years before the fathom was worth nine or ten shillings. But beaver fell in England, and that reduced the price of wampum in the colonies. The wampum was virtually redeemable in beaver, as these changes of value show. As long as the natives were active and furs were plenty there appears to have been no difficulty in passing any quantity of wampum in common with other currencies. The Bay annulled its statutes making the beads a legal tender in 1661. Rhode Island and Connecticut followed soon after. * * *

"In 1627 De Rasières, with a Dutch trading vessel, came into Plymouth from New Amsterdam. In her cargo was a lot of wampum valued at £50, for the Dutch had learned its uses as a currency in their traffic with the natives. They sent this first installment to the trading post on the river Kennebec, where it was kept in hand for two years. Meanwhile the interior Indians heard of it, and the assured supply brought a demand. For some years after the Plymouth men could hardly furnish wampum enough, etc. * * * In 1637 the trade in maize with the Indians up the Connecticut River was so important to the colonies below that they recorded an ordinance with penalties restricting it. * * * In 1638 the same authority fixed the price of corn * * * at 5s. 6d. per bushel in money, at 6s. per bushel in wampum at three a penny, or if in beaver according to the order at 9s. per pound. * * * This particular instance shows that wampum had then made itself nearly equal in purchasing power to money of any kind. The Bay authorities had fixed the rate in 1637 at six beads for a penny for any sum under 12d. In the early statutes only one rate is mentioned. Probably it was understood that the black was included at double the rate fixed for the white. In many of the later laws the two colors are mentioned in that proportion. The usual difficulty caused by a standard of value fluctuating between different markets was experienced now. Connecticut received wampum for taxes, in 1637, at four a penny. They tried to bring it to the Massachusetts standard, for the ordinance of 1640 says: 'The late order concerning Wampū at sixe a penny shall be disolued, and the former of fower a penny and two pence to be paid in the shilling shall be established.'

"In the same year Massachusetts came to the Connecticut standard, the white to pass at four and the 'bleuse' at two a penny, not above 12d. at a time, except at the will of the receiver. In 1641 they submitted to the inevitable and made the shell beads a legal tender at six a penny in sums of £10."

Mr. Weeden, whose admirable memoir* has been freely quoted herein, and who it is quite evident from numerous foot-notes has carefully gleaned the records of the colonial period in this connection, goes on to say: "Evidently the proud merchants and capitalists of the Bay had adopted the Indian money only when the absolute necessity of their community demanded the sanction of law. The precious maize which many writers have designated as an essential factor in the prosperity of the early colonists had yielded the first place, and shell money became the principal medium of intercourse with the natives. Stringent necessity forced men like Winthrop and Endicott to receive these bar-

---

* Indian Money as a Factor in New England Civilization. Baltimore, 1884.

baric trinkets on a par with solid coin of the old English realm. * * * The coin marks, the £ s. d. of their money, they adopted from the Lombard merchants who settled in London, and taught them the larger commerce. They brought these mystic symbols of civilization across the seas and stamped them on the shell treasures of Canonicus and Sassacus."

There was no restriction on the manufacture of wampum. Anybody could make it, and it was made by the whites as well as the Indians. "Seeing that profit and wealth lay in the possession of wampum the burghers [of New Amsterdam] as the easiest way of getting rich began to make it. With their tools of steel this could be done very rapidly, but with the loss of the painstaking care with which the Indians wrought came a loss of value and the wampum soon began to depreciate. To widen their market it was carried to New England." *

The inferior quality of much of the wampum in circulation about this time led to the legislation of 1648 and 1649, by Massachusetts and Connecticut, in the matter of " bad, false, and unfinished peage."

"In 1644 the Indian trade was at its height in New England. In 1661 and 1662 all the New England colonies ceased to receive wampum as a lawful currency, * * * but its use continued long after. * * * New York continued the beads in circulation longer than the regular use prevailed in New England."

The "Acts of Virginia,† 1655," show legislation as follows: " Be it enacted by this Grand Assembly that peeces of Eight that are good and of silver shall pass for five shillings sterling, and Roan only and Wompom peeke to keep their wonted value."

In 1693 they were recognized in the definite rates of the Brooklyn ferry. They continued to be circulated in the remoter districts of New England through the century, and even into the beginning of the eighteenth. ‡

It was practically in use as change and was current with silver in Connecticut in 1704.

The knowledge and use of wampum or wampum-peage extended far into the interior of the country, or perhaps more properly wampum in some form was not uncommon among the aborigines of what was then the " far West."

The territory occupied by the Five Indian Nations being between that of the coast tribes and that of the remoter western Indians, indicates a path of distribution, and justifies the supposition that the wampum of the more distant was the same as that of the sea-board tribes.

Whether the interior tribes of the continent at that time, made use of it as money or as jewelry for personal adornment is a matter of conjecture. It is however highly probable that the wampum beads used

---

* Ingersoll et al.   ‡ Weeden.
† Acts of Virginia Assembly, IV, 1655.

by them were received indirectly from the maritime or coast tribes in exchange for such articles as were peculiar to their interior position.

Without multiplying authorities, it may be safely asserted that this shell money was manufactured along the Atlantic coast from Maine to Florida, and on the Gulf coast certainly as far south as Central America. The use of this circulating medium was undoubtedly very general among the agricultural tribes east of the Mississippi River.* The ancient sepulchral tumuli of Georgia, Tennessee, Florida, and other Southern States, as well as those located in the valley of the Ohio and in valleys tributary both to it and to the Mississippi from the east, when opened, fully corroborate the historical narrative, and afford physical proof that this product of the skill and the patience of the coast tribes, sought and obtained through trade relations, was thus, and by means of subsequent migrations, widely disseminated among the red men dwelling far in the interior.

The proximity of the coast tribes to the sources whence the material was procured from which the wampum-peage was made would at once give to the latter superior commercial advantages, and it is quite likely that they were directly or indirectly liberal purchasers from the interior communities, who considered them, if not as merchants or bankers, at least as particularly fortunate and wealthy on account of the money they handled, just as the inhabitants of interior and agricultural districts among civilized people regard the traders and inhabitants of littoral cities and settlements.

There is some reason for believing that among the Five Nations wampum of home manufacture was made out of a species of fresh-water snail (shell) that lives in the streams and smaller lakes of the region occupied by said tribes.

From the foregoing some idea may be formed of the importance in the past of

SHELL MONEY AS A FACTOR IN AMERICAN CIVILIZATION.

Aside from the shell beads, or strings of shell beads, that were used as money, wampum was used for personal adornment,† and belts were made by embroidering wampum upon "strips of deer-skin," forming a girdle or scarf, and these belts and scarfs were not simply an evidence of wealth but a symbol of authority and power.

---

* C. C. Jones, Antiquities of the Southern Indians.   Appleton & Co., 1873.

† "The Queen of Pamunkey was introduced * * * she having round her head a plat of black and white wampum peague three inches broad in imitation of a corown, and was cloathed in a mantle of dresst deer skins," etc. T[homas] M[atthews] The Begining and Progress and Conclusion of Bacon's Rebellion in Virginia in the year 1675 and 1676.

"Their hair was breeded with white and Blue Peak, and hung gracefully upon a large Roll upon their shoulders. This peak consists of small cylinders cut out of a Conque shell, drilled through and strung like Beads. It serves them both for Money and Jewels, the Blue being of much greater Value than the white." [Byrd, *l. c.* 73.]

In Major Rogers's Account of North America (London, 1765), in alluding to the wampum of the Indians, he says: "When they solicit the alliance, offensive or defensive, of a whole nation, they send an embassy with a large belt of *wampum* and a bloody hatchet, inviting them to come and drink the blood of their enemies. The *wampum* made use of on these and other occasions, before their acquaintance with the Europeans, was nothing but small shells, which they picked up by the sea-coast and on the banks of the lakes; and now it is nothing but a kind of cylindrical beads, made of shells, white and black, which are esteemed among them as silver and gold are among us. They have the art of stringing, twisting, and interweaving them into their belts, collars, blankets, moccasins, etc., in ten thousand different sizes, forms, and figures, so as to be ornaments for every part of dress, and expressive to them of all their important transactions.

"They dye the *wampum* of various colors and shades, and mix and dispose them with great ingenuity and order, so as to be significant among themselves of almost everything they please; so that by these their words are kept and their thoughts communicated to one another, as ours by writing. The belts that pass from one nation to another in all treaties, declarations, and important transactions, are very carefully preserved in the cabins of their chiefs, and serve not only as a kind of record or history, but as a public treasure.

"According to the Indian conception these belts could tell, by means of an interpreter, the exact rule, provision, or transaction talked into them at the time, and of which they were the exclusive record. A strand of wampum consisting of purple and white shell beads, or a belt woven with figures formed by beads of different colors, operated on the principle of associating a particular fact with a particular string or figure; thus giving a serial arrangement to the facts as well as fidelity to the memory. These strands and belts were the only visible records of the Iroquois; but they required those trained interpreters who could draw from their strings and figures [the acts and intentions] locked up in their remembrance."*

After the defeat of the great chief Philip of the Wampanoags, Anawan, the most trusted warrior, counselor, and friend of Philip, went out quietly, brought the three or four wampum scarfs—splendid in his eyes—and gave them to his conqueror. The trinkets were not only valuable in themselves, they also symbolized and embodied a complete submission to the more mighty men whose prowess had prevailed over the Indians. The largest scarf, 9 inches wide, pictured with birds and beasts and flowers, when laid over the shoulders of the sturdy Rhode Islander, swept his ankles. Another belt designed for the head carried two flags attached to it. Governor Winslow in his letter to the King, accompanying the spoils of Philip, speaks of them as "being his Crowne, his Gorge and two Belts of their own making of their goulde

---

* Morgan, Ancient Society.

and silver." Gold it was not, coin it was not; but the governor correctly described it as "their gold." This quality gave it the attributes of a currency in the growing intercourse with the colonists. It was this quality, this costliness, which impressed the barbaric imagination and made wampum a high symbol in every ceremony, political or religious.

Whenever the Indians made an important statement in their frequent negotiations, they presented a belt to prove it, to give force to their words. "The hatchet fixed in the head," one of the most forcible of their many figures, expressing a sense of wrong, a legitimate grievance—this hatchet must be removed by something more powerful than words. A belt was presented to discharge the grievance, and not by mere purchase. The value of the beads could hardly have been of consequence to a haughty confederacy like the Iroquois or Five Nations. It marked the gravity of the apology. It gave to the words the weight of hard physical facts, and made the expression an emblem of great force and significance.*

It is not the object of this paper to present or consider the use of shells or wampum beads for other purposes than money or a medium in trade. As Mr. Holmes† remarks in his elaborate memoir, "the literature of wampum would fill a volume."

So, from a passing glance at the symbolic uses of wampum and the important mnemonic use of these insignificant shell beads to the ancient Americans of the Atlantic sea-board, we will cross the continent and consider

THE SHELL MONEY OF THE CALIFORNIA ABORIGINES.

The use of shells for the purposes of money by the Indians of the northwest coast of North America prevailed no doubt for a long time before any members of the European races had any knowledge of the aborigines of this portion of the continent. At the time of the earliest contact of white men with the red men of the Pacific slope, shell money was found to be in use, and the same forms have been obtained from the graves and ancient burial places of the aborigines of California, etc.

Our knowledge of the Indians of the west coast is, unfortunately, exceedingly limited and indefinite. Limited in time, as we find when we seek to trace back, prior to the date of the transfer of the territory of what are termed the Pacific States to the United States, and indefinite as to the minor features of the west coast Indians, in matters which pertain or relate to their ordinary habits, customs, etc.

Powers, referring to shell money, says: "Immense quantities of it were formerly in circulation among the California Indians, and the manufacture of it was large and constant to replace the continual wastage * * * caused by the sacrifice of so much upon the death of wealthy men, and by the propitiatory sacrifices performed by many

---

* Weeden.

† Art in Shell of the Ancient Americans, Ann. Rept. Bureau Ethnology, 1880–'81.

tribes, especially those of the Coast Range. From my own observations, which have not been limited, and from the statements of pioneers and the Indians themselves, I hesitate little to express the belief that every Indian in the State, in early days, possessed an average of at least $100 worth of shell money. This would represent the value of about two women (though the Nishinam never actually bought their wives), or two grizzly-bear skins, or twenty-five cinnamon-bear skins or about three average ponies. This may be considered a fair state, ment of the diffusion of wealth among them in their primitive condition."

The late George Gibbs,[*] in writing (prior to 1873) of the Indians of the northwest coast, says: "Measures of length were probably all referred to parts of the body, the principal being the extent of the outstretched arms, which was used in valuing their money, the haikwa or wampum of the Pacific."

HAIK-WA, HI-A-QUA, OR TUSK-SHELL MONEY.

Of these shells, a species of *Dentalium*, Mr. Lord writes:[†]
"The money-shells are procured upon the north end of Vancouver Island; also in the bays and inlets along the mainland coast north of

Fig. 8.
DENTALIUM.
(Pacific coast. From specimen in U. S. N. M.)

latitude of 49 degrees to Sitka, and is common likewise round Queen Charlotte's Island. The genus has an enormous geographical range, and it is, perhaps, strange that the shells from Northwest America, from California, and those obtained on our own coast, when placed side by side, scarcely present any material specific difference."[‡]

The Tusk-shells are collected in the following manner: "An Indian when shell-fishing arms himself with a long spear, the haft of which is light deal; to the end of it is fastened a strip of wood placed transversely, but driven full of teeth made of bone. The whole affair resembles a long comb affixed to the end of a stick with the teeth very wide apart. A squaw sits in the stern of the canoe, and paddles it slowly along, whilst the Indian with the spear stands in the bow. He stabs this comb-like affair into the sand at the bottom of the water, and after giving two or three prods draws it up to look at it. If he has been

---

[*] Tribes of Western Washington and Northwestern Oregon.

[†] The Naturalist in British Columbia, vol. II.

[‡] There are several unquestionably distinct species on the west coast from Sitka to Central America.

successful perhaps four or five money-shells have been impaled on the teeth of the spear. It is a very ingenious mode of procuring them, for it would be quite impracticable either to dredge or net them out, and they are never, as far as I know, found between tide-marks."

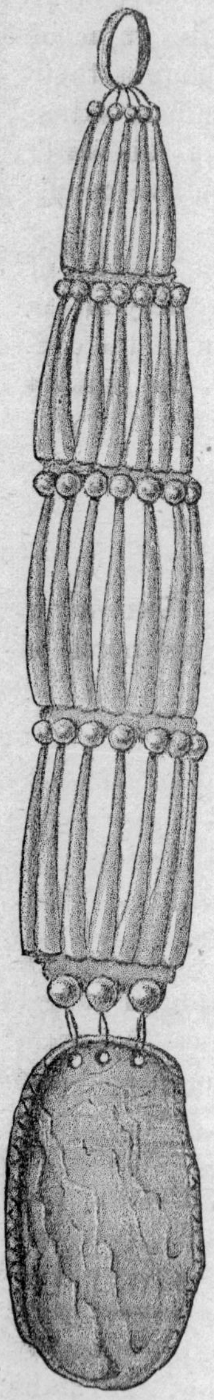

Gibbs also describes the method of obtaining them as follows: "This shell is a species of *Dentalium*, which was procured on the northern coast by letting down long poles to which was attached a piece of wood filled with spikes or teeth, between which the shell became fixed. The squaws string them very neatly. A small bit of dried sinew, taken from * * * the caribou is passed through the shell lengthwise, there being a hole at each end. The string is generally ornamented with fragments of the * * * Haliotis shell and tufts of dry wool taken from the mountain goat (*Capra americana*)."

KOP-KOPS; SHORT TUSK-SHELLS.

The short, broken, and inferior shells are strung together in the same manner, but in various lengths, and represent shillings or pence, as the string is either long or short or the shells defective. All inferior strings, irrespective of either length or quality, are called *kop-kops*. The *hi-qua* represents the sovereign, the highest standard of currency, and, as a rule, would purchase one male or two female slaves. The value of the slave, estimating it by the sum paid in blankets for a slave at the present day, would be about £50 sterling. Forty *kop-kops* equal a *hi-qua* in value, but various small bargains are made and small debts paid with *kop-kops*, only just as we pay away shillings or lesser coin.

Gibbs also says: "Its price depended entirely upon its length; forty to the fathom being the standard of value. When the shells were so short that it required more to make up the required length, they were of inferior account, but rose proportionately with increased size. A fathom of forty was formerly worth a slave, and even now will bring five dollars in money. "Single shells were shown me on the Tsihalis for which the owner refused one dollar apiece. This money is, however, becoming scarce, and is far less used than formerly, at least by the tribes who have much intercourse with the whites. It was the universal currency through an extensive district. On the Klamath River

Fig. 9.

Ear ornament made of short Tusk-shells *kop-kops* with pendant of ear-shell, *Haliotis, uhl-lo.*

(West coast of North America. From specimen in U. S. N. M.)

it is valued even more highly than on the Sound and the Columbia, and those aboriginal peddlers, the Klikitat, frequently carry it to southern Oregon for sale. * * * I have never met with mnemonical signs or pictorial help to memory."

Mr. Lord also says that the use of these shells (*Dentalium*) as money had at the time he wrote to a great extent died out. This was due to the introduction of blankets by the Hudson Bay Company. "A slave, a canoe, or a squaw is worth in these days so many blankets; formerly it was so many strings of *Dentalia*."*

Further touching the value of the tusk shell money the same writer remarks: "The value depends upon its length. Those representing the greater value are called, when strung together end to end, a *hi-qua*, but the standard by which *Dentalium* is calculated to be fit for a *hi-qua* is that twenty-five shells placed end to end must make a fathom, or 6 feet in length."

In 1810† these were the circulating medium of the country, and twenty [? shells] of them would buy a good beaver-skin.

Pickering‡ says "the Chinooks have '*wampum*' of the usual description, but strings and bands of *Dentalium* shells of somewhat similar model seem principally to subserve the purposes of currency."

"In early days, ere the red and white men knew each other, the *Dentalium* was the only currency in use. It is quite clear, and also a very curious fact, that the *hi-qua* and *kop-kop* were known and used by the Indians of the interior at some distant period, although no trace of their use or knowledge of the shell exists among them at present; for in digging out some flint implements, stone beads, and other things I need not here enumerate, from the drift, I found numbers of *dentaliums* and round buttons made of the Haliotis nacre. The distance from the nearest sea-board was about 1,000 miles, and the language spoken by these inland Indians quite incomprehensible to the Indians on the coast."§

Among the *Tah ka li* or *Ta cullies*, regarded by Gibbs as belonging to the Tinnehs, inhabiting a region extending from the Cascade Range in British Columbia eastward to the Rocky Mountains, their avarice it was said "lies in the direction of hiaqua shells,‖ which they obtain indirectly from the sea-coast or of the maritime tribes through intervening tribes."

Whymper,¶ describing an Indian muster of various tribes at or near Fort Yukon, Alaska, in 1867, said: "Their clothing was much befringed with beads, and many of them wore through the nose (as did most of the other Indian *men* present) an ornament composed of the *hya-qua*

---

* Proc. Zool. Soc. London, March, 1864.

† Harmon's Jour., Voyages and Travels, 1820.

‡ Races of Man. This was in 1841.

§ Lord, *l. c.*

‖ Harmon's Journal.

¶ Whymper's Alaska.

shell (*Dentalium entalis* or *Entalis vulgaris*).   Both of the fur companies on the river trade with them, and at very high prices." He further remarks that his spelling "*hya-qua*" conveys a closer approximation to the usual pronunciation of the word then Mr. Lord's "*hi-qua.*"

The use of these shells for nasal ornamentation,* as observed by Mr. Whymper, at Fort Yukon, is practiced by the Californian Indians.   While at Crescent City in 1861 we saw a medicine-man belonging to one of the neighboring tribes thus curiously decorated.   He had perforated the partition which separates the nostrils, and into the hole had inserted from each side, point passed by point, two of these shells.

This unique ornamentation was further improved by the sticking of the feathers of some species of wild fowl into the larger end of each of the hollow shells.

Whymper gives the scientific name of the Tusk-shell as *Dentalium entalis* or *Entalis vulgaris*.   Now, this species of Tusk-shell is a North Atlantic form; the Pacific coast species is *Dentalium indianorum.*†

The Atlantic form, which is abundantly obtained in Europe, has been largely imported for the Indian trade; it is highly probable that a great part of the Tusk-shells that have been in circulation of late years do not belong to the indigenous species, but have been worked off upon the Indians by the traders.

Among the California tribes the Tusk-shells were called *Alli-co-cheek*, or *álli-co-chick*,‡ the latter being the orthography of Mr. Powers.   The same writer observed the use of this species of money-shell among the Cahrocs or Karoks, who arrange it on strings, the shortest being worth with them 25 cents, the longest $2. * * *   The unit of currency is a string the length of a man's arm, with a certain number of the longer shells below the elbow, and a certain number of the shorter ones above. This shell money is called *állicochick*, not only on the Klamath, but from Crescent City to Eel River, though the tribes using it speak different languages.

When the Americans first arrived in the country an Indian would give from $40 to $50 in gold for a string of it; but now it is principally the old Indians who value it at all.§

" Hupa *álli-co-chick* is rated a little differently from the Karok.   The standard of measurement is a string of five shells.   Nearly every man has ten lines tattooed across the inside of his left arm, about half way between the wrist and elbow, and in measuring shell money he takes the string in his right hand, draws one end over his left thumb nail and if the other end reaches to the uppermost of the tattoo-lines the five shells are worth $25 in gold, or $5 a shell.   Of course it is only one in

---

* Mentioned also in Franklin's narrative: Journey to the Shores of the Polar Sea, vol. II, p. 84.

† Sometimes called *Dentalium pretiosum.*

‡ Meaning among the Yuroks, literally, Indian money.

§ Overland Monthly, vol. VIII.

ten thousand that is long enough to reach this high value. The longest ones usually seen are worth about $2, that is, $10 the string."

Powers says of the Indians of Del Norte County, that they are more avaricious than others in California. "Money makes the chief among them, and he is entitled to that honor who possesses the most *alli-ko-chick*."

After describing the puberty dance (*Kin'-alkh-ta*) of the Hupâs, he says: "She is now ready for marriage, and she will bring in the market from three to ten strings (about half the valuation of a man), that is, from $15 to $50."

I have heretofore referred to the *Pectens* or scallop shells, and their place in history and song. So also with the *Dentalia* or money-shells of the Indians, which it will be seen have a place in their simple rhythm and music.

Among the Moädocs, or Modoks "when a maiden arrives at woman-hood her father makes a kind of party in her honor. Her young companions assemble, and together they dance and sing wild, dithyrambic roundelays, improvised songs of the woods and the waters:

> "'Jumping echoes of the rock;
> Squirrels turning somersaults;
> Green leaves, dancing in the air;
> Fishes white as money-shells
> Running in the water, green and deep and still.
> Hi-ho, hi-ho, hi-hay!
> Hi-ho, hi-ho, hi-hay!'

"This is the substance of one of the songs, as translated for me."[*]

In describing marriage among the Yúroks or Eurocs, he says: "When a young Indian becomes enamored of a maiden and can not wait to collect the amount of shells demanded by her father, he is sometimes allowed to pay half the amount and become what is termed 'half married.' Instead of bringing her to his cabin and making her his slave, he goes to live in *her* cabin and becomes *her* slave." Again he says: "Since the advent of the Americans the honorable estate of matrimony has fallen sadly into desuetude among the young braves, because they seldom have shell money nowadays, and the old Indians prefer that in exchange for their daughters. * * * The old generation dislike the white man's money, but hoard up shell money like true misers," etc.

The Patawat have reduced the science and practice of law down to a tolerably accurate mechanism in one matter at least—that of mulctuary punishment. The average fine imposed for the murder of a man is ten strings of *ál-li-co-chik*, each string consisting of ten pieces, and for that of a squaw five strings of equal length. As the pieces of shell money generally average, and as it was first valued in American coin, these fines amount to about $100 and $50, respectively.

Among the Patwats "a wife is always acquired by purchase, and her

---

[*] Powers, Overland Monthly, vol. x.

market value is regulated on a sliding scale, on which the prices range all the way from two up to fifteen strings." Among the Hupâs or Hoopas, Powers* says: "Murder is generally compounded for by the payment of shell money."

Besides the *alli-co-cheek* or Tusk-shell money; *Dentalia,* which so far as general use as *money* is considered, had the widest circulation, we will now briefly glance at certain other forms that were used to a greater or less extent for the same purpose.

The Tusk-shell money, *al-li-ko-chik,* it seems, was principally used by the coast tribes from Mendocino, California, northward to Alaska, and by such other tribes to the eastward of the coast tribes whose territory joined on or was proximate to that of the coast tribes; and that it was known and highly prized still farther to the eastward, we have the following testimony:

"The Hidatsa,† Minnataree, or Gros Ventre Indians, are one of the three tribes which at present [1854–'62]) inhabit the permanent village at Fort Berthold, Dakota Territory, and hunt on the waters of the Upper Missouri and Yellowstone Rivers, in northwestern Dakota and eastern Montana."‡

"It appears probable that they once carried on a trade indirectly with the tribes of the Pacific coast, for they had *Dentalium* shells similar to those obtained on the Pacific, and they prized them so highly that the white traders found it advisable to obtain them for the trade. As late as 1866, ten of these shells, of inferior size, costing the traders only a cent apiece, would buy a superior buffalo robe, and formerly only two or three of the same quality were paid for a robe. Modern traders, with whom the writer has conversed, obtain their shells from the Eastern importers, and know nothing of the original source of supply. They suppose them to come from the Atlantic coast or the Great Lakes, and call them 'Iroquois shells,' which is probably their corruption of the Chinook *Hyakwa,* but it is possible the reverse is the case."

They also used, and still use as ornaments, fragments of the *Abalone* shells (one or more species of Haliotis) of the Pacific. These are now supplied to the trade under the name of California shells. Ten years ago one of these shells, unpolished, sold for a good robe. There is little doubt that they used *Abalone, Dentalium,* and other sea-shells before the traders brought them. Old traders and Indians say so. Even as late as 1833 it would seem that they had not yet become a regular part of a trader's outfit; for Maximilian§ says of the Mandans: "They do not disfigure the bodies; only they make some apertures in the outer rim of the ear, in which they have strings of beads, brass or iron rings of different sizes, or shells, the last of which they obtain from other

---

* Overland Monthly, vol. IX.

† Ethnography and Philology of the Hidatsa Indians, etc., p. 3.

‡ *Id.,* p. 28.

§ Travels in the Interior of North America by Maximilian * * * in 1832, 1833, 1834. London ed. Ackerman & Co. 1843.

Indian tribes. If they are questioned respecting these shells, they answer that they were brought from the sea."

It had but a limited use among the west-coast Indians, if we may judge by the rarity of its occurrence in old graves. Of the small number of specimens in the National Museum named in the foot-note * nearly all belong to a different species of *Dentalium*, namely, *D. hexagonum*, and it is not certain that such examples as do not belong to this species should be regarded as the same as the northern form. *D. hexagonum*, though a smaller, slenderer, and more delicate shell, and in these respects less desirable through being less serviceable than *D. indianorum*, is fully as abundant along the coast in the region around San Diego as *D. indianorum* is in the Puget Sound region.

HAWOCK OR HA-WOK.

Powers expresses the opinion "that the staple currency of all the tribes in central and southern California is made from the same mate-

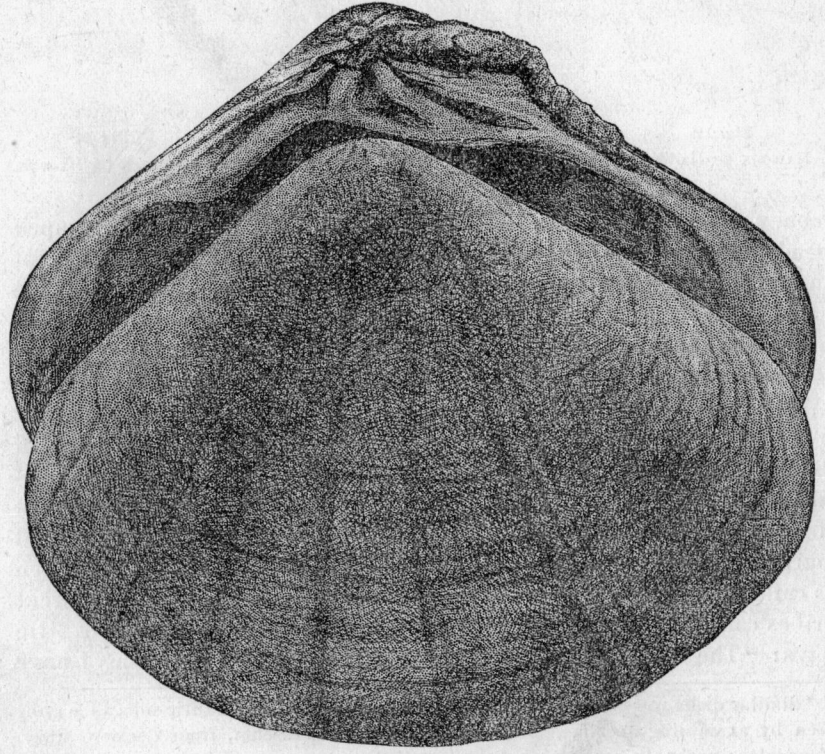

Fig. 10.

TIVELA CRASSATELLOIDES.†

(Southern coast of California. From specimen iu U. S. N. M.)

---

* San Miguel Island: *D. hexagonum* and perhaps *D. indianorum* on same string. [29144.] San Luis Obispo: Fragments of both of above, or possibly (artificially shortened and strung) beads, mixed. [21773.]

† = *Pachydesma crassatelloides*.

rial," but he is not positive of that except among the Nishinam [Maidu]. Here it is made from the heavy shells of a bivalve, a ponderous clam when adult, of very compact texture, peculiar to the southern coast of California; abundant at Morro or Estero Bay and other places southward to San Diego. This is cut into circular pieces of the diameter as shown in the annexed figures, or even smaller, the thickness of the pieces varying with the thickness of the shells, or of that portion of the valve from which the disks are made. The larger pieces* (Figs. 11 and 12) of the value of twenty-five cents are cut from the thicker part of the valves of large or adult clams of said species, and the smaller (Figs. 13 and 14) of the value of four cents each from the thinner portions. This

| Fig. 11. | Fig. 12. | Fig. 13. | Fig. 14. |
| HAWOCK OR HA-WOK. | HAWOCK OR HA-WOK. | HAWOCK OR HA-WOK. | HAWOCK OR HA-WOK. |

money, of which the smaller pieces closely resemble the disk-shaped beads of the natives of the Paumotu Islands in the South Pacific, except in being of twice the diameter and thickness, is strung upon strings the same as beads in a necklace, for which it is also used. Figs. 13 and 14 are the same in form and about the size of the pieces made from *Saxidomus aratus*,† according to Yates, and in use among the Indian Pomos [Wailakki] of Lake County,‡ and probably by the neighboring Wintuns. While on a collecting tour along the coast in the neighborhood of Bodega, in 1867 or 1868, we were told by some of the old settlers thereabout that the Indians formerly visited this region for the purpose of digging this particular species of clam. The meats were dried for food purposes and the shells were used to make this form of money, which is called *hawock*, according to Mr. Powers, though, as he says, different tribes call it by different names and attach different values to it. He says: "The Bear River Indians (*Neeshenams*) are the only ones I have

---

* Similar disks were sometimes made by the Indians of the Atlantic side, as may be seen by examining specimen 21618 in the National Museum, from Cocke County, Tennessee; probably cut out of a Busycon shell.

† = *Saxidomus gracilis*. A form closely related to the foregoing, *Saxidomus nuttallii*, is used to a certain extent by the Indians in Washington Territory for making these disk heads or money. They make two sizes of it, like the figures in this respect. *S. nuttallii* is a common clam in Puget Sound.

‡ Yates states the value of these small disks as being 80 for $1 among the Indians of Lake County.

seen who count it by the single piece; the others rate it by the foot or yard. * * * It is sometimes strung upon a string many yards long,

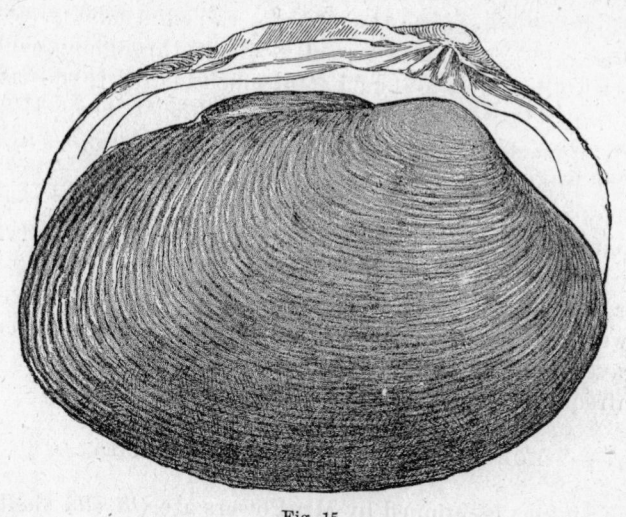

Fig. 15.
SAXIDOMUS ARATUS.
(Southern coast of California. From specimen in U. S. N. M.)

in hundreds of pieces, and doubled into lengths of about a yard. The Wai'-lak-kis make the buttons thin, then every tenth one thicker, so that it looks like a Catholic rosary, and their name for it is *tocalli*."

In a photograph of a young woman of the Bear River Indians, named Válputteh, sent to me by Mr. Powers, her person is adorned with a necklace of *hawock*, which, it is stated, is ten yards long, requiring to be wound several times about her neck. It consists of about 1,160 pieces, valued at $232. "Sometimes disks of *hawock* are made two inches in diameter and half an inch thick, which are rated at one dollar apiece, but such large pieces are seldom seen." These disk-beads or *Hawock* "are strung on strings made of the inner bark of wild cotton or milk-weed (*Asclepias*); and either all the pieces on a string or all in one section of it are of the same size."

In connection with the use of money in traffic among the interior Indians, it appears that "all the dwellers on the plains, and as far up on the mountain as the cedar line, bought all their bows and most of their arrows from the upper mountaineers. An Indian is about ten days making a bow, and it costs $3, $4, or $5, according to the workmanship; an arrow 12½ cents. Three kinds of money were employed in this traffic. White shell beads, or rather buttons, pierced in the center and strung together were rated at $5 per yard (*hawock*); periwinkles, at $1 a yard; fancy marine shells, at various prices, from $3 to $10 or $15, according to their beauty.

"Among the Yocuts, whose dominion covers the Kern and Tulare basins and the middle San Joaquin, etc., their money consists of the usual shell buttons (*hawock*), and a string of them reaching from the point of the middle finger to the elbow is valued at twenty-five cents."

The use of hāwok was quite general no doubt throughout central and southern California, and to some extent much farther to the east. One example* in the National Museum is from New Mexico. Hāwok was often made of much smaller size than the figures illustrate; as small as the smaller beads or *peage* of the Atlantic coast and equally well finished, sometimes even neatly ornamented by serrating the edges,† which must have been a difficult and painstaking work in beads so small. Again we find cylindrical beads sometimes five inches in length, either curved or straight, made from the heavy clam *Tivela;* these we may regard, however, rather as ornaments than money; they have been found in the graves on most of the islands in the Santa Barbara Channel, as well as infrequently in similar situations on the mainland.

KOL-KOL OR OLIVELLA SHELL MONEY.

The periwinkles mentioned by Mr. Powers are *Olivella* shells of the species known as *O. biplicata*, a form that is exceedingly abundant in numerous places along the Californian coast. They were prepared by simply rubbing or grinding off the apex, and were called *col-col* or *kol-kol*. This form was strung in a double string, the shells lying mouth to

Fig. 16.

OLIVELLA BIPLICATA.

(Coast of California. From specimens in U. S. N. M.)

mouth, and it is stated were "slightly esteemed." This was no doubt owing to the abundance of this species. They were, however, extensively used for personal decoration, for they have been found in ancient graves at various places in southern, central, and northern California on the mainland, and also the islands in the Santa Barbara Channel.‡

* Museum number 9538.

† Santa Barbara (15221) graves. See also specimens from San Miguel Island, 15768, 29127, 29129; Santa Rosa Island, 23696; Santa Cruz Island, 18190, 26253; Santa Barbara, 20244; Dos Pueblos, 18773; Stockton, 32316.

‡ "We found *O. biplicata* in great numbers in the graves on San Miguel Island, many of which had been bored, seemingly for the purpose of stringing. I observed also many of them with the apex ground off, so that a string might be readily passed through lengthwise."—(W. G. W. Harford, 1876.) "The shell of *Olivella biplicata* Sby., is also (or was) used as money, the writer having found them occasionally in the 'mounds' of Contra Costa and Alameda Counties mixed with small flat disks described above."—(Dr. L. G. Yates.)

These shells were not only strung whole, but disk-shaped beads were cut out of the body whorl as shown in figure. These *Olivella* shells

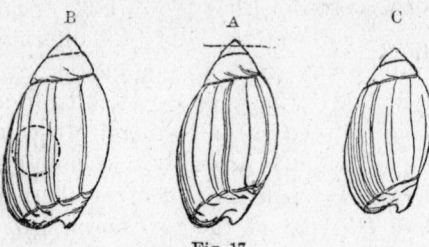

Fig. 17.

OLIVELLA BIPLICATA.

A, the portion above the line was ground off to admit of stringing; B, the circle shows the part of the shell from which the disks were cut; C, a specimen of the shell in the natural state.

(Coast of California. From specimens in U. S. N. M.)

vary considerably in size, often measuring an inch or more in length. The smaller ones were apparently preferred for stringing whole, while the larger ones were required for making the disks.

This way of treating the *Olivella* shells seems to have been formerly rather popular, if we may judge by the specimens in the National Museum* from Indian graves. In the majority of instances these disks were rather rudely finished, with rough and uneven edges, but sometimes, as shown in a specimen from Santa Rosa Island,† the disks are made quite small and very neatly finished.

Mr. Barber‡ says: "Through eastern Utah and south into Arizona many *Olivas* [Olivellas] were found scattered through the débris of crumbling walls and broken pottery. The perforation has been effected by grinding down the apex." * * * He describes other beads that "were of two sizes, and usually white. The smaller variety was flat on both sides, or slightly convex on one side and concave on the other, * * * as thin as a wafer, and the circumference of an ordinary pea. In the center a neatly bored hole enabled the owner to string them together in the form of a necklace. The larger variety was about the circumference of an average buckshot."

Capt. John Moss, of Parrott City, Colorado, says that these beads are valued highly by the present Navajo Indians to the south, a small string, when such can be found, bringing in exchange a good horse. The Navajoes are constantly grubbing about the old buildings and adjacent graves in search of these trinkets. This accounts in some measure for their great scarcity among the ruins to-day. They were undoubtedly obtained by the ancients from other tribes, who brought them, or at least the shells from which they were fashioned, from the Pacific coast. We know that these ruins extend as far west as the junction of the San Juan and Colorado Rivers, so that communication

* Santa Cruz Island, 26,425; San Miguel Island, 14988, 26428, 29024, 29623.

† Santa Rosa Island, 23693; Santa Barbara County, 21846, 21848; Santa Cruz, 18231, 26254; Contra Costa County, 9453.

‡ American Naturalist, vol. XI, 1277.

between the tribe in question and others situated along the Pacific Ocean or Gulf of California was rendered easy. Don José Cortez, writing of the tribes near the Colorado in 1799, speaks of "the white beads they get on the shores of the Gulf of California."

The more general form of kol-kol, combined or arranged in various ways, single and double strings, bracelets, etc., from as far east as southern Utah,* may be seen in the National Museum.

The finest example extant is probably that obtained by Lieutenant Ray† from the Hupa or Hoopah Indians of northern California. It is made of quite small *Olivellas* of the two species, *O. biplicata* and *O. intorta*, carefully selected specimens, and neatly strung. If extended in a single length it would measure nearly thirty feet, and includes probably over a thousand shells.

Occasionally large specimens of *O. biplicata* were cut, or more likely ground down, lengthwise‡ and then perforated, so as to admit of attachment or stringing; but this is not a common form, and was most likely for ornament only.

Powers, writing about *hawock*, says: "This may be called their silver, and is the great medium of all transactions, while the money answering to gold is made from various species of the ear shell" (*Haliotis*) and is called "*Uhl-lo* or *ül-lo*."

UHL-LO, ÜL-LO, OR ABALONE MONEY.

These shells are without doubt the "fancy marine shells" previously mentioned, which were valued at "$3 to $10, or $15, according to their beauty," and belong to one or the other of the species known to conchologists as *Haliotis rufescens*, *H. splendens*, and *H. cracherodii*, all indigenous forms, popularly known as *abalones;*§ the aulones of the Spanish.

It is not a matter of wonder that these beautiful shells excited the admiration of the savage. Many tons of them have within the last twenty years been collected and shipped to Europe and China as well as to the Eastern United States, where they are manipulated into various forms for useful and decorative purposes. The California Indians, with their primitive tools of obsidian, cut them up "into oblong strips from 1 to 2 inches in length, according to the curvature of the shell, and about a third as broad as they are long. * * * Holes are drilled near one end and they are thereby fastened to a string, * * * hanging edge to edge. Ten pieces generally constitute a string, and the larger pieces rate at $1 apiece, $10 a string; the smaller in proportion,

* 14621, also 11986, southern Utah.

† 77185, Hoopah Valley, California.

‡ San Miguel Island, California [No. 29156], in National Museum.

§ Holmes says that "*H. kamtchatkana*, which furnishes a dark-green nacre, is much used farther north." This is probably a mistake, and *H. splendens* the species intended, as the former is the least brilliant and has the thinnest shell of any of the west American species.

or less, if they are not pretty. Being susceptible of a high polish, this money forms a beautiful ornament, and is worn for necklaces on gala days. But as money it is rather too large and cumbersome, and the Indians generally seek to exchange it for the less brilliant but more useful *ha-wock*. The *ül-lo* may be considered rather as jewelry."

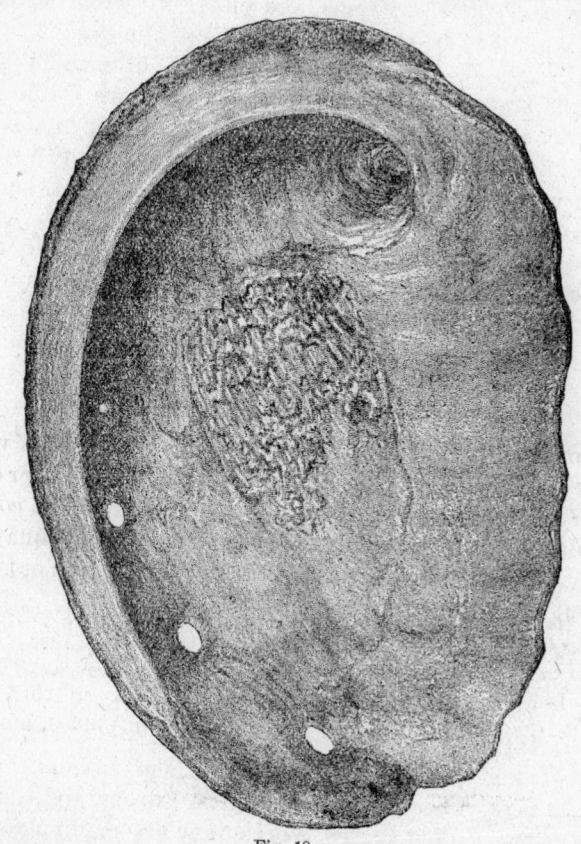

Fig. 18.

RED-BACKED ABALONE (*Haliotis rufescens*). From nature, reduced one-half.

(Coast of California. From specimen in U. S. N. M.)

The *ühl-lo* pieces are of a uniform size on the same string; they do not mix them. The dollar pieces (Figs. 19, 20) are generally about 1¼ inches long and 1 inch wide; the smaller about as long, but narrower; * * * a couple of fragments I picked up in an old Indian camp are worth twenty-five cents each.

The Indians are very ingenious and economical in working up the aulones. Wherever there is a broad, flat space they take out a dollar piece; where the curve is sharper, smaller ones. They especially value the outer edge (columella) of the whorl or lip, where the color is brilliant, and these they are obliged to cut into twenty-five-cent pieces. You will see that the *ühl-lo* is cut into pieces of different sizes, and even pieces

of the same size vary in value, according to their brilliancy. * * *
All the money that I have seen was strung on grocery twine, but they
often use sinew of various kinds; also the bark of a milkweed that
grows about here.*

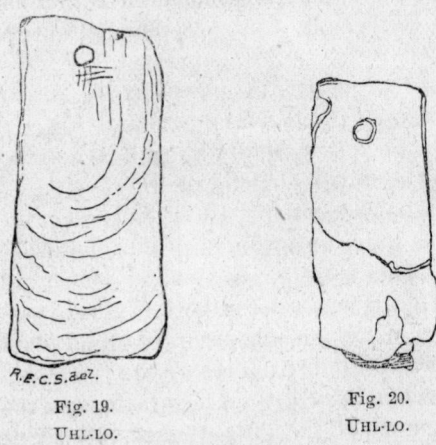

R. E. C. S. del.

Fig. 19.

UHL-LO.

Fig. 20.

UHL-LO.

"The aulone or *ühl-lo* necklace has three or four strings of very small
glass beads above the shells, forming a band about a quarter of an inch
wide, which encircles the neck. * * * A common deep conical basket, of about a bushel and a half capacity, such as the squaws use for
carrying their household effects, is worth one and one-half or two strings
of *ühl-lo*, that is, fifteen or twenty dollars."

The shells of the various species of *Haliotis* were as highly prized by
the red men of the west coast in the past as in later times, and were
worked by them into a great variety of forms. These forms, as well as
entire shells, have been found in the older burial places, mounds, and

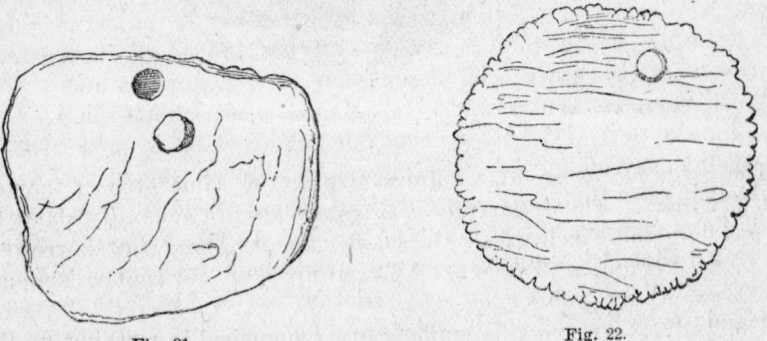

Fig. 21.

Fig. 22.

FROM INDIAN MOUND, VALLEJO, SOLANE COUNTY, CALIFORNIA. FOUND IN 1872 BY C. D. VOY.

graves throughout the entire coast, and far to the eastward in interior
localities.

* Placer County, California.

Disks of different sizes, perforated or otherwise, some with plain edges,* others with the edges crenulated† or regularly notched; also other shapes, crescentic, elliptic, lanceolate, falciform, leaf-shaped, and a number of other forms occur; but, with the exception of the discoidal pieces, which may have been sometimes used as money, it is probable that these were jewelry, and were used as pendants, buttons, spangles, etc.

One instance of the purchasing power of an abalone was related to me many years ago by Dr. Edward Palmer. While in New Mexico, upon one occasion, he was witness to a trade wherein the consideration for a horse was a California abalone shell.

How far or to what extent the use of the *uhl-lo* for the purposes of money prevailed is quite uncertain, or where the use of it as money left off or as jewelry began, is too vague even for conjecture. It is, however, highly probable that it was used in both of these ways; less as money and more as jewelry or for personal decoration, and for the ornamentation of the implements and appurtenances of the red man.

As before the termination of what may be termed the wampum period in the colonial history of the Atlantic sea-board States, shell money, "bad, false, and unfinished peage," got into circulation, so the shell money of the west coast Indians was counterfeited or made by white men with machinery, and the purchasing power consequently declined. But the decline was not from this cause alone. At the time when Mr. Powers wrote, he stated that "the younger English-speaking Indians scarcely use it at all, except in a few dealings with their elders or for gambling. One sometimes lays away a few strings of it, for he knows he can not squander it at the stores, and is thus removed from temptation and possible bankruptcy; and when he wishes for a few dollars of American money he can raise it by exchanging with some old Indian who happens to have gold. * * * It is singular how the old Indians cling to this currency, when they know that it will purchase nothing from the shops; but then their wants are few and mostly supplied from the sources of nature, and besides that, this money has a certain religious value in their minds as being alone worthy to be offered up on the funeral pyre of departed friends or famous chiefs of their tribe."

Shell money made by white men was introduced among the Indians probably more than half a century ago, and quite likely by the American Fur Company at a still earlier period. In Mr. Norton's paper‡ it is stated that Mr. Astor was one of the patrons of "The Last Wampum Coinage" or had been a customer, and Mr. Astor has always been regarded as the leading spirit and controlling genius of that famous commercial enterprise whose field of operations extended to the western

---

* San Miguel Island, 29132, 29134, 29135; Santa Rosa Island, 23711; Santa Barbara, 21854, 30398; Santa Cruz, 18319.

† San Miguel Island, 29133; Santa Barbara, 15222, 20239; Santa Cruz, 18198; Dos Pueblos, 18769. Imperforate disks: San Miguel Island, 29646; Santa Barbara, 20239.

‡ Am. Magazine, March, 1888.

shores of the continent. A large number of specimens or pieces of Au-lo-ne or Ab-a-lone money (*ühl-lo*), of recent (white man's) manufacture—all alike, too much alike to be genuine—made from the columella, or "outer edge," as Mr. Powers calls it, are in the collection of the National Museum. These came from the west coast, but they are simply samples of "false peage," as the bogus shell money of the Atlantic side was termed.

Unlike the shell money of the east coast Indians, the shell money of the red men of the west coast had no status as "a medium or currency" with the whites. The necessities of the period and of the situation that led to and caused the very general use of wampum or shell money in the intercourse and relations of the red men and white settlers of the Atlantic sea-board never existed on the western slope of the continent.

The Indian money of the west coast was practically used only among the Indians themselves. Neither, so far as we can perceive, has the hi-qua, hai-qua, or alli-co-chick, the kol-kol, ha-wock, or ühl-lo, in whatever manner or form used or combined, ever held as high or a similar place or function as or with the wampum or Indian money of the ancient Americans of the East in its symbolic, historical, governmental, and mnemonic aspects.

There is, it will be admitted, a touch of pathos, a gleam of sentiment, exhibited in the preference of the "old Indians" for *their money*, "a touch of nature" in their esteeming it "as alone worthy to be offered up on the funeral pyre of departed friends or famous chiefs of their tribe."

The Indian money of the Pacific coast* was hardly more than money, jewelry, or ornament. However used it was never more than these—an evidence of the acquisitive spirit and wealth of its possessor. The Indian money of the Atlantic coast had other uses and served higher purposes, and in these latter aspects indicated the intelligence and latent intellectual power and strength of the native red men of that side, and by comparison from this point of view serves also to show the superiority of the aborigines of the eastern to those of the western side of the continent.

SHELL MONEY AND THE SLAVE TRADE.

The use of cowry money in the African slave trade has heretofore been mentioned. It will be seen upon investigation that the shell money of the red men of North America was commonly used for a similar purpose, as well as for the compounding of crimes and the evasion of the penalties demanded by justice. In these latter respects the *black and white peage* of the east, and the *haik-wa, alli-co-chick* and *ha-wock* of the west coast, were of equal potency with the most ap-

---

* The Mojaves have a species of currency called *pook*, consisting of strings of shell beads, whose value is determined by the length. (Whipple, Pac. R. R. Reports, vol. III, p. 115.)

proved forms of gold and silver money of the present time, when applied, as the latter has been and not infrequently, to similar unworthy purposes in modern civilized communities. In other respects the Indians of the East and the West were alike, simply savages, before the advent of the white man as well as after—to use a homely expression, "chips off the same block." Lawson,* commenting upon the power of peage in the matters just presented, says:

"This is the money with which you may buy skins, furs, slaves, or anything the Indians have; it being the mammon (as our money is to us) that entices and persuades them to do anything and part with everything they possess except their children for slaves. As for their wives, they are often sold, and their daughters violated for it. With this they buy off murders; and whatsoever a man can do that is ill, this wampum will quit him of and make him, in their opinion, good and virtuous, though never so black before."

Gibbs states that among the Indians of the coast section of Oregon and Washington, "slavery is thoroughly interwoven with their social polity. East of the Cascades, though it exists it is not so common, the equestrian habit of the tribes living there probably rendering it less profitable, etc. * * * The system most likely originated in wars, all prisoners becoming slaves as a matter of course. * * * If one Indian has wronged another and failed to make compensation, or if a debtor is insolvent, he may be taken as a slave. And this slavery is final degradation. If a man purchase his father or mother they become his slave and are treated as such."

From other sources corroboratory of Gibbs, we find that "with the Classets† slaves are held by all the tribes, and are treated very much like their dogs, being looked upon as property and not within the category of humanity. For a master to kill half a dozen slaves is no wrong or cruelty ; it only tends to illustrate the owner's noble disposition in freely sacrificing his property. Slaves are obtained by kidnapping, and are sold in large numbers to northern tribes. * * * The Classets, a rich and powerful tribe, encourage the slave-hunting incursions of the Nootkas against their weaker neighbors."

Slavery, common to all the coast families, is also practiced by the Chinooks, but there is less difference here perhaps than elsewhere between the condition of the slaves and the free.

In this connection, of the tribes farther to the north we read that " the Thlinket slaves are either captured in war, bought from other tribes who may themselves have captured them, or the children of female slaves. The wars between the tribes, being now of rare occurrence, the supply of slaves is kept up by barter with the more southern tribes, and hence many of the slaves are the Flatheads of Oregon. The slaves of

---

* History of Carolina.

† Bancroft: Native Races, etc., vol. I, pp. 217-218, and elsewhere.

the Thlinkets * * * have no rights that the master is bound to respect."*

Among the Tacullies " slavery is common with them; all who can afford it keeping slaves;" and so with the Nootkas. Slavery is practiced by all the tribes and the slave trade forms an important part of their commerce. Among the Haidahs " slavery is universal, and as the life of the slave is of no value to the owner except as property, they are treated with extreme cruelty;" and Lord says of the Indians of British Columbia, " slaves are bought and sold after the fashion of dogs and horses, and shells of the *Dentalium* are the sovereigns and shillings used to pay for them."

SHELL MONEY AND THE COMPOUNDING OF CRIMES.

Proceeding along the west coast from Alaska to California, various authorities have reported that among the Kutchins of the Yukon, "in the absence of law, murder and all other crimes are compounded for."

Of the littoral or maritime tribes of British Columbia, among the Haidahs, " crimes have no punishment by law; murder is settled for with relatives of the victim by death or by the payment of a large sum." With the Indians farther to the eastward, Harmon, referring to the Tacullies, says, " Murder is not considered as a crime of great magnitude."

To the southward of Puget Sound and British Columbia, in addition to what has been incidentally quoted elsewhere in the text, powers says of the Hupas, " Murder is generally compounded for by the payment of shell money," and among the Gallinomero, a branch of the Pomos, the same author states that "no crime is known for which the malefactor can not atone with money." Among the Karoks "the murder of a man's dearest relative may be compounded for by the payment of money, the price of the average Indian's life being *i-sa-pa-só-ra* (one string). * * * "A man may own as many women for slaves as he can purchase." * * * No adultery is so flagrant but that the husband can be placated with money at about the rate that would be paid for murder."

SHELL-MONEY ARISTOCRACY.

Amid the dreary repulsiveness of sensualism and cruelty we catch a gleam of the ludicrous as well as a revelation of the weakness and vanity of these primitive barbarians, that reads like a satire or seems like a burlesque on certain facies of modern society among civilized pale-faces. The influence of the almighty dollar in many of the polite circles of nineteenth-century civilization seems like a travesty with variations and improvements upon the magic power of *haik-wa, alli-cochick, hawock,* and *kol-kol,* etc., in the matter of social status among

---

* Dall's Alaska, 1870.

the shell-money aristocracy of the Karoks, Hupas, Haidahs, and others of the ancient families of western America.

Among the Karoks "no marriage is legal or binding unless preceded by the payment of money, and that family is most aristocratic in which the most money was paid for the wife. For this reason it stands a young man well in hand to be diligent in accumulating shell money and not to be a niggard in bargaining with his father-in-law. So far is this shell aristocracy carried, that the children of a woman for whom no money was paid are accounted no better than bastards, and the whole family are condemned."

The Hupas have the same shell aristocracy as the Karok, the amount paid for the wife determining her rank in society.

Among the Haidahs "rank and power depend greatly upon wealth, which consists of implements, wives, and slaves. Wealth, which is quite as important here as in any civilized communities and of much more importance than is customary among savage nations, consists in shell money, called alli-co-chick, white deer-skins, canoes, and indirectly in women." Again: "Wives, as they must be bought, are a sign of wealth, and the owner of many is respected accordingly."

Two centuries have nearly passed since the "peage" and "wampum" of the eastern aborigines ceased to be an implement in the current activities in the colonial life of the Atlantic sea-board. A century later and the red men themselves had become as obsolete as their "coinage;" outcasts and wanderers from their native haunts, overlooked and forgotten in the tumult, or trampled out in the triumphant westward march of a conquering race.

The past of the red men of the Pacific has not yet been reached. They still live and wander, but the twilight is upon them. The glimpse that we get incidentally in our brief review is that of forty or fifty years ago rather than to day.

On the shores of British Columbia and at many places to the north, to Alaska and inclusive of that Territory, they are numerous even now. To the southward it is different. We may follow the westerly slopes of the Sierra Nevada, or either flank of the picturesque Coast Ranges, or the shore line from southern California to Puget Sound without meeting a solitary sample of the native stock. Again, perchance while hunting in the valleys or fishing in the streams a few "bucks and squaws" may be met with, disguised in the cast-off garments of the alien whites.

In the pleasant valleys where the Wintuns, Matsuns, and Shastas once roamed in all the pomp and circumstance of savage pride, adorned with glittering fragments of *aulone,* or necklaces of *hawock* or *kol-kol,* a few arrow-heads or mortars may be found to verify the traditions of former occupancy. Here and there the shriveled remnants of the tribes and families, the former tenants of this vast region, are gathered into reservations, human drift-weed in the eddies of the stream, thrust aside by the pitiless current of a resistless civilization.

BIBLIOGRAPHY.

Should the reader be desirous of pursuing this subject further, the writer would particularly recommend Mr. Holmes's memoir, as well as that of Mr. W. B. Weeden, the title of which has previously been given. These memoirs are not only especially valuable for the foot-notes and copious references to the bibliography of the subjects treated, but as well for their intelligent arrangement and the judicious comments of the authors; Stearns's "Shell Money," in the American Naturalist, vol. III, March, 1869; "Aboriginal Shell Money," Proceedings of the California Academy of Sciences, July, 1873; "Aboriginal Shell Money," in Overland Monthly (San Francisco), September, 1873; also "Aboriginal Shell Money," American Naturalist, vol. XI, 1877, with figures; Dr. L. G. Yates's Notes on the Aboriginal Money of California, American Naturalist, vol. XI, 1877; "Wampum and its History," E. Ingersoll, American Naturalist, vol. XVII, 1883; Horatio Hale "On the Origin and Nature of Wampum," American Naturalist, vol. XVIII, 1884; Stephen Powers, Contributions to North American Ethnology, vol. III, Washington, 1877 (a most entertaining volume); W. H. Pratt, Proceedings of the Davenport Academy of Natural Sciences, vol. II; J. K. Lord, "The Naturalist in British Columbia," vol. II; "The Last Wampum Coinage," by C. L. Norton, in the American Magazine, March, 1888; Bancroft's "Native Races of the Pacific States of North America," 1874.

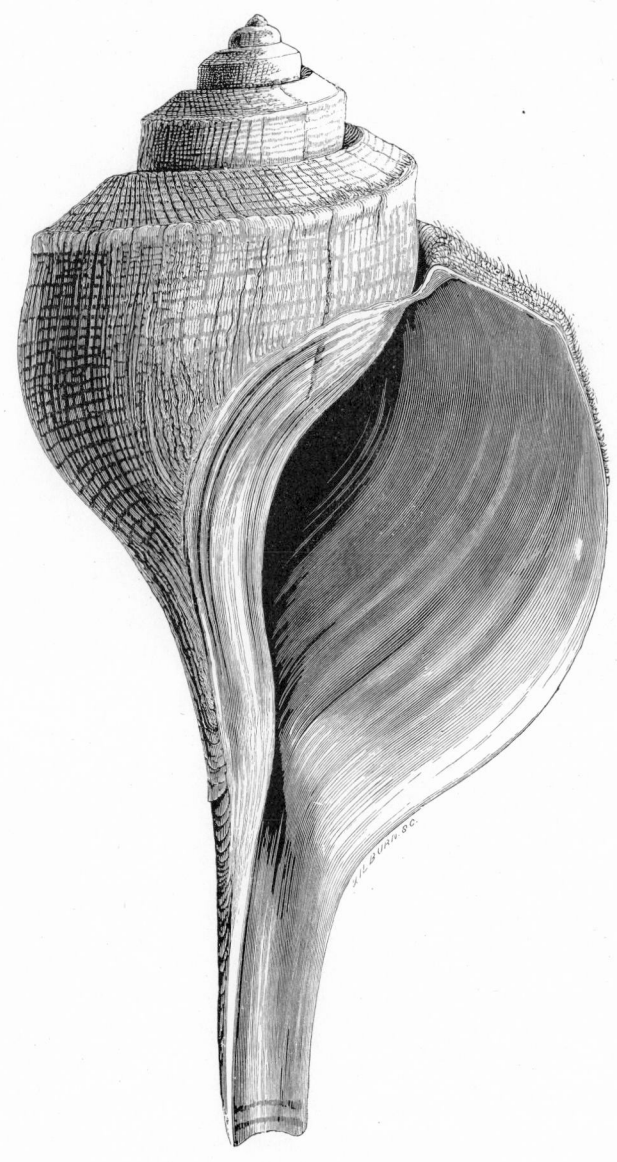

GROOVED WHELK.

Sycotypus canaliculatus Linn. (Page 305.)

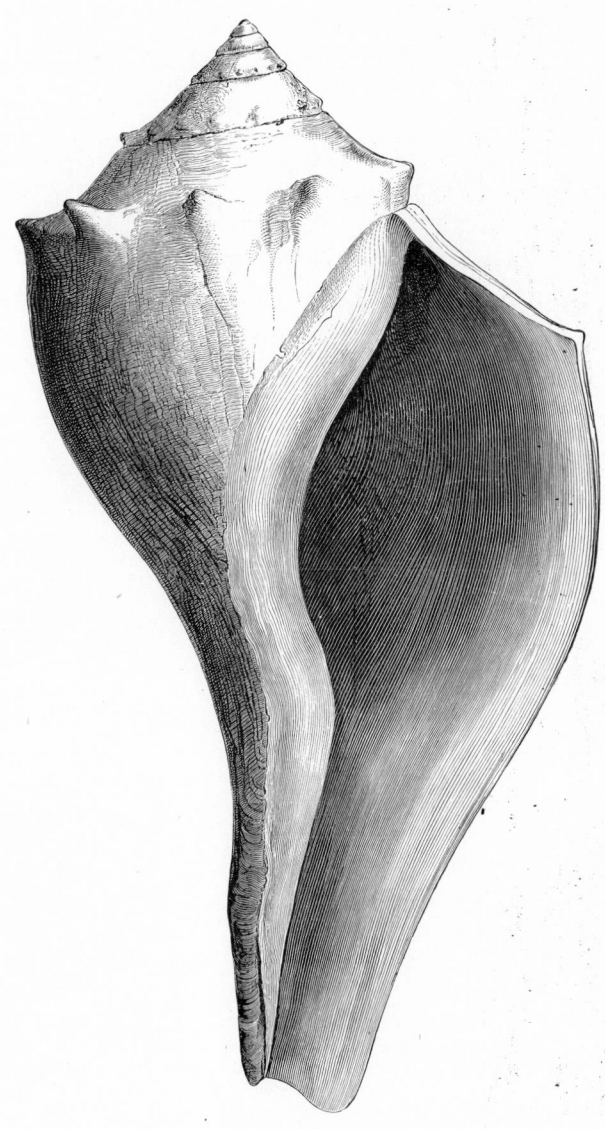

FIG WHELK.

Fulgur carica Linn. (Pages 308, 309.)

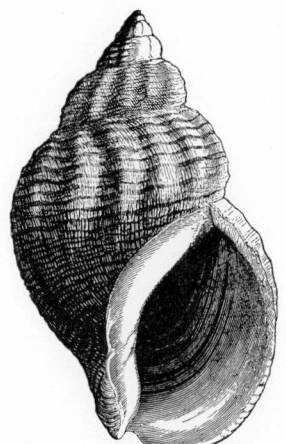

Fig. 1.

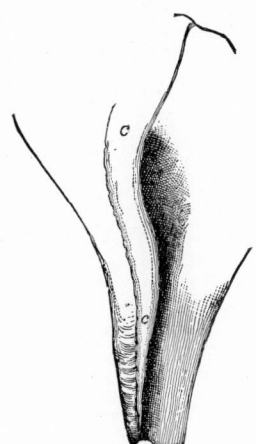

Fig. 2.

FIG. 1. *Buccinum undatum* Linn.. common whelk. (Page 308.)
FIG. 2. Columella and part of body whorl of *Fulgur carica*. *c, c*, portion from which the longer white wampum beads were made. (Page 309.)

Fig. 1.

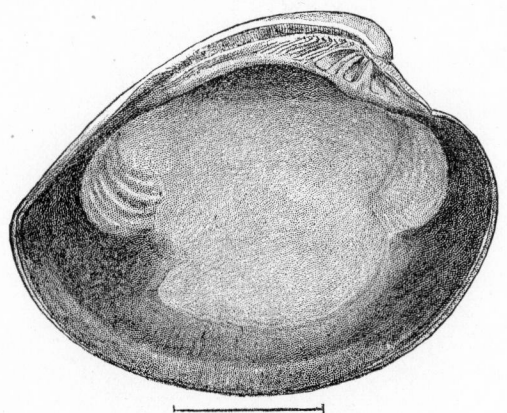

Fig. 2.

FIG. 1. The Quahaug, *Venus mercenaria*; outside view. (Pages 306, 307.)
FIG. 2. Inside view of same species.

Fig. 1.

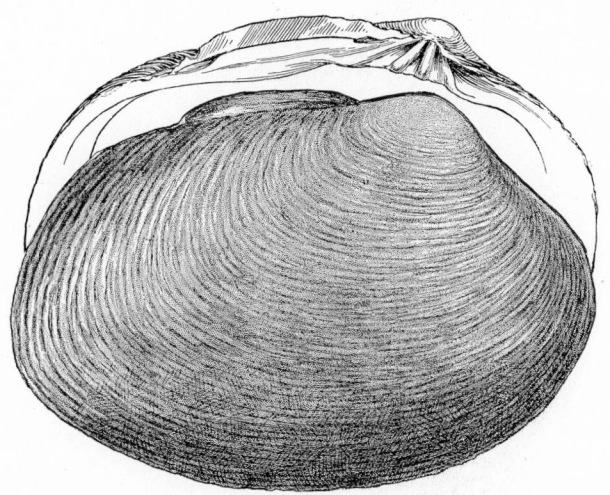

Fig. 2.

SHELLS USED IN MAKING HAWOCK. (Pages 321–323.)

FIG. 1. *Saxidomus Nuttallii.*   FIG. 2. *Saxidomus aratus.*

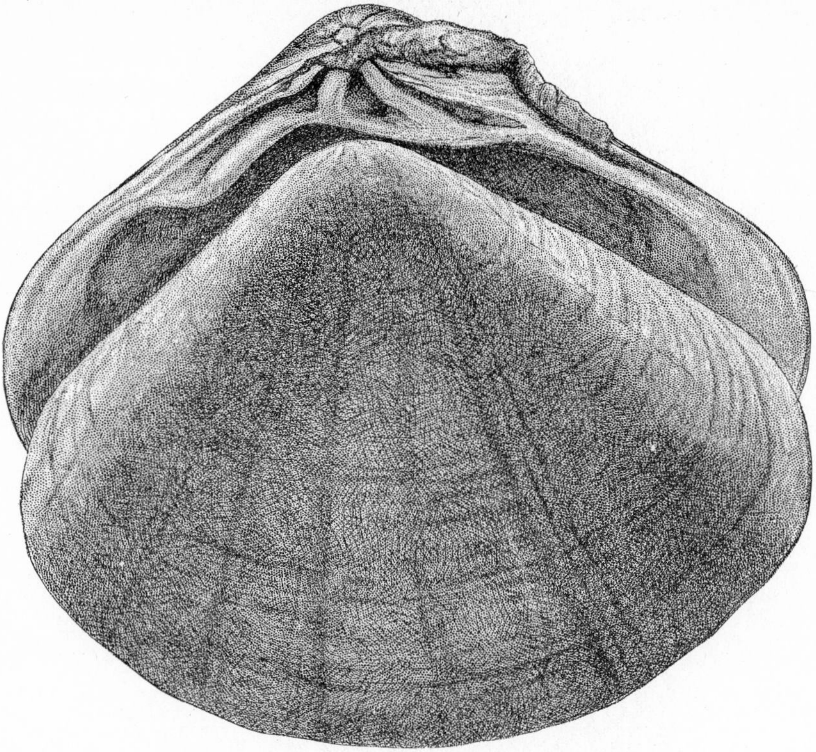

PLATE VII.

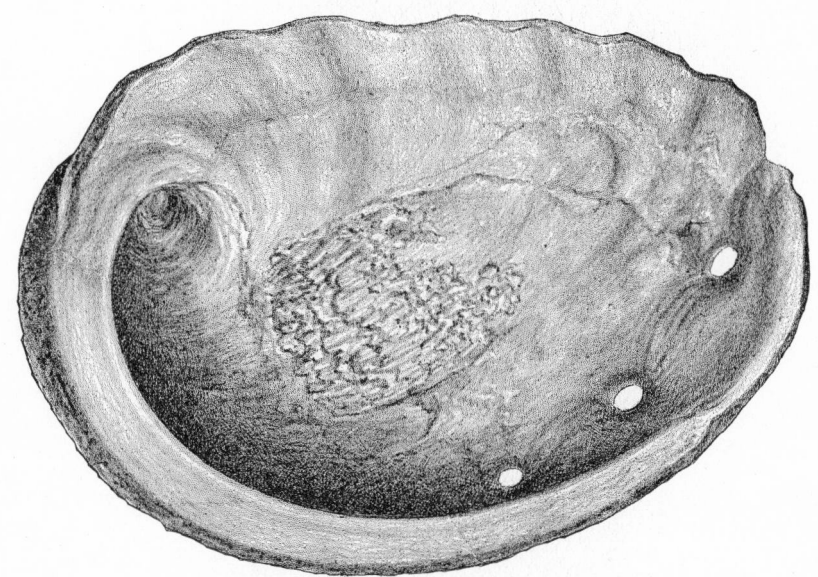

Fig. 1.

Fig. 2.

FIG. 1. Heavy Clam, *Tivela crassatelloides*. (Pages 321, 322.)
FIG. 2. Red-backed Ear-shell or Abalone, *Haliotis rufescens*. (Page 326.)

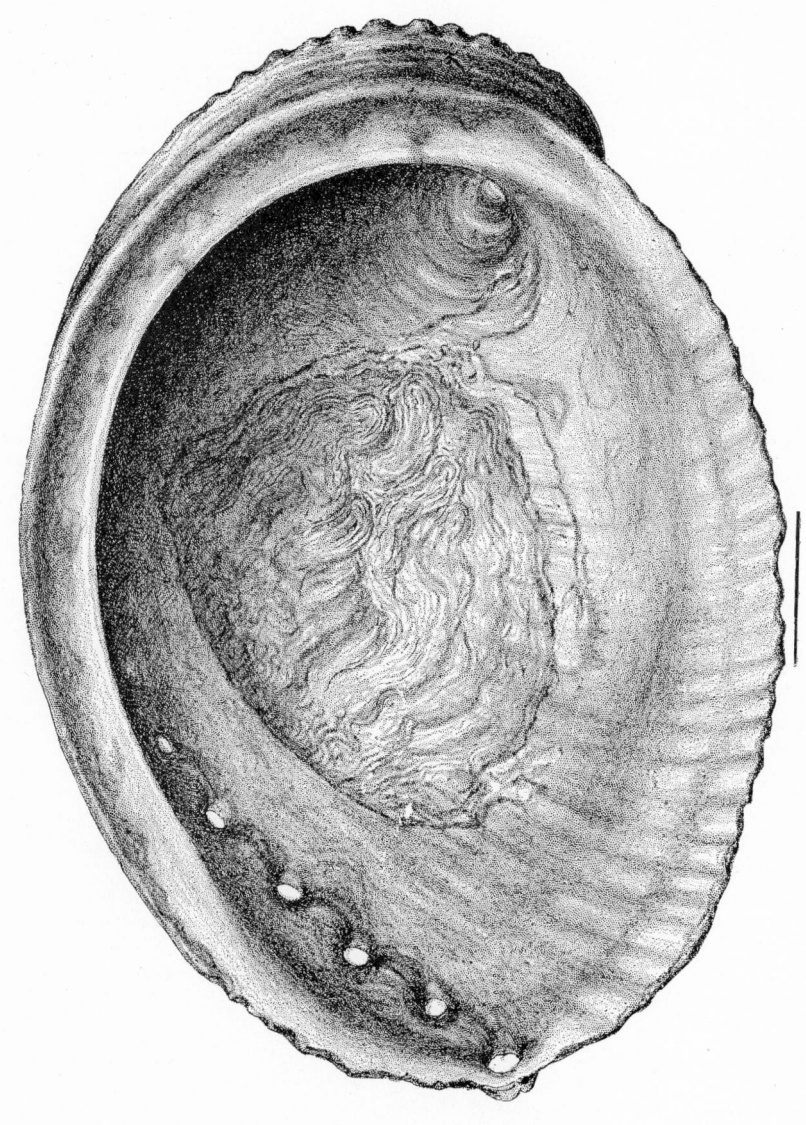

Abalone or Ear-shell, *Haliotis splendens* Reeve. (Pages 326 et seq.)

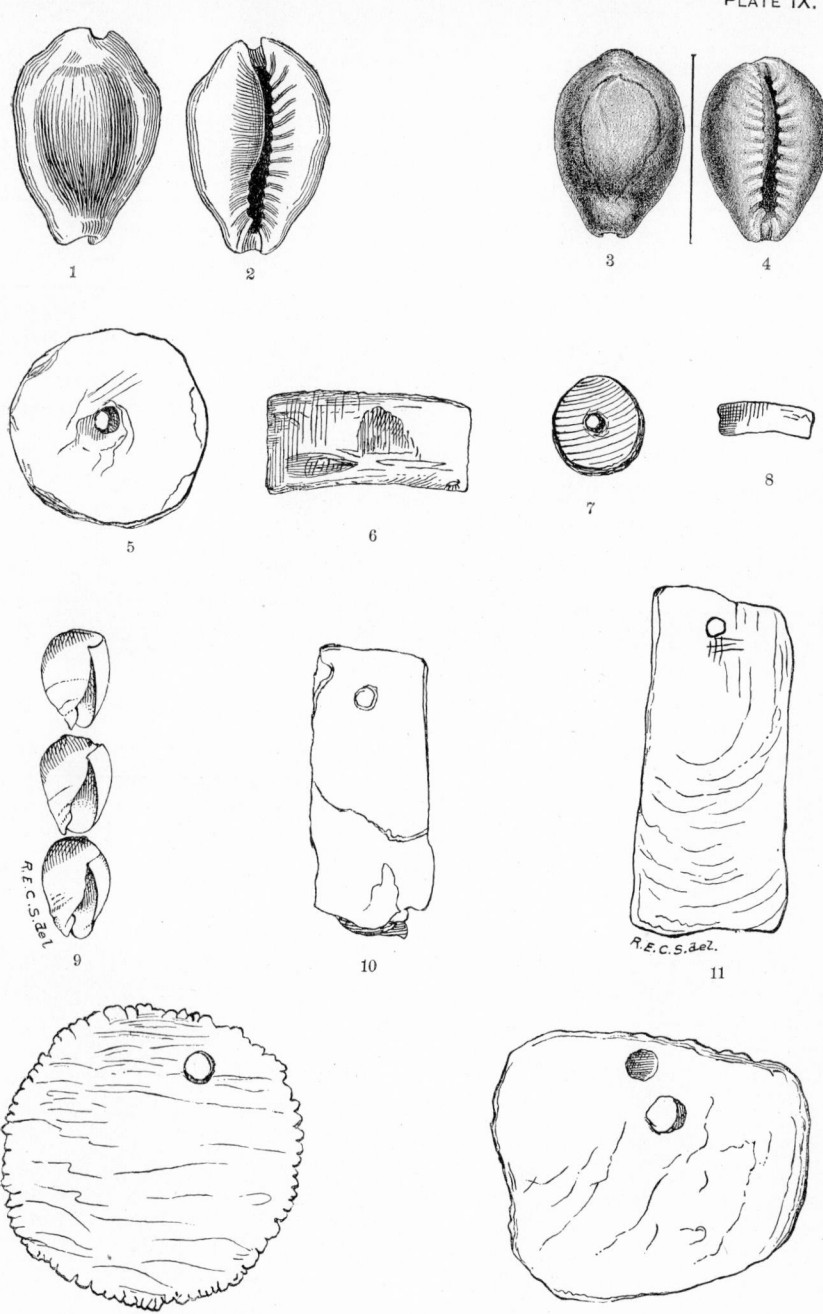

MONEY SHELLS AND SHELL MONEY.

Figs. 1, 2, 3, 4. Cowry Shells. (Pages 300 et seq.)
Figs. 5, 6, 7, 8. Hawock disks. (Pages 321 et seq.)
Fig.   9. Kolkol, of Olivella shells. (Page 324.)
Figs. 10, 11. Uhl-lo, of Ear-shells. (Pages 326–328.)
Figs. 12, 13. Uhl-lo money or jewelry. (Page 328.)

A PRELIMINARY CATALOGUE OF THE ESKIMO COLLECTION IN THE U. S. NATIONAL MUSEUM, ARRANGED GEOGRAPHICALLY AND BY USES.

By Lieut. T. Dix Bolles, U. S. Navy.

The list here presented is intended to be of service as an introduction to a complete analysis of Eskimo art.

The collection is made up of the smaller collections of R. Macfarlane, Capt. E. P. Herendeen, R. Kennicott, C. F. Hall, Prof. W. H. Dall, T. H. Bean, E. W. Nelson, L. M. Turner, L. Kumlein; Lieut. George M. Stoney, U. S. Navy; Captain Hooper, U. S. Revenue Marine; Lieut. C. L. McKay, U. S. Revenue Marine; Lieut. P. H. Ray, U. S. Army; Henry W. Elliott; Sergt. S. Applegate, U. S. Signal Corps; William J. Fisher, and others.

Nearly two years have been occupied by the compiler in reaching a result which he trusts will aid the student who may be inclined to an exhaustive comparison between the various villages or the Indian tribes whose boundaries touch the Eskimo territory.

The nomenclature is that of Ivan Petroff, from his chart in vol. viii, Tenth Census Report. Differences in spelling and even in names made it necessary to adopt some writer's plan in its entirety, even if some errors were evident. Petroff seems to me the most accurate and also has more or less official status.

In many cases the location or use of an object was wrongly given by collectors; this was misleading at first, but before long the multiplication of these errors caused serious confusion. These have been placed in their proper locality.

In the following table of places the geographical arrangement follows the coast-lines from east to west and south, taking in the outlying islands, etc., as they occur geographically.

Although similarities in many or even all respects may point to a closer connection between vicinities which are only a few miles apart, these may be separated in the list by a number of geographically-coast-line-following places; no attempt to follow these similarities will be made here.

Latitudes and longitudes are given to facilitate identification. The numbers in the columns express the whole number of specimens from a locality.

In the résumé at the end the writer notes the total number of articles handled, located, arranged, marked, and labeled.

GLOSSARY OF TERMS.

AMULETS. Objects carried by hunters to bring good luck or to avoid bad.

BABY-SEAL HOOK. Used for dragging the baby seal from its snow concealment.

BAG FASTENER. A slip of ivory tied to the end of the string, which is wrapped around the bag and then thrust under the cord to keep all tight.

BAILER, ICE. A sieve on the end of a handle to clear seal hole of small ice.

BRUSH, ICE. An implement similarly used.

BARK-SKINNER. A knife and curved bone to cut and remove birch bark.

BEAD SEPARATOR. Ivory bars placed at intervals in bead-work, and pierced, to hold the thread on which the beads are strung.

BERILS. Bone tools to round the edges of ivory or bone implements.

BLOOD-PINS. Used to close the wounds in dead animals, to save the blood for food.

BOOT-SOLE CREASER. A crimper used to prepare the seam before sewing.

BRIDGE. A small curved wedge used to tighten sinew on bows.

CHECK ON DRAG-LINE. An ivory slip to keep noose close to object inclosed.

CHECK ON WHALE-LINE. A friction check to save the hand from chafing when the line is running out.

COMBS FOR GRASS. Used to hackle grass.

DECOYS. The seal is inquisitive, and any strange noise or object, which does not frighten, will attract it and bring it into the snare.

DECOY FLOAT. Float on a net carved to resemble a bird, animal or simply a rattle.

DECOY SCRATCHER. A claw used near net or seal hole to attract seal; imitation of male seal.

DETACHER FOR HARPOON POINT. An ivory double button, on one of which the loop of the point-line is fixed, but which allows it to slip off when the point strikes.

DRAG CHAIN OR HANDLE. Used with a cord and noose to drag game on the ice.

FINGER-MASKS. Small articles of wood ornamented with hair or feathers

FINGER-REST. A check for the finger to rest against.

FIRE-BIT. A soft wood spindle, which is rapidly revolved to produce fire.

FIRE MOUTH-PIECE. A wooden piece held in the teeth. This has a stone bearing for the upper end of the fire-bit.

FIRE-SOCKET. Soft wood stick, on which the fire-bit is revolved, producing fire.

FISH BAIT. Small ivory fish or bright-colored material, used as bait.

FLOAT. The skin of a seal blown up to sustain the walrus line and act as a drag.

FLOAT MOUTH-PIECE. The orifice through which the air enters or escapes.

FLOAT PLUG. A disk, with a groove around it, used to close natural or accidental holes in seal float.

FUNGUS. Used to mix with tobacco for smoking.

GAMBLING BLOCK AND PIN. A game similar to "cup and ball."

GAMBLING DUCKS. A game similar to "heads and tails."

GAMBLING COUNTERS. A game similar to "odd and even."

GAMBLING TARGET AND LANCE. Each participant puts up a wager; the target, a netted oval ring, is hung in the air and the lance is thrown at it. If the point gets entangled the thrower has a choice of the wager laid out.

HARPOON POINT. The outer section carrying the blade.

HARPOON LOOSE SHAFT. The intermediate shaft.

HARPOON FORESHAFT. The bone or ivory socket on wooden shafts.

HARPOON BUTT. The lower extremity usually shod with a pike to give a hold on ice.

HUNTING TALLY. A bone or ivory stick on which to mark number of game.

ICE-CREEPERS. Rough pieces to tie on sole of boot.

KAYAK SUITS. Two kinds of jackets for fair and foul weather.

KNIFE, BLUBBER. With heavy blade like a cleaver.

KNIFE, CUTTING. Defense knife.

KNIFE, CARVING. To cut and carve wood or ivory.

KNIFE, FISH. For cleaning and scaling fish.

KNIFE, STABBING. To give the *coup de grace* to captured game.

KNIFE, SNOW. For clearing snow from fur garments, etc.

LEADERS. Used on dart shaft to keep the line clear from tangles.

LOUSERS. Curved ribs of animals to scrape and destroy vermin in clothes.

MASKS. Used in festivities.

MEDICINE-MAN'S WAND. Used in ceremonial to discover witch.

MOUTH-PIECE TO OIL BAG. A cup-shaped orifice used either in filling or drinking.

MUSKRAT BOW AND ARROW. The arrows are tied to the bow and used at short range.

NEEDLE BOARD. On which needle eyes are drilled.

NET WEIGHT. To hang in the mesh and keep it open while making.

PADDLE YOKE. The cross-piece for the hand on the end of the handle.

PRICKER. A large bodkin to open knots.

SCRAPERS. Used in dressing skins to remove fat and integument.

SEAL PROBE. Thrust down a seal hole to give warning of the animal's approach.

SINEW TIGHTENER. A bow-maker's tool to put the turns of sinew on smoothly and tightly.

SINEW TWIRLER. A twirling tool used while making sinew cord.

SLING BOARD. This has been spoken of in other works as a throwing-stick, but it is properly a sling, as it does not leave the hand.

SLING DART. The light harpoon, which is used with the board.

SNUFF TUBES. Inserted into the nose and box to avoid waste and to increase the dose.

SPIDER LINE. A sinew line stretched across the top of boat, under which the lance, paddle, etc., are placed to prevent their rolling about.

STOOL. Used while watching a seal-hole: to keep the feet off the ice.

WATER TUBES. Used to suck out the water and filth from the boat while *en route*.

WHIRLER. A toy to swing about the head. It makes a buzzing noise.

Table showing the latitude and longitude of the regions represented in this list.

Regions.	North.		West.		Regions.	North.		West.	
	°	″	°	″		°	″	°	″
West Greenland					Kashunuk	61	30	165	00
Ungava, Labrador	60	00	68	00	Kaialigamute	61	15	164	15
Cumberland Gulf	66	00	67	00	Ookagamute	60	50	164	40
Smith Sound	78	00	73	00	Cape Vancouver	60	40	165	10
Igloolik	69	20	81	30	Agiukchugamute	60	30	164	30
Pelly Bay	68	20	90	00	Nulokhtologamute	60	25	164	20
King William's Land	70	00	97	30	Nunivak	60	00	166	00
Cape Bathurst	70	40	127	30	Sfaganugamute	60	25	164	00
Mackenzie River	68	00	135	00	Anogogmute	59	45	163	50
Anderson River					Kongiganagamute	59	40	163	15
Herschel Island	68	40	159	00	Koolvagavigamute	59	50	162	45
Point Barrow	71	18	156	24	Chalitmute	60	00	163	40
Point Belcher	70	50	159	30	Big Lake	61	20	163	00
Icy Cape	70	25	161	42	Kuskokwim River	60	45	161	50
Cape Lisburne	69	50	166	22	Togiak River	59	10	160	10
Point Hope	68	15	166	50	Igushek	58	50	158	45
Kotzebue Sound	66	30	163	00	Tuniakput	59	20	160	15
Hotham Inlet	66	40	162	00	Nushegak	58	55	158	25
Putnam River	67	00	161	30	Bristol Bay	58	50	157	00
Cape Espenberg	66	30	163	30	Ugashik	57	40	157	50
Kegiktowik	63	40	161	20	Oonalashka	53	54	166	32
St. Michael	63	40	162	10	Chernovsky	53	30	167	00
Pikmikltolik	63	20	162	30	Bering's Island	55	00	164	00
Pastolik	62	55	162	55	Naknek	58	45	157	00
Raibozniksky	62	00	162	00	Kogginug	59	10	156	46
Sabotnisky					Wrangel Bay	57	30	156	00
Mission	62	00	161	00	Iliamna Lake	59	30	155	00
Paimute	62	30	160	00	Kadiak	57	30	153	00
Anvik	62	40	160	00	Cook's Inlet	61	00	152	00
Nulato	64	45	158	00	Nuchek	60	20	147	00
Upper Yukon	Above Nulato.				Yakutat	59	18	139	00
Tanana	65	10	152	00	Thlinkit	Southeast Alaska.			
Askinuk	61	40	166	00					

	Regions.	Mortars.	Pestles.	Forks.	Spoons.	Dishes.	Marrow-extractors.	Knives.	Trays.	Bowls.	Blood-pins.	Blubber-knives.	Cutting-knives.	Sheaths.	Fish-knives.	Handles.	Blades.	Sharpeners.	Snuff-tubes.
1	West Greenland						1						1		2				
2	Labrador				21	10		1	1						5				
3	Cumberland Gulf				3	3							1		5	2		1	
4	Smith Sound																		
5	Igloolik			10	7		1				9		1						
6	Pelly Bay																		
7	King William's Land				2														
8	Cape Bathurst																		
9	Mackenzie River				1								4	1	3				
10	Anderson River					3							4	1	2				
11	Herschel Island																		
12	Point Barrow				13	15	1		3				4		13	23	1	11	9
13	Point Belcher																		
14	Icy Cape				1	1													
15	Cape Lisburne																		
16	Point Hope																		
17	Kotzebue Sound				3										2		2	3	
18	Hotham Inlet														2				
19	Putnam River				1			1					1			1		1	1
20	Cape Espenberg				1												2		
21	Cape Prince of Wales																		
22	Diomede Island				1														
23	Cape Wankarem				1														
24	Port Clarence					2									1			4	
25	Tchukchi																		
26	King's Island																		
27	Sledge Island				7											1		2	2
28	Cape Nome				3											1		3	4
29	St. Lawrence Island				8	7									11	1	10		
30	Poonook				2										3		2		
31	Plover Bay				1								1						
32	Kaviagamute																		
33	Golovina Bay																		
34	Cape Darby														1				
35	Nubviakhchugaluk														3	2			
36	Norton Bay																		
37	Koyuk River															1	1	1	
38	Shaktolik					1											1		
39	Oonalakleet				1	1									1		2	2	
40	Kegikhtowik																		
41	St. Michael					2							3		8	3	30	3	9
42	Pikmiktalik																		
43	Pastolik					1	1											1	
44	Norton Sound																		
45	Yukon Delta and Mouth																		
46	Razboiniksky				4	4									3			8	5
47	Sabotnisky				1	1									1			1	
48	Mission				1			3							2		4		16
49	Paimute				6											1			
50	Anvik				1			3		5			3				22		
51	Nulato																2		
52	Tanana				13			1					2	1					
53	Upper Yukon				6			3											
54	Askinuk																3		8
55	Kashunuk				7										4	1	2	2	15
56	Kaialigamute				4														12
57	Ookagamute																		
58	Cape Vancouver				2	2							1						2
59	Nulokhtologamute					2		1									2	1	2
60	Agiukchugamute				1											1			2
61	Nunivak Island				4	5										2		1	6
62	Sfaganugamute				1	1									1	3			6
63	Anogogmute				2										1	1		4	5
64	Kongiganagamute				3	1										2	1		5
65	Koolvagavigamute				2														
66	Chalitmute				9	2										2			6
67	Big Lake				2	1										1			
68	Kuskokvim River				4													1	6
69	Eogiak River				1										5		6	4	
70	Tuniakhput				4										2				
71	Igushek												4		1		15		

Snuff-scrapers.	Snuff mortars and pestles.	Snuff-sieves.	Cutting-boards.	Pipes.	Pipe-molds.	Fungus.	Tobacco-boxes.	Lancets.	Lamps.	Hooks for meat.	Mouth-piece to oil-bag.	Baskets.	Dippers.	Buckets.	Handles, bucket.	Bags for tobacco, etc.	Boxes, miscellaneous.	Needles for stringing fish.	Jackets.	Breeches.	Gut shirts.	Boots.	No.
				17					16							3			4	3		4	1
																			17	3	2	1	2
																1			3	1			3
																							4
											1					2				1			5
																							6
																							7
				13															1				8
				13								3			2	7	1		5		2	6	9
																6	4		5	1		2	10
																			1	1			11
				13			9								2	2	5		6	2		2	12
																							13
																							14
																							15
															6								16
	2						2					1	1		7	1			1			1	17
							7												1				18
	1			3								1	1	1	1		2						19
																							20
				5			1								2				1		1		21
															3	1	2		2	1		1	22
															1	1							23
	1			4			1								1	3	3	1					24
																						2	25
1				1					1						3							1	26
	1			3	1		4				1				12	4	4						27
	1			4											10	24	3					2	28
														2	1	2	14						29
																	1						30
																							31
							3												1				32
							1									1				1	4	2	33
							3								7	14							34
			1				2				1				15								35
				1											1	2	1						36
															2	4							37
															4	1							38
				1			3				1				6	10	2			3	1	3	39
	1			8			3				1			1	4	5	3						40
	1			7		2	9				13				31	26	7						41
											2					1							42
	3						2				3				8	8	1		2				43
																							44
																							45
1	1	1		4		1	2									3	13	7	1	2		2	46
				1												1	5	2					47
																3	9	4					48
																							49
							3		1							3					1		50
							3									5	1						51
							2									1							52
																1			3	4		1	53
							2																54
1							3				3				3	2	4						55
							4				2	1	1			5	3						56
							1																57
							3							2		1	2		2				58
							3									3							59
							1				1												60
2				19	1		2				2				3	10	1					1	61
							1										3						62
				5			1				1				1	1	2						63
				1			1								1	1	1						64
				1											1	5							65
				6		1					1				1	5	3						66
				4							1					7	3						67
				1							3					3						1	68
				1		1			1		6				16	1	1						69
																1	1						70
																							71

	Regions.	Mortars.	Pestles.	Forks.	Spoons.	Dishes.	Marrow-extractors.	Knives.	Trays.	Bowls.	Blood-pins.	Blubber-knives.	Cutting-knives.	Sheaths.	Fish-knives.	Handles.	Blades.	Sharpeners.	Snuff-tubes.
72	Nushegak				2				1									2	
73	Bristol Bay		7		13	4							1		14			8	
74	Iliamna Lake				10	2													
75	Koggiung				4													2	
76	Naknek	1			1								2				1		
77	Oogashik				1										2				
78	Oonalashka				1														
79	Chernovsky					1												3	
80	Wrangel Bay												1				4	2	
81	Kadiak Island				6	1							4		9		6		
82	Cook's Inlet					1			1										
83	Nuchek												2						
84	Yakutat																		
85	Thlinkit														1				
86	Bering's Island																		
87	Japan																		
88	Lapland																		
89	Madison, Ohio																		1
	Total	1	7	10	193	60	7	1	19	1	9	4	48	3	121	24	118	75	113

Snuff-scrapers.	Snuff mortars and pestles.	Snuff-sieves.	Cutting-boards.	Pipes.	Pipe-molds.	Fungus.	Tobacco-boxes.	Lancets.	Lamps.	Hooks for meat.	Mouth-piece to oil-bag.	Baskets.	Dippers.	Buckets.	Handles, bucket.	Bags for tobacco, etc.	Boxes, miscellaneous.	Needles for stringing fish.	Jackets.	Breeches.	Gut shirts.	Boots.	
						1	2					2				5					5	2	72
	1						3		1			4		4		12	2		5		3	5	73
																7							74
							1										1						75
								4															76
																							77
												7				17					1	1	78
																							79
																							80
									12			1			1	3			1	2			81
																							82
																							83
	1																						84
	3														1								85
																							86
																				1		2	87
																							88
																							89
4	13	1	1	100	1	4	120	6	30	1	8	70	2	10	138	165	93	2	66	21	22	42	

Regions.	Fish-skin boots.	Shoes.	Moccasons.	Grass socks.	Fishing hats.	Shades for same.	Caps.	Mittens.	Fish-skin mittens.	Grass mittens.	Kayak suits.	Armor.	Skin robes.	Mats.	Gloves.	Buttons.	Bracelets.	Belts.	Necklaces.	Ear-rings.	Labrets.	Head-dresses.	Pendants.
1 West Greenland	5							1			5		1			6	1						
2 Labrador	3							1				4				1	2					1	6
3 Cumberland Gulf																3	1					1	9
4 Smith Sound																							
5 Igloolik							1									5			2				
6 Pelly Bay																			1				
7 King William's Land																2							1
8 Mackenzie River			1				12					4				1		2	1	1	14		25
9 Anderson River		1		1			4		2			1				2		2			8		1
10 Point Barrow							2	1				2				1		3		2	18		2
11 Point Belcher																							
12 Icy Cape																1							
13 Cape Lisburne																					5		
14 Point Hope																5					5		
15 Kotzebue Sound								1				1				34					3		
16 Hotham Inlet																4					6		
17 Putnam River								1															
18 Cape Espenberg																2					1		1
19 Cape Prince of Wales															1	19				1	2		6
20 Diomede Island												1			1	22	1	1			10		3
21 Cape Wankarem																							
22 Port Clarence			1													13					1		
23 Tchukchi									1			1											
24 King's Island								1													1		
25 Sledge Island			4													66				5	69		5
26 Cape Nome	1							1								49	1			1	15		3
27 St. Lawrence Island																3							5
28 Poonook																1							
29 Plover Bay																2							1
30 Kaviagamute																							
31 Golovina Bay			1												1	2							
32 Cape Darby																11				4	2		10
33 Nubviakhchugaluk																18				9	4		6
34 Norton Bay			1																				
35 Koyuk River																2				1	13		
36 Shaktolik																13							
37 Oonalakleet															1	4	1			1	17		1
38 Kegikhtowik																3							
39 St. Michael																102	3			62	58		36
40 Pikmiktalik																1							
41 Pastolik																					1		
42 Norton Sound																							2
43 Yukon Delta and Mouth																							
44 Razboiniksky			1	2	3	2										1					13		8
45 Sabotnisky																							
46 Mission																				5			
47 Paimute															1	1				2	4		
48 Anvik								1															
49 Nulato																				1			
50 Tanana								1								1							
51 Upper Yukon																							
52 Askinuk																3				36	5		1
53 Kashunuk				4												11				7	16		7
54 Kaialigumute																1				12	1		
55 Ookagamute																							
56 Cape Vancouver																24				15	1		10
57 Nulokhtologamute																7		1		10	2		2
58 Agiukchugamute																7				7	1		8
59 Nunivak Island																25				9	14		11
60 Sfaganugamute																5				12			5
61 Anogogmute																9				11	2		4
62 Kongiganagamute																13				23	5		7
63 Koolvagavigamute																3					1		
64 Chalitmute																9				12	1		8
65 Big Lake																2				6	2		12
66 Kuskokvim River	1															8				2	1		11
67 Togiak River																4				8	1		4
68 Tuniakhput																							
69 Igushek																							
70 Nushegak																1					2		
71 Bristol Bay								4	2							9	5	2	6	8		7	6
72 Iliamna Lake		2														3						1	
73 Koggiung																							

Hair ornaments.	Hat ornaments.	Box ornaments.	Needle-case ornaments.	Beads.	Snow-goggles.	Ice-creepers.	Snow-knives.	Lousers.	Brushes.	Combs, hair.	Spears, complete.	Spear-points.	Spears, fish.	Spears, fish, points.	Harpoons, complete.	Harpoon-points.	Harpoon loose-shafts.	Harpoon-foreshafts.	Harpoon-butts.	Stools.	Seal-probes.	Bailer for ice-hole.	Brush for ice-hole.	Harpoon-line.	Check for whale-lines.	
							2		1	2	2	3	1			9	4	2		1				2		1
			10				2	1	2	2				1	1	15	5	3	5					1		2
							2						1			5	19	5	1	2					3	3
													1										1			4
			1				1				2				2	2	2					8				5
																										6
			1													2					1					7
													1				6	1	1	1						8
	1						1			2			1	1	1	3	4	1	2					1		9
							1			6			6	7	18	5	42	4	1	3	2		1			10
							1																			11
																										12
																1										13
1						1							1													14
		5	3										4			3	1	1								15
			1			1				1			3	2										1		16
										1																17
		14					2			1			2			1	1		1							18
		1							1							2	1		1							19
									2							7	1		1				3			20
																							1	1		21
							2			1	1	2			1	8	2		2				1	1		22
																										23
													1										1	1		24
3		14	6		6		4	2		2			2			5	14	1	1	1				1		25
		1	1				3	2		1	1	2				11	6		1				1			26
					1		2	1			1				7	23	10	4	7	2			1	2		27
					1		1			1					7	1	1	1	1							28
					1		1									2	1	1	1							29
															1	1								1		30
			2												1	3								1		31
			4		2		1						4			3										32
			7				3						4			1								1		33
	1				3								2													34
	2									1			1			3								1		35
	5		1																							36
			3	1	1		1				1		3			1	1	1								37
			1								1		3			6	1	3								38
	27	6	8	1	5		6			4			3			8	5									39
							1									1	1									40
							1									1	1									41
	3		1						1																	42
							1																			43
1	5				2		1																	1		44
					1		2		3	1																45
			3		9		3						1		2											46
							2						1													47
					3		10																			48
					6											1										49
													1													50
													1													51
	3						6				3		1			1	5	3	1	2						52
	14		5		1		6						1				1	1	2							53
							1										1	2								54
							10																			55
	3						13									1	3	1								56
							5										4									57
2	2			1			2										2	1								58
	2			1									1		1	8	12	4		1						59
																	3	3								60
	1			1			1									4	2	2								61
3				1			3										1	1								62
							11																			63
				1			2									4	5	3								64
							7																			65
2			1				5						1										1			66
							3			3						3	2	2								67
																										68
																	1									69
													2				2									70
	2						1								1	10	3		2							71
																										72
							2																			73

	Region	Fish-skin boots.	Shoes.	Moccasons.	Grass socks.	Fishing hats.	Shades for same.	Caps.	Mittens.	Fish-skin mittens.	Grass mittens.	Kayak suits.	Armor.	Skin robes.	Mats.	Gloves.	Buttons.	Bracelets.	Belts.	Necklaces.	Ear-rings.	Labrets.	Head-dresses.	Pendants.
74	Naknek	..	..	..	..	..	..	..	..	..	..	..	..	..	..	..	..	..	..	..	2	..	1	..
75	Oogashik	..	..	..	..	..	..	..	..	..	..	..	..	..	..	..	2	1	1	..	2	1	1	..
76	Oonalashka	..	..	..	2	..	..	..	..	..	..	..	..	..	..	..	7	..	..	..	3	2	..	8
77	Chernovsky	..	..	..	..	..	..	..	..	..	..	..	..	..	..	..	..	..	..	..	..	..	..	..
78	Wrangel Bay	..	..	..	..	..	..	..	..	..	..	..	..	..	..	..	..	..	..	..	..	..	..	..
79	Kadiak Island	4	..	..	2	..	..	..	1	1	..	..	..	..	..	..	1	..	..	..	..	4	..	..
80	Cook's Inlet	..	..	..	..	..	..	..	..	..	..	..	..	..	..	..	3	..	..	..	..	1	..	..
81	Nuchek	..	..	..	..	..	..	..	..	..	..	..	..	..	..	..	1	..	..	..	..	..	..	..
82	Yakutat	..	..	..	..	..	..	..	..	..	..	..	..	..	..	..	..	..	..	..	..	..	..	..
83	Thlinkit	..	..	..	..	..	..	..	..	..	..	..	..	2	..	..	..	..	..	..	..	14	..	..
84	Bering's Island	..	..	..	..	..	..	..	..	..	..	..	..	..	..	..	..	..	..	..	..	..	..	..
85	Japan	..	..	..	..	..	..	..	..	..	..	..	..	..	..	..	..	..	..	..	..	..	..	..
86	Lapland	..	..	..	..	..	..	..	..	..	..	..	..	..	..	..	..	..	..	..	..	..	..	..
87	Mexico	..	..	..	..	..	..	..	..	..	..	..	..	..	..	..	..	..	..	..	..	1	..	..
	Total	5	12	1	1	8	9	1	32	9	1	5	2	12	1	10	546	20	13	10	296	332	11	236

	Hair ornaments.	Hat ornaments.	Box ornaments.	Needle-case ornaments.	Beads.	Snow-goggles.	Ice-creepers.	Snow-knives.	Lousers.	Brushes.	Combs, hair.	Spears, complete.	Spear-points.	Spears, fish.	Spears, fish, points.	Harpoons, complete.	Harpoon-points.	Harpoon loose shafts.	Harpoon-foreshafts.	Harpoon-butts.	Stools.	Seal-probes.	Bailer for ice-hole.	Brush for ice-hole.	Harpoon-line.	Check for whale-lines.
74								1					7					1	1							
75						1						3	8													
76								1					1													
77																										
78																		2	2							
79													12	1												
80																			1							
81																										
82																										
83																										
84																										
85																										
86																										
87																										
	12	46	41	58	11	40	3	139	10	5	30	29	68	10	3	71	235	45	15	29	4	10	8	1	14	3

	Regions	Lines	Check for whale-lines	Floats	Mouth-pieces, float	Float-plugs	Float-rattles	Float-handles	Float-swivels	Sling-darts, fish, complete	Sling-darts, fish, points	Sling-darts, fish, shafts	Sling-darts, fish, with float	Sling-darts, fish, rings for	Sling-darts, bird, complete	Sling-darts, bird, points	Sling-darts, bird, side prongs	Sling-boards	Detacher for harpoon point
1	West Greenland			3											3		1	1	
2	Labrador		1													1	1		
3	Cumberland Gulf			1	4										1	1	9	1	
4	Smith Sound																		
5	Igloolik				1											1	1		
6	Pelly Bay																		
7	King William's Land																		
8	Mackenzie River																		
9	Anderson River				1										3	1	1		
10	Point Barrow			2						10	2	1			4	7	3		
11	Point Belcher																		
12	Icy Cape			1															
13	Cape Lisburne			1															
14	Point Hope																		
15	Kotzebue Sound					2	3			1		1			1	1	1		
16	Hotham Inlet																		
17	Putnam River				1														
18	Cape Espenberg					1													
19	Cape Prince of Wales		1				2	2	2							1			
20	Diomede Island				4	2	3								2				
21	Cape Wankarem																		
22	Port Clarence						3				1	1					2		
23	Tchukchi																		
24	King's Island																		
25	Sledge Island		1	3	5	1	6			3	3	2					1	2	
26	Cape Nome		1	3	5	2	2			1	2	2			1	1		2	
27	St. Lawrence Island		2	5			5					5							
28	Poonook																		
29	Plover Bay																		
30	Kaviagamute			2	3	2													1
31	Golovina Bay		1							20									
32	Cape Darby			2	2					1		1							
33	Nubviakhchugaluk			3	1							2							1
34	Norton Bay		2							1	1					1			1
35	Koyuk River										2	1							
36	Shaktolik										2	1							
37	Oonalakleet			2						35	2	1			3	2	3	1	1
38	Kegikhtowik		1	1						13	1	1			1		2	1	1
39	St. Michael			1		2	2	1	1	79	5	3			24	9	3		6
40	Pikmiktalik									2							2		
41	Pastolik				4					5	3					1			
42	Norton Sound									3	3	1				2	2		
43	Yukon Delta and Mouth																		
44	Razboiniksky			2						5					8		1		2
45	Sabotnisky									6	1	1					2		
46	Mission																		
47	Paimute															1			
48	Anvik																		
49	Nulato																		
50	Tanana																		
51	Upper Yukon																		
52	Askinuk			1						13					3				3
53	Kashunuk		1	8						5					1				3
54	Kaialigumute				1					3					1		1		3
55	Ookagamute																		
56	Cape Vancouver		1	2	4					16		1					3		
57	Nulokhtologamute			2	2					4		1			3	1			2
58	Agiukchugamute				2						1								
59	Nunivak Island	1		2	1					29	3	2		5	15		13		4
60	Sfaganugamute				1						1								
61	Anogogmute			1	1												1		2
62	Kongiganagamute			5	7					6		1			1				2
63	Koolvagavigamute			7						1		2							
64	Chalitmute			2	1					9	3	3				1	2	2	
65	Big Lake									1									1
66	Kuskokvim River			3				1		1		1							
67	Togiak River			8	1						3	3							
68	Tuniakhput																		5

Leaders on shaft of harpoon.	Finger-rest on shaft of harpoon.	Ring for same.	Clasp for seal-line.	Bows.	Bow-models.	Quivers.	Wrist-guards.	Quiver-stiffener.	Muskrat bow and arrow.	Arrows, bird.	Arrows, fish.	Arrows, deer.	Arrow-points.	Darts.	Boxes for spear-points.	Hooks for fish.	Sinkers.	Lines and rods.	Tips for rods.	Bait.	Nets.	Sinkers, net.	
				8		2				23	16		17								1		1
	2			6	1						6					8					1		2
	1	1		4	1	2					13									2	1		3
	1										2												4
			2																				5
				1							1					1							6
											4												7
	2			2	1	1				5	42					17					1		8
				3	1	8					41	9				25					1	1	9
					3	2	1			2	25	24			5	23					1	1	10
										4											1		11
																					1		12
																					1		13
										1											1	1	14
	3															1	4						15
																6							16
				1		1				5			4			3					2	1	17
																							18
		1														1	8		1		1		19
	1			2		1										10	2		2			1	20
				4		1						3	4										21
	1															17	5				1		22
																	1					1	23
																						1	24
2	12										1				1	14	16		6	1		1	25
	8														2	32	35	6	6	1		1	26
	2			3		2	2	2	1	12	88		8			5	6	7	6		1	1	27
							1																28
																1	1						29
																2							30
																					1		31
1	2			1						1						6	5	1	1				32
1	1																		1				33
																			1			1	34
	1			2			11					3	7			10	1						35
							2																36
	2						1									9	1	1					37
	2			1						6	5					8	3		1			1	38
11	2			2	3		5	1		4	16	20			8	12	6		2		1		39
															1								40
				1						14						5							41
							1										3	1					42
																							43
3	1			3			2	2		3	9									3			44
				1																3	1		45
																							46
1																							47
													7										48
				2						2	1		5							1			49
										1	9												50
						1				1													51
25				3											3	6							52
20				1	2						9					2							53
4				1							3												54
										3	7												55
5				1												3	1						56
	1																						57
4	1																						58
5	1			2						3	55		2			3							59
																1							60
1																							61
1	1																						62
1	1			1																			63
				1						3	1					1							64
4	1									1	1	2				1							65
																							66
3	1															2							67
																							68

	Regions..	Lines.	Check for whale-lines.	Floats.	Mouth-pieces, float.	Float-plugs.	Float-rattles.	Float-handles.	Float-swivels.	Sling-darts, fish, complete.	Sling-darts, fish, points.	Sling-darts, fish, shafts.	Sling-darts, fish, with float.	Sling-darts, fish, rings for.	Sling-darts, bird, complete.	Sling-darts, bird, points.	Sling-darts, bird, side prongs.	Sling-boards.	Detacher for harpoon point.
69	Igushek																		
70	Nushegak									8			2		2			2	
71	Bristol Bay	3		3		2				10	3	4	2		4	1		6	
72	Iliamna Lake	4																	3
73	Koggiung									13	2								
74	Nakneek																		
75	Oogashik									2								1	
76	Oonalashka									9		1			1	2		6	
77	Chernovsky					1						2						1	
78	Wrangel Bay									1									
79	Kadiak Island	1			1	1				3	2				1			1	
80	Cook's Inlet	1								7			2					1	
81	Nuchek																		
82	Yakutat																		
83	Thlinkit																	2	
84	Bering's Island																		
85	Japan																		
86	Lapland																		
	Total	26	3	23	69	57	12	23	3	317	58	47	5	5	81	36	14	69	40

Leaders on shaft of harpoon.	Finger-rest on shaft of harpoon.	Ring for same.	Clasp for seal-line.	Bows.	Bow-models.	Quivers.	Wrist-guards.	Quiver-stiffener.	Muskrat bow and arrow.	Arrows, bird.	Arrows, fish.	Arrows, deer.	Arrow-points.	Darts.	Boxes for spear-points.	Hooks for fish.	Sinkers.	Lines and rods.	Tips for rods.	Bait.	Nets.	Sinkers, net.	
								1															69
				2						2	13												70
				5						2	8					2		1					71
																							72
																							73
																							74
		1														2		1				1	75
																						1	76
											1												77
																							78
					1						9												79
					1						2												80
											5												81
											4												82
					1					1	8												83
																							84
																							85
																							86
91	49	2	2	68	13	18	25	2	1	96	410	54	55	2	21	237	97	18	22	10	14	12	

	Regions.	Net-floats.	Decoy floats and rattles.	Handles, net.	Stabbing-knives.	Decoy-scratchers.	Seal-clubs.	Hook for baby-seal pup.	Traps and snares.	Deer-calls.	Gun-rests.	Bullets.	Bullet-mold.	Ramrods and tips.	Powder-flasks.	Powder-measures.	Cap-holders.	Gun-cases.	Belt, with shot and bullet bags.
1	West Greenland							1											
2	Labrador								3									3	
3	Cumberland Gulf							2											
4	Smith Sound																		
5	Igloolik				1														
6	Pelly Bay																		
7	King William's Land																		
8	Mackenzie River								1	3									
9	Anderson River								1										
10	Point Barrow		2		3	2			1										
11	Point Belcher																		
12	Icy Cape																		
13	Cape Lisburne								1										
14	Point Hope		6			2										1			
15	Kotzebue Sound																		
16	Hotham Inlet				2		1									2			
17	Putnam River														1				
18	Cape Espenberg						1										1		
19	Cape Prince of Wales																		
20	Diomede Island		2																
21	Cape Wankarem								2										
22	Port Clarence				19														
23	Tchukchi																		
24	King's Island																		
25	Sledge Island					4	1		3								6		
26	Cape Nome				23				1						1		1	2	
27	St. Lawrence Island	1			1	2			6								1		
28	Poonook																		
29	Plover Bay																		
30	Kaviagamute																2		
31	Golovina Bay																		
32	Cape Darby				14				1										
33	Nubviakhchugaluk																1		
34	Norton Bay															1	1		
35	Koyuk River					1			1								1		
36	Shaktolik																		
37	Oonalakleet				11				3						1	2	1		
38	Kegikhtowik		1		2	1					1								
39	St. Michael					2			9							1	5		
40	Pikmiktalik																		
41	Pastolik								5								4		
42	Norton Sound				2	1			2								2		
43	Yukon Delta and Mouth																		
44	Razboiniksky		3	2	1				3								1		
45	Sabotnisky	1																	
46	Mission																		
47	Paimute							1			1								
48	Anvik				7														
49	Nulato																		
50	Tanana									4					1				
51	Upper Yukon																		
52	Askinuk															1			
53	Kashunuk		1		30										1	1	2	2	
54	Kaialigumute				1											1			
55	Ookagamute																		
56	Cape Vancouver		1		2									1			3	1	
57	Nulokhtologamute				2												2	2	
58	Aginkchugamute																1		
59	Nunivak Island				42											1	1		
60	Sfaganugamute																1		
61	Anogogmute				11								1						
62	Kongiganagamute																		
63	Koolvagavigamute																		
64	Chalitmute				5							1				2			
65	Big Lake																		
66	Kuskokvim River				6														

No.	Wad-cutters.	Hunting-tally.	Cache-markers.	Sinew-tighteners.	Wedges.	Polishers.	Straighteners.	Feather set.	Flint-chipper.	Pricker.	Splint to strengthen bows.	Bridges.	Bevels.	Polishing-stones.	Pumice-stone.	Mouth-pieces.	Fire-bits.	Handles.	Bows.	Drills.	Fire-sockets.	Tools to skin seal.	Scrapers, complete.	Scraper-handles.	Scraper-blades.
1																				1				1	5
2																				4					1
3																2			3	1			3		
4																									
5																					2		4		
6																									
7																									
8				16	3											1		1	3	7	1		1		
9				6	3	3	1									4	1	2	3	3					
10		1	2	8	2			1	7	1						5	3	10	15	11			10		8
11																									
12															1										
13																									
14					3	9	1	8										1	3				14		
15					2	5		4	2							1		3	10	2			4	3	2
16					2	2		2	1									1	4	1			1	2	7
17								1	4									1	1	1			3		
18																									
19						2										2		3	1				4		2
20																2		3	3	1			1		
21																			1						
22																4			1			2			
23																									
24																									
25					5	5		2			2				1	1		2	8	1			8		
26					7	6		2								11		1	15	2			1		
27					3	1			1					4	1	4		1	1	2					
28																									
29						3																			
30					1																				
31																1		1	1	1					
32					2	1		1	2	1						2		1	9						1
33					2			2	2							2			5				1		1
34								2								2							1		1
35									2														1		1
36																			4	1		1	1		1
37																3	1		1				1		
38											1	1				2		1		1			10	2	
39	1	1		2			2				5	6				4		1	8	2			2		4
40																1									
41								1						1		1									
42				1			1																		
43																									
44						2		1	1		1	3	1			5		4		1			1		
45											1		1			4		1					4		
46					1																		6		
47																		1		1			1		
48																							8		
49																									
50					1																				
51																									
52																									
53					3											1							5		
54																									
55																									
56					1													2					1		
57																									
58																1									
59					3					1						2		2		1			1		
60																		1		2					
61																1		2							
62																									
63																									
64					1											6		6		1	1		3		
65					1																		6		
66																1		1							1

	Regions.	Net-floats.	Decoy floats and rattles.	Handles, net.	Stabbing-knives.	Decoy-scratchers.	Seal-clubs.	Hook for baby-seal pup.	Traps and snares.	Deer-calls.	Gun-rests.	Bullets.	Bullet-mold.	Ramrods and tips.	Powder-flasks.	Powder-measures.	Cap-holders.	Gun-cases.	Belt, with shot and bullet bags.
67	Togiak River	...	...	...	12	...	...	...	...	...	...	7	...	...	...	2	1	...	...
68	Tuniakhput	...	...	...	...	...	...	...	...	...	...	...	...	...	...	...	...	...	...
69	Igushek	...	...	...	3	...	...	...	...	...	...	...	...	...	...	1	1	...	...
70	Nushegak	...	...	...	2	...	...	...	...	...	...	...	...	...	...	...	...	...	...
71	Bristol Bay	...	...	...	5	...	...	...	16	...	...	...	...	...	1	1	1	1	1
72	Iliamna Lake	...	...	...	...	...	...	...	...	...	...	...	...	...	...	...	...	...	...
73	Koggiung	...	...	...	...	...	...	...	...	...	...	...	...	...	...	...	...	...	...
74	Naknek	...	...	...	2	...	...	...	...	...	...	...	...	...	...	...	...	...	...
75	Oogashik	...	...	...	3	...	...	...	...	...	...	...	...	...	...	...	...	...	...
76	Oonalashka	...	...	...	...	...	...	...	...	...	...	...	...	...	...	...	...	...	...
77	Chernovsky	...	...	...	?	...	...	...	...	...	...	...	...	...	...	...	...	...	...
78	Wrangel Bay	...	...	...	...	...	...	...	...	...	...	...	...	...	...	...	...	...	...
79	Kadiak Island	...	...	...	...	...	...	...	1	...	...	...	...	...	1	1	1	1	1
80	Cook's Inlet	...	...	...	...	...	...	...	...	...	...	...	...	...	...	...	...	...	...
81	Nuchek	...	...	...	...	...	...	...	...	...	...	...	...	...	...	...	...	...	...
82	Yakutat	...	...	...	...	...	...	...	...	...	...	...	...	...	...	...	...	...	...
83	Thlinkit	...	...	...	...	...	...	...	...	...	...	...	...	...	...	...	...	...	...
84	Bering's Island	...	...	...	...	...	...	...	...	...	...	...	...	...	...	...	...	...	...
85	Japan	...	...	...	...	...	...	...	...	...	...	...	...	...	...	...	...	...	...
86	Lapland	...	...	...	...	...	...	...	...	...	...	...	...	...	...	...	...	...	...
	Total	1	14	5	211	15	4	4	60	3	2	11	1	4	7	28	39	2	2

Wad-cutters.	Hunting-tally.	Cache-markers.	Sinew-tighteners.	Wedges.	Polishers.	Straighteners.	Feather set.	Flint-chipper.	Pricker.	Splint to strengthen bows.	Bridges.	Bevels.	Polishing-stones.	Pumice-stone.	Mouth-pieces.	Fire-bits.	Handles.	Bows.	Drills.	Fire-sockets.	Tools to skin seal.	Scrapers, complete.	Scraper-handles.	Scraper-blades.	
...	...	...	...	...	...	...	...	...	...	...	...	...	...	...	2	1	2	...	...	1	...	9	...	...	67
...	...	...	...	...	...	...	...	...	...	...	...	...	...	...	...	...	...	...	...	...	...	...	...	...	68
...	...	...	...	...	1	...	...	...	...	...	...	...	...	...	...	...	...	...	...	...	...	...	...	...	69
...	...	...	...	...	...	...	...	...	...	...	...	...	...	...	1	1	1	...	...	1	...	...	...	...	70
...	...	...	...	...	...	...	...	...	...	...	...	...	...	...	3	1	...	...	1	3	...	4	...	2	71
...	...	...	...	...	...	...	...	...	...	...	...	...	...	...	...	...	...	...	...	...	...	...	...	...	72
...	...	...	...	...	...	...	...	...	...	...	...	...	...	...	2	2	...	...	1	2	...	1	...	5	73
...	...	...	...	...	...	...	...	...	...	...	...	...	...	...	...	...	...	...	...	...	...	2	...	1	74
...	...	...	...	...	...	...	...	...	...	...	...	...	...	...	...	...	...	...	...	...	...	...	...	12	75
...	...	...	...	...	...	...	...	...	...	...	...	...	...	...	...	...	...	...	...	...	...	...	...	...	76
...	...	...	...	...	...	...	...	...	...	...	...	...	...	1	...	...	...	...	...	...	...	...	...	2	77
...	...	...	...	...	...	...	...	...	...	...	...	...	...	...	...	...	...	...	1	...	...	...	...	2	78
...	...	...	...	...	...	...	...	...	...	...	...	...	...	...	...	...	...	...	...	...	...	...	...	...	79
...	...	...	...	...	...	...	...	...	...	...	...	...	...	...	...	...	...	...	1	...	...	...	...	...	80
...	...	...	...	...	...	...	...	...	...	...	...	...	...	...	...	...	...	...	...	...	...	...	...	...	81
...	...	...	...	...	...	...	...	...	...	...	...	...	...	...	...	...	...	...	...	...	...	...	...	...	82
...	...	2	...	...	...	...	...	...	...	...	...	...	...	...	...	...	...	...	...	...	...	...	...	...	83
...	...	...	...	...	...	...	...	...	...	...	...	...	...	...	...	...	...	...	...	...	...	...	...	...	84
...	...	...	...	...	...	...	...	...	...	...	...	...	...	...	...	...	...	...	...	...	...	...	...	...	85
...	...	...	...	...	...	...	...	...	...	...	...	...	...	...	...	...	...	...	...	...	...	...	...	...	86
1	2	2	56	51	3	31	1	25	8	13	3	3	5	4	84	10	53	97	47	13	2	123	16	73	

No.	Regions.	Scraper-blades.	Boot-sole creasers.	Bark-skinners.	Carving-knife.	Saws.	Adzes.	Adze-handles.	Adze-blades.	Adze-heads.	Hammers.	Wedges.	Scoops.	Shovels.	Picks.	Bodkins.	Bag-fasteners.	Needles.	Needle-cases.	Thimbles.	Thimble-holders.	Needle-sharpeners.
1	West Greenland												2						5	4	4	
2	Labrador				7											3	1		5	4	4	
3	Cumberland Gulf		1		1												1	1	6			
4	Smith Sound																					
5	Igloolik				2													1	1			
6	Pelly Bay																					
7	King William's Land																		8	1	1	1
8	Mackenzie River		1	10	4	1													1			
9	Anderson River		2	17	4	1									2				3	2	5	
10	Point Barrow			42		10	2	17	11	8		3	4	8				42	4	12	5	
11	Point Belcher																					
12	Icy Cape																					
13	Cape Lisburne																					
14	Point Hope			1					5		1										3	
15	Kotzebue Sound		4	2		1										1	1		6	7	5	
16	Hotham Inlet		1						1										5	1	5	
17	Putnam River			1											1				1			
18	Cape Espenberg																					
19	Cape Prince of Wales		1	1	1				2							1				1	1	
20	Diomede Island								10							1			1			
21	Cape Wankarem															3						
22	Port Clarence		1	3												1	6		1	1	3	
23	Tchukchi															1						
24	King's Island																		1			
25	Sledge Island		9	1					8							1	6		10	1	5	
26	Cape Nome	2	7	14					3							1	6		8		1	
27	St. Lawrence Island					2		1		1		1	1			1	1		2		1	
28	Poonook												1									
29	Plover Bay																					
30	Kaviagamute		7																5	1	1	
31	Golovina Bay		1														1					
32	Cape Darby	6	4	2					3										3			3
33	Nubviakhchugaluk	3	2						1			2					4		4	2		6
34	Norton Bay		4																			2
35	Koyuk River	2										4							11			2
36	Shaktolik																		1	1		
37	Oonalakleet	2	13	2	1							3				3	2		5			1
38	Kegikhtowik		4	1											1							
39	St. Michael		28	3					5		1				1	26	39	2	19		24	
40	Pikmiktalik		3														2		6			
41	Pastolik		7						1		1				1	9	6		4			
42	Norton Sound		3															1				
43	Yukon Delta and Mouth															9	45		25			
44	Razboiniksky		5	1					1			2			1	4	29		18			
45	Sabotnisky	1		4	1											5	22		2			
46	Mission		1	1					2							1	2		2			
47	Paimute															3	8		3			
48	Anvik		1	1																		
49	Nulato		3	1					1							3						
50	Tanana								2													
51	Upper Yukon			1							1											
52	Askinuk															4	11		15			
53	Kashunuk	1	4								1					13	27		27	1	2	
54	Kaialigumute															1	5		9			
55	Ookagamute			1													2		3			
56	Cape Vancouver		1													12	33		7			
57	Nulokhtologamute		1	1												2	17		1	2		
58	Agiukchugamute															8	7		3			
59	Nunivak Island		1	4							14					5	6		14	2		
60	Sfaganugamute															2	12		4			
61	Anogogmute		1													1	5		5			
62	Kongiganagamute															4	21		2			
63	Koolvagavigamute			1																		
64	Chalitmute		1	1												9	16		9	4		
65	Big Lake	10		1												2	33		24		1	1
66	Kuskokvim River		1						2							11	28		12			
67	Togiak River	2	1									2				2	29		4	13	16	
68	Tuniakhput			1													4					
69	Igushek								1													

No.	Needle-boards	Embroidery-boards	Braiding implements	Sinew-twister	Thread-reel	Bead-separators	Shoemaker's board and tools	Tool for making belts	Combs, grass	Net-needles	Net-bobbins	Net-spacers	Net-weights	Net-prickers	Shoulder-yoke	Drag-chains	Drag-handles	Check on drag-line	Tool to pass cord under skin of seal	Blubber-hooks	Sledge	Sledge-models	Sledge-runners	Sledge-dog harness	Sledge-dog whips
1									2													1	2		
2									10														1		
3																		3					1		
4																		1							
5																		2			1				
6																									
7																									
8							1											1			1	6		1	
9							1																	1	
10								1		9		11	4	12				3	7						
11																			2						
12																									
13																									
14										1								2	3						
15										1		1	1					9	5	1					
16													1	2											
17										2	1	2	2	3											
18																			1						
19										3		1			1			5	6						
20						3	1			2		1	3					5	2						
21																									
22							1								1			2	3						
23																									
24																									1
25						2				6		9	8		3			32	24						
26						3				3		7	1					10	9						
27										3		4	4	2										6	2
28																					2		1	5	
29																									
30										1					1			5	4						
31																		3	3						
32	1									1		2	3		1	2		6	3						
33		1								1			1	2				1	2						
34											1		1										1		
35										1															
36													2					4	3						
37						1				1			1					1	1				1		
38						3				3	5	7	5				2	2	8						
39												1							1						
40							7			1															
41																									
42																									
43	1					5				3	1	4	2		3			1							
44			1							6		7	4		2										
45										3		3	4												
46										6															
47										2		2			1							1			
48										6															
49											1														
50						5				4	4							1			2				
51											9	3	10					1							
52						6			1																
53										1	1							2							
54										1	6	2													
55										2															
56												1						1		1					
57										1	20	7	5		1			4				6			
58																		3	1						
59																		2							
60												1													
61																									
62												2													
63																									
64															1										
65					1	9												1							
66						3												1							
67																		1			2				

	Regions.	Scraper-blades.	Boot-sole creasers.	Bark-skinners.	Carving-knife.	Saws.	Adzes.	Adze-handles.	Adze-blades.	Adze-heads.	Hammers.	Wedges.	Scoops.	Shovels.	Picks.	Bodkins.	Bag-fasteners.	Needles.	Needle-cases.	Thimbles.	Thimble-holders.	Needle-sharpeners.
70	Nushegak				2	6	1		1							1	4			1	2	
71	Bristol Bay		3		5				8			4							4			
72	Iliamna Lake																					
73	Koggiung		2		4									2				10		2		
74	Naknek		2																			
75	Oogashik								1													
76	Oonalashka																5			1		
77	Chernvosky																					
78	Wrangel Bay																					
79	Kadiak Island				1		3		8		1				1							
80	Cook's Inlet								2													
81	Nuchek																					
82	Yakutat																					
83	Thlinkit								1								1					
84	Bering's Island																					
85	Japan																					
86	Lapland																			2		
	Total	29	132	5	135	16	21	2	87	11	8	28	3	13	27	171	426	55	208	61	100	1

	Needle-boards.	Embroidery-boards.	Braiding implements.	Sinew-twister.	Thread-reel.	Bead-separators.	Shoemaker's board and tools.	Tool for making belts.	Combs, grass.	Net-needles.	Net-bobbins.	Net-spacers.	Net-weights.	Net-prickers.	Shoulder-yoke.	Drag-chains.	Drag-handles.	Check on drag-line.	Tool to pass cord under skin of seal.	Blubber-hooks.	Sledge.	Sledge-models.	Sledge-runners.	Sledge-dog harness.	Sledge-dog whips.
70	...	...	...	...	...	...	...	...	...	...	...	...	...	...	...	...	...	...	...	...	1	...	...	...	...
71	...	...	...	...	...	11	...	...	...	...	9	5	...	...	...	...	...	...	...	...	...	...	...	...	...
72	...	...	...	...	...	...	...	...	...	...	...	...	...	...	...	...	...	...	...	...	...	...	...	...	...
73	...	...	...	...	...	...	...	...	1	...	1	...	...	...	...	...	...	...	...	...	...	...	...	...	...
74	...	...	...	...	...	...	...	...	...	...	3	2	...	...	...	...	...	...	...	2	...	...	...	...	...
75	...	...	...	...	...	...	...	...	...	...	3	...	...	...	...	...	...	...	...	...	...	...	...	...	...
76	...	2	1	...	...	...	...	...	...	...	1	...	...	...	...	...	...	...	...	...	...	...	...	...	...
77	...	...	...	...	...	...	...	...	...	...	...	...	...	...	...	...	...	...	...	...	...	...	...	...	...
78	...	...	...	...	...	...	...	...	...	...	...	...	...	...	...	...	...	...	...	...	...	...	...	...	...
79	...	...	...	...	...	...	...	...	...	...	...	...	...	...	...	...	...	...	...	...	...	...	...	...	...
80	...	...	...	...	...	...	...	...	...	...	...	...	...	...	...	...	...	...	...	...	...	...	...	...	...
81	...	...	...	...	...	...	...	...	...	...	...	...	...	...	...	...	...	...	...	...	...	...	...	...	...
82	...	...	...	...	...	...	...	...	...	...	...	...	...	...	...	...	...	...	...	...	...	...	...	...	...
83	...	...	...	...	...	...	...	...	...	...	...	...	...	...	...	...	...	...	...	...	...	...	...	...	...
84	...	...	...	...	...	...	...	...	...	...	...	...	...	...	...	...	...	...	...	...	...	...	...	...	...
85	...	...	...	...	...	...	...	...	...	...	1	...	...	...	...	...	...	...	...	...	...	...	...	...	...
86	...	...	...	...	...	...	...	...	...	...	...	...	...	...	...	...	...	...	...	...	...	...	...	...	...
	2	3	1	3	13	46	2	1	51	28	139	67	37	16	3	4	112	90	1	13	6	19	6	2	3

	Regions.	Dog-whip butts.	Dog-harness toggles.	Dog-harness swivels.	Dog-harness blocks.	Toboggins.	Snow-shoes.	Kayaks.	Kayak-models.	Ooniaks.	Ooniak-models.	Canoes, birch-bark models.	Paddles.	Paddle-yokes.	Boat-hooks, complete.	Boat-hook hooks.	Ice-breaker for stem of kayak.	Water-tubes.	Line-racks.
1	West Greenland		2					4	8		2		4						2
2	Labrador					8	14	1	3		1		1		1				
3	Cumberland Gulf		4		2			1	4		2								
4	Smith Sound																		
5	Igloolik		1															1	
6	Pelly Bay																		
7	King William's Land																		
8	Mackenzie River						2	1	3		1								
9	Anderson River								2					1					
10	Point Barrow						3	1						1		1			
11	Point Belcher																		
12	Icy Cape				1		1												
13	Cape Lisburne																		
14	Point Hope	1								1					4	1			
15	Kotzebue Sound				8			1											
16	Hotham Inlet																		
17	Putnam River						2												
18	Cape Kruzenstern							1											
19	Cape Espenberg							1											
20	Cape Prince of Wales	1		1	1														
21	Diomede Island	1		1					1		1					1			
22	Cape Wankarem																		
23	Port Clarence																	1	
24	Tchukchi						1												
25	King's Island							1							2				
26	Sledge Island	1			5										1	2			
27	Cape Nome			2	2			1							1	2	1		
28	St. Lawrence Island	3	1		9		2	2		1		1				2			1
29	Poonook						2	1	1										
30	Plover Bay				1														
31	Kaviagamute																		
32	Golovina Bay														1				
33	Cape Darby			2	1													1	
34	Nubviakhchugaluk																		
35	Norton Bay			2						1									
36	Koyuk River			2															
37	Shakotlik																		
38	Oonalakleet	2	1		3			5											
39	Kegikhtowik							1							1	1			
40	St. Michael						1	1	1	1		1				6			
41	Pikmiktalik																1		
42	Pastolik																		
43	Norton Sound															1			
44	Yukon Delta and Mouth																		
45	Razboiniksky			2				1											
46	Sabotnisky																		
47	Mission																		
48	Paimute											2							
49	Anvik							1											
50	Nulato											4				1			
51	Tanana							1				1							
52	Upper Yukon											3							
53	Askinuk															1			
54	Kashunuk												4		1	3			
55	Kaialigumute														1				
56	Ookagamute															2			
57	Cape Vancouver							1											
58	Nulokhtologamute															1			
59	Aginkchugamute																		
60	Nunivak Island				2			2	2										
61	Sfaganugamute																		
62	Anogogmute															1			
63	Kongiganagamute																		
64	Koolvagavigamute																		
65	Chalitmute															3	1		
66	Big Lake															14			
67	Kuskokvim River																	2	
68	Togiak River															3			
69	Tuniakhput																		
70	Igushek																		

	Sail block or hook.	Cleat on kayak to hold spear.	Fork on kayak to hold spear.	Spider-line on kayak.	Sliders on kayak.	Pictures.	Paint-brushes.	Paint-dishes.	Masks.	Finger-masks.	Dance-wands.	Dance-gloves.	Dance head-dress.	Gambling block and pins.	Counters.	Shuttlecocks.	Quoits, set.	Balls, gaming.	Ducks, gaming, sets.	Dominoes, sets.	Miscellaneous toys.	Dolls, dressed.	Doll dresses.
1																							
2							5	3						1				4	1	3	2	3	
3														5				1					
4																							
5	1	1												1						3			
6																							
7																							
8			4			5												1					
9			2			5																	1
10			5						5														
11																							
12																							
13									1														
14																					2	1	
15		2		1																		4	
16																						4	
17																	2						
18																							
19																							
20		4	2															2					
21		1	1																				
22																							
23	1	1	3		4																		
24																							
25			1	2																			
26	8	13		1	2													3				2	
27	2	7		2							10	1	2									3	1
28	3			2					1							3						1	
29																							
30																		1				1	1
31																						1	
32				1	1																		1
33	1	2																				1	
34																						1	
35																						1	2
36																							
37																							
38		3							1												1		1
39																							
40		8				7			8	5		2			1							10	5
41																							
42		2								1												3	
43																							
44																							
45		2							18	5							1					6	
46									15	3												5	
47									6	3													
48		1							3													3	
49									5	1													1
50									3														
51																							
52																							1
53									3												5		
54		7																			3		
55		6																			7		
56																					2		
57		5							2												3		
58		7																			1		
59		3																					
60		13																			3		
61		4																			2		
62		5																			1		
63		1								1											2		
64																							
65		6	1							2											2		
66		1																			9		
67									32	5											1		
68									8	8			3								10		
69																							
70													2										

	Regions.	Dog-whip butts.	Dog-harness toggles.	Dog-harness swivels.	Dog-harness blocks.	Toboggins.	Snow-shoes.	Kayaks.	Kayak-models.	Ooniaks.	Ooniak-models.	Canoes, birch-bark models.	Paddles.	Paddle-yokes.	Boat-hooks, complete.	Boat-hook hooks.	Ice-breaker for stem of kayak.	Water-tubes.	Line-racks.
71	Nushegak								3						1				
72	Bristol Bay				1				4				1	1		2	2		
73	Iliamna Lake																		
74	Koggiung																		
75	Naknek																		
76	Oogashik						1												
77	Oonalashka							1	15										
78	Chernovsky																		
79	Wrangel Bay																		
80	Kadiak Island							1	4		2								
81	Cook's Inlet																		
82	Nuchek								1										
83	Yakutat																		
84	Thlinkit																		
85	Bering's Island						1	1	1										
86	Found in southeast Alaska															1			
	Total	9	7	15	35	8	29	15	69	2	15	11	6	2	14	45	3	5	3

Sail block or hook.	Cleat on kayak to hold spear.	Fork on kayak to hold spear.	Spider-line on kayak.	Sliders on kayak.	Pictures.	Paint-brushes.	Paint-dishes.	Masks.	Finger-masks.	Dance-wands.	Dance-gloves.	Dance head-dress.	Gambling block and pins.	Counters.	Shuttlecocks.	Quoits, set.	Balls, gaming.	Ducks, gaming, sets.	Dominoes, sets.	Miscellaneous toys.	Dolls, dressed.	Doll dresses.	
....		....	....	....	....	....	....	....	....		....	....	....	....	....	....	....	....	....	3	....	....	71
....	5	....	....	....	....	....	....	....	....	4	....	....	....	....	....	....	....	....	....		3	....	72
....		....	....	....	....	....	....	....	....		....	....	....	....	....	....	....	....	....			....	73
....		....	....	....	....	....	....	....	....		....	....	....	....	....	....	....	....	....			....	74
....		....	....	....	....	....	....	....	....		....	....	....	....	....	....	....	....	....			....	75
....		....	....	....	....	....	....	2	1		....	....	....	....	....	....	....	....	....			....	76
....	1	2	....	....	....	....	....	....	....		....	....	....	....	....	....	....	....	....			....	77
....		....	....	....	....	....	....	....	....		....	....	....	....	....	....	....	....	....			....	78
....		....	....	....	....	....	....	....	....		....	....	....	....	....	....	....	....	....			....	79
....		....	....	....	....	....	....	1	....		....	....	....	....	....	....	....	....	....			....	80
....		....	....	....	....	....	....	....	....		....	....	....	....	....	....	....	....	....			....	81
....		....	....	....	....	....	....	9	....		....	....	....	....	....	....	....	....	....			....	82
....		....	....	....	....	....	....	....	....		....	....	....	....	....	....	....	....	....			....	83
....		....	....	....	....	....	....	....	....		....	....	....	....	....	....	....	....	....		1	....	84
....		....	....	....	....	....	....	....	....		....	....	....	....	....	....	....	....	....			....	85
....		....	....	....	....	....	....	....	....		....	....	....	....	....	....	....	....	....			....	86
16	111	21	7	7	17	5	3	122	35	14	3	7	7	1	1	3	9	6	6	8	104	14	

	Regions.	Dolls, nude.	Tops.	Whirlers.	Target and lance game.	Drums.	Drum-handles.	Fiddle.	Guitar.	Carved bears.	Carved dogs.
1	West Greenland						1				
2	Labrador	2				3		1		1	
3	Cumberland Gulf	2									
4	Smith Sound										
5	Igloolik										
6	Pelly Bay										
7	King William's Land										
8	Mackenzie River										
9	Anderson River										
10	Point Barrow	23				3	4			8	4
11	Point Belcher										
12	Icy Cape										
13	Cape Lisburne										
14	Point Hope						4			1	
15	Kotzebue Sound	10								3	1
16	Hotham Inlet	6									
17	Putnam River	1	1								
18	Cape Espenberg	3								2	
19	Cape Prince of Wales	5	1							2	
20	Diomede Island	6								2	2
21	Cape Wankarem					1					
22	Port Clarence										
23	Tchukchi										
24	King's Island										
25	Sledge Island	16		1						4	
26	Cape Nome	12	1			2				1	13
27	St. Lawrence Island	12								8	9
28	Poonook	1							1		
29	Plover Bay									1	
30	Kaviagamute	1									
31	Golovina Bay										
32	Cape Darby	6								1	
33	Nubviakhchugaluk	3					1			1	
34	Norton Bay	3								1	
35	Koyuk River										1
36	Shaktolik	1					1				
37	Oonalakleet	6								4	
38	Kegikhtowick										
39	St. Michael	30				1	1			1	
40	Pikmiktalik					1					
41	Pastolik				1	1					
42	Norton Sound	27				2					
43	Yukon Delta and Mouth										
44	Razboiniksky	6									
45	Sabotnisky	7									
46	Missi n	14									
47	Paimute	2									
48	Anvik										
49	Nulato										
50	Tanana										
51	Upper Yukon										
52	Askinuk	3									
53	Kashunuk	3									
54	Kaialigumute	3									
55	Ookogamute										
56	Cape Vancouver	5				1	2				
57	Nulokhtologamute	1									
58	Agiukchugamute	1									
59	Nunivak Island	5									1
60	Sfaganugamute	2									
61	Anogogmute										
62	Kongigangamute	1									
63	Koolvagavigamute										
64	Chalitmute	2									
65	Big Lake	5									
66	Kuskokvim River	2									
67	Togiak River	8									
68	Tuniakhput										
69	Igushek										
70	Nushegak	3				2			3		

Carved animals, miscellaneous.	Carved fish.	Carved seals.	Carved whales.	Carved walrus.	Carved otter.	Carved birds.	Carved slings.	Carved candlesticks.	Carved padlocks.	Carved rulers.	Carved spoons.	Carved knives.	Carved forks.	Amulets.	Shaman's wand.	Grave ornaments.	
						4											1
																	2
																	3
																	4
															4		5
																	6
																	7
																	8
																	9
		6	6	3										31			10
																	11
																	12
																	13
																	14
2		7		4		11											15
																	16
4																	17
1				1													18
1		4															19
		2		1		3											20
																	21
																	22
																	23
																	24
7		6	2			2											25
2		2	1			1											26
		13	1	11		73											27
1		2		1		1											28
		1				13											29
																	30
2																	31
1		5		2													32
1		1	1														33
1																	34
3																	35
	1		1														36
2	3	2	1														37
		1															38
68	31	22	7	2	17	15	7										39
																	40
																	41
															1		42
																	43
			1		1										1		44
																	45
																	46
																	47
																	48
																	49
																	50
																	51
																	52
4	1						5								1		53
		1															54
																	55
7	10	5	11	6	3	1	6										56
	1		2														57
2				1													58
		3				1	1	2							7		59
						1											60
																	61
																	62
																	63
						2											64
																	65
			1														66
																	67
																	68
																	69
2				2	2			1	3	1	1	1	1			3	70

	Regions.	Dolls, nude.	Tops.	Whirlers.	Target and lance game.	Drums.	Drum-handles.	Fiddle.	Guitar.	Carved bears.	Carved dogs.
71	Bristol Bay			1						1	
72	Iliamna Lake										
73	Koggiung										
74	Naknek										
75	Oogashik										
76	Oonalashka					2					
77	Chernovsky										
78	Wrangel Bay										
79	Kadiak Island									1	1
80	Cook's Inlet										
81	Nuchek										
82	Yakutat	1									
83	Thlinkit								1		
84	Bering's Island					1			1		
	Total	249	3	2	1	21	14	4	4	46	31

RÉSUMÉ.—Total number of articles, 11,452.

Carved animals, miscellaneous.	Carved fish.	Carved seals.	Carved whales.	Carved walrus.	Carved otter.	Carved birds.	Carved slugs.	Carved candlesticks.	Carved padlocks.	Carved rulers.	Carved spoons.	Carved knives.	Carved forks.	Amulets.	Shaman's wand.	Grave ornaments.	
......	......	1	2	1	3	......	3	......	......	......	......	......	......	5	......	......	71
......	......	......	......	......	......	......	......	......	......	......	......	......	......	......	......	......	72
5	......	......	6	4	15	6	6	......	......	......	......	......	......	......	......	......	73
......	......	......	......	......	......	......	......	......	......	......	......	......	......	......	......	......	74
......	......	......	......	......	......	......	......	......	......	......	......	......	......	......	......	......	75
2	2	1	1	1	14	1	......	......	......	......	......	......	......	......	......	......	76
......	......	......	......	......	......	......	......	......	......	......	......	......	......	......	......	......	77
......	......	......	......	......	......	......	......	......	......	......	......	......	......	......	......	......	78
......	......	......	......	......	......	......	......	......	......	......	......	......	......	......	......	......	79
......	......	......	......	......	......	......	......	......	......	......	......	......	......	......	......	......	80
......	......	......	......	......	......	......	......	......	......	......	......	......	......	......	......	......	81
......	......	......	......	......	......	......	......	......	......	......	......	......	......	......	......	......	82
......	......	......	......	......	......	......	......	......	......	......	......	......	......	......	......	......	83
......	......	......	......	......	......	......	......	......	......	......	......	......	......	......	......	......	84
117	49	85	45	39	59	132	29	1	3	1	1	1	1	49	1	3	

THE EXTERMINATION

OF

THE AMERICAN BISON,

WITH

A SKETCH OF ITS DISCOVERY AND LIFE HISTORY.

BY

WILLIAM T. HORNADAY.

CONTENTS.

LIST OF ILLUSTRATIONS.

MAPS.

PREFATORY NOTE.

It is hoped that the following historical account of the discovery, partial utilization, and almost complete extermination of the great American bison may serve to cause the public to fully realize the folly of allowing all our most valuable and interesting American mammals to be wantonly destroyed in the same manner. The wild buffalo is practically gone forever, and in a few more years, when the whitened bones of the last bleaching skeleton shall have been picked up and shipped East for commercial uses, nothing will remain of him save his old, well-worn trails along the water-courses, a few museum specimens, and regret for his fate. If his untimely end fails even to point a moral that shall benefit the surviving species of mammals *which are now being slaughtered in like manner*, it will be sad indeed.

Although *Bison americanus* is a true bison, according to scientific classification, and not a buffalo, the fact that more than sixty millions of people in this country unite in calling him a "buffalo," and know him by no other name, renders it quite unnecessary for me to apologize for following, in part, a harmless custom which has now become so universal that all the naturalists in the world could not change it if they would.

W. T. H.

371

THE EXTERMINATION OF THE AMERICAN BISON.

By WILLIAM T. HORNADAY,
Superintendent of the National Zoological Park.

PART I.—LIFE HISTORY OF THE BISON.

I. DISCOVERY OF THE SPECIES.

The discovery of the American bison, as first made by Europeans, occurred in the menagerie of a heathen king.

In the year 1521, when Cortez reached Anahuac, the American bison was seen for the first time by civilized Europeans, if we may be permitted to thus characterize the horde of blood-thirsty plunder-seekers who fought their way to the Aztec capital. With a degree of enterprise that marked him as an enlightened monarch, Montezuma maintained, for the instruction of his people, a well-appointed menagerie, of which the historian De Solis wrote as follows (1724):

"In the second Square of the same House were the Wild Beasts, which were either presents to Montezuma, or taken by his Hunters, in strong Cages of Timber, rang'd in good Order, and under Cover: Lions, Tygers, Bears, and all others of the savage Kind which New-Spain produced; among which the greatest Rarity was the Mexican Bull; a wonderful composition of divers Animals. It has crooked Shoulders, with a Bunch on its Back like a Camel; its Flanks dry, its Tail large, and its Neck cover'd with Hair like a Lion. It is cloven footed, its Head armed like that of a Bull, which it resembles in Fierceness, with no less strength and Agility."

Thus was the first-seen buffalo described. The nearest locality from whence it could have come was the State of Coahuila, in northern Mexico, between 400 and 500 miles away, and at that time vehicles were unknown to the Aztecs. But for the destruction of the whole mass of the written literature of the Aztecs by the priests of the Spanish Conquest, we might now be reveling in historical accounts of the bison which would make the oldest of our present records seem of comparatively recent date.

Nine years after the event referred to above, or in 1530, another Spanish explorer, Alvar Nuñez Cabeza, afterwards called Cabeza de Vaca—or, in other words "Cattle Cabeza," the prototype of our own distinguished "Buffalo Bill"—was wrecked on the Gulf coast, west of the delta of the Mississippi, from whence he wandered westward through what is now the State of Texas. In southeastern Texas he discovered the American bison on his native heath. So far as can be ascertained, this was the earliest discovery of the bison in a wild state, and the description of the species as recorded by the explorer is of historical interest. It is brief and superficial. The unfortunate explorer took very little interest in animated nature, except as it contributed to the sum of his daily food, which was then the all-important subject of his thoughts. He almost starved. This is all he has to say:[*]

"Cattle come as far as this. I have seen them three times, and eaten of their meat. I think they are about the size of those in Spain. They have small horns like those of Morocco, and the hair long and flocky, like that of the merino. Some are light brown (*pardillas*) and others black. To my judgment the flesh is finer and sweeter than that of this country [Spain]. The Indians make blankets of those that are not full grown, and of the larger they make shoes and bucklers. They come as far as the sea-coast of Florida [now Texas], and in a direction from the north, and range over a district of more than 400 leagues. In the whole extent of plain over which they roam, the people who live bordering upon it descend and kill them for food, and thus a great many skins are scattered throughout the country."

Coronado was the next explorer who penetrated the country of the buffalo, which he accomplished from the west, by way of Arizona and New Mexico. He crossed the southern part of the " Panhandle" of Texas, to the edge of what is now the Indian Territory, and returned through the same region. It was in the year 1542 that he reached the buffalo country, and traversed the plains that were "full of crooke-backed oxen, as the mountaine Serena in Spaine is of sheepe." This is the description of the animal as recorded by one of his followers, Casta-ñeda, and translated by W. W. Davis:[†]

" The first time we encountered the buffalo, all the horses took to flight on seeing them, for they are horrible to the sight."

" They have a broad and short face, eyes two palms from each other, and projecting in such a manner sideways that they can see a pursuer. Their beard is like that of goats, and so long that it drags the ground when they lower the head. They have, on the anterior portion of the body, a frizzled hair like sheep's wool; it is very fine upon the croup, and sleek like a lion's mane. Their horns are very short and thick, and can scarcely be seen through the hair. They always change their hair in May, and at this season they really resemble lions. To make it drop more quickly, for they change it as adders do their skins, they roll among the brush-wood which they find in the ravines.

" Their tail is very short, and terminates in a great tuft. When they run they carry it in the air like scorpions. When quite young they are

---

[*] Davis' Spanish Conquest of New Mexico. 1869. P. 67.

[†] The Spanish Conquest of New Mexico. Davis. 1869. Pp. 206-7.

tawny, and resemble our calves; but as age increases they change color and form.

"Another thing which struck us was that all the old buffaloes that we killed had the left ear cloven, while it was entire in the young; we could never discover the reason of this.

" Their wool is so fine that handsome clothes would certainly be made of it, but it can not be dyed for it is tawny red. We were much surprised at sometimes meeting innumerable herds of bulls without a single cow, and other herds of cows without bulls."

Neither De Soto, Ponce de Leon, Vasquez de Ayllon, nor Pamphilo de Narvaez ever saw a buffalo, for the reason that all their explorations were made south of what was then the habitat of that animal. At the time De Soto made his great exploration from Florida northwestward to the Mississippi and into Arkansas (1539-'41) he did indeed pass through country in northern Mississippi and Louisiana that was afterward inhabited by the buffalo, but at that time not one was to be found there. Some of his soldiers, however, who were sent into the northern part of Arkansas, reported having seen buffalo skins in the possession of the Indians, and were told that live buffaloes were to be found 5 or 6 leagues north of their farthest point.

The earliest discovery of the bison in Eastern North America, or indeed anywhere north of Coronado's route, was made somewhere near Washington, District of Columbia, in 1612, by an English navigator named Samuell Argoll,* and narrated as follows:

"As soon as I had unladen this corne, I set my men to the felling of Timber, for the building of a Frigat, which I had left half finished at Point Comfort, the 19. of March: and returned myself with the ship into Pembrook [Potomac] River, and so discovered to the head of it, which is about 65. leagues into the Land, and navigable for any ship. And then marching into the Countrie, I found great store of Cattle as big as Kine, of which the Indians that were my guides killed a couple, which we found to be very good and wholesome meate, and are very easie to be killed, in regard they are heavy, slow, and not so wild as other beasts of the wildernesse."

It is to be regretted that the narrative of the explorer affords no clew to the precise locality of this interesting discovery, but since it is doubtful that the mariner journeyed very far on foot from the head of navigation of the Potomac, it seems highly probable that the first American bison seen by Europeans, other than the Spaniards, was found within 15 miles, or even less, of the capital of the United States, and possibly within the District of Columbia itself.

The first meeting of the white man with the buffalo on the northern boundary of that animal's habitat occurred in 1679, when Father Hen-

---

* Purchas: His Pilgrimes. (1625.) Vol. IV, p. 1765. "A letter of Sir Samuel Argoll touching his Voyage to Virginia, and actions there. Written to Master Nicholas Hawes, June, 1613."

nepin ascended the St. Lawrence to the great lakes, and finally penetrated the great wilderness as far as western Illinois.

The next meeting with the buffalo on the Atlantic slope was in October, 1729, by a party of surveyors under Col. William Byrd, who were engaged in surveying the boundary between North Carolina and Virginia.

As the party journeyed up from the coast, marking the line which now constitutes the interstate boundary, three buffaloes were seen on Sugar-Tree Creek, but none of them were killed.

On the return journey, in November, a bull buffalo was killed on Sugar-Tree Creek, which is in Halifax County, Virginia, within 5 miles of Big Buffalo Creek; longitude 78° 40″ W., and 155 miles from the coast.* "It was found all alone, tho' Buffaloes Seldom are." The meat is spoken of as "a Rarity," not met at all on the expedition up. The animal was found in thick woods, which were thus feelingly described: "The woods were thick great Part of this Day's Journey, so that we were forced to scuffle hard to advance 7 miles, being equal in fatigue to double that distance of Clear and Open Ground." One of the creeks which the party crossed was christened Buffalo Creek, and "so named from the frequent tokens we discovered of that American Behemoth."

In October, 1733, on another surveying expedition, Colonel Byrd's party had the good fortune to kill another buffalo near Sugar-Tree Creek, which incident is thus described :†

"We pursued our journey thro' uneven and perplext woods, and in the thickest of them had the Fortune to knock down a Young Buffalo 2 years old. Providence threw this vast animal in our way very Seasonably, just as our provisions began to fail us. And it was the more welcome, too, because it was change of dyet, which of all Varietys, next to that of Bed-fellows, is the most agreeable. We had lived upon Venison and Bear till our stomachs loath'd them almost as much as the Hebrews of old did their Quails. Our Butchers were so unhandy at their Business that we grew very lank before we cou'd get our Dinner. But when it came, we found it equal in goodness to the best Beef. They made it the longer because they kept Sucking the Water out of the Guts in imitation of the Catauba Indians, upon the belief that it is a great Cordial, and will even make them drunk, or at least very Gay."

A little later a solitary bull buffalo was found, *but spared*,‡ the earliest instance of the kind on record, and which had few successors to keep it company.

II. GEOGRAPHICAL DISTRIBUTION.

The range of the American bison extended over about one-third of the entire continent of North America. Starting almost at tide-water

---

* Westover Manuscript. Col. William Byrd. Vol. I, p. 172.
† Vol. II, pp. 24, 25.
‡ *Ib.*, p. 28.

on the Atlantic coast, it extended westward through a vast tract of dense forest, across the Alleghany Mountain system to the prairies along the Mississippi, and southward to the Delta of that great stream. Although the great plains country of the West was the natural home of the species, where it flourished most abundantly, it also wandered south across Texas to the burning plains of northeastern Mexico, westward across the Rocky Mountains into New Mexico, Utah, and Idaho, and northward across a vast treeless waste to the bleak and inhospitable shores of the Great Slave Lake itself. It is more than probable that had the bison remained unmolested by man and uninfluenced by him, he would eventually have crossed the Sierra Nevadas and the Coast Range and taken up his abode in the fertile valleys of the Pacific slope.

Had the bison remained for a few more centuries in undisturbed possession of his range, and with liberty to roam at will over the North American continent, it is almost certain that several distinctly recognizable varieties would have been produced. The buffalo of the hot regions in the extreme south would have become a short-haired animal like the gaur of India and the African buffalo. The individuals inhabiting the extreme north, in the vicinity of Great Slave Lake, for example, would have developed still longer hair, and taken on more of the dense hairyness of the musk ox. In the "wood" or "mountain buffalo" we already have a distinct foreshadowing of the changes which would have taken place in the individuals which made their permanent residence upon rugged mountains.

It would be an easy matter to fill a volume with facts relating to the geographical distribution of *Bison americanus* and the dates of its occurrence and disappearance in the multitude of different localities embraced within the immense area it once inhabited. The capricious shiftings of certain sections of the great herds, whereby large areas which for many years had been utterly unvisited by buffaloes suddenly became overrun by them, could be followed up indefinitely, but to little purpose. In order to avoid wearying the reader with a mass of dates and references, the map accompanying this paper has been prepared to show at a glance the approximate dates at which the bison finally disappeared from the various sections of its habitat. In some cases the date given is coincident with the death of the last buffalo known to have been killed in a given State or Territory; in others, where records are meager, the date given is the nearest approximation, based on existing records. In the preparation of this map I have drawn liberally from Mr. J. A. Allen's admirable monograph of "The American Bison," in which the author has brought together, with great labor and invariable accuracy, a vast amount of historical data bearing upon this subject. In this connection I take great pleasure in acknowledging my indebtedness to Professor Allen's work.

While it is inexpedient to include here all the facts that might be recorded with reference to the discovery, existence, and ultimate extinction of the bison in the various portions of its former habitat, it is yet worth while to sketch briefly the extreme limits of its range. In doing this, our starting point will be the Atlantic slope east of the Alleghanies, and the reader will do well to refer to the large map.

DISTRICT OF COLUMBIA.—There is no indisputable evidence that the bison ever inhabited this precise locality, but it is probable that it did. In 1612 Captain Argoll sailed up the "Pembrook River" to the head of navigation (Mr. Allen believes this was the James River, and not the Potomac) and marched inland a few miles, where he discovered buffaloes, some of which were killed by his Indian guides. If this river was the Potomac, and most authorities believe that it was, the buffaloes seen by Captain Argoll might easily have been in what is now the District of Columbia.

Admitting the existence of a reasonable doubt as to the identity of the Pembrook River of Captain Argoll, there is yet another bit of history which fairly establishes the fact that in the early part of the seventeenth century buffaloes inhabited the banks of the Potomac between this city and the lower falls. In 1624 an English fur-trader named Henry Fleet came hither to trade with the Anacostian Indians, who then inhabited the present site of the city of Washington, and with the tribes of the Upper Potomac. In his journal (discovered a few years since in the Lambeth Library, London) Fleet gave a quaint description of the city's site as it then appeared. The following is from the explorer's journal:

"Monday, the 25th June, we set sail for the town of Tohoga, where we came to an anchor 2 leagues short of the falls. * * * This place, without question, is the most pleasant and healthful place in all this country, and most convenient for habitation, the air temperate in summer and not violent in winter. It aboundeth with all manner of fish. The Indians in one night commonly will catch thirty sturgeons in a place where the river is not above 12 fathoms broad, and as for deer, buffaloes, bears, turkeys, the woods do swarm with them. * * * The 27th of June I manned my shallop and went up with the flood, the tide rising about 4 feet at this place. We had not rowed above 3 miles, but we might hear the falls to roar about 6 miles distant."[*]

MARYLAND.—There is no evidence that the bison ever inhabited Maryland, except what has already been adduced with reference to the District of Columbia. If either of the references quoted may be taken as conclusive proof, and I see no reason for disputing either, then the fact that the bison once ranged northward from Virginia into Maryland is fairly established. There is reason to expect that fossil remains of *Bison americanus* will yet be found both in Maryland and the District of Columbia, and I venture to predict that this will yet occur.

VIRGINIA.—Of the numerous references to the occurrence of the bison in Virginia, it is sufficient to allude to Col. William Byrd's meetings

---

[*] Charles Burr Todd's "Story of Washington, p. 18. New York, 1889.

with buffaloes in 1620, while surveying the southern boundary of the State, about 155 miles from the coast, as already quoted; the references to the discovery of buffaloes on the eastern side of the Virginia mountains, quoted by Mr. Allen from Salmon's "Present State of Virginia," page 14 (London, 1737), and the capture *and domestication* of buffaloes in 1701 by the Huguenot settlers at Manikintown, which was situated on the James River, about 14 miles above Richmond. Apparently, buffaloes were more numerous in Virginia than in any other of the Atlantic States.

NORTH CAROLINA.—Colonel Byrd's discoveries along the inter-state boundary between Virginia and North Carolina fixes the presence of the bison in the northern part of the latter State at the date of the survey. The following letter to Prof. G. Brown Goode, dated Birdsnest post-office, Va., August 6, 1888, from Mr. C. R. Moore, furnishes reliable evidence of the presence of the buffalo at another point in North Carolina: "In the winter of 1857 I was staying for the night at the house of an old gentleman named Houston. I should judge he was seventy then. He lived near Buffalo Ford, on the Catawba River, about 4 miles from Statesville, N. C. I asked him how the ford got its name. He told me that his grandfather told him that when he was a boy the buffalo crossed there, and that when the rocks in the river were bare they would eat the moss that grew upon them." The point indicated is in longitude 81° west and the date not far from 1750.

SOUTH CAROLINA.—Professor Allen cites numerous authorities, whose observations furnish abundant evidence of the existence of the buffalo in South Carolina during the first half of the eighteenth century. From these it is quite evident that in the northwestern half of the State buffaloes were once fairly numerous. Keating declares, on the authority of Colhoun, "and we know that some of those who first settled the Abbeville district in South Carolina, in 1756, found the buffalo there." * This appears to be the only definite locality in which the presence of the species was recorded.

GEORGIA.—The extreme southeastern limit of the buffalo in the United States was found on the coast of Georgia, near the mouth of the Altamaha River, opposite St. Simon's Island. Mr. Francis Moore, in his "Voyage to Georgia," made in 1736 and reported upon in 1744,† makes the following observation:

"The island [St. Simon's] abounds with deer and rabbits. There are no buffalo in it, though there are large herds upon the main." Elsewhere in the same document (p. 122) reference is made to buffalo-hunting by Indians on the main-land near Darien.

In James E. Oglethorpe's enumeration (A. D. 1733) of the wild beasts of Georgia and South Carolina he mentions "deer, elks, bears, wolves, and buffaloes."‡

---

* Long's Expedition to the Source of the St. Peter's River, 1823, II, p. 26.

† Coll. Georgia Hist. Soc., I, p. 117.

‡ Ibid., I, p. 51.

Up to the time of Moore's voyage to Georgia the interior was almost wholly unexplored, and it is almost certain that had not the "large herds of buffalo on the main-land" existed within a distance of 20 or 30 miles or less from the coast, the colonists would have had no knowledge of them; nor would the Indians have taken to the war-path against the whites at Darien "under pretense of hunting buffalo."

ALABAMA.—Having established the existence of the bison in north-western Georgia almost as far down as the center of the State, and in Mississippi down to the neighborhood of the coast, it was naturally expected that a search of historical records would reveal evidence that the bison once inhabited the northern half of Alabama. A most careful search through all the records bearing upon the early history and exploration of Alabama, to be found in the Library of Congress, failed to discover the slightest reference to the existence of the species in that State, or even to the use of buffalo skins by any of the Alabama Indians. While it is possible that such a hiatus really existed, in this instance its existence would be wholly unaccountable. I believe that the buffalo once inhabited the northern half of Alabama, even though history fails to record it.

LOUISIANA AND MISSISSIPPI.—At the beginning of the eighteenth century, buffaloes were plentiful in southern Mississippi and Louisiana, not only down to the coast itself, from Bay St. Louis to Biloxi, but even in the very Delta of the Mississippi, as the following record shows. In a "Memoir addressed to Count de Pontchartrain," December 10, 1697, the author, M. de Remonville, describes the country around the mouth of the Mississippi, now the State of Louisiana, and further says: [*]

"A great abundance of wild cattle are also found there, which might be domesticated by rearing up the young calves." Whether these animals were buffaloes might be considered an open question but for the following additional information, which affords positive evidence: "The trade in furs and peltry would be immensely valuable and exceedingly profitable. We could also draw from thence a great quantity of buffalo hides every year, as the plains are filled with the animals."

In the same volume, page 47, in a document entitled "Annals of Louisiana from 1698 to 1722, by M. Penicaut" (1698), the author records the presence of the buffalo on the Gulf coast on the banks of the Bay St. Louis, as follows: "The next day we left Pea Island, and passed through the Little Rigolets, which led into the sea about three leagues from the Bay of St. Louis. We encamped at the entrance of the bay, near a fountain of water that flows from the hills, and which was called at this time Belle Fountain. We hunted during several days upon the coast of this bay, and filled our boats with the meat of the deer, buffaloes, and other wild game which we had killed, and carried it to the fort (Biloxi)."

---

[*] Hist. Coll. of Louisiana and Florida, B. F. French, 1869, first series, p. 2.

The occurrence of the buffalo at Natchez is recorded,* and also (p. 115) at the mouth of Red River, as follows: "We ascended the Mississippi to Pass Manchac, where we killed fifteen buffaloes. The next day we landed again, and killed eight more buffaloes and as many deer."

The presence of the buffalo in the Delta of the Mississippi was observed and recorded by D'Iberville in 1699.†

According to Claiborne,‡ the Choctaws have an interesting tradition in regard to the disappearance of the buffalo from Mississippi. It relates that during the early part of the eighteenth century a great drought occurred, which was particularly severe in the prairie region. For three years not a drop of rain fell. The Nowubee and Tombigbee Rivers dried up and the forests perished. The elk and buffalo, which up to that time had been numerous, all migrated to the country beyond the Mississippi, and never returned.

TEXAS.—It will be remembered that it was in southeastern Texas, in all probability within 50 miles of the present city of Houston, that the earliest discovery of the American bison on its native heath was made in 1530 by Cabeza de Vaca, a half-starved, half-naked, and wholly wretched Spaniard, almost the only surviving member of the celebrated expedition which burned its ships behind it. In speaking of the buffalo in Texas at the earliest periods of which we have any historical record, Professor Allen says: "They were also found in immense herds on the coast of Texas, at the Bay of St. Bernard (Matagorda Bay), and on the lower part of the Colorado (Rio Grande, according to some authorities), by La Salle, in 1685, and thence northwards across the Colorado, Brazos, and Trinity Rivers. Joutel says that when in latitude 28° 51' "the sight of abundance of goats and bullocks, differing in shape from ours, and running along the coast, heightened our earnestness to be ashore." They afterwards landed in St. Louis Bay (now called Matagorda Bay), where they found buffaloes in such numbers on the Colorado River that they called it La Rivière aux Bœufs.§ According to Professor Allen, the buffalo did not inhabit the coast of Texas east of the mouth of the Brazos River.

It is a curious coincidence that the State of Texas, wherein the earliest discoveries and observations upon the bison were made, should also now furnish a temporary shelter for one of the last remnants of the great herd.

MEXICO.—In regard to the existence of the bison south of the Rio Grande, in old Mexico, there appears to be but one authority on record, Dr. Berlandier, who at the time of his death left in MS. a work on the mammals of Mexico. At one time this MS. was in the Smithsonian Institution, but it is there no longer, nor is its fate even ascertain-

---

* Ibid., pp. 88–91.

† Hist. Coll. of Louisiana and Florida, French, second series, p. 58.

‡ Mississippi as a Province, Territory, and State, p. 484.

§ The American Bisons, Living and Extinct, p. 132.

able. It is probable that it was burned in the fire that destroyed a portion of the Institution in 1865. Fortunately Professor Allen obtained and published in his monograph (in French) a copy of that portion of Dr. Berlandier's work relating to the presence of the bison in Mexico,* of which the following is a translation:

" In Mexico, when the Spaniards, ever greedy for riches, pushed their explorations to the north and northeast, it was not long before they met with the buffalo. In 1602 the Franciscan monks who discovered Nuevo Leon encountered in the neighborhood of Monterey numerous herds of these quadrupeds. They were also distributed in Nouvelle Biscaye (States of Chihuahua and Durango), and they sometimes advanced to the extreme south of that country. In the eighteenth century they concentrated more and more toward the north, but still remained very abundant in the neighborhood of the province of Bexar. At the commencement of the nineteenth century we see them recede gradually in the interior of the country to such an extent that they became day by day scarcer and scarcer about the settlements. Now, it is not in their periodical migrations that we meet them near Bexar. Every year in the spring, in April or May, they advance toward the north, to return again to the southern regions in September and October. The exact limits of these annual migrations are unknown; it is, however, probable that in the north they never go beyond the banks of the Rio Bravo, at least in the States of Cohahuila and Texas. Toward the north, not being checked by the currents of the Missouri, they progress even as far as Michigan, and they are found in summer in the Territories and interior States of the United States of North America. The route which these animals follow in their migrations occupies a width of several miles, and becomes so marked that, besides the verdure destroyed, one would believe that the fields had been covered with manure.

" These migrations are not general, for certain bands do not seem to follow the general mass of their kin, but remain stationary throughout the whole year on the prairies covered with a rich vegetation on the banks of the Rio de Guadelupe and the Rio Colorado of Texas, not far from the shores of the Gulf, to the east of the colony of San Felipe, precisely at the same spot where La Salle and his traveling companions saw them two hundred years before. The Rev. Father Damian Mansanet saw them also as in our days on the shores of Texas, in regions which have since been covered with the habitations, hamlets, and villages of the new colonists, and from whence they have disappeared since 1828.

" From the observations made on this subject we may conclude that the buffalo inhabited the temperate zone of the New World, and that they inhabited it at all times. In the north they never advanced beyond the 48th or 58th degree of latitude, and in the south, although

---

* The American Bisons, pp. 129–130.

HEAD OF BUFFALO BULL.

From specimen in the National Museum Group.

Reproduced from the *Cosmopolitan Magazine*, by permission of the publishers.

they may have reached as low as 25°, they scarcely passed beyond the 27th or 28th degree (north latitude), at least in the inhabited and known portions of the country."

NEW MEXICO.—In 1542 Coronado, while on his celebrated march, met with vast herds of buffalo on the Upper Pecos River, since which the presence of the species in the valley of the Pecos has been well known. In describing the journey of Espejo down the Pecos River in the year 1584, Davis says (Spanish Conquest of New Mexico, p. 260): "They passed down a river they called *Rio de las Vacas,* or the River of Oxen [the river Pecos, and the same Cow River that Vaca describes, says Professor Allen], and was so named because of the great number of buffaloes that fed upon its banks. They traveled down this river the distance of 120 leagues, all the way passing through great herds of buffaloes."

Professor Allen locates the western boundary of the buffalo in New Mexico even as far west as the western side of Rio Grande del Norte.

UTAH.—It is well known that buffaloes, though in very small numbers, once inhabited northeastern Utah, and that a few were killed by the Mormon settlers prior to 1840 in the vicinity of Great Salt Lake. In the museum at Salt Lake City I was shown a very ancient mounted head of a buffalo bull which was said to have been killed in the Salt Lake Valley. It is doubtful that such was really fact. There is no evidence that the bison ever inhabited the southwestern half of Utah, and, considering the general sterility of the Territory as a whole previous to its development by irrigation, it is surprising that any buffalo in his senses would ever set foot in it at all.

IDAHO.—The former range of the bison probably embraced the whole of Idaho. Fremont states that in the spring of 1824 "the buffalo were spread in immense numbers over the Green River and Bear River Valleys, and through all the country lying between the Colorado, or Green River of the Gulf of California, and Lewis' Fork of the Columbia River, the meridian of Fort Hall then forming the western limit of their range. [In J. K. Townsend's "Narrative of a Journey across the Rocky Mountains," in 1834, he records the occurrence of herds near the Mellade and Boise and Salmon Rivers, ten days' journey—200 miles—west of Fort Hall.] The buffalo then remained for many years in that country, and frequently moved down the valley of the Columbia, on both sides of the river, as far as the Fishing Falls. Below this point they never descended in any numbers. About 1834 or 1835 they began to diminish very rapidly, and continued to decrease until 1838 or 1840, when, with the country we have just described, they entirely abandoned all the waters of the Pacific north of Lewis's Fork of the Columbia [now called Snake] River. At that time the Flathead Indians were in the habit of finding their buffalo on the heads of Salmon River and other streams of the Columbia.

OREGON.—The only evidence on record of the occurrence of the bison in Oregon is the following, from Professor Allen's memoir (p. 119): "Respecting its former occurrence in eastern Oregon, Prof. O. C. Marsh, under date of New Haven, February 7, 1875, writes me as follows: 'The most western point at which I have myself observed remains of the buffalo was in 1873, on Willow Creek, eastern Oregon, among the foot-hills on the eastern side of the Blue Mountains. This is about latitude 44°. The bones were perfectly characteristic, although nearly decomposed.'"

The remains must have been those of a solitary and very enterprising straggler.

THE NORTHWEST TERRITORIES (British).—At two or three points only did the buffaloes of the British Possessions cross the Rocky Mountain barrier toward British Columbia. One was the pass through which the Canadian Pacific Railway now runs, 200 miles north of the international boundary. According to Dr. Richardson, the number of buffaloes which crossed the mountains at that point were sufficiently noticeable to constitute a feature of the fauna on the western side of the range. It is said that buffaloes also crossed by way of the Kootenai Pass, which is only a few miles north of the boundary line, but the number which did so must have been very small.

As might be expected from the character of the country, the favorite range of the bison in British America was the northern extension of the great pasture region lying between the Missouri River and Great Slave Lake. The most northerly occurrence of the bison is recorded as an observation of Franklin in 1820 at Slave Point, on the north side of Great Slave Lake. "A few frequent Slave Point, on the north side of the lake, but this is the most northern situation in which they were observed by Captain Franklin's party."[*]

Dr. Richardson defined the eastern boundary of the bison's range in British America as follows: "They do not frequent any of the districts formed of primitive rocks, and the limits of their range to the eastward, within the Hudson's Bay Company's territories, may be correctly marked on the map by a line commencing in longitude 97°, on the Red River, which flows into the south end of Lake Winnipeg, crossing the Saskatchewan to the westward of the Basquian Hill, and running thence by the Athapescow to the east end of Great Slave Lake. Their migrations westward were formerly limited to the Rocky Mountain range, and they are still unknown in New Caledonia and on the shores of the Pacific to the north of the Columbia River; but of late years they have found out a passage across the mountains near the sources of the Saskatchewan, and their numbers to the westward are annually increasing.[†]

Great Slave Lake.—That the buffalo inhabited the southern shore of this lake as late as 1871 is well established by the following letter from

---

[*] Sabine, Zoological Appendix to "Franklin's Journey," p. 668.
[†] Fauna Boreali-Americana, vol. 1, p. 279-280.

Mr. E. W. Nelson to Mr. J. A. Allen, under date of July 11, 1877:* "I have met here [St. Michaels, Alaska] two gentlemen who crossed the mountains from British Columbia and came to Fort Yukon through British America, from whom I have derived some information about the buffalo (*Bison americanus*) which will be of interest to you. These gentlemen descended the Peace River, and on about the one hundred and eighteenth degree of longitude made a portage to Hay River, directly north. On this portage they saw thousands of buffalo skulls, and old trails, in some instances 2 or 3 feet deep, leading east and west. They wintered on Hay River near its entrance into Great Slave Lake, and here found the buffalo still common, occupying a restricted territory along the southern border of the lake. This was in 1871. They made inquiry concerning the large number of skulls seen by them on the portage, and learned that about fifty years before, snow fell to the estimated depth of 14 feet, and so enveloped the animals that they perished by thousands. It is asserted that these buffaloes are larger than those of the plains."

MINNESOTA AND WISCONSIN.—A line drawn from Winnipeg to Chicago, curving slightly to the eastward in the middle portion, will very nearly define the eastern boundary of the buffalo's range in Minnesota and Wisconsin.

ILLINOIS AND INDIANA.—The whole of these two States were formerly inhabited by the buffalo, the fertile prairies of Illinois being particularly suited to their needs. It is doubtful whether the range of the species extended north of the northern boundary of Indiana, but since southern Michigan was as well adapted to their support as Ohio or Indiana, their absence from that State must have been due more to accident than design.

OHIO.—The southern shore of Lake Erie forms part of the northern boundary of the bison's range in the eastern United States. La Hontan explored Lake Erie in 1687 and thus describes its southern shore: "I can not express what quantities of Deer and Turkeys are to be found in these Woods, and in the vast Meads that lye upon the South side of the Lake. At the bottom of the Lake we find beeves upon the Banks of two pleasant Rivers that disembogue into it, without Cataracts or Rapid Currents."† It thus appears that the southern shore of Lake Erie forms part of the northern boundary of the buffalo's **range** in the eastern United States.

NEW YORK.—In regard to the presence of the bison in any portion of the State of New York, Professor Allen considers the evidence as fairly conclusive that it once existed in western New York, not only in the vicinity of the eastern end of Lake Erie, where now stands the city of Buffalo, at the mouth of a large creek of the same name, but also on the shore of Lake Ontario, probably in Orleans County. In his monograph

---

*American Naturalist, XI, p. 624.
†J. A. Allen's *American Bisons*, p. 107.

of "The American Bisons," page 107, he gives the following testimony and conclusions on this point:

"The occurrence of a stream in western New York, called Buffalo Creek, which empties into the eastern end of Lake Erie, is commonly viewed as traditional evidence of its occurrence at this point, but positive testimony to this effect has thus far escaped me.

"This locality, if it actually came so far eastward, must have formed the eastern limit of its range along the lakes. I have found only highly questionable allusions to the occurrence of buffaloes along the southern shore of Lake Ontario. Keating, on the authority of Colhoun, however, has cited a passage from Morton's "New English Canaan" as proof of their former existence in the neighborhood of this lake. Morton's statement is based on Indian reports, and the context gives sufficient evidence of the general vagueness of his knowledge of the region of which he was speaking. The passage, printed in 1637 is as follows: They [the Indians] have also made descriptions of great heards of well growne beasts that live about the parts of this lake [Erocoise] such as the Christian world (untill this discovery) hath not bin made acquainted with. These Beasts are of the bignesse of a Cowe, their flesh being very good foode, their hides good lether, their fleeces very usefull, being a kinde of wolle as fine almost as the wolle of the Beaver, and the Salvages doe make garments thereof. It is tenne yeares since first the relation of these things came to the eares of the English.' The 'beast' to which allusion is here made [says Professor Allen] is unquestionably the buffalo, but the locality of Lake 'Erocoise' is not so easily settled. Colhoun regards it, and probably correctly, as identical with Lake Ontario. * * * The extreme northeastern limit of the former range of the buffalo seems to have been, as above stated, in western New York, near the eastern end of Lake Erie. That it probably ranged thus far there is fair evidence."

PENNSYLVANIA.—From the eastern end of Lake Erie the boundary of the bison's habitat extends south into western Pennsylvania, to a marsh called Buffalo Swamp on a map published by Peter Kalm in 1771. Professor Allen says it " is indicated as situated between the Alleghany River and the West Branch of the Susquehanna, near the heads of the Licking and Toby's Creeks (apparently the streams now called Oil Creek and Clarion Creek)." In this region there were at one time thousands of buffaloes. While there is not at hand any positive evidence that the buffalo ever inhabited the southwestern portion of Pennsylvania, its presence in the locality mentioned above, and in West Virginia generally, on the south, furnishes sufficient reason for extending the boundary so as to include the southwestern portion of the State and connect with our starting point, the District of Columbia.

III. Abundance.

Of all the quadrupeds that have lived upon the earth, probably no other species has ever marshaled such innumerable hosts as those of the American bison. It would have been as easy to count or to estimate the number of leaves in a forest as to calculate the number of buffaloes living at any given time during the history of the species previous to 1870. Even in South Central Africa, which has always been exceedingly prolific in great herds of game, it is probable that all its quadrupeds taken together on an equal area would never have more than equaled the total number of buffalo in this country forty years ago.

To an African hunter, such a statement may seem incredible, but it appears to be fully warranted by the literature of both branches of the subject.

Not only did the buffalo formerly range eastward far into the forest regions of western New York, Pennsylvania, Virginia, the Carolinas, and Georgia, but in some places it was so abundant as to cause remark. In Mr. J. A. Allen's valuable monograph * appear a great number of interesting historical references on this subject, as indeed to every other relating to the buffalo, a few of which I will take the liberty of quoting.

In the vicinity of the spot where the town of Clarion now stands, in northwestern Pennsylvania, Mr. Thomas Ashe relates that one of the first settlers built his log cabin near a salt spring which was visited by buffaloes in such numbers that " he supposed there could not have been less than two thousand in the neighborhood of the spring." During the first years of his residence there, the buffaloes came in droves of about three hundred each.

Of the Blue Licks in Kentucky, Mr. John Filson thus wrote, in 1784: " The amazing herds of buffaloes which resort thither, by their size and number, fill the traveller with amazement and terror, especially when

---

* All who are especially interested in the life history of the buffalo, both scientific and economical, will do well to consult Mr. Allen's monograph, "The American Bisons, Living and Extinct," if it be accessible. Unfortunately it is a difficult matter for the general reader to obtain it. A reprint of the work as originally published, but omitting the map, plates, and such of the subject-matter as relates to the extinct species, appears in Hayden's "Report of the Geological Survey of the Territories," for 1875 (pp. 443–587), but the volume has for several years been out of print.

The memoir as originally published has the following titles:

Memoirs of the Geological Survey of Kentucky. | N. S. Shaler, Director. | Vol. I. Part II. | — | The American Bisons, | living and extinct. | By J. A. Allen. | With twelve plates and map. | — | University press, Cambridge: | Welch, Bigelow & Co. | 1876.

Memoris of the Museum of Comparative Zoology, | at Harvard College, Cambridge, Mass. | Vol. IV. No. 10. | — | The American Bisons, | living and extinct. | By J. A. Allen. | Published by permission of N. S. Shaler, Director of the Kentucky | Geological Survey. | With twelve plates and a map. | University press, Cambridge: | Welch, Bigelow & Co. | 1876. |

4to., pp. i–ix, 1–246, 1 col'd map, 12 pl., 13 ll. explanatory, 2 wood-cuts in text.

These two publications were simultaneous, and only differed in the titles. Unfortunately both are of greater rarity than the reprint referred to above.

he beholds the prodigious roads they have made from all quarters, as if leading to some populous city; the vast space of land around these springs desolated as if by a ravaging enemy, and hills reduced to plains; for the land near these springs is chiefly hilly. * * * I have heard a hunter assert he saw above one thousand buffaloes at the Blue Licks at once; so numerous were they before the first settlers had wantonly sported away their lives." Col. Daniel Boone declared of the Red River region in Kentucky, "The buffaloes were more frequent than I have seen cattle in the settlements, browzing on the leaves of the cane, or cropping the herbage of those extensive plains, fearless because ignorant of the violence of man. Sometimes we saw hundreds in a drove, and the numbers about the salt springs were amazing."

According to Ramsey, where Nashville now stands, in 1770 there were "immense numbers of buffalo and other wild game. The country was crowded with them. Their bellowings sounded from the hills and forest." Daniel Boone found vast herds of buffalo grazing in the valleys of East Tennessee, between the spurs of the Cumberland mountains.

Marquette declared that the prairies along the Illinois River were "covered with buffaloes." Father Hennepin, in writing of northern Illinois, between Chicago and the Illinois River, asserted that "there must be an innumerable quantity of wild bulls in that country, since the earth is covered with their horns. * * * They follow one another, so that you may see a drove of them for above a league together. * * * Their ways are as beaten as our great roads, and no herb grows therein."

Judged by ordinary standards of comparison, the early pioneers of the last century thought buffalo were abundant in the localities mentioned above. But the herds which lived east of the Mississippi were comparatively only mere stragglers from the innumerable mass which covered the great western pasture region from the Mississippi to the Rocky Mountains, and from the Rio Grande to Great Slave Lake. The town of Kearney, in south central Nebraska, may fairly be considered the geographical center of distribution of the species, as it originally existed, but ever since 1800, and until a few years ago, the center of population has been in the Black Hills of southwestern Dakota.

Between the Rocky Mountains and the States lying along the Mississippi River on the west, from Minnesota to Louisiana, the whole country was one vast buffalo range, inhabited by millions of buffaloes. One could fill a volume with the records of plainsmen and pioneers who penetrated or crossed that vast region between 1800 and 1870, and were in turn surprised, astounded, and frequently dismayed by the tens of thousands of buffaloes they observed, avoided, or escaped from. They lived and moved as no other quadrupeds ever have, in great multitudes, like grand armies in review, covering scores of square miles at once. They were so numerous they frequently stopped boats in the rivers, threatened to overwhelm travelers on the plains, and in later years derailed locomotives and cars, until railway engineers learned by experience the wisdom of stopping their trains whenever there were buffaloes crossing the track. On this feature of the buffalo's life history a few detailed observations may be of value.

Near the mouth of the White River, in southwestern Dakota, Lewis and Clark saw (in 1806) a herd of buffalo which caused them to make the following record in their journal:

"These last animals [buffaloes] are now so numerous that from an eminence we discovered more than we had ever seen before at one time; and if it be not impossible to calculate the moving multitude, which darkened the whole plains, we are convinced that twenty thousand would be no exaggerated number."

When near the mouth of the Yellowstone, on their way down the Missouri, a previous record had been made of a meeting with other herds:

"The buffalo now appear in vast numbers. A herd happened to be on their way across the river [the Missouri]. Such was the multitude of these animals that although the river, including an island over which they passed, was a mile in length, the herd stretched as thick as they could swim completely from one side to the other, and the party was obliged to stop for an hour. They consoled themselves for the delay by killing four of the herd, and then proceeded till at the distance of 45 miles they halted on an island, below which two other herds of buffalo, as numerous as the first, soon after crossed the river."[*]

Perhaps the most vivid picture ever afforded of the former abundance of buffalo is that given by Col. R. I. Dodge in his "Plains of the Great West," p. 120, *et seq.* It is well worth reproducing entire:

"In May, 1871, I drove in a light wagon from Old Fort Zara to Fort Larned, on the Arkansas, 34 miles. At least 25 miles of this distance was through one immense herd, composed of countless smaller herds of buffalo then on their journey north. The road ran along the broad level 'bottom,' or valley, of the river.   *   *   *

"The whole country appeared one great mass of buffalo, moving slowly to the northward; and it was only when actually among them that it could be ascertained that the apparently solid mass was an agglomeration of innumerable small herds, of from fifty to two hundred animals, separated from the surrounding herds by greater or less space, but still separated. The herds in the valley sullenly got out of my way, and, turning, stared stupidly at me, sometimes at only a few yards' distance. When I had reached a point where the hills were no longer more than a mile from the road, the buffalo on the hills, seeing an unusual object in their rear, turned, stared an instant, then started at full speed directly towards me, stampeding and bringing with them the

---

[*] Lewis and Clark's Exped., II, p. 395.

numberless herds through which they passed, and pouring down upon me all the herds, no longer separated, but one immense compact mass of plunging animals, mad with fright, and as irresistible as an avalanche.

"The situation was by no means pleasant. Reining up my horse (which was fortunately a quiet old beast that had been in at the death of many a buffalo, so that their wildest, maddest rush only caused him to cock his ears in wonder at their unnecessary excitement), I waited until the front of the mass was within 50 yards, when a few well-directed shots from my rifle split the herd, and sent it pouring off in two streams to my right and left. When all had passed me they stopped, apparently perfectly satisfied, though thousands were yet within reach of my rifle and many within less than 100 yards. Disdaining to fire again, I sent my servant to cut out the tongues of the fallen. This occurred so frequently within the next 10 miles, that when I arrived at Fort Larned I had twenty-six tongues in my wagon, representing the greatest number of buffalo that my conscience can reproach me for having murdered on any single day. I was not hunting, wanted no meat, and would not voluntarily have fired at these herds. I killed only in self-preservation and fired almost every shot from the wagon."

At my request Colonel Dodge has kindly furnished me a careful estimate upon which to base a calculation of the number of buffaloes in that great herd, and the result is very interesting. In a private letter, dated September 21, 1887, he writes as follows:

"The great herd on the Arkansas through which I passed could not have averaged, *at rest*, over fifteen or twenty individuals to the acre, but was, from my own observation, not less than 25 miles wide, and from reports of hunters and others it was about five days in passing a given point, or not less than 50 miles deep. From the top of Pawnee Rock I could see from 6 to 10 miles in almost every direction. This whole vast space was covered with buffalo, looking at a distance like one compact mass, the visual angle not permitting the ground to be seen. I have seen such a sight a great number of times, but never on so large a scale.

"That was the last of the great herds."

With these figures before us, it is not difficult to make a calculation that will be somewhere near the truth of the number of buffaloes actually seen in one day by Colonel Dodge on the Arkansas River during that memorable drive, and also of the number of head in the entire herd.

According to his recorded observation, the herd extended along the river for a distance of 25 miles, which was in reality the width of the vast procession that was moving north, and back from the road as far as the eye could reach, on both sides. It is making a low estimate to consider the extent of the visible ground at 1 mile on either side. This gives a strip of country 2 miles wide by 25 long, or a total of 50 square miles covered with buffalo, averaging from fifteen to twenty to the acre.* Taking the lesser number, in order to be below the truth rather than above it, we find that the number actually seen on that day by Colonel Dodge was in the neighborhood of 480,000, not counting the additional number taken in at the view from the top of Pawnee Rock, which, if added, would easily bring the total up to a round half million!

If the advancing multitude had been at all points 50 miles in length (as it was known to have been in some places at least) by 25 miles in width, and still averaged fifteen head to the acre of ground, it would have contained the enormous number of 12,000,000 head. But, judging from the general principles governing such migrations, it is almost certain that the moving mass advanced in the shape of a wedge, which would make it necessary to deduct about two-thirds from the grand total, which would leave 4,000,000 as our estimate of the actual number of buffaloes in this great herd, which I believe is more likely to be below the truth than above it.

No wonder that the men of the West of those days, both white and red, thought it would be impossible to exterminate such a mighty multitude. The Indians of some tribes believed that the buffaloes issued from the earth continually, and that the supply was necessarily inexhaustible. And yet, in four short years the southern herd was almost totally annihilated.

With such a lesson before our eyes, confirmed in every detail by living testimony, who will dare to say that there will be an elk, moose, caribou, mountain sheep, mountain goat, antelope, or black-tail deer left alive in the United States in a wild state fifty years from this date, ay, or even twenty-five?

Mr. William Blackmore contributes the following testimony to the abundance of buffalo in Kansas:†

"In the autumn of 1868, whilst crossing the plains on the Kansas Pacific Railroad, for a distance of upwards of 120 miles, between Ellsworth and Sheridan, we passed through an almost unbroken herd of buffalo. The plains were blackened with them, and more than once the train had to stop to allow unusually large herds to pass. * * * In 1872, whilst on a scout for about a hundred miles south of Fort Dodge to the Indian Territory, we were never out of sight of buffalo."

Twenty years hence, when not even a bone or a buffalo-chip remains above ground throughout the West to mark the presence of the buffalo, it may be difficult for people to believe that these animals ever existed in such numbers as to constitute not only a serious annoyance, but very

---

* On the plains of Dakota, the Rev. Mr. Belcourt (Schoolcraft's N. A. Indians, IV, p. 108) once counted two hundred and twenty-eight buffaloes, a part of a great herd, feeding on a single acre of ground. This of course was an unusual occurrence with buffaloes not stampeding, but practically at rest. It is quite possible also that the extent of the ground may have been underestimated.

† Plains of the Great West, p. xvi.

often a dangerous menace to wagon travel across the plains, and also to stop railway trains, and even throw them off the track. The like has probably never occurred before in any country, and most assuredly never will again, if the present rate of large game destruction all over the world can be taken as a foreshadowing of the future. In this connection the following additional testimony from Colonel Dodge ("Plains of the Great West," p. 121) is of interest:

"The Atchison, Topeka and Santa Fé Railroad was then [in 1871–'72] in process of construction, and nowhere could the peculiarity of the buffalo of which I am speaking be better studied than from its trains. If a herd was on the north side of the track, it would stand stupidly gazing, and without a symptom of alarm, although the locomotive passed within a hundred yards. If on the south side of the track, even though at a distance of 1 or 2 miles from it, the passage of a train set the whole herd in the wildest commotion. At full speed, and utterly regardless of the consequences, it would make for the track on its line of retreat. If the train happened not to be in its path, it crossed the track and stopped satisfied. If the train was in its way, each individual buffalo went at it with the desperation of despair, plunging against or between locomotive and cars, just as its blind madness chanced to direct it. Numbers were killed, but numbers still pressed on, to stop and stare as soon as the obstacle had passed. After having trains thrown off the track twice in one week, conductors learned to have a very decided respect for the idiosyncrasies of the buffalo, and when there was a possibility of striking a herd 'on the rampage' for the north side of the track, the train was slowed up and sometimes stopped entirely."

The accompanying illustration, reproduced from the "Plains of the Great West," by the kind permission of the author, is, in one sense, ocular proof that collisions between railway trains and vast herds of buffaloes were so numerous that they formed a proper subject for illustration. In regard to the stoppage of trains and derailment of locomotives by buffaloes, Colonel Dodge makes the following allusion in the private letter already referred to: "There are at least a hundred reliable railroad men now employed on the Atchison, Topeka and Santa Fé Railroad who were witnesses of, and sometimes sufferers from, the wild rushes of buffalo as described on page 121 of my book. I was at the time stationed at Fort Dodge, and I was personally cognizant of several of these 'accidents.'"

The following, from the ever-pleasing pen of Mr. Catlin, is of decided interest in this connection:

"In one instance, near the mouth of White River, we met the most immense herd crossing the Missouri River [in Dakota], and from an imprudence got our boat into imminent danger amongst them, from which we were highly delighted to make our escape. It was in the midst of the 'running season,' and we had heard the 'roaring' (as it is called) of the herd when we were several miles from them. When

SLAUGHTER OF BUFFALO ON THE KANSAS PACIFIC RAILROAD.

Reproduced from "*The Plains of the Great West*," by permission of the author, Col. R. I. Dodge.

we came in sight, we were actually terrified at the immense numbers that were streaming down the green hills on one side of the river, and galloping up and over the bluffs on the other. The river was filled, and in parts blackened with their heads and horns, as they were swimming about, following up their objects, and making desperate battle whilst they were swimming. I deemed it imprudent for our canoe to be dodging amongst them, and ran it ashore for a few hours, where we laid, waiting for the opportunity of seeing the river clear, but we waited in vain. Their numbers, however, got somewhat diminished at last, and we pushed off, and successfully made our way amongst them. From the immense numbers that had passed the river at that place, they had torn down the prairie bank of 15 feet in height, so as to form a sort of road or landing-place, where they all in succession clambered up. Many in their turmoil had been wafted below this landing, and unable to regain it against the swiftness of the current, had fastened themselves along in crowds, hugging close to the high bank under which they were standing. As we were drifting by these, and supposing ourselves out of danger, I drew up my rifle and shot one of them in the head, which tumbled into the water, and brought with him a hundred others, which plunged in, and in a moment were swimming about our canoe, and placing it in great danger. No attack was made upon us, and in the confusion the poor beasts knew not, perhaps, the enemy that was amongst them; but we were liable to be sunk by them, as they were furiously hooking and climbing on to each other. I rose in my canoe, and by my gestures and hallooing kept them from coming in contact with us until we were out of their reach."*

IV. CHARACTER OF THE SPECIES.

1. *The buffalo's rank amongst ruminants.*—With the American people, and through them all others, familiarity with the buffalo has bred contempt. The incredible numbers in which the animals of this species formerly existed made their slaughter an easy matter, so much so that the hunters and frontiersmen who accomplished their destruction have handed down to us a contemptuous opinion of the size, character, and general presence of our bison. And how could it be otherwise than that a man who could find it in his heart to murder a majestic bull bison for a hide worth only a dollar should form a one-dollar estimate of the grandest ruminant that ever trod the earth? Men who butcher African elephants for the sake of their ivory also entertain a similar estimate of their victims.

With an acquaintance which includes fine living examples of all the larger ruminants of the world except the musk-ox and the European bison, I am sure that the American bison is the grandest of them all. His only rivals for the kingship are the Indian bison, or gaur (*Bos gaurus*), of Southern India, and the aurochs, or European bison, both of which

---

* Catlin's North American Indians, II, p. 13.

really surpass him in height, if not in actual bulk also.   The aurochs is taller, and possesses a larger pelvis and heavier, stronger hindquarters, but his body is decidedly smaller in all its proportions, which gives him a lean and "leggy" look.   The hair on the head, neck, and forequarters of the aurochs is not nearly so long or luxuriant as on the same parts of the American bison.   This covering greatly magnifies the actual bulk of the latter animal.   Clothe the aurochs with the wonderful pelage of our buffalo, give him the same enormous chest and body, and the result would be a magnificent bovine monster, who would indeed stand without a rival.   But when first-class types of the two species are placed side by side it seems to me that *Bison americanus* will easily rank his European rival.

The gaur has no long hair upon any part of his body or head.   What little hair he has is very short and thin, his hindquarters being almost naked.   I have seen hundreds of these animals at short range, and have killed and skinned several very fine specimens, one of which stood 5 feet 10 inches in height at the shoulders.   But, despite his larger bulk, his appearance is not nearly so striking and impressive as that of the male American bison.   He seems like a huge ox running wild.

The magnificent dark brown frontlet and beard of the buffalo, the shaggy coat of hair upon the neck, hump, and shoulders, terminating at the knees in a thick mass of luxuriant black locks, to say nothing of the dense coat of finer fur on the body and hindquarters, give to our species not only an apparent height equal to that of the gaur, but a grandeur and nobility of presence which are beyond all comparison amongst ruminants.

The slightly larger bulk of the gaur is of little significance in a comparison of the two species; for if size alone is to turn the scale, we must admit that a 500-pound lioness, with no mane whatever, is a more majestic looking animal than a 450-pound lion, with a mane which has earned him his title of king of beasts.

2. *Change of form in captivity.*—By a combination of unfortunate circumstances, the American bison is destined to go down to posterity shorn of the honor which is his due, and appreciated at only half his worth.   The hunters who slew him were from the very beginning so absorbed in the scramble for spoils that they had no time to measure or weigh him, nor even to notice the majesty of his personal appearance on his native heath.

In captivity he fails to develop as finely as in his wild state, and with the loss of his liberty he becomes a tame-looking animal.   He gets fat and short-bodied, and the lack of vigorous and constant exercise prevents the development of bone and muscle which made the prairie animal what he was.

From observations made upon buffaloes that have been reared in captivity, I am firmly convinced that confinement and semi-domestication are destined to effect striking changes in the form of *Bison americanus.* While this is to be expected to a certain extent with most large species, the changes promise to be most conspicuous in the buffalo. The most striking change is in the body between the hips and the shoulders. As before remarked, it becomes astonishingly short and rotund, and through liberal feeding and total lack of exercise the muscles of the shoulders and hindquarters, especially the latter, are but feebly developed.

The most striking example of the change of form in the captive buffalo is the cow in the Central Park Menagerie, New York. Although this animal is fully adult, and has given birth to three fine calves, she is small, astonishingly short-bodied, and in comparison with the magnificently developed cows taken in 1886 by the writer in Montana, she seems almost like an animal of another species.

Both the live buffaloes in the National Museum collection of living animals are developing the same shortness of body and lack of muscle, and when they attain their full growth will but poorly resemble the splendid proportions of the wild specimens in the Museum mounted group, each of which has been mounted from a most careful and elaborate series of post-mortem measurements. It may fairly be considered, however, that the specimens taken by the Smithsonian expedition were in every way more perfect representatives of the species than have been usually taken in times past, for the simple reason that on account of the muscle they had developed in the numerous chases they had survived, and the total absence of the fat which once formed such a prominent feature of the animal, they were of finer form, more active habit, and keener intelligence than buffaloes possessed when they were so numerous. Out of the millions which once composed the great northern herd, those represented the survival of the fittest, and their existence at that time was chiefly due to the keenness of their senses and their splendid muscular powers in speed and endurance.

Under such conditions it is only natural that animals of the highest class should be developed. On the other hand, captivity reverses all these conditions, while yielding an equally abundant food supply.

In no feature is the change from natural conditions to captivity more easily noticeable than in the eye. In the wild buffalo the eye is always deeply set, well protected by the edge of the bony orbit, and perfect in form and expression. The lids are firmly drawn around the ball, the opening is so small that the white portion of the eyeball is entirely covered, and the whole form and appearance of the organ is as shapely and as pleasing in expression as the eye of a deer.

In the captive the various muscles which support and control the eyeball seem to relax and thicken, and the ball protrudes far beyond its normal plane, showing a circle of white all around the iris, and bulging out in a most unnatural way. I do not mean to assert that this is common in captive buffaloes generally, but I have observed it to be disagreeably conspicuous in many.

Another change which takes place in the form of the captive buffalo is an arching of the back in the middle, which has a tendency to make the hump look lower at the shoulders and visibly alters the outline of the back. This tendency to "hump up" the back is very noticeable in domestic cattle and horses during rainy weather. While a buffalo on his native heath would seldom assume such an attitude of dejection and misery, in captivity, especially if it be anything like close confinement, it is often to be observed, and I fear will eventually become a permanent habit. Indeed, I think it may be confidently predicted that the time will come when naturalists who have never seen a wild buffalo will compare the specimens composing the National Museum group with the living representatives to be seen in captivity and assert that the former are exaggerations in both form and size.

3. *Mounted Specimens in Museums.*—Of the "stuffed" specimens to be found in museums, all that I have ever seen outside of the National Museum, and even those within that institution up to 1886, were "stuffed" in reality as well as in name. The skins that have been rammed full of straw or excelsior have lost from 8 to 12 inches in height at the shoulders, and the high and sharp hump of the male has become a huge, thick, rounded mass like the hump of a dromedary, and totally unlike the hump of a bison. It is impossible for any taxidermist to stuff a buffalo-skin with loose materials and produce a specimen which fitly represents the species. The proper height and form of the animal can be secured and retained only by the construction of a manikin, or statue, to carry the skin. In view of this fact, which surely must be apparent to even the most casual observer, it is to be earnestly hoped that hereafter no one in authority will ever consent to mount or have mounted a valuable skin of a bison in any other way than over a properly constructed manikin.

4. *The Calf.*—The breeding season of the buffalo is from the 1st of July to the 1st of October. The young cow does not breed until she is three years old, and although two calves are sometimes produced at a birth, one is the usual number. The calves are born in April, May, and June, and sometimes, though rarely, as late as the middle of August. The calf follows its mother until it is a year old, or even older. In May, 1886, the Smithsonian expedition captured a calf alive, which had been abandoned by its mother because it could not keep up with her. The little creature was apparently between two and three weeks old, and was therefore born about May 1. Unlike the young of nearly all other *Bovidæ*, the buffalo calf during the first months of its existence is clad with hair of a totally different color from that which covers him during the remainder of his life. His pelage is a luxuriant growth of rather long, wavy hair, of a uniform brownish-yellow or "sandy" color (cinnamon, or yellow ocher, with a shade of Indian yellow) all over the head, body, and tail, in striking contrast with the darker colors of the older animals. On the lower half of the leg it is lighter, shorter, and straight.

On the shoulders and hump the hair is longer than on the other portions, being 1½ inches in length, more wavy, and already arranges itself in the tufts, or small bunches, so characteristic in the adult animal.

On the extremity of the muzzle, including the chin, the hair is very short, straight, and as light in color as the lower portions of the leg. Starting on the top of the nose, an inch behind the nostrils, and forming a division between the light yellowish muzzle and the more reddish hair on the remainder of the head, there is an irregular band of dark, straight hair, which extends down past the corner of the mouth to a point just back of the chin, where it unites. From the chin backward the dark band increases in breadth and intensity, and continues back half way to the angle of the jaw. At that point begins a sort of under mane of wavy, dark-brown hair, nearly 3 inches long, and extends back along the median line of the throat to a point between the fore legs, where it abruptly terminates. From the back of the head another streak of dark hair extends backward along the top of the neck, over the hump, and down to the lumbar region, where it fades out entirely. These two dark bands are in sharp contrast to the light sandy hair adjoining.

The tail is densely haired. The tuft on the end is quite luxuriant, and shows a center of darker hair. The hair on the inside of the ear is dark, but that on the outside is sandy.

The naked portion of the nose is light Vandyke-brown, with a pinkish tinge, and the edge of the eyelid the same. The iris is dark brown. The horn at three months is about 1 inch in length, and is a mere little black stub. In the male, the hump is clearly defined, but by no means so high in proportion as in the adult animal. The hump of the calf from which this description is drawn is of about the same relative angle and height as that of an adult cow buffalo. The specimen itself is well represented in the accompanying plate.

The measurements of this specimen in the flesh were as follows:

BISON AMERICANUS. (Male; four months old.)

(*No. 15503, National Museum collection.*)

	Feet.	Inches.
Height at shoulders	2	8
Length, head and body to insertion of tail	3	10½
Depth of chest	1	4
Depth of flank		10
Girth behind fore leg	3	½
From base of horns around end of nose	1	7½
Length of tail vertebræ		7

The calves begin to shed their coat of red hair about the beginning of August. The first signs of the change, however, appear about a month earlier than that, in the darkening of the mane under the throat, and also on the top of the neck.*

---

* Our captive had, in some way, bruised the skin on his forehead, and in June all the hair came off the top of his head, leaving it quite bald. We kept the skin well greased with porpoise oil, and by the middle of July a fine coat of black hair had grown out all over the surface that had previously been bare.

By the 1st of August the red hair on the body begins to fall off in small patches, and the growth of fine, new, dark hair seems to actually crowd off the old. As is the case with the adult animals, the shortest hair is the first to be shed, but the change of coat takes place in about half the time that it occupies in the older animals.

By the 1st of October the transformation is complete, and not even a patch of the old red hair remains upon the new suit of brown. This is far from being the case with the old bulls and cows, for even up to the last week in October we found them with an occasional patch of the old hair still clinging to the new, on the back or shoulders.

Like most young animals, the calf of the buffalo is very easily tamed, especially if taken when only a few weeks old. The one captured in Montana by the writer, resisted at first as stoutly as it was able, by butting with its head, but after we had tied its legs together and carried it to camp, across a horse, it made up its mind to yield gracefully to the inevitable, and from that moment became perfectly docile. It very soon learned to drink milk in the most satisfactory manner, and adapted itself to its new surroundings quite as readily as any domestic calf would have done. Its only cry was a low-pitched, pig-like grunt through the nose, which was uttered only when hungry or thirsty.

I have been told by old frontiersmen and buffalo-hunters that it used to be a common practice for a hunter who had captured a young calf to make it follow him by placing one of his fingers in its mouth, and allowing the calf to suck at it for a moment. Often a calf has been induced in this way to follow a horseman for miles, and eventually to join his camp outfit. It is said that the same result has been accomplished with calves by breathing a few times into their nostrils. In this connection Mr. Catlin's observations on the habits of buffalo calves are most interesting.

"In pursuing a large herd of buffaloes at the season when their calves are but a few weeks old, I have often been exceedingly amused with the curious maneuvers of these shy little things. Amidst the thundering confusion of a throng of several hundreds or several thousands of these animals, there will be many of the calves that lose sight of their dams; and being left behind by the throng, and the swift-passing hunters, they endeavor to secrete themselves, when they are exceedingly put to it on a level prairie, where naught can be seen but the short grass of 6 or 8 inches in height, save an occasional bunch of wild sage a few inches higher, to which the poor affrighted things will run, and dropping on their knees, will push their noses under it and into the grass, where they will stand for hours, with their eyes shut, imagining themselves securely hid, whilst they are standing up quite straight upon their hind feet, and can easily be seen at several miles distance. It is a familiar amusement with us, accustomed to these scenes, to retreat back over the ground where we have just escorted the herd, and approach these little trembling things, which stubbornly maintain their

PLATE IV.

Engraved by R. H. Carson.

From photograph of group in National Museum.

BUFFALO COW, CALF (FOUR MONTHS OLD), AND YEARLING.

Reproduced from the *Cosmopolitan Magazine*, by permission of the publishers.

positions, with their noses pushed under the grass and their eyes strained upon us, as we dismount from our horses and are passing around them. From this fixed position they are sure not to move until hands are laid upon them, and then for the shins of a novice we can extend our sympathy; or if he can preserve the skin on his bones from the furious buttings of its head, we know how to congratulate him on his signal success and good luck.

"In these desperate struggles for a moment, the little thing is conquered, and makes no further resistance. And I have often, in concurrence with a known custom of the country, held my hands over the eyes of the calf and breathed a few strong breaths into its nostrils, after which I have, with my hunting companions, rode several miles into our encampment with the little prisoner busily following the heels of my horse the whole way, as closely and as affectionately as its instinct would attach it to the company of its dam.

"This is one of the most extraordinary things that I have met with in the habits of this wild country, and although I had often heard of it, and felt unable exactly to believe it, I am now willing to bear testimony to the fact from the numerous instances which I have witnessed since I came into the country. During the time that I resided at this post [mouth of the Teton River] in the spring of the year, on my way up the river, I assisted (in numerous hunts of the buffalo with the fur company's men) in bringing in, in the above manner, several of these little prisoners, which sometimes followed for 5 or 6 miles close to our horse's heels, and even into the fur company's fort, and into the stable where our horses were led. In this way, before I left the headwaters of the Missouri, I think we had collected about a dozen, which Mr. Laidlaw was successfully raising with the aid of a good milch cow.*

It must be remembered, however, that such cases as the above were exceptional, even with the very young calves, which alone exhibited the trait described. Such instances occurred only when buffaloes existed in such countless numbers that man's presence and influence had not affected the character of the animal in the least. No such instances of innocent stupidity will ever be displayed again, even by the youngest calf. The war of extermination, and the struggle for life and security have instilled into the calf, even from its birth, a mortal fear of both men and horses, and the instinct to fly for life. The calf captured by our party was not able to run, but in the most absurd manner it butted our horses as soon as they came near enough, and when Private Moran attempted to lay hold of the little fellow it turned upon him, struck him in the stomach with its head, and sent him sprawling into the sagebrush. If it had only possessed the strength, it would have led us a lively chase.

During 1886 four other buffalo calves were either killed or caught by the cowboys on the Missouri-Yellowstone divide, in the Dry Creek region.

---

* North American Indians, I, 255.

All of them ran the moment they discovered their enemies. Two were shot and killed. One was caught by a cowboy named Horace Brodhurst, ear-marked, and turned loose. The fifth one was caught in September on the Porcupine Creek round-up. He was then about five months old, and being abundantly able to travel he showed a clean pair of heels. It took three fresh horses, one after another, to catch him, and his final capture was due to exhaustion, and not to the speed of any of his pursuers. The distance covered by the chase, from the point where his first pursuer started to where the third one finally lassoed him, was considered to be at least 15 miles. But the capture came to naught, for on the following day the calf died from overexertion and want of milk.

Colonel Dodge states that the very young calves of a herd have to depend upon the old bulls for protection, and seldom in vain. The mothers abandon their offspring on slight provocation, and even none at all sometimes, if we may judge from the condition of the little waif that fell into our hands. Had its mother remained with it, or even in its neighborhood, we should at least have seen her, but she was nowhere within a radius of 5 miles at the time her calf was discovered. Nor did she return to look for it, as two of us proved by spending the night in the sage-brush at the very spot where the calf was taken. Colonel Dodge declares that "the cow seems to possess scarcely a trace of maternal instinct, and, when frightened, will abandon and run away from her calf without the slightest hesitation. * * * When the calves are young they are always kept in the center of each small herd, while the bulls dispose themselves on the outside."*

Apparently the maternal instinct of the cow buffalo was easily mastered by fear. That it was often manifested, however, is proven by the following from Audubon and Bachman : †

"Buffalo calves are drowned from being unable to ascend the steep banks of the rivers across which they have just swam, as the cows cannot help them, although they stand near the bank, and will not leave them to their fate unless something alarms them.

"On one occasion Mr. Kipp, of the American Fur Company, caught eleven calves, their dams all the time standing near the top of the bank. Frequently, however, the cows leave the young to their fate, when most of them perish. In connection with this part of the subject, we may add that we were informed, when on the Upper Missouri River, that when the banks of that river were practicable for cows, and their calves could not follow them, they went down again, after having gained the top, and would remain by them until forced away by the cravings of hunger. When thus forced by the necessity of saving themselves to quit their young, they seldom, if ever, return to them. When a large herd of these wild animals are crossing a river, the calves or yearlings manage to get on the backs of the cows, and are thus conveyed safely over."

---

* Plains of the Great West, pp. 124, 125.
† Quadrupeds of North America, vol. II, pp. 38, 39.

5. *The Yearling.*—During the first five months of his life, the calf changes its coat completely, and becomes in appearance a totally different animal. By the time he is six months old he has taken on all the colors which distinguish him in after life, excepting that upon his fore quarters. The hair on the head has started out to attain the luxuriant length and density which is so conspicuous in the adult, and its general color is a rich dark brown, shading to black under the chin and throat. The fringe under the neck is long, straight, and black, and the under parts, the back of the fore-arm, the outside of thigh, and the tail-tuft are all black.

The color of the shoulder, the side, and upper part of the hind quarter is a peculiar smoky brown ("broccoli brown" of Ridgway), having in connection with the darker browns of the other parts a peculiar faded appearance, quite as if it were due to the bleaching power of the sun. On the fore quarters there is none of the bright straw color so characteristic of the adult animal. Along the top of the neck and shoulders, however, this color has at last begun to show faintly. The hair on the body is quite luxuriant, both in length and density, in both respects quite equaling, if not even surpassing, that of the finest adults. For example, the hair on the side of the mounted yearling in the Museum group has a length of 2 to $2\frac{1}{2}$ inches, while that on the same region of the adult bull, whose pelage is particularly fine, is recorded as being 2 inches only.

The horn is a straight, conical spike from 4 to 6 inches long, according to age, and perfectly black. The legs are proportionally longer and larger in the joints than those of the full-grown animal. The countenance of the yearling is quite interesting. The sleepy, helpless, innocent expression of the very young calf has given place to a wide-awake, mischievous look, and he seems ready to break away and run at a second's notice.

The measurements of the yearling in the Museum group are as follows:

BISON AMERICANUS.   (Male yearling, taken Oct. 31, 1886.   Montana.)

(*No. 15694, National Museum collection.*)

	Feet.	Inches.
Height at shoulders	3	5
Length, head and body to insertion of tail	5	
Depth of chest	1	11
Depth of flank	1	1
Girth behind fore leg	4	3
From base of horns around end of nose	2	$1\frac{1}{2}$
Length of tail vertebræ		10

6. *The Spike Bull.*—In hunters' parlance, the male buffalo between the "yearling" age and four years is called a "spike" bull, in recognition of the fact that up to the latter period the horn is a spike, either perfectly straight, or with a curve near its base, and a straight point the

rest of the way up. The curve of the horn is generally hidden in the hair, and the only part visible is the straight, terminal spike. Usually the spike points diverge from each other, but often they are parallel, and also perpendicular. In the fourth year, however, the points of the horns begin to curve inward toward each other, describing equal arcs of the same circle, as if they were going to meet over the top of the head.

In the handsome young "spike" bull in the Museum group, the hair on the shoulders has begun to take on the length, the light color, and tufted appearance of the adult, beginning at the highest point of the hump and gradually spreading. Immediately back of this light patch the hair is long, but dark and woolly in appearance. The leg tufts have doubled in length, and reveal the character of the growth that may be finally expected. The beard has greatly lengthened, as also has the hair upon the bridge of the nose, the forehead, ears, jaws, and all other portions of the head except the cheeks.

The "spike" period of a buffalo is a most interesting one. Like a seventeen-year-old boy, the young bull shows his youth in so many ways it is always conspicuous, and his countenance is so suggestive of a half-bearded youth it fixes the interest to a marked degree. He is active, alert, and suspicious, and when he makes up his mind to run the hunter may as well give up the chase.

By a strange fatality, our spike bull appears to be the only one in any museum, or even in preserved existence, as far as can be ascertained. Out of the twenty-five buffaloes killed and preserved by the Smith-sonian expedition, ten of which were adult bulls, this specimen was the only male between the yearling and the adult ages. An effort to pro-cure another entire specimen of this age from Texas yielded only two spike heads. It is to be sincerely regretted that more specimens repre-senting this very interesting period of the buffalo's life have not been preserved, for it is now too late to procure wild specimens.

The following are the post-mortem dimensions of our specimen:

BISON AMERICANUS.

("Spike" bull, two years old; taken October 14, 1886. Montana.)

(*No. 15685, National Museum collection.*)

	Feet.	Inches.
Height at shoulders	4	2
Length, head and body to insertion of tail	7	7
Depth of chest	2	3
Depth of flank	1	7
Girth behind fore leg	5	8
From base of horns around end of nose	2	8½
Length of tail vertebræ	1	

7. *The Adult Bull.*—In attempting to describe the adult male in the National Museum group, it is difficult to decide which feature is most prominent, the massive, magnificent head, with its shaggy frontlet and luxuriant black beard, or the lofty hump, with its showy covering of

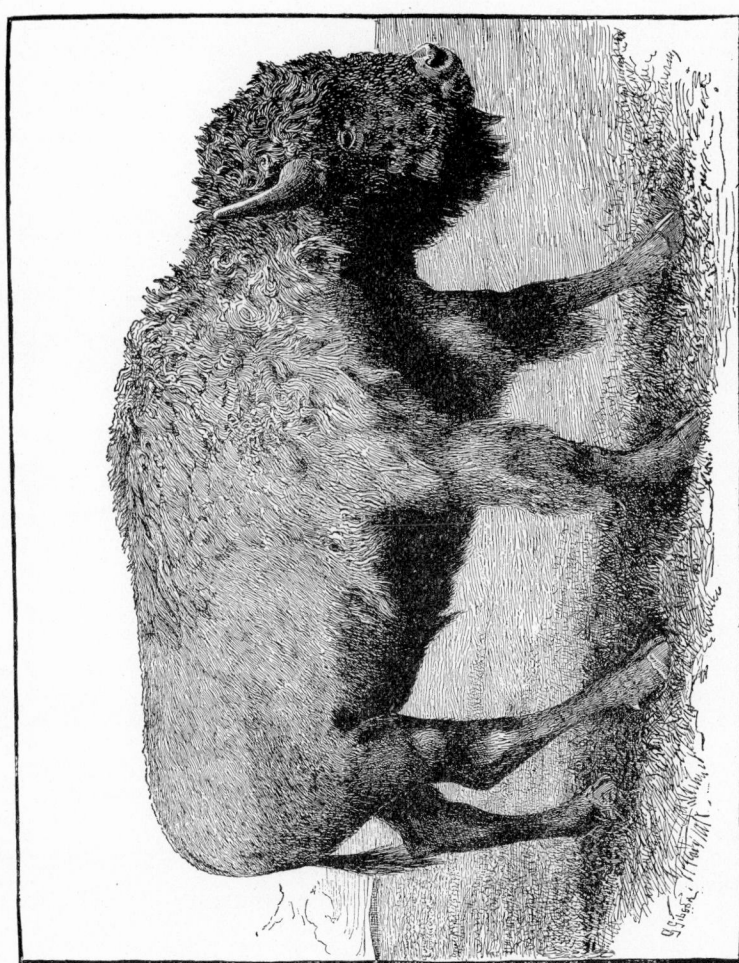

SPIKE BULL.

From the group in the National Museum.

Reproduced from the *Cosmopolitan Magazine*, by permission of the publishers.

straw-yellow hair, in thickly-growing locks 4 inches long. But the head is irresistible in its claims to precedence.

It must be observed at this point that in many respects this animal is an exceptionally fine one. In actual size of frame, and in quantity and quality of pelage, it is far superior to the average, even of wild buffaloes when they were most numerous and at their best.* In one respect, however, that of actual bulk, it is believed that this specimen may have often been surpassed. When buffaloes were numerous, and not required to do any great amount of running in order to exist, they were, in the autumn months, very fat. Audubon says: "A large bison bull will generally weigh nearly 2,000 pounds, and a fat cow about 1,200 pounds. We weighed one of the bulls killed by our party, and found it to reach 1,727 pounds, although it had already lost a good deal of blood. This was an old bull, and not fat. It had probably weighed more at some previous period."† Our specimen when killed (by the writer, December 6, 1886) was in full vigor, superbly muscled, and well fed, but he carried not a single pound of fat. For years the never-ceasing race for life had utterly prevented the secretion of useless and cumbersome fat, and his "subsistence" had gone toward the development of useful muscle. Having no means by which to weigh him, we could only estimate his weight, in which I called for the advice of my cowboys, all of whom were more or less familiar with the weight of range cattle, and one I regarded as an expert. At first the estimated weight of the animal was fixed at 1,700 pounds, but with a constitutional fear of estimating over the truth, I afterward reduced it to 1,600 pounds. This I am now well convinced was an error, for I believe the first figure to have been nearer the truth.

In mounting the skin of this animal, we endeavored by every means in our power, foremost of which were three different sets of measurements, taken from the dead animal, one set to check another, to reproduce him when mounted in exactly the same form he possessed in life—muscular, but not fat.

The color of the body and hindquarters of a buffalo is very peculiar, and almost baffles intelligent description. Audubon calls it "between a dark umber and liver-shining brown." I once saw a competent artist experiment with his oil-colors for a quarter of an hour before he finally struck the combination which exactly matched the side of our large bull. To my eyes, the color is a pale gray-brown or smoky gray. The range of individual variation is considerable, some being uniformly

---

* In testimony whereof the following extract from a letter written by General Stewart Van Vliet, on March 10, 1887, to Professor Baird, is of interest:

"My Dear Professor: On the receipt of your letter of the 6th instant I saw General Sheridan, and yesterday we called on your taxidermist and examined the buffalo bull he is setting up for the Museum. I don't think I have ever seen a more splendid specimen in my life. General Sheridan and I have seen millions of buffalo on the plains in former times. I have killed hundreds, but I never killed a larger animal than the one in the possession of your taxidermist."

† Quadrupeds of North America, vol. II, p. 44.

darker than the average type, and others lighter. While the under parts of most adults are dark brown or blackish brown, others are actually black. The hair on the body and hinder parts is fine, wavy on the outside, and woolly underneath, and very dense. Add to this the thickness of the skin itself, and the combination forms a covering that is almost impervious to cold.

The entire fore-quarter region, *e. g.*, the shoulders, the hump, and the upper part of the neck, is covered with a luxuriant growth of pale yellow hair (Naples yellow + yellow ocher), which stands straight out in a dense mass, disposed in handsome tufts. The hair is somewhat woolly in its nature, and the ends are as even as if the whole mass had lately been gone over with shears and carefully clipped. This hair is 4 inches in length. As the living animal moved his head from side to side, the hair parted in great vertical furrows, so deep that the skin itself seemed almost in sight. As before remarked, to comb this hair would utterly destroy its naturalness, and it should never be done under any circumstances. Standing as it does between the darker hair of the body on one side and the almost black mass of the head on the other, this light area is rendered doubly striking and conspicuous by contrast. It not only covers the shoulders, but extends back upon the thorax, where it abruptly terminates on a line corresponding to the sixth rib.

From the shoulder-joint downward, the color shades gradually into a dark brown until at the knee it becomes quite black. The huge fore-arm is lost in a thick mass of long, coarse, and rather straight hair 10 inches in length. This growth stops abruptly at the knee, but it hangs within 6 inches of the hoof. The front side of this mass is blackish brown, but it rapidly shades backward and downward into jet-black.

The hair on the top of the head lies in a dense, matted mass, forming a perfect crown of rich brown (burnt sienna) locks, 16 inches in length, hanging over the eyes, almost enveloping both horns, and spreading back in rich, dark masses upon the light-colored neck.

On the cheeks the hair is of the same blackish-brown color, but comparatively short, and lies in beautiful waves. On the bridge of the nose the hair is about 6 inches in length and stands out in a thick, uniform, very curly mass, which always looks as if it had just been carefully combed.

Immediately around the nose and mouth the hair is very short, straight and stiff, and lies close to the skin, which leaves the nostrils and lips fully exposed. The front part of the chin is similarly clad, and its form is perfectly flat, due to the habit of the animal in feeding upon the short, crisp buffalo grass, in the course of which the chin is pressed flat against the ground. The end of the muzzle is very massive, measuring 2 feet 2 inches in circumference just back of the nostrils.

The hair of the chin-beard is coarse, perfectly straight, jet black, and 11½ inches in length on our old bull.

Occasionally a bull is met with who is a genuine Esau amongst his kind. I once saw a bull, of medium size but fully adult, whose hair

BULL BUFFALO IN NATIONAL MUSEUM GROUP.

Drawn by Ernest E. Thompson.

was a wonder to behold. I have now in my possession a small lock of hair which I plucked from his forehead, and its length is $22\frac{1}{2}$ inches. His horns were entirely concealed by the immense mass of long hair that nature had piled upon his head, and his beard was as luxuriant as his frontlet.

The nostril opening is large and wide. The color of the hairless portions of the nose and mouth is shiny Vandyke brown and black, with a strong tinge of bluish-purple, but this latter tint is not noticeable save upon close examination, and the eyelid is the same. The iris is of an irregular pear-shaped outline, $1\frac{5}{16}$ inches in its longest diameter, very dark, reddish brown in color, with a black edging all around it. Ordinarily no portion of the white eyeball is visible, but the broad black band surrounding the iris, and a corner patch of white, is frequently shown by the turning of the eye. The tongue is bluish purple, as are the lips inside.

The hoofs and horns are, in reality, jet black throughout, but the horn often has at the base a scaly, dead appearance on the outside, and as the wrinkles around the base increase with age and scale up and gather dirt, that part looks gray. The horns of bulls taken in their prime are smooth, glossy black, and even look as if they had been half polished with oil.

As the bull increases in age, the outer layers of the horn begin to break off at the tip and pile up one upon another, until the horn has become a thick, blunt stub, with only the tip of what was once a neat and shapely point showing at the end. The bull is then known as a "stub-horn," and his horns increase in roughness and unsightliness as he grows older. From long rubbing on the earth, the outer curve of each horn is gradually worn flat, which still further mars its symmetry.

The horns serve as a fair index of the age of a bison. After he is three years old, the bison adds each year a ring around the base of his horns, the same as domestic cattle. If we may judge by this, the horn begins to break when the bison is about ten or eleven years old, and the stubbing process gradually continues during the rest of his life. Judging by the teeth, and also the oldest horns I have seen, I am of the opinion that the natural life time of the bison is about twenty-five years; certainly no less.

BISON AMERICANUS. (Male, eleven years old. Taken December 6, 1866. Montana.)

(No. 15703, *National Museum collection..*)

	Feet.	Inches.
Height at shoulders to the skin	5	8
Height at shoulders to top of hair	6	..
Length, head and body to insertion of tail	10	2
Depth of chest	3	10
Depth of flank	2	0
Girth behind fore leg	8	4
From base of horns around end of nose	3	6
Length of tail vertebræ	1	3
Circumference of muzzle back of nostrils	2	2

8. *The Cow in the third year.*—The young cow of course possesses the same youthful appearance already referred to as characterizing the "spike" bull. The hair on the shoulders has begun to take on the light straw-color, and has by this time attained a length which causes it to arrange itself in tufts, or locks. The body colors have grown darker, and reached their permanent tone. Of course the hair on the head has by no means attained its full length, and the head is not at all handsome.

The horns are quite small, but the curve is well defined, and they distinctly mark the sex of the individual, even at the beginning of the third year.

BISON AMERICANUS. (Young cow, in third year. Taken October 14, 1886. Montana.)

(No. 15686, *National Museum collection.*)

	Feet.	Inches.
Height at shoulders	4	5
Length, head and body to insertion of tail	7	7
Depth of chest	2	4
Depth of flank	1	4
Girth behind fore leg	5	4
From base of horns around end of nose	2	8½
Length of tail vertebræ	1	..

9. *The adult Cow.*—The upper body color of the adult cow in the National Museum group (see Plate) is a rich, though not intense, Vandyke brown, shading imperceptibly down the sides into black, which spreads over the entire under parts and inside of the thighs. The hair on the lower joints of the leg is in turn lighter, being about the same shade as that on the loins. The fore-arm is concealed in a mass of almost black hair, which gradually shades lighter from the elbow upward and along the whole region of the humerus. On the shoulder itself the hair is pale yellow or straw-color (Naples yellow+yellow ocher), which extends down in a point toward the elbow. From the back of the head a conspicuous band of curly, dark-brown hair extends back like a mane along the neck and to the top of the hump, beyond which it soon fades out.

The hair on the head is everywhere a rich burnt-sienna brown, except around the corners of the mouth, where it shades into black.

The horns of the cow bison are slender, but solid for about two-thirds of their length from the tip, ringed with age near their base, and quite black. Very often they are imperfect in shape, and out of every five pairs at least one is generally misshapen. Usually one horn is "crumpled," *e. g.*, dwarfed in length and unnaturally thickened at the base, and very often one horn is found to be merely an unsightly, misshapen stub.

The udder of the cow bison is very small, as might be expected of an animal which must do a great deal of hard traveling, but the milk is said to be very rich. Some authorities declare that it requires the

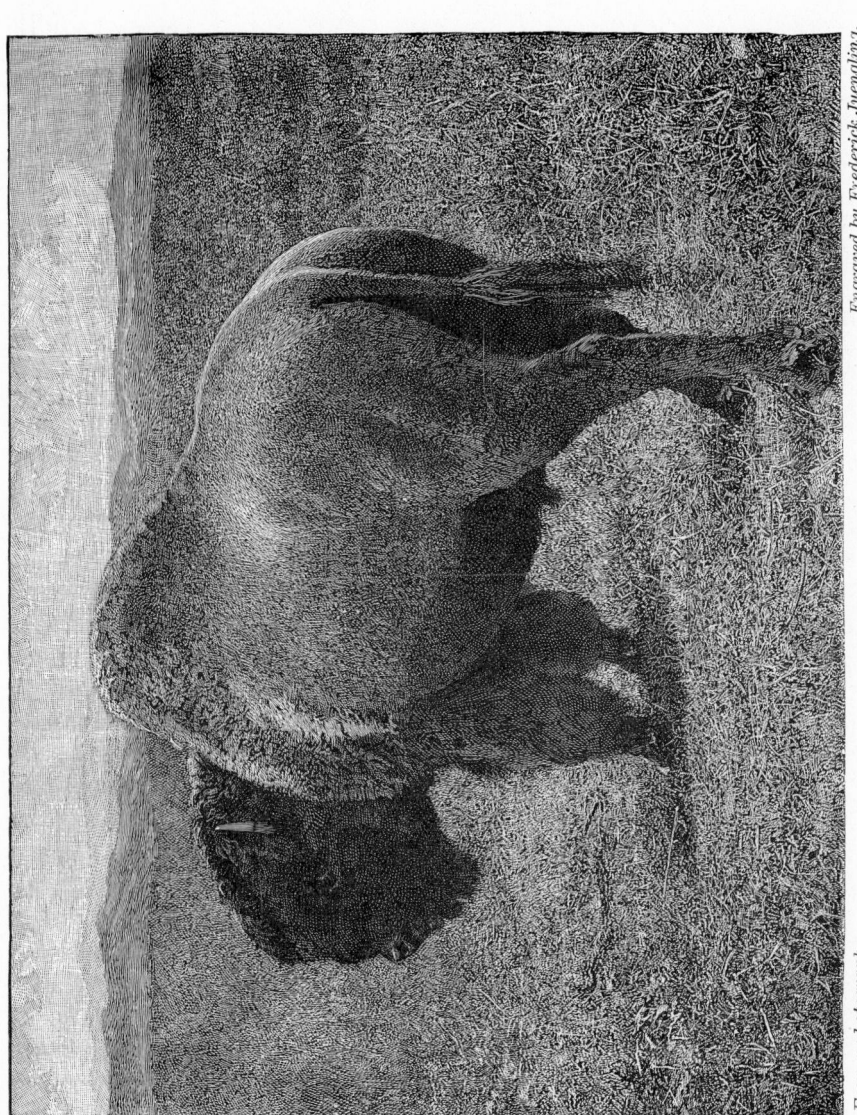

From a photograph.

Engraved by Frederick Juengling.

BULL BUFFALO. (REAR VIEW.)

Reproduced from the *Cosmopolitan Magazine*, by permission of the publishers.

milk of two domestic cows to satisfy one buffalo calf, but this, I think, is an error. Our calf began in May to consume 6 quarts of domestic milk daily, which by June 10 had increased to 8, and up to July 10, 9 quarts was the utmost it could drink. By that time it began to eat grass, but the quantity of milk disposed of remained about the same.

BISON AMERICANUS. (Adult cow, eight years old. Taken November 18, 1886. Montana.)

(*No. 15767, National Museum collection.*)

	Feet.	Inches.
Height at shoulders	4	10
Length, head and body to insertion of tail	8	6
Depth of chest	3	7
Depth of flank	1	7
Girth behind fore leg	6	10
From base of horns around end of nose	3	3
Length of tail vertebræ	1	

10. *The "Wood," or "Mountain" Buffalo.*—Having myself never seen a specimen of the so called "mountain buffalo" or "wood buffalo," which some writers accord the rank of a distinct variety, I can only quote the descriptions of others. While most Rocky Mountain hunters consider the bison of the mountains quite distinct from that of the plains, it must be remarked that no two authorities quite agree in regard to the distinguishing characters of the variety they recognize. Colonel Dodge states that "His body is lighter, whilst his legs are shorter, but much thicker and stronger, than the plains animal, thus enabling him to perform feats of climbing and tumbling almost incredible in such a huge and unwieldy beast." [*]

The belief in the existence of a distinct mountain variety is quite common amongst hunters and frontiersmen all along the eastern slope the Rocky Mountains as far north as the Peace River. In this connection the following from Professor Henry Youle Hind [†] is of general interest:

"The existence of two kinds of buffalo is firmly believed by many hunters at Red River; they are stated to be the prairie buffalo and the buffalo of the woods. Many old hunters with whom I have conversed on this subject aver that the so-called wood buffalo is a distinct species, and although they are not able to offer scientific proofs, yet the difference in size, color, hair, and horns, are enumerated as the evidence upon which they base their statement. Men from their youth familiar with these animals in the great plains, and the varieties which are frequently met with in large herds, still cling to this opinion. The buffalo of the plains are not always of the dark and rich bright brown which forms their characteristic color. They are sometimes seen from white to almost black, and a gray buffalo is not at all uncommon. Buffalo

---

[*] Plains of the Great West, p. 144.
[†] Red River, Assinniboine and Saskatchewan Expedition, ii, p. 104-105.

emasculated by wolves are often found on the prairies, where they grow to an immense size; the skin of the buffalo ox is recognized by the shortness of the wool and by its large dimensions. The skin of the so-called wood buffalo is much larger than that of the common animal, the the hair is very short, mane or hair about the neck short and soft, and altogether destitute of curl, which is the common feature in the hair or wool of the prairie animal. Two skins of the so-called wood buffalo, which I saw at Selkirk Settlement, bore a very close resemblance to the skin of the Lithuanian bison, judging from the specimens of that species which I have since had an opportunity of seeing in the British Museum.

"The wood buffalo is stated to be very scarce, and only found north of the Saskatchewan and on the flanks of the Rocky Mountains. It never ventures into the open plains. The prairie buffalo, on the contrary, generally avoids the woods in summer and keeps to the open country; but in winter they are frequently found in the woods of the Little Souris, Saskatchewan, the Touchwood Hills, and the aspen groves on the Qu'Appelle. There is no doubt that formerly the prairie buffalo ranged through open woods almost as much as he now does through the prairies."

Mr. Harrison S Young, an officer of the Hudson's Bay Fur Company, stationed at Fort Edmonton, writes me as follows in a letter dated October 22, 1887: "In our district of Athabasca, along the Salt River, there are still a few wood buffalo killed every year; but they are fast diminishing in numbers, and are also becoming very shy."

In Prof. John Macoun's "Manitoba and the Great Northwest," page 342, there occurs the following reference to the wood buffalo: "In the winter of 1870 the last buffalo were killed north of Peace River; but in 1875 about one thousand head were still in existence between the Athabasca and Peace Rivers, north of Little Slave Lake. These are called wood buffalo by the hunters, but differ only in size from those of the plain."

In the absence of facts based on personal observations, I may be permitted to advance an opinion in regard to the wood buffalo. There is some reason for the belief that certain changes of form may have taken place in the buffaloes that have taken up a permanent residence in rugged and precipitous mountain regions. Indeed, it is hardly possible to understand how such a radical change in the habitat of an animal could fail, through successive generations, to effect certain changes in the animal itself. It seems to me that the changes which would take place in a band of plains buffaloes transferred to a permanent mountain habitat can be forecast with a marked degree of certainty. The changes that take place under such conditions in cattle, swine, and goats are well known, and similar causes would certainly produce similar results in the buffalo.

The scantier feed of the mountains, and the great waste of vital energy called for in procuring it, would hardly produce a larger buffalo than the plains-fed animal, who acquires an abundance of daily food of the best quality with but little effort.

We should expect to see the mountain buffalo smaller in body than the plains animal, with better leg development, and particularly with stronger hind quarters. The pelvis of the plains buffalo is surprisingly small and weak for so large an animal. Beyond question, constant mountain climbing is bound to develop a maximum of useful muscle and bone and a minimum of useless fat. If the loss of mane sustained by the African lions who live in bushy localities may be taken as an index, we should expect the bison of the mountains, especially the " wood buffalo," to lose a great deal of his shaggy frontlet and mane on the bushes and trees which surrounded him. Therefore, we would naturally expect to find the hair on those parts shorter and in far less perfect condition than on the bison of the treeless prairies. By reason of the more shaded condition of his home, and the decided mitigation of the sun's fierceness, we should also expect to see his entire pelage of a darker tone. That he would acquire a degree of agility and strength unknown in his relative of the plain is reasonably certain. In the course of many centuries the change in his form might become well defined, constant, and conspicuous; but at present there is apparently not the slightest ground for considering that the "mountain buffalo" or "wood buffalo" is entitled to rank even as a variety of *Bison americanus*.

Colonel Dodge has recorded some very interesting information in regard to the "mountain, or wood buffalo," which deserves to be quoted entire.*

" In various portions of the Rocky Mountains, especially in the region of the parks, is found an animal which old mountaineers call the 'bison.' This animal bears about the same relation to a plains buffalo as a sturdy mountain pony does to an American horse. His body is lighter, whilst his legs are shorter, but much thicker and stronger, than the plains animal, thus enabling him to perform feats of climbing and tumbling almost incredible in such a huge and apparently unwieldy beast.

"These animals are by no means plentiful, and are moreover excessively shy, inhabiting the deepest, darkest defiles, or the craggy, almost precipitous, sides of mountains inaccessible to any but the most practiced mountaineers.

" From the tops of the mountains which rim the parks the rains of ages have cut deep gorges, which plunge with brusque abruptness, but nevertheless with great regularity, hundreds or even thousands of feet to the valley below. Down the bottom of each such gorge a clear, cold stream of purest water, fertilizing a narrow belt of a few feet of alluvial, and giving birth and growth to a dense jungle of spruce, quaking asp, and other mountain trees. One side of the gorge is generally a

---

* Plains of the Great West, p. 144–147.

thick forest of pine, while the other side is a meadow-like park, covered with splendid grass. Such gorges are the favorite haunt of the mountain buffalo. Early in the morning he enjoys a bountiful breakfast of the rich nutritious grasses, quenches his thirst with the finest water, and, retiring just within the line of jungle, where, himself unseen, he can scan the open, he crouches himself in the long grass and reposes in comfort and security until appetite calls him to his dinner late in the evening. Unlike their plains relative, there is no stupid staring at an intruder. At the first symptom of danger they disappear like magic in the thicket, and never stop until far removed from even the apprehension of pursuit. I have many times come upon their fresh tracks, upon the beds from which they had first sprung in alarm, but I have never even seen one.

"I have wasted much time and a great deal of wind in vain endeavors to add one of these animals to my bag. My figure is no longer adapted to mountain climbing, and the possession of a bison's head of my own killing is one of my blighted hopes.

"Several of my friends have been more fortunate, but I know of no sportsman who has bagged more than one.*

"Old mountaineers and trappers have given me wonderful accounts of the number of these animals in all the mountain region 'many years ago;' and I have been informed by them that their present rarity is due to the great snow-storm of 1844–'45, of which I have already spoken as destroying the plains buffalo in the Laramie country.

"One of my friends, a most ardent and pertinacious sportsman, determined on the possession of a bison's head, and, hiring a guide, plunged into the mountain wilds which separate the Middle from South Park. After several days fresh tracks were discovered. Turning their horses loose on a little gorge park, such as described, they started on foot on the trail; for all that day they toiled and scrambled with the utmost caution—now up, now down, through deep and narrow gorges and pine thickets, over bare and rocky crags, sleeping where night overtook them. Betimes next morning they pushed on the trail, and about 11 o'clock, when both were exhausted and well-nigh disheartened, their route was intercepted by a precipice. Looking over, they descried, on a projecting ledge several hundred feet below, a herd of about 20 bisons lying down. The ledge was about 300 feet at widest, by probably 1,000 feet long. Its inner boundary was the wall of rock on the top of which they stood; its outer appeared to be a sheer precipice of at least 200 feet. This ledge was connected with the slope of the mountain by a narrow neck. The wind being right, the hunters succeeded in reaching this neck unobserved. My friend selected a magnificent head, that of a

---

*Foot-note by William Blackmore: "The author is in error here, as in a point of the Tarryall range of mountains, between Pike's Peak and the South Park, in the autumn of 1871, two mountain buffaloes were killed in one afternoon. The skin of the finer was presented to Dr. Frank Buckland."

fine bull, young but full grown, and both fired. At the report the bisons all ran to the far end of the ledge and plunged over.

"Terribly disappointed, the hunters ran to the spot, and found that they had gone down a declivity, not actually a precipice, but so steep that the hunters could not follow them.

"At the foot lay a bison. A long, a fatiguing detour brought them to the spot, and in the animal lying dead before him my friend recognized his bull—his first and last mountain buffalo. None but a true sportsman can appreciate his feelings.

"The remainder of the herd was never seen after the great plunge, down which it is doubtful if even a dog could have followed unharmed."

In the issue of Forest and Stream of June 14, 1888, Dr. R. W. Shufeldt, in an article entitled "The American Buffalo," relates a very interesting experience with buffaloes which were pronounced to be of the "mountain" variety, and his observations on the animals are well worth reproducing here. The animals (eight in number) were encountered on the northern slope of the Big Horn Mountains, in the autumn of 1877. "We came upon them during a fearful blizzard of heavy hail, during which our animals could scarcely retain their feet. In fact, the packer's mule absolutely lay down on the ground rather than risk being blown down the mountain side, and my own horse, totally unable to face such a violent blow and the pelting hail (the stones being as large as big marbles), positively stood stock-still, facing an old buffalo bull that was not more than 25 feet in front of me. * * * Strange to say, this fearful gust did not last more than ten minutes, when it stopped as suddenly as it had commenced, and I deliberately killed my old buffalo at one shot, just where he stood, and, separating two other bulls from the rest, charged them down a rugged ravine. They passed over this and into another one, but with less precipitous sides and no trees in the way, and when I was on top of the intervening ridge I noticed that the largest bull had halted in the bottom. Checking my horse, an excellent buffalo hunter, I fired down at him without dismounting. The ball merely barked his shoulder, and to my infinite surprise he turned and charged me up the hill. * * * Stepping to one side of my horse, with the charging and infuriated bull not 10 feet to my front, I fired upon him, and the heavy ball took him square in the chest, bringing him to his knees, with a gush of scarlet blood from his mouth and nostrils. * * *

"Upon examining the specimen, I found it to be an old bull, apparently smaller and very much blacker than the ones I had seen killed on the plains only a day or so before. Then I examined the first one I had shot, as well as others which were killed by the packer from the same bunch, and I came to the conclusion that they were typical representatives of the variety known as the 'mountain buffalo,' a form much more active in movement, of slighter limbs, blacker, and far more dangerous to attack. My opinion in the premises remains unaltered to-day. In all this I may be mistaken, but it was also the opinion held by the old buffalo hunter who accompanied me, and who at once remarked when he saw them that they were 'mountain buffalo,' and not the plains variety.   *   *   *

"These specimens were not actually measured by me in either case, and their being considered smaller only rested upon my judging them by my eye. But they were of a softer pelage, black, lighter in limb, and when discovered were in the timber, on the side of the Big Horn Mountains."

The band of bison in the Yellowstone Park must, of necessity, be of the so-called " wood " or " mountain " variety, and if by any chance one of its members ever dies of old age, it is to be hoped its skin may be carefully preserved and sent to the National Museum to throw some further light on this question.

11. *The shedding of the winter pelage.*—In personal appearance the buffalo is subject to striking, and even painful, variations, and the estimate an observer forms of him is very apt to depend upon the time of the year at which the observation is made. Toward the end of the winter the whole coat has become faded and bleached by the action of the sun, wind, snow, and rain, until the freshness of its late autumn colors has totally disappeared. The bison takes on a seedy, weathered, and rusty look. But this is not a circumstance to what happens to him a little later. Promptly with the coming of the spring, if not even in the last week of February, the buffalo begins the shedding of his winter coat. It is a long and difficult task, and with commendable energy he sets about it at the earliest possible moment. It lasts him more than half the year, and is attended with many positive discomforts.

The process of shedding is accomplished in two ways: by the new hair growing into and forcing off the old, and by the old hair falling off in great patches, leaving the skin bare. On the heavily-haired portions—the head, neck, fore quarters, and hump—the old hair stops growing, dies, and the new hair immediately starts through the skin and forces it off. The new hair grows so rapidly, and at the same time so densely, that it forces itself into the old, becomes hopelessly entangled with it, and in time actually lifts the old hair clear of the skin. On the head the new hair is dark brown or black, but on the neck, fore quarters, and hump it has at first, and indeed until it is 2 inches in length, a peculiar gray or drab color, mixed with brown, totally different from its final and natural color. The new hair starts first on the head, but the actual shedding of the old hair is to be seen first along the lower parts of the neck and between the fore legs. The heavily-haired parts are never bare, but, on the contrary, the amount of hair upon them is about the same all the year round. The old and the new hair cling together with provoking tenacity long after the old coat should fall, and on several of the bulls we killed in October there were patches of it still sticking tightly to the shoulders, from which it had to be forcibly plucked away. Under all such patches the new hair was of a different color from that around them.

The other process of shedding takes place on the body and hind quarters, from which the old hair loosens and drops off in great woolly flakes a foot square, more or less. The shedding takes place very unevenly, the old hair remaining much longer in some places than in others. During April, May, and June the body and hind quarters present a most ludicrous and even pitiful spectacle. The island-like patches of persistent old hair alternating with patches of bare brown skin are adorned (?) by great ragged streamers of loose hair, which flutter in the wind like signals of distress. Whoever sees a bison at this period is filled with a desire to assist nature by plucking off the flying streamers of old hair; but the bison never permits anything of the kind, however good one's intentions may be. All efforts to dislodge the old hair are resisted to the last extremity, and the buffalo generally acts as if the intention were to deprive him of his skin itself. By the end of June, if not before, the body and hind quarters are free from the old hair, and as bare as the hide of a hippopotamus. The naked skin has a shiny brown appearance, and of course the external anatomy of the animal is very distinctly revealed. But for the long hair on the fore quarters, neck, and head the bison would lose all his dignity of appearance with his hair. As it is, the handsome black head, which is black with new hair as early as the first of May, redeems the animal from utter homeliness.

After the shedding of the body hair, the naked skin of the buffalo is burned by the sun and bitten by flies until he is compelled to seek a pool of water, or even a bed of soft mud, in which to roll and make himself comfortable. He wallows, not so much because he is so fond of either water or mud, but in self-defense; and when he emerges from his wallow, plastered with mud from head to tail, his degradation is complete. He is then simply not fit to be seen, even by his best friends.

By the first of October, a complete and wonderful transformation has taken place. The buffalo stands forth clothed in a complete new suit of hair, fine, clean, sleek, and bright in color, not a speck of dirt nor a lock awry anywhere. To be sure, it is as yet a trifle short on the body, where it is not over an inch in length, and hardly that; but it is growing rapidly and getting ready for winter.

From the 20th of November to the 20th of December the pelage is at its very finest. By the former date it has attained its full growth, its colors are at their brightest, and nothing has been lost either by the elements or by accidental causes. To him who sees an adult bull at this period, or near it, the grandeur of the animal is irresistibly felt. After seeing buffaloes of all ages in the spring and summer months the contrast afforded by those seen in October, November, and December was most striking and impressive. In the later period, as different individuals were wounded and brought to bay at close quarters, their hair was so clean and well-kept, that more than once I was led to exclaim: "He looks as if he had just been combed."

It must be remarked, however, that the long hair of the head and fore quarters is disposed in locks or tufts, and to comb it in reality would utterly destroy its natural and characteristic appearance.

Inasmuch as the pelage of the domesticated bison, the only representatives of the species which will be found alive ten years hence, will in all likelihood develop differently from that of the wild animal, it may some time in the future be of interest to know the length, by careful measurement, of the hair found on carefully-selected typical wild specimens. To this end the following measurements are given. It must be borne in mind that these specimens were not chosen because their pelage was particularly luxuriant, but rather because they are fine average specimens.

The hair of the adult bull is by no means as long as I have seen on a bison, although perhaps not many have greatly surpassed it. It is with the lower animals as with man—the length of the hairy covering is an individual character only. I have in my possession a tuft of hair, from the frontlet of a rather small bull bison, which measures 22½ inches in length. The beard on the specimen from which this came was correspondingly long, and the entire pelage was of wonderful length and density.

LENGTH OF THE HAIR OF BISON AMERICANUS.

[Measurements, in inches, of the pelage of the specimens composing the group in the National Museum.]

	Old bull, killed Dec. 6.	Old cow, killed Nov. 18.	Spike bull, killed Oct. 14.	Young cow, killed Oct. 14.	Yearling calf, killed Oct. 31.	Young calf, four months old.
Length of hair on the shoulder (over scapula)	3¾	4¾	3½	3¼	3	1½
Length of hair on top of hump	6½	7	5¼	5½	4½	2
Length of hair on the middle of the side	2	1½	2¼	1½	2¼	1¼
Length of hair on the hind quarter	1¾	1¼	¾	¾	2	1
Length of hair on the forehead	16	8½	6½	5	3½	½
Length of the chin beard	11½	9½	6¾	5	5	0
Length of the breast tuft	8	8½	8	6	5	3
Length of tuft on fore leg	10½	8	8	4½	3	1½
Length of the tail tuft	19	15	15	13	7½	4½

Albinism.—Cases of albinism in the buffalo were of extremely rare occurrence. I have met many old buffalo hunters, who had killed thousands and seen scores of thousands of buffaloes, yet never had seen a white one. From all accounts it appears that not over ten or eleven white buffaloes, or white buffalo skins, were ever seen by white men. Pied individuals were occasionally obtained, but even they were rare. Albino buffaloes were always so highly prized that not a single one, so far as I can learn, ever had the good fortune to attain adult size, their appearance being so striking, in contrast with the other members of the herd, as to draw upon them an unusual number of enemies, and cause their speedy destruction.

At the New Orleans Exposition, in 1884–'85, the Territory of Dakota exhibited, amongst other Western quadrupeds, the mounted skin of a two-year-old buffalo which might fairly be called an albino. Although not really white, it was of a uniform dirty cream-color, and showed not a trace of the bison's normal color on any part of its body.

Lieut. Col. S. C. Kellogg, U. S. Army, has on deposit in the National Museum a tanned skin which is said to have come from a buffalo. It is from an animal about one year old, and the hair upon it, which is short, very curly or wavy, and rather coarse, is pure white. In length and texture the hair does not in any one respect resemble the hair of a yearling buffalo save in one particular,—along the median line of the neck and hump there is a rather long, thin mane of hair, which has the peculiar woolly appearance of genuine buffalo hair on those parts. On the shoulder portions of the skin the hair is as short as on the hind quarters. I am inclined to believe this rather remarkable specimen came from a wild half-breed calf, the result of a cross between a white domestic cow and a buffalo bull. At one time it was by no means uncommon for small bunches of domestic cattle to enter herds of buffalo and remain there permanently.

I have been informed that the late General Marcy possessed a white buffalo skin. If it is still in existence, and is really *white*, it is to be hoped that so great a rarity may find a permanent abiding place in some museum where the remains of *Bison americanus* are properly appreciated.

V. The Habits of the Buffalo.

The history of the buffalo's daily life and habits should begin with the "running season." This period occupied the months of August and September, and was characterized by a degree of excitement and activity throughout the entire herd quite foreign to the ease-loving and even slothful nature which was so noticable a feature of the bison's character at all other times.

The mating season occurred when the herd was on its summer range. The spring calves were from two to four months old. Through continued feasting on the new crop of buffalo-grass and bunch-grass—the most nutritious in the world, perhaps—every buffalo in the herd had grown round-sided, fat, and vigorous. The faded and weather-beaten suit of winter hair had by that time fallen off and given place to the new coat of dark gray and black, and, excepting for the shortness of his hair, the buffalo was in prime condition.

During the "running season," as it was called by the plainsmen, the whole nature of the herd was completely changed. Instead of being broken up into countless small groups and dispersed over a vast extent of territory, the herd came together in a dense and confused mass of many thousand individuals. so closely congregated as to actually blacken the face of the landscape. As if by a general and irresistible impulse, every straggler would be drawn to the common center, and for miles on every side of the great herd the country would be found entirely deserted.

At this time the herd itself became a seething mass of activity and excitement. As usual under such conditions, the bulls were half the time chasing the cows, and fighting each other during the other half. These actual combats, which were always of short duration and over in a few seconds after the actual collision took place, were preceded by the usual threatening demonstrations, in which the bull lowers his head until his nose almost touches the ground, roars like a fog-horn until the earth seems to fairly tremble with the vibration, glares madly upon his adversary with half-white eyeballs, and with his fore feet paws up the dry earth and throws it upward in a great cloud of dust high above his back. At such times the mingled roaring—it can not truthfully be described as lowing or bellowing—of a number of huge bulls unite and form a great volume of sound like distant thunder, which has often been heard at a distance of from 1 to 3 miles. I have even been assured by old plainsmen that under favorable atmospheric conditions such sounds have been heard five miles.

Notwithstanding the extreme frequency of combats between the bulls during this season, their results were nearly always harmless, thanks to the thickness of the hair and hide on the head and shoulders, and the strength of the neck.

Under no conditions was there ever any such thing as the pairing off or mating of male and female buffaloes for any length of time. In the entire process of reproduction the bison's habits were similar to those of domestic cattle. For years the opinion was held by many, in some cases based on misinterpreted observations, that in the herd the identity of each family was partially preserved, and that each old bull maintained an individual harem and group of progeny of his own. The observations of Colonel Dodge completely disprove this very interesting theory; for at best it was only a picturesque fancy, ascribing to the bison a degree of intelligence which he never possessed.

At the close of the breeding season the herd quickly settles down to its normal condition. The mass gradually resolves itself into the numerous bands or herdlets of from twenty to a hundred individuals, so characteristic of bison on their feeding grounds, and these gradually scatter in search of the best grass until the herd covers many square miles of country.

In his search for grass the buffalo displayed but little intelligence or power of original thought. Instead of closely following the divides between water-courses where the soil was best and grass most abundant, he would not hesitate to wander away from good feeding-grounds into barren "bad lands," covered with sage-brush, where the grass was very thin and very poor. In such broken country as Montana, Wyoming, and southwestern Dakota, the herds, on reaching the best grazing grounds on the divides, would graze there day after day until increasing thirst compelled them to seek for water. Then, actuated by a common impulse, the search for a water-hole was begun in a business-like way. The leader of a herd, or "bunch," which post was usually filled by an old cow, would start off down the nearest "draw," or stream-heading, and all the rest would fall into line and follow her. From the moment this start was made there was no more feeding, save as a mouth-ful of grass could be snatched now and then without turning aside. In single file, in a line sometimes half a mile long and containing between one and two hundred buffaloes, the procession slowly marched down the coulée, close alongside the gully as soon as the water-course began to cut a pathway for itself. When the gully curved to right or left the leader would cross its bed and keep straight on until the narrow ditch completed its wayward curve and came back to the middle of the coulée. The trail of a herd in search of water is usually as good a piece of engineering as could be executed by the best railway surveyor, and is governed by precisely the same principles. It always follows the level of the valley, swerves around the high points, and crosses the stream repeatedly in order to avoid climbing up from the level. The same trail is used again and again by different herds until the narrow path, not over a foot in width, is gradually cut straight down into the soil to a depth of several inches, as if it had been done by a 12-inch grooving-plane. By the time the trail has been worn down to a depth of 6 or 7 inches, without having its width increased in the least, it is no longer a pleasant path to walk in, being too much like a narrow ditch. Then the buffaloes abandon it and strike out a new one alongside, which is used until it also is worn down and abandoned.

To-day the old buffalo trails are conspicuous among the very few classes of objects which remain as a reminder of a vanished race. The herds of cattle now follow them in single file just as the buffaloes did a few years ago, as they search for water in the same way. In some parts of the West, in certain situations, old buffalo trails exist which the wild herds wore down to a depth of 2 feet or more.

Mile after mile marched the herd, straight down-stream, bound for the upper water-hole. As the hot summer drew on, the pools would dry up one by one, those nearest the source being the first to disappear. Toward the latter part of summer, the journey for water was often a long one. Hole after hole would be passed without finding a drop of water. At last a hole of mud would be found, below that a hole with a little muddy water, and a mile farther on the leader would arrive at a shallow pool under the edge of a "cut bank;" a white, snow-like deposit of alkali on the sand encircling its margin, and incrusting the blades of grass and rushes that grew up from the bottom. The damp earth around the pool was cut up by a thousand hoof-prints, and the water was warm, strongly impregnated with alkali, and yellow with animal impurities, but it was *water*. The nauseous mixture was quickly surrounded by a throng of thirsty, heated, and eager buffaloes of all ages, to which the oldest and strongest asserted claims of priority. There was much crowding and some fighting, but eventually all were satisfied. After such a long journey to water, a herd would usually remain by it for some hours, lying down, resting, and drinking at intervals until completely satisfied.

Having drunk its fill, the herd would never march directly back to the choice feeding grounds it had just left, but instead would leisurely stroll off at a right angle from the course it came, cropping for awhile the rich bunch grasses of the bottom-lands, and then wander across the hills in an almost aimless search for fresh fields and pastures new. When buffaloes remained long in a certain locality it was a common thing for them to visit the same watering-place a number of times, at intervals of greater or less duration, according to circumstances.

When undisturbed on his chosen range, the bison used to be fond of lying down for an hour or two in the middle of the day, particularly when fine weather and good grass combined to encourage him in luxurious habits. I once discovered with the field-glass a small herd of buffaloes lying down at midday on the slope of a high ridge, and having ridden hard for several hours we seized the opportunity to unsaddle and give our horses an hour's rest before making the attack. While we were so doing, the herd got up, shifted its position to the opposite side of the ridge, and again laid down, every buffalo with his nose pointing to windward.

Old hunters declare that in the days of their abundance, when feeding on their ranges in fancied security, the younger animals were as playful as well-fed domestic calves. It was a common thing to see them cavort and frisk around with about as much grace as young elephants, prancing and running to and fro with tails held high in air "like scorpions."

Buffaloes are very fond of rolling in dry dirt or even in mud, and this habit is quite strong in captive animals. Not only is it indulged in during the shedding season, but all through the fall and winter. The two live buffaloes in the National Museum are so much given to rolling, even in rainy weather, that it is necessary to card them every few days to keep them presentable.

Bulls are much more given to rolling than the cows, especially after they have reached maturity. They stretch out at full length, rub their heads violently to and fro on the ground, in which the horn serves as the chief point of contact and slides over the ground like a sled-runner. After thoroughly scratching one side on mother earth they roll over and treat the other in like manner. Notwithstanding his sharp and lofty hump, a buffalo bull can roll completely over with as much ease as any horse.

The vast amount of rolling and side-scratching on the earth indulged in by bull buffaloes is shown in the worn condition of the horns of

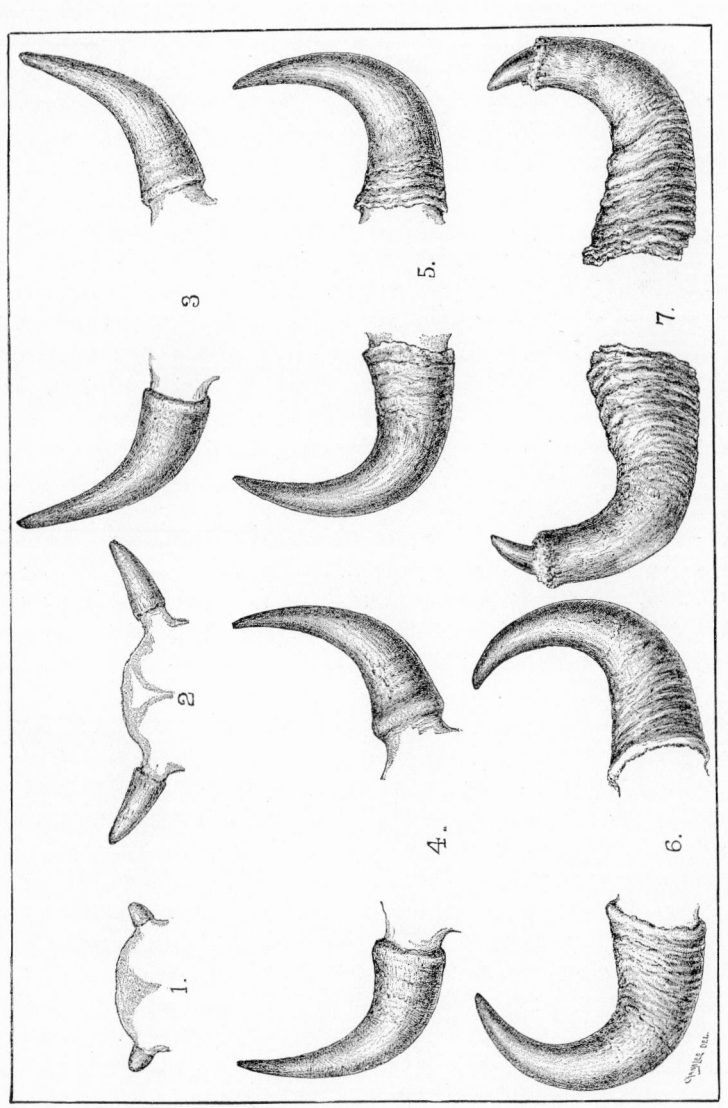

DEVELOPMENT OF THE HORNS OF THE AMERICAN BISON.

1. The Calf.
2. The Yearling.
3. Spike Bull, 2 years old.

4. Spike Bull, 3 years old.
5. Bull, 4 years old.

6. Bull, 11 years old.
7. Old "stub-horn" Bull, 20 years old.

every old specimen. Often a thickness of half an inch is gone from the upper half of each horn on its outside curve, at which point the horn is worn quite flat. This is well illustrated in the horns shown in the accompanying plate, fig. 6.

Mr. Catlin* affords some very interesting and valuable information in regard to the bison's propensity for wollowing in mud, and also the origin of the "fairy circles," which have caused so much speculation amongst travelers:

"In the heat of summer, these huge animals, which no doubt suffer very much with the great profusion of their long and shaggy hair, or fur, often graze on the low grounds of the prairies, where there is a little stagnant water lying amongst the grass, and the ground underneath being saturated with it, is soft, into which the enormous bullt lowered down upon one knee, will plunge his horns, and at last his head, driving up the earth, and soon making an excavation in the ground into which the water filters from amongst the grass, forming for him in a few moments a cool and comfortable bath, into which he plunges like a hog in his mire.

"In this delectable laver he throws himself flat upon his side, and forcing himself violently around, with his horns and his huge hump on his shoulders presented to the sides, he ploughs up the ground by his rotary motion, sinking himself deeper and deeper in the ground, continually enlarging his pool, in which he at length becomes nearly immersed, and the water and mud about him mixed into a complete mortar, which changes his color and drips in streams from every part of him as he rises up upon his feet, a hideous monster of mud and ugliness, too frightful and too eccentric to be described!

"It is generally the leader of the herd that takes upon him to make this excavation, and if not (but another one opens the ground), the leader (who is conqueror) marches forward, and driving the other from it plunges himself into it; and, having cooled his sides and changed his color to a walking mass of mud and mortar, he stands in the pool until inclination induces him to step out and give place to the next in command who stands ready, and another, and another, who advance forward in their turns to enjoy the luxury of the wallow, until the whole band (sometimes a hundred or more) will pass through it in turn,† each one throwing his body around in a similar manner and each one adding a little to the dimensions of the pool, while he carries away in his hair an equal share of the clay, which dries to a gray or whitish color and gradually falls off. By this operation, which is done perhaps in the space of half an hour, a circular excavation of fifteen or twenty feet in diameter and two feet in depth is completed and left for the water to run into, which soon fills it to the level of the ground.

---

* North American Indians, vol. I, p. 249, 250.

† In the District of Columbia work-house we have a counterpart of this in the public bath-tub, wherein forty prisoners were seen by a *Star* reporter to bathe one after another in the same water!

"To these sinks, the waters lying on the surface of the prairies are continually draining and in them lodging their vegetable deposits, which after a lapse of years fill them up to the surface with a rich soil, which throws up an unusual growth of grass and herbage, forming conspicuous circles, which arrest the eye of the traveler and are calculated to excite his surprise for ages to come."

During the latter part of the last century, when the bison inhabited Kentucky and Pennsylvania, the salt springs of those States were resorted to by thousands of those animals, who drank of the saline waters and licked the impregnated earth. Mr. Thomas Ashe* affords us a most interesting account, from the testimony of an eye-witness, of the behavior of a bison at a salt spring. The description refers to a locality in western Pennsylvania, where "an old man, one of the first settlers of this country, built his log house on the immediate borders of a salt spring. He informed me that for the first several seasons the buffaloes paid him their visits with the utmost regularity; they traveled in single files, always following each other at equal distances, forming droves, on their arrival, of about 300 each.

"The first and second years, so unacquainted were these poor brutes with the use of this man's house or with his nature, that in a few hours they *rubbed* the house completely down, taking delight in turning the logs off with their horns, while he had some difficulty to escape from being trampled under their feet or crushed to death in his own ruins. At that period he supposed there could not have been less than 2,000 in the neighborhood of the spring. They sought for no manner of food, but only bathed and drank three or four times a day and rolled in the earth, or reposed with their flanks distended in the adjacent shades; and on the fifth and sixth days separated into distinct droves, bathed, drank, and departed in single files, according to the exact order of their arrival. They all rolled successively in the same hole, and each thus carried away a coat of mud to preserve the moisture on their skin and which, when hardened and baked in the sun, would resist the stings of millions of insects that otherwise would persecute these peaceful travelers to madness or even death."

It was a fixed habit with the great buffalo herds to move southward from 200 to 400 miles at the approach of winter. Sometimes this movement was accomplished quietly and without any excitement, but at other times it was done with a rush, in which considerable distances would be gone over on the double-quick. The advance of a herd was often very much like that of a big army, in a straggling line, from four to ten animals abreast. Sometimes the herd moved forward in a dense mass, and in consequence often came to grief in quicksands, alkali bogs, muddy crossings, and on treacherous ice. In such places thousands of buffaloes lost their lives, through those in the lead being forced into danger by pressure of the mass coming behind. In this manner, in the

---

* Travels in America in 1806. London, 1808.

summer of 1867, over two thousand buffaloes, out of a herd of about four thousand, lost their lives in the quicksands of the Platte River, near Plum Creek, while attempting to cross. One winter, a herd of nearly a hundred buffaloes attempted to cross a lake called Lac-qui-parle, in Minnesota, upon the ice, which gave way, and drowned the entire herd. During the days of the buffalo it was a common thing for voyagers on the Missouri River to see buffaloes hopelessly mired in the quicksands or mud along the shore, either dead or dying, and to find their dead bodies floating down the river, or lodged on the upper ends of the islands and sand-bars.

Such accidents as these, it may be repeated, were due to the great number of animals and the momentum of the moving mass. The forced marches of the great herds were like the flight of a routed army, in which helpless individuals were thrust into mortal peril by the irresistible force of the mass coming behind, which rushes blindly on after their leaders. In this way it was possible to decoy a herd toward a precipice and cause it to plunge over en masse, the leaders being thrust over by their followers, and all the rest following of their own free will, like the sheep who cheerfully leaped, one after another, through a hole in the side of a high bridge because their bell-wether did so.

But it is not to be understood that the movement of a great herd, because it was made on a run, necessarily partook of the nature of a stampede in which a herd sweeps forward in a body. The most graphic account that I ever obtained of facts bearing on this point was furnished by Mr. James McNaney, drawn from his experience on the northern buffalo range in 1882. His party reached the range (on Beaver Creek, about 100 miles south of Glendive) about the middle of November, and found buffaloes already there; in fact they had begun to arrive from the north as early as the middle of October. About the first of December an immense herd arrived from the north. It reached their vicinity one night, about 10 o'clock, in a mass that seemed to spread everywhere. As the hunters sat in their tents, loading cartridges and cleaning their rifles, a low rumble was heard, which gradually increased to "a thundering noise," and some one exclaimed, "There! that's a big herd of buffalo coming in!" All ran out immediately, and hallooed and discharged rifles to keep the buffaloes from running over their tents. Fortunately, the horses were picketed some distance away in a grassy coulée, which the buffaloes did not enter. The herd came at a jog-trot, and moved quite rapidly. "In the morning the whole country was black with buffalo." It was estimated that 10,000 head were in sight. One immense detachment went down on to a "flat" and laid down. There it remained quietly, enjoying a long rest, for about ten days. It gradually broke up into small bands, which strolled off in various directions looking for food, and which the hunters quietly attacked.

A still more striking event occurred about Christmas time at the same place. For a few days the neighborhood of McNaney's camp had been entirely deserted by buffaloes, not even one remaining. But one morning about daybreak a great herd which was traveling south began to pass their camp. A long line of moving forms was seen advancing rapidly from the northwest, coming in the direction of the hunters' camp. It disappeared in the creek valley for a few moments, and presently the leaders suddenly came in sight again at the top of " a rise " a few hundred yards away, and came down the intervening slope at full speed, within 50 yards of the two tents. After them came a living stream of followers, all going at a gallop, described by the observer as " a long lope," from four to ten buffaloes abreast. Sometimes there would be a break in the column of a minute's duration, then more buffaloes would appear at the brow of the hill, and the column went rushing by as before. The calves ran with their mothers, and the young stock got over the ground with much less exertion than the older animals. For about four hours, or until past 11 o'clock, did this column of buffaloes gallop past the camp over a course no wider than a village street. Three miles away toward the south the long dark line of bobbing humps and hind quarters wound to the right between two hills and disappeared. True to their instincts, the hunters promptly brought out their rifles, and began to fire at the buffaloes as they ran. A furious fusilade was kept up from the very doors of the tents, and from first to last over fifty buffaloes were killed. Some fell headlong the instant they were hit, but the greater number ran on until their mortal wounds compelled them to halt, draw off a little way to one side, and finally fall in their death struggles.

Mr. McNaney stated that the hunters estimated the number of buffaloes *on that portion* of the range that winter (1881–'82) at 100,000.

It is probable, and in fact reasonably certain, that such forced-march migrations as the above were due to snow-covered pastures and a scarcity of food on the more northern ranges. Having learned that a journey south will bring him to regions of less snow and more grass, it is but natural that so lusty a traveler should migrate. The herds or bands which started south in the fall months traveled more leisurely, with frequent halts to graze on rich pastures. The advance was on a very different plan, taking place in straggling lines and small groups dispersed over quite a scope of country.

Unless closely pursued, the buffalo never chose to make a journey of several miles through hilly country on a continuous run. Even when fleeing from the attack of a hunter, I have often had occasion to notice that, if the hunter was a mile behind, the buffalo would always walk when going uphill; but as soon as the crest was gained he would begin to run, and go down the slope either at a gallop or a swift trot. In former times, when the buffalo's world was wide, when retreating from an attack he always ran against the wind, to avoid running upon a new danger, which showed that he depended more upon his sense of smell than his eye-sight. During the last years of his existence, however, this habit almost totally disappeared, and the harried survivors learned to run for the regions which offered the greatest safety. But even to-day, if a Texas hunter should go into the Staked Plains, and descry in the distance a body of animals running against the wind, he would, without a moment's hesitation, pronounce them buffaloes, and the chances are that he would be right.

In winter the buffalo used to face the storms, instead of turning tail and "drifting" before them helplessly, as domestic cattle do. But at the same time, when beset by a blizzard, he would wisely seek shelter from it in some narrow and deep valley or system of ravines. There the herd would lie down and wait patiently for the storm to cease. After a heavy fall of snow, the place to find the buffalo was in the flats and creek bottoms, where the tall, rank bunch-grasses showed their tops above the snow, and afforded the best and almost the only food obtainable.

When the snow-fall was unusually heavy, and lay for a long time on the ground, the buffalo was forced to fast for days together, and some-times even weeks. If a warm day came, and thawed the upper surface of the snow sufficiently for succeeding cold to freeze it into a crust, the outlook for the bison began to be serious. A man can travel over a crust through which the hoofs of a ponderous bison cut like chisels and leave him floundering belly-deep. It was at such times that the Indians hunted him on snow-shoes, and drove their spears into his vitals as he wallowed helplessly in the drifts. Then the wolves grew fat upon the victims which they, also, slaughtered almost without effort.

Although buffaloes did not often actually perish from hunger and cold during the severest winters (save in a few very exceptional cases), they often came out in very poor condition. The old bulls always suffered more severely than the rest, and at the end of winter were frequently in miserable plight.

Unlike most other terrestrial quadrupeds of America, so long as he could roam at will the buffalo had settled migratory habits.* While the elk and black-tail deer change their altitude twice a year, in conformity with the approach and disappearance of winter, the buffalo makes a radical change of latitude. This was most noticeable in the great western pasture region, where the herds were most numerous and their movements most easily observed.

---

* On page 248 of his "North American Indians," vol. i, Mr. Catlin declares pointedly that "these animals are, truly speaking, gregarious, but not migratory; they graze in immense and almost incredible numbers at times, and roam about and over vast tracts of country from east to west and from west to east as often as from north to south, which has often been supposed they naturally and habitually did to accommodate themselves to the temperature of the climate in the different latitudes." Had Mr. Catlin resided continuously in any one locality on the great buffalo range, he would have found that the buffalo had decided migratory habits. The abundance of proof on this point renders it unnecessary to enter fully into the details of the subject.

At the approah of winter the whole great system of herds which ranged from the Peace River to the Indian Territory moved south a few hundred miles, and wintered under more favorable circumstances than each band would have experienced at its farthest north. Thus it happened that nearly the whole of the great range south of the Saskatchewan was occupied by buffaloes even in winter.

The movement north began with the return of mild weather in the early spring. Undoubtedly this northward migration was to escape the heat of their southern winter range rather than to find better pasture; for as a grazing country for cattle all the year round, Texas is hardly surpassed, except where it is overstocked. It was with the buffaloes a matter of choice rather than necessity which sent them on their annual pilgrimage northward.

Col. R. I. Dodge, who has made many valuable observations on the migratory habits of the southern buffaloes, has recorded the following: *

"Early in spring, as soon as the dry and apparently desert prairie had begun to change its coat of dingy brown to one of palest green, the horizon would begin to be dotted with buffalo, single or in groups of two or three, forerunners of the coming herd. Thicker and thicker and in larger groups they come, until by the time the grass is well up the whole vast landscape appears a mass of buffalo, some individuals feeding, others standing, others lying down, but the herd moving slowly, moving constantly to the northward. * * * Some years, as in 1871, the buffalo appeared to move northward in one immense column oftentimes from 20 to 50 miles in width, and of unknown depth from front to rear. Other years the northward journey was made in several parallel columns, moving at the same rate, and with their numerous flankers covering a width of a hundred or more miles.

"The line of march of this great spring migration was not always the same, though it was confined within certain limits. I am informed by old frontiersmen that it has not within twenty-five years crossed the Arkansas River east of Great Bend nor west of Big Sand Creek. The most favored routes crossed the Arkansas at the mouth of Walnut Creek, Pawnee Fork, Mulberry Creek, the Cimarron Crossing, and Big Sand Creek.

"As the great herd proceeds northward it is constantly depleted, numbers wandering off to the right and left, until finally it is scattered in small herds far and wide over the vast feeding grounds, where they pass the summer.

"When the food in one locality fails they go to another, and towards fall, when the grass of the high prairie becomes parched by the heat and drought, they gradually work their way back to the south, concentrating on the rich pastures of Texas and the Indian Territory, whence, the same instinct acting on all, they are ready to start together on the northward march as soon as spring starts the grass."

---

* Our Wild Indians, p. 283, et seq.

So long as the bison held undisputed possession of the great plains his migratory habits were as above—regular, general, and on a scale that was truly grand. The herds that wintered in Texas, the Indian Territory, and New Mexico probably spent their summers in Nebraska, southwestern Dakota, and Wyoming. The winter herds of northern Colorado, Wyoming, Nebraska, and southern Dakota went to northern Dakota and Montana, while the great Montana herds spent the summer on the Grand Coteau des Prairies lying between the Saskatchewan and the Missouri. The two great annual expeditions of the Red River half-breeds, which always took place in summer, went in two directions from Winnipeg and Pembina—one, the White Horse Plain division, going westward along the Qu'Appelle to the Saskatchewan country, and the other, the Red River division, southwest into Dakota. In 1840 the site of the present city of Jamestown, Dakota, was the northeastern limit of the herds that summered in Dakota, and the country lying between that point and the Missouri was for years the favorite hunting ground of the Red River division.

The herds which wintered on the Montana ranges always went north in the early spring, usually in March, so that during the time the hunters were hauling in the hides taken on the winter hunt the ranges were entirely deserted. It is equally certain, however, that a few small bands remained in certain portions of Montana throughout the summer. But the main body crossed the international boundary, and spent the summer on the plains of the Saskatchewan, where they were hunted by the half-breeds from the Red River settlements and the Indians of the plains. It is my belief that in this movement nearly all the buffaloes of Montana and Dakota participated, and that the herds which spent the summer in Dakota, where they were annually hunted by the Red River half-breeds, came up from Kansas, Colorado, and Nebraska.

While most of the calves were born on the summer ranges, many were brought forth en route. It was the habit of the cows to retire to a secluded spot, if possible a ravine well screened from observation, bring forth their young, and nourish and defend them until they were strong enough to join the herd. Calves were born all the time from March to July, and sometimes even as late as August. On the summer ranges it was the habit of the cows to leave the bulls at calving time, and thus it often happened that small herds were often seen composed of bulls only. Usually the cow produced but one calf, but twins were not uncommon. Of course many calves were brought forth in the herd, but the favorite habit of the cow was as stated. As soon as the young calves were brought into the herd, which for prudential reasons occurred at the earliest possible moment, the bulls assumed the duty of protecting them from the wolves which at all times congregated in the vicinity of a herd, watching for an opportunity to seize a calf or a wounded buffalo which might be left behind. A calf always follows its mother until its successor is appointed and installed, unless separated from her by force of circumstances. They suck until they are nine months old, or even older, and Mr. McNaney once saw a lusty calf suck its mother (in January) on the Montana range several hours after she had been killed for her skin.

When a buffalo is wounded it leaves the herd immediately and goes off as far from the line of pursuit as it can get, to escape the rabble of hunters, who are sure to follow the main body. If any deep ravines are at hand the wounded animal limps away to the bottom of the deepest and most secluded one, and gradually works his way up to its very head, where he finds himself in a perfect cul-de-sac, barely wide enough to admit him. Here he is so completely hidden by the high walls and numerous bends that his pursuer must needs come within a few feet of his horns before his huge bulk is visible. I have more than once been astonished at the real impregnability of the retreats selected by wounded bison. In following up wounded bulls in ravine headings it always became too dangerous to make the last stage of the pursuit on horseback, for fear of being caught in a passage so narrow as to insure a fatal accident to man or horse in case of a sudden discovery of the quarry. I have seen wounded bison shelter in situations where a single bull could easily defend himself from a whole pack of wolves, being completely walled in on both sides and the rear, and leaving his foes no point of attack save his head and horns.

Bison which were nursing serious wounds must often have gone many days at a time without either food or water, and in this connection it may be mentioned that the recuperative power of a bison is really wonderful. Judging from the number of old leg wounds, fully healed, which I have found in freshly killed bisons, one may be tempted to believe that a bison never died of a broken leg. One large bull which I skeletonized had had his humerus shot squarely in two, but it had united again more firmly than ever. Another large bull had the head of his left femur and the hip socket shattered completely to pieces by a big ball, but he had entirely recovered from it, and was as lusty a runner as any bull we chased. We found that while a broken leg was a misfortune to a buffalo, it always took something more serious than that to stop him.

VI. THE FOOD OF THE BISON.

It is obviously impossible to enumerate all the grasses which served the bison as food on his native heath without presenting a complete list of all the plants of that order found in a given region; but it is at least desirable to know which of the grasses of the great pasture region were his favorite and most common food. It was the nutritious character and marvelous abundance of his food supply which enabled the bison to exist in such absolutely countless numbers as characterized his occupancy of the great plains. The following list comprises the grasses which were the bison's principal food, named in the order of their importance:

Bouteloua oligostachya (buffalo, grama, or mesquite grass).—This remarkable grass formed the *pièce de résistance* of the bison's bill of fare in the days when he flourished, and it now comes to us daily in the form of beef produced of primest quality and in greatest quantity on what was until recently the great buffalo range. This grass is the most abundant and widely distributed species to be found in the great pasture region between the eastern slope of the Rocky Mountains and the nineteenth degree of west longitude. It is the principal grass of the plains from Texas to the British Possessions, and even in the latter territory it is quite conspicuous. To any one but a botanist its first acquaintance means a surprise. Its name and fame lead the unacquainted to expect a grass which is tall, rank, and full of "fodder," like the "blue-joint" (*Andropogon provincialis*). The grama grass is very short, the leaves being usually not more than 2 or 3 inches in length and crowded together at the base of the stems. The flower stalk is about a foot in height, but on grazed lands are eaten off and but seldom seen. The leaves are narrow and inclined to curl, and lie close to the ground. Instead of developing a continuous growth, this grass grows in small, irregular patches, usually about the size of a man's hand, with narrow strips of perfectly bare ground between them. The grass curls closely upon the ground, in a woolly carpet or cushion, greatly resembling a layer of Florida moss. Even in spring-time it never shows more color than a tint of palest green, and the landscape which is dependent upon this grass for color is never more than "a gray and melancholy waste." Unlike the soft, juicy, and succulent grasses of the well-watered portions of the United States, the tiny leaves of the grama grass are hard, stiff, and dry. I have often noticed that in grazing neither cattle nor horses are able to bite off the blades, but instead each leaf is pulled out of the tuft, seemingly by its root.

Notwithstanding its dry and uninviting appearance, this grass is highly nutritious, and its fat-producing qualities are unexcelled. The heat of summer dries it up effectually without destroying its nutritive elements, and it becomes for the remainder of the year excellent hay, cured on its own roots. It affords good grazing all the year round, save in winter, when it is covered with snow, and even then, if the snow is not too deep, the buffaloes, cattle, and horses paw down through it to reach the grass, or else repair to wind-swept ridges and hill-tops, where the snow has been blown off and left the grass partly exposed. Stock prefer it to all the other grasses of the plains.

On bottom-lands, where moisture is abundant, this grass develops much more luxuriantly, growing in a close mass, and often to a height of a foot or more, if not grazed down, when it is cut for hay, and sometimes yields $1\frac{1}{2}$ tons to the acre. In Montana and the north it is generally known as "buffalo-grass," a name to which it would seem to be fully entitled, notwithstanding the fact that this name is also applied, and quite generally, to another species, the next to be noticed.

Buchloë dactyloides (Southern buffalo-grass).—This species is next in value and extent of distribution to the grama grass. It also is found all over the great plains south of Nebraska and southern Wyoming, but not further north, although in many localities it occurs so sparsely as to be of little account. A single bunch of it very greatly resembles *Bouteloua oligostachya*, but its general growth is very different. It is very short, its general mass seldom rising more than 3 inches above the ground. It grows in extensive patches, and spreads by means of stolons, which sometimes are 2 feet in length, with joints every 3 or 4 inches. Owing to its southern distribution this might well be named the Southern buffalo grass, to distinguish it from the two other species of higher latitudes, to which the name "buffalo" has been fastened forever.

Stipa spartea (Northern buffalo-grass; wild oat).—This grass is found in southern Manitoba, westwardly across the plains to the Rocky Mountains, and southward as far as Montana, where it is common in many localities. On what was once the buffalo range of the British Possessions this rank grass formed the bulk of the winter pasturage, and in that region is quite as famous as our grama grass. An allied species (*Stipa viridula*, bunch-grass) is "widely diffused over our Rocky Mountain region, extending to California and British America, and furnishing a considerable part of the wild forage of the region." *Stipa spartea* bears an ill name among stockmen on account of the fact that at the base of each seed is a very hard and sharp-pointed callus, which under certain circumstances (so it is said) lodges in the cheeks of domestic animals that feed upon this grass when it is dry, and which cause much trouble. But the buffalo, like the wild horse and half-wild range cattle, evidently escaped this annoyance. This grass is one of the common species over a wide area of the northern plains, and is always found on soil which is comparatively dry. In Dakota, Minnesota, and northwest Iowa it forms a considerable portion of the upland prairie hay.

Of the remaining grasses it is practically impossible to single out any one as being specially entitled to fourth place in this list. There are several species which flourish in different localities, and in many respects appear to be of about equal importance as food for stock. Of these the following are the most noteworthy:

Aristida purpurea (Western beard-grass; purple "bunch-grass" of Montana).—On the high, rolling prairies of the Missouri-Yellowstone divide this grass is very abundant. It grows in little solitary bunches, about 6 inches high, scattered through the curly buffalo-grass (*Bouteloua oligostachya*). Under more favorable conditions it grows to a height of 12 to 18 inches. It is one of the prettiest grasses of that region, and in the fall and winter its purplish color makes it quite noticeable. The Montana stockmen consider it one of the most valuable grasses of that region for stock of all kinds. Mr. C. M. Jacobs assured me that the buffalo used to be very fond of this grass, and that "wherever this grass grew in abundance there were the best hunting-grounds for the bison." It appears that *Aristida purpurea* is not sufficiently abundant elsewhere in the Northwest to make it an inportant food for stock; but Dr. Vesey declares that it is "abundant on the plains of Kansas, New Mexico, and Texas."

Kœleria cristata.—Very generally distributed from Texas and New Mexico to the British Possessions; sand hills and arid soils; mountains, up to 8,000 feet.

Poa tenuifolia (blue-grass of the plains and mountains).—A valuable "bunch-grass," widely distributed throughout the great pasture region; grows in all sorts of soils and situations; common in the Yellowstone Park.

Festuca scabrella (bunch-grass).—One of the most valuable grasses of Montana and the Northwest generally; often called the "great bunch-grass." It furnishes excellent food for horses and cattle, and is so tall it is cut in large quantities for hay. This is the prevailing species on the foot-hills and mountains generally, up to an altitude of 7,000 feet, where it is succeeded by *Festuca ovina.*

Andropogon provincialis (blue-stem).—An important species, extending from eastern Kansas and Nebraska to the foot-hills of the Rocky Mountains, and from Northern Texas to the Saskatchewan; common in Montana on alkali flats and bottom lands generally. This and the preceding species were of great value to the buffalo in winter, when the shorter grasses were covered with snow.

Andropogon scoparius (bunch-grass; broom sedge; wood-grass).—Similar to the preceding in distribution and value, but not nearly so tall.

None of the buffalo-grasses are found in the mountains. In the mountain regions which have been visited by the buffalo and in the Yellowstone Park, where to-day the only herd remaining in a state of nature is to be found (though not by the man with a gun), the following are the grasses which form all but a small proportion of the ruminant food: *Kœleria cristata; Poa tenuifolia* (Western blue-grass); *Stipa viridula* (feather-grass); *Stipa comata; Agropyrum divergens; Agropyrum caninum.*

When pressed by hunger, the buffalo used to browse on certain species of sage-brush, particularly *Atriplex canescens* of the Southwest. But he was discriminating in the matter of diet, and as far as can be ascertained he was never known to eat the famous and much-dreaded "loco" weed (*Astragalus molissimus*), which to ruminant animals is a veritable drug of madness. Domestic cattle and horses often eat this plant where it is abundant, and become demented in consequence.

VII. MENTAL CAPACITY AND DISPOSITION.

(1) *Reasoning from cause to effect.*—The buffalo of the past was an animal of a rather low order of intelligence, and his dullness of intel-

lect was one of the important factors in his phenomenally swift extermination. He was provokingly slow in comprehending the existence and nature of the dangers that threatened his life, and, like the stupid brute that he was, would very often stand quietly and see two or three score, or even a hundred, of his relatives and companions shot down before his eyes, with no other feeling than one of stupid wonder and curiosity. Neither the noise nor smoke of the still-hunter's rifle, the falling, struggling, nor the final death of his companions conveyed to his mind the idea of a danger to be fled from, and so the herd stood still and allowed the still-hunter to slaughter its members at will.

Like the Indian, and many white men also, the buffalo seemed to feel that their number was so great it could never be sensibly diminished. The presence of such a great multitude gave to each of its individuals a feeling of security and mutual support that is very generally found in animals who congregate in great herds. The time was when a band of elk would stand stupidly and wait for its members to be shot down one after another; but it is believed that this was due more to panic than to a lack of comprehension of danger.

The fur seals who cover the "hauling grounds" of St. Paul and St. George Islands, Alaska, in countless thousands, have even less sense of danger and less comprehension of the slaughter of thousands of their kind, which takes place daily, than had the bison. They allow themselves to be herded and driven off landwards from the hauling-ground for half a mile to the killing-ground, and, finally, with most cheerful indifference, permit the Aleuts to club their brains out.

It is to be added that whenever and wherever seals or sea-lions inhabit a given spot, with but few exceptions, it is an easy matter to approach individuals of the herd. The presence of an immense number of individuals plainly begets a feeling of security and mutual support. And let not the bison or the seal be blamed for this, for man himself exhibits the same foolish instinct. Who has not met the woman of mature years and full intellectual vigor who is mortally afraid to spend a night entirely alone in her own house, but is perfectly willing to do so, and often does do so without fear, when she can have the company of one small and helpless child, or, what is still worse, three or four of them?

But with the approach of extermination, and the utter breaking up of all the herds, a complete change has been wrought in the character of the bison. At last, but alas! entirely too late, the crack of the rifle and its accompanying puff of smoke conveyed to the slow mind of the bison a sense of deadly danger to himself. At last he recognized man, whether on foot or horseback, or peering at him from a coulée, as his mortal enemy. At last he learned to run. In 1886 we found the scattered remnant of the great northern herd the wildest and most difficult animals to kill that we had ever hunted in any country. It had been only through the keenest exercise of all their powers of self-preservation that those buffaloes had survived until that late day, and we found them almost as swift as antelopes and far more wary. The instant a buffalo caught sight of a man, even though a mile distant, he was off at the top of his speed, and generally ran for some wild region several miles away.

In our party was an experienced buffalo-hunter, who in three years had slaughtered over three thousand head for their hides. He declared that if he could ever catch a " bunch" at rest he could " get a stand" the same as he used to do, and kill several head before the rest would run. It so happened that the first time we found buffaloes we discovered a bunch of fourteen head, lying in the sun at noon, on the level top of a low butte, all noses pointing up the wind. We stole up within range and fired. At the instant the first shot rang out up sprang every buffalo as if he had been thrown upon his feet by steel springs, and in a second's time the whole bunch was dashing away from us with the speed of race-horses.

Our buffalo-hunter declared that in chasing buffaloes we could count with certainty upon their always running against the wind, for this had always been their habit. Although this was once their habit, we soon found that those who now represent the survival of the fittest have learned better wisdom, and now run (1) away from their pursuer and (2) toward the best hiding place. Now they pay no attention whatever to the direction of the wind, and if a pursuer follows straight behind, a buffalo may change his course three or four times in a 10-mile chase. An old bull once led one of our hunters around three-quarters of a circle which had a diameter of 5 or 6 miles.

The last buffaloes were mentally as capable of taking care of themselves as any animals I ever hunted. The power of original reasoning which they manifested in scattering all over a given tract of rough country, like hostile Indians when hotly pressed by soldiers, in the Indian-like manner in which they hid from sight in deep hollows, and, as we finally proved, in *grazing only in ravines and hollows*, proved conclusively that *but for the use of fire-arms* those very buffaloes would have been actually safe from harm by man, and that they would have increased indefinitely. As they were then, the Indians' arrows and spears could never have been brought to bear upon them, save in rare instances, for they had thoroughly learned to dread man and fly from him for their lives. Could those buffaloes have been protected from rifles and revolvers the resultant race would have displayed far more active mental powers, keener vision, and finer physique than the extinguished race possessed.

In fleeing from an enemy the buffalo ran against the wind, in order that his keen scent might save him from the disaster of running upon new enemies; which was an idea wholly his own, and not copied by any other animal so far as known.

But it must be admitted that the buffalo of the past was very often a most stupid reasoner. He would deliberately walk into a quicksand, where hundreds of his companions were already ingulfed and in their death-struggle. He would quit feeding, run half a mile, and rush head-long into a moving train of cars that happened to come between him and the main herd on the other side of the track. He allowed himself to be impounded and slaughtered by a howling mob in a rudely constructed pen, which a combined effort on the part of three or four old bulls would have utterly demolished at any point. A herd of a thousand buffaloes would allow an armed hunter to gallop into their midst, very often within arm's-length, when any of the bulls nearest him might easily have bowled him over and had him trampled to death in a moment. The hunter who would ride in that manner into a herd of the Cape buffaloes of Africa (*Bubalus caffer*) would be unhorsed and killed before he had gone half a furlong.

(2) *Curiosity.*—The buffalo of the past possessed but little curiosity; he was too dull to entertain many unnecessary thoughts. Had he possessed more of this peculiar trait, which is the mark of an inquiring mind, he would much sooner have accomplished a comprehension of the dangers that proved his destruction. His stolid indifference to everything he did not understand cost him his existence, although in later years he displayed more interest in his environment. On one occasion in hunting I staked my success with an old bull I was pursuing on the chance that when he reached the crest of a ridge his curiosity would prompt him to pause an instant to look at me. Up to that moment he had had only one quick glance at me before he started to run. As he climbed the slope ahead of me, in full view, I dismounted and made ready to fire the instant he should pause to look at me. As I expected, he did come to a full stop on the crest of the ridge, and turned half around to look at me. But for his curiosity I should have been obliged to fire at him under very serious disadvantages.

(3) *Fear.*—With the buffalo, fear of man is now the ruling passion. Says Colonel Dodge: "He is as timid about his flank and rear as a raw recruit. When traveling nothing in front stops him, but an unusual object in the rear will send him to the right-about [toward the main body of the herd] at the top of his speed."

(4) *Courage.*—It was very seldom that the buffalo evinced any courage save that of despair, which even cowards possess. Unconscious of his strength, his only thought was flight, and it was only when brought to bay that he was ready to fight. Now and then, however, in the chase, the buffalo turned upon his pursuer and overthrew horse and rider. Sometimes the tables were completely turned, and the hunter found his only safety in flight. During the buffalo slaughter the butchers sometimes had narrow escapes from buffaloes supposed to be dead or mortally wounded, and a story comes from the great northern range south of Glendive of a hunter who was killed by an old bull whose tongue he had actually cut out in the belief that he was dead.

Sometimes buffalo cows display genuine courage in remaining with their calves in the presence of danger, although in most cases they left their offspring to their fate. During a hunt for live buffalo calves, undertaken by Mr. C. J. Jones of Garden City, Kans., in 1886, and very graphically described by a staff correspondent of the American Field in a series of articles in that journal under the title of "The Last of the Buffalo," the following remarkable incident occurred:[*]

"The last calf was caught by Carter, who roped it neatly as Mr. Jones cut it out of the herd and turned it toward him. This was a fine heifer calf, and was apparently the idol of her mother's heart, for the latter came very near making a casualty the price of the capture. As soon as the calf was roped, the old cow left the herd and charged on Carter viciously, as he bent over his victim. Seeing the danger, Mr. Jones rode in at just the nick of time, and drove the cow off for a moment; but she returned again and again, and finally began charging him whenever he came near; so that, much as he regretted it, he had to shoot her with his revolver, which he did, killing her almost immediately."

The mothers of the thirteen other calves that were caught by Mr. Jones's party allowed their offspring to be "cut out," lassoed, and tied, while they themselves devoted all their energies to leaving them as far behind as possible.

(5) *Affection.*—While the buffalo cows manifested a fair degree of affection for their young, the adult bulls of the herd often displayed a sense of responsibility for the safety of the calves that was admirable, to say the least. Those who have had opportunities for watching large herds tell us that whenever wolves approached and endeavored to reach a calf the old bulls would immediately interpose and drive the enemy away. It was a well-defined habit for the bulls to form the outer circle of every small group or section of a great herd, with the calves in the center, well guarded from the wolves, which regarded them as their most choice prey.

Colonel Dodge records a remarkable incident in illustration of the manner in which the bull buffaloes protected the calves of the herd.[†]

"The duty of protecting the calves devolved almost entirely on the bulls. I have seen evidences of this many times, but the most remarkable instance I have ever heard of was related to me by an army surgeon, who was an eye-witness.

"He was one evening returning to camp after a day's hunt, when his attention was attracted by the curious action of a little knot of six or eight buffalo. Approaching sufficiently near to see clearly, he discovered that this little knot were all bulls, standing in a close circle, with their heads outwards, while in a concentric circle at some 12 or 15 paces distant sat, licking their chaps in impatient expectancy, at least a dozen large gray wolves (excepting man, the most dangerous enemy of the buffalo).

---

[*]American Field, July 24, 1886, p. 78.
†Plains of the Great West, p. 125.

"The doctor determined to watch the performance. After a few mo.
ments the knot broke up, and, still keeping in a compact mass, started
on a trot for the main herd, some half a mile off. To his very great as-
tonishment, the doctor now saw that the central and controlling figure
of this mass was a poor little calf so newly born as scarcely to be able
to walk. After going 50 or 100 paces the calf laid down, the bulls disposed themselves in a circle as before, and the wolves, who had trotted
along on each side of their retreating supper, sat down and licked their
chaps again; and though the doctor did not see the finale, it being late
and the camp distant, he had no doubt that the noble fathers did their
whole duty by their offspring, and carried it safely to the herd."

(6) *Temper.*—I have asked many old buffalo hunters for facts in regard to the temper and disposition of herd buffaloes, and all agree that
they are exceedingly quiet, peace-loving, and even indolent animals at
all times save during the rutting season. Says Colonel Dodge: "The
habits of the buffalo are almost identical with those of the domestic
cattle. Owing either to a more pacific disposition, or to the greater
number of bulls, there is very little fighting, even at the season when it
might be expected. I have been among them for days, have watched
their conduct for hours at a time, and with the very best opportunities
for observation, but have never seen a regular combat between bulls.
They frequently strike each other with their horns, but this seems to be
a mere expression of impatience at being crowded."

In referring to the "running season." of the buffalo, Mr. Catlin says:
"It is no uncommon thing at this season, at these gatherings, to see
several thousands in a mass eddying and wheeling about under a cloud
of dust, which is raised by the bulls as they are pawing in the dirt, or
engaged in desperate combats, as they constantly are, plunging and
butting at each other in a most furious manner."

On the whole, the disposition of the buffalo is anything but vicious.
Both sexes yield with surprising readiness to the restraints of captivity,
and in a remarkably short time become, if taken young, as fully domesticated as ordinary cattle. Buffalo calves are as easily tamed as domestic
ones, and make very interesting pets. A prominent trait of character
in the captive buffalo is a mulish obstinacy or headstrong perseverance
under certain circumstances that is often very annoying. When a buffalo makes up his mind to go through a fence, he is very apt to go
through, either peaceably or by force, as occasion requires. Fortunately,
however, the captive animals usually accept a fence in the proper spirit,
and treat it with a fair degree of respect.

VIII. VALUE OF THE BUFFALO TO MAN.

It may fairly be supposed that if the people of this country could have
been made to realize the immense money value of the great buffalo
herds as they existed in 1870, a vigorous and successful effort would
have been made to regulate and restrict the slaughter. The fur

seal of Alaska, of which about 100,000 are killed annually for their skins, yield an annual revenue to the Government of $100,000, and add $900,000 more to the actual wealth of the United States. It pays to protect those seals, and we mean to protect them against all comers who seek their unrestricted slaughter, no matter whether the poachers be American, English, Russian, or Canadian. It would be folly to do otherwise, and if those who would exterminate the fur seal by shooting them in the water will not desist for the telling, then they must by the compelling.

The fur seal is a good investment for the United States, and their number is not diminishing. As the buffalo herds existed in 1870, 500,000 head of bulls, young and old, could have been killed every year for a score of years without sensibly diminishing the size of the herds. At a low estimate these could easily have been made to yield various products worth $5 each, as follows: Robe, $2.50; tongue, 25 cents; meat of hind-quarters, $2; bones, horns, and hoofs, 25 cents; total, $5. And the amount annually added to the wealth of the United States would have been $2,500,000.

On all the robes taken for the market, say, 200,000, the Government could have collected a tax of 50 cents each, which would have yielded a sum doubly sufficient to have maintained a force of mounted police fully competent to enforce the laws regulating the slaughter. Had a contract for the protection of the buffalo been offered at $50,000 per annum, ay, or even half that sum, an army of competent men would have competed for it every year, and it could have been carried out to the letter. But, as yet, the American people have not learned to spend money for the protection of valuable game; and by the time they do learn it, there will be no game to protect.

Even despite the enormous waste of raw material that ensued in the utilization of the buffalo product, the total cash value of all the material derived from this source, if it could only be reckoned up, would certainly amount to many millions of dollars—perhaps twenty millions, all told. This estimate may, to some, seem high, but when we stop to consider that in eight years, from 1876 to 1884, a single firm, that of Messrs. J. & A. Boskowitz, 105 Greene street, New York, paid out the enormous sum of $923,070 (nearly one million) for robes and hides, and that in a single year (1882) another firm, that of Joseph Ullman, 165 Mercer street, New York, paid out $216,250 for robes and hides, it may not seem so incredible.

Had there been a deliberate plan for the suppression of all statistics relating to the slaughter of buffalo in the United States, and what it yielded, the result could not have been more complete barrenness than exists to-day in regard to this subject. There is only one railway company which kept its books in such a manner as to show the kind and quantity of its business at that time. Excepting this, nothing is known definitely.

Fortunately, enough facts and figures were recorded during the hunting operations of the Red River half-breeds to enable us, by bringing them all together, to calculate with sufficient exactitude the value of the buffalo to them from 1820 to 1840. The result ought to be of interest to all who think it is not worth while to spend money in preserving our characteristic game animals.

In Ross's "Red River Settlement," pp. 242–273, and Schoolcraft's "North American Indians," Part IV, pp. 101–110, are given detailed accounts of the conduct and results of two hunting expeditions by the half-breeds, with many valuable statistics. On this data we base our calculation.

Taking the result of one particular day's slaughter as an index to the methods of the hunters in utilizing the products of the chase, we find that while "not less than 2,500 animals were killed," out of that number only 375 bags of pemmican and 240 bales of dried meat were made. "Now," says Mr. Ross, "making all due allowance for waste, 750 animals would have been ample for such a result. What, then, we might ask, became of the remaining 1,750? * * * Scarcely one-third in number of the animals killed is turned to account."

A bundle of dried meat weighs 60 to 70 pounds, and a bag of pemmican 100 to 110 pounds. If economically worked up, a whole buffalo cow yields half a bag of pemmican (about 55 pounds) and three-fourths of a bundle of dried meat (say 45 pounds). The most economical calculate that from eight to ten cows are required to load a single Red River cart. The proceeds of 1,776 cows once formed 228 bags of pemmican, 1,213 bales of dried meat, 166 sacks of tallow, each weighing 200 pounds, 556 bladders of marrow weighing 12 pounds each, and the value of the whole was $8,160. The total of the above statement is 132,657 pounds of buffalo product for 1,776 cows, or within a fraction of 75 pounds to each cow. The bulls and young animals killed were not accounted for.

The expedition described by Mr. Ross contained 1,210 carts and 620 hunters, and returned with 1,089,000 pounds of meat, making 900 pounds for each cart, and 200 pounds for each individual in the expedition, of all ages and both sexes. Allowing, as already ascertained, that of the above quantity of product every 75 pounds represents one cow saved and two and one-third buffaloes wasted, it means that 14,520 buffaloes were killed and utilized and 33,250 buffaloes were killed and eaten fresh or wasted, and 47,770 buffaloes were killed by 620 hunters, or an average of 77 buffaloes to each hunter. The total number of buffaloes killed for each cart was 39.

Allowing, what was actually the case, that every buffalo killed would, if properly cared for, have yielded meat, fat, and robe worth at least $5, the total value of the buffaloes slaughtered by that expedition amounted to $238,850, and of which the various products actually utilized represented a cash value of $72,600 added to the wealth of the Red River half-breeds.

In 1820 there went 540 carts to the buffalo plains; in 1825, 680; in 1830, 820; in 1835, 970; in 1840, 1,210.

From 1820 to 1825 the average for each year was 610; from 1825 to 1830, 750; from 1830 to 1835, 895; from 1835 to 1840, 1,090.

Accepting the statements of eye-witnesses that for every buffalo killed two and one-third buffaloes are wasted or eaten on the spot, and that every loaded cart represented thirty-nine dead buffaloes which were worth when utilized $5 each, we have the following series of totals:

From 1820 to 1825 five expeditions, of 610 carts each, killed 118,950 buffaloes, worth $594,750.

From 1825 to 1830 five expeditions, of 750 carts each, killed 146,250 buffaloes, worth $731,250.

From 1830 to 1835 five expeditions, of 895 carts each, killed 174,525 buffaloes, worth $872,625.

From 1835 to 1840 five expeditions, of 1,090 carts each, killed 212,550 buffaloes, worth $1,062,750.

Total number of buffaloes killed in twenty years,* $652,275; total value of buffaloes killed in twenty years,* $3,261,375; total value of the product utilized* and added to the wealth of the settlements, $978,412.

The Eskimo has his seal, which yields nearly everything that he requires; the Korak of Siberia depends for his very existence upon his reindeer; the Ceylon native has the cocoa-nut palm, which leaves him little else to desire, and the North American Indian had the American bison. If any animal was ever designed by the hand of nature for the express purpose of supplying, at one stroke, nearly all the wants of an entire race, surely the buffalo was intended for the Indian.

And right well was this gift of the gods utilized by the children of nature to whom it came. Up to the time when the United States Government began to support our Western Indians by the payment of annuities and furnishing quarterly supplies of food, clothing, blankets, cloth, tents, etc., the buffalo had been the main dependence of more than 50,000 Indians who inhabited the buffalo range and its environs. Of the many different uses to which the buffalo and his various parts were put by the red man, the following were the principal ones:

The body of the buffalo yielded fresh meat, of which thousands of tons were consumed; dried meat, prepared in summer for winter use; pemmican (also prepared in summer), of meat, fat, and berries; tallow, made up into large balls or sacks, and kept in store; marrow, preserved in bladders; and tongues, dried and smoked, and eaten as a delicacy.

The skin of the buffalo yielded a robe, dressed with the hair on, for clothing and bedding; a hide, dressed without the hair, which made a teepee cover, when a number were sewn together; boats, when sewn together in a green state, over a wooden framework. Shields, made

---

* By the Red River half-breeds only.

from the thickest portions, as rawhide; ropes, made up as rawhide; clothing of many kinds; bags for use in traveling; coffins, or winding sheets for the dead, etc.

Other portions utilized were sinews, which furnished fiber for ropes, thread, bow-strings, snow-shoe webs, etc.; hair, which was sometimes made into belts and ornaments; "buffalo chips," which formed a valuable and highly-prized fuel; bones, from which many articles of use and ornament were made; horns, which were made into spoons, drinking vessels, etc.

After the United States Government began to support the buffalo-hunting Indians with annuities and supplies, the woolen blanket and canvas tent took the place of the buffalo robe and the skin-covered teepee, and "Government beef" took the place of buffalo meat. But the slaughter of buffaloes went on just the same, and the robes and hides taken were traded for useless and often harmful luxuries, such as canned provisions, fancy knickknacks, whisky, fire-arms of the most approved pattern, and quantities of fixed ammunition. During the last ten years of the existence of the herds it is an open question whether the buffalo did not do our Indians more harm than good. Amongst the Crows, who were liberally provided for by the Government, horse-racing was a common pastime, and the stakes were usually dressed buffalo robes.*

The total disappearance of the buffalo has made no perceptible difference in the annual cost of the Indians to the Government. During the years when buffaloes were numerous and robes for the purchase of fire-arms and cartridges were plentiful, Indian wars were frequent, and always costly to the Government. The Indians were then quite independent, because they could take the war-path at any time and live on buffalo indefinitely. Now, the case is very different. The last time Sitting Bull went on the war-path and was driven up into Manitoba, he had the doubtful pleasure of living on his ponies and dogs until he became utterly starved out. Since his last escapade, the Sioux have been compelled to admit that the game is up and the war-path is open to them no longer. Should they wish to do otherwise they know that they could survive only by killing cattle, and cattle that are guarded by cow-boys and ranchmen are no man's game. Therefore, while we no longer have to pay for an annual campaign in force against hostile Indians, the total absence of the buffalo brings upon the nation the entire support of the Indian, and the cash outlay each year is as great as ever.

The value of the American bison to civilized man can never be calculated, nor even fairly estimated. It may with safety be said, however, that it has been probably tenfold greater than most persons have

---

* On one occasion, which is doubtless still remembered with bitterness by many a Crow of the Custer Agency, my old friend Jim McNaney backed his horse Ogalalla against the horses of the whole Crow tribe. The Crows forthwith formed a pool, which consisted of a huge pile of buffalo robes, worth about $1,200, and with it backed their best race-horse. He was forthwith "beaten out of sight" by Ogalalla, and another grievance was registered against the whites.

ever supposed. It would be a work of years to gather statistics of the immense bulk of robes and hides, undoubtedly amounting to millions in the aggregate; the thousands of tons of meat, and the train-loads of bones which have been actually utilized by man. Nor can the effect of the bison's presence upon the general development of the great West ever be calculated. It has sunk into the great sum total of our progress, and well-nigh lost to sight forever.

As a mere suggestion of the immense value of "the buffalo product" at the time when it had an existence, I have obtained from two of our leading fur houses in New York City, with branches elsewhere, a detailed statement of their business in buffalo robes and hides during the last few years of the trade. They not only serve to show the great value of the share of the annual crop that passed through their hands, but that of Messrs. J. & A. Boskowitz is of especial value, because, being carefully itemized throughout, it shows the decline and final failure of the trade in exact figures. I am under many obligations to both these firms for their kindness in furnishing the facts I desired, and especially to the Messrs. Boskowitz, who devoted considerable time and labor to the careful compilation of the annexed statement of their business in buffalo skins.

Memorandum of buffalo robes and hides bought by Messrs. J. & A. Boskowitz, 101–105 Greene street, New York, and 202 Lake street, Chicago, from 1876 to 1884.

Year.	Buffalo robes.		Buffalo hides.	
	Number.	Cost.	Number.	Cost.
1876	31,838	$39,620	None.	....
1877	9,353	35,660	None.	....
1878	41,268	150,500	None.	....
1879	28,613	110,420	None.	....
1880	34,901	176,200	4,570	$13,140
1881	23,355	151,800	26,601	89,030
1882	2,124	15,600	15,464	44,140
1883	5,690	29,770	21,869	67,190
1884	None.	....	529	1,720
Total	177,142	709,570	69,033	215,220

Total number of buffalo skins handled in nine years, 246,175; total cost, $924,790.

I have also been favored with some very interesting facts and figures regarding the business done in buffalo skins by the firm of Mr. Joseph Ullman, exporter and importer of furs and robes, of 165–167 Mercer street, New York, and also 353 Jackson street, St. Paul, Minnesota. The following letter was written me by Mr. Joseph Ullman on November 12, 1887, for which I am greatly indebted:

"Inasmuch as you particularly desire the figures for the years 1880–'86, I have gone through my buffalo robe and hide accounts of those years, and herewith give you approximate figures, as there are a good many things to be considered which make it difficult to give exact figures.

"In 1881 we handled about 14,000 hides, average cost about $3.50, and 12,000 robes, average cost about $7.50.

"In 1882 we purchased between 35,000 and 40,000 hides, at an average cost of about $3.50, and about 10,000 robes, at an average cost of about $8.50.

"In 1883 we purchased from 6,000 to 7,000 hides and about 1,500 to 2,000 robes at a slight advance in price against the year previous.

"In 1884 we purchased less than 2,500 hides, and in my opinion these were such as were carried over from the previous season in the Northwest, and were not fresh-slaughtered skins. The collection of robes this season was also comparatively small, and nominally robes carried over from 1883.

"In 1885 the collection of hides amounted to little or nothing.

"The aforesaid goods were all purchased direct in the Northwest, that is to say, principally in Montana, and shipped in care of our branch house at St. Paul, Minnesota, to Joseph Ullman, Chicago. The robes mentioned above were Indian-tanned robes and were mainly disposed of to the jobbing trade both East and West.

"In 1881 and the years prior, the hides were divided into two kinds, viz, robe hides, which were such as had a good crop of fur and were serviceable for robe purposes, and the heavy and short-furred bull hides. The former were principally sold to the John S. Way Manufacturing Company, Bridgeport, Connecticut, and to numerous small robe tanners, while the latter were sold for leather purposes to various hide-tanners throughout the United States and Canada, and brought 5½ to 8½ cents per pound. A very large proportion of these latter were tanned by the Wilcox Tanning Company, Wilcox, Pennsylvania.

"About the fall of 1882 we established a tannery for buffalo robes in Chicago, and from that time forth we tanned all the good hides which we received into robes and disposed of them in the same manner as the Indian-tanned robes.

"I don't know that I am called upon to express an opinion as to the benefit or disadvantage of the extermination of the buffalo, but nevertheless take the liberty to say that I think that some proper law restricting the unpardonable slaughter of the buffalo should have been enacted at the time. It is a well-known fact that soon after the Northern Pacific Railroad opened up that portion of the country, thereby making the transportation of the buffalo hides feasible, that is to say, reducing the cost of freight, thousands upon thousands of buffaloes were killed for the sake of the hide alone, while the carcasses were left to rot on the open plains.

"The average prices paid the buffalo hunters [from 1880 to 1884] was about as follows: For cow hides [robes?], $3; bull hides, $2.50; yearlings, $1.50; calves, 75 cents; and the cost of getting the hides to market brought the cost up to about $3.50 per hide."

The amount actually paid out by Joseph Ullman, in four years, for buffalo robes and hides was about $310,000, and this, too, long after the great southern herd had ceased to exist, and when the northern herd furnished the sole supply. It thus appears that during the course of eight years business (leaving out the small sum paid out in 1884), on the part of the Messrs. Boskowitz, and four years on that of Mr. Joseph Ullman, these two firms alone paid out the enormous sum of $1,233,070 for buffalo robes and hides which they purchased to sell again at a good profit. By the time their share of the buffalo product reached the consumers it must have represented an actual money value of about $2,000,000.

Besides these two firms there were at that time many others who also handled great quantities of buffalo skins and hides for which they paid out immense sums of money. In this country the other leading firms engaged in this business were I. G. Baker & Co., of Fort Benton; P. B. Weare & Co., Chicago; Obern, Hoosick & Co., Chicago and Saint Paul; Martin Bates & Co., and Messrs. Shearer, Nichols & Co. (now Hurlburt, Shearer & Sanford), of New York. There were also many others whose names I am now unable to recall.

In the British Possessions and Canada the frontier business was largely monopolized by the Hudson's Bay Fur Company, although the annual "output" of robes and hides was but small in comparison with that gathered in the United States, where the herds were far more numerous. Even in their most fruitful locality for robes—the country south of the Saskatchewan—this company had a very powerful competitor in the firm of I. G. Baker & Co., of Fort Benton, which secured the lion's share of the spoil and sent it down the Missouri River.

It is quite certain that the utilization of the buffalo product, even so far as it was accomplished, resulted in the addition of several millions of dollars to the wealth of the people of the United States. That the total sum, could it be reckoned up, would amount to at least fifteen millions, seems reasonably certain; and my own impression is that twenty millions would be nearer the mark. It is much to be regretted that the exact truth can never be known, for in this age of universal slaughter a knowledge of the cash value of the wild game of the United States that has been killed up to date might go far toward bringing about the actual as well as the theoretical protection of what remains.

UTILIZATION OF THE BUFFALO BY WHITE MEN.

Robes.—Ordinarily the skin of a large ruminant is of little value in comparison with the bulk of toothsome flesh it covers. In fattening domestic cattle for the market, the value of the hide is so insignificant that it amounts to no more than a butcher's perquisite in reckoning up the value of the animal. With the buffalo, however, so enormous was the waste of the really available product that probably nine-tenths of the total value derived from the slaughter of the animal came from his skin alone. Of this, about four-fifths came from the utilization of the furry robe and one-fifth from skins classed as "hides," which were either taken in the summer season, when the hair was very short or almost absent, and used for the manufacture of leather and leather goods, or else were the poorly-furred skins of old bulls.

The season for robe-taking was from October 15 to February 15, and a little later in the more northern latitudes. In the United States the hair of the buffalo was still rather short up to the first of November; but by the middle of November it was about at its finest as to length, density, color, and freshness. The Montana hunters considered that the finest robes were those taken from November 15 to December 15. Before the former date the hair had not quite attained perfection in length, and after the latter it began to show wear and lose color. The winter storms of December and January began to leave their mark upon the robes by the 1st of February, chiefly by giving the hair a bleached and weathered appearance. By the middle of February the pelage was decidedly on the wane, and the robe-hunter was also losing his energy. Often, however, the hunt was kept up until the middle of March, until either the deterioration of the quality of the robe, the migration of the herds northward, or the hunter's longing to return "to town" and "clean up," brought the hunt to an end.

On the northern buffalo range, the hunter, or "buffalo skinner," removed the robe in the following manner:

When the operator had to do his work alone, which was almost always the case, he made haste to skin his victims while they were yet warm, if possible, and before *rigor mortis* had set in; but, at all hazards, before they should become hard frozen. With a warm buffalo he could easily do his work single-handed, but with one rigid or frozen stiff it was a very different matter.

His first act was to heave the carcass over until it lay fairly upon its back, with its feet up in the air. To keep it in that position he wrenched the head violently around to one side, close against the shoulder, at the point where the hump was highest and the tendency to roll the greatest, and used it very effectually as a chock to keep the body from rolling back upon its side. Having fixed the carcass in position he drew forth his steel, sharpened his sharp-pointed "ripping-knife," and at once proceeded to make all the opening cuts in the skin. Each leg was girdled to the bone, about 8 inches above the hoof, and the skin of the leg ripped open from that point along the inside to the median line of the body. A long, straight cut was then made along the middle of the breast and abdomen, from the root of the tail to the chin. In skinning cows and young animals, nothing but the skin of the forehead and nose was left on the skull, the skin of the throat and cheeks being left on the hide; but in skinning old bulls, on whose heads the skin was very thick and tough, the whole head was left unskinned, to save labor and time. The skin of the neck was severed in a circle around the neck, just behind the ears. It is these huge heads of bushy brown hair, looking, at a lit-

FIG. 1. A DEAD BULL.

From a photograph by L. A. Huffman.

FIG. 2. BUFFALO SKINNERS AT WORK.

From a photograph by L. A. Huffman.

tle distance, quite black, in sharp contrast with the ghastly whiteness of the perfect skeletons behind them, which gives such a weird and ghostly appearance to the lifeless prairies of Montana where the bone-gatherer has not yet done his perfect work. The skulls of the cows and young buffaloes are as clean and bare as if they had been carefully macerated, and bleached by a skilled osteologist.

The opening cuts having been made, the broad-pointed "skinning-knife" was duly sharpened, and with it the operator fell to work to detach the skin from the body in the shortest possible time. The tail was always skinned and left on the hide. As soon as the skin was taken off it was spread out on a clean, smooth, and level spot of ground, and stretched to its fullest extent, inside uppermost. On the northern range, very few skins were "pegged out," *i. e.*, stretched thoroughly and held by means of wooden pegs driven through the edges of the skin into the earth. It was practiced to a limited extent on the southern range during the latter part of the great slaughter, when buffaloes were scarce and time abundant. Ordinarily, however, there was no time for pegging, nor were pegs available on the range to do the work with. A warm skin stretched on the curly buffalo-grass, hair side down, sticks to the ground of itself until it has ample time to harden. On the northern range the skinner always cut the initials of his outfit in the thin subcutaneous muscle which was always found adhering to the skin on each side, and which made a permanent and very plain mark of ownership.

In the south, the traders who bought buffalo robes on the range sometimes rigged up a rude press, with four upright posts and a huge lever, in which robes that had been folded into a convenient size were pressed into bales, like bales of cotton. These could be transported by wagon much more economically than could loose robes. An illustration of this process is given in an article by Theodore R. Davis, entitled "The Buffalo Range," in *Harper's Magazine* for January, 1869, Vol. XXXVIII, p. 163. The author describes the process as follows:

"As the robes are secured, the trader has them arranged in lots of ten each, with but little regard for quality other than some care that particularly fine robes do not go too many in one lot. These piles are then pressed into a compact bale by means of a rudely constructed affair composed of saplings and a chain."

On the northern range, skins were not folded until the time came to haul them in. Then the hunter repaired to the scene of his winter's work, with a wagon surmounted by a hay-rack (or something like it), usually drawn by four horses. As the skins were gathered up they were folded once, lengthwise down the middle, with the hair inside. Sometimes as many as 100 skins were hauled at one load by four horses.

On one portion of the northern range the classification of buffalo peltries was substantially as follows: Under the head of *robes* was included all cow skins taken during the proper season, from one year old upward, and all bull skins from one to three years old. Bull skins over three years of age were classed as *hides*, and while the best of them were finally tanned and used as robes, the really poor ones were converted into leather. The large robes, when tanned, were used very generally throughout the colder portions of North America as sleigh robes and wraps, and for bedding in the regions of extreme cold. The small robes, from the young animals, and likewise many large robes, were made into overcoats, at once the warmest and the most cumbersome that ever enveloped a human being. Thousands of old bull robes were tanned with the hair on, and the body portions were made into overshoes, with the woolly hair inside—absurdly large and uncouth, but very warm.

I never wore a pair of buffalo overshoes without being torn by conflicting emotions—mortification at the ridiculous size of my combined foot-gear, big boots inside of huge overshoes, and supreme comfort derived from feet that were always warm.

Besides the ordinary robe, the hunters and fur buyers of Montana recognized four special qualities, as follows:

The "beaver robe," with exceedingly fine, wavy fur, the color of a beaver, and having long, coarse, straight hairs coming through it. The latter were of course plucked out in the process of manufacture. These were very rare. In 1882 Mr. James McNaney took one, a cow robe, the only one out of 1,200 robes taken that season, and sold it for $75, when ordinary robes fetched only $3.50.

The "black-and-tan robe" is described as having the nose, flanks, and inside of fore legs black-and-tan (whatever that may mean), while the remainder of the robe is jet black.

A "buckskin robe" is from what is always called a "white buffalo," and is in reality a dirty cream color instead of white. A robe of this character sold in Miles City in 1882 for $200, and was the only one of that character taken on the northern range during that entire winter. A very few pure white robes have been taken, so I have been told, chiefly by Indians, but I have never seen one.

A "blue robe" or "mouse-colored (?) robe" is one on which the body color shows a decidedly bluish cast, and at the same time has long, fine fur. Out of his 1,200 robes taken in 1882, Mr. McNaney picked out 12 which passed muster as the much sought-for blue robes, and they sold at $16 each.

As already intimated, the price paid on the range for ordinary buffalo skins varied according to circumstances, and at different periods, and in different localities, ranged all the way from 65 cents to $10. The latter figure was paid in Texas in 1887 for the last lot of "robes" ever taken. The lowest prices ever paid were during the tremendous slaughter which annihilated the southern herd. Even as late as 1876, in the southern country, cow robes brought on the range only from 65

FIG. 1. FIVE MINUTES' WORK.

Photographed by L. A. Huffman.

FIG. 2. SCENE ON THE NORTHERN BUFFALO RANGE.

Photographed by L. A. Huffman.

to 90 cents, and bull robes $1.15.   On the northern range, from 1881 to 1883, the prices paid were much higher, ranging from $2.50 to $4.

A few hundred dressed robes still remain in the hands of some of the largest fur dealers in New York, Chicago, and Montreal, which can be purchased at prices much lower than one would expect, considering the circumstances.   In 1888, good robes, Indian tanned, were offered in New York at prices ranging from $15 to $30, according to size and quality, but in Montreal no first-class robes were obtainable at less than $40.

Hides.—Next in importance to robes was the class of skins known commercially as hides.   Under this head were classed all skins which for any reason did not possess the pelage necessary to a robe, and were therefore fit only for conversion into leather.   Of these, the greater portion consisted of the skins of old bulls on which the hair was of poor quality and the skin itself too thick and heavy to ever allow of its being made into a soft, pliable, and light-weight robe.   The remaining portion of the hides marketed were from buffaloes killed in spring and summer, when the body and hind-quarters were almost naked.   Apparently the quantity of summer-killed hides marketed was not very great, for it was only the meanest and most unprincipled ones of the grand army of buffalo-killers who were mean enough to kill buffaloes in summer simply for their hides.   It is said that at one time summer-killing was practiced on the southern range to an extent that became a cause for alarm to the great body of more respectable hunters, and the practice was frowned upon so severely that the wretches who engaged in it found it wise to abandon it.

Bones.—Next in importance to robes and hides was the bone product, the utilization of which was rendered possible by the rigorous climate of the buffalo plains.   Under the influence of the wind and sun and the extremes of heat and cold, the flesh remaining upon a carcass dried up, disintegrated, and fell to dust, leaving the bones of almost the entire skeleton as clean and bare as if they had been stripped of flesh by some powerful chemical process.   Very naturally, no sooner did the live buffaloes begin to grow scarce than the miles of bleaching bones suggested the idea of finding a use for them.   A market was readily found for them in the East, and the prices paid per ton were sufficient to make the business of bone-gathering quite remunerative.   The bulk of the bone product was converted into phosphate for fertilizing purposes, but much of it was turned into carbon for use in the refining of sugar.

The gathering of bones became a common industry as early as 1872, during which year 1,135,300 pounds were shipped over the Atchison, Topeka and Santa Fé Railroad.   In the year following the same road shipped 2,743,100 pounds, and in 1874 it handled 6,914,950 pounds more.   This trade continued from that time on until the plains have been gleaned so far back from the railway lines that it is no longer profitable to seek them. For that matter, however, it is said that south of the Union Pacific nothing worth the seeking now remains.

The building of the Northern Pacific Railway made possible the shipment of immense quantities of dry bones. Even as late as 1886 overland travelers saw at many of the stations between Jamestown, Dakota, and Billings, Montana, immense heaps of bones lying alongside the track awaiting shipment. In 1885 a single firm shipped over 200 tons of bones from Miles City.

The valley of the Missouri River was gleaned by teamsters who gathered bones from as far back as 100 miles and hauled them to the river for shipment on the steamers. An operator who had eight wagons in the business informed me that in order to ship bones on the river steamers it was necessary to crush them, and that for crushed bones, shipped in bags, a Michigan fertilizer company paid $18 per ton. Uncrushed bones, shipped by the railway, sold for $12 per ton.

It is impossible to ascertain the total amount or value of the bone product, but it is certain that it amounted to many thousand tons, and in value must have amounted to some hundreds of thousands of dollars. But for the great number of railroads, river steamers, and sea-going vessels (from Texas ports) engaged in carrying this product, it would have cut an important figure in the commerce of the country, but owing to the many interests between which it was divided it attracted little attention.

Meat.—The amount of fresh buffalo meat cured and marketed was really very insignificant. So long as it was to be had at all it was so very abundant that it was worth only from 2 to 3 cents per pound in the market, and many reasons combined to render the trade in fresh buffalo meat anything but profitable. Probably not more than one one-thousandth of the buffalo meat that might have been saved and utilized was saved. The buffalo carcasses that were wasted on the great plains every year during the two great periods of slaughter (of the northern and southern herds) would probably have fed to satiety during the entire time more than a million persons.

As to the quality of buffalo meat, it may be stated in general terms that it differs in no way whatever from domestic beef of the same age produced by the same kind of grass. Perhaps there is no finer grazing ground in the world than Montana, and the beef it produces is certainly entitled to rank with the best. There are many persons who claim to recognize a difference between the taste of buffalo meat and domestic beef; but for my part I do not believe any difference really exists, unless it is that the flesh of the buffalo is a little sweeter and more juicy. As for myself, I feel certain I could not tell the difference between the flesh of a three-year old buffalo and that of a domestic beef of the same age, nor do I believe any one else could, even on a wager. Having once seen a butcher eat an elephant steak in the belief that it was beef from his own shop, and another butcher eat *loggerhead turtle* steak for beef, I have become somewhat skeptical in regard to the intelligence of the human palate.

As a matter of experiment, during our hunt for buffalo we had buffalo meat of all ages, from one year up to eleven, cooked in as many different ways as our culinary department could turn out. We had it broiled, fried with batter, roasted, boiled, and stewed. The last method, when employed upon slices of meat that had been hacked from a frozen hindquarter, produced results that were undeniably tough and not particularly good. But it was an unfair way to cook any kind of meat, and may be guarantied to spoil the finest beef in the world.

Hump meat from a cow buffalo not too old, cut in slices and fried in batter, *a la cow-boy*, is delicious—a dish fit for the gods. We had tongues in plenty, but the ordinary meat was so good they were not half appreciated. Of course the tenderloin was above criticism, and even the round steaks, so lightly esteemed by the epicure, were tender and juicy to a most satisfactory degree.

It has been said that the meat of the buffalo has a coarser texture or " grain " than domestic beef. Although I expected to find such to be the case, I found no perceptible difference whatever, nor do I believe that any exists. As to the distribution of fat I am unable to say, for the reason that our buffaloes were not fat.

It is highly probable that the distribution of fat through the meat, so characteristic of the shorthorn breeds, and which has been brought about only by careful breeding, is not found in either the beef of the buffalo or common range cattle. In this respect, shorthorn beef no doubt surpasses both the others mentioned, but in all other points, texture, flavor, and general tenderness, I am very sure it does not.

It is a great mistake for a traveler to kill a patriarchal old bull buffalo, and after attempting to masticate a small portion of him to rise up and declare that buffalo meat is coarse, tough, and dry. A domestic bull of the same age would taste as tough. It is probably only those who have had the bad taste to eat bull-beef who have ever found occasion to asperse the reputation of *Bison americanus* as a beef animal.

Until people got tired of them, buffalo tongues were in considerable demand, and hundreds, if not even thousands, of barrels of them were shipped east from the buffalo country.

Pemmican.—Out of the enormous waste of good buffalo flesh one product stands forth as a redeeming feature—pemmican. Although made almost exclusively by the half-breeds and Indians of the Northwest, it constituted a regular article of commerce of great value to overland travelers, and was much sought for as long as it was produced. Its peculiar " staying powers," due to the process of its manufacture, which yielded a most nourishing food in a highly condensed form, made it of inestimable value to the overland traveler who must travel light or not at all. A handful of pemmican was sufficient food to constitute a meal when provisions were at all scarce. The price of pemmican in Winnipeg was once as low as 2*d.* per pound, but in 1883 a very small quantity which was brought in sold at 16 cents per pound. This was probably the last buffalo pemmican made. H. M. Robinson states that in 1878 pemmican was worth 1*s.* 3*d.* per pound.

The manufacture of pemmican, as performed by the Red River half-breeds, was thus described by the Rev. Mr. Belcourt, a Catholic priest, who once accompanied one of the great buffalo-hunting expeditions: *

"Other portions which are destined to be made into pimikehigan, or pemmican, are exposed to an ardent heat, and thus become brittle and easily reducible to small particles by the use of a flail, the buffalo-hide answering the purpose of a threshing-floor. The fat or tallow, being cut up and melted in large kettles of sheet-iron, is poured upon this pounded meat, and the whole mass is worked together with shovels until it is well amalgamated, when it is pressed, while still warm, into bags made of buffalo skin, which are strongly sewed up, and the mixture gradually cools and becomes almost as hard as a rock. If the fat used in this process is that taken from the parts containing the udder, the meat is called fine pemmican. In some cases, dried fruits, such as the prairie pear and cherry, are intermixed, which forms what is called seed pemmican. The lovers of good eating judge the first described to be very palatable; the second, better; the third, excellent. A taurean of pemmican weighs from 100 to 110 pounds. Some idea may be formed of the immense destruction of buffalo by these people when it is stated that a whole cow yields one-half a bag of pemmican and three fourths of a bundle of dried meat; so that the most economical calculate that from eight to ten cows are required for the load of a single vehicle."

It is quite evident from the testimony of disinterested travelers that ordinary pemmican was not very palatable to one unaccustomed to it as a regular article of food. To the natives, however, especially the Canadian *royageur*, it formed one of the most valuable food products of the country, and it is said that the demand for it was generally greater than the supply.

Dried, or "jerked" meat.—The most popular and universal method of curing buffalo meat was to cut it into thin flakes, an inch or less in thickness and of indefinite length, and without salting it in the least to hang it over poles, ropes, wicker-frames, or even clumps of standing sage brush, and let it dry in the sun. This process yielded the famous "jerked" meat so common throughout the West in the early days, from the Rio Grande to the Saskatchewan. Father Belcourt thus described the curing process as it was practiced by the half-breeds and Indians of the Northwest:

"The meat, when taken to camp, is cut by the women into long strips about a quarter of an inch thick, which are hung upon the lattice-work prepared for that purpose to dry. This lattice-work is formed of small pieces of wood, placed horizontally, transversely, and equidistant from

---

* Schoolcraft's History, Condition and Prospects of the Indian Tribes, IV, p. 107.

each other, not unlike an immense gridiron, and is supported by wooden uprights (trepieds). In a few days the meat is thoroughly desiccated, when it is bent into proper lengths and tied into bundles of 60 or 70 pounds weight. This is called dried meat (viande seche). To make the hide into parchment (so called) it is stretched on a frame, and then scraped on the inside with a piece of sharpened bone and on the out-side with a small but sharp-curved iron, proper to remove the hair. This is considered, likewise, the appropriate labor of women. The men break the bones, which are boiled in water to extract the marrow to be used for frying and other culinary purposes. The oil is then poured into the bladder of the animal, which contains, when filled, about 12 pounds, being the yield of the marrow-bones of two buffaloes."

In the Northwest Territories dried meat, which formerly sold at 2d. per pound, was worth in 1878 10d. per pound.

Although I have myself prepared quite a quantity of jerked buffalo meat, I never learned to like it. Owing to the absence of salt in its curing, the dried meat when pounded and made into a stew has a " far away" taste which continually reminds one of hoofs and horns. For all that, and despite its resemblance in flavor to Liebig's Extract of Beef, it is quite good, and better to the taste than ordinary pemmican.

The Indians formerly cured great quantities of buffalo meat in this way—in summer, of course, for use in winter—but the advent of that popular institution called "Government beef" long ago rendered it un-necessary for the noble red man to exert his squaw in that once honorable field of labor.

During the existence of the buffalo herds a few thrifty and enter-prising white men made a business of killing buffaloes in summer and drying the meat in bulk, in the same manner which to-day produces our popular "dried beef." Mr. Allen states that "a single hunter at Hays City shipped annually for some years several hundred barrels thus prepared, which the consumers probably bought for ordinary beef."

Uses of bison's hair.—Numerous attempts have been made to utilize the woolly hair of the bison in the manufacture of textile fabrics. As early as 1729 Col. William Byrd records the fact that garments were made of this material, as follows:

" The Hair growing upon his Head and Neck is long and Shagged, and so Soft that it will spin into Thread not unlike Mohair, and might be wove into a sort of Camlet. Some People have Stockings knit of it, that would have served an Israelite during his forty Years march thro' the Wilderness." *

In 1637 Thomas Morton published, in his " New English Canaan," p. 98,† the following reference to the Indians who live on the south-ern shore of Lake Erocoise, supposed to be Lake Ontario:

" These Beasts [buffaloes, undoubtedly] are of the bignesse of a

---

* Westover MSS., I, p. 172.

† Quoted by Professor Allen, "American Bisons," p. 107.

Cowe, their flesh being very good foode, their hides good lether, their fleeces very usefull, being a kind of wolle, as fine as the wolle of the Beaver, and the Salvages doe make garments thereof."

Professor Allen quotes a number of authorities who have recorded statements in regard to the manufacture of belts, garters, scarfs, sacks, etc., from buffalo wool by various tribes of Indians.* He also calls attention to the only determined efforts ever made by white men on a liberal scale for the utilization of buffalo " wool" and its manufacture into cloth, an account of which appears in Ross's " Red River Settlement," pp. 69–72. In 1821 some of the more enterprising of the Red River (British) colonists conceived the idea of making fortunes out of the manufacture of woolen goods from the fleece of the buffalo, and for that purpose organized the Buffalo Wool Company, the principal object of which was declared to be " to provide a substitute for wool, which substitute was to be the wool of the wild buffalo, which was to be collected in the plains and manufactured both for the use of the colonists and for export." A large number of skilled workmen of various kinds were procured from England, and also a plant of machinery and materials. When too late, it was found that the supply of buffalo wool obtainable was utterly insufficient, the raw wool costing the company 1s. 6d. per pound, and cloth which it cost the company £2 10s. per yard to produce was worth only 4s. 6d. per yard in England. The historian states that universal drunkenness on the part of all concerned aided very materially in bringing about the total failure of the enterprise in a very short time.

While it is possible to manufacture the fine, woolly fur of the bison into cloth or knitted garments, provided a sufficient supply of the raw material could be obtained (which is and always has been impossible), nothing could be more visionary than an attempt to thus produce salable garments at a profit.

Articles of wearing apparel made of buffalo's hair are interesting as curiosities, for their rarity makes them so, but that is the only end they can ever serve so long as there is a sheep living.

In the National Museum, in the section of animal products, there is displayed a pair of stockings made in Canada from the finest buffalo wool, from the body of the animal. They are thick, heavy, and full of the coarse, straight hairs, which it seems can never be entirely separated from the fine wool. In general texture they are as coarse as the coarsest sheep's wool would produce.

With the above are also displayed a rope-like lariat, made by the Comanche Indians, and a smaller braided lasso, seemingly a sample more than a full-grown lariat, made by the Otoe Indians of Nebraska. Both of the above are made of the long, dark-brown hair of the head and shoulders, and in spite of the fact that they have been twisted as

---

* The American Bison, p. 197.

hard as possible, the ends of the hairs protude so persistently that the surface of each rope is extremely hairy.

Buffalo chips—Last, but by no means least in value to the traveler on the treeless plains, are the droppings of the buffalo, universally known as "buffalo chips." When over one year old and thoroughly dry, this material makes excellent fuel. Usually it occurs only where fire-wood is unobtainable, and thousands of frontiersmen have a million times found it of priceless value. When dry, it catches easily, burns readily, and makes a hot fire with but very little smoke, although it is rapidly consumed. Although not as good for a fire as even the poorest timber it is infinitely better than sage-brush, which, in the absence of chips, is often the traveler's last resort.

It usually happens that chips are most abundant in the sheltered creek-bottoms and near the water-holes, the very situations which travelers naturally select for their camps. In these spots the herds have gathered either for shelter in winter or for water in summer, and remained in a body for some hours. And now, when the cow-boy on the round-up, the surveyor, or hunter, who must camp out, pitches his tent in the grassy coulée or narrow creek-bottom, his first care is to start out with his largest gunning-bag to "rustle some buffalo chips" for a camp-fire. He, at least, when he returns well laden with the spoil of his humble chase, still has good reason to remember the departed herd with feelings of gratitude. Thus even the last remains of this most useful animal are utilized by man in providing for his own imperative wants.

IX. The Present Value of the Bison to Cattle-Growers.

The bison in captivity and domestication.—Almost from time immemorial it has been known that the American bison takes kindly to captivity, herds contentedly with domestic cattle, and crosses with them with the utmost readiness. It was formerly believed, and indeed the tradition prevails even now to quite an extent, that on account of the hump on the shoulders a domestic cow could not give birth to a half-breed calf. This belief is entirely without foundation, and is due to theories rather than facts.

Numerous experiments in buffalo breeding have been made, and the subject is far from being a new one. As early as 1701 the Hugenot settlers at Manikintown, on the James River, a few miles above Richmond, began to domesticate buffaloes. It is also a matter of historical record that in 1786, or thereabouts, buffaloes were domesticated and bred in captivity in Virginia, and Albert Gallatin states that in some of the northwestern counties the mixed breed was quite common: In 1815 a series of elaborate and valuable experiments in cross-breeding the buffalo and domestic cattle was begun by Mr. Robert Wickliffe, of Lexington, Ky., and continued by him for upwards of thirty years.*

---

* For a full account of Mr. Wickliffe's experiments, written by himself, see Audubon and Bachman's "Quadrupeds of North America," vol. II, pp. 52-54.

Quite recently the buffalo-breeding operations of Mr. S. L. Bedson, of Stony Mountain, Manitoba, and Mr. C. J. Jones, of Garden City, Kans., have attracted much attention, particularly for the reason that the efforts of both these gentlemen have been directed toward the practical improvement of the present breeds of range cattle. For this reason the importance of the work in which they are engaged can hardly be over-estimated, and the results already obtained by Mr. Bedson, whose experiments antedate those of Mr. Jones by several years, are of the greatest interest to western cattle-growers. Indeed, unless the stock of pure-blood buffaloes now remaining proves insufficient for the purpose, I fully believe that we will gradually see a great change wrought in the character of western cattle by the introduction of a strain of buffalo blood.

The experiments which have been made thus far prove conclusively that—

(1) The male bison crosses readily with the opposite sex of domestic cattle, but a buffalo cow has never been known to produce a half-breed calf.

(2) The domestic cow produces a half-breed calf successfully.

(3) The progeny of the two species is fertile to any extent, yielding half-breeds, quarter, three-quarter breeds, and so on.

(4) The bison breeds in captivity with perfect regularity and success.

Need of an improvement in range cattle.—Ever since the earliest days of cattle-ranching in the West, stockmen have had it in their power to produce a breed which would equal in beef-bearing qualities the best breeds to be found upon the plains, and be so much better calculated to survive the hardships of winter, that their annual losses would have been very greatly reduced. Whenever there is an unusually severe winter, such as comes about three times in every decade, if not even oftener, range cattle perish by thousands. It is an absolute impossibility for every ranchman who owns several thousand, or even several hundred, head of cattle to provide hay for them, even during the severest portion of the winter season, and consequently the cattle must depend wholly upon their own resources. When the winter is reasonably mild, and the snows never very deep, nor lying too long at a time on the ground, the cattle live through the winter with very satisfactory success. Thanks to the wind, it usually happens that the falling snow is blown off the ridges as fast as it falls, leaving the grass sufficiently uncovered for the cattle to feed upon it. If the snow-fall is universal, but not more than a few inches in depth, the cattle paw through it here and there, and eke out a subsistence, on quarter rations it may be, until a friendly chinook wind sets in from the southwest and dissolves the snow as if by magic in a few hours' time.

But when a deep snow comes, and lies on the ground persistently, week in and week out, when the warmth of the sun softens and moistens its surface sufficiently for a returning cold wave to freeze it into a hard crust, forming a universal wall of ice between the luckless steer and his only food, the cattle starve and freeze in immense numbers. Being totally unfitted by nature to survive such unnatural conditions, it is not strange that they succumb.

Under present conditions the stockman simply stakes his cattle against the winter elements and takes his chances on the results, which are governed by circumstances wholly beyond his control. The losses of the fearful winter of 1886–'87 will probably never be forgotten by the cattlemen of the great Western grazing ground. In many portions of Montana and Wyoming the cattlemen admitted a loss of 50 per cent. of their cattle, and in some localities the loss was still greater. The same conditions are liable to prevail next winter, or any succeeding winter, and we may yet see more than half the range cattle in the West perish in a single month.

Yet all this time the cattlemen have had it in their power, by the easiest and simplest method in the world, to introduce a strain of hardy native blood in their stock which would have made it capable of successfully resisting a much greater degree of hunger and cold. It is really surprising that the desirability of cross-breeding the buffalo and domestic cattle should for so long a time have been either overlooked or disregarded. While cattle-growers generally have shown the greatest enterprise in producing special breeds for milk, for butter, or for beef, cattle with short horns and cattle with no horns at all, only two or three men have had the enterprise to try to produce a breed particularly hardy and capable.

A buffalo can weather storms and outlive hunger and cold which would kill any domestic steer that ever lived. When nature placed him on the treeless and blizzard-swept plains, she left him well equipped to survive whatever natural conditions he would have to encounter. The most striking feature of his entire *tout ensemble* is his magnificent suit of hair and fur combined, the warmest covering possessed by any quadruped save the musk-ox. The head, neck, and fore quarters are clothed with hide and hair so thick as to be almost, if not entirely, impervious to cold. The hair on the body and hind quarters is long, fine, very thick, and of that peculiar woolly quality which constitutes the best possible protection against cold. Let him who doubts the warmth of a good buffalo robe try to weather a blizzard with something else, and then try the robe. The very form of the buffalo—short, thick legs, and head hung very near the ground—suggests most forcibly a special fitness to wrestle with mother earth for a living, snow or no snow. A buffalo will flounder for days through deep snow-drifts without a morsel of food, and survive where the best range steer would literally freeze on foot, bolt upright, as hundreds did in the winter of 1886–'87. While range cattle turn tail to a blizzard and drift helplessly, the buffalo faces it every time, and remains master of the situation.

It has for years been a surprise to me that Western stockmen have not seized upon the opportunity presented by the presence of the buffalo to improve the character of their cattle. Now that there are no longer any buffalo calves to be had on the plains for the trouble of catching them, and the few domesticated buffaloes that remain are worth fabulous prices, we may expect to see a great deal of interest manifested in this subject, and some costly efforts made to atone for previous lack of forethought.

The character of the buffalo—domestic hybrid.—The subjoined illustration from a photograph kindly furnished by Mr. C. J. Jones, represents a ten months' old half-breed calf (male), the product of a buffalo bull and domestic cow. The prepotency of the sire is apparent at the first glance, and to so marked an extent that the illustration would pass muster anywhere as having been drawn from a full-blood buffalo. The head, neck, and hump, and the long woolly hair that covers them, proclaim the buffalo in every line. Excepting that the hair on the shoulders (below the hump) is of the same length as that on the body and hind quarters, there is, so far as one can judge from an excellent photograph, no difference whatever observable between this lusty young half-breed and a full-blood buffalo calf of the same age and sex. Mr. Jones describes the color of this animal as "iron-gray," and remarks: "You will see how even the fur is, being as long on the hind parts as on the shoulders and neck, very much unlike the buffalo, which is so shaggy about the shoulders and so thin farther back." Upon this point it is to be remarked that the hair on the body of a yearling or two-year-old buffalo is always very much longer in proportion to the hair on the forward parts than it is later in life, and while the shoulder hair is always decidedly longer than that back of it, during the first two years the contrast is by no means so very great. A reference to the memoranda of hair measurements already given will afford precise data on this point.

In regard to half-breed calves, Mr. Bedson states in a private letter that "the hump does not appear until several months after birth."

Altogether, the male calf described above so strongly resembles a pure-blood buffalo as to be generally mistaken for one; the form of the adult half-blood cow promptly proclaims her origin. The accompanying plate, also from a photograph supplied by Mr. Jones, accurately represents a half-breed cow, six years old, weighing about 1,800 pounds. Her body is very noticeably larger in proportion than that of the cow buffalo, her pelvis much heavier, broader, and more cow-like, therein being a decided improvement upon the small and weak hind quarters of the wild species. The hump is quite noticeable, but is not nearly so high as in the pure buffalo cow. The hair on the fore quarters, neck, and head is decidedly shorter, especially on the head; the frontlet and chin beard being conspicuously lacking. The tufts of long, coarse, black hair which clothe the fore-arm of the buffalo cow are almost absent, but apparently the hair on the body and hind quarters has lost

HALF-BREED (BUFFALO-DOMESTIC) CALF.—HERD OF C. J. JONES, GARDEN CITY, KANSAS.

Drawn by Ernest E. Thompson.

but little, if any, of its length, density, and fine, furry quality. The horns are decidedly cow-like in their size, length, and curvature.

Regarding the general character of the half-breed buffalo, and his herd in general, Mr. Bedson writes me as follows, in a letter dated September 12, 1888:

"The nucleus of my herd consisted of a young buffalo bull and four heifer calves, which I purchased in 1877, and the increase from these few has been most rapid, as will be shown by a tabular statement farther on.

"Success with the breeding of the pure buffalo was followed by experiments in crossing with the domestic animal. This crossing has generally been between a buffalo bull and an ordinary cow, and with the most encouraging results, since it had been contended by many that although the cow might breed a calf from the buffalo, yet it would be at the expense of her life, owing to the hump on a buffalo's shoulder; but this hump does not appear until several months after birth. This has been proved a fallacy respecting *this herd* at least, for calving has been attended with no greater percentage of losses than would be experienced in ranching with the ordinary cattle. Buffalo cows and crosses have dropped calves at as low a temperature as 20° below zero, and the calves were sturdy and healthy.

"The half-breed resulting from the cross as above mentioned has been again crossed with the thoroughbred buffalo bull, producing a three quarter breed animal closely resembling the buffalo, the head and robe being quite equal, if not superior. The half-breeds are very prolific. The cows drop a calf annually. They are also very hardy indeed, as they take the instinct of the buffalo during the blizzards and storms, and do not drift like native cattle. They remain upon the open prairie during our severest winters, while the thermometer ranges from 30 to 40 degrees below zero, with little or no food except what they rustled on the prairie, and no shelter at all. In nearly all the ranching parts of North America foddering and housing of cattle is imperative in a more or less degree,* creating an item of expense felt by all interested in cattle-raising; but the buffalo [half]breed retains all its native hardihood, needs no housing, forages in the deepest snows for its own food, yet becomes easily domesticated, and consequently needs but little herding. Therefore the progeny of the buffalo is easily reared, cheaply fed, and requires no housing in winter; three very essential points in stock-raising.

"They are always in good order, and I consider the meat of the half-breed much preferable to domestic animals, while the robe is very fine indeed, the fur being evened-up on the hind parts, the same as on the shoulders. During the history of the herd, accident and other causes have compelled the slaughtering of one or two, and in these instances

---

* On nearly all the great cattle ranches of the United States it is absolutely impossible, and is not even attempted.—W. T. H.

the carcasses have sold for 18 cents per pound; the hides in their dressed state for $50 to $75 each. A half-breed buffalo ox (four years old, crossed with buffalo bull and Durham cow) was killed last winter, and weighed 1,280 pounds dressed beef. One pure buffalo bull now in my herd weighs fully 2,000 pounds, and a [half]breed bull 1,700 to 1,800 pounds.

"The three-quarter breed is an enormous animal in size, and has an extra good robe, which will readily bring $40 to $50 in any market where there is a demand for robes. They are also very prolific, and I consider them the coming cattle for our range cattle for the Northern climate, while the half and quarter breeds will be the animals for the more Southern district. The half and three-quarter breed cows, when really matured, will weigh from 1,400 to 1,800 pounds.

"I have never crossed them except with a common grade of cows, while I believe a cross with the Galloways would produce the handsomest robe ever handled, and make the best range cattle in the world. I have not had time to give my attention to my herd, more than to let them range on the prairies at will. By proper care great results can be accomplished."

Hon. C. J. Jones, of Garden City, Kans., whose years of experience with the buffalo, both as old-time hunter, catcher, and breeder, has earned for him the sobriquet of "Buffalo Jones," five years ago became deeply interested in the question of improving range cattle by crossing with the buffalo. With characteristic Western energy he has pursued the subject from that time until the present, having made five trips to the range of the only buffaloes remaining from the great southern herd, and captured sixty-eight buffalo calves and eleven adult cows with which to start a herd. In a short article published in the Farmers' Review (Chicago, August 22, 1888), Mr. Jones gives his views on the value of the buffalo in cross-breeding as follows:

"In all my meanderings I have not found a place but I could count more carcasses [of cattle] than living animals. Who has not ridden over some of the Western railways and counted dead cattle by the thousands? The great question is, Where can we get a race of cattle that will stand blizzards, and endure the drifting snow, and will not be driven with the storms against the railroad fences and pasture fences, there to perish for the want of nerve to face the northern winds for a few miles, to where the winter grasses could be had in abundance? Realizing these facts, both from observation and pocket, we pulled on our 'thinking cap,' and these points came vividly to our mind:

"(1) We want an animal that is hardy.

"(2) We want an animal with nerve and endurance.

"(3) We want an animal that faces the blizzards and endures the storms.

"(4) We want an animal that will rustle the prairies, and not yield to discouragement.

HALF-BREED (BUFFALO-DOMESTIC) COW.—HERD OF C. J. JONES, GARDEN CITY, KANSAS.

Drawn by Ernest E. Thompson.

"(5) We want an animal that will fill the above bill, and make good beef and plenty of it.

"All the points above could easily be found in the buffalo, excepting the fifth, and even that is more than filled as to the quality, but not in quantity. Where is the 'old timer' who has not had a cut from the hump or sirloin of a fat buffalo cow in the fall of the year, and where is the one who will not make affidavit that it was the best meat he ever ate? Yes, the fat was very rich, equal to the marrow from the bone of domestic cattle. * * *

"The great question remained unsolved as to the quantity of meat from the buffalo. I finally heard of a half-breed buffalo in Colorado, and immediately set out to find it. I traveled at least 1,000 miles to find it, and found a five-year-old half-breed cow that had been bred to domestic bulls and had brought forth two calves—a yearling and a sucking calf that gave promise of great results.

"The cow had never been fed, but depended altogether on the range, and when I saw her, in the fall of 1883, I estimated her weight at 1,800 pounds. She was a brindle, and had a handsome robe even in September; she had as good hind quarters as ordinary cattle; her fore parts were heavy and resembled the buffalo, yet not near so much of the hump. The offspring showed but very little of the buffalo, yet they possessed a woolly coat, which showed clearly that they were more than domestic cattle. * * *

"What we can rely on by having one-fourth, one-half, and three-fourths breeds might be analyzed as follows:

"We can depend upon a race of cattle unequaled in the world for hardiness and durability; a good meat-bearing animal; the best and only fur-bearing animal of the bovine race; the animal always found in a storm where it is overtaken by it; a race of cattle so clannish as never to separate and go astray; the animal that can always have free range, as they exist where no other animal can live; the animal that can water every third day and keep fat, ranging from 20 to 30 miles from water; in fact, they are the perfect animal for the plains of North America. One-fourth breeds for Texas, one-half breeds for Colorado and Kansas, and three-fourths breeds for more northern country, is what will soon be sought after more than any living animal. Then we will never be confronted with dead carcarsses from starvation, exhaustion, and lack of nerve, as in years gone by."

The bison as a beast of burden.—On account of the abundance of horses for all purposes throughout the entire country, oxen are so seldem used they almost constitute a curiosity. There never has existed a necessity to break buffaloes to the yoke and work them like domestic oxen, and so few experiments have been made in this direction that reliable data on this subject is almost wholly wanting. While at Miles City, Mont., I heard of a German "granger" who worked a small farm in the Tongue River Valley, and who once had a pair of cow buffaloes trained to the yoke. It was said that they were strong, rapid walkers, and capable of performing as much work as the best domestic oxen, but they were at times so uncontrollably headstrong and obstinate as to greatly detract from their usefulness. The particular event of their career on which their historian dwelt with special interest occurred when their owner was hauling a load of potatoes to town with them. In the course of the long drive the buffaloes grew very thirsty, and upon coming within sight of the water in the river they started for it in a straight course. The shouts and blows of the driver only served to hasten their speed, and presently, when they reached the edge of the high bank, they plunged down it without the slightest hesitation, wagon, potatoes, and all, to the loss of everything except themselves and the drink they went after!

Mr. Robert Wickliffe states that trained buffaloes make satisfactory oxen. " I have broken them to the yoke, and found them capable of making excellent oxen; and for drawing wagons, carts, or other heavily laden vehicles on long journeys they would, I think, be greatly preferable to the common ox."

It seems probable that, in the absence of horses, the buffalo would make a much more speedy and enduring draught animal than the domestic ox, although it is to be doubted whether he would be as strong. His weaker pelvis and hind quarters would surely count against him under certain circumstances, but for some purposes his superior speed and endurance would more than counterbalance that defect.

BISON HERDS AND INDIVIDUALS IN CAPTIVITY AND DOMESTICATION, JANUARY 1, 1889.

Herd of Mr. S. L. Bedson, Stony Mountain, Manitoba.—In 1877 Mr. Bedson purchased 5 buffalo calves, 1 bull, and 4 heifers, for which he paid $1,000. In 1888 his herd consisted of 23 full-blood bulls, 35 cows, 3 half-breed cows, 5 half-breed bulls, and 17 calves, mixed and pure;* making a total of 83 head. These were all produced from the original 5, no purchases having been made, nor any additions made in any other way. Besides the 83 head constituting the herd when it was sold, 5 were killed and 9 given away, which would otherwise make a total of 97 head produced since 1877. In November, 1888, this entire herd was purchased, for $50,000, by Mr. C. J. Jones, and added to the already large herd owned by that gentleman in Kansas.

Herd of Mr. C. J. Jones, Garden City, Kans.—Mr. Jones's original herd of 57 buffaloes constitute a living testimonial to his individual enterprise, and to his courage, endurance, and skill in the chase. The majority of the individuals composing the herd he himself ran down,

---

* In summing up the total number of buffaloes and mixed-breeds now alive in captivity, I have been obliged to strike an average on this lot of calves "mixed and pure," and have counted twelve as being of pure breed and five mixed, which I have reason to believe is very near the truth.

PLATE XIII.

YOUNG HALF-BREED (BUFFALO-DOMESTIC) BULL.—HERD OF C. J. JONES, GARDEN CITY, KANSAS.

Drawn by Ernest E. Thompson.

lassoed, and tied with his own hands. For the last five years Mr. Jones has made an annual trip, in June, to the uninhabited "panhandle" of Texas, to capture calves out of the small herd of from one hundred to two hundred head which represented the last remnant of the great southern herd. Each of these expeditions involved a very considerable outlay in money, an elaborate "outfit" of men, horses, vehicles, camp equipage, and lastly, but most important of all, a herd of a dozen fresh milch cows to nourish the captured calves and keep them from dying of starvation and thirst. The region visited was fearfully barren, almost without water, and to penetrate it was always attended by great hardship. The buffaloes were difficult to find, but the ground was good for running, being chiefly level plains, and the superior speed of the running horses always enabled the hunters to overtake a herd whenever one was sighted, and to "cut out" and lasso two, three, or four of its calves. The degree of skill and daring displayed in these several expeditions are worthy of the highest admiration, and completely surpass anything I have ever seen or read of being accomplished in connection with hunting, or the capture of live game. The latest feat of Mr. Jones and his party comes the nearest to being incredible. During the month of May, 1888, they not only captured seven calves, but also *eleven adult cows*, of which some were lassoed in full career on the prairie, thrown, tied, and hobbled! The majority, however, were actually "rounded up," herded, and held in control until a bunch of tame buffaloes was driven down to meet them, so that it would thus be possible to drive all together to a ranch. This brilliant feat can only be appreciated as it deserves by those who have lately hunted buffalo, and learned by dear experience the extent of their wariness, and the difficulties, to say nothing of the dangers, inseparably connected with their pursuit.

The result of each of Mr. Jones's five expeditions is as follows: In 1884 no calves found; 1885, 11 calves captured, 5 died, 6 survived; 1886, 14 calves captured, 7 died, 7 survived; 1887, 36 calves captured, 6 died, 30 survived; 1888, 7 calves captured, all survived; 1888, 11 old cows captured, all survived. Total, 79 captures, 18 losses, 57 survivors.

The census of the herd is exactly as follows: Adult cows, 11; three-year olds, 7, of which 2 are males and 5 females; two-year olds, 4, of which all are males; yearling, 28, of which 15 are males and 13 females; calves, 7, of which 3 are males and 4 females. Total herd, 57; 24 males and 33 females. To this, Mr. Jones's original herd, must now be added the entire herd formerly owned by Mr. Bedson.

Respecting his breeding operations Mr. Jones writes: "My oldest [bull] buffaloes are now three years old, and I am breeding one hundred domestic cows to them this year. Am breeding the Galloway cows quite extensively; also some Shorthorns, Herefords, and Texas cows. I expect best results from the Galloways. If I can get the black luster of the latter and the fur of a buffalo, I will have a robe that will bring more money than we get for the average range steer."

In November, 1888, Mr. Jones purchased Mr. Bedson's entire herd, and in the following month proceeded to ship a portion of it to Kansas City. Thirty-three head were separated from the remainder of the herd on the prairie near Stony Mountain, 12 miles from Winnipeg, and driven to the railroad. Several old bulls broke away en route and ran back to the herd, and when the remainder were finally corraled in the pens at the stock-yards "they began to fight among themselves, and some fierce encounters were waged between the old bulls. The younger cattle were raised on the horns of their seniors, thrown in the air, and otherwise gored." While on the way to St. Paul three of the half-breed buffaloes were killed by their companions. On reaching Kansas City and unloading the two cars, 13 head broke away from the large force of men that attempted to manage them, stampeded through the city, and finally took refuge in the low-lands along the river. In due time, however, all were recaptured.

Since the acquisition of this northern herd and the subsequent press comment that it has evoked, Mr. Jones has been almost overwhelmed with letters of inquiry in regard to the whole subject of buffalo breeding, and has found it necessary to print and distribute a circular giving answers to the many inquiries that have been made.

Herd of Mr. Charles Allard, Flathead Indian Reservation, Montana.— This herd was visited in the autumn of 1888 by Mr. G. O. Shields, of Chicago, who reports that it consists of thirty-five head of pure-blood buffaloes, of which seven are calves of 1888, six are yearlings, and six are two-year olds. Of the adult animals, four cows and two bulls are each fourteen years old, " and the beards of the bulls almost sweep the ground as they walk."

Herd of Hon. W. F. Cody ("Buffalo Bill").—The celebrated " Wild West Show" has, ever since its organization, numbered amongst its leading attractions a herd of live buffaloes of all ages. At present this herd contains eighteen head, of which fourteen were originally purchased of Mr. H. T. Groome, of Wichita, Kansas, and have made a journey to London and back. As a proof of the indomitable persistence of the bison in breeding under most unfavorable circumstances, the fact that four of the members of this herd are calves which were born in 1888 in London, at the American Exposition, is of considerable interest.

This herd is now (December, 1888) being wintered on General Beale's farm, near the city of Washington. In 1886–'87, while the Wild West Show was at Madison Square Garden, New York City, its entire herd of twenty buffaloes was carried off by pleuro-pneumonia. It is to be greatly feared that sooner or later in the course of its travels the present herd will also disappear, either through disease or accident.

Herd of Mr. Charles Goodnight, Clarendon, Texas.—Mr. Goodnight writes that he has " been breeding buffaloes in a small way for the past ten years," but without giving any particular attention to it. At present his herd consists of thirteen head, of which two are three-year-old bulls and four are calves. There are seven cows of all ages, one of which is a half-breed.

Herd at the Zoological Society's Gardens, Philadelphia, Arthur E. Brown, superintendent.—This institution is the fortunate possessor of a small herd of ten buffaloes, of which four are males and six females. Two are calves of 1877. In 1886 the Gardens sold an adult bull and cow to Hon. W. F. Cody for $300.

Herd at Bismarck Grove, Kansas, owned by the Atchison, Topeka and Santa Fé Railroad Company.—A small herd of buffaloes has for several years past been kept at Bismarck Grove as an attraction to visitors. At present it contains ten head, one of which is a very large bull, another in a four-year-old bull, six are cows of various ages, and two are two-year olds. In 1885 a large bull belonging to this herd grew so vicious and dangerous that it was necessary to kill him.

The following interesting account of this herd was published in the Kansas City Times of December 8, 1888:

"Thirteen years ago Colonel Stanton purchased a buffalo bull calf for $8 and two heifers for $25. The descendants of these three buffaloes now found at Bismarck Grove, where all were born, number in all ten. There were seventeen, but the rest have died, with the exception of one, which was given away. They are kept in an inclosure containing about 30 acres immediately adjoining the park, and there may be seen at any time. The sight is one well worth a trip and the slight expense that may attach to it, especially to one who has never seen the American bison in his native state.

"The present herd includes two fine bull calves dropped last spring, two heifers, five cows, and a bull six years old and as handsome as a picture. The latter has been named Cleveland, after the colonel's favorite Presidential candidate. The entire herd is in as fine condition as any beef cattle, though they were never fed anything but hay and are never given any shelter. In fact they don't take kindly to shelter, and whether a blizzard is blowing, with the mercury 20 degrees below zero, or the sun pouring down his scorching rays, with the thermometer 110 degrees above, they set their heads resolutely toward storm or sun and take their medicine as if they liked it. Hon. W. F. Cody, "Buffalo Bill," tried to buy the whole herd two years ago to take to Europe with his Wild West Show, but they were not for sale at his own figures, and, indeed, there is no anxiety to dispose of them at any figures. The railroad company has been glad to furnish them pasturage for the sake of adding to the attractions of the park, in which there are also forty-three head of deer, including two as fine bucks as ever trotted over the national deer trail toward the salt-licks in northern Utah.

"While the bison at Bismark Grove are splendid specimens of their class, "Cleveland" is decidedly the pride of the herd, and as grand a creature as ever trod the soil of Kansas on four legs. He is just six years old and is a perfect specimen of the kings of the plains. There is royal blood in his veins, and his coat is finer than the imperial purple. It is not possible to get at him to measure his stature and weight. He must weigh fully 3,000 pounds, and it is doubtful if there is to-day living on the face of the earth a handsomer buffalo bull than he. "Cleveland's" disposition is not so ugly as old Barney's was, but at certain seasons he is very wild, and there is no one venturesome enough to go into the in-closure. It is then not altogether safe to even look over the high and heavy board fence at him, for he is likely to make a run for the visitor, as the numerous holes in the fence where he has knocked off the boards will testify."

Herd of Mr. Frederick Dupree, Cheyenne Indian Agency, near Fort Bennett, Dakota.—This herd contains at present nine pure-blood buf-faloes, five of which are cows and seven mixed bloods. Of the former, there are two adult bulls and four adult cows. Of the mixed blood animals, six are half-breeds and one a quarter-breed buffalo.

Mr. Dupree obtained the nucleus of his herd in 1882, at which time he captured five wild calves about 100 miles west of Fort Bennett. Of these, two died after two months of captivity and a third was killed by an Indian in 1885.

Mr. D. F. Carlin, of the Indian service, at Fort Bennett, has kindly furnished me the following information respecting this herd, under date of November 1, 1888 :

"The animals composing this herd are all in fine condition and are quite tame. They keep by themselves most of the time, except the oldest bull (six years old), who seems to appreciate the company of do-mestic cattle more than that of his own family. Mr. Dupree has kept one half-breed bull as an experiment; he thinks it will produce a hardy class of cattle. His half-breeds are all black, with one exception, and that is a roan; but they are all built like the buffalo, and when young they grunt more like a hog than like a calf, the same as a full-blood buffalo.

"Mr. Dupree has never lost a [domestic] cow in giving birth to a half-breed calf, as was supposed by many people would be the case. There have been no sales from this herd, although the owner has a standing offer of $650 for a cow and bull. The cows are not for sale at any price.

Herd at Lincoln Park, Chicago, Mr. W. P. Walker, superintendent.— This very interesting and handsomely-kept herd is composed of seven individuals of the following character: One bull eight years old, one bull four years old, two cows eight years old, two cows two years old in the spring of 1888, and one ♀ calf born in the spring of 1888.

Zoological Gardens, Cincinnati, Ohio.—This collection contains four bison, an adult bull and cow, and one immature specimen.

Dr. V. T. McGillicuddy, Rapid City, Dakota, has a herd of four pure buffaloes and one half-breed. Of the former, the two adults, a bull and cow seven years old, were caught by Sioux Indians near the Black Hills for the owner in the spring of 1882. The Indians drove two milch cows to the range to nourish the calves when caught. These have produced two calves, one of which, a bull, is now three years old, and the other is a yearling heifer.

Central Park Menagerie, New York, Dr. W. A. Conklin, director.—This much-visited collection contains four bison, an adult bull and cow, a two-year-old calf, and a yearling.

Mr. John H. Starin, Glen Island, near New York City.—There are four buffaloes at this summer resort.

The U. S. National Museum, Washington, District of Columbia.—The collection of the department of living animals at this institution contains two fine young buffaloes; a bull four years old in July, 1888, and a cow three years old in May of the same year. These animals were captured in western Nebraska, when they were calves, by H. R. Jackett, of Ogalalla, and kept by him on his ranch until 1888. In April, 1888, Hon. Eugene G. Blackford, of New York, purchased them of Mr. Frederick D. Nowell, of North Platte, Nebraska, for $400 for the pair, and presented them to the National Museum, in the hope that they might form the nucleus of a herd to be owned and exhibited by the United States Government in or near the city of Washington. The two animals were received in Ogalalla by Mr. Joseph Palmer, of the National Museum, and by him they were brought on to Washington in May, in fine condition. Since their arrival they have been exhibited to the public in a temporary inclosure on the Smithsonian Grounds, and have attracted much attention.

Mr. B. C. Winston, of Hamline, Minnesota, owns a pair of buffaloes, one of which, a young bull, was caught by him in western Dakota in the spring of 1886, soon after its birth. The cow was purchased at Rosseau, Dakota Territory, a year later, for $225.

Mr. I. P. Butler, of Colorado, Texas, is the owner of a young bull buffalo and a half-breed calf.

Mr. Jesse Huston, of Miles City, Montana, owns a fine five-year-old bull buffalo.

Mr. L. F. Gardner, of Bellwood, Oregon, is the owner of a large adult bull.

The Riverside Ranch Company, south of Mandan, Dakota, owns a pair of full-blood buffaloes.

In Dakota, in the hands of parties unknown, there are four full-blood buffaloes.

Mr. James R. Hitch, of Optima, Indian Territory, has a pair of young buffaloes, which he has offered for sale for $750.

Mr. Joseph A. Hudson, of Estell, Nebraska, owns a three-year-old bull buffalo, which is for sale.

In other countries there are live specimens of *Bison americanus* reported as follows: two at Belleview Gardens, Manchester, England;

one at the Zoological Gardens, London; one at Liverpool, England (purchased of Hon. W. F. Cody in 1888); two at the Zoological Gardens, Dresden; one at the Zoological Gardens, Calcutta.

Statistics of full-blood buffaloes in captivity January 1, 1889.

Number kept for breeding purposes 216
Number kept for exhibition 40

Total pure-blood buffaloes in captivity 256
Wild buffaloes under Government protection in the Yellowstone Park 200
Number of mixed-breed buffalo—domestics 40

There are, without doubt, a few half-breeds in Manitoba of which I have no account. It is probable there are also a very few more captive buffaloes scattered singly here and there which will be heard of later, but the total will be a very small number, I am sure.

PART II.—THE EXTERMINATION.

I. Causes of the Extermination.

The causes which led to the practical extinction (in a wild state, at least) of the most economically valuable wild animal that ever inhabited the American continent, are by no means obscure. It is well that we should know precisely what they were, and by the sad fate of the buffalo be warned in time against allowing similar causes to produce the same results with our elk, antelope, deer, moose, caribou, mountain sheep, mountain goat, walrus, and other animals. It will be doubly deplorable if the remorseless slaughter we have witnessed during the last twenty years carries with it no lessons for the future. A continuation of the record we have lately made as wholesale game butchers will justify posterity in dating us back with the mound-builders and cave-dwellers, when man's only known function was to slay and eat.

The primary cause of the buffalo's extermination, and the one which embraced all others, was the descent of civilization, with all its elements of destructiveness, upon the whole of the country inhabited by that animal. From the Great Slave Lake to the Rio Grande the home of the buffalo was everywhere overrun by the man with a gun; and, as has ever been the case, the wild creatures were gradually swept away, the largest and most conspicuous forms being the first to go.

The secondary causes of the extermination of the buffalo may be catalogued as follows:

(1) Man's reckless greed, his wanton destructiveness, and improvidence in not husbanding such resources as come to him from the hand of nature ready made.

(2) The total and utterly inexcusable absence of protective measures and agencies on the part of the National Government and of the Western States and Territories.

(3) The fatal preference on the part of hunters generally, both white

and red, for the robe and flesh of the cow over that furnished by the bull.

(4) The phenomenal stupidity of the animals themselves, and their indifference to man.

(5) The perfection of modern breech-loading rifles and other sporting fire-arms in general.

Each of these causes acted against the buffalo with its full force, to offset which there was *not even one* restraining or preserving influence, and it is not to be wondered at that the species went down before them. Had any one of these conditions been eliminated the result would have been reached far less quickly. Had the buffalo, for example, possessed one-half the fighting qualities of the grizzly bear he would have fared very differently, but his inoffensiveness and lack of courage almost leads one to doubt the wisdom of the economy of nature so far as it relates to him.

II. Methods of Slaughter.

1. *The still-hunt.*—Of all the deadly methods of buffalo slaughter, the still-hunt was the deadliest. Of all the methods that were unsportsmanlike, unfair, ignoble, and utterly reprehensible, this was in every respect the lowest and the worst. Destitute of nearly every element of the buoyant excitement and spice of danger that accompanied genuine buffalo hunting on horseback, the still-hunt was mere butchery of the tamest and yet most cruel kind. About it there was none of the true excitement of the chase; but there was plenty of greedy eagerness to "down" as many "head" as possible every day, just as there is in every slaughter-house where the killers are paid so much per head. Judging from all accounts, it was about as exciting and dangerous work as it would be to go out now and shoot cattle on the Texas or Montana ranges. The probabilities are, however, that shooting Texas cattle would be the most dangerous; for, instead of running from a man on foot, as the buffalo used to do, range cattle usually charge down upon him, from motives of curiosity, perhaps, and not infrequently place his life in considerable jeopardy.

The buffalo owes his extermination very largely to his own unparalleled stupidity; for nothing else could by any possibility have enabled the still-hunters to accomplish what they did in such an incredibly short time. So long as the chase on horseback was the order of the day, it ordinarily required the united efforts of from fifteen to twenty-five hunters to kill a thousand buffalo in a single season; but a single still-hunter, with a long-range breech-loader, who knew how to make a "sneak" and get "a stand on a bunch," often succeeded in killing from one to three thousand in one season by his own unaided efforts. Capt. Jack Brydges, of Kansas, who was one of the first to begin the final slaughter of the southern herd, killed, by contract, one thousand one hundred and forty-two buffaloes in six weeks.

So long as the buffalo remained in large herds their numbers gave each individual a feeling of dependence upon his fellows and of general security from harm, even in the presence of strange phenomena which he could not understand. When he heard a loud report and saw a little cloud of white smoke rising from a gully, a clump of sage-brush, or the top of a ridge, 200 yards away, he wondered what it meant, and held himself in readiness to follow his leader in case she should run away. But when the leader of the herd, usually the oldest cow, fell bleeding upon the ground, and no other buffalo promptly assumed the leadership of the herd, instead of acting independently and fleeing from the alarm, he merely did as he saw the others do, and waited his turn to be shot. Latterly, however, when the herds were totally broken up, when the few survivors were scattered in every direction, and it became a case of every buffalo for himself, they became wild and wary, ever ready to start off at the slightest alarm, and run indefinitely. Had they shown the same wariness seventeen years ago that the survivors have manifested during the last three or four years, there would now be a hundred thousand head alive instead of only about three hundred in a wild and unprotected state.

Notwithstanding the merciless war that had been waged against the buffalo for over a century by both whites and Indians, and the steady decrease of its numbers, as well as its range, there were several million head on foot, not only up to the completion of the Union Pacific Railway, but as late as the year 1870. Up to that time the killing done by white men had been chiefly for the sake of meat, the demand for robes was moderate, and the Indians took annually less than one hundred thousand for trading. Although half a million buffaloes were killed by Indians, half-breeds, and whites, the natural increase was so very considerable as to make it seem that the evil day of extermination was yet far distant.

But by a coincidence which was fatal to the buffalo, with the building of three lines of railway through the most populous buffalo country there came a demand for robes and hides, backed up by an unlimited supply of new and marvellously accurate breech-loading rifles and fixed ammunition. And then followed a wild rush of hunters to the buffalo country, eager to destroy as many head as possible in the shortest time. For those greedy ones the chase on horseback was "too slow" and too unfruitful. That was a retail method of killing, whereas they wanted to kill by wholesale. From their point of view, the still-hunt or "sneak" hunt was the method *par excellence*. If they could have obtained Gatling guns with which to mow down a whole herd at a time, beyond a doubt they would have gladly used them.

The still-hunt was seen at its very worst in the years 1871, 1872, and 1873, on the southern buffalo range, and ten years later at its best in Montana, on the northern. Let us first consider it at its best, which in principle was bad enough.

The great rise in the price of robes which followed the blotting out of the great southern herd at once put buffalo-hunting on a much more comfortable and respectable business basis in the North than it had ever occupied in the South, where prices had all along been phenomenally low.

In Montana it was no uncommon thing for a hunter to invest from $1,000 to $2,000 in his "outfit" of horses, wagons, weapons, ammunition, provisions, and sundries.

One of the men who accompanied the Smithsonian Expedition for Buffalo, Mr. James McNaney, of Miles City, Montana, was an ex-buffalo hunter, who had spent three seasons on the northern range, killing buffalo for their robes, and his standing as a hunter was of the best. A brief description of his outfit and its work during its last season on on the range (1882–'83) may fairly be taken as a typical illustration of the life and work of the still-hunter at its best. The only thing against it was the extermination of the buffalo.

During the winters of 1880 and 1881 Mr. McNaney had served in Maxwell's outfit as a hunter, working by the month, but his success in killing was such that he decided to work the third year on his own account. Although at that time only seventeen years of age, he took an elder brother as a partner, and purchased an outfit in Miles City, of which the following were the principal items: Two wagons, 2 four-horse teams, 2 saddle-horses, 2 wall-tents, 1 cook-stove with pipe, 1 40–90 Sharp's rifle (breech-loading), 1 45–70 Sharps rifle (breech-loading), 1 45–120 Sharps rifle (breech-loading), 50 pounds gunpowder, 550 pounds lead, 4,500 primers, 600 brass shells, 4 sheets patch-paper, 60 Wilson skinning knives, 3 butcher's steels, 1 portable grindstone, flour, bacon, baking-powder, coffee, sugar, molasses, dried apples, canned vegetables, beans, etc., in quantity.

The entire cost of the outfit was about $1,400. Two men were hired for the season at $50 per month, and the party started from Miles City on November 10, which was considered a very late start. The usual time of setting out for the range was about October 1.

The outfit went by rail northeastward to Terry, and from thence across country south and east about 100 miles, around the head of O'Fallon Creek to the head of Beaver Creek, a tributary of the Little Missouri. A good range was selected, without enroachment upon the domains of the hunters already in the field, and the camp was made near the bank of the creek, close to a supply of wood and water, and screened from distant observation by a circle of hills and ridges. The two rectangular wall-tents were set up end to end, with the cook-stove in the middle, where the ends came together. In one tent the cooking and eating was done, and the other contained the beds.

It was planned that the various members of the party should cook turn about, a week at a time, but one of them soon developed such a rare and conspicuous talent for bread-making and general cookery that he was elected by acclamation to cook during the entire season. To the other three members fell the hunting. Each man hunted separately from the others, and skinned all the animals that his rifle brought down.

There were buffalo on the range when the hunters arrived, and the killing began at once. At daylight the still-hunter sallied forth on foot, carrying in his hand his huge Sharps rifle, weighing from 16 to 19 pounds, with from seventy-five to one hundred loaded cartridges in his two belts or his pockets. At his side, depending from his belt, hung his "hunter's companion," a flat leather scabbard, containing a ripping knife, a skinning knife, and a butcher's steel upon which to sharpen them. The total weight carried was very considerable, seldom less than 36 pounds, and often more.

Inasmuch as it was highly important to move camp as seldom as possible in the course of a season's work, the hunter exercised the greatest precaution in killing his game, and had ever before his mind the necessity of doing his killing without frightening away the survivors.

With ten thousand buffaloes on their range, it was considered the height of good luck to find a "bunch" of fifty head in a secluded "draw" or hollow, where it was possible to "make a kill" without disturbing the big herd.

The still-hunter usually went on foot, for when buffaloes became so scarce as to make it necessary for him to ride his occupation was practically gone. At the time I speak of, the hunter seldom had to walk more than 3 miles from camp to find buffalo, in case there were any at all on his range, and it was usually an advantage to be without a horse. From the top of a ridge or high butte the country was carefully scanned, and if several small herds were in sight the one easiest to approach was selected as the one to attack. It was far better to find a herd lying down or quietly grazing, or sheltering from a cold wind, than to find it traveling, for while a hard run of a mile or two often enabled the hunter to "head off" a moving herd and kill a certain number of animals out of it, the net results were never half so satisfactory as with herds absolutely at rest.

Having decided upon an attack, the hunter gets to leeward of his game, and approaches it according to the nature of the ground. If it is in a hollow, he secures a position at the top of the nearest ridge, as close as he can get. If it is in a level "flat," he looks for a gully up which he can skulk until within good rifle-shot. If there is no gully, he may be obliged to crawl half a mile on his hands and knees, often through snow or amongst beds of prickly pear, taking advantage of even such scanty cover as sage-brush affords. Some Montana still-hunters adopted the method of drawing a gunny-sack over the entire upper half of the body, with holes cut for the eyes and arms, which simple but unpicturesque arrangement often enabled the hunter to

STILL-HUNTING BUFFALOES ON THE NORTHERN RANGE.

From a painting by J. H. Moser, in the National Museum.

approach his game much more easily and more closely than would otherwise have been possible.

Having secured a position within from 100 to 250 yards of his game (often the distance was much greater), the hunter secures a comfortable rest for his huge rifle, all the time keeping his own person thoroughly hidden from view, estimates the distance, carefully adjusts his sights, and begins business. If the herd is moving, the animal in the lead is the first one shot, close behind the fore leg and about a foot above the brisket, which sends the ball through the lungs. If the herd is at rest, the oldest cow is always supposed to be the leader, and she is the one to kill first. The noise startles the buffaloes, they stare at the little cloud of white smoke and feel inclined to run, but seeing their leader hesitate they wait for her. She, when struck, gives a violent start forward, but soon stops, and the blood begins to run from her nostrils in two bright crimson streams. In a couple of minutes her body sways unsteadily, she staggers, tries hard to keep her feet, but soon gives a lurch sidewise and falls. Some of the other members of the herd come around her and stare and sniff in wide-eyed wonder, and one of the more wary starts to lead the herd away. But before she takes half a dozen steps "bang!" goes the hidden rifle again, and her leadership is ended forever. Her fall only increases the bewilderment of the survivors over a proceeding which to them is strange and unaccountable, because the danger is not visible. They cluster around the fallen ones, sniff at the warm blood, bawl aloud in wonderment, and do everything but run away.

The policy of the hunter is to not fire too rapidly, but to attend closely to business, and every time a buffalo attempts to make off, shoot it down. One shot per minute was a moderate rate of firing, but under pressure of circumstances two per minute could be discharged with deliberate precision. With the most accurate hunting rifle ever made, a "dead rest," and a large mark practically motionless, it was no wonder that nearly every shot meant a dead buffalo. The vital spot on a buffalo which stands with its side to the hunter is about a foot in diameter, and on a full-grown bull is considerably more. Under such conditions as the above, which was called getting "a stand," the hunter nurses his victims just as an angler plays a big fish with light tackle, and in the most methodical manner murders them one by one, either until the last one falls, his cartridges are all expended, or the stupid brutes come to their senses and run away. Occasionally the poor fellow was troubled by having his rifle get too hot to use, but if a snow-bank was at hand he would thrust the weapon into it without ceremony to cool it off.

A success in getting a stand meant the slaughter of a good-sized herd. A hunter whom I met in Montana, Mr. Harry Andrews, told me that he once fired one hundred and fifteen shots from one spot and killed sixty-three buffalo in less than an hour. The highest number Mr. McNancy ever knew of being killed in one stand was ninety-one head, but

Colonel Dodge once counted one hundred and twelve carcasses of buffalo "inside of a semicircle of 200 yards radius, all of which were killed by one man from the same spot, and in less than three-quarters of an hour."

The "kill" being completed, the hunter then addressed himself to the task of skinning his victims. The northern hunters were seldom guilty of the reckless carelessness and lack of enterprise in the treatment of robes which at one time was so prominent a feature of work on the southern range. By the time white men began to hunt for robes on the northern range, buffalo were becoming comparatively scarce, and robes were worth from $2 to $4 each. The fur-buyers had taught the hunters, with the potent argument of hard cash, that a robe carefully and neatly taken off, stretched, and kept reasonably free from blood and dirt, was worth more money in the market than one taken off in a slovenly manner, and contrary to the nicer demands of the trade. After 1880, buffalo on the northern range were skinned with considerable care, and amongst the robe-hunters not one was allowed to become a loss when it was possible to prevent it. Every full-sized cow robe was considered equal to $3.50 in hard cash, and treated accordingly. The hunter, or skinner, always stretched every robe out on the ground to its fullest extent while it was yet warm, and cut the initials of his employer in the thin subcutaneous muscle which always adhered to the inside of the skin. A warm skin is very elastic, and when stretched upon the ground the hair holds it in shape until it either dries or freezes, and so retains its full size. On the northern range skins were so valuable that many a dispute arose between rival outfits over the ownership of a dead buffalo, some of which produced serious results.

2. *The chase on horseback or "running buffalo."*—Next to the still-hunt the method called "running buffalo" was the most fatal to the race, and the one most universally practiced. To all hunters, save greedy white men, the chase on horseback yielded spoil sufficient for every need, and it also furnished sport of a superior kind—manly, exhilarating, and well spiced with danger. Even the horses shared the excitement and eagerness of their riders.

So long as the weapons of the Indian consisted only of the bow and arrow and the spear, he was obliged to kill at close quarters or not at all. And even when fire-arms were first placed in his hands their caliber was so small, the charge so light, and the Indian himself so poor a marksman at long range, that his best course was still to gallop alongside the herd on his favorite "buffalo horse" and kill at the shortest possible range. From all accounts, the Red River half-breeds, who hunted almost exclusively with fire-arms, never dreamed of the deadly still-hunt, but always killed their game by "running" it.

In former times even the white men of the plains did the most of their buffalo hunting on horseback, using the largest-sized Colt's revolver, sometimes one in each hand, until the repeating-rifle made its appearance, which in a great measure displaced the revolver in running buffalo. But about that time began the mad warfare for "robes" and "hides," and the only fair and sportsmanlike method of hunting was declared too slow for the greedy buffalo-skinners.

Then came the cold-blooded butchery of the still-hunt. From that time on the buffalo as a game animal steadily lost caste. It soon came to be universally considered that there was no sport in hunting buffalo. True enough of still-hunting, where the hunter sneaks up and shoots them down one by one at such long range the report of his big rifle does not even frighten them away. So far as sportsmanlike fairness is concerned, that method was not one whit more elevated than killing game by poison.

But the chase on horseback was a different thing. Its successful prosecution demanded a good horse, a bold rider, a firm seat, and perfect familiarity with weapons. The excitement of it was intense, the dangers not to be despised, and, above all, the buffalo had a fair show for his life, or partially so, at least. The mode of attack is easily described.

Whenever the hunters discovered a herd of buffalo, they usually got to leeward of it and quietly rode forward in a body, or stretched out in a regular skirmish line, behind the shelter of a knoll, perhaps, until they had approached the herd as closely as could be done without alarming it. Usually the unsuspecting animals, with a confidence due more to their great numbers than anything else, would allow a party of horsemen to approach within from 200 to 400 yards of their flankers, and then they would start off on a slow trot. The hunters then put spurs to their horses and dashed forward to overtake the herd as quickly as possible. Once up with it, each hunter chooses the best animal within his reach, chases him until his flying steed carries him close alongside, and then the arrow or the bullet is sent into his vitals. The fatal spot is from 12 to 18 inches in circumference, and lies immediately back of the fore leg, with its lowest point on a line with the elbow.

This, the true chase of the buffalo, was not only exciting, but dangerous. It often happened that the hunter found himself surrounded by the flying herd, and in a cloud of dust, so that neither man nor horse could see the ground before them. Under such circumstances fatal accidents to both men and horses were numerous. It was not an uncommon thing for half-breeds to shoot each other in the excitement of the chase; and, while now and then a wounded bull suddenly turned upon his pursuer and overthrew him, the greatest number of casualties were from falls.

Of the dangers involved in running buffalo Colonel Dodge writes as follows : *

"The danger is not so much from the buffalo, which rarely makes an effort to injure his pursuer, as from the fact that neither man nor horse

---

* Plains of the Great West, p. 127.

can see the ground, which may be rough and broken, or perforated with prairie-dog or gopher holes. This danger is so imminent, that a man who runs into a herd of buffalo may be said to take his life in his hand. I have never known a man hurt by a buffalo in such a chase. I have known of at least six killed, and a very great many more or less injured, some very severely, by their horses falling with them."

On this point Catlin declares that to engage in running buffalo is "at the hazard of every bone in one's body, to feel the fine and thrilling exhilaration of the chase for a moment, and then as often to upbraid and blame himself for his folly and imprudence."

Previous to my first experience in "running buffalo" I had entertained a mortal dread of ever being called upon to ride a chase across a prairie-dog town. The mouth of a prairie-dog's burrow is amply large to receive the hoof of a horse, and the angle at which the hole descends into the earth makes it just right for the leg of a running horse to plunge into up to the knee and bring down both horse and rider instantly; the former with a broken leg, to say the least of it. If the rider sits loosely, and promptly resigns his seat, he will go flying forward, as if thrown from a catapult, for 20 feet or so, perhaps to escape with a few broken bones, and perhaps to have his neck broken, or his skull fractured on the hard earth. If he sticks tightly to his saddle, his horse is almost certain to fall upon him, and perhaps kill him. Judge, then, my feelings when the first bunch of buffalo we started headed straight across the largest prairie-dog town I had ever seen up to that time. And not only was the ground honey-combed with gaping round holes, but it was also crossed here and there by treacherous ditch-like gullies, cut straight down into the earth to an uncertain depth, and so narrow as to be invisible until it was almost time to leap across them.

But at such a time, with the game thundering along a few rods in advance, the hunter thinks of little else except getting up to it. He looks as far ahead as possible, and helps his horse to avoid dangers, but to a great extent the horse must guide himself. The rider plies his spurs and looks eagerly forward, almost feverish with excitement and eagerness, but at the same time if he is wise he *expects* a fall, and holds himself in readiness to take the ground with as little damage as he can.

Mr. Catlin gives a most graphic description of a hunting accident, which may fairly be quoted in full as a type of many such. I must say that I fully sympathize with M. Chardon in his estimate of the hardness of the ground he fell upon, for I have a painful recollection of a fall I had from which I arose with the settled conviction that the ground in Montana is the hardest in the world! It seemed more like falling upon cast-iron than prairie turf.

"I dashed along through the thundering mass as they swept away over the plain, scarcely able to tell whether I was on a buffalo's back or my horse, hit and hooked and jostled about, till at length I found myself alongside my game, when I gave him a shot as I passed him.

I saw guns flash about me in several directions, but I heard them not. Amidst the trampling throng Mons. Chardon had wounded a stately bull, and at this moment was passing him with his piece leveled for another shot. They were both at full speed and I also, within the reach of the muzzle of my gun, when the bull instantly turned, receiving the horse upon his horns, and the ground received poor Chardon, who made a frog's leap of some 20 feet or more over the bull's back and almost under my horse's heels. I wheeled my horse as soon as possible and rode back where lay poor Chardon, gasping to start his breath again, and within a few paces of him his huge victim, with his heels high in the air, and the horse lying across him. I dismounted instantly, but Chardon was raising himself on his hands, with his eyes and mouth full of dirt, and feeling for his gun, which lay about 30 feet in advance of him. 'Heaven spare you! are you hurt, Chardon?' 'Hi–hic—hic—hic—hic——no;—hic—no—no, I believe not. Oh, this is not much, Mons. Cataline—this is nothing new—but this is a d—d hard piece of ground here—hic—oh! hic!' At this the poor fellow fainted, but in a few moments arose, picked up his gun, took his horse by the bit, which then opened *its* eyes, and with a *hic* and a ugh—*ughk!*—sprang upon its feet, shook off the dirt, and here we were, all upon our legs again, save the bull, whose fate had been more sad than that of either."*

The following passage from Mr. Alexander Ross's graphic description of a great hunt,† in which about four hundred hunters made an onslaught upon a herd, affords a good illustration of the dangers in running buffalo:

"On this occasion the surface was rocky and full of badger-holes. Twenty-three horses and riders were at one moment all sprawling on the ground; one horse, gored by a bull, was killed on the spot; two more were disabled by the fall; one rider broke his shoulder-blade; another burst his gun and lost three of his fingers by the accident; and a third was struck on the knee by an exhausted ball. These accidents will not be thought overnumerous, considering the result, for in the evening no less than thirteen hundred and seventy-five tongues were brought into camp.

It really seems as if the horses of the plains entered willfully and knowingly into the war on the doomed herds. But for the willingness and even genuine eagerness with which the "buffalo horses" of both white men and Indians entered into the chase, hunting on horseback would have been attended with almost insurmountable difficulties, and the results would have been much less fatal to the species. According to all accounts the horses of the Indians and half-breeds were far better trained than those of their white rivals, no doubt owing to the fact that the use of the bow, which required the free use of both hands,

---

* North American Indians, I, pp. 25-26.
† Red River Settlement, p. 256.

was only possible when the horse took the right course of his own free will or else could be guided by the pressure of the knees. If we may believe the historians of that period, and there is not the slightest reason to doubt them, the "buffalo horses" of the Indians displayed almost as much intelligence and eagerness in the chase as did their human riders. Indeed, in "running buffalo" with only the bow and arrow, nothing but the willing co-operation of the horse could have possibly made this mode of hunting either satisfactory or successful.

In Lewis and Clarke's Travels, volume II, page 387, appears the following record:

"He [Sergeant Pryor] had found it almost impossible with two men to drive on the remaining horses, for as soon as they discovered a herd of buffaloes the loose horses immediately set off in pursuit of them, and surrounded the buffalo herd with almost as much skill as their riders could have done. At last he was obliged to send one horseman forward and drive all the buffaloes from the route."

The Hon. H. H. Sibley, who once accompanied the Red River half-breeds on their annual hunt, relates the following: *

"One of the hunters fell from his saddle, and was unable to overtake his horse, which continued the chase as if he of himself could accomplish great things, so much do these animals become imbued with a passion for this sport! On another occasion a half-breed left his favorite steed at the camp, to enable him to recruit his strength, enjoining upon his wife the necessity of properly securing the animal, which was not done. Not relishing the idea of being left behind, he started after us and soon was alongside, and thus he continued to keep pace with the hunters in their pursuit of the buffalo, seeming to await with impatience the fall of some of them to the earth. The chase ended, he came neighing to his master, whom he soon singled out, although the men were dispersed here and there for a distance of miles."

Col. R. I. Dodge, in his Plains of the Great West, page 129, describes a meeting with two Mexican buffalo-hunters whose horses were so fleet and so well trained that whenever a herd of buffalo came in sight, instead of shooting their game wherever they came up with it, the one having the best horse would dash into the herd, cut out a fat two-year old, and, with the help of his partner, then actually drive it to their camp before shooting it down. "They had a fine lot of meat and a goodly pile of skins, and they said that every buffalo had been driven into camp and killed as the one I saw. 'It saves a heap of trouble packing the meat to camp,' said one of them, naively."

Probably never before in the history of the world, until civilized man came in contact with the buffalo, did whole armies of men march out in true military style, with officers, flags, chaplains, and rules of war, and make war on wild animals. No wonder the buffalo has been exterminated. So long as they existed north of the Missouri in any con-

---

* Schoolcraft's "North American Indians," 108.

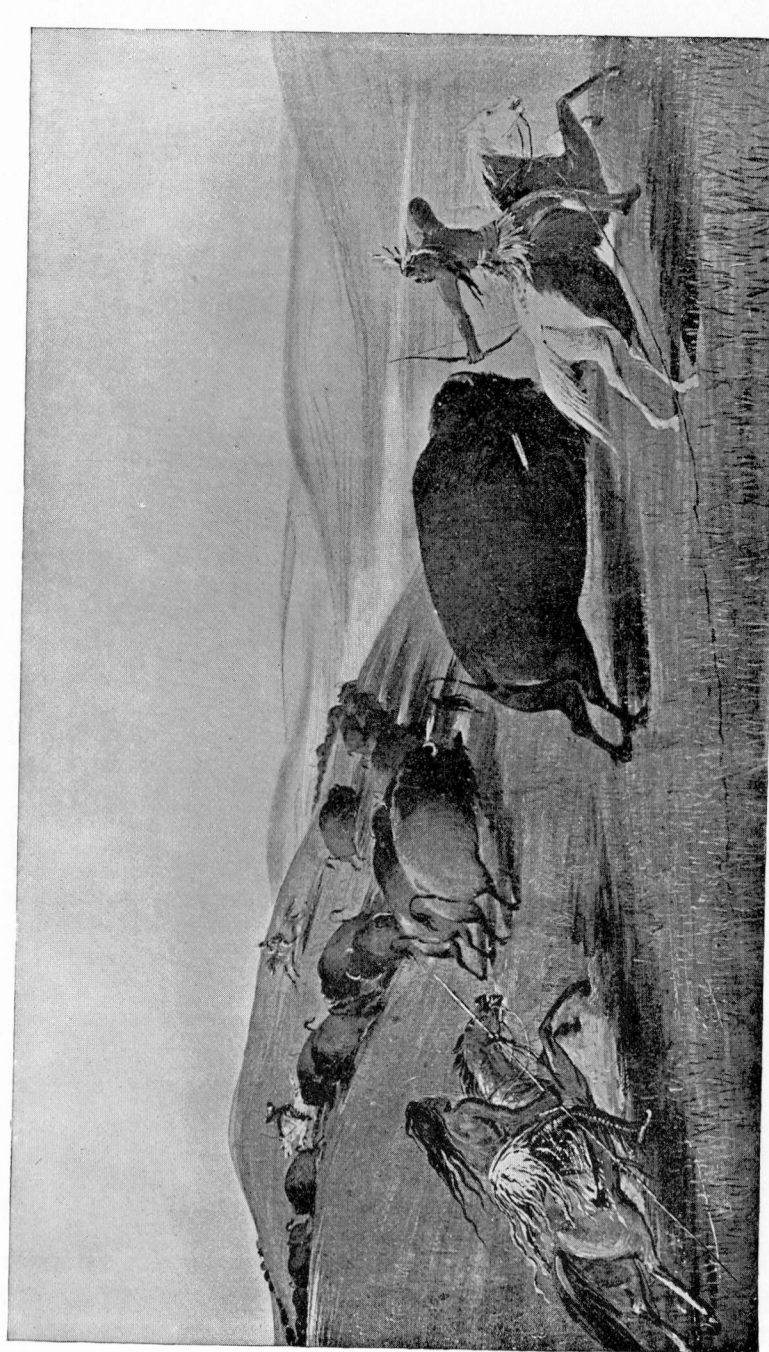

THE CHASE ON HORSEBACK.

From a painting in the National Museum by George Catlin.

siderable number, the half-breeds and Indians of the Manitoba Red River settlement used to gather each year in a great army, and go with carts to the buffalo range. On these great hunts, which took place every year from about the 15th of June to the 1st of September, vast numbers of buffalo were killed, and the supply was finally exhausted. As if Heaven had decreed the extirpation of the species, the half-breed hunters, like their white robe-hunting rivals farther south, always killed *cows* in preference to bulls so long as a choice was possible, the very course best calculated to exterminate any species in the shortest possible time.

The army of half-breeds and Indians which annually went forth from the Red River settlement to make war on the buffalo was often far larger than the army with which Cortez subdued a great empire. As early as 1846 it had become so great, that it was necessary to divide it into two divisions, one of which, the White Horse Plain division, was accustomed to go west by the Assinniboine River to the "rapids crossing-place," and from there in a southwesterly direction. The Red River division went south to Pembina, and did the most of their hunting in Dakota. The two divisions sometimes met (says Professor Hind), but not intentionally. In 1849 a Mr. Flett took a census of the White Horse Plain division, in Dakota Territory, and found that it contained 603 carts, 700 half-breeds, 200 Indians, 600 horses, 200 oxen, 400 dogs, and 1 cat.

In his "Red River Settlement" Mr. Alexander Ross gives the following census of the number of carts assembled in camp for the buffalo hunt at five different periods:

Number of carts assembled for the first trip.

In 1820	540
In 1825	680
In 1830	820
In 1835	970
In 1840	1,210

The expedition which was accompanied by Rev. Mr. Belcourt, a Catholic priest, whose account is set forth in the Hon. Mr. Sibley's paper on the buffalo,* was a comparatively small one, which started from Pembina, and very generously took pains not to spoil the prospects of the great Red River division, which was expected to take the field at the same time. This, therefore, was a small party, like others which had already reached the range; but it contained 213 carts, 55 hunters and their families, making 60 lodges in all. This party killed 1,776 cows (bulls not counted, many of which were killed, though "not even a tongue was taken"), which yielded 228 bags of pemmican, 1,213 bales of dried meat, 166 sacks of tallow, and 556 bladders full of marrow. But this was very moderate slaughter, being about 33 buffalo to each family. Even as late as 1872, when buffalo were getting scarce, Mr.

---

* Schoolcraft, pp. 101–110.

Grant * met a half-breed family on the Qu'Appelle, consisting of man, wife, and seven children, whose six carts were laden with the meat and robes yielded by *sixty* buffaloes; that number representing this one hunter's share of the spoils of the hunt.

To afford an idea of the truly military character of those Red River expeditions, I have only to quote a page from Prof. Henry Youle Hind : †

"After the start from the settlement has been well made, and all stragglers or tardy hunters have arrived, a great council is held and a president elected. A number of captains are nominated by the president and people jointly. The captains then proceed to appoint their own policemen, the number assigned to each not exceeding ten. Their duties are to see that the laws of the hunt are strictly carried out. In 1840, if a man ran a buffalo without permission before the general hunt began, his saddle and bridle were cut to pieces for the first offense; for the second offense his clothes were cut off his back. At the present day these punishments are changed to a fine of 20 shillings for the first offense. No gun is permitted to be fired when in the buffalo country before the 'race' begins. A priest sometimes goes with the hunt, and mass is then celebrated in the open prairies.

"At night the carts are placed in the form of a circle, with the horses and cattle inside the ring, and it is the duty of the captains and their policemen to see that this is rightly done. All laws are proclaimed in camp, and relate to the hunt alone. All camping orders are given by signal, a flag being carried by the guides, who are appointed by election. Each guide has his turn of one day, and no man can pass a guide on duty without subjecting himself to a fine of 5 shillings. No hunter can leave the camp to return home without permission, and no one is permitted to stir until any animal or property of value supposed to be lost is recovered. The policemen, at the order of their captains, can seize any cart at night-fall and place it where they choose for the public safety, but on the following morning they are compelled to bring it back to the spot from which they moved it the previous evening. This power is very necessary, in order that the horses may not be stampeded by night attacks of the Sioux or other Indian tribes at war with the half-breeds. A heavy fine is imposed in case of neglect in extinguishing fires when the camp is broken up in the morning.

"In sight of buffalo all the hunters are drawn up in line, the president, captains, and police being a few yards in advance, restraining the impatient hunters. 'Not yet! Not yet!' is the subdued whisper of the president. The approach to the herd is cautiously made. 'Now!' the president exclaims; and as the word leaves his lips the charge is made, and in a few minutes the excited half-breeds are amongst the bewildered buffalo."

"After witnessing one buffalo hunt," says Prof. John Macoun, " I can

---

* Ocean to Ocean, p. 116.

† Assinniboine and Saskatch. Exp. Exped., II, p. 111.

not blame the half-breed and the Indian for leaving the farm and wildly making for the plains when it is reported that buffalo have crossed the border."

The "great fall hunt" was a regular event with about all the Indian tribes living within striking distance of the buffalo, in the course of which great numbers of buffalo were killed, great quantities of meat dried and made into pemmican, and all the skins taken were tanned in various ways to suit the many purposes they were called upon to serve.

Mr. Francis La Flesche informs me that during the presence of the buffalo in western Nebraska and until they were driven south by the Sioux, the fall hunt of the Omahas was sometimes participated in by three hundred lodges, or about 3,000 people all told, six hundred of whom were warriors, and each of whom generally killed about ten buffaloes. The laws of the hunt were very strict and inexorable. In order that all participants should have an equal chance, it was decreed that any hunter caught "still-hunting" should be soundly flogged. On one occasion an Indian was discovered in the act, but not caught. During the chase which was made to capture him many arrows were fired at him by the police, but being better mounted than his pursuers he escaped, and kept clear of the camp during the remainder of the hunt. On another occasion an Omaha, guilty of the same offense, was chased, and in his effort to escape his horse fell with him in a coulée and broke one of his legs. In spite of the sad plight of the Omaha, his pursuers came up and flogged him, just as if nothing had happened.

After the invention of the Colt's revolver, and breech-loading rifles generally, the chase on horseback speedily became more fatal to the bison than it ever had been before. With such weapons, it was possible to gallop into the midst of a flying herd and, during the course of a run of 2 or 3 miles, discharge from twelve to forty shots at a range of only a few yards, or even a few feet. In this kind of hunting the heavy Navy revolver was the favorite weapon, because it could be held in one hand and fired with far greater precision than could a rifle held in both hands. Except in the hands of an expert, the use of the rifle was limited, and often attended with risk to the hunter; but the revolver was good for all directions; it could very often be used with deadly effect where a rifle could not have been used at all, and, moreover, it left the bridle-hand free. Many cavalrymen and hunters were able to use a revolver with either hand, or one in each hand. Gen. Lew. Wallace preferred the Smith and Wesson in 1867, which he declared to be "the best of revolvers" then.

It was his marvelous skill in shooting buffaloes with a rifle, from the back of a galloping horse, that earned for the Hon. W. F. Cody the sobriquet by which he is now familiarly known to the world—"Buffalo Bill." To the average hunter on horseback the galloping of the horse makes it easy for him to aim at the heart of a buffalo and shoot clear over its back. No other shooting is so difficult, or requires such consummate dexterity as shooting with any kind of a gun, especially a rifle, from the back of a running horse. Let him who doubts this statement try it for himself and he will doubt no more. It was in the chase of the buffalo on horseback, armed with a rifle, that "Buffalo Bill" acquired the marvelous dexterity with the rifle which he has since exhibited in the presence of the people of two continents. I regret that circumstances have prevented my obtaining the exact figures of the great kill of buffaloes that Mr. Cody once made in a single run, in which he broke all previous records in that line, and fairly earned his title. In 1867 he entered into a contract with the Kansas Pacific Railway, then in course of construction through western Kansas, at a monthly salary of $500, to deliver all the buffalo meat that would be required by the army of laborers engaged in building the road. In eighteen months he killed 4,280 buffaloes.

3. *Impounding or Killing in Pens.*—At first thought it seems hard to believe that it was ever possible for Indians to build pens and drive wild buffaloes into them, as cowboys now corral their cattle, yet such wholesale catches were of common occurrence among the Plains Crees of the south Saskatchewan country, and the same general plan was pursued, with slight modifications, by the Indians of the Assinniboine, Blackfeet, and Gros Ventres, and other tribes of the Northwest. Like the keddah elephant-catching operations in India, this plan was feasible only in a partially wooded country, and where buffalo were so numerous that their presence could be counted upon to a certainty. The "pound" was simply a circular pen, having a single entrance; but being unable to construct a gate of heavy timbers, such as is made to drop and close the entrance to an elephant pen, the Indians very shrewdly got over the difficulty by making the opening at the edge of a perpendicular bank 10 or 12 feet high, easy enough for a buffalo to jump down, but impossible for him to scale afterward. It is hardly probable that Indians who were expert enough to attack and kill buffalo on foot would have been tempted to undertake the labor that building a pound always involved, had it not been for the wild excitement attending captures made in this way, and which were shared to the fullest possible extent by warriors, women, and children alike.

The best description of this method which has come under our notice is that of Professor Hind, who witnessed its practice by the Plains Crees, on the headwaters of the Qu'Appelle River, in 1858. He describes the pound he saw as a fence, constructed of the trunks of trees laced together with green withes, and braced on the outside by props, inclosing a circular space about 120 feet in diameter. It was placed in a pretty dell between sand-hills, and leading from it in two diverging rows (like the guiding wings of an elephant pen) were the two rows of bushes which the Indians designate "dead men," which serve to guide the buffalo into the pound. The "dead men" extended a distance of 4 miles into the prairie. They were placed about 50 feet apart, and the

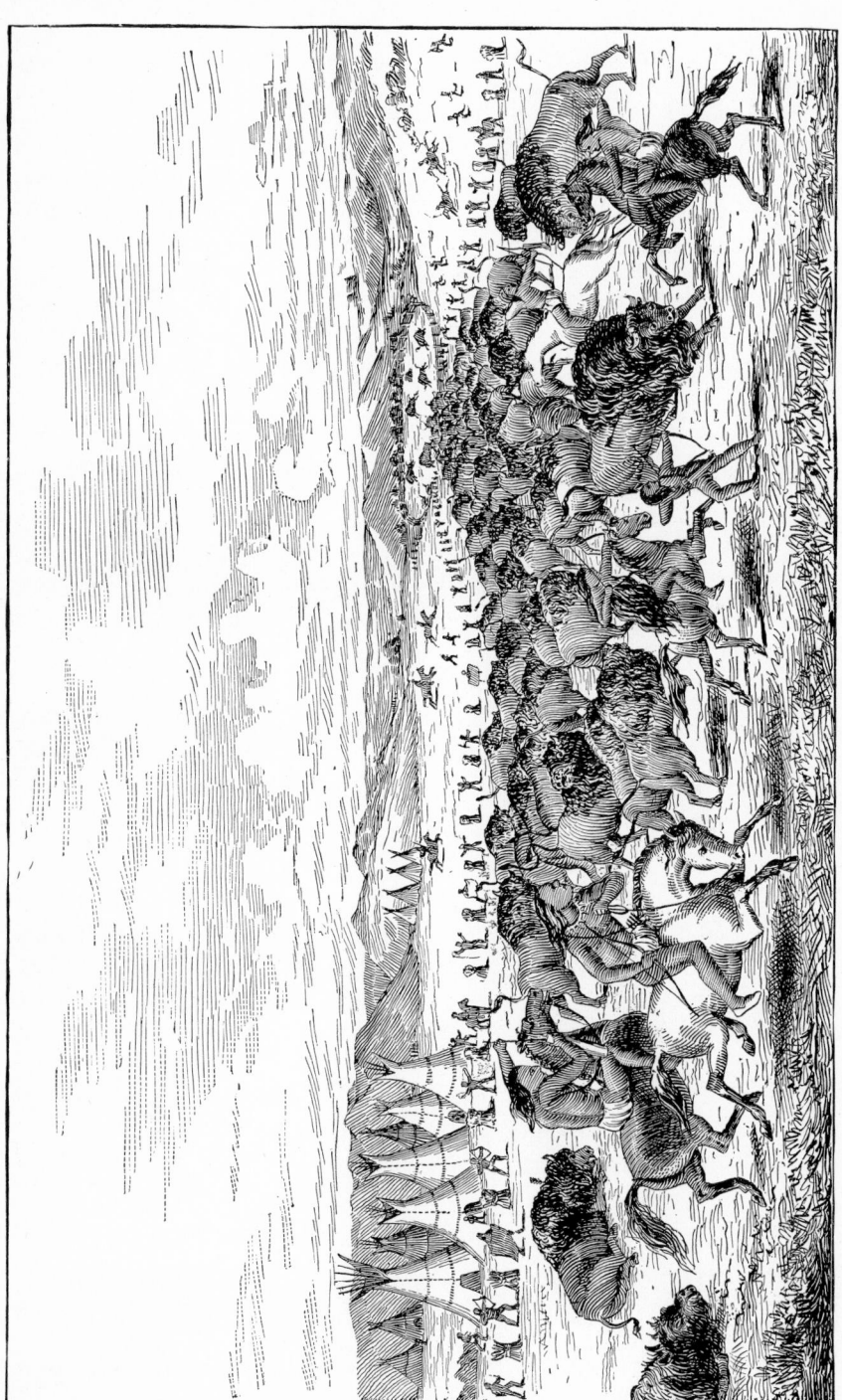

CREE INDIANS IMPOUNDING BUFFALOES.

Reproduced from Prof. H. Y. Hind's "Red River, Assinniboine, and Saskatchewan Expedition."

two rows gradually diverged until at their extremities they were from 1½ to 2 miles apart.

"When the skilled hunters are about to bring in a herd of buffalo from the prairie," says Professor Hind, "they direct the course of the gallop of the alarmed animals by confederates stationed in hollows or small depressions, who, when the buffalo appear inclined to take a direction leading from the space marked out by the 'dead men,' show themselves for a moment and wave their robes, immediately hiding again. This serves to turn the buffalo slightly in another direction, and when the animals, having arrived between the rows of 'dead men,' endeavor to pass through them, Indians stationed here and there behind a 'dead man' go through the same operation, and thus keep the animals within the narrowing limits of the converging lines. At the entrance to the pound there is a strong trunk of a tree placed about a foot from the ground, and on the inner side an excavation is made sufficiently deep to prevent the buffalo from leaping back when once in the pound. As soon as the animals have taken the fatal spring, they begin to gallop round and round the ring fence, looking for a chance to escape, but with the utmost silence women and children on the outside hold their robes before every orifice until the whole herd is brought in; then they climb to the top of the fence, and, with the hunters who have followed closely in the rear of the buffalo, spear or shoot with bows and arrows or fire-arms at the bewildered animals, rapidly becoming frantic with rage and terror, within the narrow limits of the pound.

"A dreadful scene of confusion and slaughter then begins; the oldest and strongest animals crush and toss the weaker; the shouts and screams of the excited Indians rise above the roaring of the bulls, the bellowing of the cows, and the piteous moaning of the calves. The dying struggles of so many huge and powerful animals crowded together create a revolting and terrible scene, dreadful from the excess of its cruelty and waste of life, but with occasional displays of wonderful brute strength and rage; while man in his savage, untutored, and heathen state shows both in deed and expression how little he is superior to the noble beasts he so wantonly and cruelly destroys."*

The last scene of the bloody tragedy is thus set forth a week later:

"Within the circular fence * * * lay, tossed in every conceivable position, over two hundred dead buffalo. [The exact number was 240.] From old bulls to calves of three months' old, animals of every age were huddled together in all the forced attitudes of violent death. Some lay on their backs, with eyes starting from their heads and tongue thrust out through clotted gore. Others were impaled on the horns of the old and strong bulls. Others again, which had been tossed, were lying with broken backs, two and three deep. One little calf hung suspended on the horns of a bull which had impaled it in the wild race round and round the pound. The Indians looked upon the dreadful and sickening

---

*Assinniboine and Saskatchewan Expedition, p. 358.

sight with evident delight, and told how such and such a bull or cow had exhibited feats of wonderful strength in the death-struggle. The flesh of many of the cows had been taken from them, and was drying in the sun on stages near the tents. It is needless to say that the odor was overpowering, and millions of large blue flesh-flies, humming and buzzing over the putrefying bodies, was not the least disgusting part of the spectacle."

It is some satisfaction to know that when the first "run" was made, ten days previous, the herd of two hundred buffaloes was no sooner driven into the pound than a wary old bull espied a weak spot in the fence, charged it at full speed, and burst through to freedom and the prairie, followed by the entire herd.

Strange as it may seem to-day, this wholesale method of destroying buffalo was once practiced in Montana. In his memoir on "The American Bison," Mr. J. A. Allen states that as late as 1873, while journeying through that Territory in charge of the Yellowstone Expedition, he "several times met with the remains of these pounds and their converging fences in the region above the mouth of the Big Horn River." Mr. Thomas Simpson states that in 1840 there were three camps of Assinniboine Indians in the vicinity of Carlton House, each of which had its buffalo pound into which they drove forty or fifty animals daily.

4. *The "Surround."*—During the last forty years the final extermination of the buffalo has been confidently predicted by not only the observing white man of the West, but also nearly all the Indians and halfbreeds who formerly depended upon this animal for the most of the necessities, as well as luxuries, of life. They have seen the great herds driven westward farther and farther, until the plains were left tenantless, and hunger took the place of feasting on the choice tid-bits of the chase. And is it not singular that during this period the Indian tribes were not moved by a common impulse to kill sparingly, and by the exercise of a reasonable economy in the chase to make the buffalo last as long as possible.

But apparently no such thoughts ever entered their minds, so far as *they themselves* were concerned. They looked with jealous eyes upon the white hunter, and considered him as much of a robber as if they had a brand on every buffalo. It has been claimed by some authors that the Indians killed with more judgment and more care for the future than did the white man, but I fail to find any evidence that such was ever the fact. They all killed wastefully, wantonly, and always about five times as many head as were really necessary for food. It was always the same old story, whenever a gang of Indians needed meat a whole herd was slaughtered, the choicest portions of the finest animals were taken, and about 75 per cent. of the whole left to putrefy and fatten the wolves. And now, as we read of the appalling slaughter, one can scarcely repress the feeling of grim satisfaction that arises when we also read that many of the ex-slaughterers are almost starving for the millions of pounds of fat and juicy buffalo meat they wasted a few years ago. Verily, the buffalo is in a great measure avenged already.

The following extract from Mr. Catlin's "North American Indians," I, page 199–200, serves well to illustrate not only a very common and very deadly Indian method of wholesale slaughter—the "surround"—but also to show the senseless destructiveness of Indians even when in a state of semi-starvation, which was brought upon them by similar acts of improvidence and wastefulness.

"The Minatarees, as well as the Mandans, had suffered for some months past for want of meat, and had indulged in the most alarming fears that the herds of buffalo were emigrating so far off from them that there was great danger of their actual starvation, when it was suddenly announced through the village one morning at an early hour that a herd of buffaloes was in sight. A hundred or more young men mounted their horses, with weapons in hand, and steered their course to the prairies. * * *

"The plan of attack, which in this country is familiary called a surround, was explicity agreed upon, and the hunters, who were all mounted on their 'buffalo horses' and armed with bows and arrows or long lances, divided into two columns, taking opposite directions, and drew themselves gradually around the herd at a mile or more distance from them, thus forming a circle of horsemen at equal distances apart, who gradually closed in upon them with a moderate pace at a signal given. The unsuspecting herd at length 'got the wind' of the approaching enemy and fled in a mass in the greatest confusion. To the point where they were aiming to cross the line the horsemen were seen, at full speed, gathering and forming in a column, brandishing their weapons, and yelling in the most frightful manner, by which they turned the black and rushing mass, which moved off in an opposite direction, where they were again met and foiled in a similar manner, and wheeled back in utter confusion; by which time the horsemen had closed in from all directions, forming a continuous line around them, whilst the poor affrighted animals were eddying about in a crowded and confused mass, hooking and climbing upon each other, when the work of death commenced. I had rode up in the rear and occupied an elevated position at a few rods' distance, from which I could (like the general of a battle-field) survey from my horse's back the nature and the progress of the grand mêlée, but (unlike him) without the power of issuing a command or in any way directing its issue.

"In this grand turmoil [see illustration] a cloud of dust was soon raised, which in parts obscured the throng where the hunters were galloping their horses around and driving the whizzing arrows or their long lances to the hearts of these noble animals; which in many instances, becoming infuriated with deadly wounds in their sides, erected their shaggy manes over their bloodshot eyes and furiously plunged forward at the sides of their assailants' horses, sometimes goring them to death at a lunge and putting their dismounted riders to flight for their lives. Sometimes their dense crowd was opened, and the blinded horsemen, too intent on their prey amidst the cloud of dust, were hemmed and wedged in amidst the crowding beasts, over whose backs they were obliged to leap for security, leaving their horses to the fate that might await them in the results of this wild and desperate war. Many were the bulls that turned upon their assailants and met them with desperate resistance, and many were the warriors who were dismounted and saved themselves by the superior muscles of their legs; some who were closely pursued by the bulls wheeled suddenly around, and snatching the part of a buffalo robe from around their waists, threw it over the horns and eyes of the infuriated beast, and darting by its side drove the arrow or the lance to its heart; others suddenly dashed off upon the prairie by the side of the affrighted animals which had escaped from the throng, and closely escorting them for a few rods, brought down their heart's blood in streams and their huge carcasses upon the green and enameled turf.

" In this way this grand hunt soon resolved itself into a desperate battle, *and in the space of fifteen minutes resulted in the total destruction of the whole herd*, which in all their strength and fury were doomed, like every beast and living thing else, to fall before the destroying hands of mighty man.

"I had sat in trembling silence upon my horse and witnessed this extraordinary scene, which allowed not one of these animals to escape out of my sight. Many plunged off upon the prairie for a distance, but were overtaken and killed, and although I could not distinctly estimate the number that were slain, yet I am sure that some hundreds of these noble animals fell in this grand *mêlée*. * * * Amongst the poor affrighted creatures that had occasionally dashed through the ranks of their enemy and sought safety in flight upon the prairie (and in some instances had undoubtedly gained it), I saw them stand awhile, looking back, when they turned, and, as if bent on their own destruction, retraced their steps, and mingled themselves and their deaths with those of the dying throng. Others had fled to a distance on the prairies, and for want of company, of friends or of foes, had stood and gazed on till the battle-scene was over, seemingly taking pains to stay and hold their lives in readiness for their destroyers until the general destruction was over, when they fell easy victims to their weapons, making the slaughter complete."

It is to be noticed that *every animal* of this entire herd of several hundred was slain on the spot, and there is no room to doubt that at least half (possibly much more) of the meat thus taken was allowed to become a loss. People who are so utterly senseless as to wantonly destroy their own source of food, as the Indians have done, certainly deserve to starve.

This " surround" method of wholesale slaughter was also practiced

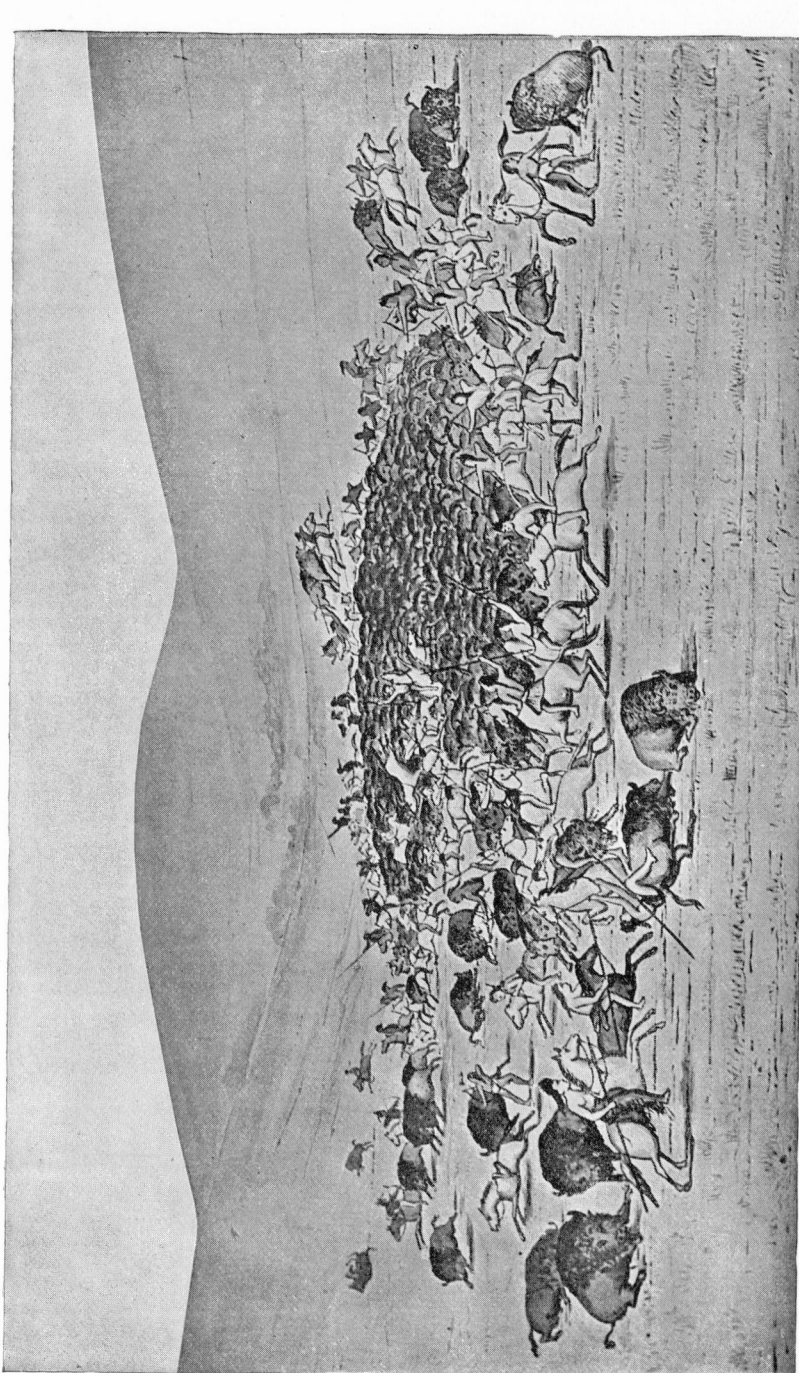

by the Cheyennes, Arapahoes, Sioux, Pawnees, Omahas, and probably many other tribes.

5. *Decoying and Driving.*—Another method of slaughtering by wholesale is thus described by Lewis and Clarke, I, 235. The locality indicated was the Missouri River, in Montana, just above the mouth of Judith River:

"On the north we passed a precipice about 120 feet high, under which lay scattered the fragments of at least one hundred carcasses of buffaloes, although the water which had washed away the lower part of the hill must have carried off many of the dead. These buffaloes had been chased down a precipice in a way very common on the Missouri, and by which vast herds are destroyed in a moment. The mode of hunting is to select one of the most active and fleet young men, who is disguised by a buffalo skin round his body; the skin of the head with the ears and horns fastened on his own head in such a way as to deceive the buffaloes. Thus dressed, he fixes himself at a convenient distance between a herd of buffaloes and any of the river precipices, which sometimes extend for some miles.

"His companions in the mean time get in the rear and side of the herd, and at a given signal show themselves, and advance towards the buffaloes. They instantly take alarm, and, finding the hunters beside them, they run toward the disguised Indian or decoy, who leads them on at full speed toward the river, when, suddenly securing himself in some crevice of the cliff which he had previously fixed on, the herd is left on the brink of the precipice; it is then in vain for the foremost to retreat or even to stop; they are pressed on by the hindmost rank, who, seeing no danger but from the hunters, goad on those before them till the whole are precipitated and the shore is strewed with their dead bodies. Sometimes in this perilous seduction the Indian is himself either trodden under foot by the rapid movements of the buffaloes, or, missing his footing in the cliff, is urged down the precipice by the falling herd. The Indians then select as much meat as they wish, and the rest is abandoned to the wolves, and creates a most dreadful stench."

Harper's Magazine, volume 38, page 147, contains the following from the pen of Theo. R. Davis, in an article entitled "The Buffalo Range:"

"As I have previously stated, the best hunting on the range is to be found between the Platte and Arkansas Rivers. Here I have seen the Indians have recourse to another method of slaughtering buffalo in a very easy, but to me a cruel way, for where one buffalo is killed several are sure to be painfully injured; but these, too, are soon killed by the Indians, who make haste to lance or shoot the cripples.

"The mode of hunting is somewhat as follows: A herd is discovered grazing on the table-lands. Being thoroughly acquainted with the country, the Indians are aware of the location of the nearest point where the table-land is broken abruptly by a precipice which descends a hundred or more feet. Toward this 'devil-jump' the Indians head the herd, which is at once driven pell-mell to and over the precipice. Meanwhile a number of Indians have taken their way by means of routes known to them, and succeed in reaching the cañon through which the crippled buffalo are running in all directions. These are quickly killed, so that out of a very considerable band of buffalo but few escape, many having been killed by the fall and others dispatched while limping off. This mode of hunting is sometimes indulged in by harum-scarum white men, but it is done more for deviltry than anything else. I have never known of its practice by army officers or persons who professed to hunt buffalo as a sport."

VI. *Hunting on Snow-shoes.*—"In the dead of the winters," says Mr. Catlin,* "which are very long and severely cold in this country, where horses can not be brought into the chase with any avail, the Indian runs upon the surface of the snow by aid of his snow-shoes, which buoy him up, while the great weight of the buffaloes sinks them down to the middle of their sides, and, completely stopping their progress, insures them certain and easy victims to the bow or lance of their pursuers. The snow in these regions often lies during the winter to the depth of 3 and 4 feet, being blown away from the tops and sides of the hills in many places, which are left bare for the buffaloes to graze upon, whilst it is drifted in the hollows and ravines to a very great depth, and rendered almost entirely impassable to these huge animals, which, when closely pursued by their enemies, endeavor to plunge through it, but are soon wedged in and almost unable to move, where they fall an easy prey to the Indian, who runs up lightly upon his snow-shoes and drives his lance to their hearts. The skins are then stripped off, to be sold to the fur-traders, and the carcasses left to be devoured by the wolves. [Owing to the fact that the winter's supply of meat was procured and dried in the summer and fall months, the flesh of all buffalo killed in winter was allowed to become a total loss.] This is the season in which the greatest number of these animals are destroyed for their robes; they are most easily killed at this time, and their hair or fur, being longer and more abundant, gives greater value to the robe."

IV. PROGRESS OF THE EXTERMINATION.

1. THE PERIOD OF DESULTORY DESTRUCTION, FROM 1730 TO 1830.

The disappearance of the buffalo from all the country east of the Mississippi was one of the inevitable results of the advance of civilization. To the early pioneers who went forth into the wilderness to wrestle with nature for the necessities of life, this valuable animal might well have seemed a gift direct from the hand of Providence. During the first few years of the early settler's life in a new country, the few domestic animals he had brought with him were far too valua-

---

* North American Indians, I, 253.

INDIANS ON SNOW-SHOES HUNTING BUFFALOES.

From a painting in the National Museum by George Catlin.

ble to be killed for food, and for a long period he looked to the wild animals of the forest and the prairie for his daily supply of meat. The time was when no one stopped to think of the important part our game animals played in the settlement of this country, and even now no one has attempted to calculate the lessened degree of rapidity with which the star of empire would have taken its westward way without the bison, deer, elk, and antelope. The Western States and Territories pay little heed to the wanton slaughter of deer and elk now going on in their forests, but the time will soon come when the "grangers" will enter those regions and find the absence of game a very serious matter.

Although the bison was the first wild species to disappear before the advance of civilization, he served a good purpose at a highly critical period. His huge bulk of toothsome flesh fed many a hungry family, and his ample robe did good service in the settler's cabin and sleigh in winter weather. By the time game animals had become scarce, domestic herds and flocks had taken their place, and hunting became a pastime instead of a necessity.

As might be expected, from the time the bison was first seen by white men he has always been a conspicuous prize, and being the largest of the land quadrupeds, was naturally the first to disappear. Every man's hand has been against him. While his disappearance from the eastern United States was, in the main, due to the settler who killed game as a means of subsistence, there were a few who made the killing of those animals a regular business. This occurred almost exclusively in the immediate vicinity of salt springs, around which the bison congregated in great numbers, and made their wholesale slaughter of easy accomplishment. Mr. Thomas Ashe* has recorded some very interesting facts and observations on this point. In speaking of an old man who in the latter part of the last century built a log house for himself "on the immediate borders of a salt spring," in western Pennsylvania, for the purpose of killing buffaloes out of the immense droves which frequented that spot, Mr. Ashe says:

"In the first and second years this old man, with some companions, killed from six to seven hundred of these noble creatures merely for the sake of their skins, which to them were worth only 2 shillings each; and after this 'work of death' they were obliged to leave the place till the following season, or till the wolves, bears, panthers, eagles, rooks, ravens, etc., had devoured the carcasses and abandoned the place for other prey. In the two following years the same persons killed great numbers out of the first droves that arrived, skinned them, and left their bodies exposed to the sun and air; but they soon had reason to repent of this, for the remaining droves, as they came up in succession, stopped, gazed on the mangled and putrid bodies, sorrowfully moaned or furiously lowed aloud, and returned instantly to the wilderness in an unusual run, without tasting their favorite spring or licking the im-

---

* Travels in America in 1806. London, 1808.

pregnated earth, which was also once their most agreeable occupation; nor did they nor any of their race ever revisit the neighborhood.

"The simple history of this spring is that of every other in the settled parts of this Western World; the carnage of beasts was everywhere the same. I met with a man who had killed two thousand buffaloes with his own hand, and others no doubt have done the same thing. In consequence of such proceedings not one buffalo is at this time to be found east of the Mississippi, except a few domesticated by the curious, or carried through the country on a public show."

But, fortunately, there is no evidence that such slaughter as that described by Mr. Ashe was at all common, and there is reason for the belief that until within the last forty years the buffalo was sacrificed in ways conducive to the greatest good of the greatest number.

From Coronado to General Frémont there has hardly been an explorer of United States territory who has not had occasion to bless the bison, and its great value to mankind can hardly be overestimated, although by many it can readily be forgotten.

The disappearance of the bison from the eastern United States was due to its consumption as food. It was very gradual, like the march of civilization, and, under the circumstances, absolutely inevitable. In a country so thickly peopled as this region speedily became, the mastodon could have survived extinction about as easily as the bison. Except when the latter became the victim of wholesale slaughter, there was little reason to bemoan his fate, save upon grounds that may be regarded purely sentimental. He served a most excellent purpose in the development of the country. Even as late as 1875 the farmers of eastern Kansas were in the habit of making trips every fall into the western part of that State for wagon loads of buffalo meat as a supply for the succeeding winter. The farmers of Texas, Nebraska, Dakota, and Minnesota also drew largely upon the buffalo as long as the supply lasted.

The extirpation of the bison west of the Rocky Mountains was due to legitimate hunting for food and clothing rather than for marketable peltries. In no part of that whole region was the species ever numerous, although in the mountains themselves, notably in Colorado, within easy reach of the great prairies on the east, vast numbers were seen by the early explorers and pioneers. But to the westward, away from the mountains, they were very rarely met with, and their total destruction in that region was a matter of easy accomplishment. According to Prof. J. A. Allen the complete disappearance of the bison west of the Rocky Mountains took place between 1838 and 1840.

2. The Period of Systematic Slaughter, from 1830 to 1838.

We come now to a history which I would gladly leave unwritten. Its record is a disgrace to the American people in general, and the Territorial, State, and General Government in particular. It will cause succeeding generations to regard us as being possessed of the leading characteristics of the savage and the beast of prey—cruelty and greed. We will be likened to the blood-thirsty tiger of the Indian jungle, who slaughters a dozen bullocks at once when he knows he can eat only one.

In one respect, at least, the white men who engaged in the systematic slaughter of the bison were savages just as much as the Piegan Indians, who would drive a whole herd over a precipice to secure a week's rations of meat for a single village. The men who killed buffaloes for their tongues and those who shot them from the railway trains for sport were murderers. In no way does civilized man so quickly revert to his former state as when he is alone with the beasts of the field. Give him a gun and something which he may kill without getting himself in trouble, and, presto! he is instantly a savage again, finding exquisite delight in bloodshed, slaughter, and death, if not for gain, then solely for the joy and happiness of it. There is no kind of warfare against game animals too unfair, too disreputable, or too mean for white men to engage in if they can only do so with safety to their own precious carcasses. They will shoot buffalo and antelope from running railway trains, drive deer into water with hounds and cut their throats in cold blood, kill does with fawns a week old, kill fawns by the score for their spotted skins, slaughter deer, moose, and caribou in the snow at a pitiful disadvantage, just as the wolves do; exterminate the wild ducks on the whole Atlantic seaboard with punt guns for the metropolitan markets; kill off the Rocky Mountain goats for hides worth only 50 cents apiece, destroy wagon loads of trout with dynamite, and so on to the end of the chapter.

Perhaps the most gigantic task ever undertaken on this continent in the line of game-slaughter was the extermination of the bison in the great pasture region by the hide-hunters. Probably the brilliant rapidity and success with which that lofty undertaking was accomplished was a matter of surprise even to those who participated in it. The story of the slaughter is by no means a long one.

The period of systematic slaughter of the bison naturally begins with the first organized efforts in that direction, in a business-like, wholesale way. Although the species had been steadily driven westward for a hundred years by the advancing settlements, and had during all that time been hunted for the meat and robes it yielded, its extermination did not begin in earnest until 1820, or thereabouts. As before stated, various persons had previous to that time made buffalo killing a business in order to sell their skins, but such instances were very exceptional. By that time the bison was totally extinct in all the region lying east of the Mississippi River except a portion of Wisconsin, where it survived until about 1830. In 1820 the first organized buffalo hunting expedition on a grand scale was made from the Red River settlement, Manitoba, in which five hundred and forty carts proceeded to the range. Previous to that time the buffaloes were found near enough to the settlements around Fort Garry that every settler could hunt independently; but as the herds were driven farther and farther away, it required an organized effort and a long journey to reach them.

The American Fur Company established trading posts along the Missouri River, one at the mouth of the Teton River and another at the mouth of the Yellowstone. In 1826 a post was established at the eastern base of the Rocky Mountains, at the head of the Arkansas River, and in 1832 another was located in a corresponding situation at the head of the South Fork of the Platte, close to where Denver now stands. Both the latter were on what was then the western border of the buffalo range. Elsewhere throughout the buffalo country there were numerous other posts, always situated as near as possible to the best hunting ground, and at the same time where they would be most accessible to the hunters, both white and red.

As might be supposed, the Indians were encouraged to kill buffaloes for their robes, and this is what Mr. George Catlin wrote at the mouth of the Teton River (Pyatt County, Dakota) in 1832 concerning this trade:*

"It seems hard and cruel (does it not ?) that we civilized people, with all the luxuries and comforts of the world about us, should be drawing from the backs of these useful animals the skins for our luxury, leaving their carcasses to be devoured by the wolves; that we should draw from that country some one hundred and fifty or two hundred thousand of their robes annually, the greater part of which are taken from animals that are killed expressly for the robe, at a season when the meat is not cured and preserved, and for each of which skins the Indian has received but a pint of whisky! Such is the fact, and that number, or near it, are annually destroyed, in addition to the number that is necessarily killed for the subsistence of three hundred thousand Indians, who live chiefly upon them."

The author further declared that the fur trade in those "great western realms" was then limited chiefly to the purchase of buffalo robes.

1. *The Red River half-breeds.*—In June, 1840, when the Red River half-breeds assembled at Pembina for their annual expedition against the buffalo, they mustered as follows:

Carts 1,210
Hunters .... 620 ⎫
Women... 650 ⎬ 1,630
Boys and girls .... 360 ⎭
Horses (buffalo runners) 403
Dogs 542
Cart horses 655
Draught oxen.. 586
Skinning knives 1,240

The total value of the property employed in this expedition and the working time occupied by it (two months) amounted to the enormous sum of £24,000.

---

* North American Indians, I, p. 263.

Although the bison formerly ranged to Fort Garry (near Winnipeg), they had been steadily killed off and driven back, and in 1840 none were found by the expedition until it was 250 miles from Pembina, which is situated on the Red River, at the international boundary. At that time the extinction of the species from the Red River to the Cheyenne was practically complete. The Red River settlers, aided, of course, by the Indians of that region, are responsible for the extermination of the bison throughout northeastern Dakota as far as the Cheyenne River, northern Minnesota, and the whole of what is now the province of Manitoba. More than that; as the game grew scarce and retired farther and faither, the half-breeds, who despised agriculture as long as there was a buffalo to kill, extended their hunting operations westward along the Qu'Appelle until they encroached upon the hunting-grounds of the Plain Crees, who lived in the Saskatchewan country.

Thus was an immense inroad made in the northern half of the herd which had previously covered the entire pasture region from the Great Slave Lake to central Texas. This was the first visible impression of the systematic killing which began in 1820. Up to 1840 it is reasonably certain, as will be seen by figures given elsewhere, that by this business-like method of the half-breeds, at least 652,000 buffaloes were destroyed by them alone.

Even as early as 1840 the Red River hunt was prosecuted through Dakota southwestwardly to the Missouri River and a short distance beyond it. Here it touched the wide strip of territory, bordering that stream, which was even then being regularly drained of its animal resources by the Indian hunters, who made the river their base of operations, and whose robes were shipped on its steam-boats.

It is certain that these annual Red River expeditions into Dakota were kept up as late as 1847, and as long thereafter as buffaloes were to be found in any number between the Cheyenne and the Missouri. At the same time, the White Horse Plains division, which hunted westward from Fort Garry, did its work of destruction quite as rapidly and as thoroughly as the rival expedition to the United States.

In 1857 the Plains Crees, inhabiting the country around the head-waters of the Qu'Appelle River (250 miles due west from Winnipeg), assembled in council, and "determined that in consequence of promises often made and broken by the white men and half-breeds, and the rapid destruction by them of the buffalo they fed on, they would not permit either white men or half-breeds to hunt in their country, or travel through it, except for the purpose of trading for their dried meat, pemmican, skins and robes."

In 1858 the Crees reported that between the two branches of the Saskatchewan buffalo were "very scarce." Professor Hind's expedition saw only one buffalo in the whole course of their journey from Winnipeg until they reached Sand Hill Lake, at the head of the Qu'Appelle, near the south branch of the Saskatchewan, where the first herd was encountered. Although the species was not totally extinct on the Qu'Appelle at that time, it was practically so.

2. *The country of the Sioux.*—The next territory completely depopulated of buffaloes by systematic hunting was very nearly the entire southern half of Dakota, southwestern Minnesota, and northern Nebraska as far as the North Platte. This vast region, once the favorite range for hundreds of thousands of buffaloes, had for many years been the favorite hunting ground of the Sioux Indians of the Missouri, the Pawnees, Omahas, and all other tribes of that region. The settlement of Iowa and Minnesota presently forced into this region the entire body of Mississippi Sioux from the country west of Prairie du Chien and around Fort Snelling, and materially hastened the extermination of all the game animals which were once so abundant there. It is absolutely certain that if the Indians had been uninfluenced by the white traders, or, in other words, had not been induced to take and prepare a large number of robes every year for the market, the species would have survived very much longer than it did. But the demand quickly proved to be far greater than the supply. The Indians, of course, found it necessary to slaughter annually a great number of buffaloes for their own wants—for meat, robes, leather, teepees, etc. When it came to supplementing this necessary slaughter by an additional fifty thousand or more every year for marketable robes, it is no wonder that the improvident savages soon found, when too late, that the supply of buffaloes was not inexhaustible. Naturally enough, they attributed their disappearance to the white man, who was therefore a robber, and a proper subject for the scalping-knife. Apparently it never occurred to the minds of the Sioux that they themselves were equally to blame; it was always *the paleface* who killed the buffaloes; and it was always *Sioux* buffaloes that they killed. The Sioux seemed to feel that they held a chattel mortgage on all the buffaloes north of the Platte, and it required more than one pitched battle to convince them otherwise.

Up to the time when the great Sioux Reservation was established in Dakota (1875–77), when 33,739 square miles of country, or nearly the whole southwest quarter of the Territory, was set aside for the exclusive occupancy of the Sioux, buffaloes were very numerous throughout that entire region. East of the Missouri River, which is the eastern boundary of the Sioux Reservation, from Bismarck all the way down, the species was practically extinct as early as 1870. But at the time when it became unlawful for white hunters to enter the territory of the Sioux nation there were tens of thousands of buffaloes upon it, and their subsequent slaughter is chargable to the Indians alone, save as to those which migrated into the hunting grounds of the whites.

3. *Western railways, and their part in the extermination of the buffalo.*— The building of a railroad means the speedy extermination of all the big game along its line. In its eagerness to attract the public and

build up "a big business," every new line which traverses a country containing game does its utmost, by means of advertisements and posters, to attract the man with a gun. Its game resorts are all laid bare, and the market hunters and sportsmen swarm in immediately, slaying and to slay.

Within the last year the last real retreat for our finest game, the only remaining stronghold for the mountain sheep, goat, caribou, elk, and deer—northwestern Montana, northern Idaho, and thence westward—has been laid open to the very heart by the building of the St. Paul, Minneapolis and Manitoba Railway, which runs up the valley of the Milk River to Fort Assinniboine, and crosses the Rocky Mountains through Two Medicine Pass. Heretofore that region has been so difficult to reach that the game it contains has been measurably secure from general slaughter; but now it also must " go."

The marking out of the great overland trail by the Argonauts of '49 in their rush for the gold fields of California was the foreshadowing of the great east-and-west breach in the universal herd, which was made twenty years later by the first transcontinental railway.

The pioneers who "crossed the plains" in those days killed buffaloes for food whenever they could, and the constant harrying of those animals experienced along the line of travel, soon led them to retire from the proximity of such continual danger. It was undoubtedly due to this cause that the number seen by parties who crossed the plains in 1849 and subsequently, was surprisingly small. But, fortunately for the buffaloes, the pioneers who would gladly have halted and turned aside now and then for the excitement of the chase, were compelled to hurry on, and accomplish the long journey while good weather lasted. It was owing to this fact, and the scarcity of good horses, that the buffaloes found it necessary to retire only a few miles from the wagon route to get beyond the reach of those who would have gladly hunted them.

Mr. Allen Varner, of Indianola, Illinois, has kindly furnished me with the following facts in regard to the presence of the buffalo, as observed by him during his journey westward, over what was then known as the Oregon Trail.

"The old Oregon trail ran from Independence, Missouri, to old Fort Laramie, through the South Pass of the Rocky Mountains, and thence up to Salt Lake City. We left Independence on May 6, 1849, and struck the Platte River at Grand Island. The trail had been traveled but very little previous to that year. We saw no buffaloes whatever until we reached the forks of the Platte, on May 20, or thereabouts. There we saw seventeen head. From that time on we saw small bunches now and then; never more than forty or fifty together. We saw no great herds anywhere, and I should say we did not see over five hundred head all told. The most western point at which we saw buffaloes was about due north of Laramie Peak, and it must have been about the 20th of June. We killed several head for meat during our trip, and found them all rather thin in flesh. Plainsmen who claimed to know, said that all the buffaloes we saw had wintered in that locality, and had not had time to get fat. The annual migration from the south had not yet begun, or rather had not yet brought any of the southern buffaloes that far north."

In a few years the tide of overland travel became so great, that the buffaloes learned to keep away from the dangers of the trail, and many a pioneer has crossed the plains without ever seeing a live buffalo.

4. *The division of the universal herd.*—Until the building of the first transcontinental railway made it possible to market the " buffalo product," buffalo hunting as a business was almost wholly in the hands of the Indians. Even then, the slaughter so far exceeded the natural increase that the narrowing limits of the buffalo range was watched with anxiety, and the ultimate extinction of the species confidently predicted. Even without railroads the extermination of the race would have taken place eventually, but it would have been delayed perhaps twenty years. With a recklessness of the future that was not to be expected of savages, though perhaps perfectly natural to civilized white men, who place the possession of a dollar above everything else, the Indians with one accord singled out the *cows* for slaughter, because their robes and their flesh better suited the fastidious taste of the noble redskin. The building of the Union Pacific Railway began at Omaha in 1865, and during that year 40 miles were constructed. The year following saw the completion of 265 miles more, and in 1867 245 miles were added, which brought it to Cheyenne. In 1868, 350 miles were built, and in 1869 the entire line was open to traffic.

In 1867, when Maj. J. W. Powell and Prof. A. H. Thompson crossed the plains by means of the Union Pacific Railway as far as it was constructed and thence onward by wagon, they saw during the entire trip only one live buffalo, a solitary old bull, wandering aimlessly along the south bank of the Platte River.

The completion of the Union Pacific Railway divided forever the buffaloes of the United States into two great herds, which thereafter became known respectively as the northern and southern herds. Both retired rapidly and permanently from the railway, and left a strip of country over 50 miles wide almost uninhabited by them. Although many thousand buffaloes were killed by hunters who made the Union Pacific Railway their base of operations, the two great bodies retired north and south so far that the greater number were beyond striking distance from that line.

5. *The destruction of the southern herd.*—The geographical center of the great southern herd during the few years of its separate existence previous to its destruction was very near the present site of Garden City, Kansas. On the east, even as late as 1872, thousands of buffaloes ranged within 10 miles of Wichita, which was then the headquarters

of a great number of buffalo-hunters, who plied their occupation vigorously during the winter. On the north the herd ranged within 25 miles miles of the Union Pacific, until the swarm of hunters coming down from the north drove them farther and farther south. On the west, a few small bands ranged as far as Pike's Peak and the South Park, but the main body ranged east of the town of Pueblo, Colorado. In the southwest, buffaloes were abundant as far as the Pecos and the Staked Plains, while the southern limit of the herd was about on a line with the southern boundary of New Mexico. Regarding this herd, Colonel Dodge writes as follows: "Their most prized feeding ground was the section of country between the South Platte and Arkansas rivers, watered by the Republican, Smoky, Walnut, Pawnee, and other parallel or tributary streams, and generally known as the Republican country. Hundreds of thousands went south from here each winter, but hundreds of thousands remained. It was the chosen home of the buffalo."

Although the range of the northern herd covered about twice as much territory as did the southern, the latter contained probably twice as many buffaloes. The number of individuals in the southern herd in the year 1871 must have been at least three millions, and most estimates place the total much higher than that.

During the years from 1866 to 1871, inclusive, the Atchison, Topeka and Santa Fé Railway and what is now known as the Kansas Pacific, or Kansas division of the Union Pacific Railway, were constructed from the Missouri River westward across Kansas, and through the heart of the southern buffalo range. The southern herd was literally cut to pieces by railways, and every portion of its range rendered easily accessible. There had always been a market for buffalo robes at a fair price, and as soon as the railways crossed the buffalo country the slaughter began. The rush to the range was only surpassed by the rush to the gold mines of California in earlier years. The railroad builders, teamsters, fortune-seekers, "professional" hunters, trappers, guides, and every one out of a job turned out to hunt buffalo for hides and meat. The merchants who had already settled in all the little towns along the three great railways saw an opportunity to make money out of the buffalo product, and forthwith began to organize and supply hunting parties with arms, ammunition, and provisions, and send them to the range. An immense business of this kind was done by the merchants of Dodge City (Fort Dodge), Wichita, and Leavenworth, and scores of smaller towns did a corresponding amount of business in the same line. During the years 1871 to 1874 but little else was done in that country except buffalo killing. Central depots were established in the best buffalo country, from whence hunting parties operated in all directions. Buildings were erected for the curing of meat, and corrals were built in which to heap up the immense piles of buffalo skins that accumulated. At Dodge City, as late as 1878, Professor Thompson saw a lot of baled buffalo skins in a corral, the solid cubical contents of which he calculated to equal 120 cords.

At first the utmost wastefulness prevailed. Every one wanted to kill buffalo, and no one was willing to do the skinning and curing. Thousands upon thousands of buffaloes were killed for their tongues alone, and never skinned. Thousands more were wounded by unskillful marksmen and wandered off to die and become a total loss. But the climax of wastefulness and sloth was not reached until the enterprising buffalo-butcher began to skin his dead buffaloes by horse-power. The process is of interest, as showing the depth of degradation to which a man can fall and still call himself a hunter. The skin of the buffalo was ripped open along the belly and throat, the legs cut around at the knees, and ripped up the rest of the way. The skin of the neck was divided all the way around at the back of the head, and skinned back a few inches to afford a start. A stout iron bar, like a hitching-post, was then driven through the skull and about 18 inches into the earth, after which a rope was tied very firmly to the thick skin of the neck, made ready for that purpose. The other end of this rope was then hitched to the whiffletree of a pair of horses, or to the rear axle of a wagon, the horses were whipped up, and the skin was forthwith either torn in two or torn off the buffalo with about 50 pounds of flesh adhering to it. It soon became apparent to even the most enterprising buffalo-skinner that this method was not an unqualified success, and it was presently abandoned.

The slaughter which began in 1871 was prosecuted with great vigor and enterprise in 1872, and reached its height in 1873. By that time, the buffalo country fairly swarmed with hunters, each party putting forth its utmost efforts to destroy more buffaloes than its rivals. By that time experience had taught the value of thorough organization, and the butchering was done in a more business-like way. By a coincidence that proved fatal to the bison, it was just at the beginning of the slaughter that breech-loading, long-range rifles attained what was practically perfection. The Sharps 40–90 or 45–120, and the Remington were the favorite weapons of the buffalo-hunter, the former being the one in most general use. Before the leaden hail of thousands of these deadly breech-loaders the buffaloes went down at the rate of several thousand daily during the hunting season.

During the years 1871 and 1872 the most wanton wastefulness prevailed. Colonel Dodge declares that, though hundreds of thousands of skins were sent to market, they scarcely indicated the extent of the slaughter. Through want of skill in shooting and want of knowledge in preserving the hides of those slain by green hunters, *one hide sent to market represented three, four, or even five dead buffalo.* The skinners and curers knew so little of the proper mode of curing hides, that at least half of those actually taken were lost. In the summer and fall of 1872 one hide sent to market represented at least *three* dead buffalo.

This condition of affairs rapidly improved; but such was the furor for slaughter, and the ignorance of all concerned, that every hide sent to market in 1871 represented no less than *five* dead buffalo.

By 1873 the condition of affairs had somewhat improved, through better organization of the hunting parties and knowledge gained by experience in curing. For all that, however, buffaloes were still so exceedingly plentiful, and shooting was so much easier than skinning, the latter was looked upon as a necessary evil and still slighted to such an extent that every hide actually sold and delivered represented two dead buffaloes.

In 1874 the slaughterers began to take alarm at the increasing scarcity of buffalo, and the skinners, having a much smaller number of dead animals to take care of than ever before, were able to devote more time to each subject and do their work properly. As a result, Colonel Dodge estimated that during 1874, and from that time on, one hundred skins delivered represented not more than one hundred and twenty-five dead buffaloes; but that "no parties have ever got the proportion lower than this."

The great southern herd was slaughtered by still-hunting, a method which has already been fully described. A typical hunting party is thus described by Colonel Dodge: *

"The most approved party consisted of four men—one shooter, two skinners, and one man to cook, stretch hides, and take care of camp. Where buffalo were very plentiful the number of skinners was increased. A light wagon, drawn by two horses or mules, takes the outfit into the wilderness, and brings into camp the skins taken each day. The outfit is most meager: a sack of flour, a side of bacon, 5 pounds of coffee, tea, and sugar, a little salt, and possibly a few beans, is a month's supply. A common or "A" tent furnishes shelter; a couple of blankets for each man is a bed. One or more of Sharps or Remington's heaviest sporting rifles, and an unlimited supply of ammunition, is the armament; while a coffee-pot, Dutch-oven, frying-pan, four tin plates, and four tin cups constitute the kitchen and table furniture.

"The skinning knives do duty at the platter, and 'fingers were made before forks.' Nor must be forgotten one or more 10-gallon kegs for water, as the camp may of necessity be far away from a stream. The supplies are generally furnished by the merchant for whom the party is working, who, in addition, pays each of the party a specified percentage of the value of the skins delivered. The shooter is carefully selected for his skill and knowledge of the habits of the buffalo. He is captain and leader of the party. When all is ready, he plunges into the wilderness, going to the center of the best buffalo region known to him, not already occupied (for there are unwritten regulations recognized as laws, giving to each hunter certain rights of discovery and occupancy).

---

* Plains of the Great West, p. 134.

Arrived at the position, he makes his camp in some hidden ravine or thicket, and makes all ready for work."

Of course the slaughter was greatest along the lines of the three great railways—the Kansas Pacific, the Atchison, Topeka and Santa Fé, and the Union Pacific, about in the order named. It reached its height in the season of 1873. During that year the Atchison, Topeka and Santa Fé Railroad carried out of the buffalo country 251,443 robes, 1,617,600 pounds of meat, and 2,743,100 pounds of bones. The end of the southern herd was then near at hand. Could the southern buffalo range have been roofed over at that time it would have made one vast charnelhouse. Putrifying carcasses, many of them with the hide still on, lay thickly scattered over thousands of square miles of the level prairie, poisoning the air and water and offending the sight. The remaining herds had become mere scattered bands, harried and driven hither and thither by the hunters, who now swarmed almost as thickly as the buffaloes. A cordon of camps was established along the Arkansas River, the South Platte, the Republican, and the few other streams that contained water, and when the thirsty animals came to drink they were attacked and driven away, and with the most fiendish persistency kept from slaking their thirst, so that they would again be compelled to seek the river and come within range of the deadly breech-loaders. Colonel Dodge declares that in places favorable to such warfare, as the south bank of the Platte, a herd of buffalo has, by shooting at it by day and by lighting fires and firing guns at night, been kept from water until it has been entirely destroyed. In the autumn of 1873, when Mr. William Blackmore traveled for some 30 or 40 miles along the north bank of the Arkansas River to the east of Fort Dodge, " there was a continuous line of putrescent carcasses, so that the air was rendered pestilential and offensive to the last degree. The hunters had formed a line of camps along the banks of the river, and had shot down the buffalo, night and morning, as they came to drink. In order to give an idea of the number of these carcasses, it is only necessary to mention that I counted sixty-seven on one spot not covering 4 acres."

White hunters were not allowed to hunt in the Indian Territory, but the southern boundary of the State of Kansas was picketed by them, and a herd no sooner crossed the line going north than it was destroyed. Every water-hole was guarded by a camp of hunters, and whenever a thirsty herd approached, it was promptly met by rifle-bullets.

During this entire period the slaughter of buffaloes was universal. The man who desired buffalo meat for food almost invariably killed five times as many animals as he could utilize, and after cutting from each victim its very choicest parts—the *tongue alone*, possibly, or perhaps the hump and hind quarters, one or the other, or both—fully four-fifths of the really edible portion of the carcass would be left to the wolves. It was no uncommon thing for a man to bring in two barrels of salted buffalo tongues, without another pound of meat or a solitary robe. The tongues were purchased at 25 cents each and sold in the markets farther east at 50 cents. In those days of criminal wastefulness it was a very common thing for buffaloes to be slaughtered for their tongues alone. Mr. George Catlin* relates that a few days previous to his arrival at the mouth of the Teton River (Dakota), in 1832, "an immense herd of buffaloes had showed themselves on the opposite side of the river," whereupon a party of five or six hundred Sioux Indians on horseback forded the river, attacked the herd, recrossed the river about sunset, and came into the fort with fourteen hundred fresh buffalo tongues, which were thrown down in a mass, and for which they required only a few gallons of whisky, which was soon consumed in "a little harmless carouse." Mr. Catlin states that from all that he could learn not a skin or a pound of meat, other than the tongues, was saved after this awful slaughter.

Judging from all accounts, it is making a safe estimate to say that probably no fewer than fifty thousand buffaloes have been killed for their tongues alone, and the most of these are undoubtedly chargeable against white men, who ought to have known better.

A great deal has been said about the slaughter of buffaloes by foreign sportsmen, particularly Englishmen; but I must say that, from all that can be ascertained on this point, this element of destruction has been greatly exaggerated and overestimated. It is true that every English sportsman who visited this country in the days of the buffalo always resolved to have, and did have, "a buffalo hunt," and usually under the auspices of United States Army officers. Undoubtedly these parties did kill hundreds of buffaloes, but it is very doubtful whether the aggregate of the number slain by foreign sportsmen would run up higher than ten thousand. Indeed, for myself, I am well convinced that there are many old ex-still-hunters yet living, each of whom is accountable for a greater number of victims than all buffaloes killed by foreign sportsmen would make added together. The professional butchers were very much given to crying out against "them English lords," and holding up their hands in holy horror at buffaloes killed by them for their heads, instead of for hides to sell at a dollar apiece; but it is due the American public to say that all this outcry was received at its true value and deceived very few. By those in possession of the facts it was recognized as "a blind," to divert public opinion from the real culprits.

Nevertheless it is very true that many men who were properly classed as sportsmen, in contradistinction from the pot-hunters, did engage in useless and inexcusable slaughter to an extent that was highly reprehensible, to say the least. A sportsman is not supposed to kill game wantonly, when it can be of no possible use to himself or any one else, but a great many do it for all that. Indeed, the sportsman who

---

* North American Indians, I, 256.

kills sparingly and conscientiously is rather the exception than the rule. Colonel Dodge thus refers to the work of some foreign sportsmen:

"In the fall of that year [1872] three English gentlemen went out with me for a short hunt, and in their excitement bagged more buffalo than would have supplied a brigade." As a general thing, however, the professional sportsmen who went out to have a buffalo hunt for the excitement of the chase and the trophies it yielded, nearly always found the bison so easy a victim, and one whose capture brought so little glory to the hunter, that the chase was voted very disappointing, and soon abandoned in favor of nobler game. In those days there was no more to boast of in killing a buffalo than in the assassination of a Texas steer.

It was, then, the hide-hunters, white and red, but especially white, who wiped out the great southern herd in four short years. The prices received for hides varied considerably, according to circumstances, but for the green or undressed article it usually ranged from 50 cents for the skins of calves to $1.25 for those of adult animals in good condition. Such prices seem ridiculously small, but when it is remembered that, when buffaloes were plentiful it was no uncommon thing for a hunter to kill from forty to sixty head in a day, it will readily be seen that the *chances* of making very handsome profits were sufficient to tempt hunters to make extraordinary exertions. Moreover, even when the buffaloes were nearly gone, the country was overrun with men who had absolutely nothing else to look to as a means of livelihood, and so, no matter whether the profits were great or small, so long as enough buffaloes remained to make it possible to get a living by their pursuit, they were hunted down with the most determined persistency and pertinacity.

6. *Statistics of the slaughter.*—The most careful and reliable estimate ever made of results of the slaughter of the southern buffalo herd is that of Col. Richard Irving Dodge, and it is the only one I know of which furnishes a good index of the former size of that herd. Inasmuch as this calculation was based on actual statistics, supplemented by personal observations and inquiries made in that region during the great slaughter, I can do no better than to quote Colonel Dodge almost in full.*

The Atchison, Topeka and Santa Fé Railroad furnished the following statistics of the buffalo product carried by it during the years 1872, 1873, and 1874:

Buffalo product.

Year.	No. of skins carried.	Meat carried.	Bone carried.
		Pounds.	Pounds.
1872.....	165, 721	....	1, 135, 300
1873.....	251, 443	1, 617, 600	2, 743, 100
1874.....	42, 289	632, 800	6, 914, 950
Total .	459, 453	2, 250, 400	10, 793, 350

* Plains of the Great West, pp. 139–144.

The officials of the Kansas Pacific and Union Pacific railroads either could not or would not furnish any statistics of the amount of the buffalo product carried by their lines during this period, and it became necessary to proceed without the actual figures in both cases. Inas much as the Kansas Pacific road cuts through a portion of the buffalo country which was in every respect as thickly inhabited by those animals as the region traversed by the Atchison, Topeka and Santa Fé, it seemed absolutely certain that the former road hauled out fully as many hides as the latter, if not more, and its quota is so set down. The Union Pacific line handled a much smaller number of buffalo hides than either of its southern rivals, but Colonel Dodge believes that this, "with the smaller roads which touch the buffalo region, taken together, carried about as much as either of the two principal buffalo roads."

Colonel Dodge consi.lers it reasonably certain that the statistics furnished by the Atchison, Topeka and Santa Fê road represent only one-third of the entire buffalo product, and there certainly appears to be good ground for this belief. It is therefore in order to base further calculations upon these figures.

According to evidence gathered on the spot by Colonel Dodge during the period of the great slaughter, one hide sent to market in 1872 represented three dead buffaloes, in 1873 two, and in 1874 one hundred skins delivered represented one hundred and twenty-five dead animals. The total slaughter by white men was therefore about as below:

Year.	Hides shipped by A., T. and S. F. railway.	Hides shipped by other roads, same period (estimated).	Total number of buffaloes utilized.	Total number killed and wasted.	Total of buffaloes slaughtered by whites.
1872	165,721	331,442	497,163	994,326	1,491,489
1873	251,443	502,886	754,329	754,329	1,508,658
1874	42,289	84,578	126,867	31,716	158,583
Total	459,453	918,906	1,378,359	1,780,461	3,158,730

During all this time the Indians of all tribes within striking distance of the herds killed an immense number of buffaloes every year. In the summer they killed for the hairless hides to use for lodges and for leather, and in the autumn they slaughtered for robes and meat, but particularly robes, which were all they could offer the white trader in exchange for his goods. They were too lazy and shiftless to cure much buffalo meat, and besides it was not necessary, for the Government fed them. In regard to the number of buffaloes of the southern herd killed by the Indians, Colonel Dodge arrives at an estimate, as follows:

"It is much more difficult to estimate the number of dead buffalo represented by the Indian-tanned skins or robes sent to market. This number varies with the different tribes, and their greater or less contact with the whites. Thus, the Cheyennes, Arapahoes, and Kiowas of the southern plains, having less contact with whites, use skins for their lodges, clothing, bedding, par-fléches, saddles, lariats, for almost everything. The number of robes sent to market represent only what we may call the foreign exchange of these tribes, and is really not more than one-tenth of the skins taken. To be well within bounds I will assume that one robe sent to market by these Indians represents six dead buffaloes.

"Those bands of Sioux who live at the agencies, and whose peltries are taken to market by the Union Pacific Railroad, live in lodges of cotton cloth furnished by the Indian Bureau. They use much civilized clothing, bedding, boxes, ropes, etc. For these luxuries they must pay in robes, and as the buffalo range is far from wide, and their yearly 'crop' small, more than half of it goes to market."

Leaving out of the account at this point all consideration of the killing done north of the Union Pacific Railroad, Colonel Dodge's figures are as follows:

Southern buffaloes slaughtered by southern Indians.

Indians.	Sent to market.	No. of dead buffaloes represented.
Kiowas, Comanches, Cheyennes, Arapahoes, and other Indians whose robes go over the Atchison, Topeka and Santa Fé Railroad..	19,000	114,000
Sioux at agencies, Union Pacific Railroad....	10,000	16,000
Total slaughtered per annum...........	29,000	130,000
Total for the three years 1872–1874.....		390,000

Reference has already been made to the fact that during those years an immense number of buffaloes were killed by the farmers of eastern Kansas and Nebraska for their meat. Mr. William Mitchell, of Wabaunsee, Kansas, stated to the writer that "in those days, when buffaloes were plentiful in western Kansas, pretty much everybody made a trip West in the fall and brought back a load of buffalo meat. Everybody had it in abundance as long as buffaloes remained in any considerable number. Very few skins were saved; in fact, hardly any, for the reason that nobody knew how to tan them, and they always spoiled. At first a great many farmers tried to dress the green hides that they brought back, but they could not succeed, and finally gave up trying. Of course, a great deal of the meat killed was wasted, for only the best parts were brought back."

The Wichita (Kansas) *World* of February 9, 1889, contains the following reference:

"In 1871 and 1872 the buffalo ranged within 10 miles of Wichita, and could be counted by the thousands. The town, then in its infancy, was the headquarters for a vast number of buffalo-hunters, who plied their occupation vigorously during the winter. The buffalo were killed principally for their hides, and daily wagon trains arrived in town loaded with them. Meat was very cheap in those days; fine, tender buffalo steak selling from 1 to 2 cents per pound. * * * The business was quite profitable for a time, but a sudden drop in the price of hides brought them down as low as 25 and 50 cents each. * * * It was a very common thing in those days for people living in Wichita to start out in the morning and return by evening with a wagon load of buffalo meat."

Unquestionably a great many thousand buffaloes were killed annually by the settlers of Kansas, Nebraska, Texas, New Mexico, and Colorado, and the mountain Indians living west of the great range. The number so slain can only be guessed at, for there is absolutely no data on which to found an estimate. Judging merely from the number of people within reach of the range, it may safely be estimated that the total number of buffaloes slaughtered annually to satisfy the wants of this heterogeneous element could not have been less than fifty thousand, and probably was a much higher number. This, for the three years, would make one hundred and fifty thousand, and the grand total would therefore be about as follows:

The slaughter of the southern herd.

Killed by "professional" white hunters in 1872, 1873, and 1874	3,158,730
Killed by Indians, same period	390,000
Killed by settlers and mountain Indians	150,000
Total slaughter in three years	3,698,730

These figures seem incredible, but unfortunately there is not the slightest reason for believing they are too high. There are many men now living who declare that during the great slaughter they each killed from twenty-five hundred to three thousand buffaloes every year. With thousands of hunters on the range, and such possibilities of slaughter before each, it is, after all, no wonder that an average of nearly a million and a quarter of buffaloes fell each year during that bloody period.

By the close of the hunting season of 1875 the great southern herd had ceased to exist. As a body, it had been utterly annihilated. The main body of the survivors, numbering about ten thousand head, fled southwest, and dispersed through that great tract of wild, desolate, and inhospitable country stretching southward from the Cimarron country across the "Public Land Strip," the Pan-handle of Texas, and the Llano Estacado, or Staked Plain, to the Pecos River. A few small bands of stragglers maintained a precarious existence for a few years longer on the headwaters of the Republican River and in southwestern Nebraska, near Ogalalla, where calves were caught alive as late as 1885. Wild buffaloes were seen in southwestern Kansas for the last time in 1886, and the two or three score of individuals still living in the Canadian River country of the Texas Pan-handle are the last wild survivors of the great Southern herd.

The main body of the fugitives which survived the great slaughter of 1871-'74 continued to attract hunters who were very "hard up," who pursued them, often at the risk of their own lives, even into the terrible Llano Estacado. In Montana in 1886 I met on a cattle ranch an ex-buffalo-hunter from Texas, named Harry Andrews, who from 1874 to 1876 continued in pursuit of the scattered remnants of the great southern herd through the Pan-handle of Texas and on into the Staked Plain itself. By that time the market had become completely overstocked with robes, and the prices received by Andrews and other hunters was only 65 cents each for cow robes and $1.15 each for bull robes, delivered on the range, the purchaser providing for their transportation to the railway. But even at those prices, which were so low as to make buffalo killing seem like downright murder, Mr. Andrews assured me that he "made big money." On one occasion, when he "got a stand" on a large bunch of buffalo, he fired one hundred and fifteen shots from one spot, and killed sixty-three buffaloes in about an hour.

In 1880 buffalo hunting as a business ceased forever in the Southwest, and so far as can be ascertained, but one successful hunt for robes has been made in that region since that time. That occurred in the fall and winter of 1887, about 100 miles north of Tascosa, Texas, when two parties, one of which was under the leadership of Lee Howard, attacked the only band of buffaloes left alive in the Southwest, and which at that time numbered about two hundred head. The two parties killed fifty-two buffaloes, of which ten skins were preserved entire for mounting. Of the remaining forty-two, the heads were cut off and preserved for mounting and the skins were prepared as robes. The mountable skins were finally sold at the following prices: Young cows, $50 to $60; adult cows, $75 to $100; adult bull, $150. The unmounted heads sold as follows: Young bulls, $25 to $30; adult bulls, $50; young cows, $10 to $12; adult cows, $15 to $25. A few of the choicest robes sold at $20 each, and the remainder, a lot of twenty-eight, of prime quality and in excellent condition, were purchased by the Hudson's Bay Fur Company for $350.

Such was the end of the great southern herd. In 1871 it contained certainly no fewer than three million buffaloes, and by the beginning of 1875 its existence as a herd had utterly ceased, and nothing but scattered, fugitive bands remained.

7. *The Destruction of the Northern Herd.*—Until the building of the Northern Pacific Railway there were but two noteworthy outlets for the buffalo robes that were taken annually in the Northwestern Territories of the United States. The principal one was the Missouri River, and the Yellowstone River was the other. Down these streams the hides were transported by steam-boats to the nearest railway shipping point. For fifty years prior to the building of the Northern Pacific Railway in 1880-'82, the number of robes marketed every year by way of these streams was estimated variously at from fifty to one hundred

thousand. A great number of hides taken in the British Possessions fell into the hands of the Hudson's Bay Company, and found a market in Canada.

In May, 1881, the Sioux City (Iowa) *Journal* contained the following information in regard to the buffalo robe "crop" of the previous hunting season—the winter of 1880–'81 :

"It is estimated by competent authorities that one hundred thousand buffalo hides will be shipped out of the Yellowstone country this season. Two firms alone are negotiating for the transportation of twenty-five thousand hides each. * * * Most of our citizens saw the big load of buffalo hides that the *C. K. Peck* brought down last season, a load that hid everything about the boat below the roof of the hurricane deck. There were ten thousand hides in that load, and they were all brought out of the Yellowstone on one trip and transferred to the *C. K. Peck*. How such a load could have been piled on the little *Terry* not even the men on the boat appear to know. It hid every part of the boat, barring only the pilot-house and smoke-stacks. But such a load will not be attempted again. For such boats as ply the Yellowstone there are at least fifteen full loads of buffalo hides and other pelts. Reckoning one thousand hides to three car loads, and adding to this fifty cars for the other pelts, it will take at least three hundred and fifty box-cars to carry this stupendous bulk of peltry East to market. These figures are not guesses, but estimates made by men whose business it is to know about the amount of hides and furs awaiting shipment.

"Nothing like it has ever been known in the history of the fur trade. Last season the output of buffalo hides was above the average, and last year only about thirty thousand hides came out of the Yellowstone country, or less than a third of what is there now awaiting shipment. The past severe winter caused the buffalo to bunch themselves in a few valleys where there was pasturage, and there the slaughter went on all winter. There was no sport about it, simply shooting down the famine-tamed animals as cattle might be shot down in a barn-yard. To the credit of the Indians it can be said that they killed no more than they could save the meat from. The greater part of the slaughter was done by white hunters, or butchers rather, who followed the business of killing and skinning buffalo by the month, leaving the carcasses to rot."

At the time of the great division made by the Union Pacific Railway the northern body of buffalo extended from the valley of the Platte River northward to the southern shore of Great Slave Lake, eastward almost to Minnesota, and westward to an elevation of 8,000 feet in the Rocky Mountains. The herds were most numerous along the central portion of this region (see map), and from the Platte Valley to Great Slave Lake the range was continuous. The buffalo population of the southern half of this great range was, according to all accounts, nearly three times as great as that of the northern half. At that time, or, let us say, 1870, there were about four million buffaloes south of the Platte River, and probably about one million and a half north of it. I am aware that the estimate of the number of buffaloes in the great northern herd is usually much higher than this, but I can see no good grounds for making it so. To my mind, the evidence is conclusive that, although the northern herd ranged over such an immense area, it was numerically less than half the size of the overwhelming multitude which actually crowded the southern range, and at times so completely consumed the herbage of the plains that detachments of the United States Army found it difficult to find sufficient grass for their mules and horses.[*]

The various influences which ultimately led to the complete blotting out of the great northern herd were exerted about as follows:

In the British Possessions, where the country was immense and game of all kinds except buffalo very scarce indeed; where, in the language of Professor Kenaston, the explorer, "there was a great deal of country around every wild animal," the buffalo constituted the main dependence of the Indians, who would not cultivate the soil at all, and of the half-breeds, who would not so long as they could find buffalo. Under such circumstances the buffaloes of the British Possessions were hunted much more vigorously and persistently than those of the United States, where there was such an abundant supply of deer, elk, antelope, and other game for the Indians to feed upon, and a paternal government to support them with annuities besides. Quite contrary to the prevailing idea of the people of the United States, viz., that there were great herds of buffaloes in existence in the Saskatchewan country long after ours had all been destroyed, the herds of British America had been almost totally exterminated by the time the final slaughter of our northern herd was inaugurated by the opening of the Northern Pacific Railway in 1880. The Canadian Pacific Railway played no part whatever in the extermination of the bison in the British Possessions, for it had already taken place. The half-breeds of Manitoba, the Plains Crees of Qu'Appelle, and the Blackfeet of the South Saskatchewan country swept bare a great belt of country stretching east and west between the Rocky Mountains and Manitoba. The Canadian Pacific Railway found only bleaching bones in the country through which it passed. The buffalo had disappeared from that entire region before 1879 and left the Blackfeet Indians on the verge of starvation. A few thousand buffaloes still remained in the country around the headwaters of the Battle River, between the North and South Saskatchewan, but they were surrounded and attacked from all sides, and their numbers diminished very rapidly until all were killed.

---

[*] As an instance of this, see *Forest and Stream*, vol. II, p. 184: "Horace Jones, the interpreter here [Fort Sill], says that on his first trip along the line of the one hundredth meridian, in 1859, accompanying Major Thomas—since our noble old general—they passed continuous herds for over 60 miles, which left so little grass behind them that Major Thomas was seriously troubled about his horses."

The latest information I have been able to obtain in regard to the disappearance of this northern band has been kindly furnished by Prof. C. A. Kenaston, who in 1881, and also in 1883, made a thorough exploration of the country between Winnipeg and Fort Edmonton for the Canadian Pacific Railway Company. His four routes between the two points named covered a vast scope of country, several hundred miles in width. In 1881, at Moose Jaw, 75 miles southeast of The Elbow of the South Saskatchewan, he saw a party of Cree Indians, who had just arrived from the northwest with several carts laden with fresh buffalo meat. At Fort Saskatchewan, on the North Saskatchewan River; just above Edmonton, he saw a party of English sportsmen who had recently been hunting on the Battle and Red Deer Rivers, between Edmonton and Fort Kalgary, where they had found buffaloes, and killed as many as they cared to slaughter. In one afternoon they killed fourteen, and could have killed more had they been more blood-thirsty. In 1883 Professor Kenaston found the fresh trail of a band of twenty-five or thirty buffaloes at The Elbow of the South Saskatchewan. Excepting in the above instances he saw no further traces of buffalo, nor did he hear of the existence of any in all the country he explored. In 1881 he saw many Cree Indians at Fort Qu'Appelle in a starving condition, and there was no pemmican or buffalo meat at the fort. In 1883, however, a little pemmican found its way to Winnipeg, where it sold at 15 cents per pound; an exceedingly high price. It had been made that year, evidently in the month of April, as he purchased it in May for his journey.

The first really alarming impression made on our northern herd was by the Sioux Indians, who very speedily exterminated that portion of it which had previously covered the country lying between the North Platte and a line drawn from the center of Wyoming to the center of Dakota. All along the Missouri River from Bismarck to Fort Benton, and along the Yellowstone to the head of navigation, the slaughter went bravely on. All the Indian tribes of that vast region—Sioux, Cheyennes, Crows, Blackfeet, Bloods, Piegans, Assinniboines, Gros Ventres, and Shoshones—found their most profitable business and greatest pleasure (next to scalping white settlers) in hunting the buffalo. It took from eight to twelve buffalo hides to make a covering for one ordinary teepee, and sometimes a single teepee of extra size required from twenty to twenty-five hides.

The Indians of our northwestern Territories marketed about seventy-five thousand buffalo robes every year so long as the northern herd was large enough to afford the supply. If we allow that for every skin sold to white traders four others were used in supplying their own wants, which must be considered a very moderate estimate, the total number of buffalos slaughtered annually by those tribes must have been about three hundred and seventy-five thousand.

The end which so many observers had for years been predicting really began (with the northern herd) in 1876, two years after the great annihilation which had taken place in the South, although it was not until four years later that the slaughter became universal over the entire range. It is very clearly indicated in the figures given in a letter from Messrs. I. G. Baker & Co., of Fort Benton, Montana, to the writer, dated October 6, 1887, which reads as follows:

"There were sent East from the year 1876 from this point about seventy-five thousand buffalo robes. In 1880 it had fallen to about twenty thousand, in 1883 not more than five thousand, and in 1884 none whatever. We are sorry we can not give you a better record, but the collection of hides which exterminated the buffalo was from the Yellowstone country on the Northern Pacific, instead of northern Montana."

The beginning of the final slaughter of our northern herd may be dated about 1880, by which time the annual robe crop of the Indians had diminished three-fourths, and when summer killing for hairless hides began on a large scale. The range of this herd was surrounded on three sides by tribes of Indians, armed with breech-loading rifles and abundantly supplied with fixed ammunition. Up to the year 1880 the Indians of the tribes previously mentioned killed probably three times as many buffaloes as did the white hunters, and had there not been a white hunter in the whole Northwest the buffalo would have been exterminated there just as surely, though not so quickly by perhaps ten years, as actually occurred. Along the north, from the Missouri River to the British line, and from the reservation in northwestern Dakota to the main divide of the Rocky Mountains, a distance of 550 miles as the crow flies, the country was one continuous Indian reservation, inhabited by eight tribes, who slaughtered buffalo in season and out of season, in winter for robes and in summer for hides and meat to dry. In the Southeast was the great body of Sioux, and on the Southwest the Crows and Northern Cheyennes, all engaged in the same relentless warfare. It would have required a body of armed men larger than the whole United States Army to have withstood this continuous hostile pressure without ultimate annihilation.

Let it be remembered, therefore, that the American Indian is as much responsible for the extermination of our northern herd of bison as the American citizen. I have yet to learn of an instance wherein an Indian refrained from excessive slaughter of game through motives of economy, or care for the future, or prejudice against wastefulness. From all accounts the quantity of game killed by an Indian has always been limited by two conditions only—lack of energy to kill more, or lack of more game to be killed. White men delight in the chase, and kill for the "sport" it yields, regardless of the effort involved. Indeed, to a genuine sportsman, nothing in hunting is "sport" which is not obtained at the cost of great labor. An Indian does not view the matter in that light, and when he has killed enough to supply his wants, he stops, because he sees no reason why he should exert himself any further.

This has given rise to the statement, so often repeated, that the Indian killed only enough buffaloes to supply his wants. If an Indian ever attempted, or even showed any inclination, to husband the resources of nature in any way, and restrain wastefulness *on the part of Indians*, it would be gratifying to know of it.

The building of the Northern Pacific Railway across Dakota and Montana hastened the end that was fast approaching; but it was only an incident in the annihilation of the northern herd. Without it the final result would have been just the same, but the end would probably not have been reached until about 1888.

The Northern Pacific Railway reached Bismarck, Dakota, on the Missouri River, in the year 1876, and from that date onward received for transportation eastward all the buffalo robes and hides that came down the two rivers, Missouri and Yellowstone.

Unfortunately the Northern Pacific Railway Company kept no separate account of its buffalo-product business, and is unable to furnish a statement of the number of hides and robes it handled. It is therefore impossible to even make an estimate of the total number of buffaloes killed on the northern range during the six years which ended with the annihilation of that herd.

In regard to the business done by the Northern Pacific Railway, and the precise points from whence the bulk of the robes were shipped, the following letter from Mr. J. M. Hannaford, traffic manager of the Northern Pacific Railroad, under date of September 3, 1887, is of interest.

"Your communication, addressed to President Harris, has been referred to me for the information desired.

"I regret that our accounts are not so kept as to enable me to furnish you accurate data; but I have been able to obtain the following general information, which may prove of some value to you:

"From the years 1876 and 1880 our line did not extend beyond Bismarck, which was the extreme easterly shipping point for buffalo robes and hides, they being brought down the Missouri River from the north for shipment from that point. In the years 1876, 1877, 1878, and 1879 there were handled at that point yearly from three to four thousand bales of robes, about one-half the bales containing ten robes and the other half twelve robes each. During these years practically no hides were shipped. In 1880 the shipment of hides, dry and untanned, commenced,* and in 1881 and 1882 our line was extended west, and the shipping points increased, reaching as far west as Terry and Sully Springs, in Montana. During these years, 1880, 1881, and 1882, which practically finished the shipments of hides and robes, it is impossible

---

* It is to be noted that hairless hides, *taken from buffaloes killed in summer*, are what the writer refers to. It was not until 1881, when the end was very near, that hunting buffalo in summer as well as winter became a wholesale business. What hunting can be more disgraceful than the slaughter of females and young *in summer*, when skins are almost worthless.

for me to give you any just idea of the number shipped. The only figures obtainable are those of 1881, when over seventy-five thousand dry and untanned buffalo hides came down the river for shipment from Bismarck. Some robes were also shipped from this point that year, and a considerable number of robes and hides were shipped from several other shipping points.

"The number of pounds of buffalo meat shipped over our line has never cut any figure, the bulk of the meat having been left on the prairie, as not being of sufficient value to pay the cost of transportation.

"The names of the extreme eastern and western stations from which shipments were made are as follows: In 1880, Bismarck was the only shipping point. In 1881, Glendive, Bismarck, and Beaver Creek. In 1882, Terry and Sully Springs, Montana, were the chief shipping points, and in the order named, so far as numbers and amount of shipments are concerned. Bismarck on the east and Forsyth on the west were the two extremities.

"Up to the year 1880, so long as buffalo were killed only for robes, the bands did not decrease very materially; but beginning with that year, when they were killed for their hides as well, a most indiscriminate slaughter commenced, and from that time on they disappeared very rapidly. Up to the year 1881 there were two large bands, one south of the Yellowstone and the other north of that river. In the year mentioned those south of the river were driven north and never returned, having joined the northern band, and become practically extinguished.

"Since 1882 there have, of course, been occasional shipments both of hides and robes, but in such small quantities and so seldom that they cut practically no figure, the bulk of them coming probably from north Missouri points down the river to Bismarck."

In 1880 the northern buffalo range embraced the following streams: The Missouri and all its tributaries, from Fort Shaw, Montana, to Fort Bennett, Dakota, and the Yellowstone and all its tributaries. Of this region, Miles City, Montana, was the geographical center. The grass was good over the whole of it, and the various divisions of the great herd were continually shifting from one locality to another, often making journeys several hundred miles at a time. Over the whole of this vast area their bleaching bones lie scattered (where they have not as yet been gathered up for sale) from the Upper Marias and Milk Rivers, near the British boundary, to the Platte, and from the James River, in central Dakota, to an elevation of 8,000 feet in the Rocky Mountains. Indeed, as late as October, 1887, I gathered up on the open common, within half a mile of the Northern Pacific Railway depot at the city of Helena, the skull, horns, and numerous odd bones of a large bull buffalo which had been killed there.

Over many portions of the northern range the traveler may even now ride for days together without once being out of sight of buffalo

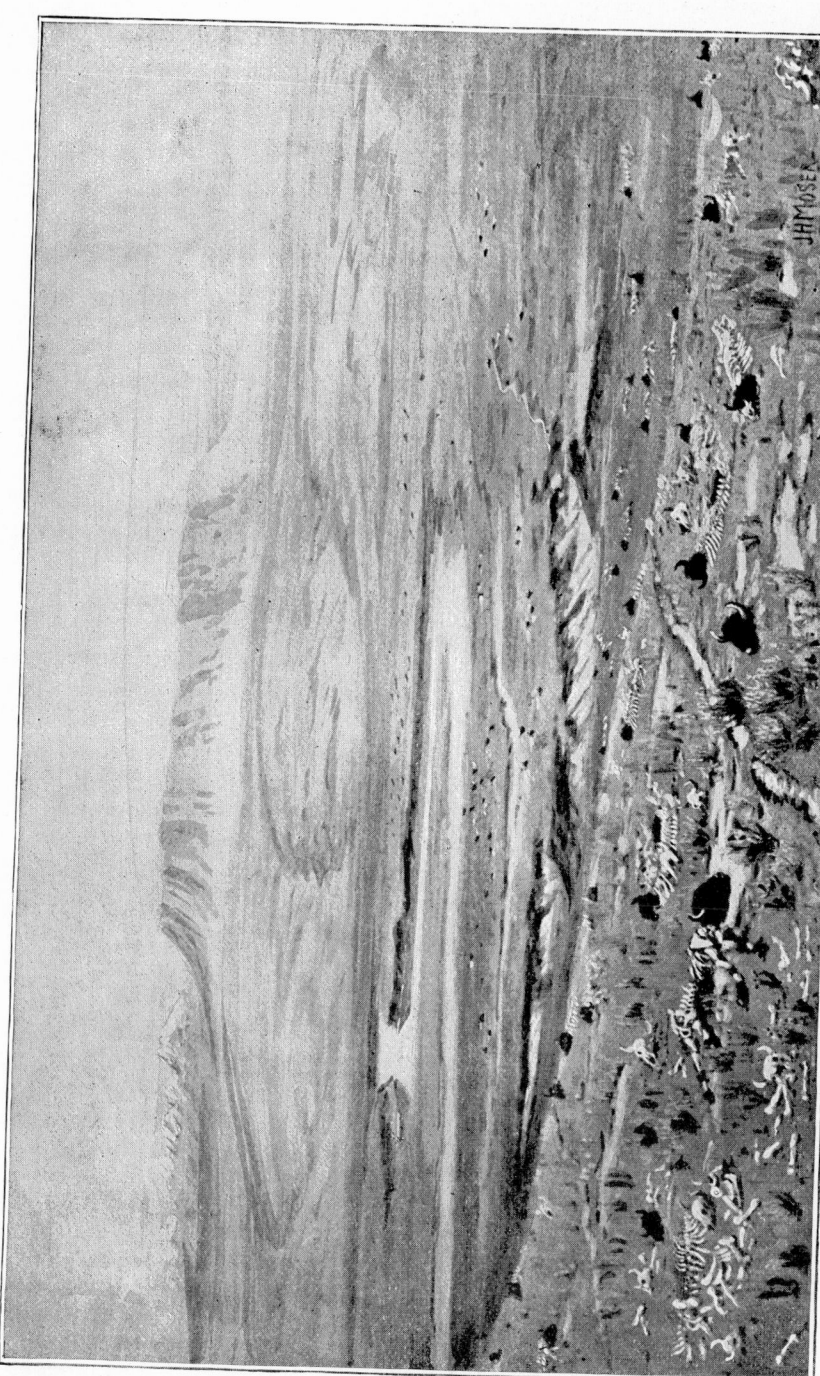

WHERE THE MILLIONS HAVE GONE.

From a painting by J. H. Moser, in the National Museum.

carcasses, or bones. Such was the case in 1886 in the country lying between the Missouri and the Yellowstone, northwest of Miles City. Go wherever we might, on divides, into bad lands, creek-bottoms, or on the highest plateaus, we always found the inevitable and omnipresent grim and ghastly skeleton, with hairy head, dried-up and shriveled nostrils, half-skinned legs stretched helplessly upon the gray turf, and the bones of the body bleached white as chalk.

The year 1881 witnessed the same kind of a stampede for the northern buffalo range that occurred just ten years previously in the south. At that time robes were worth from two to three times as much as they ever had been in the south, the market was very active, and the successful hunter was sure to reap a rich reward as long as the buffaloes lasted. At that time the hunters and hide-buyers estimated that there were five hundred thousand buffaloes within a radius of 150 miles of Miles City, and that there were still in the entire northern herd not far from one million head. The subsequent slaughter proved that these estimates were probably not far from the truth. In that year Fort Custer was so nearly overwhelmed by a passing herd that a detachment of soldiers was ordered out to turn the herd away from the post. In 1882 an immense herd appeared on the high, level plateau on the north side of the Yellowstone which overlooks Miles City and Fort Keogh in the valley below. A squad of soldiers from the Fifth Infantry was sent up on the bluff, and in less than an hour had killed enough buffaloes to load six four-mule teams with meat. In 1886 there were still about twenty bleaching skeletons lying in a group on the edge of this plateau at the point where the road from the ferry reaches the level, but all the rest had been gathered up.

In 1882 there were, so it is estimated by men who were in the country, no fewer than five thousand white hunters and skinners on the northern range. Lieut. J. M. T. Partello declares that " a cordon of camps, from the Upper Missouri, where it bends to the west, stretched toward the setting sun as far as the dividing line of Idaho, completely blocking in the great ranges of the Milk River, the Musselshell, Yellowstone, and the Marias, and rendering it impossible for scarcely a single bison to escape through the chain of sentinel camps to the Canadian northwest. Hunters of Nebraska, Wyoming, and Colorado drove the poor hunted animals north, directly into the muzzles of the thousands of repeaters ready to receive them. * * * Only a few short years ago, as late as 1883, a herd of about seventy-five thousand crossed the Yellowstone River a few miles south of here [Fort Keogh], scores of Indians, pot-hunters, and white butchers on their heels, bound for the Canadian dominions, where they hoped to find a haven of safety. Alas! not five thousand of that mighty mass ever lived to reach the British border line."

It is difficult to say (at least to the satisfaction of old hunters) which were the most famous hunting grounds on the northern range. Lieutenant Partello states that when he hunted in the great triangle bounded by the three rivers, Missouri, Musselshell, and Yellowstone, it contained, to the best of his knowledge and belief, two hundred and fifty thousand buffaloes. Unquestionably that region yielded an immense number of buffalo robes, and since the slaughter *thousands of tons* of bones have been gathered up there. Another favorite locality was the country lying between the Powder River and the Little Missouri, particularly the valleys of Beaver and O'Fallon Creeks. Thither went scores of "outfits" and hundreds of hunters and skinners from the Northern Pacific Railway towns from Miles City to Glendive. The hunters from the towns between Glendive and Bismarck mostly went south to Cedar Creek and the Grand and Moreau Rivers. But this territory was also the hunting ground of the Sioux Indians from the great reservation farther south.

Thousands upon thousands of buffaloes were killed on the Milk and Marias Rivers, in the Judith Basin, and in northern Wyoming.

The method of slaughter has already been fully described under the head of " the still-hunt," and need not be recapitulated. It is some gratification to know that the shocking and criminal wastefulness which was so marked a feature of the southern butchery was almost wholly unknown in the north. Robes were worth from $1.50 to $3.50, according to size and quality, and were removed and preserved with great care. Every one hundred robes marketed represented not more than one hundred and ten dead buffaloes, and even this small percentage of loss was due to the escape of wounded animals which afterward died and were devoured by the wolves. After the skin was taken off the hunter or skinner stretched it carefully upon the ground, inside uppermost, cut his initials in the adherent subcutaneous muscle, and left it until the season for hauling in the robes, which was always done in the early spring, immediately following the hunt.

As was the case in the south, it was the ability of a single hunter to destroy an entire bunch of buffalo in a single day that completely annihilated the remaining thousands of the northern herd before the people of the United States even learned what was going on. For example, one hunter of my acquaintance, Vic. Smith, the most famous hunter in Montana, killed one hundred and seven buffaloes in one " stand," in about one hour's time, and without shifting his point of attack. This occurred in the Red Water country, about 100 miles northeast of Miles City, in the winter of 1881–'82. During the same season another hunter, named " Doc." Aughl, killed eighty-five buffaloes at one " stand," and John Edwards killed seventy-five. The total number that Smith claims to have killed that season is " about five thousand." Where buffaloes were at all plentiful, every man who called himself a hunter was expected to kill between one and two thousand during the hunting season— from November to February—and when the buffaloes were to be found it was a comparatively easy thing to do.

During the year 1882 the thousands of bison that still remained alive on the range indicated above, and also marked out on the accompanying map, were distributed over that entire area very generally. In February of that year a Fort Benton correspondent of *Forest and Stream* wrote as follows: "It is truly wonderful how many buffalo are still left. Thousands of Indians and hundreds of white men depend on them for a living. At present nearly all the buffalo in Montana are between Milk River and Bear Paw Mountains. There are only a few small bands between the Missouri and the Yellowstone." There were plenty of buffalo on the Upper Marias River in October, 1882. In November and December there were thousands between the Missouri and the Yellowstone Rivers. South of the Northern Pacific Railway the range during the hunting season of 1882-'83 was thus defined by a hunter who has since written out the "Confessions of a Buffalo Butcher" for *Forest and Stream* (vol. XXIV, p. 489): "Then [October, 1882] the western limit was defined in a general way by Powder River, and extending eastward well toward the Missouri and south to within 60 or 70 miles of the Black Hills. It embraces the valleys of all tributaries to Powder River from the east, all of the valleys of Beaver Creek, O'Fallon Creek, and the Little Missouri and Moreau Rivers, and both forks of the Cannon Ball for almost half their length. This immense territory, lying almost equally in Montana and Dakota, had been occupied during the winters by many thousands of buffaloes from time immemorial, and many of the cows remained during the summer and brought forth their young undisturbed."

The three hunters composing the party whose record is narrated in the interesting sketch referred to, went out from Miles City on October 23, 1882, due east to the bad lands between the Powder River and O'Fallon Creek, and were on the range all winter. They found comparatively few buffaloes, and secured only two hundred and eighty-six robes, which they sold at an average price of $2.20 each. They saved and marketed a large quantity of meat, for which they obtained 3 cents per pound. They found the whole region in which they hunted fairly infested with Indians and half-breeds, all hunting buffalo.

The hunting season which began in October, 1882, and ended in February, 1883, finished the annihilation of the great northern herd, and left but a few small bands of stragglers, numbering only a very few thousand individuals all told. A noted event of the season was the retreat northward across the Yellowstone of the immense herd mentioned by Lieutenant Partello as containing seventy-five thousand head; others estimated the number at fifty thousand; and the event is often spoken of to-day by frontiersmen who were in that region at the time. Many think that the whole great body went north into British territory, and that there is still a goodly remnant of it in some remote region between the Peace River and the Saskatchewan, or somewhere there, which will yet return to the United States. Nothing could be more illusory than this belief. In the first place, the herd never reached the British line, and, if it had, it would have been promptly annihilated by the hungry Blackfeet and Cree Indians, who were declared to be in a half-starved condition, through the disappearance of the buffalo, as early as 1879.

The great herd that "went north" was utterly extinguished by the white hunters along the Missouri River and the Indians living north of it. The only vestige of it that remained was a band of about two hundred individuals that took refuge in the labyrinth of ravines and creek bottoms that lie west of the Musselshell between Flat Willow and Box Elder Creeks, and another band of about seventy-five which settled in the bad lands between the head of the Big Dry and Big Porcupine Creeks, where a few survivors were found by the writer in 1886.

South of the Northern Pacific Railway, a band of about three hundred settled permanently in and around the Yellowstone National Park, but in a very short time every animal outside of the protected limits of the park was killed, and whenever any of the park buffaloes strayed beyound the boundary they too were promptly killed for their heads and hides. At present the number remaining in the park is believed by Captain Harris, the superintendent, to be about two hundred; about one-third of which is due to breeding in the protected territory.

In the southeast the fate of that portion of the herd is well known. The herd which at the beginning of the hunting season of 1883 was known to contain about ten thousand head, and ranged in western Dakota, about half way between the Black Hills and Bismarck, between the Moreau and Grand Rivers, was speedily reduced to about one thousand head. Vic. Smith, who was "in at the death," says there were eleven hundred, others say twelve hundred. Just at this juncture (October, 1883) Sitting Bull and his whole band of nearly one thousand braves arrived from the Standing Rock Agency, and in two days' time slaughtered the entire herd. Vic. Smith and a host of white hunters took part in the killing of this last ten thousand, and he declares that "when we got through the hunt there was not a hoof left. That wound up the buffalo in the Far West, only a stray bull being seen here and there afterwards."

Curiously enough, not even the buffalo-hunters themselves were at the time aware of the fact that the end of the hunting season of 1882–'83 was also the end of the buffalo, at least as an inhabitant of the plains and a source of revenue. In the autumn of 1883 they nearly all outfitted as usual, often at an expense of many hundreds of dollars, and blithely sought "the range" that had up to that time been so prolific in robes. The end was in nearly every case the same—total failure and bankruptcy. It was indeed hard to believe that not only the millions, but also the thousands, had actually gone, and forever.

I have found it impossible to ascertain definitely the number of robes and hides shipped from the northern range during the last years of the slaughter, and the only reliable estimate I have obtained was made for me, after much consideration and reflection, by Mr. J. N. Davis, of Minneapolis, Minnesota. Mr. Davis was for many years a buyer of furs, robes, and hides on a large scale throughout our Northwestern Territories, and was actively engaged in buying up buffalo robes as long as there were any to buy. In reply to a letter asking for statistics, he wrote me as follows, on September 27, 1887:

"It is impossible to give the exact number of robes and hides shipped out of Dakota and Montana from 1876 to 1883, or the exact number of buffalo in the northern herd; but I will give you as correct an account as any one can. In 1876 it was estimated that there were half a million buffaloes within a radius of 150 miles of Miles City. In 1881 the Northern Pacific Railroad was built as far west as Glendive and Miles City. At that time the whole country was a howling wilderness, and Indians and wild buffalo were too numerous to mention. The first shipment of buffalo robes, killed by white men, was made that year, and the stations on the Northern Pacific Railroad between Miles City and Mandan sent out about fifty thousand hides and robes. In 1882 the number of hides and robes bought and shipped was about two hundred thousand, and in 1883 forty thousand. In 1884 I shipped from Dickinson, Dakota Territory, the only car load of robes that went East that year, and it was the last shipment ever made."

For a long time the majority of the ex-hunters cherished the fond delusion that the great herd had only "gone north" into the British Possessions, and would eventually return in great force. Scores of rumors of the finding of herds floated about, all of which were eagerly believed at first. But after a year or two had gone by without the appearance of a single buffalo, and likewise without any reliable information of the existence of a herd of any size, even in British territory, the butchers of the buffalo either hung up their old Sharps rifles, or sold them for nothing to the gun-dealers, and sought other means of livelihood. Some took to gathering up buffalo bones and selling them by the ton, and others became cowboys.

V. Congressional Legislation for the Protection of the Bison.

The slaughter of the buffalo down to the very point of extermination has been so very generally condemned, and the general Government has been so unsparingly blamed for allowing such a massacre to take place on the public domain, it is important that the public should know all the facts in the case. To the credit of Congress it must be said that several very determined efforts were made betwen the years 1871 and 1876 looking toward the protection of the buffalo. The failure of all those well-meant efforts was due to our republican form of Government. Had this Goverment been a monarchy the buffalo would have been protected; but unfortunately in this case (perhaps the only one on record wherein a king could have accomplished more than the representatives of the people) the necessary act of Congress was so hedged in and beset by obstacles that it never became an accomplished fact. Even when both houses of Congress succeeded in passing a suitable act (June 23, 1874) it went to the President in the last days of the session only to be pigeon-holed, and die a natural death.

The following is a complete history of Congressional legislation in regard to the protection of the buffalo from wanton slaughter and ultimate extinction. The first step taken in behalf of this persecuted animal was on March 13, 1871, when Mr. McCormick, of Arizona, introduced a bill (H. R. 157), which was ordered to be printed. Nothing further was done with it. It read as follows:

Be it enacted, etc., That, excepting for the purpose of using the meat for food or preserving the skin, it shall be unlawful for any person to kill the bison, or buffalo, found anywhere upon the public lands of the United States; and for the violation of this law the offender shall, upon conviction before any court of competent jurisdiction, be liable to a fine of $100 for each animal killed, one-half of which sum shall, upon its collection, be paid to the informer.

On February 14, 1872, Mr. Cole, of California, introduced in the Senate the following resolution, which was considered by unanimous consent and agreed to:

Resolved, That the Committee on Territories be directed to inquire into the expediency of enacting a law for the protection of the buffalo, elk, antelope, and other useful animals running wild in the Territories of the United States against indiscriminate slaughter and extermination, and that they report by bill or otherwise.

On February 16, 1872, Mr. Wilson, of Massachusetts, introduced a bill in the Senate (S. 655) restricting the killing of the buffalo upon the public lands; which was read twice by its title and referred to the Committee on Territories.

On April 5, 1872, Mr. R. C. McCormick, of Arizona, made a speech in the House of Representatives, while it was in Committee of the Whole, on the restriction of the killing of buffalo.

He mentioned a then recent number of *Harper's Weekly*, in which were illustrations of the slaughter of buffalo, and also read a partly historical extract in regard to the same. He related how, when he was once snow-bound upon the Kansas Pacific Railroad, the buffalo furnished food for himself and fellow-passengers. Then he read the bill introduced by him March 13, 1871, and also copies of letters furnished him by Henry Bergh, president of the American Society for the Prevention of Cruelty to Animals, which were sent to the latter by General W. B. Hazen, Lieut. Col. A. G. Brackett, and E. W. Wynkoop. He also read a statement by General Hazen to the effect that he knew of a man who killed ninety-nine buffaloes with his own hand in one day. He also spoke on the subject of cross-breeding the buffalo with common cattle, and read an extract in regard to it from the San Francisco *Post*.[*]

On April 6, 1872, Mr. McCormick asked leave to have printed in the

---

[*] Congressional Globe (Appendix), second session Forty-second Congress.

Globe some remarks he had prepared regarding restricting the killing of buffalo, which was granted.*

On January 5, 1874, Mr. Fort, of Illinois, introduced a bill (H. R. 921) to prevent the useless slaughter of buffalo within the Territories of the United States; which was read and referred to the Committee on the Territories.†

On March 10, 1874, this bill was reported to the House from the Committee on the Territories, with a recommendation that it be passed.‡

The first section of the bill provided that it shall be unlawful for any person, who is not an Indian, to kill, wound, or in any way destroy any female buffalo of any age, found at large within the boundaries of any of the Territories of the United States.

The second section provided that it shall be, in like manner, unlawful for any such person to kill, wound, or destroy in said Territories any greater number of male buffaloes than are needed for food by such person, or than can be used, cured, or preserved for the food of other persons, or for the market. It shall in like manner be unlawful for any such person, or persons, to assist, or be in any manner engaged or concerned in or about such unlawful killing, wounding, or destroying of any such buffaloes; that any person who shall violate the provisions of the act shall, on conviction, forfeit and pay to the United States the sum of $100 for each offense (and each buffalo so unlawfully killed, wounded, or destroyed shall be and constitute a separate offense), and on a conviction of a second offense may be committed to prison for a period not exceeding thirty days; and that all United States judges, justices, courts, and legal tribunals in said Territories shall have jurisdiction in cases of the violation of the law.

Mr. Cox said he had been told by old hunters that it was impossible to tell the sex of a running buffalo; and he also stated that the bill gave preference to the Indians.

Mr. Fort said the object was to prevent early extermination; that thousands were annually slaughtered for skins alone, and thousands for their tongues alone; that perhaps hundreds of thousands are killed every year in utter wantonness, with no object for such destruction. He had been told that the sexes could be distinguished while they were running.§

This bill does not prohibit any person joining in a reasonable chase and hunt of the buffalo.

Said Mr. Fort, "So far as I am advised, gentlemen upon this floor representing all the Territories are favorable to the passage of this bill."

---

* Congressional Globe, April 6, 1872, Forty-second Congress, second session.

† Congressional Record, vol. 2, part 1, Forty-third Congress, p. 371.

‡ Congressional Record, vol. 2, part 3, Forty-third Congress, first session, pp. 2105, 2109.

§ I know of no greater affront that could be offered to the intelligence of a genuine buffalo-hunter than to accuse him of not knowing enough to tell the sex of a buffalo "on the run" by its form alone.—W. T. H.

Mr. Cox wanted the clause excepting the Indians from the operations of the bill stricken out, and stated that the Secretary of the Interior had already said to the House that the civilization of the Indian was impossible while the buffalo remained on the plains.

The Clerk read for Mr. McCormick the following extract from the *New Mexican*, a paper published in Santa Fé:

The buffalo slaughter, which has been going on the past few years on the plains, and which increases every year, is wantonly wicked, and should be stopped by the most stringent enactments and most vigilant enforcements of the law. Killing these noble animals for their hides simply, or to gratify the pleasure of some Russian duke or English lord, is a species of vandalism which can not too quickly be checked. United States surveying parties report that there are two thousand hunters on the plains killing these animals for their hides. One party of sixteen hunters report having killed twenty-eight thousand buffaloes during the past summer. It seems to us there is quite as much reason why the Government should protect the buffaloes as the Indians.

Mr. McCormick considered the subject important, and had not a doubt of the fearful slaughter. He read the following extract from a letter that he had received from General Hazen:

I know a man who killed with his own hand ninety-nine buffaloes in one day, without taking a pound of the meat. The buffalo for food has an intrinsic value about equal to an average Texas beef, or say $20. There are probably not less than a million of these animals on the western plains. If the Government owned a herd of a million oxen they would at least take steps to prevent this wanton slaughter. The railroads have made the buffalo so accessible as to present a case not dissimilar.

He agreed with Mr. Cox that some features of the bill would probably be impracticable, and moved to amend it. He did not believe any bill would entirely accomplish the purpose, but he desired that such wanton slaughter should be stopped.

Said he, "It would have been well both for the Indians and the white men if an enactment of this kind had been placed on our statute-books years ago. * * * I know of no one act that would gratify the red men more."

Mr. Holman expressed surprise that Mr. Cox should make any objection to parts of the measure. The former regarded the bill as "an effort in a most commendable direction," and trusted that it would pass.

Mr. Cox said he would not have objected to the bill but from the fact that it was partial in its provisions. He wanted a bill that would impose a penalty on every man, red, white, or black, who may wantonly kill these buffaloes.

Mr. Potter desired to know whether more buffaloes were slaughtered by the Indians than by white men.

Mr. Fort thought the white men were doing the greatest amount of killing.

Mr. Eldridge thought there would be just as much propriety in killing the fish in our rivers as in destroying the buffalo in order to compel the Indians to become civilized.

Mr. Conger said: "As a matter of fact, every man knows the range of the buffalo has grown more and more confined year after year; that they have been driven westward before advancing civilization." But he opposed the bill!

Mr. Hawley, of Connecticut, said: " I am glad to see this bill. I am in favor of this law, and hope it will pass."

Mr. Lowe favored the bill, and thought that the buffalo ought to be protected for proper utility.

Mr. Cobb thought they ought to be protected for the settlers, who depended partly on them for food.

Mr. Parker, of Missouri, intimated that the policy of the Secretary of the Interior was a sound one, and that the buffaloes ought to be exterminated, to prevent difficulties in civilizing the Indians.

Said Mr. Conger, " I do not think the measure will tend at all to protect the buffalo."

Mr. McCormick replied: " This bill will not prevent the killing of buffaloes for any useful purpose, but only their wanton destruction."

Mr. Kasson said: " I wish to say one word in support of this bill, because I have had some experience as to the manner in which these buffaloes are treated by hunters. The buffalo is a creature of vast utility, * * * . This animal ought to be protected; * * * ."

The question being taken on the passage of the bill, there were—ayes 132, noes not counted.

So the bill was passed.

On June 23, 1874, this bill (H. R. 921) came up in the Senate.*

Mr. Harvey moved, as an amendment, to strike out the words " who is not an Indian."

Said Mr. Hitchcock, "That will defeat the bill."

Mr. Frelinghuysen said: " That would prevent the Indians from killing the buffalo on their own ground. I object to the bill."

Mr. Sargent said: " I think we can pass the bill in the right shape without objection. Let us take it up. It is a very important one."

Mr. Frelinghuysen withdrew his objection.

Mr. Harvey thought it was a very important bill, and withdrew his amendment.

The bill was reported to the Senate, ordered to a third reading, read the third time, and passed. It went to President Grant for signature, and expired in his hands at the adjournment of that session of Congress.

On February 2, 1874, Mr. Fort introduced a bill (H. R. 1689) to tax buffalo hides; which was referred to the Committee on Ways and Means.

On June 10, 1874, Mr. Dawes, from the Committee on Ways and Means, reported back the bill adversely, and moved that it be laid on the table.

---

* Congressional Globe, Vol. 2, part 6, Forty-third Congress, first session.

Mr. Fort asked to have the bill referred to the Committee of the Whole, and it was so referred.

On February 2, 1874, Mr. R. C. McCormick, of Arizona, introduced in the House a bill (H. R. 1728) restricting the killing of the bison, or buffalo, on the public lands; which was referred to the Committee on the Public Lands, and never heard of more.

On January 31, 1876, Mr. Fort introduced a bill (H. R. 1719) to prevent the useless slaughter of buffaloes within the Territories of the United States, which was referred to the Committee on the Territories.[*]

The Committee on the Territories reported back the bill without amendment on February 23, 1876.[†] Its provisions were in every respect identical with those of the bill introduced by Mr. Fort in 1874, and which passed both houses.

In support of it Mr. Fort said: "The intention and object of this bill is to preserve them [the buffaloes] for the use of the Indians, whose homes are upon the public domain, and to the frontiersmen, who may properly use them for food. * * * They have been and are now being slaughtered in large numbers. * * * Thousands of these noble brutes are annually slaughtered out of mere wontonness. * * * This bill, just as it is now presented, passed the last Congress. It was not vetoed, but fell, as I understand, merely for want of time to consider it after having passed both houses." He also intimated that the Government was using a great deal of money for cattle to furnish the Indians, while the buffalo was being wantonly destroyed, whereas they might be turned to their good.

Mr. Crounse wanted the words "who is not an Indian" struck out, so as to make the bill general. He thought Indians were to blame for the wanton destruction.

Mr. Fort thought the amendment unnecessary, and stated that he was informed that the Indians did not destroy the buffaloes wantonly.

Mr. Dunnell thought the bill one of great importance.

The Clerk read for him a letter from A. G. Brackett, lieutenant-colonel, Second United States Cavalry, stationed at Omaha Barracks, in which was a very urgent request to have Congress interfere to prevent the wholesale slaughter then going on.

Mr. Reagan thought the bill proper and right. He knew from personal experience how the wanton slaughtering was going on, and also that the Indians were *not* the ones who did it.

Mr. Townsend, of New York, saw no reason why a white man should not be allowed to kill a female buffalo as well as an Indian. He said it would be impracticable to have a separate law for each.

Mr. Maginnis did not agree with him. He thought the bill ought to pass as it stood.

Mr. Throckmorton thought that while the intention of the bill was a

---

* Forty-fourth Congress, first session, vol. 4, part 2, pp. 1237–1241.
† Forty-fourth Congress first session, vol. 4, part 1, p. 773.

good one, yet it was mischievous and difficult to enforce, and would also work hardship to a large portion of our frontier people. He had several objections. He also thought a cow buffalo could not be distinguished at a distance.

Mr. Hancock, of Texas, thought the bill an impolicy, and that the sooner the buffalo was exterminated the better.

Mr. Fort replied by asking him why all the game—deer, antelope, etc.—was not slaughtered also. Then he went on to state that to exterminate the buffalo would be to starve innocent children of the red man, and to make the latter more wild and savage than he was already.

Mr. Baker, of Indiana, offered the following amendment as a substitute for the one already offered:

Provided, That any white person who shall employ, hire, or procure, directly or indirectly, any Indian to kill any buffalo forbidden to be killed by this act, shall be deemed guilty of a misdemeanor and punished in the manner provided in this act.

Mr. Fort stated that a certain clause in his bill covered the object of the amendment.

Mr. Jenks offered the following amendment:

Strike out in the fourth line of the second section the word "can" and insert "shall;" and in the second line of the same section insert the word "wantonly" before "kill;" so that the clause will read:

"That it shall be in like manner unlawful for any such person to wantonly kill, wound, or destroy in the said Territories any greater number of male buffaloes than are needed for food by such person, or than shall be used, cured, or preserved for the food of other persons, or for the market."

Mr. Conger said: "I think the whole bill is unwise. I think it is a useless measure."

Mr. Hancock said: "I move that the bill and amendment be laid on the table."

The motion to lay the bill upon the table was defeated, and the amendment was rejected.

Mr. Conger called for a division on the passage of the bill. The House divided, and there were—ayes 93, noes 48. He then demanded tellers, and they reported—ayes 104, noes 36. So the bill was passed.

On February 25, 1876, the bill was reported to the Senate, and referred to the Committee on Territories, from whence it never returned.

On March 20, 1876, Mr. Fort introduced a bill (H. R. 2767) to tax buffalo hides; which was referred to the Committee on Ways and Means, and never heard of afterward.

This was the last move made in Congress in behalf of the buffalo. The philanthropic friends of the frontiersman, the Indian, and of the buffalo himself, despaired of accomplishing the worthy object for which they had so earnestly and persistently labored, and finally gave up the fight. At the very time the effort in behalf of buffalo protection was abandoned the northern herd still flourished, and might have been preserved from extirpation.

At various times the legislatures of a few of the Western States and

Territories enacted laws vaguely and feebly intended to provide some sort of protection to the fast-disappearing animals. One of the first was the game law of Colorado, passed in 1872, which declared that the killers of game should not leave any flesh to spoil. The western game laws of those days amounted to about as much as they do now; practically nothing at all. I have never been able to learn of a single instance, save in the Yellowstone Park, wherein a western hunter was prevented by so simple and innocuous a thing as a game law from killing game. Laws were enacted, but they were always left to enforce themselves. The idea of the frontiersman (the average, at least) has always been to kill as much game as possible before some other fellow gets a chance at it, *and before it is all killed off!* So he goes at the game, and as a general thing kills all he can while it lasts, and with it feeds himself and family, his dogs, and even his hogs, to repletion. I knew one Montana man north of Miles City who killed for his own use twenty-six black-tail deer in one season, and had so much more venison than he could consume or give away that a great pile of carcasses lay in his yard until spring and spoiled.

During the existence of the buffalo it was declared by many an impossibility to stop or prevent the slaughter. Such an accusation of weakness and imbecility on the part of the General Government is an insult to our strength and resources. The protection of game is now and always has been simply a question of money. A proper code of game laws and a reasonable number of salaried game-wardens, sworn to enforce them and punish all offenses against them, would have afforded the buffalo as much protection as would have been necessary to his continual existence. To be sure, many buffaloes would have been killed on the sly in spite of laws to the contrary, but it was wholesale slaughter that wrought the extermination, and that could easily have been prevented. A tax of 50 cents each on buffalo robes would have maintained a sufficient number of game-wardens to have reasonably regulated the killing, and maintained for an indefinite period a bountiful source of supply of food, and also raiment for both the white man of the plains and the Indian. By judicious management the buffalo could have been made to yield an annual revenue equal to that we now receive from the fur-seals—$100,000 per year.

During the two great periods of slaughter—1870-'75 and 1880-'84—the principal killing grounds were as well known as the stock-yards of Chicago. Had proper laws been enacted, and had either the general or territorial governments entered with determination upon the task of restricting the killing of buffaloes to proper limits, their enforcement would have been, in the main, as simple and easy as the collection of taxes. Of course the solitary hunter in a remote locality would have bowled over his half dozen buffaloes in secure defiance of the law; but such desultory killing could not have made much impression on the great mass for many years. The business-like, wholesale slaughter, wherein one hunter would openly kill five thousand buffaloes and market perhaps two thousand hides, could easily have been stopped forever. Buffalo hides could not have been dealt in clandestinely, for many reasons, and had there been no sale for ill-gotten spoils the still-hunter would have gathered no spoils to sell. It was an undertaking of considerable magnitude, and involving a cash outlay of several hundred dollars to make up an "outfit" of wagons, horses, arms and ammunition, food, etc., for a trip to "the range" after buffaloes. It was these wholesale hunters, both in the North and the South, who exterminated the species, and to say that all such undertakings could not have been effectually prevented by law is to accuse our law-makers and law-officers of imbecility to a degree hitherto unknown. There is nowhere in this country, nor in any of the waters adjacent to it, a living species of any kind which the United States Government can not fully and perpetually protect from destruction by human agencies if it chooses to do so. The destruction of the buffalo was a loss of wealth perhaps twenty times greater than the sum it would have cost to conserve it, and this stupendous waste of valuable food and other products was committed by one class of the American people and permitted by another with a prodigality and wastefulness which even in the lowest savages would be inexcusable.

VI. COMPLETENESS OF THE EXTERMINATION.

(May 1, 1889.)

Although the existence of a few widely-scattered individuals enables us to say that the bison is not yet absolutely extinct in a wild state, there is no reason to hope that a single wild and unprotected individual will remain alive ten years hence. The nearer the species approaches to complete extermination, the more eagerly are the wretched fugitives pursued to the death whenever found. Western hunters are striving for the honor (?) of killing the last buffalo, which, it is to be noted, has already been slain about a score of times by that number of hunters.

The buffaloes still alive in a wild state are so very few, and have been so carefully "marked down" by hunters, it is possible to make a very close estimate of the total number remaining. In this enumeration the small herd in the Yellowstone National Park is classed with other herds in captivity and under protection, for the reason that, had it not been for the protection afforded by the law and the officers of the Park, not one of these buffaloes would be living to-day. Were the restrictions of the law removed now, every one of those animals would be killed within three months. Their heads alone are worth from $25 to $50 each to taxidermists, and for this reason every buffalo is a prize worth the hunter's winning. Had it not been for stringent laws, and a rigid enforcement of them by Captain Harris, the last of the Park buffaloes would have been shot years ago by Vic. Smith, the Rea Brothers, and other hunters, of whom there is always an able contingent around the Park.

In the United States the death of a buffalo is now such an event that it is immediately chronicled by the Associated Press and telegraphed all over the country. By reason of this, and from information already in hand, we are able to arrive at a very fair understanding of the present condition of the species in a wild state.

In December, 1886, the Smithsonian expedition left about fifteen buffaloes alive in the bad lands of the Missouri-Yellowstone divide, at the head of Big Porcupine Creek. In 1887 three of these were killed by cowboys, and in 1888 two more, the last death recorded being that of an old bull killed near Billings. There are probably eight or ten stragglers still remaining in that region, hiding in the wildest and most broken tracts of the bad lands, as far as possible from the cattle ranches, and where even cowboys seldom go save on a round-up. From the fact that no other buffaloes, at least so far as can be learned, have been killed in Montana during the last two years, I am convinced that the bunch referred to are the last representatives of the species remaining in Montana.

In the spring of 1886 Mr. B. C. Winston, while on a hunting trip about 75 miles west of Grand Rapids, Dakota, saw seven buffaloes—five adult animals and two calves; of which he killed one, a large bull, and caught a calf alive. On September 11, 1888, a solitary bull was killed 3 miles from the town of Oakes, in Dickey County. There are still three individuals in the unsettled country lying between that point and the Missouri, which are undoubtedly the only wild representatives of the race east of the Missouri River.

On April 28, 1887, Dr. William Stephenson, of the United States Army, wrote me as follows from Pilot Butte, about 30 miles north of Rock Springs, Wyoming:

"There are undoubtedly buffalo within 50 or 60 miles of here, two having been killed out of a band of eighteen some ten days since by cowboys, and another band of four seen near there. I hear from cattlemen of their being seen every year north and northeast of here."

This band was seen once in 1888. In February, 1889, Hon. Joseph M. Carey, member of Congress from Wyoming, received a letter informing him that this band of buffaloes, consisting of twenty-six head, had been seen grazing in the Red Desert of Wyoming, and that the Indians were preparing to attack it. At Judge Carey's request the Indian Bureau issued orders which it was hoped would prevent the slaughter. So, until further developments, we have the pleasure of recording the presence of twenty-six wild buffaloes in southern Wyoming.

There are no buffaloes whatever in the vicinity of the Yellowstone Park, either in Wyoming, Montana, or Idaho, save what wander out of that reservation, and when any do, they are speedily killed.

There is a rumor that there are ten or twelve mountain buffaloes still on foot in Colorado, in a region called Lost Park, and, while it lacks confirmation, we gladly accept it as a fact. In 1888 Mr. C. B. Cory, of Boston, saw in Denver, Colorado, eight fresh buffalo skins, which it was said had come from the region named above. In 1885 there was a herd of about forty "mountain buffalo" near South Park, and although some of the number may still survive, the indications are that the total number of wild buffaloes in Colorado does not exceed twenty individuals.

In Texas a miserable remnant of the great southern herd still remains in the "Pan-handle country," between the two forks of the Canadian River. In 1886 about two hundred head survived, which number by the summer of 1887 had been reduced to one hundred, or less. In the hunting season of 1887–'88 a ranchman named Lee Howard fitted out and led a strong party into the haunts of the survivors, and killed fifty-two of them. In May, 1888, Mr. C. J. Jones again visited this region for the purpose of capturing buffaloes alive. His party found, from first to last, thirty-seven buffaloes, of which they captured eighteen head, eleven adult cows and seven calves; the greatest feat ever accomplished in buffalo-hunting. It is highly probable that Mr. Jones and his men saw about all the buffaloes now living in the Pan-handle country, and it therefore seems quite certain that not over twenty-five individuals remain. These are so few, so remote, and so difficult to reach, it is to be hoped no one will consider them worth going after, and that they will be left to take care of themselves. It is greatly to be regretted that the State of Texas does not feel disposed to make a special effort for their protection and preservation.

In regard to the existence of wild buffaloes in the British Possessions, the statements of different authorities are at variance, by far the larger number holding the opinion that there are in all the Northwest Territory only a few almost solitary stragglers. But there is still good reason for the hope, and also the belief, that there still remain in Athabasca, between the Athabasca and Peace Rivers, at least a few hundred "wood buffalo." In a very interesting and well-considered article in the London *Field* of November 10, 1888, Mr. Miller Christy quotes all the available positive evidence bearing on this point, and I gladly avail myself of the opportunity to reproduce it here:

"The Hon. Dr. Schulz, in the recent debate on the Mackenzie River basin, in the Canadian senate, quoted Senator Hardisty, of Edmonton, of the Hudson's Bay Company, to the effect that the wood buffalo still existed in the region in question. 'It was,' he said, 'difficult to estimate how many; but probably five or six hundred still remain in scattered bands.' There had been no appreciable difference in their numbers, he thought, during the last fifteen years, as they could not be hunted on horseback, on account of the wooded character of the country, and were, therefore, very little molested. They are larger than the buffalo of the great plains, weighing at least 150 pounds more. They are also coarser haired and straighter horned.

"The doctor also quoted Mr. Frank Oliver, of Edmonton, to the effect that the wood buffalo still exists in small numbers between the Lower Peace and Great Slave Rivers, extending westward from the latter to the Salt River in latitude 60 degrees, and also between the Peace and Athabasca Rivers. He states that 'they are larger than the prairie buffalo, and the fur is darker, but practically they are the same animal.' * * * Some buffalo meat is brought in every winter to the Hudson's Bay Company's posts nearest the buffalo ranges.

"Dr. Schulz further stated that he had received the following testimony from Mr. Donald Ross, of Edmonton: The wood buffalo still exists in the localities named. About 1870 one was killed as far west on Peace River as Fort Dunvegan. They are quite different from the prairie buffalo, being nearly double the size, as they will dress fully 700 pounds."

It will be apparent to most observers, I think, that Mr. Ross's statement in regard to the size of the wood buffalo is a random shot.

In a private letter to the writer, under date of October 22, 1887, Mr. Harrison S. Young, of the Hudson's Bay Company's post at Edmonton, writes as follows:

"The buffalo are not yet extinct in the Northwest. There are still some stray ones on the prairies away to the south of this, but they must be very few. I am unable to find any one who has personal knowledge of the killing of one during the last two years, though I have since the receipt of your letter questioned a good many half-breeds on the subject. In our district of Athabasca, along the Salt River, there are still a few wood buffalo killed every year, but they are fast diminishing in numbers and are also becoming very shy."

In his "Manitoba and the Great Northwest" Prof. John Macoun has this to say regarding the presence of the wood buffalo in the region referred to:

"The wood buffalo, when I was on the Peace River in 1875, were confined to the country lying between the Athabasca and Peace Rivers north of latitude 57° 30', or chiefly in the Birch Hills. They were also said to be in some abundance on the Salt and Hay Rivers, running into the Slave River north of Peace River. The herds thirteen years ago [now nineteen] were supposed to number about one thousand, all told. I believe many still exist, as the Indians of that region eat fish, which are much easier procured than either buffalo or moose, and the country is much too difficult for white men."

All this evidence, when carefully considered, resolves itself into simply this and no more: The only evidence in favor of the existence of any live buffaloes between the Athabasca and Peace Rivers is in the form of very old rumors, most of them nearly fifteen years old; time enough for the Indians to have procured fire-arms in abundance and killed all those buffaloes two or three times over.

Mr. Miller Christy takes "the mean of the estimates," and assumes that there are now about five hundred and fifty buffaloes in the region named. If we are to believe in the existence there of any stragglers his estimate is a fair one, and we will gladly accept it. The total is therefore as follows:

Number of American bison running wild and unprotected on January 1, 1889.

In the Pan-handle of Texas	25
In Colorado	20
In southern Wyoming	26
In the Musselshell country, Montana	10
In western Dakota	4
Total number in the United States	85
In Athabasca, Northwest Territory (estimated)	550
Total in all North America	635

Add to the above the total number already recorded in captivity (256) and those under Government protection in the Yellowstone Park (200), and the whole number of individuals of *Bison americanus* now living is 1,091.

From this time it is probable that many rumors of the sudden appearance of herds of buffaloes will become current. Already there have been three or four that almost deserve special mention. The first appeared in March, 1887, when various Western newspapers published a circumstantial account of how a herd of about three hundred buffaloes swam the Missouri River about 10 miles above Bismarck, near the town of Painted Woods, and ran on in a southwesterly direction. A letter of inquiry, addressed to Mr. S. A. Peterson, postmaster at Painted Woods, elicited the following reply:

"The whole rumor is false, and without any foundation. I saw it first in the —— newspaper, where I believe it originated."

In these days of railroads and numberless hunting parties, there is not the remotest possibility of there being anywhere in the United States a herd of a hundred, or even fifty, buffaloes which has escaped observation. Of the eighty-five head still existing in a wild state it may safely be predicted that not even one will remain alive five years hence. A buffalo is now so great a prize, and by the ignorant it is considered so great an honor (?) to kill one, that extraordinary exertions will be made to find and shoot down without mercy the "last buffalo."

There is no possible chance for the race to be perpetuated in a wild state, and in a few years more hardly a bone will remain above ground to mark the existence of the most prolific mammalian species that ever existed, so far as we know.

VII. EFFECTS OF THE EXTERMINATION.

The buffalo supplied the Indian with food, clothing, shelter, bedding, saddles, ropes, shields, and innumerable smaller articles of use and ornament. In the United States a paternal government takes the place of the buffalo in supplying all these wants of the red man, and it costs several millions of dollars annually to accomplish the task.

The following are the tribes which depended very largely—some almost wholly—upon the buffalo for the necessities, and many of the luxuries, of their savage life until the Government began to support them:

Sioux	30,561	Kiowas and Comanches	2,756
Crow	3,226	Arapahoes	1,217
Piegan, Blood, and Blackfeet	2,026	Apache	332
Cheyenne	3,477	Ute	978
Gros Ventres	856	Omaha	1,160
Arickaree	517	Pawnee	998
Mandan	283	Winnebago	1,222
Bannack and Shoshone	2,001		
Nez Percé	1,460	Total	54,758
Assinniboine	1,688		

This enumeration (from the census of 1886) leaves entirely out of consideration many thousands of Indians living in the Indian Territory and other portions of the Southwest, who drew an annual supply of meat and robes from the chase of the buffalo, notwithstanding the fact that their chief dependence was upon agriculture.

The Indians of what was once the buffalo country are not starving and freezing, for the reason that the United States Government supplies them regularly with beef and blankets in lieu of buffalo. Does any one imagine that the Government could not have regulated the killing of buffaloes, and thus maintained the supply, for far less money than it now costs to feed and clothe those 54,758 Indians?

How is it with the Indians of the British Possessions to-day?

Prof. John Macoun writes as follows in his "Manitoba and the Great Northwest," page 342:

"During the last three years [prior to 1883] the great herds have been kept south of our boundary, and, as the result of this, our Indians have been on the verge of starvation. When the hills were covered with countless thousands [of buffaloes] in 1877, the Blackfeet were dying of starvation in 1879."

During the winter of 1886–'87, destitution and actual starvation prevailed to an alarming extent among certain tribes of Indians in the Northwest Territory who once lived bountifully on the buffalo. A terrible tale of suffering in the Athabasca and Peace River country has recently (1888) come to the minister of the interior of the Canadian government, in the form of a petition signed by the bishop of that diocese, six clergymen and missionaries, and several justices of the peace. It sets forth that "owing to the destruction of game, the Indians, both last winter and last summer, have been in a state of starvation. They are now in a complete state of destitution, and are utterly unable to provide themselves with clothing, shelter, ammunition, or food for the coming winter." The petition declares that on account of starvation, and consequent cannibalism, a party of twenty-nine Cree Indians was reduced to three in the winter of 1886.* Of the Fort Chippewyan Indians, be-tween twenty and thirty starved to death last winter, and the death of many more was hastened by want of food and by famine diseases. Many other Indians—Crees, Beavers, and Chippewyans—at almost all points where there are missions or trading posts, would certainly have starved to death but for the help given them by the traders and missionaries at those places. It is now declared by the signers of the memorial that scores of families, having lost their heads by starvation, are now per-fectly helpless, and during the coming winter must either starve to death or eat one another unless help comes. Heart-rending stories of suffering and cannibalism continue to come in from what was once the buffalo plains.

If ever thoughtless people were punished for their reckless improvi-dence, the Indians and half-breeds of the Northwest Territory are now paying the penalty for the wasteful slaughter of the buffalo a few short years ago. The buffalo is his own avenger, to an extent his remorseless slayers little dreamed he ever could be.

VIII. Preservation of the Species from Absolute Extinction.

There is reason to fear that unless the United States Government takes the matter in hand and makes a special effort to prevent it, the pure-blood bison will be lost irretrievably through mixture with do-mestic breeds and through in-and-in breeding.

The fate of the Yellowstone Park herd is, to say the least, highly un-certain. A distinguished Senator, who is deeply interested in legisla-tion for the protection of the National Park reservation, has declared that the pressure from railway corporations, which are seeking a foot-hold in the park, has become so great and so aggressive that he fears the park will "eventually be broken up." In any such event, the destruc-tion of the herd of park buffaloes would be one of the very first results. If the park is properly maintained, however, it is to be hoped that the buffaloes now in it will remain there and increase indefinitely.

As yet there are only two captive buffaloes in the possession of the Government, viz, those in the Department of Living Animals of the Na-tional Museum, presented by Hon. E. G. Blackford, of New York. The buffaloes now in the Zoological Gardens of the country are but few in number, and unless special pains be taken to prevent it, by means of judicious exchanges, from time to time, these will rapidly deteriorate in size, and within a comparatively short time run out entirely, through continued in-and-in breeding. It is said that even the wild aurochs in the forests of Lithuania are decreasing in size and in number from this cause.

---

* It was the Cree Indians who used to practice impounding buffaloes, slaughtering a penful of two hundred head at a time with most fiendish glee, and leaving all but the very choicest of the meat to putrefy.

With private owners of captive buffaloes, the temptations to produce cross-breeds will be so great that it is more than likely the breeding of pure-blood buffaloes will be neglected. Indeed, unless some stockman like Mr. C. J. Jones takes particular pains to protect his full-blood buffaloes, and keep the breed absolutely pure, in twenty years there will not be a pure-blood animal of that species on any stock farm in this country. Under existing conditions, the constant tendency of the numerous domestic forms is to absorb and utterly obliterate the few wild ones.

If we may judge from the examples set us by European governments, it is clearly the duty of our Government to act in this matter, and act promptly, with a degree of liberality and promptness which can not be otherwise than highly gratifying to every American citizen and every friend of science throughout the world. The Fiftieth Congress, at its last session, responded to the call made upon it, and voted $200,000 for the establishment of a National Zoological Park in the District of Columbia on a grand scale. One of the leading purposes it is destined to serve is the preservation and breeding in comfortable, and so far as space is concerned, luxurious captivity of a number of fine specimens of every species of American quadruped now threatened with extermination.*

At least eight or ten buffaloes of pure breed should be secured very soon by the Zoological Park Commission, by gift if possible, and cared for with special reference to keeping the breed absolutely pure, and *keeping the herd from deteriorating and dying out through in-and-in breeding.*

The total expense would be trifling in comparison with the importance of the end to be gained, and in that way we might, in a small measure, atone for our neglect of the means which would have protected the great herds from extinction. In this way, by proper management, it will be not only possible but easy to preserve fine living representatives of this important species for centuries to come.

The result of continuing in-breeding is certain extinction. Its progress may be so slow as to make no impression upon the mind of a herd-owner, but the end is only a question of time. The fate of a majority of the herds of British wild cattle (*Bos urus*) warn us what to expect with the American bison under similar circumstances. Of the fourteen herds of wild cattle which were in existence in England and Scotland during the early part of the present century, direct descendants of the

---

* It is indeed an unbounded satisfaction to be able to now record the fact that this important task, in which every American citizen has a personal interest, is actually to be undertaken. Last year we could only say it ought to be undertaken. In its accomplishment, the Government expects the co-operation of private individuals all over the country in the form of gifts of desirable living animals, for no government could afford to purchase all the animals necessary for a great Zoological Garden, provide for their wants in a liberal way, and yet give the public free access to the collection, as is to be given to the National Zoological Park.

wild herds found in Great Britain, nine have become totally extinct through in-breeding.

The five herds remaining are those at Somerford Park, Blickling Hall, Woodbastwick, Chartley, and Chillingham.

PART III.—THE SMITHSONIAN EXPEDITION FOR MUSEUM SPECIMENS.

I. The Exploration.

During the first three months of the year 1886 it was ascertained by the writer, then chief taxidermist of the National Museum, that the extermination of the American bison had made most alarming progress. By extensive correspondence it was learned that the destruction of all the large herds, both North and South, was already an accomplished fact. While it was generally supposed that at least a few thousand individuals still inhabited the more remote and inaccessible regions of what once constituted the great northern buffalo range, it was found that the actual number remaining in the whole United States was probably less than three hundred.

By some authorities who were consulted it was considered an impossibility to procure a large series of specimens anywhere in this country, while others asserted positively that there were no wild buffaloes south of the British possessions save those in the Yellowstone National Park. Canadian authorities asserted with equal positiveness that none remained in their territory.

A careful inventory of the specimens in the collection of the National Museum revealed the fact that, with the exception of one mounted female skin, another unmounted, and one mounted skeleton of a male buffalo, the Museum was actually without presentable specimens of this most important and interesting mammal.

Besides those mentioned above, the collection contained only two old, badly mounted, and dilapidated skins, (one of which had been taken in summer, and therefore was not representative), an incomplete skeleton, some fragmentary skulls of no value, and two mounted heads. Thus it appeared that the Museum was unable to show a series of specimens, good or bad, or even one presentable male of good size.

In view of this alarming state of affairs, coupled with the already declared extinction of *Bison americanus*, the Secretary of the Smithsonian Institution, Prof. Spencer F. Baird, determined to send a party into the field at once to find wild buffalo, if any were still living, and in case any were found to collect a number of specimens. Since it seemed highly uncertain whether any other institution, or any private individual, would have the opportunity to collect a large supply of specimens before it became too late, it was decided by the Secretary that the Smithsonian Institution should undertake the task of providing for the future as liberally as possible. For the benefit of the smaller scientific museums of the country, and for others which will come into existence during the next half century, it was resolved to collect at all hazards, in case buffalo could be found, between eighty and one hundred specimens of various kinds, of which from twenty to thirty should be skins, an equal number should be complete skeletons, and of skulls at least fifty.

In view of the great scarcity of buffalo and the general belief that it might be a work of some months to find any specimens, even if it were possible to find any at all, it was determined not to risk the success of the undertaking by delaying it until the regular autumn hunting season, but to send a party into the field at once to prosecute a search. It was resolved to discover at all hazards the whereabouts of any buffalo that might still remain in this country in a wild state, and, if possible, to reach them before the shedding of their winter pelage. It very soon became apparent, however, that the latter would prove an utter impossibility.

Late in the month of April a letter was received from Dr. J. C. Merrill, United States Army, dated at Huntley, Montana, giving information of reports that buffalo were still to be found in three localities in the Northwest, viz: on the headwaters of the Powder River, Wyoming; in Judith Basin, Montana; and on Big Dry Creek, also in Montana. The reports in regard to the first two localities proved to be erroneous. It was ascertained to a reasonable certainty that there still existed in southwestern Dakota a small band of six or eight wild buffaloes, while from the Panhandle of Texas there came reports of the existence there, in small scattered bands, of about two hundred head. The buffalo known to be in Dakota were far too few in number to justify a long and expensive search, while those in Texas, on the Canadian River, were too difficult to reach to make it advisable to hunt them save as a last resort. It was therefore decided to investigate the localities named in the Northwest.

Through the courtesy of the Secretary of War, an order was sent to the officer commanding the Department of Dakota, requesting him to furnish the party, through the officers in command at Forts Keogh, Maginnis, and McKinney, such field transportation, escort, and camp equipage as might be necessary, and also to sell to the party such commissary stores as might be required, at cost price, plus 10 per cent. The Secretary of the Interior also favored the party with an order, directing all Indian agents, scouts, and others in the service of the Department to render assistance as far as possible when called upon.

In view of the public interest attaching to the results of the expedition, the railway transportation of the party to and from Montana was furnished entirely without cost to the Smithsonian Institution. For these valuable courtesies we gratefully acknowledge our obligations to Mr. Frank Thomson, of the Pennsylvania Railroad; Mr. Roswell Miller, of the Chicago, Milwaukee and St. Paul; and Mr. Robert Harris, of the Northern Pacific.

Under orders from the Secretary of the Smithsonian Institution, the writer left Washington on May 6, accompanied by A. H. Forney, assistant in the department of taxidermy, and George H. Hedley, of Medina, New York. It had been decided that Miles City, Montana, might properly be taken as the first objective point, and that town was reached on May 9.

Diligent inquiry in Miles City and at Fort Keogh, 2 miles distant, revealed the fact that no one knew of the presence of any wild buffalo anywhere in the Northwest, save within the protected limits of the Yellowstone Park. All inquiries elicited the same reply: "There are no buffalo any more, and you can't get any anywhere." Many persons who were considered good authority declared most positively that there was not a live buffalo in the vicinity of Big Dry Creek, nor anywhere between the Yellowstone and Missouri Rivers. An army officer from Fort Maginnis testified to the total absence of buffalo in the Judith Basin, and ranchmen from Wyoming asserted that none remained in the Powder River country.

Just at this time it was again reported to us, and most opportunely confirmed by Mr. Henry R. Phillips, owner of the L U-bar ranch on Little Dry Creek, that there still remained a chance to find a few buffalo in the country lying south of the Big Dry. On the other hand, other persons who seemed to be fully informed regarding that very region and the animal life it contained, assured us that not a single buffalo remained there, and that a search in that direction would prove fruitless. But the balance of evidence, however, seemed to lie in favor of the Big Dry country, and we resolved to hunt through it with all possible dispatch.

On the afternoon of May 13 we crossed the Yellowstone and started northwest up the trail which leads along Sunday Creek. Our entire party consisted of the two assistants already mentioned, a non-commissioned officer, Sergeant Garone, and four men from the Fifth Infantry acting as escort; Private Jones, also from the Fifth Infantry, detailed to act as our cook, and a teamster. Our conveyance consisted of a six-mule team, which, like the escort, was ordered out for twenty days only, and provided accordingly. Before leaving Miles City we purchased two saddle-horses for use in hunting, the equipments for which were furnished by the ordnance department at Fort Keogh.

During the first two days' travel through the bad lands north of the Yellowstone no mammals were seen save prairie-dogs and rabbits. On the third day a few antelope were seen, but none killed. It is to be borne in mind that this entire region is absolutely treeless everywhere save along the margins of the largest streams. Bushes are also entirely absent, with the exception of sage-brush, and even that does not occur to any extent on the divides.

On the third day two young buck antelopes were shot at the Red Buttes. One had already commenced to shed his hair, but the other had not quite reached that point. We prepared the skin of the first specimen and the skeleton of the other. This was the only good antelope skin we obtained in the spring, those of all the other specimens taken being quite worthless on account of the looseness of the hair. During the latter part of May, and from that time on until the long winter hair is completely shed, it falls off in handfuls at the slightest pressure, leaving the skin clad only with a thin growth of new, mouse-colored hair an eighth of an inch long.

After reaching Little Dry Creek and hunting through the country on the west side of it nearly to its confluence with the Big Dry we turned southwest, and finally went into permanent camp on Phillips Creek, 8 miles above the LU-bar ranch and 4 miles from the Little Dry. At that point we were about 80 miles from Miles City.

From information furnished us by Mr. Phillips and the cowboys in his employ, we were assured that about thirty-five head of buffalo ranged in the bad lands between Phillips Creek and the Musselshell River and south of the Big Dry. This tract of country was about 40 miles long from east to west by 25 miles wide, and therefore of about 1,000 square miles in area. Excepting two temporary cowboy camps it was totally uninhabited by man, treeless, without any running streams, save in winter and spring, and was mostly very hilly and broken.

In this desolate and inhospitable country the thirty-five buffaloes alluded to had been seen, first on Sand Creek, then at the head of the Big Porcupine, again near the Musselshell, and latest near the head of the Little Dry. As these points were all from 15 to 30 miles distant from each other, the difficulty of finding such a small herd becomes apparent.

Although Phillips Creek was really the eastern boundary of the buffalo country, it was impossible for a six-mule wagon to proceed beyond it, at least at that point. Having established a permanent camp, the Government wagon and its escort returned to Fort Keogh, and we proceeded to hunt through the country between Sand Creek and the Little Dry. The absence of nearly all the cowboys on the spring round-up, which began May 20, threatened to be a serious drawback to us, as we greatly needed the services of a man who was acquainted with the country. We had with us as a scout and guide a Cheyenne Indian, named Dog, but it soon became apparent that he knew no more about the country than we did. Fortunately, however, we succeeded in occasionally securing the services of a cowboy, which was of great advantage to us.

It was our custom to ride over the country daily, each day making a circuit through a new locality, and covering as much ground as it was possible to ride over in a day. It was also our custom to take trips of from two to four days in length, during which we carried our blankets and rations upon our horses and camped wherever night overtook us, provided water could be found.

Our first success consisted in the capture of a buffalo calf, which from excessive running had become unable to keep up with its mother, and had been left behind. The calf was caught alive without any difficulty, and while two of the members of our party carried it to camp across a horse, the other two made a vigorous effort to discover the band of adult animals. The effort was unsuccessful, for, besides the calf, no other buffaloes were seen.

Ten days after the above event two bull buffaloes were met with on the Little Dry, 15 miles above the L U-bar ranch, one of which was overtaken and killed, but the other got safely away. The shedding of the winter coat was in full progress. On the head, neck, and shoulders the old hair had been entirely replaced by the new, although the two coats were so matted together that the old hair clung in tangled masses to the other. The old hair was brown and weather-beaten, but the new, which was from 3 to 6 inches long, had a peculiar bluish-gray appearance. On the head the new hair was quite black, and contrasted oddly with the lighter color. On the body and hind quarters there were large patches of skin which were perfectly bare, between which lay large patches of old, woolly, brown hair. This curious condition gave the animal a very unkempt and "seedy" appearance, the effect of which was heightened by the long, shaggy locks of old, weather-beaten hair which clung to the new coat of the neck and shoulders like tattered signals of distress, ready to be blown away by the first gust of wind.

This specimen was a large one, measuring 5 feet 4 inches in height. Inasmuch as the skin was not in condition to mount, we took only the skeleton, entire, and the skin of the head and neck.

The capture of the calf and the death of this bull proved conclusively that there were buffaloes in that region, and also that they were breeding in comparative security. The extent of the country they had to range over made it reasonably certain that their number would not be diminished to any serious extent by the cowboys on the spring round-up, although it was absolutely certain that in a few months the members of that band would all be killed. The report of the existence of a herd of thirty-five head was confirmed later by cowboys, who had actually seen the animals, and killed two of them merely for sport, as usual. They saved a few pounds of hump meat, and all the rest became food for the wolves and foxes.

It was therefore resolved to leave the buffaloes entirely unmolested until autumn, and then, when the robes would be in the finest condition, return for a hunt on a liberal scale. Accordingly, it was decided to return to Washington without delay, and a courier was dispatched with a request for transportation to carry our party back to Fort Keogh.

While awaiting the arrival of the wagons, a cowboy in the employ of the Phillips Land and Cattle Company killed a solitary bull buffalo about 15 miles west of our camp, near Sand Creek. This animal had completely shed the hair on his body and hind quarters. In addition to the preservation of his entire skeleton, we prepared the skin also, as an example of the condition of the buffalo immediately after shedding.

On June 6 the teams from Fort Keogh arrived, and we immediately returned to Miles City, taking with us our live buffalo calf, two fresh buffalo skeletons, three bleached skeletons, seven skulls, one skin entire, and one head skin, in addition to a miscellaneous collection of skins and skeletons of smaller mammals and birds. On reaching Miles City we hastily packed and shipped our collection, and, taking the calf with us, returned at once to Washington.

II. THE HUNT.

On September 24 I arrived at Miles City a second time, fully equipped for a protracted hunt for buffalo; this time accompanied only by W. Harvey Brown, a student of the University of Kansas, as field assistant, having previously engaged three cowboys as guides and hunters—Irwin Boyd, James McNaney, and L. S. Russell. Messrs. Boyd and Russell were in Miles City awaiting my arrival, and Mr. McNaney joined us in the field a few days later. Mr. Boyd acted as my foreman during the entire hunt, a position which he filled to my entire satisfaction.

Thanks to the energy and good-will of the officers at Fort Keogh, of which Lieutenant-Colonel Cochran was then in command, our transportation, camp equipage, and stores were furnished without an hour's delay. We purchased two months' supplies of commissary stores, a team, and two saddle-horses, and hired three more horses, a light wagon, and a set of double harness. Each of the cowboys furnished one horse; so that in our outfit we had ten head, a team, and two good saddle-horses for each hunter. The worst feature of the whole question of subsistence was the absolute necessity of hauling a supply of grain from Miles City into the heart of the buffalo country for our ten horses. For such work as they had to encounter it was necessary to feed them constantly and liberally with oats in order to keep them in condition to do their work. We took with us 2,000 pounds of oats, and by the beginning of November as much more had to be hauled up to us.

Thirty six hours after our arrival in Miles City our outfit was complete, and we crossed the Yellowstone and started up the Sunday Creek trail. We had from Fort Keogh a six-mule team, an escort of four men, in charge of Sergeant Bayliss, and an old veteran of more than twenty years' service, from the Fifth Infantry, Private Patrick McCanna, who was detailed to act as cook and camp-guard for our party during our stay in the field.

On September 29 we reached Tow's ranch, the **HV**, on Big Dry Creek (erroneously called Big Timber Creek on most maps of Montana), at the mouth of Sand Creek, which here flows into it from the southwest. This point is said to be 90 miles from Miles City. Here we received our freight from the six-mule wagon, loaded it with bleached skeletons and skulls of buffalo, and started it back to the post. One member of the escort, Private C. S. West, who was then on two months' furlough, elected to join our party for the hunt, and accordingly remained with us to its

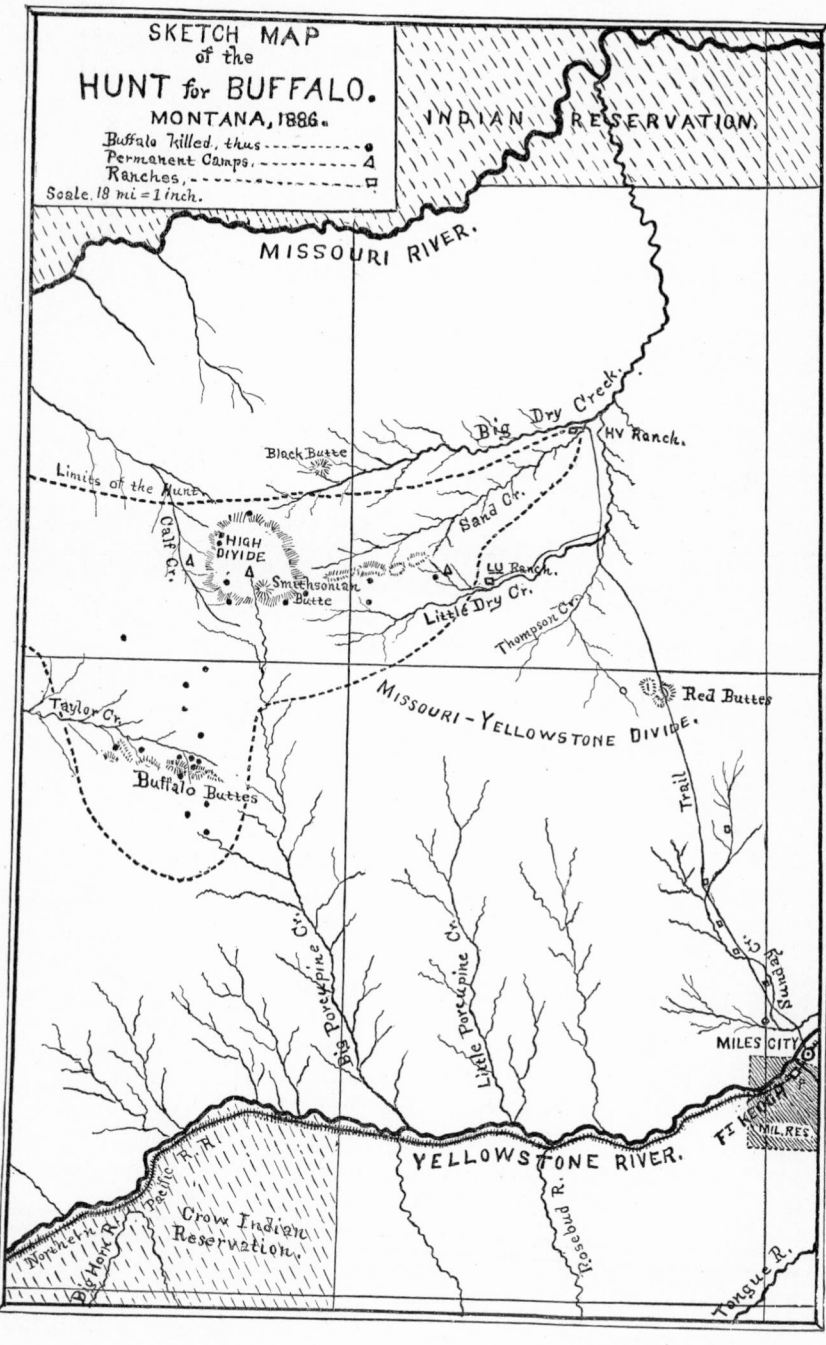

close. Leaving half of our freight stored at the **HV** ranch, we loaded the remainder upon our own wagon, and started up Sand Creek.

At this point the hunt began. As the wagon and extra horses proceeded up the Sand Creek trail in the care of W. Harvey.Brown, the three cowboys and I paired off, and while two hunted through the country along the south side of the creek, the others took the north. The whole of the country bordering Sand Creek, quite up to its source, consists of rugged hills and ridges, which sometimes rise to considerable height, cut between by great yawning ravines and hollows, such as persecuted game loves to seek shelter in. Inasmuch as the buffalo we were in search of had been seen hiding in those ravines, it became necessary to search through them with systematic thoroughness; a proceeding which was very wearing upon our horses. Along the south side of Sand Creek, near its source, the divide between it and Little Dry Creek culminates in a chain of high, flat-topped buttes, whose summits bear a scanty growth of stunted pines, which serve to make them conspicuous landmarks. On some maps these insignificant little buttes are shown as mountains, under the name of "Piny Buttes."

It was our intention to go to the head of Sand Creek, and beyond, in case buffaloes were not found earlier. Immediately westward of its source there is a lofty level plateau, about 3 miles square, which, by common consent, we called the High Divide. It is the highest ground anywhere between the Big Dry and the Yellowstone, and is the starting point of streams that run northward into the Missouri and Big Dry, eastward into Sand Creek and the Little Dry, southward into Porcupine Creek and the Yellowstone, and westward into the Musselshell. On three sides—north, east, and south—it is surrounded by wild and rugged butte country, and its sides are scored by intricate systems of great yawning ravines and hollows, steep-sided and very deep, and bad lands of the worst description.

By the 12th of October the hunt had progressed up Sand Creek to its source, and westward across the High Divide to Calf Creek, where we found a hole of wretchedly bad water and went into permanent camp. We considered that the spot we selected would serve us as a key to the promising country that lay on three sides of it, and our surmise that the buffalo were in the habit of hiding in the heads of those great ravines around the High Divide soon proved to be correct. Our camp at the head of Calf Creek was about 20 miles east of the Musselshell River, 40 miles south of the Missouri, and about 135 miles from Miles City, as the trail ran. Four miles north of us, also on Calf Creek, was the line camp of the **STV** ranch, owned by Messrs. J. H. Conrad & Co., and 18 miles east, near the head of Sand Creek, was the line camp of the **N**-bar ranch, owned by Mr. Newman. At each of these camps there were generally from two to four cowboys. From all these gentlemen we received the utmost courtesy and hospitality on all occasions, and all the information in regard to buffalo which it was in their power to give. On many occasions they rendered us valuable assistance, which is hereby gratefully acknowledged.

We saw no buffalo, nor any signs of any, until October 13. On that day, while L. S. Russell was escorting our second load of freight across the High Divide, he discovered a band of seven buffaloes lying in the head of a deep ravine. He fired upon them, but killed none, and when they dashed away he gave chase and followed them 2 or 3 miles. Being mounted on a tired horse, which was unequal to the demands of the chase, he was finally distanced by the herd, which took a straight course and ran due south. As it was then nearly night, nothing further could be done that day except to prepare for a vigorous chase on the morrow. Everything was got in perfect readiness for an early start, and by daybreak the following morning the three cowboys and the writer were mounted on our best horses, and on our way through the bad lands to take up the trail of the seven buffaloes.

Shortly after sunrise we found the trail, not far from the head of Calf Creek, and followed it due south. We left the rugged butte region behind us, and entered a tract of country quite unlike anything we had found before. It was composed of a succession of rolling hills and deep hollows, smooth enough on the surface, to all appearances, but like a desert of sand-hills to traverse. The dry soil was loose and crumbly, like loose ashes or scoriæ, and the hoofs of our horses sank into it half-way to the fetlocks at every step. But there was another feature which was still worse. The whole surface of the ground was cracked and seamed with a perfect net-work of great cracks, into which our horses stepped every yard or so, and sank down still farther, with many a tiresome wrench of the joints. It was terrible ground to go over. To make it as bad as possible, a thick growth of sage-brush or else grease-wood was everywhere present for the horses to struggle through, and when it came to dragging a loaded wagon across that 12-mile stretch of "bad grounds" or "gumbo ground," as it was called, it was killing work.

But in spite of the character of this ground, in one way it was a benefit to us. Owing to its looseness on the surface we were able to track the buffaloes through it with the greatest ease, whereas on any other ground in that country it would have been almost impossible. We followed the trail due south for about 20 miles, which brought us to the head of a small stream called Taylor Creek. Here the bad grounds ended, and in the grassy country which lay beyond, tracking was almost impossible. Just at noon we rode to a high point, and on scanning the hills and hollows with the binocular discovered the buffaloes lying at rest on the level top of a small butte 2 miles away. The original bunch of seven had been joined by an equal number.

We crept up to within 200 yards of the buffaloes, which was as close as we could go, fired a volley at them just as they lay, and did not even kill a calf! Instantly they sprang up and dashed away at astonishing speed, heading straight for the sheltering ravines around the High Divide.

We had a most exciting and likewise dangerous chase after the herd through a vast prairie-dog town, honey-combed with holes just right for a running horse to thrust a leg in up to the knee and snap it off like a pipe-stem, and across fearfully wide gullies that either had to be leaped or fallen into. McNaney killed a fine old bull and a beautiful two-year old, or "spike" bull, out of this herd, while I managed to kill a cow and another large old bull, making four for that day, all told. This herd of fourteen head was the largest that we saw during the entire hunt.

Two days later, when we were on the spot with the wagon to skin our game and haul in the hides, four more buffaloes were discovered within 2 miles of us, and while I worked on one of the large bull skins to save it from spoiling, the cowboys went after the buffalo, and by a really brilliant exploit killed them all. The first one to fall was an old cow, which was killed at the beginning of the chase, the next was an old bull, who was brought down about 5 miles from the scene of the first attack, then 2 miles farther on a yearling calf was killed. The fourth buffalo, an immense old bull, was chased fully 12 miles before he was finally brought down.

The largest bull fell about 8 miles from our temporary camp, in the opposite direction from that in which our permanent camp lay, and at about 3 o'clock in the afternoon. There not being time enough in which to skin him completely and reach our rendezvous before dark, Messrs. McNaney and Boyd dressed the carcass to preserve the meat, partly skinned the legs, and came to camp.

As early as possible the next morning we drove to the carcass with the wagon, to prepare both skin and skeleton and haul them in. When we reached it we found that during the night a gang of Indians had robbed us of our hard-earned spoil. They had stolen the skin and all the eatable meat, broken up the leg-bones to get at the marrow, and even cut out the tongue. And to injury the skulking thieves had added insult. Through laziness they had left the head unskinned, but on one side of it they had smeared the hair with red war-paint, the other side they had daubed with yellow, and around the base of one horn they had tied a strip of red flannel as a signal of defiance. Of course they had left for parts unknown, and we never saw any signs of them afterward. The gang visited the LU-bar ranch a few days later, so we learned subsequently. It was then composed of eleven braves (!), who claimed to be Assinniboines, and were therefore believed to be Piegans, the most notorious horse and cattle thieves in the Northwest.

On October 22d Mr. Russell ran down in a fair chase a fine bull buffalo, and killed him in the rough country bordering the High Divide on the south. This was the ninth specimen. On the 26th we made another trip with the wagon to the Buffalo Buttes, as, for the sake of convenience, we had named the group of buttes near which eight head had already been taken. While Mr. Brown and I were getting the wagon across the bad grounds, Messrs. McNaney and Boyd discovered a solitary bull buffalo feeding in a ravine within a quarter of a mile of our intended camping place, and the former stalked him and killed him at long range. The buffalo had all been attracted to that locality by some springs which lay between two groups of hills, and which was the only water within a radius of about 15 miles. In addition to water, the grass around the Buffalo Buttes was most excellent.

During all this time we shot antelope and coyotes whenever an opportunity offered, and preserved the skins and skeletons of the finest until we had obtained a very fine series of both. At this season the pelts of these animals were in the finest possible condition, the hair having attained its maximum length and density, and, being quite new, had lost none of its brightness of color, either by wear or the action of the weather. Along Sand Creek and all around the High Divide antelope were moderately plentiful (but really scarce in comparison with their former abundance), so much so that had we been inclined to slaughter we could have killed a hundred head or more, instead of the twenty that we shot as specimens and for their flesh. We have it to say that from first to last not an antelope was killed which was not made use of to the fullest extent.

On the 31st of October, Mr. Boyd and I discovered a buffalo cow and yearling calf in the ravines north of the High Divide, within 3 miles of our camp, and killed them both. The next day Private West arrived with a six mule team from Fort Keogh, in charge of Corporal Clafer and three men. This wagon brought us another 2,000 pounds of oats and various commissary stores. When it started back, on November 3, we sent by it all the skins and skeletons of buffalo, antelope, etc., which we had collected up to that date, which made a heavy load for the six mules. On this same day Mr. McNaney killed two young cow buffaloes in the bad lands south of the High Divide, which brought our total number up to fourteen.

On the night of the 3d the weather turned very cold, and on the day following we experienced our first snow-storm. By that time the water in the hole, which up to that time had supplied our camp, became so thick with mud and filth that it was unendurable; and having discovered a fine pool of pure water in the bottom of a little cañon on the southern slope of the High Divide we moved to it forthwith. It was really the upper spring of the main fork of the Big Porcupine, and a finer situation for a camp does not exist in that whole region. The spot which nature made for us was sheltered on all sides by the high walls of the cañon, within easy reach of an inexhaustible supply of good water, and also within reach of a fair supply of dry fire-wood, which we found half a mile below. This became our last permanent camp, and its advantages made up for the barrenness and discomfort of our camp on Calf Creek. Immediately south of us, and 2 miles distant there rose a lofty conical butte about 600 feet high, which forms a very conspicuous landmark from the south. We were told that it was visible from 40 miles down the Porcupine. Strange to say, this valuable landmark was without a name, so far as we could learn; so, for our own convenience, we christened it Smithsonian Butte.

The two buffalo cows that Mr. McNaney killed just before we moved our camp seemed to be the last in the country, for during the following week we scouted for 15 miles in three directions, north, east, and south, without finding as much as a hoof-print. At last we decided to go away and give that country absolute quiet for a week, in the hope that some more buffalo would come into it. Leaving McCanna and West to take care of the camp, we loaded a small assortment of general equipage into the wagon and pulled about 25 miles due west to the Musselshell River.

We found a fine stream of clear water, flowing over sand and pebbles, with heavy cottonwood timber and thick copses of willow along its banks, which afforded cover for white-tailed deer. In the rugged brakes, which led from the level river bottom into a labyrinth of ravines and gullies, ridges and hog-backs, up to the level of the high plateau above, we found a scanty growth of stunted cedars and pines, which once sheltered great numbers of mule deer, elk, and bear. Now, however, few remain, and these are very hard to find. Even when found, the deer are nearly always young. Although we killed five mule deer and five white-tails, we did not kill even one fine buck, and the only one we saw on the whole trip was a long distance off. We saw fresh tracks of elk, and also grizzly bear, but our most vigorous efforts to discover the animals themselves always ended in diappointment. The many bleaching skulls and antlers of elk and deer, which we found everywhere we went, afforded proof of what that country had been as a home for wild animals only a few years ago. We were not a little surprised at finding the fleshless carcasses of three head of cattle that had been killed and eaten by bears within a few months.

In addition to ten deer, we shot three wild geese, seven sharp-tailed grouse, eleven sage grouse, nine Bohemian waxwings, and a magpie, for their skeletons. We made one trip of several miles up the Musselshell, and another due west, almost to the Bull Mountains, but no signs of buffalo were found. The weather at this time was quite cold, the thermometer registering 6 degrees below zero; but, in spite of the fact that we were without shelter and had to bivouac in the open, we were, generally speaking, quite comfortable.

Having found no buffalo by the 17th, we felt convinced that we ought to return to our permanent camp, and did so on that day. Having brought back nearly half a wagon-load of specimens in the flesh or half skinned, it was absolutely necessary that I should remain at camp all the next day. While I did so, Messrs. McNaney and Boyd rode over to the Buffalo Buttes, found four fine old buffalo cows, and, after a hard chase, killed them all.

Under the circumstances, this was the most brilliant piece of work of the entire hunt. As the four cows dashed past the hunters at the Buffalo Buttes, heading for the High Divide, fully 20 miles distant, McNaney killed one cow, and two others went off wounded. Of course the cowboys gave chase. About 12 miles from the starting-point one of the wounded cows left her companions, was headed off by Boyd, and killed. About 6 miles beyond that one, McNaney overhauled the third cow and killed her, but the fourth one got away for a short time. While McNaney skinned the third cow and dressed the carcass to preserve the meat, Boyd took their now thoroughly exhausted horses to camp and procured fresh mounts. On returning to McNaney they set out in pursuit of the fourth cow, chased her across the High Divide, within a mile or so of our camp, and into the ravines on the northern slope, where she was killed. She met her death nearly if not quite 25 miles from the spot where the first one fell.

The death of these four cows brought our number of buffaloes up to eighteen, and made us think about the possibilities of getting thirty. As we were proceeding to the Buffalo Buttes on the day after the "kill" to gather in the spoil, Mr. Brown and I taking charge of the wagon, Messrs. McNaney and Boyd went ahead in order to hunt. When within about 5 miles of the Buttes we came unexpectedly upon our companions, down in a hollow, busily engaged in skinning another old cow, which they had discovered traveling across the bad grounds, waylaid, and killed.

We camped that night on our old ground at the Buffalo Buttes, and although we all desired to remain a day or two and hunt for more buffalo, the peculiar appearance of the sky in the northwest, and the condition of the atmosphere, warned us that a change of weather was imminent. Accordingly, the following morning we decided without hesitation that it was best to get back to camp that day, and it soon proved very fortunate for us that we so decided.

Feeling that by reason of my work on the specimens I had been deprived of a fair share of the chase, I arranged for Mr. Boyd to accompany the wagon on the return trip, that I might hunt through the bad lands west of the Buffalo Buttes, which I felt must contain some buffalo. Mr. Russell went northeast and Mr. McNaney accompanied me. About 4 miles from our late camp we came suddenly upon a fine old solitary bull, feeding in a hollow between two high and precipitous ridges. After a short but sharp chase I succeeded in getting a fair shot at him, and killed him with a ball which broke his left humerus and passed into his lungs. He was the only large bull killed on the entire trip by a single shot. He proved to be a very fine specimen, measuring 5 feet 6 inches in height at the shoulders. The wagon was overtaken and called back to get the skin, and while it was coming I took a complete series of measurements and sketches of him as he lay.

Although we removed the skin very quickly, and lost no time in again starting the wagon to our permanent camp, the delay occasioned by the death of our twentieth buffalo,—which occurred on November 20, precisely two months from the date of our leaving Washington to collect twenty buffalo, if possible,—caused us all to be caught in a snow-storm, which burst upon us from the northwest. The wagon had to be abandoned about 12 miles from camp in the bad lands. Mr. Brown packed the bedding on one of the horses and rode the other, he and Boyd reaching camp about 9 o'clock that night in a blinding snow-storm. Of course the skins in the wagon were treated with preservatives and covered up. It proved to be over a week that the wagon and its load had to remain thus abandoned before it was possible to get to it and bring it to camp, and even then the task was one of great difficulty. In this connection I can not refrain from recording the fact that the services rendered by Mr. W. Harvey Brown on all such trying occasions as the above were invaluable. He displayed the utmost zeal and intelligence, not only in the more agreeable kinds of work and sport incident to the hunt, but also in the disagreeable drudgery, such as team-driving and working on half-frozen specimens in bitter cold weather.

The storm which set in on the 20th soon developed into a regular blizzard. A fierce and bitter cold wind swept down from the northwest, driving the snow before it in blinding gusts. Had our camp been poorly sheltered we would have suffered, but at it was we were fairly comfortable.

Having thus completed our task (of getting twenty buffaloes), we were anxious to get out of that fearful country before we should get caught in serious difficulties with the weather, and it was arranged that Private C. S. West should ride to Fort Keogh as soon as possible, with a request for transportation. By the third day, November 23, the storm had abated sufficiently that Private West declared his willingness to start. It was a little risky, but as he was to make only 10 miles the first day and stop at the N-bar camp on Sand Creek, it was thought safe to let him go. He dressed himself warmly, took my revolver, in order not to be hampered with a rifle, and set out.

The next day was clear and fine, and we remarked it as an assurance of Mr. West's safety during his ride from Sand Creek to the LU-bar ranch, his second stopping-place. The distance was about 25 miles, through bad lands all the way, and it was the only portion of the route which caused me anxiety for our courier's safety. The snow on the levels was less than 6 inches deep, the most of it having been blown into drifts and hollows; but although the coulées were all filled level to the top, our courier was a man of experience and would know how to avoid them.

The 25th day of November was the most severe day of the storm, the mercury in our sheltered cañon sinking to —16 degrees. We had hoped to kill at least five more buffaloes by the time Private West should arrive with the wagons; but when at the end of a week the storm had spent itself, the snow was so deep that hunting was totally impossible save in the vicinity of camp, where there was nothing to kill. We expected the wagons by the 3d of December, but they did not come that day nor within the next three. By the 6th the snow had melted off sufficiently that a buffalo hunt was once more possible, and Mr. McNaney and I decided to make a final trip to the Buffalo Buttes. The state of the ground made it impossible for us to go there and return the same day, so we took a pack-horse and arranged to camp out.

When a little over half-way to our old rendezvous we came upon three buffaloes in the bad grounds, one of which was an enormous old bull, the next largest was an adult cow, and the third a two-year-old heifer. Mr. McNaney promptly knocked down the old cow, while I devoted my attention to the bull; but she presently got up and made off unnoticed at the precise moment Mr. McNaney was absorbed in watching my efforts to bring down the old bull. After a short chase my horse carried me alongside my buffalo, and as he turned toward me I gave him a shot through the shoulder, breaking the fore leg and bringing him promptly to the ground. I then turned immediately to pursue the young cow, but by that time she had got on the farther side of a deep gully which was filled with snow, and by the time I got my horse safely across she had distanced me. I then rode back to the old bull. When he saw me coming he got upon his feet and ran a short distance, but was easily overtaken. He then stood at bay, and halting within 30 yards of him I enjoyed the rare opportunity of studying a live bull buffalo of the largest size on foot on his native heath. I even made an outline sketch of him in my note-book. Having studied his form and outlines as much as was really necessary, I gave him a final shot through the lungs, which soon ended his career.

This was a truly magnificent specimen in every respect. He was a "stub-horn" bull, about eleven years old, much larger every way than any of the others we collected. His height at the shoulder was 5 feet 8 inches perpendicular, or 2 inches more than the next largest of our collection. His hair was in remarkably fine condition, being long, fine, thick, and well colored. The hair in his frontlet is 16 inches in length, and the thick coat of shaggy, straw-colored tufts which covered his neck and shoulders measured 4 inches. His girth behind the fore leg was 8 feet 4 inches, and his weight was estimated at 1,600 pounds.

I was delighted with our remarkably good fortune in securing such a prize, for, owing to the rapidity with which the large buffaloes are being found and killed off these days, I had not hoped to capture a really old individual. Nearly every adult bull we took carried old bullets in his body, and from this one we took four of various sizes that had been fired

TROPHIES OF THE HUNT.

Mounted by the author in the U. S. National Museum.

Reproduced from the *Cosmopolitan Magazine*, by permission of the publishers.

into him on various occasions. One was found sticking fast in one of the lumbar vertebræ.*

After a chase of several miles Mr. McNaney finally overhauled his cow and killed her, which brought the number of buffaloes taken on the fall hunt up to twenty-two. We spent the night at the Buffalo Buttes and returned to camp the next day. Neither on that day nor the one following did the wagons arrive, and on the evening of the 8th we learned from the cowboys of the N-bar camp on Sand Creek that our courier, Private West, had not been seen or heard from since he left their camp on November 24, and evidently had got lost and frozen to death in the bad lands.

The next day we started out to search for Private West, or news of him, and spent the night with Messrs. Brodhurst and Andrews, at their camp on Sand Creek. On the 10th, Mr. McNaney and I hunted through the bad lands over the course our courier should have taken, while Messrs. Russell and Brodhurst looked through the country around the head of the Little Dry. When McNaney and I reached the LU-bar ranch that night we were greatly rejoiced at finding that West was alive, although badly frost-bitten, and in Fort Keogh.

It appears that instead of riding due east to the LU bar ranch, he lost his way in the bad lands, where the buttes all look alike when covered with snow, and rode southwest. It is at all times an easy matter for even a cowboy to get lost in Montana if the country is new to him, and when there is snow on the ground the difficulty of finding one's way is increased tenfold. There is not only the danger of losing one's way, but the still greater danger of getting ingulfed in a deep coulée full of loose snow, which may easily cause both horse and rider to perish miserably. Even the most experienced riders sometimes ride into coulées which are level full of snow and hidden from sight.

Private West's experience was a terrible one, and also a wonderful case of self-preservation. It shows what a man with a cool head and plenty of grit can go through and live. When he left us he wore two undershirts, a heavy blanket shirt, a soldier's blouse and overcoat, two pairs of drawers, a pair of soldier's woolen trousers, and a pair of overalls. On his feet he wore three pairs of socks, a pair of *low shoes* with canvas leggins, and he started with his feet tied up in burlaps. His head and hands were also well protected. He carried a 38-caliber revolver, but, by a great oversight, only six matches. When he left the N-bar camp, instead of going due east toward the LU-bar ranch, he swung around and went southwest, clear around the head of the Little Dry, and finally struck the Porcupine south of our camp. The first night out he made a fire with sage-brush, and kept it going all night. The second night he also had a fire, but it took his last match to make it. During the first three days he had no food, but on the fourth he

---

* This specimen is now the commanding figure of the group of buffalo which has recently been placed on exhibition in the Museum.

shot a sage-cock with his revolver, and ate it raw. This effort, however, cost him his last cartridge. Through hard work and lack of food his pony presently gave out, and necessitated long and frequent stops for rest. West's feet threatened to freeze, and he cut off the skirts of his overcoat to wrap them with, in place of the gunny sacking, that had been worn to rags. Being afraid to go to sleep at night, he slept by snatches in the warmest part of the day, while resting his horse.

On the 5th day he began to despair of succor, although he still toiled southward through the bad lands toward the Yellowstone, where people lived. On the envelopes which contained my letters he kept a diary of his wanderings, which could tell his story when the cowboys would find his body on the spring round-up.

On the afternoon of the sixth day he found a trail and followed it until nearly night, when he came to Cree's sheep ranch, and found the solitary ranchman at home. The warm-hearted frontiersman gave the starving wanderers, man and horse, such a welcome as they stood in need of. West solemnly declares that in twenty-four hours he ate a whole sheep. After two or three days of rest and feeding both horse and rider were able to go on, and in course of time reached Fort Keogh.

Without the loss of a single day Colonel Gibson started three teams and an escort up to us, and notwithstanding his terrible experience, West had the pluck to accompany them as guide. His arrival among us once more was like the dead coming to life again. The train reached our camp on the 13th, and on the 15th we pulled out for Miles City, loaded to the wagon-bows with specimens, forage, and camp plunder.

From our camp down to the **HV** ranch, at the mouth of Sand Creek, the trail was in a terrible condition. But, thanks to the skill and judgment of the train-master, Mr. Ed. Haskins, and his two drivers, who also knew their business well, we got safely and in good time over the dangerous part of our road. Whenever our own tired and overloaded team got stuck in the mud, or gave out, there was always a pair of mules ready to hitch on and help us out. As a train-master, Mr. Haskins was a perfect model, skillful, pushing, good-tempered, and very obliging.

From the **HV** ranch to Miles City the trail was in fine condition, and we went in as rapidly as possible, fearing to be caught in the snow-storm which threatened us all the way in. We reached Miles City on December 20, with our collection complete and in fine condition, and the next day a snow-storm set in which lasted until the 25th, and resulted in over a foot of snow. The ice running in the Yellowstone stopped all the ferry-boats, and it was with good reason that we congratulated ourselves on the successful termination of our hunt at that particular time. Without loss of time Mr. Brown and I packed our collection, which filled twenty-one large cases, turned in our equipage at Fort Keogh, sold our horses, and started on our homeward journey. In due course of time the collection reached the Museum in good condition, and a series of the best specimens it contains has already been mounted.

At this point it is proper to acknowledge our great indebtedness to the Secretary of War for the timely co-operation of the War Department, which rendered the expedition possible. Our thanks are due to the officers who were successively in command at Fort Keogh during our work, Col. John D. Wilkins, Col. George M. Gibson, and Lieut. Col. M. A. Cochran, and their various staff officers; particularly Lieut. C. B. Thompson, quartermaster, and Lieut. H. K. Bailey, adjutant. It is due these officers to state that everything we asked for was cheerfully granted with a degree of promptness which contributed very greatly to the success of the hunt, and lightened its labors very materially.

I have already acknowledged our indebtedness to the officers of the Pennsylvania; the Chicago, Milwaukee and St. Paul; and Northern Pacific railways for the courtesies so liberally extended in our emergency. I take pleasure in adding that all the officers and employés of the Northern Pacific Railway with whom we had any relations, particularly Mr. C. S. Fee, general passenger and ticket agent, treated our party with the utmost kindness and liberality throughout the trip. We are in like manner indebted to the officers of the Chicago, Milwaukee and St. Paul Railway for valuable privileges granted with the utmost cordiality.

Our thanks are also due to Dr. J. C. Merrill, and to Mr. Henry R. Phillips, of the Phillips Land and Cattle Company, on Little Dry Creek, for valuable information at a critical moment, and to the latter for hospitality and assistance in various ways, t times when both were keenly appreciated.

Counting the specimens taken in the spring, our total catch of buffalo amounted to twenty-five head, and constituted as complete and fine a series as could be wished for. I am inclined to believe that in size and general quality of pelage the adult bull and cow selected and mounted for our Museum group are not to be surpassed, even if they are ever equaled, by others of their kind.

The different ages and sexes were thus represented in our collection: 10 old bulls, 1 young bull, 7 old cows, 4 young cows, 2 yearling calves, 1 three-months calf*; total, 25 specimens.

Our total collection of specimens of *Bison americanus*, including everything taken, contained the following: 24 fresh skins, 1 head skin, 8 fresh skeletons, 8 dry skeletons, 51 dry skulls, 2 fœtal young; total, 94 specimens.

Our collection as a whole also included a fine series of skins and skeletons of antelope, deer of two species, coyotes, jack rabbits, sage grouse (of which we prepared twenty-four rough skeletons for the Department of Comparative Anatomy), sharp-tailed grouse, and specimens of all the other species of birds and small mammals to be found in

* Caught alive, but died in captivity July 26, 1886, and now in the mounted group.

that region at that season. From this *matériel* we now have on exhibition besides the group of buffaloes, a family group of antelope, another of coyotes, and another of prairie dogs, all with natural surroundings.

III. THE MOUNTED GROUP IN THE NATIONAL MUSEUM.

The result of the Smithsonian expedition for bison which appeals most strongly to the general public is the huge group of six choice specimens of both sexes and all ages, mounted with natural surroundings, and displayed in a superb mahogany case. The dimensions of the group are as follows: Length, 16 feet; width, 12 feet, and height, 10 feet. The subjoined illustration is a very fair representation of the principal one of its four sides, and the following admirable description (by Mr. Harry P. Godwin), from the Washington *Star* of March 10, 1888, is both graphic and accurate:

A SCENE FROM MONTANA—SIX OF MR. HORNADAY'S BUFFALOES FORM A PICTURESQUE GROUP—A BIT OF THE WILD WEST REPRODUCED AT THE NATIONAL MUSEUM—SOMETHING NOVEL IN THE WAY OF TAXIDERMY—REAL BUFFALO-GRASS, REAL MONTANA DIRT, AND REAL BUFFALOES.

A little bit of Montana—a small square patch from the wildest part of the wild West—has been transferred to the National Museum. It is so little that Montana will never miss it, but enough to enable one who has the faintest glimmer of imagination to see it all for himself—the hummocky prairie, the buffalo-grass, the sagebrush, and the buffalo. It is as though a little group of buffalo that have come to drink at a pool had been suddenly struck motionless by some magic spell, each in a natural attitude, and then the section of prairie, pool, buffalo, and all had been carefully cut out and brought to the National Museum. All this is in a huge glass case, the largest ever made for the Museum. This case and the space about it, at the south end of the south hall, has been inclosed by high screens for many days while the taxidermist and his assistants have been at work. The finishing touches were put on to-day, and the screens will be removed Monday, exposing to view what is regarded as a triumph of the taxidermist's art. The group, with its accessories, has been prepared so as to tell in an attractive way to the general visitor to the Museum the story of the buffalo, but care has been taken at the same time to secure an accuracy of detail that will satisfy the critical scrutiny of the most technical naturalist.

THE ACCESSORIES.

The pool of water is a typical alkaline water-hole, such as are found on the great northern range of bison, and are resorted to for water by wild animals in the fall when the small streams are dry. The pool is in a depression in the dry bed of a coulée or small creek. A little mound that rises beside the creek has been partially washed away by the water, leaving a crumbling bank, which shows the strata of the earth, a very thin layer of vegetable soil, beneath a stratum of grayish earth, and a layer of gravel, from which protrude a fossil bone or two. The whole bank shows the marks of erosion by water. Near by the pool a small section of the bank has fallen. A buffalo trail passes by the pool in front. This is a narrow path, well beaten down, depressed, and bare of grass. Such paths were made by herds of bison all over their pasture region as they traveled down water-courses, in single file, searching for water. In the grass some distance from the pool lie the bleaching skulls of two buffalo who have fallen victims to hunters who have cruelly lain in wait to get a shot at the animals as they come to drink. Such relics, strewn all over the plain, tell the story of the extermination of the American bison. About the pool and the sloping mound grow the low buffalo-grass, tufts of tall bunch-grass and sage-brush, and a species of prickly pear. The pool is clear and tranquil. About its edges is a white deposit of alkali. These are the scenic accessories of the buffalo group, but they have an interest almost equal to that of the buffaloes themselves, for they form really and literally a genuine bit of the West. The homesick Montana cowboy, far from his wild haunts, can here gaze upon his native sod again ; for the sod, the earth that forms the face of the bank, the sage-brush, and all were brought from Montana—all except the pool. The pool is a glassy delusion, and very perfect in its way. One sees a plant growing beneath the water, and in the soft, oozy bottom, near the edge, are the deep prints made by the fore feet of a big buffalo bull. About the soft, moist earth around the pool, and in the buffalo trail are the foot-tracks of the buffalo that have tramped around the pool, some of those nearest the edge having filled with water.

THE SIX BUFFALOES.

The group comprises six buffaloes. In front of the pool, as if just going to drink, is the huge buffalo bull, the giant of his race, the last one that was secured by the Smithsonian party in 1888, and the one that is believed to be the largest specimen of which there is authentic record. Near by is a cow eight years old, a creature that would be considered of great dimensions in any other company than that of the big bull. Near the cow is a suckling calf, four months old. Upon the top of the mound is a "spike" bull, two and a half years old; descending the mound away from the pool is a young cow three years old, on one side, and on the other a male calf a year and a half old. All the members of the group are disposed in natural attitudes. The young cow is snuffing at a bunch of tall grass ; the old bull and cow are turning their heads in the same direction apparently, as if alarmed by something approaching ; the others, having slaked their thirst, appear to be moving contentedly away. The four months' old calf was captured alive and brought to this city. It lived for some days in the Smithsonian grounds, but pined for its prairie home, and finally died. It is around the great bull that the romance and main interest of the group centers.

*   *   *   *   *   *   *

It seemed as if Providence had ordained that this splendid animal, perfect in limb, noble in size, should be saved to serve as a monument to the greatness of his race, that once roamed the prairies in myriads. Bullets found in his body showed that he had been chased and hunted before, but fate preserved him for the immortality of a Museum exhibit. His vertical height at the shoulders is 5 feet 8 inches. The thick hair adds enough to his height to make it full 6 feet. The length of his head and body is 9 feet 2 inches, his girth 8 feet 4 inches and his weight is, or was, about 1,600 pounds.

THE TAXIDERMIST'S OBJECT LESSONS.

This group, with its accessories, is, in point of size, about the biggest thing ever attempted by a taxidermist. It was mounted by Mr. Hornaday, assisted by Messrs. J. Palmer and A. H. Forney. It represents a new departure in mounting specimens for museums. Generally such specimens have been mounted singly, upon a flat surface. The American mammals, collected by Mr. Hornaday, will be mounted in a manner that will make each piece or group an object lesson, telling something of the history and the habits of the animal. The first group produced as one of the results of the Montana hunt comprised three coyotes. Two of them are struggling, and one might almost say snarling, over a bone. They do not stand on a painted board, but on a little patch of soil. Two other groups designed by Mr. Hornaday, and executed by Mr. William Palmer, are about to be placed in the Museum. One of these represents a family of prairie-dogs. They are disposed about a prairie-dog mound. One sits on its haunches eating; others are running about.   Across the mouth of the burrow, just ready to disappear into it, is another one, startled for the moment by the sudden appearance of a little burrowing owl that has alighted on one side of the burrow. The owl and the dog are good friends and live together in the same burrow, but there appears to be strained relations between the two for the moment.

THE PRESERVATION OF MUSEUM SPECIMENS FROM INSECTS AND THE EFFECTS OF DAMPNESS.

By WALTER HOUGH, A. M.

The preservation of museum specimens is of no less importance than their acquisition. Periodically the attack of some new insect, or the infesting of some new material, is brought to the notice of curators, and hitherto many specimens have been destroyed which it would be now impossible to replace. In a great museum the abundance of the material will not permit its frequent examination, so that all specimens should be thoroughly poisoned before they get out of sight. There are many things which one would not think it necessary to poison, yet all should be, for nearly all organic structures have peculiar enemies in the insect world. As instances, woodwork, basketry, textiles, botanical specimens, etc., should be poisoned with corrosive sublimate, as it coagulates the albuminoid principles in vegetation and thereby prevents decay as well as the attacks of insects.

The ravages of moths have been experienced from remote times, and though the preservation of materials from the attacks of these and other insects has been repeatedly attempted, all efforts, it seems, have so far been ineffectual. Most of the chemical substances suggested are too poisonous to be used on articles brought in contact with the person, as in every-day wear. Happily this is no objection here, for with ordinary precautions the specimens sent to the Museum can be treated with the strongest poisons, the main difficulty being to avoid damaging the material in their application.

First in rank of destructiveness are the moths, of which four species have been observed at active work in the Museum. These are *Tinea flavifrontella* Linn., the common, or clothes, moth; *T. tapetzella* Linn., or carpet moth; *T. pellionella* Linn., or fur moth, and *T. granella* Linn., or grain moth. These Tineids are night-flying insects, though the little fluttering " millers " are often seen flying in darkened rooms in the daytime. Their natural habitat is in dry animal and fibrous vegetable substances, and sometimes on the fur of living animals; in houses they infest woolens, furs, grain, etc., and the destruction caused by the larvæ is well known. They begin to fly about actively in May. I have observed them in warm rooms as early as March, and have found the larvæ all through the winter. In the stage in which this insect does its destructive work, it is a plump white caterpillar provided with strong mandibles and sixteen legs. It nips the fiber, beginning as soon as hatched from the egg, and builds a case which is enlarged as the insect grows. These insects are known to travel in search of other quarters; they are very hard to kill, extreme cold does not affect them, and many of the domestic preventives, such as camphor, tobacco, etc., entirely fail to destroy them.

All articles subject to injury from these moths should be often examined and shaken, especially in spring and early summer, to dislodge the eggs.

Another very serious pest is the "buffalo bug" (*Anthrenus lepidus* Linn.), and its relative the "carpet bug" (*A. varius* Fabr.). The adult is a small round sluggish beetle, brown, with white or variegated scales on the wing covers. The larvæ are short, plump worms with numerous stiff, brown hairs. This insect is on the increase; its ravages seem to have attracted the notice of the public, and much was written about it a few years ago, in 1882 and 1883. Like the *tinea* larva, the buffalo-bug larva cuts leather, woolen, or fur, and builds an incoherent case from the fragments. These insects multiply very rapidly, and are also unaffected by ordinary insect preventives.

The larvæ of the "basket beetle" (*Sitodrepa panicea* Linn.) are small worm-like creatures with six minute feet. They are furnished with strong cutting-jaws by means of which they eat their way into basketry and old wood, or similar substances, boring little holes as round as if made with a fine drill. The adult insect is a little, sluggish, brown beetle which simulates death on being disturbed.

Another insect, the subject of a letter to Science, May 28, 1886, and there called "A New Museum Pest," is the "silver fish" (*Lepisma domestica*). The adult is a shining fish-shaped insect, wingless, but very quick in its movements. It prefers starch for food, and attacks everything that contains that substance, such as labels pasted or sized with starch or mucilage, cotton or linen laundered goods, etc. This insect is extremely obnoxious to librarians, being attracted by the paste used in binding books.

Other insects are often introduced into the Museum on specimens and by other means, but these are of less consequence, as they do not breed there and are usually not harmful.

It has been thought well to introduce here a paper by Mr. John B. Smith, assistant curator of entomology in the Museum, relating to the care of insect collections. It was published in the Proceedings of the Entomological Society of Washington,* under the title "Some Observations on Museum Pests."

One of the duties of a person in charge of a large collection of insects is keeping out museum pests, as the various species that feed on the dried insects are generically called. In a large collection, like that of the National Museum, no inconsiderable time is required for that purpose, as it takes at least two weeks to go through all the boxes carefully.

It has been the fashion to recommend as a certain preventive tight boxes, and quarantining all specimens before putting into the collection, and undoubtedly this is an excellent precaution, saving much future labor. It is, however, by no means the certain remedy it has been claimed to be. The boxes and cabinets in use in the Museum are as perfect, as far as safety is concerned, as it is possible to get them at present, yet withal constant care is required. *Psocidæ* will find their way into the tightest boxes, and though they do little damage ordinarily, yet in a collection of *Tineidæ*, or minute *Diptera*, they can do considerable damage. For these pests I have found naphthaline a perfect remedy. A single half-ounce cone is a perfect protection, and lasts about three months ordinarily.

Tineid larvæ are rather rarely found in the collections on the larger moths, and are not always easily discovered, since they make no dust, as do the *Anthreni*. On one occasion I found that one pair of wings of a *C. regalis* suddenly collapsed without apparent cause. Close examination showed a Tineid larva that had been feeding on the dense, long vestiture, making galleries in all directions in such a way that when I took hold of one end of the gallery, the vestiture of the under side came off in large sheets, leaving the wings almost clean, the veins broken here and there, which produced the collapse. They rarely burrow into the specimen, never in my experience. *Ptinidæ* are sometimes found, but are exceedingly rare in our collection. One box lined with corn pith was riddled by them, and a very few specimens were attacked. By all odds the most dangerous enemies are the larvæ of the *Dermestidæ*, which are pests pure and simple. The principal enemy in our collection is *Anthrenus varius*, though *Trogoderma* is not uncommon.

My experience with these is, that in the uniformly high temperature preserved in the laboratory they breed all the year around, and have no definite broods; a few larvæ appear at all times, though during the summer, when the beetles come in from the grounds, and from other parts of the Museum, exposed specimens are attacked at more regular intervals. The rule is to keep naphthaline in all boxes at all times, but, like all rules, it is not always possible to adhere strictly to it. The boxes not so protected are usually first attacked. In a cabinet not quite tight I coned a number of drawers and left the others unprotected. In the course of the summer the unprotected drawers nearly all became infested, while as a rule the others were free. The naphthaline seems to act as a repellant. I have found, however, that it does not annoy the larvæ to any very great extent, and Mr. Lugger has shown me a naphthaline cone in a hollow of which a larva had pupated. I have reason to believe, however, that it does retard the development of young larvæ. A large number of boxes, nearly one hundred, were received from North Carolina, containing a collection, principally Coleoptera. They were overhauled and found to be pretty generally infested with *Trogoderma*, this being the only species found. No *Anthrenus* larvæ were noticed. Bisulphide of carbon was freely used, and naphthaline cones were placed in all the boxes. For awhile the boxes were frequently examined and no larvæ developed. Throughout the summer the boxes were examined at intervals and remained free. With the approach of cold weather they were left for a longer period and the cones nearly all evaporated. In December this was noticed, and the boxes were again overhauled, and it was found that a very general development of larvæ had begun, all of them *Trogoderma*, and none of them more than 2 to 3 millimeters in length, most of them apparently just hatched. The entire collection was scrutinized, and an occasional *Anthrenus* larva was found, but no other *Trogoderma*, even in the most exposed boxes.

I conclude from this that the collection when received was infested, and that there were eggs everywhere ready to develop; some had begun to develop, and these were destroyed by the use of bisulphide of carbon, which also served to check the development of the eggs. The boxes were quite large, and two large cones were put in each; they were also quite secure, and the atmosphere in them was fully impregnated with the odor of naphthaline. Throughout the summer, when under ordinary circumstances they would have developed, the eggs remained dormant, but after the naphthaline had evaporated completely, development began. I might add here that *Trogoderma* is an exceedingly rare pest in New York, and not common in Washington; farther south it seems to replace *Anthrenus*. For all these pests bisulphide of carbon is a sovereign remedy, except when they are burrowing in large Coleoptera or Lepidoptera. I have repeatedly soaked large Bombycids with chloroform or bisulphide, and a week later found them still infested. I worked for a month over some large Lucanids (*Proculejus*), and finally separated the parts so that I could fill the body cavity with chloroform. In one case, that was somewhat exposed and contained old material of little value, I found a specimen destroyed by *Microgaster*, a rare parasite for *Anthrenus*. How they got at this box is difficult to explain, since it was tight enough to prevent the entrance of the insect.

I have noticed also that boxes on the lower tier of shelves are much more liable to attack than those on upper tiers, and this leads me to believe that the parent beetle will deposit eggs outside of the boxes or on the floor of the cases, and the young larvæ will work their way into the smallest crevices. It seems difficult to account for isolated larvæ in boxes containing only old insects.

Finally I find the danger of infection comparatively greater at Washington than in New York, principally because the warm season begins earlier and lasts longer, increasing the chances of infection. I find, too, that the only real chance of safety consists in constant examination, tight boxes, and a free use of chloroform or bisulphide of carbon.

As to naphthaline, I consider that it is a good general preventive. I know that it keeps out Psocids and ants. It enhances the tendency to grease and to verdigris, and in tight boxes it seems to exercise a relaxing tendency, causing the wings to droop.

There are several classes of substances to be poisoned, in which the colors, fabric, or character of material, and therefore the kind of poison and the strength of solution, are important factors. For instance, goods not fast dyed (especially cotton), or which are dyed with colors that contain solutions, will start; also fabrics or substances which may be corroded or hardened, or otherwise injured, as feathers, fur, dressed deer-skin, etc. Too strong a solution may also cause a deposit on fur, etc., with a dulling effect. As a test for this, a black feather should be dipped in the solution, if it is of corrosive sublimate or arsenic in alcohol. If the solution be too strong, it will produce a white coating when dry. Any solution should exert its action in two ways, first to repel the adult insect, and second, to destroy the hatched larva. Pungent odors are noxious to moths and the higher orders of insects, but this is hardly true in the case of the beetles to which we have before alluded. The pungency of odor can not be made to last long, so that the poisoning quality is of prime importance. The substances used for solutions are deadly poisons, and no one who has not had experience in handling them had better undertake to apply them. Corrosive sublimate will attack the finger-nails and the skin. It is also volatile. Arsenic is prejudicial to the health; the dust, it is said, produces catarrh, both gastric and nasal, though this has not been confirmed by my observation.

Before poisoning, all objects should be treated with benzine, by putting them in a close box or vessel, and pouring the benzine in, leaving them tightly closed therein for several days. This operation destroys any larvæ or eggs. They should then be hung up until the benzine evaporates before proceeding with the poisoning solutions. Bisulphide of carbon is more volatile and more quickly effective than benzine, and may be used, if preferred. There is reason to believe that both kill the eggs—quickly if the fluid comes in contact with them and less rapidly if they are directly affected only by the fumes in the vapor. Great care must be taken not to allow fire of any kind to come in contact with the vapor of bisulphide of carbon. There are several reasons why benzine is preferable, and the latter is sure to be effective when followed by the arsenic-naphtha solution. The solution found most satisfactory for poisoning nearly every kind of specimens is as follows:

Saturated solution of arsenic acid and alcohol	1 pint.
Strong carbolic acid	25 drops.
Strychnine	20 grains.
Alcohol (strong)	1 quart.
Naphtha, crude or refined	1 pint.

The use of strychnine is not absolutely necessary; but it is a very good agent and adds much to the value of the solution. Other solutions and poisons will be noticed below. It will be found advisable to apply solutions in the form of spray to delicate objects, such as feathers or specimens of similar character. In this treatment an atomizer may be used. Some small specimens may be dipped and allowed to drain, and the solution may be applied with a brush to a large class of objects, taking care to saturate every part. The specimens can then be hung up to dry or laid away as they are. They should be kept free from dust, which is exceedingly injurious to them. As soon as poisoned, they ought, if intended for exhibition, to be mounted in dust-tight cases, or carefully stowed away in close-fitting drawers or boxes. In unit or costume boxes a small packet of naphthaline may be concealed behind the specimens, and the junction of the lid should be made dust-proof by pasting on strips of paper with paste containing arsenic or corrosive sublimate.

Some specimens present problems that do not fall under any rule and have to be left to judgment and experiment. As an instance in point, we mention a fine deer-skin robe collected by Mr. Turner, beautifully tawed, with the hair on, and ornamented with a medium which will not stand wetting. It is obvious that no solution can be used in this case, since alcohol or water will harden the buck-skin and destroy the decoration. Satisfactory results might be obtained by judicious spraying, but there would be doubt as to the completeness of the poisoning. It would be better to rub into the kid surface a powder made of precipitated chalk and white arsenic. The fur side should then be well rubbed, care being taken to allow the powder to penetrate into the roots of the hair. By all means protect the hands with gloves. Powdered soap would also be a good medium for the arsenic. Great care should be taken in applying this poison and in handling a specimen poisoned in this way. Such specimens should be at once closed up tightly and put on exhibition.

Corrosive sublimate has been much used for poisoning and is a valuable agent. Several specimens in the Museum, which were poisoned years ago with this substance, were so filled with it that they are dusty. They are made of fur-skin, and are stiff and unpresentable for exhibition. I do not know what was the condition of the articles when they were acquired; they are, however, undeniably moth-proof. I have found numerous adult moths destroyed in the act of laying their eggs. A careful use of corrosive sublimate is very effective, if it is not brought in contact with skins, as it coagulates albumen. It is also volatile, and Dr. G. H. Beyer, U. S. Navy, has proposed to take advantage of this property in preventing the growth of fungi on materia-medica specimens in jars. One objection to corrosive sublimate is that it crystallizes out very easily; this might be obviated by adding a little naphtha to the alcoholic solution.

Naphthaline is used by Mr. J. B. Smith, of the Museum, and by other entomologists, to preserve insect collections from *Acari*, *Psoci*, *Dermestes*, *Anthreni*, and other museum pests.* It destroys the two former, but only tends to repel the others. It also acts as an antiseptic, destroying schizomycetes, moulds, bacteria, etc. The salt is perfectly neutral, is not poisonous to man, and is cheap. It is customary in this department to put a small packet or cones in cases containing mounted costumes.

Vaseline may be called perfect grease, since it does not become rancid or corrosive. It is especially useful to protect iron and steel from rust, and no doubt would preserve woodwork from extraneous attack. It is also good to soften leather which has become hard. In the case of clubs, spears, and implements of hard wood, like those of Polynesia, a fine polish may be obtained by using vaseline. I regard vaseline as a good vehicle in which to apply white arsenic to skins, as is done with arsenic soap. It penetrates very well, especially if thinned a little with naphtha. Vaseline is also used on book-backs to soften them, to prevent mould, and to keep insects away.

A few recipes germane to this subject, and which may be useful in other departments of the Museum, are appended:

Mr. Hornaday has used arsenical soap prepared in the following manner:

White soap	2	pounds.
Powdered white arsenic	2	do.
Camphor	5	ounces.
Subcarbonate of potash	6	do.
Alcohol	8	do.

See p. 555.

Slice the soap, melt it, add the potash, stir in the arsenic, and add the camphor previously dissolved in the alcohol. Stir, when cooling, to prevent the arsenic from sinking to the bottom. For use, mix a small quantity with water until it resembles buttermilk, and apply with a common paint-brush. This is a mechanical mixture. Mr. Hornaday has obtained results of the highest order from its use. The following is believed to be a more correct chemical combination:

White soap	1 ounce.
Arseniate of potash	2 do.
Water	6 drachms.
Camphor	2 do.
Strychnine (ad lib.)	15 grains.

The following ingredients make an effective preservative powder:

White arsenic	1 pound.
Burnt alum	1 do.
Powdered oak bark	2 do.
Camphor	$\frac{1}{2}$ do.

This should be powdered well, sifted and kept in well-stoppered bottles. It should be applied to the wet surface of skin and rubbed in well. The hands should be protected with gloves. I have never tried this preparation.

The following solution has been prepared by Wickersheimer for the preservation of objects in the natural state:

Alum	500	grains.
Salt	125	do.
Saltpeter	60	do.
Potash	300	do.
Arsenic trioxide (white arsenic)	100	do.

Dissolve in 1 quart of boiling water. Cool and filter, and for 1 quart of the solution add 4 quarts of glycerine and 1 quart of alcohol. Either soak the objects in the solution, or inject them with it. This solution is said to do very well except in tropical climates.

For botanical specimens this is said to be an excellent preservative:

One ounce of corrosive sublimate to 1 quart of alcohol, diluted 50 per cent. The best plan is to dip the specimens and then carefully dry them. The poison can also be painted on with a camel's-hair brush.

For the preservation of entomological specimens, the strongest solution used should be corrosive sublimate in alcohol, 1 to 100, and the weakest 0.1 to 100. (See remarks on naphthaline, *ante*.)

For insects on plants, the following solutions are recommended:

First solution.		*Second solution.*	
Salt	$2\frac{1}{2}$ pounds.	First solution	1 quart.
Saltpeter	4 ounces.	Arseniate of potash	2 ounces.
Water	1 gallon.	Water	1 gallon.
Filter.			

A cheaper solution can be made by taking—

White arsenic	1 pound.
Sal soda	4 ounces.
Water	1 gallon.

Boil till a solution is made. Take 1 quart to 40 gallons of water. These solutions have been found by the Department of Agriculture to be very useful in destroying the scale-bug and the red spider, so harmful to plants.

The following method is employed by furriers in the treatment of fur skins for the purpose of rendering them pliable: The skin is steeped and scoured in a bath of alum, bran, and salt, in order to remove greasiness; then in a bath of soap and soda, to remove the oil from the fur. When thoroughly washed and dried it is found that the pelt has become tawed or kid leather.

To soften and cleanse buck-skin or chamois leather, rub plenty of castile soap into the skin and soak for two hours in a weak solution of sal soda in warm water and rub well until quite clean. Afterwards rinse in a weak solution of sal soda and soap in water; after rinsing, wring it dry in a coarse towel, and when fully dry beat it until soft and smooth.

For domestic purposes the following preventives from moth ravages are suggested: Dissolve in 200 parts of alcohol 2 parts of salicylic acid and 2 parts of thymol; perfume with oil of lemon. This is a neutral solution and will not injure colors or texture, and has a pleasant odor, but is rather expensive.

A good preparation to sprinkle among furs being packed away in a close box or drawer, is naphthaline and menthol or thymol, in proportion of 1 ounce of the former to 20 grains of either of the latter, rubbed together. The odor will disappear from the furs or goods after they have been aired for a short time. Even if moths are present and are hatched, they will not feed when closely shut up in the odor of this mixture, and in this respect it is far superior to camphor. Thymol alone is very good. Naphthaline is now on the market in a very convenient shape called "moth marbles," and seems to be going into general use.

In the following list of apparatus only those things have been mentioned that have been found necessary or very useful in the operations at the National Museum. Doubtless at other places, where such a range of subjects for poisoning is not presented, some of the articles can be dispensed with:

Gutta-percha atomizer, which may bought for one dollar. The bottle can be easily wired to a handle for convenience. (Fig. 1.)

Fig. 1. Gutta-percha atomizer.

Galvanized sheet-iron tank (Fig. 2) used for subjecting specimens to bisulphide of carbon. The lid and air-hole cap on the lid both fit into a slot (Fig. 2a) that is to be filled with water to prevent escape of gas. The tank should be set out in the open air if possible. The size of the tank used here is 3 by 2 by 2 feet, and it has handles on the ends and on the lid. (Fig. 2.)

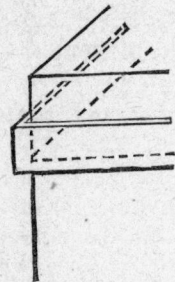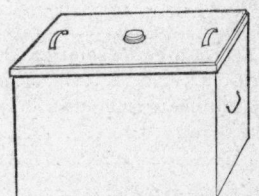

FIG. 2a. Showing adjustment of lid of tank.   FIG. 2. Galvanized sheet-iron tank.

Shaw and Geary No. 2 air compressor (cost $15), and four-nozzle gutta-percha atomizer, cost $2.50. These are found necessary only when much spraying is to be done.

Stock solution jar, jar for mixed solution, benzine jar or jug, graduate, 1 pint; glass funnel, 3 paint brushes, not too large; several stoneware jars with closely fitting lids for smaller specimens. With good-sized jars, or even a closely-joined box, the galvanized tank may be dispensed with, especially when benzine is to be used.

The poison tags should not be large. They are convenient for showing whether specimens are poisoned or not, and when, and are sometimes a good test whether they are well poisoned. They may be printed with death's-head and word "poisoned," with space for date and museum number.

The long established "Museum standard" cases are provided with bead and groove (Figs. 3 and 4) which effectually exclude dust and insects, the two worst foes of museum collections. In putting up perish-

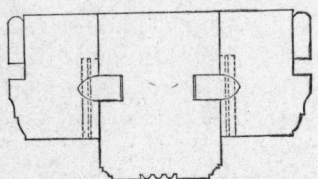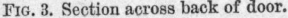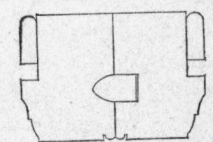

FIG. 3. Section across back of door.   FIG. 4. Section across junction of door.

able specimens permanently in the glazed Museum unit boxes, etc., the backs are made of tin, and to guard against the minute, insinuating, newly-hatched moth larva, the junction of the lid with the sides is pasted over with strips of paper or muslin with glue, poisoned with corrosive sublimate or arsenic. This, with naphthaline cones inside, is the highest triumph of the preservation of museum specimens.

In the following table are given the approximate prices of chemicals which have been referred to in this paper:

Alcohol, 95 per cent	$2.50	per gallon.
Arsenic acid, Merck's	.40	per pound.
Arseniate of potash		do.
Arsenic, white	.10	do.
Benzine	.15	per gallon.
Bisulphide of carbon	.25	per pound.
Burnt alum	.10	do.
Camphor	.25	do.
Carbolic acid, Calvert's solution	.60	do.
Chloroform	.75	do.
Corrosive sublimate (mercuric chloride)	.90	do.
Ether	.85	do.
Glycerine	.30	do.
Menthol	.50	per ounce.
Naphtha		per gallon.
Naphthaline crystals	.25	per pound.
Naphthaline cones	1.25	per 100.
Naphthaline "moth marbles"	.10	per box.
Oak bark, powdered, or tannin	.10-.25	per pound.
Oil of lemon	.20	per ounce.
Salicylic acid	2.25	per pound.
Saltpeter	.35	do.
Sal soda	.05	do.
Strychnine	.20	per ½-ounce.
Subcarbonate of potash	.25	per pound.
Thymol	.60	per ounce.
Vaseline, Cheeseborough's	.50	per pound.

SECTION IV.

BIBLIOGRAPHY OF THE U. S. NATIONAL MUSEUM DURING THE FISCAL YEAR ENDING JUNE 30, 1887.

BIBLIOGRAPHY OF THE U. S. NATIONAL MUSEUM DURING THE FISCAL YEAR ENDING JUNE 30, 1887.

I.—PUBLICATIONS OF THE MUSEUM.

Department of the Interior: | U. S. National Museum. | —— | Proceedings | of the | United States National Museum. | Vol. IX. | 1886. | —— | Published under the direction of the Smithsonian Institution | —— | Washington: | Government Printing Office. | 1887.

8vo. pp. i–viii, 1–714. Plates i–xxv.

The following is a list of signatures of the Proceedings of the U. S National Museum, published between July 1, 1886, and June 30, 1887, and forming volume ix and part of volume x:

Date of publication.	Signature number.	Pages.	Date of publication.	Signature number.	Pages.
1886.			Dec. 8	28	433–448
VOLUME IX.			Dec. 8	29	449–464
			Nov. 26	30	465–480
Aug. 14	1	1– 16	Nov. 26	31	481–496
Aug. 14	2	17– 32	Nov. 26	32	497–512
Aug. 21	3	33– 48	Nov. 26	33	513–528
Aug. 23	4	49– 64	Dec. 2	34	529–544
Aug. 26	5	65– 80			
Aug. 26	6	81– 96	**1887.**		
Sept. 2	7	97–112	Jan. 25	35	545–560
Sept. 13	8	113–128	Feb. 8	36	561–576
Sept. 15	9	129–144	Feb. 9	37	577–592
Sept. 17	10	145–160	Feb. 11	38	593–608
Sept. 28	11	161–176	Feb. 11	39	609–624
Sept. 28	12	177–192	Feb. 11	40	625–640
Sept. 28	13	193–208	Feb. 14	41	641–656
Oct. 11	14	209–224	Feb. 25	42	657–672
Oct. 13	15	225–240		43	673–688
Oct. 13	16	241–256		44	689–714
Oct. 13	17	257–272			
Oct. 13	18	273–288	VOLUME X.		
Oct. 19	19	289–304			
Oct. 19	20	305–[320]	Apr. 25	1	1–16
[Oct. 19]	[21]	321–336	Apr. 25	2	17–32
Oct. 19	22	337–352	May 17	3	33–48
Oct. 30	23	353–368	May 17	4	49–64
Oct. 30	24	369–384	May 17	5	65–80
Oct. 30	25	385–400	May 17	6	81–96
Oct. 30	26	401–416			
Dec. 7	27	417–432	Total	50	810

Department of the Interior: | U. S. National Museum | Bulletin | of the | United States National Museum | No. 31. | Synopsis of the North American Syrphidæ | By | Samuel W. Williston, M. D., Ph. D. | —— | With twelve plates | —— | Washington: | Government Printing Office. | 1886. |

8vo. pp. i–xxv, 1–335.

Annual Report | of the | Board of Regents | of the | Smithsonian Institution | showing | the Operations, Expeditions, and Condition | of the Institution | for | the year 1884 | Part II | ——Washington: | Government Printing Office | 1886. |

> 8vo. pp. i–ix, 1–458. 105 plates.
> This report is divided into five parts.
> Part   I. Report of the Assistant Director.
> Part   II. Report of the Curators and Acting Curators.
> Part III. Papers descriptive of collections in the National Musem.
> Part IV. Bibliography, 18-4.
> Part   V. List of accessions in 1884.

II.—PAPERS BY OFFICERS OF THE NATIONAL MUSEUM AND OTHER INVESTIGATORS WHOSE WRITINGS ARE BASED DIRECTLY OR INDIRECTLY ON MUSEUM MATERIAL.

ALPHABETICAL LIST OF NAMES.

Allen, J. A., American Museum of Natural History, New York City.

Baird, Spencer F., Secretary, Smithsonian Institution.

Baker, J. G., U. S. Geological Survey.

Batchelder, Charles F., Cambridge, Massachusetts.

Bean, Tarleton H., U. S. Fish Commission, Honorary Curator, Department of Fishes, U. S. National Museum.

Beckham, Charles Wickliffe, Bardstown, Kentucky.

Benedict, James E., Naturalist, U. S. Fish Commission.

Beyer, Henry G., U. S. Navy, Honorary Curator, Section of Materia Medica, U. S. National Museum.

Binney, William G., Burlington, New Jersey.

Blakiston, Thomas, London, Ohio.

Boehmer, George H., Smithsonian Institution.

Bollman, Charles H., Indiana University, Bloomington, Indiana.

Brewster, William, Cambridge, Massachusetts.

Brooks, W. Edwin, Milton, Ontario.

Bush, Katherine J., Sheffield Scientific School, Yale College, New Haven, Connecticut.

Clark, A. Howard, Assistant Curator, Section of Historical Relics, U. S. National Museum.

Clarke, F. W., U. S. Geological Survey, Honorary Curator, Department of Minerals, U. S. National Museum.

Coale, H. K., Chicago, Illinois.

Collins, Joseph William, U. S. Fish Commission, Honorary Curator, Section of Naval Architecture, U. S. National Museum.

Cope, E. D., Philadelphia, Pennsylvania.

Cory, Charles B., Boston, Massachusetts.

Dall, William Healey, U. S. Geological Survey, Honorary Curator, Department of Mollusks, U. S. National Museum.

Dewey, Frederick Perkins, Curator, Department of Metallurgy and Economic Geology, U. S. National Museum.

Doering, George E., Section of Materia Medica, U. S. National Museum.

Edwards, Charles L., Minneapolis, Minnesota.

Eigenmann, Carl H., Indiana University, Bloomington, Indiana.

Emerson, W. Otto, Haywards, California.

Everman, Barton W., Indiana University, Bloomington, Indiana.

Fewkes, J. Walter, Museum of Comparative Zoology, Cambridge, Massachusetts.

Fordice, Morton W., Indiana University, Bloomington, Indiana.

Fox William H., New York City.

Gault, B. F., Chicago, Illinois.

Geare, Randolph I., U. S. National Museum.

Gilbert, G. K., U. S. Geological Survey.

Goode, G. Brown, Assistant Secretary, Smithsonian Institution, in charge of U. S. National Museum.

Goss, N S., Topeka, Kansas.

Henshaw, H. W., U. S. Geological Survey.

Hitchcock, Romyn, Acting Curator, Section of Textiles and Foods, U. S. National Museum.

Holmes, W. H., Bureau of Ethnology, Honorary Curator, Department of American Aboriginal Pottery, U. S. National Museum.

Hornaday, William T., Chief Taxidermist, U. S. National Museum.

Hough, Walter, Department of Ethnology, U. S. National Museum.

Hughes, Elizabeth G., Indiana University, Bloomington, Indiana.

Jordan, David S., President, Indiana University, Bloomington, Indiana.

Knowlton, Frank H., Assistant Curator, Department of Fossil Plants, U. S. National Museum.

Lawrence, George N., New York City.

Lesquereux, Leo, Columbus, Ohio.

Linton, Edwin, Washington and Jefferson College, Washington, Pennsylvania.

Lucas, Frederic A., Osteologist, U. S. National Museum.

McDonald, Marshall, Chief of Division of Distribution, U. S. Fish Commission.

Marcou, John B., U. S. Geological Survey, Assistant, Department of Mesozoic Invertebrate Fossils, U. S. National Museum.

Mason, Otis T., Curator, Department of Ethnology, U. S. National Museum.

Mazyck, William G., Charleston, South Carolina.

Merrill, George Perkins, Curator, Department of Lithology and Physical Geology, U. S. National Museum.

Merriam, C. Hart, Ornithologist, Department of Agriculture.

Miner, R. H., Ensign, U. S. Navy.

Murdoch, John, Librarian, Smithsonian Institution.

Nye, Willard, jr., U. S. Fish Commission.

Pelseneer, Paul, Museum of Brussels, Belgium.

Rau, Charles, Curator, Department of Antiquities, U. S. National Museum.

Rathbun, Richard, U. S. Fish Commission, Honorary Curator, Department of Marine Invertebrates, U. S. National Museum.

Ridgway, Robert, Curator, Department of Birds, U. S. National Museum.

Riley, Charles Valentine, Entomologist, Department of Agriculture, Honorary Curator, Department of Insects, U. S. National Museum.

Ryder, John A., University of Pennsylvania, Philadelphia, Pennsylvania.

Sclater, P. L., Secretary of the Zoological Society of London, London, England.

Sennett, George B., New York City.

Seton, Ernest E. T., New York City.

Shufeldt, R. W., Captain, Medical Corps, U. S. Army, Fort Wingate, New Mexico.

Slade, D. D., Museum of Comparative Zoology, Cambridge, Massachusetts.

Smith, Hugh M., U. S. Fish Commission.

Smith, John B., Assistant Curator, Department of Insects, U. S. National Museum.

Smith, Rosa, San Diego, California.

Stearns, R. E. C., Adjunct Curator, Department of Mollusks, U. S. National Museum.

Stejneger, Leonhard, Assistant Curator, Department of Birds, U. S. National Museum.

Tanner, Z. L., Lieutenant-Commander, U. S. Navy, U. S. Fish Commission Steamer *Albatross*.

Toppan, George L., Chicago, Illinois.

Townsend, Charles H., U. S. Fish Commission.

True, Frederick W., Curator, Department of Mammals, U. S. National Museum.

Verrill, Addison E., Professor of Zoology, Yale College, New Haven, Connecticut.

Walcott, Charles Doolittle, U. S. Geological Survey, Honorary Curator, Department of Invertebrate Fossils (Paleozoic), U. S. National Museum.

Ward, Lester F., U. S. Geological Survey, Honorary Curator, Departments of Fossil and Recent Plants, U. S. National Museum.

Wells, John Grant, Grenada, West Indies.

White, Charles A., U. S. Geological Survey, Honorary Curator, Department of Mesozoic Invertebrate Fossils, U. S. National Museum.

Williston, Dr. Samuel W., Peabody Museum, New Haven, Connecticut.

Yarrow, Henry Crécy, M. D., U. S. Army, Honorary Curator, Department of Reptiles, U. S. National Museum.

LIST OF PAPERS.

J. A. ALLEN. The Masked Bob White (*Colnius ridgwayi*) of Arizona, and its Allies.

Bull. Amer. Mus. N. H., I, 1886, pp. 273–290, pl. (colored) xxiii.

A full monograph of this species, including comparisons with allied species. In the preparation of this monograph the author was materially aided by the loan of specimens in the National Museum.

SPENCER F. BAIRD. Occurrence of Cory's Shearwater (*Puffinus borealis*) and several species of Jaegers in large numbers in the vicinity of Gay Head, Massachusetts, during the autumn of 1886.

The Auk, IV, 1887, pp. 71, 72.

"Enormous numbers of *Puffinus* and *Stercorarius* followed the young herring in shore towards the end of September, the former being almost exclusively *P. borealis*, with a few *P. stricklandi*, the latter consisting principally of *S. parasiticus* and *S. pomarinus* in every stage of coloration. The Jaegers were shyer, but the Shearwaters very tame, so that a dozen birds were killed by the discharge of two guns from a launch. About a hundred specimens were secured, and thousands could easily have been killed if necessary."

J. G. BAKER. Mr. J. J. Cooper's Costa Rica Ferns.

The Journal of Botany, British and Foreign. London, XXV, pp. 24–26.

Gives list of the ferns sent for determination by the National Museum with descriptions of new species.

CHARLES F. BATCHELDER. The North Carolina Mountains in Winter.

The Auk, III, 1886, pp. 307–314.

Two of the specimens of *Junco hyemalis carolinensis*, mentioned on page 312, were presented by the author to the National Museum.

TARLETON H. BEAN. Cruise of the *Grampus* on the Southern Mackerel Grounds.

Boston Herald, May 9, May 26, and June 6, 1887.

TARLETON H. BEAN. Extract from the report of A. Annaniassen on his voyage to Iceland.* (Translation.)

Rep. U. S. Fish Com., XII, 1886, 309–313.

TARLETON H. BEAN. Report on Examination of Clupeoids from Carp Ponds.

Bull. U. S. Fish Com., VI, No. 28, March 24, 1887, pp. 441, 442.

Clupea æstivalis, C. vernalis, and *C. sapidissima*. Ten thousand young shad were put into one of the ponds in April, 1885; nearly seven thousand of these were caught December 10, 1885- the maximum length being five inches.

TARLETON H. BEAN. Report on the Department of Fishes in the United States National Museum, 1884.

Report Smithsonian Institution, 1884 (1886) II, pp. 161–178.

(See under GOODE and BEAN.)

CHARLES WICKLIFFE BECKHAM. Additional Notes on the Birds of Pueblo County, Colorado.

The Auk, IV, 1887, pp. 120–125.

Specimens of some of the species mentioned were presented to the National Museum by the author.

---

* From *Selskabet for de norske Fiskeriers Fremme, Aarsbereting*, 1883, pp. 3–10.

JAMES E. BENEDICT. Report of the Naturalist. (See Z. L. TANNER.)

(Report on the work of the U. S. Fish Commission steamer *Albatross* for the year ending December 31, 1883, pp. 117-236, by Lieut. Commander Z. L. Tanner, U. S. Navy, commanding.)

Report U. S. Commissioner of Fish and Fisheries, Part XI, 1883, pp. 175-177.

JAMES E. BENEDICT. Report of the Naturalist.

(Report on the work of the U. S. Fish Commission steamer *Albatross* for the year ending December 31, 1884, by Lieut. Commander Z. L. Tanner, U. S. Navy, commanding.)

Report U. S. Commissioner of Fish and Fisheries, Part XII, for 1884, pp. 86-103.

JAMES E. BENEDICT. Descriptions of ten species and one genus of Annelids from the dredgings of the U. S. Fish Commission steamer *Albatross*.

Proc. U. S. Nat. Mus., IX, 1886, pp. 547-553, plates 20-25.

Describes one new genus, *Crucigera* of the family Serpulidæ (p. 550), and the following species, all of which are figured: *Protula diomedeæ* B., sp. nov., off Cape Hatteras, 43 fathoms; *Protula alba* B., sp. nov., St. Thomas, West Indies; *Hydroides dianthus* Ver., Chesapeake Bay; *Hydroides spongicola* B., sp. nov., Gulf of Mexico, 26 fathoms; *Hydroides protulicola* B., sp. nov., off Cape Hatteras, 43 fathoms; *Crucigera Websteri* B., sp. nov., Gulf of Mexico, 26 fathoms; *Pomatostegus stellatus* Schmarda, Jamaica and Curaçao; *Spirobranchus giganteu*, Mörch, St. Thomas and Curaçao; *Spirobranchus incrassatus* (Kröyer) Mörch, Vera Cruz; *Spirobranchus dendropoma* Mörch, St. Thomas, Jamaica, and Curaçao.

H. G. BEYER. The direct action of calcium, sodium, potassium, and ammonium salts on the human blood vessels.

Medical News, September 4, 1886.

When these investigations were begun, comparatively little was known with regard to the action of these salts on the blood-vessels. The results which had been recorded were rather indefinite and contradictory, and the methods used rather imperfect. It was of especial importance to ascertain by means of new and improved methods, as accurately as possible, the action of potassium salts on the vascular system, and, as far as this was done in these observations, the few points of interest will here be briefly stated.

Bromide of potassium, when administered in certain doses, is known to produce sleep, and acts, therefore, as an hypnotic. This effect, it is supposed, is produced by a condition of cerebral anæmia induced by the drug, owing to contraction of the blood-vessels, which is said to ensue when this drug is administered.

In the above investigations it was found that all the potassium salts tried, namely, the iodide, bromide, and chloride, invariably produced dilatation pure and simple with large and small doses, and no contraction whatever resulted at any time of the experiments. It is therefore rendered exceedingly probable by the results obtained in these experiments that contraction of the blood-vessels is no part of, at least, the direct action of these salts, and if the latter produce dilatation at all, it can only be owing to an effect which they might possibly exert on the vaso-motor center in the medulla.

Cerebral anæmia, however, might still be produced even without the assumption of such an effect on the vaso-motor center, in about the following manner: In all the experiments which were made with potassium salts on the blood-vessels, considerable œdema of those organs through which the drug was allowed to flow was noticed. Hence, it must be assumed that one of the characteristic effects produced by these salts is to favor the transudation of fluids from out of the vessels into the surrounding lymphatics. The perivascular lymphatics, however, when completely filled, must necessarily compress to a certain extent the vascular lumen, and hence cause a much diminished flow of blood to the part, besides compressing the tissues outside of and immediately against them.

The conclusions drawn from these experiments are as follows:

(1) Calcium salts cause the vessels to contract by virtue of their stimulating influence on the vaso-motor ganglia.

(2) Sodium and ammonium salts excite, first, the ganglia of the vaso-dilators; next, those of the vaso-motors; hence producing at first dilatation, and afterwards contraction of the vessels.

(3) Potassium salts stimulate the ganglia of the vaso-dilator only, and consequently produce dilatation; if, however, as was shown in two observations, the dilatation which they produce is followed by contraction, this contraction is so extremely slight that it may practically be neglected; therefore, any stimulating influence on the vaso-motor ganglia which they might possess is insignificant when compared with that which they exert over the vaso-dilators.

H. G. BEYER. On the micro-organisms of lactic fermentation.

Medical News, November 6, 1886.

This paper is an experimental inquiry into the causes of the souring of milk.

The presence of microörganisms in liquids undergoing fermentation has hitherto been interpreted and explained in various ways. While some looked at those low forms of life as the

H. G. BEYER—Continued.

mere associates of these processes, attributing the real cause of the resulting decomposition to chemical ferments, others, though believing in the causation of fermentation by microörganisms, looked at these processes as physiological ones or else attributed them to a certain power of adaptability possessed by certain microbes to different conditions of life.

Lister was, perhaps, the first clearly to point out the fact that the peculiar and characteristic fermentative process by which milk becomes sour is initiated or directly caused by a certain species of microbe. While, however, Lister had proved this fact, it did not necessarily follow from his experiments alone that the same process might not also be called into existence by a chemical ferment produced by the lacteal glands, and which was contained in the milk when it left these glands.

The matter, therefore, even after Lister's famous experiments, remained as undecided as ever, and the contention which has grown up between chemists and biologists for ages past had not been diminished in any way.

In the mean time our methods of bacteriological research having been greatly improved by the patient and admirable researche of Prof. Robert Koch, it had become necessary to reinvestigate this whole question. The task has, indeed, been most ably performed by Dr. Heuppe, whose researches will be found embodied in a recent contribution to our knowledge of lactic acid fermentation and fermentation in general, published in the *Mittheilungen d. kaiserlichen Gesundheitsamtes*, Berlin, 1884.

In this paper Heuppe has, we think, successfully demonstrated the fact that lactic acid fermentation, or the process of the souring of milk, by which the sugar contained in milk is converted into lactic and carbonic acids, is directly dependent on or caused by a certain definite variety of microörganism, the morphological and physiological character of which renders it sufficiently distinct from any other known microbe.

Heuppe has demonstrated his point in the following manner: First, by showing that this particular organism is constantly associated with lactic-acid fermentation; second, by separating it from other microörganisms; third, by cultivating it outside the original media in which it occurs, so as to separate chemical by-products; fourth, by the inoculation of pure cultures into the proper media producing the characteristic decomposition; fifth, by ascertaining the biological conditions under which this process of fermentation is brought about in the best manner.

Although Heuppe himself is exceedingly guarded in his conclusions, the results obtained by him from the very accurate series of experiments made according to the most modern and advanced methods, will, no doubt, be fully realized by even those who are but slightly familiar with the history of fermentation and the long struggle which has existed for ages, and still exists between chemists and biologists with regard to the nature and causes of fermentation. This alone would, no doubt, form sufficient pretext for a critical examination and repetition of at least a portion of Heuppe's experiments. But aside from this, and in spite of the fact that importation of Heuppe's lactic-acid germ is most likely to be an almost daily occurrence on this side of the Atlantic, the identity between it and the germs which cause the same decomposition in American milk must be proven by the same methods and experiments, in order to make this mere supposition a certainty.

With this object in view, I gladly took advantage of an opportunity kindly offered to me this summer by Drs. E. D. Salmon and Theobald Smith, of the Bureau of Animal Industry, U. S. Department of Agriculture, of working out this problem in their well-equipped laboratory.

In repeating Heuppe's experiments, so far as th is was done by me, it was, of course, thought best to follow out the same course of experimenting and to use the same methods as were used by him, and the first question, therefore, which naturally arose was, What microörganisms, if any, do we find in sour milk as it occurs in our market?

Bacterium lactis may be described as a short, thick, plump, little rod, distinctly ovoidal in shape, about half as broad as long, and varying in length from 1 to 2μ, its breadth remaining tolerably uniform. The best specimens may be found in milk cultures, the smallest in beef-infusion-pepton-gelatine cultures. As the bacterium lengthens a slight constriction about its middle portion becomes noticeable, which soon broadens and deepens, giving rise, just before complete division takes place, to the figure-8 form. This form becomes more especially noticeable in preparations stained with methyl-violet, which leaves a very minute central portion of the protoplasm unstained. The germ does not liquefy gelatine, and when examined on the hollow side it is found to be motionless. With regard to spore-formation our experiments have not been attended by very positive results, although everything else seems to indicate that they do form spores. The settlement of this question will form one of the subjects of future investigations.

The results of the foregoing experiments have led me to agree fully with those obtained by Heuppe, namely, lactic-acid fermentation, or the process of the souring of milk during which the sugar contained in the latter is converted into lactic and carbonic acids, is directly dependent or caused by the life and growth of a certain definite variety of microörganism, the

H. G. BEYER—Continued.

  physiological characters of which are sufficiently distinct to differentiate it from any other known organism, and which, therefore, may be properly designated as *Bacterium lactis*.

H. G. BEYER. The direct action of Atropine, Hyoscine, Hyoscyamine, and Daturine on the Heart of the Dog, Terrapin, and Frog.

  American Journal of the Medical Sciences, April, 1887.

  The question of the action of atropine and its congeners on the vascular system of animals has, perhaps, been the most difficult and perplexing which ever presented itself to the physiologist.

  For a period of fifty years physiologists have been engaged with this problem, many experiments having been made, many bitter controversies having been fought out during this time, and yet the question could hardly be said to have been satisfactorily answered.

  So far as the action of atropia on the heart is concerned, the best authorities still differ in about the following points : (1) That its action may be fully explained by assuming that a paralyzing influence is exerted on the terminal filaments of the pneumogastrics; (2) that atropia at first stimulates and then paralyzes these filaments ; (3) that it not only paralyzes these filaments, but also, and at the same time, stimulates the vaso-motor apparatus of the heart.

  It seemed to me that the question of the action of atropine had gained anew in interest and importance with the discoveries of Gaskell on the origin, course, and distribution of the nerves supplying certain viscera. He found, for instance, that the heart of both cold and warm blooded animals was supplied with two kinds of nerve-filaments, the stimulation of the one accelerating and augmenting the heart's action, that of the other retarding or altogether stopping its action.

  It was thought that by a careful study of the action of atropine on the isolated heart it might be possible to attain good evidence as to how it affected at least the peripheral portions of this double nerve-supply and whether it stimulates or paralyzes the one kind of nerves to the exclusion of the other, or whether it affected both alike, and if so, how is this action influenced by the quantity of the drug administered at the time ?

  After a great many experiments of this kind, the conclusions which were finally reached were as follows:

  (1) Atropine, homatropine, hyoscine, hyoscyamine, and daturine are stimulants of the sympathetic nerve-apparatus of the heart.

  (2) The vaso-motor portion of this nerve-apparatus is affected by comparatively small doses of the drugs, giving rise to either acceleration or augmentation of the heart's action.

  (3) The inhibitory portion is excited by large doses only, giving rise to slowing of the heart's action, and, finally, causing diastolic arrest.

  (4) The muscular substance of the heart is greatly excited by atropine, homatropine, and daturine, and only slightly so by hyoscine and hyoscyamine.

  (5) The vaso-motor nerves and their ganglia are the first to become exhausted, the inhibitory ganglia and their nerves are the next, and the muscular substance is exhausted last of all.

  (6) The slowing of the heart's action which follows the administration of these drugs in the intact animal may be sufficiently accounted for by their influence on the inhibitory nerves and ganglia of the heart itself.

  (7) The acceleration following the administration of certain doses of these drugs can not be sufficiently accounted for by their action on the accelerator nerves and ganglia within the heart, but is principally due to causes resident outside this organ.

  The essential points brought out by these experiments are that both vaso-motor as well as inhibitory nerves are stimulated by the atropines, but that the former are affected by small doses, the latter by large doses only; hence a large dose causing an excitation of the vaso-inhibitory portion of this nerve-apparatus may entirely cover up the vaso-motor excitement which is present simultaneously with that of the vaso-inhibitory portion of the nerve-apparatus. Inasmuch, however, as large doses quickly paralyze the vaso-motor apparatus, and also as the vaso-motor become exhausted sooner than the vaso-inhibitory nerves, the slowing of the heart's action following primary acceleration must be looked upon as a sign of much greater danger than the latter, and is indicative of much more profound action, for if this influence is not arrested it will terminate in diastolic arrest.

  A point of interest needing to be emphasized is that different doses of the same drug may produce results on the same organ that are diametrically opposed to each other.

  The influence of atropine on organs of similar innervation, as is the heart, is assumed to be identical with that exerted on the heart.

H. G. BEYER. On some of the problems to be solved by pharmaco-physiology, with a new outline classification of Pharmacology.

  Medical News, 1887.

  In this paper some of the more important problems in pharmaco-physiology are discussed.

H. G. BEYER—Continued.

Particular attention is called to the necessity of investigating the action of drugs with due regard to the chemical constitution of the latter, and examples are cited showing, beyond doubt the relation which exists between chemical constitution and physiological action.

A new outline classification of the whole science of pharmacology is included in this article, with explanatory notes of each of the terms used in this classification, which is as follows:

Pharmacology
- Descriptive..
  - Pharmaco-mineralogy..
  - Pharmaco-botany ......
  - Pharmaco-zoology......
- Experimental
  - Pharmaco-physics......
  - Pharmaco-chemistry ...
  - Pharmaco-physiology ..
  - Pharmaco-pathology ..
} Pharmaco-therapy.

H. G. BEYER. The action of Tropin Hydrochlorate and Sodium Tropate on the peripheral blood-vessels.

American Journal of the Medical Sciences, 1887.

By a careful experimental study of the influence of atropine on isolated organs we have been able to furnish good pharmacological evidence in proof of the fact that this alkaloid exerts a double action on those organs which are supplied by both motor and inhibitory sympathetic-nerve structure.

It has been shown that very small doses of the drug will stimulate the motor-nerve elements and that larger doses of it will stimulate the inhibitory portion of the nerve-supply of these organs. Thus, very small doses of atropine will give rise to contraction of the pupil, to acceleration of the heart's action, to increased peristalsis of the intestine; large doses, on the contrary, produce dilatation of the pupil, arrest the heart in diastole, and stop the peristaltic movements of the intestine. Furthermore, in view of the important researches of Ladenburg on the chemical constitution of atropine, it seemed to me strongly advisable to try and ascertain if this double action of atropine could possibly be explained by a careful study and comparison of the action of its two constituents, tropin and tropic acid.

The pupil did not seem to me a sufficiently typical object for the determination of this all-important point, and I therefore concluded to try the blood-vessels, more especially since it is now looked upon generally as a well-settled question in physiology that the blood-vessels are supplied by two kinds of nerve structures, namely, vaso-motor and vaso-inhibitory, or dilator, the stimulation of the former causing vaso-constriction, that of the latter giving rise to vaso-dilatation.

Consequently, we might argue that tropic acid is that part of the molecule of atropine which causes pupillary dilation, and if we have, furthermore, reasons to believe that tissues which are identical, both in histological structure and physiological function, are al o similarly affected by the same chemical stimuli, then it ought to follow that this same portion of the molecule of atropine should give rise to vaso-dilatation. Atropine, however, producing also vaso-constriction (in small doses at least), it would perhaps further follow that the remaining portion of the molecule should give rise to vaso-constriction.

In these experiments on the blood-vessels with sodium tropate and tropin hydrochlorate an improved method was used. Instead of an artificial heart and lung to arterialize and pump the blood through the blood-vessels, as had been used in the latest researches of this kind by Drs. von Frey and Gruber, a natural heart and lung were interposed between the blood-reservoirs and the blood-vessels. Hence this method is free from all those objections which still cling to the old method, and, consequently, the result ought to be reliable.

After making a number of experiments, it was found that tropin hydrochlorate produced vaso-constriction, and that sodium tropate gave rise to vaso-dilatation. We have here, then, an important and very decided illustration of the relation of chemical constitution to physiological action, and, at the same time, a very striking explanation of the double action of the alkaloid atropin.

H. G. BEYER. Report on the Section of Materia Medica in the U. S. National Museum, 1884.

Report Smithsonian Institution, 1884 (1886) II, pp. 75–77.

WILLIAM G. BINNEY. A second supplement to the fifth volume of the Terrestrial Air-breathing Mollusks of the United States and adjacent Territories.

Bull. Mus. Comp. Zoology, Harvard College, XIII, No. 2, Dec., 1886, pp. 23–48, Pl. I–III.

Contains a list of the locally introduced species, of the universally distributed species, and the species of the Central and Pacific provinces, with notes and new facts regarding them. The paper is partly based on material furnished by the Department of Mollusks, U. S. National Museum.

THOMAS BLAKISTON. Water birds of Japan.

 Proc. U. S. Nat. Mus., IX, 1886 Feb. 14, 1887, pp. 652–660.

 An important paper comparing the Japanese fauna of water-birds with that of the Pacific coast of North America.

GEORGE H. BOEHMER. Norsk Naval Architecture.

 Proc. U. S. Nat. Mus., IX, Dec. 8, 1886, pp. 443–459, 5 plates.

CHARLES H. BOLLMAN. Notes on a collection of Fishes from the Escambia River, with description of a new species of *Zygonectes* (*Zygonectes escambiæ*).

 Proc. U. S. Nat. Mus., IX, Nov. 26, 1886, pp. 462–465.

 Twenty-two species of Alabama fishes noted, most of them briefly. *Zygonectes cingulatus* and *Etheostoma squamiceps* described. Note on name of the Striped Bass.

WILLIAM BREWSTER. Additional notes on Peale's Petrel (*Æstrelata gularis*).

 The Auk, III, 1886, pp. 389–393.

 Æstrelata scalaris described as a new species and compared with the types of *Æ. gularis* (Peale) and *Æ. fisheri* Ridgw. belonging to the National Museum.

WILLIAM BREWSTER. Three New Forms of North American Birds.

 The Auk, IV, 1887, pp. 145–149.

 The new forms are named as follows: *Symphemia semipalmata inornata; Phalænoptilus nuttalli nitidus;* and *Vireo noveboraceensis maynardi.* The types of the latter belong to the National Museum, and additional Museum material was also utilized by the author.

WILLIAM BREWSTER. The Redpolls of Massachusetts.

 The Auk, IV, 1887, pp. 163, 164.

 The specimens in question were forwarded to the National Museum for comparison and identification.

W. EDWIN BROOKS. Additional Notes on the Genus *Acanthis*.

 The Ibis, 1886, pp. 359–364.

 Based chiefly on material borrowed from the National Museum.

KATHARINE J. BUSH. List of Deep-Water Mollusca dredged by the United States Fish Commission steamer *Fish Hawk* in 1880, 1881, and 1882, with their range in depth.

 Report U. S. Commissioner of Fish and Fisheries, Part XI, for 1883, pp. 701–727.

 This list is intended to include all the Mollusca dredged by the *Fish Hawk* in the region of the Gulf Stream, that have been determined. In general, only those species that have been taken below 60 fathoms are included, except the surface species inhabiting the same region. The total number of species recorded is 269, distributed among the several groups as follows: Cephalopoda, 17 species; Gasteropoda, 142 species; Pteropoda, 13 species; Solenochoncha, 8 species; Lamellibranchiata, 88 species; Brachiopoda, 1 species.

A. HOWARD CLARK. The American Whale Fishery, 1877–1886.

 Science, IX, No. 217, April 1, 1887, pp. 321–324.

A. HOWARD CLARK. Fish Preservation by Acids.

 Forest and Stream, XXVIII, No. 22, June 23, 1887, p. 479.

A. HOWARD CLARK. The Iced and Frozen Fish Trade.

 Forest and Stream, XXVII, No. 3, Aug. 12, 1886, p. 50.

A. HOWARD CLARK. Notes on the History of preparing fish for market, by freezing.

 Bull. U. S. Fish Com., VI, No. 29, March 27, 1886, pp. 467–469.

F. W. CLARKE. Researches on the Lithia Micas.

 Amer. Jour. of Science, XXXII, Nov., 1886, pp. 353–361.

 Discusses the composition of the Maine lepidolites and the iron micas of Cape Ann.

F. W. CLARKE. A Check-List of the Meteorites represented in the collection of the U. S. National Museum.

 Circular U. S. Nat. Mus., pp. 1–4.

F. W. CLARKE. The New Alchemy.

 The Epoch, Feb. 25, 1887.

F. W. CLARKE. Saccharin.

 The Epoch, June 17, 1887.

F. W. CLARKE. Administrative Report of the Division of Chemistry and Physics, U. S. Geological Survey.

Sixth Annual Report U. S. Geological Survey, pp. 86-88.

F. W. CLARKE and J. S. DILLER. Turquoise from New Mexico.

Amer. Jour. of Science, XXXII, Sept., 1886, pp. 211-217.

The turquoise from Los Cerillos.

F. W. CLARKE and others. A Report of the Work done in the Division of Chemistry and Physics, mainly during the fiscal year 1884-'85.

Bull. U. S. Geologial Survey, 27, pp. 3-80 ; also in Sixth Annual Report, pp. 535-610.

F. W. CLARKE. [Various abstracts of papers upon Atomic Weight, published in the Journal of Analytical Chemistry.]

F. W. CLARKE. [Report on the] Department of Mineralogy [in the U. S. National Museum, 1884].

Report Smithsonian Institution, 1884 (1886) II, pp. 221-225.

H. K. COALE. Geographical variations between *Chondestes grammacus* (Say) and *Chondestes grammacus strigatus* (Swains.).

Ridgway Ornith. Club, Bull. No. 2, 1887, pp. 24, 25.

Points out the distinguishing characters of the two races, the demonstration being in part based on specimens borrowed from the National Museum.

H. K. COALE. Description of a new species and subspecies of the genus *Dendroica*.

Ridgway Ornith. Club, Bull. No. 2, 1887, pp. 82, 83.

Based almost entirely on specimens in the National Museum, two of which are also the type specimens of the two new forms described as *D. œstiva worcomi* and *D. dugesi.*

J. W. COLLINS. Notes on an Investigation of the Great Fishing Banks of the Western Atlantic.

Bull. U. S. Fish. Com., VI, No. 24, Dec. 31, 1886, pp. 369-381.

These notes relate to researches made during a cruise of the U. S. Fish Commission steamer *Albatross*, from June 17 to July 16, 1885, with the object of investigating the fauna and fishing grounds of the chain of great ocean banks between Cape Cod and Newfoundland. Many references are made to the fishes and marine invertebrates taken in the trawls and dredges, and by means of hooks and lines. These specimens are now in the National Museum.

J. W. COLLINS. A curious Knife found in the Head of a Cod-fish.

Bull. U. S. Fish Com., VI, No. 24, Dec. 31, 1886, pp. 381-383, 1 cut.

J. W. COLLINS. Notes on the Red-Snapper Fishery.

Bull. U. S. Fish Com., VI, No. 19, Nov. 18, 1886, pp. 299, 300.

J. W. COLLINS. Report of J. W. Collins [Report on the work of the United States Fish Commission schooner *Albatross* for the year ending December 31, 1883, pp. 117-236. By Lieut. Commander Z. L. Tanner, U. S. Navy, commanding].

Report U. S. Commissioner of Fish and Fisheries, part XI, for 1883 (1886), pp. 164-174.

J. W. COLLINS. Report on the Section of Naval Architecture in the U. S. National Museum, 1884.

Report Smithsonian Institution, 1884 (1886) II, pp. 85-106.

E. D. COPE. [Descriptions of new species of Mexican Reptiles, constituting part III of Catalogue of animals collected by the Geographical and Exploring Commission of the Republic of Mexico. By Fernando Ferrari-Perez.]

Proc. U. S. Nat. Mus., IX, Sept. 28, 1886, pp. 182-199.

CHARLES B. CORY. The Birds of the West Indies, including the Bahama Islands, the Greater and the Lesser Antilles, excepting the Islands of Tobago and Trinidad. (Continued.)

The Auk, III, 1886, pp. 337-381, pp. 454-472 ; IV, 1887, pp. 137-151, pp. 108-120.

In the preparation of this paper the author has been assisted by loan of specimens in the National Museum.

CHARLES B. CORY. Description of Thirteen New Species of Birds from the Island of Grand Cayman, West Indies.

The Auk, III, 1886, pp. 497-501.

The new species which were compared with material in the National Museum are named as follows: *Certhiola sharpei ; Dendroica vitellina ; Chrysotis caymanensis ; Colaptes gundlachi ; Engyptila collaris ; Zenaida spadicea ; Centurus caymanensis ; Mimocichla ravida ; Quiscalus caymanensis ; Spindalis salvini ; Vireo alleni ; Myiarchus denigratus ; Icterus bairdi*

BIBLIOGRAPHY. 571

CHARLES B. CORY. A List of the Birds collected in the Island or Grand Cayman, West Indies, by W. D. Richardson, during the Summer of 1886.

The Auk, III, 1886, pp. 501, 502.

Enumerates 40 species. The National Museum acquired a number of them in exchange with Mr. Cory.

WILLIAM HEALEY DALL. Report on the Mollusca.

Part 1. Brachiopoda and Pelecypoda. *Bulletin of the Museum of Comparative Zoology*, XII, No. 6.

(Reports on the results of dredging under the supervision of Alexander Agassiz in the Gulf of Mexico (1877-'78) and in the Caribbean Sea (1879-'80) by the U. S. Coast Survey steamer *Blake*, Lieut. Commander C. D. Sigsbee, U. S. Navy, and Commander J. R. Bartlett, U. S. Navy, commanding. No. XXIX. 8vo, pp. 171-318, Plates I-IX, Cambridge, the Museum. September, 1886.)

This paper comprises the first part of the report on the deep-sea Mollusca collected on the *Blake* expeditions, and consists, first, of a general discussion of the conditions of molluscan life at various depths, the effect of these conditions upon variation and specific equilibrium, a classification of the regions of the sea bottom, and a review of the fauna of the depths as now known; second, of a description of the brachiopods and pelecypods of the *Blake* collection and illustrative species amounting to thirteen species and varieties of brachiopods and two hundred and fourteen of pelecypods (beside thirty mentioned or described as illustrative), comprising three new families, twelve new subgenera or sections, and eighty-one new species, beside those previously known.

In addition to description of the shells, etc., anatomical details of high importance and previously unknown are given for many species of the *Pectenidæ*; for Dimya, previously known only as a fossil for species of *Modiola* and *Arca*, for the new family *Poromyidæ*, and for the *Verticordiidæ*, *Cuspidariidæ*, and species of *Anatinidæ*.

The important fact of the absence of gills in the genus *Cuspidaria* (formerly known as *Neæra*) is established, with many details and a re-arrangement of the genera and sections of the group as well as of the *Poromyidæ* and *Verticordiidæ*.

A new and recent species of the genus *Isocardia*, section *Meiocardia*, hitherto represented by a single species in oriental seas, is shown to inhabit the Antilles, and the nomenclature of many American mollusks is revised and corrected.

WILLIAM HEALEY DALL. Report on the Mollusks collected by L. M. Turner, at Ungava Bay, North Labrador, and from the adjacent Arctic seas.

Proc. U. S. Nat. Mus., IX, Oct. 11, 1886, pp. 202-208, pl. iii, figs. 1-3.

This report enumerates four pulmonates, two pteropods, nine marine gastropods, eight pelecypods, and one brachiopod, with notes. Of these, one genus, *Aquilonaria*, with its type *A. turneri*, is described as new.

WILLIAM HEALEY DALL. Contribution to the Natural History of the Commander Islands. No. 6. Report on Bering Island Mollusca, collected by Mr. Nicholas Grebnitzki.

Proc. U. S. Nat. Mus., IX, Oct. 11, 1886, pp. 209-219.

In this paper seventy-five species are enumerated, with notes and a summary and revision of the existing knowledge as to the Mollusk fauna of the Commander Islands. The name *Osteochiton* is proposed for the group typified by *Placiphora sinuata* Carpenter; *Haloconcha* for Lacunella Dall. (pre-occupied by Deshayes), and a new variety, *atkana*, of *Litorina sitkana* Phil., is described.

WILLIAM HEALEY DALL. Supplementary notes on some species of Mollusks of the Bering Sea and vicinity.

Proc. U. S. Nat. Mus., IX, Oct. 19, 1886, pp. 297-309, pls. iii and iv.

In this paper besides numerous notes and corrections in regard to previously known species, the following are described and figured:

Bela sculpturata, *B. krausei*, *B. solida*; *Cerithiopsis truncatum*, *Velutina conica*, *Cingula robusta* var. *martyni* and var. *scipio*, *Onoba cerinella*, *O. aleutica*, *Alvania castanea* var. *alaskana*, *A. castanella*, *A. aurivillii*, and *Macoma* var. *middendorffii*.

The following are figured for the first time: *Mangilia aleutica*, *Bela lævigata*, *B. harpa*, and *Trophon muriciformis*. *Mangilia funebrale* Dall is shown to be a synonym of *M. levidensis* Cpr., and *Trophon Stuarti* Smith of *T. orpheus* Gould.

WILLIAM HEALEY DALL. Alleged early Chinese voyages to America.

Science, VIII, No. 196, Nov. 5, 1886, pp. 402, 403.

Calls attention to the uncertain character of the evidence generally adduced in favor of these voyages, and corrects several wide-spread erroneous statements bearing on this topic.

WILLIAM HEALEY DALL. The Religion of the Uapé.
Science, VIII, No. 197, Nov. 12, 1886, pp. 437, 438.
Summarizes the religious system and practices of this South American people.

WILLIAM HEALEY DALL. The People on the Kongo.
Science, VIII, No. 197, Nov. 12, 1886, pp. 441, 442.
A summary of Walck's observations.

WILLIAM HEALEY DALL. Isaac Lea, LL. D.
Science, VIII, No. 202, Dec. 17, 1886, pp. 556–558.
Notice of Dr. Lea's life and services, with portrait.

WILLIAM HEALEY DALL. Museums of Ethnology and their classification.
Science, IX, No. 228, June 17, 1887, p. 587.
States the problems which confront a curator with a museum of ethnology to classify, and the results which may be attained by adopting either solution.

WILLIAM HEALEY DALL. The Nestor of American Naturalists.
Swiss Cross, I, No. 2, Feb. 1887, pp. 43, 44.
A biographical notice, for young readers, of the life and works of Dr. Isaac Lea.

WILLIAM HEALEY DALL. Report on the Department of Mollusks in the United States National Museum, 1884.
Report Smithsonian Institution, 1884 (1886) II, pp. 179–184.

FREDERIC P. DEWEY. [Report on the] Department of Metallurgy and Economic Geology [in the National Museum, 1884].
Report Smithsonian Institution, 1884 (1886) II, pp. 239–276.

GEORGE E. DOERING. Analyses of the Cinchona Barks on exhibition in the Materia Medica Section, U. S. National Museum.
Proc. U. S. Nat. Mus., IX, Oct. 30, 1886, pp. 438–442.

CHARLES L. EDWARDS. (See under JORDAN and EDWARDS.)

CARL H. EIGENMANN and ELIZABETH G. HUGHES. A Review of the North American Species of the Genera Lagodon, Archosargus, and Diplodus.
Proc. U. S. Nat. Mus., X, May 17, 1887, pp. 65–74.
Key to the genera Sparus, Lagodon, Archosargus, Diplodus, Stenotomus, and Calamus, and to the species of each genus. Notes on skeletons.
(See under JORDAN and EIGENMANN.)

W. OTIS EMERSON. Ornithological Observations in San Diego County.
Bulletin Calif. Acad. Science, II, 1887, pp. 419–431.
Several of the specimens identified by Mr. Ridgway from specimens sent to the National Museum for the purpose.

BARTON W. EVERMANN. (See under JORDAN and EVERMANN.)

FERNANDO FERRARI-PEREZ. Catalogue of Animals collected by the Geographical and Exploring Commission of the Republic of Mexico.*
Proc. U. S. Nat. Mus., IX, 1886, pp. 125–199.
This catalogue includes the following subjects: I. Mammals; II. Birds; III. Reptiles.

J. WALTER FEWKES. Report on the Medusæ collected by the U. S. Fish Commission steamer Albatross in the region of the Gulf Stream in 1883–'84.
Report U. S. Commissioner of Fish and Fisheries, Part XII, for 1884 (1886), pp. 927–980, pl. 1–10.
The following new families, genera, and species are described:

ACRASPEDA.

Periphylla humilis, sp. nov., p. 931.
Atolla Bairdii, sp. nov., pl. 1–3, p. 936.
Verrillii, sp. nov., pl. 4–5, p. 939.
Nauphantopsis, gen. nov., pl. 6, p. 944.
Diomedeæ, sp. nov., pl. 6, p. 946.
Ephyroides, gen. nov., pl. 7, p. 948.
rotaformis, sp. nov., pl. 7, p. 949

NARCOMEDUSÆ.

Halicreasidæ, fam. nov., p. 952.
Solmaris incisa, sp. nov., pl. 9, p. 954.

HYDROIDA.

Polycanna Americana, sp. nov., p. 959.
Mesonema Bairdii, sp. nov., p. 962.

PNEUMATOPHORÆ.

Rhizophysa uvaria, sp. nov., p. 967.
Pterophysa, gen. nov., pl. 10, p. 968.
grandis, sp. nov., pl. 10, figs. 1–3, p. 969.
Angelidæ, fam. nov., p. 971.
Angelopsis, gen. nov., p. 971.
globosa, sp. nov., pl. 10, fi, s. 4, 5, p. 972.

*A great many of the specimens enumerated have become the property of the National Museum.

MORTON W. FORDICE. (See under JORDAN and FORDICE.)

WILLIAM H. FOX. List of Birds found in Roane County, Tennessee, during April, 1884, and March and April, 1885.

> *The Auk*, III, 1886, pp. 315–320.
>
> "The present list is one of special importance as being the first pertaining to the birds of Tennessee of which I have any knowledge. With the exception of the few not marked with an asterisk (prefixed to the number) the species are verified by specimens in the National Museum collection, which have been kindly presented by Dr. Fox." (From a foot-note by R. Ridgway.)

WILLIAM H. FOX. *Vireo solitarius alticola* in Tennessee.

> *The Auk*, IV, 1887, p. 164.
>
> The specimens referred to are in the National Museum.

B T. GAULT. *Ammodromus beldingi* Ridgw. (Belding's March Sparrow.)

> *Ridgway Ornith. Club*, Bull. No. 2, 1887, pp. 58–60.
>
> One of the three specimens mentioned was sent to the National Museum for identification.

RANDOLPH I. GEARE. Mexican Antiquities.

> *Popular Science Monthly*, XXXI, No. 1, May, 1887, pp. 79–83. Four cuts.

CHARLES H. GILBERT. Description of new and little known Etheostomoids.

> *Proc. U. S. Nat. Mus.*, X, May 17, 1887, pp. 47–64.
>
> The species are all referred to *Etheostoma* with *Ulocentra, Cottogaster, Hadropterus, Rhothœca, Etheostoma*, and *Alvarius* as subgeneric subdivisions. *Ulocentra histrio, Cottogaster uranidea, Hadropterus ouachitæ, H. squamatus, H. cymatotænia, H. nianguæ, Rothœca blennius, R. rupestre, Etheostoma luteovinctum, E. parvipinne, E. tuscumbia, Alvarius fonticola*, nn. spp.; *Etheostoma nianguæ spilotum, E. whipplei alabamæ,* nn. sub-spp.
>
> (See under JORDAN and GILBERT.)

G. BROWN GOODE. Report upon the Condition and Progress of the U. S. National Museum, 1884.

> *Report Smithsonian Institution*, 1884 (1886) II, pp. 3–72.

G. BROWN GOODE. A Century of Electricity.

> *The Epoch*, New York, I, pp. 239–240, April 15, 1887.
>
> Review of T. C. Mendenhall's book of the same title.

G. BROWN GOODE. Scientific Men and Institutions in America

> *The Epoch*, New York, I, pp. 467–469, June 24, 1887.
>
> On the inadequacy of the organization of Science in the United States.

G. BROWN GOODE and TARLETON H. BEAN. Description of thirteen species and two genera of Fishes from the *Blake* Collection.

> *Bull Mus. Comp. Zool.*, XII, No. 5, pp. 153–170.
>
> *Barathronus* and *Benthosaurus*, nn. gg., *Aphyonus* and *Bregmaceros* represented by new Atlantic species.

N. S. GOSS. The Snowy Plover on the Salt Plains of the Indian Territory and Kansas.

> *The Auk*, III, 1886, p. 409.
>
> Colonel Goss's birds were sent to the Museum for comparison.

N. S. GOSS. Additions to the Catalogue of the Birds of Kansas.

> *The Auk*, IV, 1887, p. 7–11.
>
> Specimens compared in National Museum.

H. W. HENSHAW. Description of a New Jay from California.

> *The Auk*, III, 1886, pp. 452, 453.
>
> Described as *Aphelocoma insularis*, from specimens in the National Museum.

H. W. HENSHAW. Occurrence of *Ammodromus caudacutus nelsoni* in Massachusetts.

> *The Auk*, III, 1886, p. 416.
>
> Refers partly to specimens in the National Museum.

ROMYN HITCHCOCK. Report on the Section of Textile Industries in the U. S. National Museum, 1884.

> *Report Smithsonian Institution*, 1884 (1886) II, pp. 79–84.

ROMYN HITCHCOCK. Report on the Section of Foods of the U. S. National Museum. 1884.

> *Report Smithsonian Institution*, 1884 (1885) II, pp. 107, 108.

WILLIAM H. HOLMES. Ancient Pottery of the Mississippi Valley.

> *Fourth Annual Report of the Bureau of Ethnology*, pp. 257–260.

WILLIAM H. HOLMES.   Pottery of the Ancient Pueblos.
Fourth Annual Report of the Bureau of Ethnology, pp. 361-436.

WILLIAM H. HOLMES.   Origin and Development of Form and Ornament in the Ceramic Art.
Fourth Annual Report of the Bureau of Ethnology, pp. 437-465.

WILLIAM H. HOLMES.   A sketch of the Great Serpent Mound.
Science, VIII, No. 204, Dec. 31, 1886, p. 624-628.

WILLIAM T. HORNADAY.   "The Last Buffalo Hunt:" A series of eight newspaper letters, published weekly, from March 6, 1887, to April 24, inclusive, in the New York *Sun*, Boston *Globe*, Philadelphia *Press*, Pittsburgh *Dispatch*, Chicago *Inter-Ocean*, Detroit *Tribune*, Indianapolis *Journal*, St. Louis *Globe-Democrat*, Washington *Star*, St. Paul *Pioneer-Press*, Omaha *Herald*, Portland *Oregonian*.
The sub-titles of the letters were as follows:
  I. The Extermination of the Great American Bison.
  II. Closing in on the Remnant.
  III. The Game Begins to Fall.
  IV. The Pursuit of the Pronghorn.
  V. Robbed by Redskins.
  VI. Deer Hunting on the Musselshell.
  VII. The Death of the Twentieth Buffalo.
  VIII. Buffalo Hunters in a Blizzard.
  An informal narrative of the Smithsonian Exploration for American Bison in 1886, prefaced by a statement of the causes which made it necessary, and the condition of the species at the present day. Its total extinction in a wild state is predicted to take place in less than five years.

WALTER HOUGH.   Thumb Marks.
Science, VIII, No. 185, Aug. 20, 1886, p. 166.
Notice of the anthropological investigation of the markings on the skin of the hand, especially of the thumb, with regard to its value as a racial characteristic. Also notes used in China for purposes of identification and by women and illiterates in signing papers.

WALTER HOUGH.   A Bayanzi execution.
Science, IX, No. 229, June 24, 1887, p. 615, 1 fig.
Description of the executioner's sword and mode of execution among the Bayanzi of the Congo. The sword figured was presented to the Museum by Lieut. E. H Taunt, U. S. Navy.

WALTER HOUGH.   Notes on the Bernadou Corean collection.
New Dominion, Morgantown, West Virginia, Aug. 7, 1887.

ELIZABETH G. HUGHES.   (See under EIGENMANN and HUGHES and JORDAN and HUGHES.)

DAVID S. JORDAN.   A record of collections of Fishes made under the auspices of the U. S. Fish Commission and the U. S. National Museum from 1875 to 1885.
Report Smithsonian Institution, 1884, II (1886), pp. 169-178.
This forms a portion of Dr. T. H. Bean's report on the Department of Fishes in the U. S. National Museum, 1884.

DAVID S. JORDAN.   A preliminary list of the Fishes of the West Indies.
Proc. U. S. Nat. Mus., IX, 1886 (Jan. 25, 1887), pp. 554-608.
Eight hundred and seventy-five species, besides a supplementary list of fifty-one species not yet found in, but properly belonging to, the West Indies.

DAVID S. JORDAN.   List of Fishes collected at Havana, Cuba, in December, 1883, with notes and descriptions.
Proc. U. S. Nat. Mus., IX (Aug. 14, 1886), pp. 31-55.
Two hundred and four species collected in the markets. Spanish names in use at Havana are given. Color notes and brief descriptions of many species. Some species are fully described. *Prionotus rubio, Citharichthys œthalion*, nn. spp.; *Scartella* Poey, n. g.

DAVID S. JORDAN.   Notes on Fishes collected at Beaufort, North Carolina, with a revised list of the species known from that locality.
Proc. U. S. Nat. Mus., IX, Aug. 14, 1886, pp. 25-30.
List of one hundred and fourteen species, with the names only, except in regard to *Serranus dispilurus* (= *subligarius*), *Gobionellus encœomus, Hypleurochilus geminatus, Etropus microstomus, Hippocampus punctulatus*.

DAVID S. JORDAN. Notes on some Fishes collected at Pensacola, by Mr. Silas Stearns, with description of one new species (*Chœtodon aya*).

    Proc. U. S. Nat. Mus., IX, Oct. 11, 1886, pp. 225–229.

    Nine species. Full descriptions of *Chœtodon aya*, *Cryptotomus ustus*, and *Prionotus stearnsi*. Key to American species of *Cryptotomus*.

DAVID S. JORDAN. Notes on typical specimens of Fishes described by Cuvier and Valenciennes, and preserved in the Musée d'Histoire Naturelle in Paris.

    Proc. U. S. Nat. Mus., IX, Nov. 26, 1886, pp. 525–546.

    Eighty-eight types examined and identified. *Marcgravia*, n. g., for *Batrachus cryptocentrus* C. and V.

DAVID S. JORDAN and CHARLES L. EDWARDS. A review of the American species of *Tetraodontidæ*.

    Proc. U. S. Nat. Mus., IX, Oct. 13, 1886, pp. 230–247.

    Fourteen species, belonging to the genera *Lagocephalus*, *Sphæroides*, *Tetraodon*, *Colomesus*, and *Canthigaster*.

DAVID S. JORDAN and CARL H. EIGENMANN. A review of the *Gobiidæ* of North America.

    Proc. U. S. Nat. Mus., IX, Nov. 26, 1886, pp. 477–518.

    Genera admitted: *Ioglossus*, *Gobiomorus*, *Dormitator*, *Guavina*, *Eleotris*, *Erotelis*, *Gymneleotris*, *Sicydium*, *Sicyopterus*, *Evorthodus*, *Lophogobius*, *Gobius*, *Chonophorus*, *Lepidogobius*, *Microgobius*, *Gobiosoma*, *Gillichthys*, *Typhlogobius*, *Tyntlastes*, and *Gobioides*. Keys to all the species. Notes on skeletons.

DAVID S. JORDAN and BARTON W. EVERMANN. Description of six new species of Fishes from the Gulf of Mexico, with notes on other species.

    Proc. U. S. Nat. Mus., IX, Nov. 26, 1886, pp. 466–476.

    Callechelys murœna, *Serranus ocyurus*, *Scarus evermanni*, *S. bollmani*, *Prionotus roseus*, nn. spp.; *Steinegeria rubescens*, n. g. and n. sp. Descriptions of *Narcine brasiliensis*, *Sidera nigromarginata*, *Myrophis punctatus*, and *Pronotogrammus vivanus*, besides brief notes on other species.

DAVID S. JORDAN and MORTON W. FORDICE. A review of the American species of *Belonidœ*.

    Proc. U. S. Nat. Mus., IX, Oct. 19, 1886, pp. 339–361.

    Genera admitted: *Belone*, *Tylosurus*, and *Potamorrhaphis*. Keys to all the species (21). *Belone belone*, *Tylosurus notatus*, *subtruncatus*, *euryops*, *exilis*, *marinus*, *raphidoma*, *acus*, *hians*, and *Potamorrhaphis guianensis* described.

DAVID S. JORDAN and CHARLES H. GILBERT. List of Fishes collected in Arkansas, Indian Territory, and Texas, in September, 1884, with notes and descriptions.

    Proc. U. S. Nat. Mus., IX, Aug. 14, 1886, pp. 1–25.

    Notropis sabinœ, n. sp.; *Hybopsis œstivalis marconis*, var. nov.

DAVID S. JORDAN and ELIZABETH G. HUGHES. A review of the species of the genus *Prionotus*.

    Proc. U. S. Nat. Mus., IX, Oct. 19, 1886, pp. 337, 338.

    Fifteen species discussed. Key to all. Critical notes on many species.

DAVID S. JORDAN and ELIZABETH G. HUGHES. A review of the genera and species of *Julidinæ* found in American waters.

    Proc. U. S. Nat. Mus., IX, Aug. 23, 1886, pp. 56–70.

    Genera admitted: *Platyglossus*, *Oxyjulis*, *Pseudojulis*, and *Thalassoma*. Keys to all the species. Critical notes on many; color notes on some.

F. H. KNOWLTON, Additions to the Flora of Washington and vicinity, from April 1, 1884, to April 1, 1886.

    Proc. Biological Society, Washington, III, 1884, pp. 106–132.

    The paper is divided into the following heads:

        I. List of vascular plants added to the flora from April 1, 1884, to April, 1886.

        II. Revision of Musci and Hepaticæ of Washington and vicinity.

        III. List of the lichens of Washington and vicinity.

        IV. Changes in nomenclature.

        V. New localities for rare species.

        VI. Species excluded.

F. H. KNOWLTON. A résumé of the Algo-Lichen hypothesis.

The American Monthly Microscopical Journal, Washington, VII, pp. 101–105.

Sums up briefly the principal arguments used in defense of the anatomy of the plants called lichens, being the results largely of recent European investigations.

F. H. KNOWLTON. A collection of Exotics.

The Botanical Gazette, XI, p. 250.

Describes the collection of exotics belonging to the U. S. National Museum.

F. H. KNOWLTON. Alaskan plants.

The Botanical Gazette, XI, p. 340.

Gives a list of twenty-four species of plants collected at Ounalaska by Mr. S. Applegate of the U. S. Signal Service.

F. H. KNOWLTON. Felix's "Die Fossilen Hölzer West Indiens."

The Botanical Gazette, XII, pp. 90, 91.

A short review of this important work on the fossil woods of the West Indies.

F. H. KNOWLTON. *Solidago bicolor* L., and var. *concolor* Torr. and Gray.

The Botanical Gazette, XII, p. 111.

Mentions the discovery of both these forms growing from the same root.

F. H. KNOWLTON. *Solidago erecta* Prush.

The Botanical Gazette, XII, p. 114.

Mentions the fact that this species has recently been reinstated by Dr. Gray and that the National Museum has a series for exchanges.

GEORGE N. LAWRENCE. Description of a new species of Thrush from the Island of Grenada, West Indies.

Annals N. Y. Acad. Science, VI, 1887, pp. 23, 24.

The new species is named *Margarops albiventris*. The type belongs to the National Museum.

GEORGE N. LAWRENCE. Description of new species of Birds of the families Sylviidæ, Troglodytidæ, and Tyrannidæ.

Annals N. Y. Acad. Science, VI, 1887, pp. 66–68.

The new species, which are named *Regulus satrapa aztecus, Troglodytes brachyurus, Octhœca flaviventris*, were compared with specimens of allied forms in the National Museum.

(See also under JOHN G. WELLS.)

LEO LESQUEREUX. List of recently identified fossil plants belonging to the U. S. National Museum, with descriptions of several new species. [Compiled and prepared for publication by F. H. Knowlton.]

Proceedings of the U. S. National Museum, X, pp. 21–46, pl. i–iv.

Gives list of two hundred and three species of fossil plants, identified from large mass of miscellaneous material accumulated through a long period of years by the Smithsonian Institution and National Museum.

EDWIN LINTON. Notes on two forms of Cestoid Embryos.

American Naturalist, Feb., 1887, pp. 1–7, pl. x.

Studies made at the Wood's Holl Station of the U. S. Fish Commission. The forms described and figured are, an embryo *Rhynchobothrium*, from the peritoneum of the blu fish, *Pomatomus saltatrix*, and an embryo *Tetrarhynchobothrium*, from the surface of the liver of the Cero, *Cymbium regale*.

FREDERIC A. LUCAS. The mounting of Mungo.

Science, VIII, No. 193, Oct. 15, 1886, pp. 337–341.

A description of the manner in which the young African elephant "Mungo" was mounted at the U. S. National Museum, with illustrations by W. H. Chandlee.

FREDERIC A. LUCAS. The affinities of *Chœtura*.

The Auk, III, No. 4, Oct., 1886, pp. 444–451.

A comparison of the skeleton of the Chimney Swift (*Chœtura pelasgia*) with that of the Swallows and Humming-birds, the conclusion being drawn that the affinities of the Swift were with the Humming-birds rather than with the Passeres.

FREDERIC A. LUCAS. Notes of a Bird-catcher.

The Auk, IV, No. 1, Jan., 1887, pp. 1–6.

Notes of the capture, habits, and distribution of some of the Antarctic *Procellaridœ*.

FREDERIC A. LUCAS. Official extermination.
Forest and Stream, XXVIII, No. 6, March 3, 1887, p. 104.
A reply to letter in Forest and Steam, denouncing the killing of the sea elephants collected for the U. S. National Museum.

FREDERIC A. LUCAS. Classification of the Macrochires.
The Auk, IV, No. 2, April, 1887, pp. 171, 172.
A reply to certain comments by Dr. R. W. Shufeldt on the affinities of *Chætura*.

FREDERIC A. LUCAS. Lepidoptera at Sea.
Science, IX, No. 218, April 8, 1887, pp. 340, 341.
Noting a remarkable occurrence of nocturnal Lepidoptera about 1, 000 miles from the coast of Brazil.

FREDERIC A. LUCAS. The rudimentary metacarpals of Bison.
Science, IX, No. 219, April 5, 1887, p. 363.
A letter referring to a previous communication by Dr. D. D. Slade, and questioning if there was as much difference between the metacarpals of the European and the American bison as Dr. Slade had been led to believe.

FREDERIC A. LUCAS. [Osteological notes on the rudimentary metacarpals of Bison.]
Science, IX, No. 223, May 13, 1887, pp. 460, 461.
(See also under D. D. SLADE and F.W. TRUE.)
This letter treats of the same subject as that referred to in the foregoing note. Mr. Lucas shows conclusively that the American bison possesses two rudimentary metacarpals.

FREDERIC A. LUCAS. The maxillo-palatines of *Tachycineta*.
Science, IX, No. 223, May 13, 1887, pp. 461, 462.
Reply to a letter of Dr. R. W. Shufeldt.

MARSHALL McDONALD. California Trout for the Ozark Mountain region.
Bull. U. S. Fish Com., VI, No. 28, March 24, 1887, pp. 447, 448.
Salmo irideus successfully introduced into Missouri. Specimens are in the National Museum.

JOHN BELKNAP MARCOU. Supplement to the list of Mesozoic and Cenozoic invertebrate types in the collections of the National Museum.
Proc. U. S. Nat. Mus., IX, Oct. 13, 1886, pp. 250–254.

O. T. MASON. Report on the Department of Ethnology in the U. S. National Museum, 1884.
Report Smithsonian Institution, 1884 (1886) II, pp. 109–122.

O. T. MASON. Throwing-sticks in the National Museum.
Report Smithsonian Institution, 1884 (1886) II, pp. 279-289, pls. i-xvii.

O. T. MASON. Basket-work of the North American Aborigines.
Report Smithsonian Institution, 1884 (1886) II, pp. 291-306, pls. i-lxiv·

O. T. MASON. Corea by native Artists.
Science, VIII, No. 183, Aug. 6, 1886, pp. 115-118, pl. 2.

O. T. MASON. Archæolological Enigmas.
Science, VIII, No. 201, Dec. 10, 1886, p. 528.

O. T. MASON. Guadalajara Pottery.
Science, VIII, No. 196, Nov. 5, 1886, pp. 405-408, pl. 2.

O. T. MASON. Planting and Exhuming a Prayer
Science, VIII, No. 179, July 9, 1886, p. 24, pl. 1.

O. T. MASON. Arrangement of Museums.
Science, IX, No. 225, May 27, 1887, p. 534.

O. T. MASON. Synechdochical Magic.
Science, IX, No. 205, Jan. 7, 1887, p. 17.

O. T. MASON. A Hairy Human Family.
Science, IX, No. 205, Jan. 7, 1887, p. 16.

O. T. MASON. The Aboriginal Miller.
Science, IX, No. 206, Jan. 14, 1887, pp. 25-28 ; 2 plates, 31 figures. Also in *The Swiss Cross*, I, Jan., 1887, pp. 19-22 ; 2 plates.

O. T. MASON. The Hupa Indians.
Science, IX, No. 221, Feb. 18, 1887, pp. 149-152 ; 2 plates, 33 figures.

O. T. MASON. Indian Cradles.
Science, IX, No. 229, Jan. 24, 1887, pp. 617–620 ; 2 plates.

O. T. MASON. Anthropological Notes in American Naturalist.
Davenport Academy Proceedings, vol. IV, July, 1886, p. 671.
Vocabulary of Archery, July, 1886, p. 673.
Anthropology in Brazil, Sept., 1886, p. 831.
Californian and Polynesian fish-hooks, Sept., 1886, p. 833.
Ancient Egyptian Classification of Races of Men, Sept., 1886, p. 834.
The Peabody Museum, Oct., 1887, p. 907.
West Indian Stone Implements, Oct., 1887, p. 908.
Indian Children's Games, Oct., 1887, p. 908.
Ancient Commerce, Oct., 1887, p. 909.
Melanesia, Oct., 1887, p. 910.
Archæological Frauds, Oct., 1887, p. 910.
Folk-lore, Nov., 1886, pp. 991–995.
Arrow Release, Nov., 1886, p. 995.
The Origin of Languages, Nov., 1886, p. 997.
Australian Medicine Men, Dec., 1886, p. 1067.
The Iconographic Encyclopædia, Dec., 1886, p. 1070.
Chinese Jade in America, vol. XXI, No. 1, Jan., 1887, p. 96.
Head-flattenings, Jan., 1887, p. 98.
Love and Anthropology, Jan., 1887, p. 98.
The Races of Man, Feb., 1887, p. 204.
Folk-lore, June, 1887, pp. 590–594.

WILLIAM G. MAZYCK. A new Land-shell from California, with note on *Selenites Duranti* N.
Proc. U. S. Nat. Mus., IX, December 8, 1886, pp. 460, 61.
Describes and figures *S. cœlata* n. sp., and figures *S. Duranti* Newcomb.

C. HART MERRIAM. Preliminary description of a new Pocket-Gopher from California.
Science, VIII, No. 203, Decem. 24, 1886, p. 558.

GEORGE P. MERRILL. [Report on the] Department of Lithology and Physical Geology [in the U. S. National Museum, 1884].
Report Smithsonian Institution, 1884 (1886) II, pp. 227–238.

GEORGE P. MERRILL. Fulgurites, or Lightning Holes.
Popular Science Monthly, XXX, No. 4, Feb., 1887, pp. 529–539, 4 figures.
This paper gives a popular account of the formation and composition of fulgurites and some of the ideas formerly prevailing concerning their origin. The figures are the same as those in the preceding paper.

GEORGE P. MERRILL. Stones for Building and Decoration.
Building, New York, April 16, and March 26, 1887.
These two numbers, the only ones that have appeared up to the expiration of the time covered by this report, are portions of a series of articles on the subject designed to appear from time to time in the pages of this journal. They differ but little from matters that will ultimately appear in my hand-book of the collections.

GEORGE P. MERRILL. Notes on the Composition of certain "Pliocene Sandstones" from Montana and Idaho.
Am. Jour. Sci. Nat., XXVII, No. —, 1886, pp. 199–204, 3 figures.
This paper shows that certain peculiar rocks collected by Dr. A. C. Peale, of the Hayden Survey, in 1871, and considered at the time as sandstone of Pliocene age, were composed almost wholly of finely comminuted particles of pumice dust. Given details of microscopic structure, illustrated by figures, and results of chemical analyses.

GEORGE P. MERRILL. Our Building-stone Supply.
Scientific American, Jan. 8, 1887, and Scientific American Supplement, Jan. 22 and 29, 1887.
This paper is merely a popular article on the source and qualities of the building and ornamental stone of the Mine Comumn. Text and seven illustrations.

GEORGE P. MERRILL. On Fulgurites.
Proc. U. S. Nat. Mus., IX, Aug. 26, 1886, pp. 83–91, 1 plate.
Describes fulgurites found in Whiteside County, Illinois, and now in the Museum collection. Gives results of chemical and microscopical examinations.

R. H. MINER. Report of Ensign R. H. Miner, U. S. Navy, Department of Fishes. (Report on the work of the U. S. Fish Commission Steamer *Albatross* for the year ending December 31, 1883, pp. 117–236. By Lieut. Commander Z. L. Tanner, U. S. Navy, commanding.)

> *Report U. S. Commission of Fish and Fisheries*, part XI, for 1883, pp. 178–203.

JOHN MURDOCH. A study of the Eskimo Bows in the U. S. National Museum.

> *Report Smithsonian Institution*, 1884, II (1886), pp. 307–316, pls. I–XII.

JOHN MURDOCH. A few legendary Fragments from the Point Barrow Eskimos.

> *American Naturalist*, XX, No. 7, July, 1886, pp. 593–599.

JOHN MURDOCH. Shore-Bird Nomenclature.

> *Forest and Stream*, XXVII, No. 20, Dec. 9, 1886, p. 382.

JOHN MURDOCH. Shore-Bird Nomenclature.

> *Forest and Stream*, XXVII, No. 15, Nov. 4, 1886, p. 287.

JOHN MURDOCH. Alaska Trout and the Fly.

> *Forest and Stream*, XXVII, No. 19, Dec. 2, 1886, pp. 366, 367.

JOHN MURDOCH. The Parts of an Eskimo Harpoon.

> *American Naturalist*, XX, Sept., 1886, pp. 828–831.

JOHN MURDOCH. The East Greenlanders.

> *American Naturalist*, XXI, No. 2, Feb., 1887, pp. 133–138.
> Abstract and review of Dr. Rink's paper in "Deutsche Geographische Blätter," IX, No. 3, 1886.

JOHN MURDOCH. On some popular errors in regard to the Eskimos.

> *American Naturalist*, XXI, No. 1, Jan., 1887, pp. 9–16.

JOHN MURDOCH. Note on Eider Ducks.

> *Zoologist* [3], XI, 123, March, 1887, p. 108.
> Unhurt birds dropping when shot at on the wing.

JOHN MURDOCH. The Blue Plover.

> *Forest and Stream*, XXVII, No. 16, Nov. 11, 1886, p. 309.
> Brief note identifying this trivial name.

JOHN MURDOCH. Weapons in Game.

> *Forest and Stream*, XXVII, No. 20, Dec. 9, 1886, p. 383.
> Brief note, identifying as Eskimo a bone arrow-head found in a goose; mentioned in *Forest and Stream* for Nov. 25, 1886.

WILLARD NYE, JR. Fish and Fishing at Abaco Island.

> *Bulletin U. S. Fish Com.*, VI, No. 8, June 15, 1886, pp. 125, 126.
> Notes on some of the species taken by the *Albatross* in the West Indies.

WILLIARD NYE, JR. Habits of Whiting or Frost Fish (*Merlucius bilinearis*, Mitch.).

> *Bulletin U. S. Fish Com.*, VI, No. 13, Sept. 11, 1886, p. 208.

PAUL PELSENEER. Description d'un nouveau genre de Ptéropode gymnosome.

> *Bull. Scientifique du département du Nord.* 2me sér., 9me année, No. 6. Paris, Octave Doin, 1886. 11 pp., 8vo. Title on cover.
> Describes *Notabranchœa Macdonaldi*, n. sp. et gen., from a specimen obtained by the U. S. Fish Commission steamer *Albatross*, and furnished to the writer by the U. S. National Museum.

RICHARD RATHBUN. Descriptions of Parasitic Copepoda belonging to the genera *Pandarus* and *Chondracanthus* (with seven plates).

> *Proc. U. S. Nat. Mus.*, IX, Oct. 19, 1886, pp. 310–234, plates 5–11.
> The following species are described and figured; they are all from the collections of the U. S. Fish Commission, and were obtained on or off the southern coast of New England. *Pandarus sinuatus* Say, parasitic on the sand shark (*Carcharias americanus*), Atwood's shark (*Carcharodon Atwoodi*), and the dogfish (*Mustelus canis*). *Pandarus Smithii* Rathbun, sp. nov., parasitic on the dusky shark (*Carcharhinus obscurus*) and the sand shark (*Odontaspis littoralis*). *Chondracanthus galeritus* Rathbun, sp. nov., parasitic on the common flounder (*Paralichthys dentatus*). *Chondracanthus phycidis* Rathbun, sp. nov., parasitic on the common hake (*Phycis tenuis*). *Chondrac nthus cottunculi* Rathbun, sp. nov., parasitic on *Cottunculus torvus* and microps. A figure is also given of *Pandarus Cranchii* Leach.

RICHARD RATHBUN. Catalogue of the species of Corals belonging to the genus *Madrepora*, contained in the U. S. National Museum.

> *Proc. U. S. Nat. Mus.*, x, April 10, 1887, pp. 10–19.
>
> Fifty-nine species are enumerated, of which forty-seven are represented by the type specimens described by Prof. J. D. Dana from the collections made by the United States exploring expedition around the world, 1838–1842. Forty-eight new species were described by Dana from that collection, one of which had not been found at the time of the publication of this paper. It has, however, since been discovered, having been accidentally mislaid, and the series of his types is now complete. The six species described by Prof. A. E. Verrill from the collection of the North Pacific exploring expedition, 1853–1856, are also represented by the type specimens.

RICHARD RATHBUN. Report on the Department of Marine Invertebrates in the U. S. National Museum, 1884.

> *Report Smithsonian Institution*, 1884 (1886) II, pp. 189–202.

RICHARD RATHBUN. Catalogue of the collection of recent Echini in the U. S. National Museum (corrected to July 1, 1886).

> *Proc. U. S. Nat. Mus.*, IX, Oct. 13, 1886, pp. 255–293.
>
> The collection is second, in this country, only to that of the Museum of Comparative Zoology at Harvard College. It contains one hundred and fifty-two determined species, many of which are represented by large series of specimens, covering a wide range of distribution, both geographical and bathymetrical. Fifty-four species were derived from the explorations of the U. S. Fish Commission, and the dredgings of the U. S. Coast Survey steamer *Blake* are represented by a nearly complete series of the species mentioned and described by Mr. Alexander Agassiz. The collection also contains all the species known from the western coast of North America, including a very large amount of material from Alaska. Most of the species obtained by Dr. William Stimpson, as naturalist of the North Pacific exploring expedition, 1853–1856, are also preserved, and miscellaneous accessions from various sources have added many forms. The catalogue is arranged systematically with respect to the species, under which each lot of specimens is recorded separately and in geographical order, with full data as to localities, depths, etc. Notes are given under a few of the species.

RICHARD RATHBUN. Sponges and the Sponge Fishery.

> *The Chautauquan*, March, 1887, pp. 352–354.
>
> A popular account.

CHARLES RAU. Report on the Department of Antiquities in the U. S. National Museum, 1884.

> *Report Smithsonian Institution*, 1884 (1886) II, pp 123–127.

ROBERT RIDGWAY. Report on the Department of Birds in the U. S. [National] Museum, 1884.

> *Report Smithsonian Institution*, 1884 (1886) II, pp. 143–155.

ROBERT RIDGWAY. Description of an apparently new species of *Picolaptes*, from the Lower Amazon.

> *Proc. U. S. Nat. Mus.*, IX, Nov. 26, 1886, p. 523.
>
> The new species is named *Picolaptes rikeri* Ridgw.

ROBERT RIDGWAY. Description of a new species of *Cotinga* from the Pacific coast of Costa Rica.

> *Proc. U. S. Nat. Mus.*, x, April 25, 1887, pp. 1–2, pl. vi, figs. 3 and 4.
>
> The new species is named *Cotinga ridgwayi* Zeledon.

ROBERT RIDGWAY. Description of a new form of *Spindalis* from the Bahamas.

> *Proc. U. S. Nat. Mus.*, x, April 25, 1887, p. 3.
>
> New subspecies, named *Spindalis zena townsendi.*

ROBERT RIDGWAY. Description of the adult female of *Carpodectes antoniæ* Zeledon; with critical remarks, notes on habits, etc., by José C. Zeledon.

> *Proc. U. S. Nat. Mus.*, x, April 25, 1887, p. 20.

ROBERT RIDGWAY. A | Nomenclature of Colors | for Naturalists, | and | Compendium of Useful Knowledge | for Ornithologists, | By | Robert Ridgway, | Curator, Department of Birds, United States National Museum. | —— | With Ten Colored Plates and Seven Plates | of Outline Illustrations | —— | Bos'on : | Little, Brown and Company. | 1886. | 8vo, 129 pp., 17 pl.

ROBERT RIDGWAY—Continued.

This book, which is dedicated to Prof. S. F. Baird, consists of two parts, the first one being a "Nomenclature of Colors," containing: Preface; principles of color and general remarks; colors required by the zoological or botanical artist; comparative vocabulary of colors and bibliography; the second part being the "Ornithologists' Compendium," comprising: Glossary of technical terms used in descriptive ornithology; table for converting millimeters into English inches and decimals; and table for converting English inches and decimals into millimeters.

ROBERT RIDGWAY. Descriptions of some new species of Birds, supposed to be from the interior of Venezuela.

Proc. U. S. Nat. Mus., IX, Aug. 26, 1886, pp. 92–94.

The species described as new are *Pyroderus masoni* and *Aulacorhamphus dimidiatus*; the third species is given as "*Myiopsitta lineola* (Cassin)?" A synoptical table of all the known species of the genus *Pyroderus* is also given.

ROBERT RIDGWAY. On *Æstrelata sandwichensis* Ridgw.

Proc. U. S. Nat Mus., IX, Aug. 26, 1886, pp. 95, 96.

Points out the differences between this species and *Æ. hæsitata*, and intimates that it may be identical with *Æ. phæopygia* Salv.

ROBERT RIDGWAY. Description of a melanistic specimen of *Buteo latissimus* (Wils.).

Proc. U. S. Nat. Mus., IX, Oct. 13, 1886, pp. 248, 249.

Full description, and comparison with *B. fuliginosus.*

ROBERT RIDGWAY. Description of a new subspecies of *Cyclorhis* from Yucatan.

Proc. U. S. Nat. Mus., IX, Nov. 26, 1886, p. 519.

New subspecies named *Cyclorhis flaviventris yucatanensis.*

ROBERT RIDGWAY. Description of a recently new Oyster-catcher (*Hæmatopus galapagensis*) from the Galapagos Islands.

Proc. U. S. Nat. Mus., IX, Oct. 19, 1886, pp. 325, 326.

Full description, with a synoptical table of the American Pied Oyster-catchers.

ROBERT RIDGWAY. Description of a new species of *Myiarchus*, presumably from the Orinoco district of South America.

Proc. U. S. Nat. Mus., IX, Nov. 26, 1886, p. 520.

The new species named *Myiarchus coalei* Ridgw.

ROBERT RIDGWAY. On a probable Hybrid between *Dryobates nuttallii* (Gamb.) and *D. pubescens gairdnerii* (Aud.).

Proc. U. S. Nat. Mus., IX, Nov. 26, 1886, pp. 521, 522.

With full comparative description of the two species and the supposed hybrid, which came from San Francisco, California.

ROBERT RIDGWAY. On the Glaucous Gull of Bering Sea and contiguous waters.

The Auk, III, 1886, pp. 330, 331.

Describes as a new species *Larus barrovianus* Ridgw.

ROBERT RIDGWAY. Description of a new species of Oyster-catcher from the Galapagos Islands.

The Auk, III, 1886, p. 331.

Hæmatopus galapagensis Ridgw., sp. nov.

ROBERT RIDGWAY. Preliminary descriptions of some new species of Birds from southern Mexico, in the collection of the Mexican Geographical and Exploring Commission.

The Auk, III, 1886, pp. 331–333.

Diagnosis of the following species published in advance by permission of the Director of the National Museum: *Amphispiza ferrariperezi*; *Pipilo submaculatus*; *P. complexus*; *Anas diazi*; *Philortyx personatus.*

ROBERT RIDGWAY. Description of two species of Birds supposed to be from the interior of Venezuela.

The Auk, III, 1886, p. 333.

Brief diagnosis of *Pyroderus masoni* and *Aulacorhamphus dimidiatus*, published in advance.

ROBERT RIDGWAY. Descriptions of a new species of Elf Owl from Socorro Island, western Mexico.

The Auk, III, 1886, pp. 333, 334.

Brief diagnosis of *Micrathene graysoni* Ridgw.

ROBERT RIDGWAY. Description of a new genus of *Oceanitidæ*.

> *The Auk*, III, 1886, p. 334.
> *Pealea* Ridgw., gen. nov., type *Thalassidroma lineata* Peale.

ROBERT RIDGWAY. Description of four new species of Birds from the Bahama Islands.

> *The Auk*, III, 1886, pp. 334–337.
> These species were collected by the naturalists of the Fish Commission steamer *Albatross* during the cruise in Bahaman waters, March and April, 1886. They were named as follows: *Geothlypis coryi; G. tanneri; Centurus nyeanus; C. blakei.*

ROBERT RIDGWAY. Description of a new genus of *Tyrannidæ* from Santo Domingo.

> *The Auk*, III, 1886, pp. 382, 383.
> *Lawrencia* Ridgw., gen. nov., type *Empidonax nanus* Lawr.

ROBERT RIDGWAY. [Reply to Dr. J. G. Cooper's article entitled "The Water Birds of North America, Explanations," in The Auk, III, 1886, pp. 401, 402.]

> *The Auk*, III, 1886, pp. 403, 404.
> Concluding remarks in the controversy originally started by Dr. Cooper in an earlier number of The Auk.

ROBERT RIDGWAY. A singularly marked Specimen of *Sphyropicus thyroideus*.

> *The Auk*, IV, 1887, pp. 75, 76.
> The specimen, which was shot in Blue Cañon, California, is remarkable for the excessive development of the red color on the head.

ROBERT RIDGWAY. The Imperial Woodpecker (*Campephilus imperialis*) in northern Sonora.

> *The Auk*, IV, 1887, p. 161.
> The head of a female of this species, shot by Lieut. H. C. Benson, U. S. Army, within 50 miles of the Arizona boundary, was received by the National Museum.

ROBERT RIDGWAY. The Coppery-tailed Trogon (*Trogon ambiguus*) breeding in southern Arizona.

> *The Auk*, IV, 1887, pp. 161, 162.
> Refers to the nestling collected by Lieutenant Benson in the Huachuca Mountains.

ROBERT RIDGWAY. Descriptions of a new species of the Genus *Empidonax* from Guatemala.

> *The Ibis*, 1886, pp. 459, 460.
> The new species is named *E. salvini* Ridgw.; the type is in the National Museum.

ROBERT RIDGWAY. On *Empidochanes fuscatus* (Max.) and *Empidonax brunneus* (Ridgw.).

> *The Ibis*, 1886, pp. 460, 461.
> Demonstrates the distinctness of the species, based upon comparison of the type specimens of both. Gives a synopsis of the species of *Empidochanes* and proposes conditionally the name *E. vireoninus* for the species from Tobago.

ROBERT RIDGWAY. On the species of the genus *Empidonax*.

> *The Ibis*, 1886, pp. 461–468.
> A synoptical table, with descriptions of all the species known to belong to this genus. The article was prepared at the request of Dr. P. L. Sclater, secretary Zoological Society, London, who sent his entire collection of these birds to the author for examination and determination.

ROBERT RIDGWAY. List of Birds found breeding within the corporate limits of Mount Carmel, Illinois.

> *Ridgway Ornith. Club*, Bulletin 2, 1887, pp. 26–35.
> Enumerates eighty-four species which have been positively identified as breeding within the town limits.

ROBERT RIDGWAY. Description of a new Plumed Partridge from Sonora (*Callipepla elegans bensoni*).

> *Forest and Stream*, XXVIII, No. 6, 1887, p. 106.
> Based on specimens presented to the National Museum by Lieut. Harry C. Benson, U. S. Army.

ROBERT RIDGWAY. [Descriptions of five new species of Birds, and critical remarks on others of greater or less rarity or interest; constituting part II of Catalogue of Animals collected by the Geographical and Exploring Commission of the Republic of Mexico. By Fernando Ferrari-Perez.]

> *Proc. U. S. Nat. Mus.*, IX, Sept. 15, 1886, pp. 130–182.

ROBERT RIDGWAY—Continued.

The new species are as follows: *Amphispiza ferrariperezi; Pipilo submaculatus; P. complexus; Anas diazi*, and *Philortyx personatus*. *Micrathene graysoni* Ridgway, from Socorro I land, is also described, and a synoptical table of the North American and Mexican species of the restricted genus *Anas* is given.

CHARLES V. RILEY. Report on the Department of Insects in the U. S. National Museum, 1884.

Report of Smithsonian Institution, 1884, (1886) II, pp. 185–188.

CHARLES V. RILEY. The present status and future prospects of Silk Culture in the United States. (Abstract.)

Proc. Am. Assn. Adv. Sci., XXXIV, Ann Arbor meeting, Aug. 1885, p. 516. (Author's extras issued July 1, 1886.)

The author concludes that the adaptability of the United States to silk culture is proven; that the profits are very small; that the encouragement given by Congress has been productive of good, and has intensified interest in the subject; but once withdrawn a reaction would set in; that no permanent advantage to American silk-growers can be secured unless by a protective tariff which will recognize that the so-called "raw silk" is a manufactured article and entitled to protection.

CHARLES V. RILEY. The probabilities of Locust or "Grasshopper" injury in the near future, and a new method of counteracting their injury. (Abstract.)

Proc. Am. Assn. Adv. Sci., XXXIV, pp. 519, 520, Ann Arbor meeting, 1885. (Author's extras issued July, 1886.)

Shows that there is a certain periodicity in locust visitations; analyzes the indications for 1886, and concludes that there is some danger of injury for that year, though adverse weather may yet modify or avert the danger. The new remedy, somewhat extensively used on the Pacific coast recently, is a mixture of bran, sugar, arsenic, and water, which is placed as a bait throughout the infested localities.

CHARLES V. RILEY. Notes on *Feniseca Tarquinius* Fabr.

Canadian Entomologist, XVIII, Oct., 1886, pp. 191–193.

Comments on Mr. W. H. Edwards's article on this species in Canadian Entomologist, XVIII, 141–153, and gives an explanation of the manner in which the carnivorous habits of *Feniseca* were discovered after long and careful observation, extending from 1880 to 1885.

CHARLES V. RILEY. The Mulberry Silk-worm; being a manual of instructions in silk-culture. Sixth revised edition, with illustrations.

Bull. No. 9, U. S. Department of Agriculture, Division of Entomology, pp. vii, 65, pl. i and ii, figs. 1–29.

Letter of submittal. Preface to 2d edition. Preface to 6th edition, giving a history of past work done, future prospects, advice to beginners, and explanation of techinal terms. Chapter I, Physiology and Life History of the Silk-worm. Chapter II, Wintering and Hatching the Eggs. Chapter III, Implements that facilitate the raising of Silk. Chapter IV, The Rearing of Silk-worms. Chapter V, Enemies and Diseases of the Silk-worms. Chapter VI, Reproduction. Chapter VII, Choking the Chrysalis. Chapter VIII, Silk-reeling. Chapter IX, Physical Properties of reeled Silk. Chapter X, Food-plants; Glossary of terms used; Explanation to Plates; Index.

CHARLES V. RILEY. Our Shade Trees and their Insect Defoliators; being a consideration of the four most injurious species which affect the trees of the capital, with means of destroying them.

Bulletin No. 10, U. S. Department of Agriculture, Division of Entomology, pp. 1–69, figs. 1–27.

Treats of the Imported Elm Leaf-beetle (*Galeruca xanthomelæna*); the Bag or Drop Worm (*Thyridopteryx ephemeræformis*); the White Marked Tussock-moth (*Orgyia leucostigma*); and the Fall Web-worm (*Hyphantria cunea*).

Of each species the full life history is given, details as to structure and other characters, methods of work, amount of damage, trees most or least affected, natural enemies and parasites, and what means may be employed to check their ravages. Arsenical sprays are still the most effective when it becomes necessary to use insecti ides on a large scale. Effect of winter work in destroying each species; effect of whitewashing trees, as well as of tree boxes; injurious as well as beneficial effects of shade trees of Washington; prospects for the ensuing year.

CHARLES V. RILEY. Reports of Experiments with Insecticide Substances chiefly upon Insects affecting garden crops, made under direction of the Entomologist.

Bull. No. 11, U. S. Department of Agriculture, Division of Entomology, pp. 1–34.

CHARLES V. RILEY—Continued.

Contains: Letter of submittal. Experiments with Insecticides, giving an explanation of reasons for having a variety of substances tested, and methods employed. Opinions on the value of some of them. Report of experiments at Lafayette, Indiana, by F. M. Webster. Gives the results of eighty-five experiments on twelve species of insects. Report of Experiments at Ames, Iowa, by Prof. Herbert Osborn. Gives the results of experiments with eleven different mixtures. Report of Experiments at Trenton, New Jersey, by Thomas Bennett. Gives the results of experiments with decoctions of *Datura stramonium, Lycopersicum esculentum, Sambucus, Ailanthus, Podophyllum, Peltatum,* and *Tanacetum.*

CHARLES V. RILEY. Miscellaneous notes on the work of the Division of Entomology for the season of 1885, prepared by the Entomologist. With illustrations.

Bull. No. 12, U. S. Department of Agriculture, Division of Entomology, pp. 1–46, pl. i.

Contains notes of some of the work done under the direction of the Entomologist during the time mentioned, and special reports, as follows: Production and Manufacture of Buhach, by D. W. Coquillett. Additions to the Third Report on the causes of the destruction of the Evergreen and other Forest Insects in northern New England, by A. S. Packard. The Periodical Cicada in southeaastern Indiana, by Amos W. Butler, and Notes of the Year. These notes contain items of information regarding "The Colorado Potato Beetle in Georgia," "The Sugarcane Beetle Injuring Corn," "The Corn-root Web-worm, an old pest in Indiana," "*Monephora bicincta* damaging Bermuda Grass," "A new Enemy to the Persimmon," The Black Scale of California," "The Black Scale of California found in South Carolina," "*Bibio albipennis* as an injurious Insect," "An Enemy to Silk Worms," Great Damage to Beans by Blister Beetles," "*Anthomyia angustifrons,* a lignivorous Insect," "The Tile-horned *Prionus* in Prairie Land," "The Clover-seed Midge in Wisconsin," "*Colaspis flavida* injuring the LeConte Pear," "Great Damage by the Cottonwood Borer," "*Leptocoris trivittata* injuring Apples," "*Proconia undata* in injurious numbers," "Occurrences of the Army Worm during the Season," "California Remedies for the Woolly Aphis," "The Hessian Fly in California," "*Agonoderus pallipes* injurious to Corn."

CHARLES V. RILEY. Mr. Hulst's Observations on *Pronuba yuccasella.*

Entomologica Americana, ii, March, 1887, pp. 233–236.

Criticises Mr. Hulst's observations, p. 184, same volume, to the effect that yucca may be fertilized by other insects than *P. yuccasella.* Gives a history of his work on the subject, and details the reasons for his conclusions; also cites the admitted exceptions to the rule as given by him. Discredits Mr. Hulst's conclusions as unsupported by facts.

CHARLES V. RILEY. Showers of Sulphur; Pine Pollen.

The Evening Star, Washington, March 9, 1887.

Refers to the recent reports of supposed sulphur showers, and states that they consist of the pollen of *Pinus longifolia,* citing other similar instances in previous years.

CHARLES V. RILEY. Remarks on the Insect Defoliators of our Shade Trees, made by Dr. C. V. Riley, U. S. Entomologist. Stenographic report by James W. Tooley of an address before the New York Farmers, at a meeting held March 10, 1887.

Printed by the Globe Stationery and Printing Co., N. Y., 1887.

Prelude: Imported and native injurious insects. Speaks of the Imported Elm Leaf-beetle (*Galeruca xanthomelœna*), the Bag-worm (*Thyridopteryx ephemerœformis*), the White-marked Tussock-moth (*Orgyia leucostigma*), and the Fall Web-worm (*Hyphantria cunea*). Gives a brief popular history of each species, their method of injury, the time and amount of damage, and what measures for their destruction can be taken. Arsenical sprays and washes are recommended, and their use explained and defended.

CHARLES V. RILEY. Address at the semi-annual State Convention of Fruit-Growers of California.

Pacific Rural Press, April 23, 1887, pp. 361–364.

Remarks principally on *Icerya purchasi* Mask., giving a review of the nomenclature, the geographical distribution and probable origin of the species, a list of the food-plants, possibility and mode of spreading, characteristics of the insect, natural enemies, and a very exhaustive review of the measures for the prevention of the spread of the pest and means of applying them, and the results of some experiments made by him or under his direction; also refers to parasites, and suggests the visit of an experienced observer to Australia to study the species in its native home, and artificially introduce any parasite there found preying on it; urges appointment of State entomologists, and makes suggestions as to best law; importance of prevention; prosperity *vs.* insect injury, etc.

CHARLES V. RILEY. Bumble-Bees *vs.* Red Clover.

Rural New Yorker, April 23, 1887, vol. 46, p. 273.

Records the fact as to settlement in Europe of the question of the more or less complete dependence of Red Clover for fertilization upon the Bumble-Bees. Records the recent experiences in New Zealand where this clover was nearly sterile. After the European Bumble-Bee was introduced and had spread rapidly, the beneficial effects on Red Clover were immediately perceptible in a much more liberal seeding.

CHARLES V. RILEY. Notes on Icerya. Its probable origin on the Islands of Bourbon and Mauritius.

Pacific Rural Press, June 4, 1887, pp. 506, 507.

Discusses the question of the identity of *Icerya purchasi* Maskell, with *I. sacchari* Signoret. Expresses the opinion that they will be found identical. The question of synonomy here is an important one, as it bears on the question of the original home of the species. If the two are identical, Mauritius and Bourbon are probably the points or origin, as specimens are easily transported with sugar from those points.

To this are added extracts from correspondence bearing on this subject of origin as follows:
Letter from Roland Trimen, of Cape Town, February 8, 1887.
Letter from Frazer S. Crawford, of Adelaide, February 21, 1887.
Letter from Baron von Muller, of Melbourne, March 21, 1887.
Letter from L. M. Kirk, Wellington, New Zealand, March 25, 1887.
Extract from an article by E. J. Dunn, in Melbourne Argus, August, 1886.

CHARLES V. RILEY. The Hop Plant Louse.

Waterville Times and Reflex June 17, 1887.

Gives an account of recent discoveries in the life history of *Phorodon humuli.* It is now definitely established that the winter eggs are laid on Plum; that from these eggs hatch lice that for three generations live on Plum, then become winged and migrate to the Hop, where they increase and go through the well-known life history. Refutes the views heretofore held on the subject, and explains how he was led to discover the true state of the case, and the important bearing of the discovery to hop-growers in regions not yet infested with the pest.

CHARLES V. RILEY. Two new Insect Pests.

Rural New Yorker, June 25, 1887, vol. 46, p. 416.

Treats of "A new apple pest," the Apple-leaf Flea-beetle (*Haltica punctipennis* Leconte), and "A new destructive Cricket in Louisiana." The former had been found on Hawthorn by the author as long ago as 1872. This year it appeared in great numbers near Gainesville and Galveston, Texas, and did great damage. Paris green has been used against it successfully. The latter has appeared in Catahoula Parish, Louisiana, in destructive numbers. It is a true *Gryllus,* species as yet unknown, which eats a great variety of cultivated plants. Its method of work is described, and a bran, sugar, and arsenic mash suggested as a remedy.

CHARLES V. RILEY. Report of the Entomologist.

Report of the Commissioner of Agriculture, 1886, pp. 459–592, plates i-xi.

Contains divisions and chapters with titles as follows:
Introduction, pp. 459–465, containing a review of the work of the year in the division, with comments on the reports of agents, a specification of plans and of work now under way.
Miscellaneous insects, pp. 446–546, pl. I-XI, divided as follows: The Cottony Cushion-scale (*Icerya purchasi* Maskell), pp. 466–492, pl. I-V; Buffalo-gnats, pp. 492–517, pl. VI-IX; the Fall Web-worm, pp. 518–539, pl. X-XI; Joint-worms, pp. 539–546.
Silk-culture, pp. 546–552.
Reports of agents: Report on remedies for the Cottony Cushion-scale, pp. 552–557, by D. W. Coquillett; report upon supplementary experiments on the Red Scale, by Albert Koebele, pp. 558–572; insects affecting small grains and grasses, by F. M. Webster, special agent, pp. 573–582; report on experiments in apiculture, by N. W. McLain, pp. 582–591.

CHARLES V. RILEY. The Cottony Cushion-scale (*Icerya purchasi* Maskell).

Report of the Entomologist, Department of Agriculture, 1886, pp. 466–492, pl. i-v.

Gives first an account of the dates of first acquaintance with the insect; geographical distribution, looking more particularly to its probable point of origin, its spread, and limitation in California; the range of food-plants in Australia, New Zealand, and California. The life-history in all its stages is given in great detail and illustrated. The rate of growth is discussed, as are also its habits. The sweet secretion, called "honey-dew," is extremely abundant, and attractive to other insects. Details mode of spread and distribution, gives a list of natural enemies, among them a Microlepidopteron, *Blastobasis iceryæella,* n. sp., which is described. A chalcid parasite has also been discovered, belonging to a new genus, characterized as *Isodromus* Howard, and described as *I. iceryæ,* n. sp. Remedies and preventives are discussed, and spray solutions with a base of kerosene recommended as most likely to be effective.

CHARLES V. RILEY.   Buffalo-gnats.

Report of the Entomologist, Department of Agriculture, 1886, pp. 492–517, pl. vi–x.

Gives first a brief review, showing origin of names and the kind of injury done by them. Treats in detail: The Southern Buffalo-gnat (Simulium pecuarum, n. sp.) ; gives the geographical distribution; the early history; time of appearance; duration of an invasion; character of a swarm; mode of attack; animals injured; effect of the bites; how animals protect themselves; preventives; remedies for the bites; attack on man and results; damage done in various years; popular opinions about the early stages of the Buffalo-gnat; habits and natural history; treating of the egg (not yet discovered) ; the larva, its habits and food, pupa and cocoon and imago; number of broods; enemies of the Buffalo-gnat; technical description of S. pecuarum and S. meridionale, sp. nov. Discusses the remedies tried and proposed against the larvæ, the connection between overflows and gnats, and number of brood.

CHARLES V. RILEY.   The Fall Web-worm (Hyphantria cunea Drury).

Report of the Entomologist, Department of Agriculture, 1886, pp. 518–539, pls. x and xi.

The paper contains subdivisions indicating its contents as follows: Natural history, giving the life cycle of the species in all stages and in great detail ; injury done in 1886 ; proportionate injury to different plants and shade trees ; peculiar effects of the defoliation on some plants ; enemies of the web-worm other than insects ; predaceous insect enemies ; fungus disease of the web-worm ; experiments to obtain percentage of diseased caterpillars ; true parasites of the web-worm ; secondary parasites ; describes the new species Telenomous bifidus (parasitic in the eggs), Meteorus hyphantriæ, and Apanteles hyphantriæ; remedies; review of the various appliances for burning, pruning, and spraying ; arsenical poisons still most satisfactory and effective.

CHARLES V. RILEY.   Joint Worms.

Report of the Entomologist, Department of Agriculture, 1886, pp. 539–546.

The common Joint Worm (Isosoma hordei Harr.) has been increasing in number of late years ; comparison of injury with that caused by the Hessian Fly (Cecidomyia destructor). Review of points at which injury was done. Isosoma nigrum Cook, is a re-description of this old species. Some details as to breeding and some notes on parasites. The Wheat-straw Isosoma (Isosoma tritici Riley) has been carefully studied, and the results of the studies are here given. The species proves dimorphic in the female form, the dimorphic variety having been described as I. grande Riley. Details of manner in which this was established. Summary of life history. Geographical distribution. Appearance in Kansas for the first time.

CHARLES V. RILEY.   Silk-Culture.

Report of the Entomologist, Department of Agriculture. 1886, pp. 546–551.

General work ; an experimental filature set up in Washington ; Osage Orange vs. Mulberry as a food-plant ; the Serrell reel ; cost of work, a daily deficiency the result thus far; causes leading to it ; the distribution of eggs and races preferred ; choking of cocoons ; table showing cocoons produced in the United States in 1886, and the various States where produced.

JOHN A. RYDER.   On the value of the Fin-rays and their Characteristics of Development in the Classification of the Fishes, together with Remarks on the Theory of Degeneration.

Proc. U. S. Nat. Mus., IX, Aug. 26, 1886, pp. 71–82.

JOHN A. RYDER.   On the Origin of the Heterocercy and the Evolution of the Fins and Fin-rays of Fishes.

Report U. S. Fish Com., XII, 1886, pp. 981–1107, 11 plates.

JOHN A. RYDER.   On the intraovarian Gestation of the Redfish (Sebastes marinus).

Bull. U. S. Fish Com., VI, p. 92.

JOHN A. RYDER.   Preliminary Notice of the Development of the Toad-fish (Batrachus tau).

Bull. U. S. Fish Com., VI, 1886, p. 4.

JOHN A. RYDER.   On the earlier Stages of Cleavage of the Blastodisk of Raia erinacea.

Bull. U. S. Fish Com., VI, 1886, p. 8.

P. L. SCLATER.   On Empidonax brunneus and its allied species.

The Ibis, 1887, pp. 64–66.

Based chiefly on material belonging to the National Museum. The author maintains that E. brunneus is the same as Muscipeta bimaculata d'Orb and Lafr., and that Empidochanes vireoninus is identical with Ochthœca arenacea Scl. and Salv

GEORGE B. SENNETT. Descriptions of two new sub-species of Titmice from Texas.
> *The Auk*, IV, 1887, pp. 28–30.
> The new sub-species are named *Parus atricristatus castaneifrons* and *Parus bicolor texensis*.
> National Museum specimens were borrowed for comparison.

ERNEST E. T. SETON. The Birds of Western Manitoba (concluded).
> *The Auk*, III, 1886, pp. 320–329 and p. 453.
> The author borrowed specimens belonging to the National Museum for purposes of identifying and comparing the birds upon which the present paper is based.

R. W. SHUFELDT. Observations upon the Habits of *Micropus melanoleucus*, with critical notes on its Plumage and external Charac ers.
> *The Ibis*, 1887, pp. 151–158, one color plate.
> Based in part upon specimens belonging to the National Museum, and borrowed for comparison.

D. D. SLADE and F. A. LUCAS. Osteological Notes.
> *Science*, IX, No. 223, May 13, 1887, p. 460.
> On the metacarpal bones of the bison and auroch.

HUGH M. SMITH. Birds new to the District of Columbia.
> *The Auk*, III, 1886, pp. 139, 140.

HUGH M. SMITH. Peculiar Nest of *Chelidon erythrogaster*.
> *The Auk*, III, 1886, p. 278.

HUGH M. SMITH. The Red Phalarope in the District of Columbia.
> *The Auk*, III, 1886, p. 482.
> Refers to a specimen in the National Museum.

JOHN B. SMITH. Collection Note.
> *Entomologica Americana*, II, July, 1886, p. 71.
> Describes the use of smoke in driving out insects from their places of concealment.

JOHN B. SMITH. Food-plants of *Chalcophora*.
> *Entomologica Americana*, II, July, 1886, p. 71.
> Gives the food-plant of *C. campestris* as sycamore. All other species feed on evergreen, so far as known.

JOHN B. SMITH. Scent Organs in some Bombycid Moths.
> *Entomologica Americana*, II, July, 1886, pp. 79, 80, 2 figures.
> Describes in detail and figures the peculiar extensile organs in the abdomen of the male *Leucarctia acræa* and *Pytrharctia isabella*.

JOHN B. SMITH. Hop Vine Insects.
> *Waterville Times and Hop Reporter*, Waterville, New York, vol. XXVIII, No. 29, July 16, 1886, p. 2, col. 2.
> An answer to the editor in response to a letter of inquiry in regard to the hop aphis.

JOHN B. SMITH. Larva of *Aphorista vittata* Fabr.
> *Entomologica Americana*, II, Aug., 1886, pp. 85–87, 6 figures.
> Describes and illustrates in detail the larva and pupa of the above species.

JOHN B. SMITH. Obituary Note on Capt. D. H. Murdock, Ninth U. S. Infantry, and Dr. Gustav Haller, of Berne, Switzerland.
> *Entomologica Americana*, II, Aug., 1886, p. 101.

JOHN B. SMITH. Ants' Nests and their Inhabitants.
> *American Naturalist*, XX, No. 8, Aug., 1886, pp. 679–689.
> Gives a list of the species found in ants' nests as guests, parasites, and visitors, and the habits and functions of each, as far as known.

JOHN B. SMITH. Polydactylism.
> *Science*, VIII, No. 187, Sept. 3, 1886, p. 213.
> Gives the history of an occurrence of six-fingered and six-toed individuals of one family,

JOHN B. SMITH. Notice of Dr. Horn's Paper on the *Eucnemidæ*, etc., of the United States.
> *Entomologica Americana*, II, Sept., 1886, p. 117.
> Gives an appreciative notice of his paper in Trans. Am. Ent. Soc., XIII, p. 58.

JOHN B. SMITH. Note on *Quadrina diazoma* Grote.
> *Entomologica Americana*, II, Sept., 1886, p. 124.
> Gives a review of the structure of the species, criticises Mr Grote's location of it in the *Ceratocampidæ*, and places it with the *Cossidæ*.

JOHN B. SMITH. Notes on *Scolytus unispinosus*.

Entomologica Americana, II, Nov., 1886, pp. 125–127.

Describes and figures the galleries of this species on *Abies Douglassi*, and gives list of food plants of the American species, showing that no others feed on conifers.

JOHN B. SMITH. Note on *Dynastes tityus*.

Entomologica Americana, II, Nov., 1886, p. 163.

Unusual abundance of the species, and notes on its habits and odor.

JOHN B. SMITH. Sexual Brush of the Male *Lyranthœcia marginata*.

Entomologica Americana, II, Nov., 1886, p. 164.

Describes a secondary sexual character of the species, consisting of a long concealed brush of hair at the base of the abdomen.

JOHN B. SMITH. A Revision of the lepidopterous Family Saturniidæ.

Proc. U. S. Nat. Mus., IX, Dec., 1886, pp. 414–437, plates xii, xiii, and xiv.

Gives a synopsis and description of the genera and species; draws in the genera *Platysamia* and *Callosamia* (=*Attacus*); limits the family and describes *Calosaturnia*, new genus, for *Saturnia mendocino* Behr.

JOHN B. SMITH. Beetles as a Nuisance.

Popular Science Monthly, XXX, Jan., 1887, p. 409, 410.

Describes an unusual swarm of *Dynastes tityus*, and the annoyance caused by their peculiarly fetid odor.

JOHN B. SMITH. Interesting notes from the Proceedings of the Berliner Ent. Verein.

Entomologica Americana, III, March, 1887, pp. 19, 20.

Miscellaneous scraps of interest, translated from the Berl. Ent. Zeitschrift for 1886.

JOHN B. SMITH. Note on the genus *Cressonia*.

Societas Entomologica, II, April 1, 1887, p. 3.

Gives a brief description of the structure of the genus, and especially of the antennæ.

JOHN B. SMITH. Antennal structure of the genus *Cressonia*.

Entomologica Americana, III, April, 1887, pp. 2, 3.

Describes the unique antennal structure of this sphinged genus.

JOHN B. SMITH. Note on Minot's researches into the structure of the skin of Larvæ.

Entomologica Americana, III, April, 1887, p. 16.

Gives a brief abstract of Minot's paper in Archiv. für Micr. Anat., XXVIII, pp. 37–48.

JOHN B. SMITH. *Euerythra trimaculata*, new species.

Entomologica Americana, III, April, 1887, p. 17.

Describes a species from Texas under the above name.

JOHN B. SMITH. Die Formiciden der Vereinigten Staaten von Nord Amerika, von Dr. Gustav Mayr.

Entomologica Americana, III, April, 1887, p. 19.

A notice of and brief abstract of contents.

JOHN B. SMITH. The genus *Quadrina*.

Canadian Entomologist, XIX, May, 1887, p. 100.

Correction of a misstatement by Mr. Grote in reference to the location of this genus.

JOHN B. SMITH. New species of *Callimorpha*.

Entomologica Americana, III, May, 1887, pp. 25, 26.

Describes as new *C. lactata* from Texas, and *C. suffusa*, widely spread.

JOHN B. SMITH. Notes on a paper by Mr. Butler entitled "Notes on certain North American species of the group called by M. Guénée 'Acronycta.'"

Entomologica Americana, III, May, 1887, pp. 35, 36.

Of the species mentioned by Mr. Butler, *A. hilus* does not seem to be described, while *A. modica* has been dropped from the lists for want of identification.

JOHN B. SMITH. A Voice from the Wilderness.

Entomologica Americana, III, May, 1887, p. 39.

A letter from E. A. Schwarz to J. B. Smith describing insect collecting at Key West, and comments thereon by Mr. Smith.

JOHN B. SMITH. Criticism of an article on *Orgyia* in Science, by Le Metayer de Guichainville.

Entomologica Americana, III, June, 1887, p. 55.

JOHN B. SMITH. Notes on *Apion*, with description of a new species.
Entomologica Americana, III, June, 1887, p. 56.
Describes as new *Apion lividum* from District of Columbia. Notices a secondary sexual character of one gronp, and corrects the synonomy of four species.

JOHN B. SMITH. Williston's synopsis of the North American *Syrphidæ*.
Entomologica Americana, III, June, 1887, p. 59.
Appreciative notice of the paper above mentioned.

JOHN B. SMITH. Interesting entomological literature.
Entomologica Americana, III, June, 1887, p. 60.
Calls attention to a fierce personal controversy in *Ent. Nachrichten* between Drs. Kraatz and Kolbe.

ROSA SMITH. On the occurrence of a new species of *Rhinoptera* (*R. encenadæ*) in Todos Santos Bay, Lower California.
Proc. U. S. Nat. Mus., IX, Oct. 11, 1886, p. 220.

ROBERT E. C. STEARNS. The death of Dr. Albert Kellogg.
Science, IX, No. 220, April 22, 1887, p. 391.

ROBERT E. C. STEARNS. The death of William Ashburner.
Science, IX, No. 223, May 13, 1887, p. 462.

ROBERT E. C. STEARNS. *Araujia albens* as a moth-trap.
American Naturalist, XXI, No. 8, June, 1887, pp. 501–507.
Describes the mechanism by which the plant entraps moths, and gives a list of species taken.

LEONHARD STEJNEGER. Notes on the northern palæarctic Bullfinches.
Proc. U. S. Nat. Mus., X, 1887, pp. 103–110.
Shows that *Pyrrhula cassini* Baird as the older name must take precedence over *P. cineracea* Cabanis; also that *P. rosacea* Seebohm is identical with *P. griseiventris* Lafr.

LEONHARD STEJNEGER. Contributions to the natural history of the Commander Islands, No. 7. Revised and annotated catalogue of the birds inhabiting the Commander Islands. (With three plates.)
Proc. U. S. Nat. Mus., X, 1887, pp. 117–145, pls. vii, viii, ix.
Enumerated one hundred and forty-three species. A Flycatcher from Bering Island named conditionally *Butalis pallescens*.

LEONHARD STEJNEGER. Review of Japanese Birds. I. The Woodpeckers. (With a colored plate.)
Proc. U. S. Nat. Mus., IX, Sept. 2, 1886, pp. 99–124, pl. ii.
The first of a series of articles forming a kind of "Prodromus" of a contemplated larger work on the birds of Japan. The present part of the "review" treats of twelve species and subspecies of woodpeckers, three of which are described as new, viz, *Picus canus jessoensis*, *Dryobates subcirris*, and *D. namiyei*, the latter being figured on the plate.

LEONHARD STEJNEGER. The British Marsh-tit.
Proc. U. S. Nat. Mus., IX, Sept. 28, 1886, pp. 200, 201.
Described as a new subspecies, *Parus palustris dresseri* Stejn.

LEONHARD STEJNEGER. Notes on the species of the Australian genus *Pardalotus*.
Proc. U. S. Nat. Mus., IX, Oct. 19, 1886, pp. 294–296.
Maintains that *P. assimilis* belongs to *P. affinis* as a subspecies, and not to *P. ornatus*. A "Key to the Species" is given, as well as a catalogue of the species, contained in the National Museum.

LEONHARD STEJNEGER. Description of *Rallus jouyi*, with remarks on *Rallus striatus* and *Rallus gularis*.
Proc. U. S. Nat. Mus., IX, Oct. 30, 1886, pp. 362–364.
The former described as a new species; the other two shown to be distinct.

LEONHARD STEJNEGER. On *Turdus alpestris* and *Turdus torquatus*, two distinct species of European Thrushes.
Proc. U. S. Nat. Mus., IX, Oct. 30, 1886, pp. 365–373.
Proves conclusively that *T. alpestris* is a distinct species inhabiting the mountains of southern Europe; in fact "that there exist two distinct species of ring-thrushes in Europe, notwithstanding the fact that hardly a single European ornithologist of the present generation even dreams of it."

LEONHARD STEJNEGER.   Review of Japanese Birds.   II. Tits and Nut-hatches.

Proc. U. S. Nat. Mus., IX, Oct. 30, 1886, pp. 374–394.

Treats of twelve species, of which one is described as new, viz, *Sitta amurensis clara*, while two are new to the Japanese fauna. *Remiza* proposed as a new generic term instead of *Ægi-thalus*, preoccupied.

LEONHARD STEJNEGER.   Review of Japanese Birds.   III. Rails, Gallinules, and Coots.

Proc. U. S. Nat. Mus., IX, Oct. 30, 1886, pp. 395–409.

Nine Japanese species are treated of, besides several other extra-limital species.

LEONHARD STEJNEGER.   On the status of *Synthliboramphus wumizusume* as a North American bird.

Proc. U. S. Nat. Mus., IX, Nov. 26, 1886, pp. 524.

Maintains that this species has no right to a place in the North American fauna.

LEONHARD STEJNEGER.   On a collection of Birds made by Mr. M. Namiye, in the Liu Kiu Islands, Japan, with description of new species.

Proc. U. S. Nat. Mus., IX, 1886 (Feb. 11, 1887), pp. 634–651.

This collection was made by Mr. M. Namiye, under the auspices of the Tokio Educational Museum, Tokio, Japan, and forwarded to the National Museum. The new species described are: *Treron permagna*, *Hypsipetes pryeri*, *Icoturus namiyei*, *Chelidon namiyei*, *Pericrocotus tegimœ*. Three other species are new to the Japanese fauna. A new genus, *Icoturus*, was created for the reception of *I. namiyei* Stejn. and *I. komadori* (Temm.).

LEONHARD STEJNEGER.   Review of Japanese Birds.   IV. Synopsis of the genus *Turdus*.

Proc. U. S. Nat. Mus., X, April 25, 1887, pp. 4, 5.

Eight species, of which one is described as new, *Turdus jouyi*.

LEONHARD STEJNEGER.   Birds of Kauai Island, Hawaiian Archipelago, collected by Mr. Valdemar Knudsen, with descriptions of new species.

Proc. U. S. Nat. Mus., X, May 17, 1887, pp. 75–102, pl. vi, figs. 1 and 2.

Enumerates twenty-one species, of which the following are described as new: *Himantopus knudseni*, *Chasiempis ridgwayi*, *Ch. dolei*, *Phæornis myadestina*, *Himatione parva*, *Oreomyza bairdi*. *Oreomyza* is characterized as a new genus. *Moho braccata* Cassin shown to be different from *M. nobilis*. Several species added to the fauna of the archipelago. A synopsis of the species of *Chasiempis* is given, as well as a "Key to the Genera of the Hawaiian *Dicœidœ*."

LEONHARD STEJNEGER.   Madarasz's "Zeitschrift für Ornithologie."

The Auk, III, 1886, pp. 398–399.

A review calling the attention of American ornithologists to this Journal.

LEONHARD STEJNEGER.   Dr. Shufeldt on the Osteology of the *Trochilidœ Caprimulgidœ*, and *Cypselidœ*.

The Auk, III, 1886, pp. 404–406.

A review of a paper by Dr. Shufeldt in the Proceedings of the Zool. Soc. London, criticising his conclusions in regard to the Swifts and Hummingbirds, maintaining that these two families are closely related, and should be included in the same order.

LEONHARD STEJNEGER.   Further Notes on the genus *Acanthis*.

The Auk, IV, 1887, pp. 30–35.

Treats especially of the British Redpoll. The only Japanese species unquestionably identified is *A. holbœlli*.

LEONHARD STEJNEGER.   Pleske on the Birds of the Kola Peninsula.

The Auk, IV, 1887, pp. 61–63.

A review of the bird volume of Pleske's "Uebersicht der Säugethiere und Vögel der Kola-Halbinsel." St. Petersburg, 1886.

LEONHARD STEJNEGER.   W. E. Brooks on the genus *Acanthis*.

The Auk, IV, 1887, p. 63.

A review of two papers by Brooks in "The Ibis," 1885 and 1886.

LEONHARD STEJNEGER.   Supplementary Notes on the genus *Acanthis*.

The Auk, IV, 1887, pp. 144, 145.

Notes on four specimens of *A. cabaret*, from Austria, submitted to the author for examination by Ritter von Tschusi zu Schmidhoffen.

LEONHARD STEJNEGER.   Classification of the Macrochires.

The Auk, IV, 1887, pp. 170, 171.

Letter to the editors of "The Auk" in reply to a letter from Dr. Shufeldt commenting on the writer's criticism of Dr. Shufeldt's original paper. (See above.)

LEONHARD STEJNEGER. [Letter to the editors of "The Ibis."]
The Ibis, 1886, pp. 381, 382.
Maintaining that "to use the oldest available name in every case, where it can be proved, and to spell it exactly as it was spelled when published for the first time," is the only rule of zoological nomenclature which can be carried out with safety.

LEONHARD STEJNEGER. Description of a new species of Fruit-Pigeon (*Janthœnas jouyi*) from the Liu Kiu Islands, Japan.
American Naturalist, 1887, pp. 583, 584.
Based upon a specimen submitted to the author for examination by the authorities of the Tokio Educational Museum.

LEONHARD STEJNEGER. On *Brachyramphus perdix* (Pall.) and its nearest allies (plate vii).
Zeitschr. Ges. Ornith., III, 1886, pp. 210-219. One plate.
Shows that *B. perdix* should be separated from *B. marmoratus.*

LEONHARD STEJNEGER. Lundefuglene det Stille Hav.
Naturen, 1887, pp. 33-38.
An account of the Puffins and Auklets of the Northern Pacific Ocean.

LEONHARD STEJNEGER. On the extermination of the Great Northern Sea-Cow (*Rytina*), a reply to Prof. A. E. Nordenskiöld.
Bulletin Amer. Geograph. Soc., 1886, No. 4, pp. 317-328.
Disproves Nordenskiold's allegation that living Rytinas have been seen since 1768, the year given by Sauer as the year of extinction of the Great Northern Sea-Cow.

Z. L. TANNER. Report on the work of the United States Fish Commission steamer *Albatross* for the year ending December 31, 1883. By Lieut. Commander Z. L. Tanner, U. S. Navy, commanding.
Report U. S. Commissioner of Fish and Fisheries, part XI, for 1883-1886, pp. 117-236, 1885.
Gives a narrative of the several cruises made during the year, and includes the following special reports: Report of the naturalist, Mr. James E. Benedict, pp. 175-177; Report of Ensign R. H. Miner, U. S. Navy, Department of Fishes, pp. 178-203; Dredging and Trawling Record, Stations 2001-2116, pp. 219-221.

Z. L. TANNER. Report on the work of the United States Fish Commission steamer *Albatross* for the year ending December 31, 1884. By Lieut. Commander Z. L. Tanner, U. S. Navy, commanding.
Report U. S. Commissioner of Fish and Fisheries, part XII, for 1884-1886, pp. 1-116, plates 1-3.
A narrative of the cruises during the year, with the report of the naturalist, Mr. James E. Benedict (pp. 86-103), and the records of the dredging and trawling stations, 2117-2310 (pp. 106-110).

Z. L. TANNER. Record of hydrographic soundings and dredging stations occupied by the steamer *Albatross* in 1886. By Lieut. Commander Z. L. Tanner, U. S. Navy, commanding.
Bull. U. S. Fish Com., VI, 1886, pp. 277-285.
A list of the localities (Stations 2629-2735) from which specimens, now in the collection of the National Museum, were obtained. The following data are given with respect to each locality: Serial number, date, position, temperature, depth, character of bottom, apparatus used, etc.

GEORGE L. TOPPAN. A Contribution to our Knowledge of Albinism.
Ridgway Ornith. Club, Bull. No. 2, 1887, pp. 61-77.
The author enumerates one hundred and fifty-four North American species which have been found in albinistic plumage, making special reference to twenty-eight species in the National Museum examined by him.

CHARLES H. TOWNSEND. List of the Midsummer Birds of the Kowak River, northern Alaska.
The Auk, IV, 1887, pp. 11-13.
Enumerates fifty-two species. The specimens collected are in the collection of the National Museum.

FREDERICK W. TRUE. Report on the Department of Mammals in the U. S. National Museum, 1884.
Report Smithsonian Institution, 1884 (1886) II, pp. 129-142.

FREDERICK W. TRUE. On a Spotted Dolphin apparently identical with the *Prodelphinus doris* of Gray.

Report Smithsonian Institution, 1884, II, 1886, pp. 317–324, pls. i–vi.

FREDERICK W. TRUE. The Florida Musk-rat, *Neofiber alleni* True.

Report Smithsonian Institution, 1884, II, 1886, pp. 325–330, pls. i–iii.

FREDERICK W. TRUE and F. A. LUCAS. On the West Indian Seal, *Monachus tropicalis* Gray.

Report Smithsonian Institution, 1884, II, 1886, pp. 331–335, pls. i–iii.

FREDERICK W. TRUE. A new study of the genus *Dipodomys*.

Proc. U. S. Nat. Mus., IX, Oct. 30, 1886, pp. 409–413.

(Read before the Biological Society of Washington, November 28, 1885.)

FREDERICK W. TRUE. An annotated list of the Mammals collected by the late Mr. Charles L. McKay in the vicinity of Bristol Bay, Alaska.

Proc. U. S. Nat. Mus., IX, Oct. 11, 1886, pp. 221–224.

FREDERICK W. TRUE. Description of a new genus and species of mole, *Dymecodon pilirostris*, from Japan.

Proc. U. S. Nat. Mus., IX, Aug. 26, 1886, pp. 97, 98.

FREDERICK W. TRUE. A new Bat from Puget Sound.

Science, VIII., Dec. 24, 1886, p. 588.

A diagnosis of *Vespertilio longicrus* sp. n.

FREDERICK W. TRUE. Description of a new species of Bat, *Vespertilio longicrus*, from Puget Sound.

Proc. U. S. Nat. Mus., X, April 25, 1887, pp. 6, 7.

FREDERICK W. TRUE. The Almiqui.

Science, VIII, No. 190, Sept. 24, 1886, p. 282; one cut.

Notes on the acquisition of a living specimen.

FREDERICK W. TRUE. An Ass with abnormally developed hoofs.

Science, VIII, No. 191, Oct. 1, 1886, p. 304.

An account of a remarkable case of hypertrophy of the hoofs.

FREDERICK W. TRUE. Some distinctive cranial characters of the Canada Lynx.

Proc. U. S. Nat. Mus., X, April 25, 1887, pp. 8, 9.

A. E. VERRILL. Results of the explorations made by the steamer *Albatross* off the northern coast of the United States in 1883.

Report U. S. Com. Fish and Fisheries, part XI, for 1883 (1886), pp. 513–699, pls. 1–44, 1885.

This report is divided into the following topics: "Character of the deep-sea deposits." "List of the stations occupied by the *Albatross* in 1883." "Fauna of the deep water." "Fauna of the northern waters." "Lists of species dredged by the *Albatross* in 1883, and by the *Fish Hawk* in 1880–'82." "Fauna of the shallow water near Cape Hatteras." "List of the shallow water Mollusca dredged off Cape Hatteras by the *Albatross* in 1883, by Miss K. J. Bush." "Fauna of the surface water of the Gulf Stream." "Preliminary list of Acalephæ collected by the *Albatross* in 1883, in the region of the Gulf Stream, by J. W. Fewkes."

The plates contain 245 figures covering most of the groups of marine invertebrates, and mainly representing species that had been previously described.

The following new forms are described:

Mollusca.

Mangilia ephamilla Bush, p. 80.
Mangilia melanitica Dall, var. *oxia* Bush., p. 580.
Mangilia oxytata Bush, p. 582.
Mangilia (?) *glypta* Bush, p. 582.
Niso æglëes Bush, p. 585.
Dentalium leptum Bush, p. 586.
Cadulus Carolinensis Bush, p. 587.
Neæra costata Bush, p. 587.

Tunicata.

Culeolus Tanneri Ver., p. 529 (foot-note).

Echinodermata.

Synapta brychia Ver., p. 539.
Ophiacantha fraterna Ver., p. 545.
Ophiacantha varispina Ver., p. 545.
Ophiacantha gracilis Ver., p. 548.
Amphiura fragilis Ver., p. 549.

Acalephæ.

Atolla Verrillii Fewkes, p. 596.
Nauphantopsis Diomedeæ Fewkes, gen. et sp. nov., p. 596.
Pterophysa grandis Fewkes, gen, et sp. nov., p. 598.
Angelopsis globosa Fewkes, gen. et sp. nov., p. 599.

CHARLES D. WALCOTT. [Report on the] Dep artment of Invertebrate Fossils, Paleo zoic [in the National Museum, 1884].

Report Smithsonian Institution, 1884, II (1886), pp. 203-214.

CHARLES D. WALCOTT. Classification of the Cambrian system of North America.

Amer. Jour. Sci., XXXIII, art. xvi, August, 1866, pp. 138-157, 9 figures.

CHARLES D. WALCOTT. Cambrian age of the Roofing Slates of Granville, Washington County, New York.

Proc. Amer. Assoc. Adv. Sci., Buffalo meeting, August, 1886. (One page extract.) Salem Press, December, 1886.

CHARLES D. WALCOTT. The Taconic System.

Amer. Jour. Sci., XXXIII, February, 1887. (One page extract.)

LESTER F. WARD. [Report on the] Department of Fossil Plants [in the U. S. National Museum, 1884].

Report Smithsonian Institution, 1884, II (1886), pp. 219, 220.

LESTER F. WARD. Broadening the Way to Success.

The Forum, New York, II, December, 1886, pp. 340-350.

Condensed from a lecture delivered at the National Museum, May 1, 1886, on "Heredity and Opportunity." It is argued that undue attention is paid to genius and too little to the extension of equal opportunities to all.

LESTER F. WARD. The Use and Abuse of Wealth.

The Forum, New York, II, February, 1887, pp. 549-558.

Some of the ways in which persons of ample means might profitably employ it are pointed out, and the use of wealth as an aid to thorough and efficient work is suggested as a partial solution of the question of restricting fortune.

LESTER F. WARD. Science and Immortality.

The Christian Register, Boston, LXVI, April 7, 1887, pp. 211, 212.

Contribution to a "Symposium" of scientific men on the subject of the title. The article was copied in Public Opinion, Washington, III, April 16, 1887, and the Symposium has since been issued in pamphlet form.

LESTER F. WARD. The Immortality that Science teaches.

The Open Court, Chicago, I, May 26, 1887, pp. 199-201. One of the propositions contained in the preceding contribution is here more fully expanded.

LESTER F. WARD. False notions of Government.

The Forum, New York, III, June, 1887, pp. 364-372.

Some of the current fallacies respecting the powers and duties are exposed in this article and the direction in which state functions should be enlarged is pointed out.

LESTER F. WARD. Administrative Report to the Director of the U. S. Geological Survey of the operations of the Division of Paleobotany for the year ending June 30, 1885.

Sixth Annual Report of the U. S. Geological Survey, 1884-'85. Washington, 1885, issued June, 1887, pp. 81-85.

LESTER F. WARD. Synopsis of the Flora of the Laramie Group.

Sixth Annual Report of the U. S. Geological Survey, 1884-'85. Washington, 1885. Extras, Washington, 1886, issued June 1887, pp. 399-557, pls. xxxi-lxv.

Contains an historical review of opinion relative to the age, the nature and extent of the groups and of the vegetation of the Laramie Group, an extensive table of distribution of Laramie, Devonian, and Eocene plants, and a thorough discussion of the same. Concludes with a report upon recent collections from the Laramie Group, especially the results of the author's personal studies in Colorado and Wyoming, in 1881, and on the Lower Yellowstone and Upper Missouri (Fort Union Group) in 1883, still in process of elaboration, giving a list of 140 species identified at that date, 85 of which were new to science. These 140 species are illustrated on 35 double plates, containing 409 figures, by the photo-engraving process. No descriptions nor discussions of the botanical affinities of these fossil plants accompany the list of names and illustrations, these being reserved for the publication described under the next title.

LESTER F. WARD. Types of the Laramie Flora.

Bull. of the U. S. Geological Survey, No. 37, 354 pages, 57 double plates, 8vo, Washington, 1887.

The figures published in the "Synopsis of the Flora of the Laramie Group" (see last title) are here reproduced on smaller plates, and are preceded by 115 pages of letter-press devoted to their thorough systematic description, with synonymy and full discussion of the relationships of the species.

JOHN GRANT WELLS.   A Catalogue of the Birds of Grenada, West Indies, with observations thereon.   [Edited by George N. Lawrence.]

> *Proc. U. S. Nat. Mus.*, IX, 1886, Feb. 11, 1887, pp. 609–633.
>
> Most of the species given in this catalogue have been presented by Mr. Wells to the National Museum.   Ninety-two species are enumerated.   The paper is interspersed with numerous notes by Mr. Lawrence included in brackets and signed "G. N. L."

C. A. WHITE.   On the Fresh-water Invertebrates of the North American Jurassic.

> *Bull.* 29, *U. S. Geological Survey*, pp. 1–41.   Four plates.

C. A. WHITE.   On the relation of the Laramie Molluscan Fauna to that of the succeeding Fresh-water Eocene and other groups.

> *Bull.* 34, *U. S. Geological Survey*, Washington, 1886, pp. 1 (388)–54 (442), pls. i–v.

C. A. WHITE.   On new generic forms of Cretaceous Mollusca and their relation to other forms.

> *Proc. Phil. Acad. Nat. Sci.*, Jan., 1887, pp. 32–37, pl. ii.

C. A. WHITE.   On the Cretaceous Formations of Texas and their relation to those of other portions of North America.

> *Proc. Phila. Acad. Nat. Sci.*, Feb., 1887, pp. 39–47.

C. A. WHITE.   On the inter-relation of contemporaneous fossil Faunas and Floras.

> *Amer. Jour. Sci.* (3rd ser.), XXXIII, pp. 364–374.

C. A. WHITE.   On the age of the Coal found in the region traversed by the Rio Grande.

> *Amer. Jour. Sci.* (3rd ser.), vol. XXXIII, pp. 18–20.

C. A. WHITE.   (Report on the) Department of Invertebrate Fossils, Mesozoic and Cenozoic (in the U. S. National Museum, 1884).

> *Report Smithsonian Institution*, 1884, II (1886), pp. 215–217.

SAMUEL W. WILLISTON, M. D.   Synopsis of the North American Syrphidæ.

> *Bull.* 31, *U. S. Nat. Mus.*, 1886, 8vo, pp. i–xxx+1–335, pl. i to xii.
>
> Gives a definition of the family, its extent, characters, and classifications, and a synoptic table of subfamilies, tribes, and genera.   This forms Part I of the work.
>
> In Part II are given detailed descriptions of the sixty-five genera into which the family is divided, and of over three hundred species (many of them new), together with a full synonymy and bibliography.
>
> Part III. Conclusion.   Gives the habits of the species, a résumé of the larval habits as far as known, structure of the family, sexual differences, geographical distribution, geological distribution, chronological list of genera, and a definition of terms.
>
> The Appendix contains a few added species, modifications of synopsis, and general notes.

H. C. YARROW.   Report on the Department of Herpetology in the U. S. National Museum, 1884.

> *Report Smithsonian Institution*, 1884, II (1886), pp. 157–160.

H. C. YARROW.   Recurrence of symptoms of Poisoning after Snake-bites.

> *Medical News.* 1887, I, p. 623.

H. C. YARROW.   Navajo methods of curing Ague.

> *Forest and Stream*, XXVIII, No. 6, March 3, 1887, pp. 104, 105

SECTION V.

LIST OF ACCESSIONS TO THE U. S. NATIONAL MUSEUM DURING THE FISCAL YEAR 1886–'87, WITH DESCRIPTIVE NOTES.

LIST OF ACCESSIONS.

JULY, 1886.

ENGRAVER'S TOOLS (one set), including graver-square and handle, graver-gouge and handle, etching-point and etching-ground, eye-glass, scraper, burnisher, and roller.

    JOHN SELLERS & SONS, New York City. 17705. '86. (I)

MONKEY, *Macacus maurus*, in the flesh.

    ZOOLOGICAL SOCIETY OF PHILADELPHIA. (Through Arthur E. Brown, Esq.). 17706. '86. (IV)

MOLLUSKS.

    S. F. CHENEY, Grand Manan, New Brunswick. 17707. '86. (IX)

SEA CUCUMBERS, crabs, etc.

    S. F. CHENEY, Grand Manan, New Brunswick. 17707. '86. (XI)

PYROXENIC ROCK containing some pyrrhotite; for examination.

    GEORGE W. WATKINS, Moriah, Essex County, New York. 17708. '86 (XVI)

INSECTS caught near an electric light; for examination.

    WILLIAM H. ASHMEAD, Jacksonville, Florida. 17709. '86. (X)

COPPERHEAD SNAKE, *Ancistrodon piscivorus*.

    GEORGE CHANDLER, West Washington, District of Columbia. 17710. '86. (VI)

KANGAROO RAT, *Dipodomys agilis*.

    F. N. DICK, North Platte, Nebraska. 17711. '86. (IV)

MOLE, *Scalops aquaticus*.

    BENJAMIN MILLER, West Washington, District of Columbia. 17712. '86. (IV)

FOSSIL, *Spirifera logani*; a fine specimen.

    WILEY BRITTON, Harrisonville, Missouri. (Through Dr. C. Hart Merriam.) 17713. '86. (XIII, A)

FOSSIL (Mesozoic). Lower valve of *Radiolites austinensis*, Roemer, an extinct genus of the Rudistæ; for examination.

    SAMUEL HAMMONTREE, Bonham, Texas. 17714. '86. (XIII, B)

CONFEDERATE SEAL, Treasury Department, stamped on paper manufactured in the Confederate States during the war.

    PAUL BECKWITH, U. S. National Museum. 17715. '86. (I)

ORNAMENTED GOLD DISK, from a mound.

    S. A. ROBINSON, Orlando, Orange County, Florida. 17716. '86. (III)

PESTLES, sinkers, fragment of a pot-stone bowl, natural formations slightly modified, etc.

    GEORGE MIDDLETOWN and W. H. H. CHAMBERS, Lumberton, New Jersey. 17717. '86. (III)

STUFFED CROCODILE.

    JAMES W. SILER, Cape Town, Africa. 17718. '86.

AMERICAN HERCULES BEETLE, *Dynastes tityus*; for examination.

    "*Memphis Avalanche*," Memphis, Tennessee. 17719. '86. (X)

LIZARD, *Eumeces fasciatus*.

    F. W. HAYWARD, Oakley, South Carolina. 17720. '86. (VI)

STONE AX, arrow-head, broken flint, pebbles, etc. (Exchange.)

    Dr. A. D. THOMAS, Terre Haute, Missouri. 17721. '86. (III)

INDIAN OBJECTS made of pot-stone.

J. S. RATHBONE, Waynesville, North Carolina. 17722. '86. (III)

WATER from a large salt lake near Pecos, Texas; for examination.

J. K. HARRINGTON, Pecos, Texas. 17723. '86. (XVI)

COPPER ORES.

L. STADTMULLER, New Haven, Connecticut. 17724. '86. (XVIII)

CARVED HORN, a relic of the English and French wars.

C. McMICHAEL BARTON, Orangeburgh, South Carolina. 17725. '86. (I)

SEA HERRING, Clupea harengus; for examination.

J. T. CHURCH, Tiverton, Rhode Island. 17726. '86. (VIII)

CHINESE LANTERN. (Returned.)

Major T. B. FERGUSON, Washington, District of Columbia. 17727. '86. (II, A)

PUPA and cast-off skins of a species of the higher Bombycidæ (?).

B. F. STALKER, New Providence, Indiana. 17728. '86. (X)

STAR-NOSED MOLE, Condylura cristata, in the flesh.

D. W. LAWSON, West Winsted, Connecticut. 17729. '86. (IV)

MINERALS; from Rockbridge County, Virginia.

Prof. J. H. MORRISON, Lexington, Virginia. 17730. '86. (XVI)

TORPEDO, cramp-fish, or electric ray, Torpedo occidentalis.

J. B. EDWARDS, Amagansett, New York. 17731. '86. (VII)

STURGEON, Acipenser sturio (head).

E. G. BLACKFORD, New York City. 17732. '86. (VII)

STONE METATE.

JOSÉ C. ZELEDON, San José, Costa Rica. 17733. '86. (III)

BIRD, Crax globicera (skin); new to the collection.

JOSÉ C. ZELEDON, San José, Costa Rica. 17733. '86. (V, A)

SHELLS.

JOSÉ C. ZELEDON, San José, Costa Rica. 17733. '86. (IX)

MINNOWS, fat-head and black-head, Pimephales promelas; said to have fallen from rain clouds at Harvard, Nebraska.

W. L. MAY, Fremont, Nebraska. 17734. '86. (VII)

ROUGH-WINGED SWALLOW, Stelgidopteryx serripennis, from Alexandria County, Virginia.

ROBERT RIDGWAY, U. S. National Museum. 17735. '86. (V, A)

SHELLS, Parapholas californica and Pholas (Zirphœa) crispola, from Queen Charlotte Islands.

W. B. ANDERSON, Fort Simpson, British Columbia. 17736. '86. (IX)

FLYING-SQUIRREL, Sciuropterus volucella (skin).

W. B. ANDERSON, Fort Simpson, British Columbia. 17736. '86. (IV)

BIRD-SKINS, Turdus aonalaschkœ, Cyanocitta annectens, Aphriza virgata, and Tringa canutus (4 specimens).

W. B. ANDERSON, Fort Simpson, British Columbia. 17736. '86. (V, A)

SPONGE, Chelina sp. (2 specimens).

W. B. ANDERSON, Fort Simpson, British Columbia. 17736. '86. (XI)

OYSTER-SHELL taken from the bottom of the frigate Constellation when she was at anchor at the dry-dock in Charlestown, after her return from the West Indies.

Dr. E. STERLING, Cleveland, Ohio. 17737. '86. (IX)

GOLDFINCH, a cross between a female canary, Serinus canariensis, and a male goldfinch, Carduelis carduelis.

LOUIS SCHMID & SONS, Washington, District of Columbia. 17738. '86. (V, A)

PLANT; for examination.

Dr. C. M. CASE, Honey Spring, Texas. 17739. '86. (XV)

MOTH, Anisota virginiensis; for examination.

WILLIAM BRADFORD, Centre, Alabama. 17740. '86. (X)

MANGANESE MINERAL and silicious material stained with various particles of decomposition products; for examination.

Mrs. E. W. P. GUYE, Seattle, Washington Territory. 17741. '86. (XVIII)

SHELL, *Unio rubiginosus* Lea; for examination.

Dr. W. S. NEWLON, Oswego, Kansas. 17742. '86. (IX)

BLISTERING BEETLES,* *Epicauta maculata;* for examination.

Capt. HENRY ROMEYN, U. S. Army, Fort Keogh, Montana. 17742. '86. (X)

COINS, ancient Grecian and Roman.

FRANK REYNOLDS, U. S. National Museum. 17744. '86. (I)

GLACIAL FLUTING and striation, from the North quarry, Kelley's Island, Western Lake Erie.

Mrs. E. K. HUNTINGTON. (Through T. C. Chamberlin, U. S. Geological Survey.) 17745. '86. (XVII)

PHOTOGRAPHS of Winnebago, Ute, and Osage Indians (39).

BUREAU OF ETHNOLOGY, Washington, District of Columbia. 17746. '86. (II, A)

METEORITES (187 specimens).

CHARLES U. SHEPARD, Charleston, South Carolina. 17747. '86. (XVI)

FISH, specimen of "LOOK DOWN," *Vomer setipinnis;* for examination.

E. M. McCOMAS, Washington, District of Columbia. 17748. '86. (VII)

NOTCHED SINKER; for examination.

D. C. HARROWER, Tioga, Tioga County, Pennsylvania. 17749. '86. (III)

MAMMAL SKINS AND SKELETONS:

Bison americanus.	*Hesperomys leucopus.*
Antilocapra americana.	*Lepus campestris.*
Fiber zibethicus.	*L. sylvaticus.*
Spermophilus 13-*lineata.*	*Canis latrans* (2) juv.
Tamias asiaticus pallidus.	

Collected by W. T. Hornaday, in Montana.

SMITHSONIAN INSTITUTION, Washington, District of Columbia. 17750. '86. (IV)

BIRD-SKINS from Montana (7 specimens). Collected by W. T. Hornaday.

SMITHSONIAN INSTITUTION, Washington, District of Columbia. 17750. '86. (V, A)

DUCKS' EGGS (96 specimens). Collected by W. T. Hornaday.

SMITHSONIAN INSTITUTION, Washington, District of Columbia. 17750. '86. (V, B)

QUARTZ containing a small amount of mica; for examination.

J. HOWELL. (Through Hon. M. W. Ransom, U. S. Senate.) 17751. '86. (XVIII)

SNAKE EGGS.

REUBEN WRIGHT, Clifton Station, Virginia. 17752. '86. (VI)

COPPER COIN, 3 *schwaren,* Bremen, Germany, 1858.

GEORGE ECKERT, Jr., Washington, District of Columbia. 17753. '86. (I)

HEAD OF ELK, *Cervus canadensis* (deposited).

Col. JOHN D. WILKINS, Fort Keogh, Montana. 17754. '86. (IV)

ALBINO ROBIN, *Merula migratoria.*

GEORGE MARSHALL, Laurel, Maryland. 17755. '86. (V, A)

IRON PYRITES; for examination.

P. H. SPEARS, Morrillton, Arkansas. (Through Hon. James H. Berry.) 17756. '86. (XVI)

CROCIDOLITE IN QUARTZ; four cut stones artificially colored.

GEORGE F. KUNZ, Hoboken, New Jersey. 17757. '86. (XVI)

METEORIC IRON; four fragments from Augusta County, Virginia, and eleven fragments from Jenny's Creek, West Virginia. (In exchange.)

GEORGE F. KUNZ, Hoboken, New Jersey. 17758. '86. (XVI)

---

* See Report on Department of Insects, Part II.

RED ELDER, *Sambucus pubens*, from Forest, Ontario; for name.

L. H. SMITH, Forest, Ontario. 17759. '86. (XV)

HERB, apparently *Lithospermum multiflorum;* for name.

W. R. BROWN, Sanders, Fresno County, California. 17760. '86. (I)

FOSSIL SHELLS, from the Pebas Group in the valley of the Amazon.

Dr. O. BÖTTGER, Frankfort-am-Main, Germany. 17761. '86. (XIII, B)

ARCHÆOLOGICAL OBJECTS: Hammer-stone, 14 chips and flakes, 7 rude implements, 4 leaf-shaped implements, 6 spear-heads, 55 arrow-heads, rude chipped ax, grooved ax, 2 fragments of pierced tablets, 3 fragments of pot-stone bowls, 5 fragments of split bones, 70 fragments of pottery, 14 Unio and oyster shells, presented. Also 26 rude implements and 107 arrow-heads, in exchange.

O. N. BRYAN, Marshall Hall, Maryland. 17762. '86. (III)

CHLORITIC MATERIAL, decomposed; for examination.

Hon. W. C. WHITTHORNE, United States Senate. 17763. '86. (XVIII)

FOSSIL CEPHALOPOD, *Belemnitella quadrata* (4 specimens), from Germany.

Prof. C. SCHLÜTER, Bonn on Rhine, Germany. (Through Dr. C. A. White.) 17764. '86. (XIII, B)

INVERTEBRATE FOSSILS, *Cyclostoma antiquus* (7), *Cyclostoma tricarinata* (7), *Cyrena livata* (2).

Prof. F. SANDBERGER, Wurzburg, Bavaria. 17765. '86. (XIII, B)

LEADS.

A. EILERS, Colorado Smelting Company, South Pueblo, Colorado. 17766. '86. (XVIII)

WOOD of *Abies Douglassi*, bored by *Scolytus unispinosus;* from Sylvania, California. Collected by L. E. Ricksecker.

J. B. SMITH, U. S. National Museum. 17767. '86. (X)

PLANT, *Hibiscus moschatus*, L.; for examination.

HARVEY C. MEDFORD, Tupelo, Mississippi. 17768. '86. (XV)

DECOMPOSED TOURMALINE from New York; for examination.

GEORGE W. WATKINS, Moriah, New York. 17769. (XVIII)

ROOT (Rhizome); for examination.

P. E. DUPUY, Richmond, Virginia. 17770. '86. (I)

FERRUGINOUS CONCRETION, from near Havre-de-Grace, Maryland.

U. S. GEOLOGICAL SURVEY, Washington, District of Columbia. (Through W J McGee.) 17771. '86. (XVII)

TETRADYMITE.

BUSH and MEYERS, Sheridan, Montana. 17772. '86. (XVIII)

PLANT, *Hypericum galioides*, Lam.; for examination.

J. C. MCGAHA, Cedar Mountain, Transylvania County, North Carolina. 17773. '86. (XV)

HEAD OF VIRGINIA DEER, *Cariacus virginianus* (mounted).

H. H. MINER, Saranac Lake, New York. 17774. '86. (IV)

PILOT-BOAT (model). Schooner-rigged pilot-boat *Glyn*, of Brunswick, Georgia. Designed by G. L. Daboll and built by Robert Palmer & Sons, Noank, in 1884. The top of model represents deck line, above which was a bulwark 20 inches high, including the rail. Keel, 12 inches deep forward and 24 inches deep aft. Length over all, 78 feet; on water-line, 68 feet; top of keel to top of deck, 9 feet 4 inches; beam, 20 feet. A marked characteristic is the strong rake of the stem, and the considerable flare of the bow above water.

G. L. DABOLL, Noank, Connecticut. 17775. '86. (I)

FRESH-WATER SHELLS.

H. G. HODGE, York, Clark County, Illinois. 17776. '86. (IX)

SCOURING RUSH, *Equisetum hyemale*, and *Nelumbium luteum*.

H. G. HODGE, York, Clark County, Illinois. 17776. '86. (XV)

MOLLUSKS AND BRACHIOPODS. Two hundred and five species; about 500 specimens dry and alcoholic, dredged by U. S. Coast Survey steamer *Blake*, 1876–'78; from the Gulf of Mexico and the West Indies.

Prof. ALEXANDER AGASSIZ, Cambridge, Massachusetts. (Through Dr. W. H. Dall.) 17777. '86. (IX)

ROCKFISH, *Roccus lineatus;* from the Susquehanna River, at Bainbridge, Pennsylvania.

BERNARD DOYLE, Bainbridge, Pennsylvania. 17778. '86. (VII)

BIRD-SKINS,* from New Zealand:

Hieracidea novæ-zealandiæ, Lath. (2 specimens.)

Hieracidea ferox, Peale.

Circus gouldi, Bonap. (2 specimens.)

Athene novæ-zealandiæ, Gml. (2 specimens.)

Halcyon vagans, Less. (3 specimens.)

Prosthemadera novæ-zealandiæ, Gml. (4 specimens.)

Anthornis melanura, Sparr. (2 specimens.)

Zosterops lateralis, Lath. (2 specimens.)

Orthonyx ochrocephala, Gml. (2 specimens.)

Certhiparus novæ-zealandiæ. (2 specimens.)

Petrœca longipes, Less. (2 specimens.)

Petrœca macrocephala, Gml. (2 specimens.)

Anthus novæ-zealandiæ, Gml. (2 specimens.)

Turnagra crassirostris, Gml.

Rhipidura flabellifera, Gml. (2 specimens.)

Rhipidura fuliginosa, Sparr. (2 specimens.)

Charadrius obscurus, Gml. (4 specimens.)

Charadrius bicinctus, Jard. (3 specimens.)

Anarhynchus frontalis, Q. & G. (4 specimens.)

Hæmatopus unicolor, Frost.

Botaurus pœciloptilus, Wagl.

Limosa baueri, Maum. (3 specimens.)

Tringa canutus, L.

Ocydromus earli, Gray. (2 specimens.)

Ocydromus earli, Gray. Juv.

Ocydromus australis, Sparr. (2 specimens.)

Rallus philippensis, L. (3 specimens.)

Ortygometra tabuensis, Gml.

Porphyrio melanotus, Temm. (2 specimens.)

Anas superciliosa, Gml.

Podiceps cristatus, L.

Podiceps rufipectus, Gray.

Larus dominicanus, Licht. (2 specimens.)

Creadion carunculatus, Gml. (2 specimens.)

Heteralocha acutirostris, Gould. (2 specimens.)

Stringops habroptilus, Gray. (2 specimens.)

Platycercus novæ-zealandiæ, Sparr. (2 specimens.)

Platycercus auriceps, Kuhl. (2 specimens.)

Nestor meridionalis, Gml. (2 specimens.)

Nestor notabilis, Gould. (2 specimens.)

Eudynamis taitensis, Sparr. (2 specimens.)

Carpophaga novæ-zealandiæ, Gml. (2 specimens.)

Apteryx mantelli, Bartl. (2 specimens.)

Larus scopulinus, Forst. (2 specimens.)

Sterna frontalis, Gray. (2 specimens.)

Sterna antarctica, Frost. (2 specimens.)

Puffinus tristis, Forst.

Procellaria parkinsoni, Gray.

Procellaria cookii, Gray.

Thalassidroma fregata, L.

Dysporus serrator, Banks. Juv.

Phalacrocorax melanoleucus, Viell.

Phalacrocorax brevirostris, Gould.

Phalacrocorax varius, Gml.

Phalacrocorax punctatus, Sparr. (2 specimens.)

Eudyptes pachyrhynchus, Gray. (2 specimens.)

The nomenclature is that of Buller's Manual of the Birds of New Zealand, Wellington, 1882.

AUCKLAND MUSEUM, Auckland, New Zealand. (Through Prof. T. F. Cheeseman, curator.) 17779. '86. (V, A)

* See Report on Department of Birds, Part II.

Coke:

GEOLOGICAL SURVEY OF KENTUCKY, Lexington, Kentucky. (Through Prof. J. B. Proctor.) 17780. '86. (XVIII)

GEOMETRIC COMPASS, from China.

Dr. D. B. McCARTEE, Washington, District of Columbia. 17781. '86. (II, A)

"*The New England Nut Courant*," No. 80, 1723. Printed and sold by Benjamin Franklin.

THOMAS A. RICH, Boston, Massachusetts. 17782. '86. (I)

RECEIPTED BILL, dated October 15, 1864—a relic of the Confederacy.

E. R. TODD, U. S. National Museum. 17783. '86. (I)

PYRRHOTITE, containing nickel; for examination.

A. H. CROWKHITE and GEORGE B. HENDERSON, Denver, Colorado. 17784. '86. (XVI)

KAOLIN; for examination.

A. J. BARNETT & BRO., Leakey, Texas. 17785. '86. (XVI)

PLANT, large-leaved form of *Lilium canadensis*, L. (?); for name.

W. H. ADAMS, Elmore, Illinois. 17786. '86. (XV)

LEAD BUCKLES, made in the factory of Harrison Bros. & Co.

HARRISON BROTHERS & Co., Philadelphia, Pennsylvania. 17787. '86. (XVIII)

LIMESTONE, supposed by sender to contain silver or zinc; for examination.

S. FLETCHER, Phebe, Tennessee. 17788. '86. (XVIII)

PHOTOGRAVURES to accompany the metallurgical collection from the Works of the Colorado Smelting Company.

COLORADO SMELTING COMPANY, South Pueblo, Colorado. 17789. '86. (XVIII)

ORES, consisting chiefly of magnetic oxide of iron, from Arizona; for examination.

J. D. EMMERSLEY, Dos Cabezos, Arizona. 17790. '86. (XVIII)

FOSSIL SHELLS (68 species). (Exchange.)

Prof. M. NEUMEYER, Vienna, Austria. 17791, '86. (XIII, B)

RHIZOMES of *Nuphar pumilum* (?) and *Nymphœa alba* var. *candida*, from Prussia.

Prof. D. R. CASPARY, Konigsberg, Prussia. 17792. '86. (Sent to the carp ponds.)

FOSSILS, *Dictyophyton tuberosum, Zaphrentis solida, Chonophyllum, Chœtetes lycoperdon, Monticulipora, Productus cora, Zaphrentis*. (Sixteen specimens.)

W. R. LEIGHTON, Creston, Iowa. 17793. '86. (XIII, A)

COTTON, handspun yarn, quilt, purple dye, and shell-fish from which the dye is made; from the Indians of Acapulco.

JOHN A. SUTTER, U. S. consul, Acapulco, Mexico. (Through Quartermaster's Department, U. S. A.). 17794. '86. (I)

PEARLS (998), taken from the following species of Californian mollusks: *Tivela crassatelloides, Chione fluctifraga, Vomer mercenaria, Haliotis splendens, Haliotis Crachordii, Haliotis rubescens*.

C. R. ORCUTT, San Diego, California. 17795. '86. (IX)

MOCKING BIRD, *Mimus polyglottos* (skeleton), from Virginia.

W. C. WEEDEN, U. S. National Museum. 17796. '86. (XII)

PIECE OF WRECK from George's Banks, supposed to be a part of the quarter-rail of an old fishing vessel, brought up by a hand-line fish-hook, lat. 41° 55', long. 66° 5C'.

P. A. MERCHANT, Schooner *Ethel*, Gloucester, Massachusetts. (Through W. A. Wilcox.) 17797. '86. (I)

OIL PORTRAIT of Sin-Sin, painted in Shanghai, China. Also carved frame, made in Ningpo.

Dr. D. B. McCARTEE, Washington, District of Columbia. 17798. '86. (II, A)

COMMON ATLANTIC SALMON, *Salmo wilmotii*, and California trout, *Salmo irideus*.

Dr. FRANCIS DAY, Cheltenham, England. 17799. '86. (VII)

ETHNOLOGICAL OBJECTS: Model of child's sledge; snow-knife made of wood from Dr. Kane's ship; Dr. Boas' seal-skin parka, from Cumberland Gulf. Also Venetian pitcher, and wine goblet of the seventeenth century. (Exchange.)

Dr. EMIL BESSELS, Washington, District of Columbia. 17800. '86. (II, A)

BIRD SKINS AND SKELETONS (14), from California.
LOREN W. GREEN, Redding, California. 17801. '86. (IV)

SCREECH OWL, *Megascops asio*, from Maryland.
GEORGE MARSHALL, Laurel, Maryland. 17802. '86. (V, A)

RED PHALAROPE, *Crymophilus fulicarius.* Shot on Eastern Branch, District of Columbia.
F. S. WEBSTER, Washington, District of Columbia. 17803. '86. (V, A)

FISHES, *Lepomis pallidus, Micropterus salmoides, Ambloplites rupestris, Amia calva, Esox lucius, Stizostedium vitreum, Pomoxys sparoides, Perca americana, Amiurus natalis* var. *cupreus, Lepomis gibbosus, Coregonus* sp., *Percina caprodes, Lota maculosa, Uranidea,* sp.
F. L. WASHBURN, Minneapolis, Minnesota. 17804. '86. (VII)

TORTOISE, from Darlington, South Carolina.
FRANK BURNS, U. S. Geological Survey. 17805. '86. (VI)

HUMMING-BIRDS, from South America. (6 skins.)
F. S. WEBSTER, Washington, District of Columbia. 17806. '86. (V, A)

WHIP-POOR-WILL, *Antrostomus vociferus*, from Maryland.
GEORGE MARSHALL, Laurel, Maryland. 17807. '86. (V, A)

AMBER-FISH, *Seriola lalandi*, from Wood's Holl, Massachusetts.
U. S. FISH COMMISSION, Wood's Holl, Massachusetts. 17808. '86. (VII)

*BIRD SKIN, *Picolaptes rikeri*, nov. sp., from South America.
C. B. RIKER, 301 Produce Exchange, New York. 17809. '86. (V, A)

OXIDE OF LEAD, supposed to be an artificial product; for examination.
.CHARLES MASON, Edge Hill, Virginia. 17810. '86. (XVIII)

PIPE, probably of Indian manufacture.
LEVI W. MENGEL, 620 Penn street, Reading, Pennsylvania. 17811. '86. (II, A)

MAMMALS, *Plecotus auritus, Vespertilio bechsteinii, Vesperus borealis, Vespertilio mystacinus, Arvicola rufocanus* (skins); *Putorius fœtidus, Ursus arctos* (skulls); *Gulo borealis* (skeleton).
Prof. TYCHO TULLBERG, Upsala, Sweden. 17812. '86. (IV)

GALENA (sulphide of lead); for examination.
Dr. H. M. RECTOR, Hot Springs, Arkansas. 17813. '86. (XVIII)

FOSSIL TEETH OF MAMMOTH, *Elephas americanus*, and Horse, *Equus*, sp., from Sulphur Valley, Arizona Territory; for inspection. (Returned.)
THOMAS J. NEWLAND, Wilcox, Arizona Territory. 17814. '86. (XII)

CANARY BIRD, *Serinus canariensis*, in the flesh.
LOUIS SCHMID & SONS, Washington, District of Columbia. 17815. '86. (V, A)

CEREMONIAL WEAPON, from Orangeburgh, South Carolina.
FRANK BURNS, U. S. Geological Survey. 17816. '86. (III)

FROG, from Darlington, South Carolina.
FRANK BURNS, U. S. Geological Survey. 17816. '86. (VI)

FISHES, *Phoxinus stagnalis* sp. nov. (2 species); from Russia. (In exchange.)
ZOOLOGICAL MUSEUM, ACADEMY OF SCIENCES, St. Petersburg, Russia. 17817. '86. (VII)

METEORIC IRON. Shavings (machine turnings) from the San Bernardino meteorite, with two photographs.
STATE MINING BUREAU OF CALIFORNIA. (Through Prof. H. S. Durden.) 17818. '86. (XVI)

TIN ORE, from Etta Mine.
CHARLES A. HOWARD, Rapid City, Dakota. 17819. '86. (XVIII)

IGUANA, from Big Swan Island, Honduras.
Capt. E. S. STONE, Brooklyn, New York. 17820. '86. (VI)

---

* For description of this new species see Proceedings U. S. National Museum, vol. 9, p. 523.

STURGEON, *Acipenser sturio* var. *oxyrhynchus.*

R. H. WALKER, Columbia, Alabama. 17821. '86. (VII)

JAPANESE SCREEN.

FONG LEE. (Through New Orleans Exposition.) 17822. '86. (II)

PHARYNGEALS of fresh-water Drum, *Aplodinotus grunniens;* for examination.

JOHN A. HARPER, Pittsburgh, Pennsylvania. 17823. '86. (VII)

QUARTZ mixed with gold and tetradymite; for examination.

GEORGE TULLOCK, Sheridan, Montana. 17824. '86. (XVIII)

TERRAPINS.

J. W. P. JENKS, Middleborough, Massachusetts. 17825. '86. (XII)

FIJI WAR CLUB.

Dr. BROWERS, Dunellen, New Jersey. 17826. '86. (II, A)

LIMESTONE. Two pieces; for examination.

J. F. BUMBELOUGH, Shingle, Tennessee. 17827. '86. (XVI)

MOCKING BIRD, *Mimus polyglottos.*

Dr. EMIL BESSELS, Washington, District of Columbia. 17828. '86. (XII)

ARCHÆOLOGICAL OBJECTS: 4 cutting tools, 3 perforators, 3 scrapers, 44 arrow and spear heads, 6 celts, 2 grooved axes, 2 pestles, and a fragment of pottery; from Hamilton County, Ohio. (Exchange.)

W. C. CONE, Sater, Hamilton County, Ohio. 17829. '86. (III)

ARCHÆOLOGICAL OBJECTS: 2 grooved axes, arrow-shaft straightener, fish-hook (steatite), and 5 chipped flint implements; from Ohio. (Returned.)

K. Q. SMITH, Columbus, Ohio. 17830. '86. (III)

FRETWORK, interlaced, after the Moorish patterns.

C. S. RANSOM & CO., Cleveland, Ohio. 17831. '86. (I)

FIELD MOUSE, *Hesperomys leucopus;* harvest mouse, *Ochetodon humilis;* common mouse, *Mus musculus;* for examination.

G. H. RAGSDALE, Gainesville, Texas. 17832. '86. (IV)

TWO-SPOTTED TREE-HOPPER, *Membracis binotata*, ord. *Hemiptera Homoptera;* for examination.

W. G. BLISH, Niles, Michigan. 17833. '86. (X)

DIGGER WASP, *Stizus speciosus;* for examination.

Dr. Z. D. WALTERS, Marietta, Ohio. 17834. '86. (X)

AUGUST.

ORE; for examination.

M. A. BONVILLE, Dardanelle, Arkansas. 17835. '86. (XVIII)

MACKEREL, *Scomber pneumatophorus* (alcoholic).

U. S. FISH COMMISSION, Wood's Holl, Massachusetts. 17836. '86. (VII)

ENGLISH REDPOLL and linnet (skins). (Exchange.)

R. BOWDLER SHARPE, London, England. 17837. '86. (V, A)

MUSSEL SHELL, with images of Buddha on inside; from Ningpo, China.

Dr. D. B. MCCARTEE, Washington, District of Columbia. 17838. '86. (II, A)

MOCKING BIRD, *Mimus polyglottos.*

W. C. WEEDEN, U. S. National Museum. 17839. '86. (V, A)

WEATHERED MAGNESIAN LIMESTONE.

S. S. BUCK, engineer, Niagara Suspension Bridge. 17840. '86. (XVII)

MINERALS, 126 specimens. (Exchanged.)

JOSEPH WILCOX, Media, Pennsylvania. 17841. '86. (XVI)

FISHES (alcoholic).

HERBERT M. KNOWLES, Point Judith, Rhode Island. 17842. '86. (VII)

WHITE GLASS (fused).

C. RUNGE, New Ulm, Texas. 17843. '86. (XVI)

SANDSTONE; for examination.

N. A. RAMSEY, Asheville, North Carolina. 17844. '86. (XVII)

GREAT KINGFISHER, *Dacelo gigas*, from Australia; skeleton.

ZOOLOGICAL SOCIETY OF PHILADELPHIA. (Through Arthur E. Brown, Esq.). 17845. '86. (XII)

SAIL-FISH, *Histiophorus gladius*.

U. S. FISH COMMISSION. 17846. '86. (VII)

IRON RAIL.

J. E. WATKINS, Camden, New Jersey. 17847. '86. (I)

LEPIDOPTERA: 17 species, 21 specimens; for examination.

Miss MARY E. MURTFELDT, Kirkwood, Montana. 17848. '86. (X)

FIBERS, FABRICS, ETC.

GOVERNMENT OF GUATEMALA. (Through Enrique Toriello, Chargé d'affaires of the Republic of Guatemala.) 17849. '86. (I)

WOODS, from Guatemala.

GOVERNMENT OF GUATEMALA. (Through Enrique Toriello.) 17849. '86. (XV)

MOLE CRICKET, *Gryllotalpa* sp.; American Hercules beetle, *Dynastes tityus;* for examination.

JOHN A. RAMSEY, Salisbury, North Carolina. 17850. '86. (X)

WILD RYE, *Elymus canadensis* and *E. virginicus;* for examination.

A. E. BOVAY, Glen Ullin, Dakota. 17851. '86. (XV)

LINNET, *Linota cannabina* (skeleton).

LOUIS SCHMID & SONS, Washington, District of Columbia. 17852. '86. (XII)

MOCKING BIRD, *Mimus polyglottos* (in flesh).

Dr. EMIL BESSELS, Smithsonian Institution. 17853. '86. (V, A)

ETHNOLOGICAL OBJECTS collected in Greenland by Dr. Octave Pavy, U. S. Army, surgeon and naturalist of the Greely Arctic Expedition: Greenland kyak model complete, with spear, harpoon and line, throwing-stick, line-rack, paddle, lance, and snow-knife; similar model, mounted for hunting birds; umiak model, with paddles complete; set of dog-harness and whip; sledge, named "Lilla;" pair of long Greenland boots, embroidered; pair of seal-skin slippers; embroidered leather belt, with carved ivory clasps; square work-bag of embroidered seal-skin; hand-bag of seal-skin, embroidered; three embroidered leather mats; hassock of black and white hair seal-skin; cape of eider-duck skins; cloak of eider-duck skins; muff of eider-duck skins; pair of wristlets of eider-duck skins; muff of bird-skins and eider-down; foot-warmer of eider skins; three samples of skins; beaded collar; photograph of *Gulnare*, at St. John's, Newfoundland; piece of *Polaris* flag, given to Dr. Pavy by Colonel Lupton; lace made by Danish women in Southern Greenland; ivory counters (93 pieces); two letters commending Dr. Pavy: 1. By Dr. K. Smith; 2. By members of the Greely party; North American Review articles on Dr. Pavy's journal; three photos found with Dr. Pavy's effects; portion of his neckerchief; newspaper clippings with account of official papers; memorial services at St. Louis, August 24, 1884; Arctic flowers gathered north of Lady Franklin Bay by Dr. Pavy, naturalist of the Greely expedition; nine photographs of Dr. Pavy, Mrs. Pavy, and groups of the Greely party. (Deposited.)

Mrs. LILLA MAY PAVY, New York City. 17854. '86. (III)

ETHNOLOGICAL OBJECTS, from Burmah and India.

Rev. C. H. A. DALL, Calcutta, India. (Through W. H. Dall.) 17855. '86. (II, A)

SANDSTONE; for examination.

CLARENCE L. BARRETT, Clearfield, Pennsylvania. 17856. '86. (XVII)

CALCITE, from neighborhood of Campeche, State of Campeche, Mexico.

Dr. CHARLES RAU, Smithsonian Institution. 17857. (XVI)

MUSSELS AND LAND SHELLS, from South Carolina, and fresh-water shells from the Potomac River.

FRANK BURNS, U. S. Geological Survey. 17858. '86. (IX)

Bog Manganese.

C. G. Viele, Garrett, North Carolina. 17859. '86. (xvi)

Internode of *Calamites* or *Equisetum* (fragment).

H. Shriver, Wytheville, Virginia. 17860. '86. (xiv)

Epidote and Quartz (fragment).

H. Shriver, Wytheville, Virginia. 17860. '86. (xvi)

Chipped Flints (95 specimens); for examination.

H. Shriver, Wytheville, Virginia. 17860. '86. (iii)

Conglomerate Rock, for examination.

William Rawe, Judsonia, White County, Arkansas. 17861. '86. (xvi)

Photograph of Owl captured near Somerset, Pennsylvania.

W. H. Welfley, Somerset, Pennsylvania. 17862. '86. (v, a)

Western Savanna Sparrows, *Ammodramus sandwichensis alaudinus* (6); and Hybrid Flickers, *Colaptes auratus* and *Colaptes mexicanus.*

W. Otto Emerson, Haywards, California. 17863. '86. (v, a)

Nests and Eggs of Black-throated Bunting, *Spiza americana,* Gm.

D. L. Beckham, Bardstown, Kentucky. 17864. '86 (v, b)

Steel Sleeper, with a short piece of 90-pound rail, etc., the standard iron road superstructure on the London and Northwestern Railway.

J. E. Watkins, Camden, New Jersey. 17865. '87. (i)

Teapoys (2) of Cashmir lacquer, from Lahore, Cashmir, India.

Mrs. Helen Tompkins, Calcutta, India. 17866. '86. (ii, a)

Pipe and Case, from Lapland. Brass portion of English make; pipe probably Dutch.

Dr. Emil Bessels, Smithsonian Institution. 17867. '86. (ii, a)

Picture representing the pursing of mackerel with large purse seines.

American Net and Twine Company, Boston, Massachusetts. 17868. '86. (i)

Imitation Turquoise (four specimens).

Israel Farjeon, New York City. (Received in 1880.) 17869. '86. (xvi)

Black Tern, *Hydrochelidon nigra;* for examination.

J. W. Bowman, Aleman, New Mexico. 17870. '86. (xii)

Galena and White Marble, containing a silicate of lime; for examination.

Hicks and Sitgreaves, Bristol, Tennessee. 17871. '86. (xviii)

Sucker-fish, *Echeneis remora;* for examination.

J. M. C. Eaton, Irvington, New Jersey. 17872. '86. (vii)

Flat-head Minnow, *Pimephales promelas;* for examination.

M. M. Bostwick, Iowa City, Iowa. 17873. '86, (vii)

Loggerhead Turtles (three specimens). (Purchased.)

Fred S. Allen, Cuttyhunk, Massachusetts. 17874. '86. (vi)

Leather Jacket, *Oligoplites saurus.*

James M. Southwick, Providence, Rhode Island. 17875. '86. (vii)

Monkey, *Cynopithecus niger.*

Zoological Society of Philadelphia. (Through Arthur E. Brown, Esq.). 17876. '86. (iv)

Decomposed Schistose Rock; for examination.

Charles Spurlock, Dardanelle, Arkansas. 17877. '86. (xviii)

Shark's Teeth (fossil).

G. V. Young, Aberdeen, Mississippi. 17878. '86. (vii)

Fossil Shells, apparently belonging to the *Veneridæ.*

G. V. Young, Aberdeen Mississippi. 17878. '86. (ix)

Fossil Wood, probably dicotyledonous; from blue rock bluffs on Matubbie Creek.

G. V. Young, Aberdeen, Mississippi. 17878. '86. (xiv)

Sandstone Concretion; for examination.

James M. Dougherty, Doylestown, Pennsylvania. 17879. '86. (xvii)

Woodchuck, *Arctomys monax.*

J. C. Wilson, Sligo, Maryland. 17880. '86. (xii)

NIGHT-HAWK, *Chordeiles virginianus*, and Red-headed Woodpecker, *Melanerpes erythro-cephalus*, from Virginia.

R. RIDGWAY, U. S. National Museum. 17881. '86. (V, A)

PHOTOGRAPH of Large-billed Shrike, *Lanius robustus*.

Dr. L. STEJNEGER, U. S. National Museum. 17882. '86. (V, A)

INDIAN FOODS.

Dr. H. W. HARKNESS, San Francisco, California. 17883. '86. (I)

RICHARDSON'S SPERMOPHILE, *Spermophilus richardsoni* (skins); from Manitoba.

ERNEST E. T. SETON, New York City. 17884. '86. (IV)

BIRDS' EGGS: Bartram's Sandpiper, *Bartramia longicauda;* Northern Sharp-tailed Grouse, *Pediocœtes phasianellus;* Gray Ruffed Grouse, *Bonasa umbellus umbelloides; Colymbus auritus;* from Manitoba.

ERNEST E. T. SETON, New York City. 17884. '86. (V, B)

RICHARDSON'S SPERMOPHILE, *Spermophilus richardsoni* (skulls); from Manitoba.

ERNEST E. T. SETON, New York City. 17884. '86. (XII)

BIRD-SKINS (6 specimens, 6 species).

ERNEST E. T. SETON, New York City. 17884. '86. (V, A)

PHOTOGRAPHS of Labrador Gyrfalcon, *Falco rusticolus obsoletus;* Prairie Hens, *Tym-panuchus cupido*, ♂ and ♀ ads., and Pallas's Cormorant, *Phalacrocorax perspicillatus.*

R. RIDGWAY, U. S. National Museum. 17885. '86. (V, A)

MUSTARD SEED, black and white varieties; for examination.

JOHN W. SCHWANER, Guide Rock, Nebraska. 17886. '86. (I)

ROCK, drift bowlder of quartz porphyry.

F. M. & C. O. MERICA, Garrett, Indiana. 17887. '86. (XVII)

AMERICAN WATER BUG, *Belostoma americanum;* for examination.

E. J. JONES, Batesburgh, South Carolina. 17888. '86. (X)

SKIN OF MUSKRAT, dressed for fur; specimen caught near Richmond, Virginia.

M. BOWSKY, New York City. 17889. '86. (I)

RATTLESNAKE, *Crotalus* (?).

Dr. J. R. MATHERS, Buckhannon, Upshur County, West Virginia. 17890. '86. (VI)

FISHES: *Moxostoma macrolepidotum, Ictiobus velifer, Lepomis humilis, Hybopsis storerianus, Pimephales notatus, P. confertus, Notropis lutrensis, N. œneolus, N. topeka, N. macro-stoma, N. germanus* (type), *N. deliciosus, Etheostoma lepida, Lepomis cyanellus, Ceratich-thys biguttatus, Semotilus atromaculatus, Fundulus zebrinus, Lepidosteus osseus, Phe-nacobius mirabilis, Noturus flavus*, and *Boleosoma olmstedi;* from Indiana.

O. P. HAY, Irvington, Indiana. 17891. '86. (VII)

SEMI-OPALS (94 specimens).

U. S. GEOLOGICAL SURVEY, Washington, District of Columbia. (Through L. C. Johnson.) 17892. '86. (XVI)

HAIR WORMS, *Gordius* sp. (?); from New Mexico; for examination.

Dr. M. N. VAN FLEET, Weed, Lincoln County, New Mexico. 17893. '86. (XI)

MOUND REMAINS, consisting of bones, teeth, fragments of flint, pottery, etc.

Dr. J. C. MCCORMICK, Strawberry Plains, Jefferson County, Tennessee. 17894. '86. (III)

LEECHES (8 specimens).

Prof. ALFRED DUGÈS, Guanajuato, Mexico. 17895. '86. (XI)

QUARTZ CRYSTAL (large), two feldspar crystals (large), and emerald green mica; from Maine.

Prof. HENRY CARMICHAEL, Boston, Massachusetts. 17896. '86. (XVI)

AMERICAN HERCULES BEETLE, *Dynastes tityus;* from Virginia; for name.

W. L. ALEXANDER, Lick Run, Botetourt County, Virginia. 17897. '86. (X)

RED OCHER and a flinty conglomerate; for examination.

RICHARD BENNETT, Whitcomb, Carroll County, Arkansas. 17898. '86. (XVI)

RICHARDSON'S MERLIN, *Falco richardsoni*, Ridgw.; from Colorado.

ROBERT RIDGWAY, U. S. National Museum. 17899. '86. (V, A)

OLD BLANKET.
> Donor not known. 17900. '86. (II, A)

GALENA (sulphide of lead); 2 specimens.
> M. T. NEWSON, Brookhaven, Mississippi. 17901. '86. (XVIII)

MAGNETITE; octrahedral crystals with a little quartz; limestone containing a large variety of sulphides of copper, lead, zinc, and iron; for examination.
> HARRY D. MUSSER, Roherstown, Lancaster County, Pennsylvania. 17902. '86. (XVIII)

MENHADEN, *Brevoortia tyrannus.*
> J. T. CHURCH, Tiverton, Rhode Island. 17903. '86. (VII)

SILVER ORES, from the "Silver King" and "Goodenough" mines in Pinal County, Arizona.
> C. P. CULVER, Washington, District of Columbia. 17904. '86. (XVIII)

MYRIOPODA,* 27 species, from Bloomington, Indiana, and Pensacola, Florida; for name.
> C. H. BOLLMAN, Indiana University, Bloomington, Indiana. 17905. '86. (X)

HEN'S EGG; malformation.
> A. G. HATFIELD, Washington, District of Columbia. 17906. '86. (V, B)

HERB,* *Solidago californica,* Nutt., a plant possessing aromatic, stimulant, and diaphoretic properties.
> W. R. BROWN, Sanders, Fresno County, California. 17907. '86. (I)

ARCHÆOLOGICAL OBJECTS: Human skulls and bones, 2 clay bowls, shell and glass beads, iron knife-blade, and piece of baked clay; from a grave. Also 2 stone implements, flint implements, shells and fragment of pottery (222 specimens); from bank of Coosa River, Cherokee County, Alabama.
> HENRY J. BIDDLE and I. C. RUSSELL, Centre, Cherokee County, Alabama. 17908. '86. (III)

SAIL-FISH, *Histiophorus* sp. (skull), and Tunny or Horse Mackerel, *Orcynus thynnus;* from Wood's Holl, Massachusetts.
> U. S. FISH COMMISSION. 17909. '86. (VII)

(Accession 17910 canceled.)

ORE; for examination.
> Dr. J. A. SEWELL, Rockwood, Tennessee. 17911. '86. (XVIII)

INSECT, *Prionotus cristatus;* for examination.
> FRANK S. GOLD, Rest, Virginia. 17912. '86. (X)

CHINA PLATE belonging to the set of George Washington. Blue and white china with insignia of "Society of Cincinnati."
> Judge JOSEPH HOLT, Washington, District of Columbia. 17913. '86. (I)

AMERICAN HERCULES BEETLE, *Dynastes tityus;* for name.
> Miss ESTELLE BURTHE, Liberty, Virginia. 17914. '86. (X)

† TREMATODE, taken from the white of a freshly laid egg; for examination.
> C. H. SLAYTON, Berlin, Wisconsin. 17915. '86. (XI)

LIMONITE; for examination.
> Dr. C. S. COOPER, Roanoke, Virginia. 17916. '86. (XVI)

INSECT, *Mantis carolina.*
> GEORGE M. FORTUNE, Argonia, Sumner County, Kansas. 17917. '86. (X)

FIELD SPARROW, *Spizella pusilla,* and Nighthawk, *Chordeiles virginiana* (3 skeletons).
> R. RIDGWAY, U. S. National Museum. 17918. '86. (XII)

TIGER CUB, *Felis tigris.*
> W. A. CONKLIN, Esq., Central Park Menagerie, New York City, New York. 17919. '86. (IV)

ALMIQUI, *Solenodon cubanus* (♂, ♀, and juv.). Living and alcoholic specimens. (Purchased.)
> JOHN GUNDLACH, Santiago, Cuba. 17920. '86. (IV)

---

* See Proceedings U. S. National Museum, vol. 10, pp. 323 and 328.

† This specimen is the subject of a paper by Dr. Edwin Linton, in vol. 10, Proceedings of the U. S. National Museum, pp. 367–369.

September.

Pipe, found near Piqua (cast).

C. T. Williams, Piqua, Miami County, Ohio. 17921. '86. (iii)

Vases (from the *Manufacture Nationale de Sèvres*):

Form of vase "Stephanus," after an architect of that name; decorated in the style of vases made by Ducerceau, epoch of Louis XIV; medallions of "The Four Seasons," modeled by Dorat; gray ground.

Form of vase "Stephanus," after an architect of that name; Limoges style; blue ground; enameled with a circle of Cupids (or children) by Seiffert.

Form of vase, "Boizot," after a sculptor of that name; gray ground decorated with modelings in clay, and gilded.

Form of vase, "Mycenæ," Grecian; speckled blue-green ground; figures modeled in clay by Gobert.

Form of vase, "Parent," called after a decorator of that name in the last century; Saxon style; flowers by Cabau; medallions by Paillet.

Form of vase, "The Gourd of Asti;" salmon ground; figures "The Vintage," modeled by Archelais.

Form of vase, "Fizen;" engraved with flower-garlands in white and gold.

Form of vases (pair), old Chinese; decorated with the nasturtium vine, in blue on white ground, gilt.

Tapestries:

From the *Manufacture Nationale des Gobelins:* Six pieces of tapestry, the work of the first hundred exercises of the scholars. One piece of tapestry made by one of the scholars. One bench (?), ground color yellow, decorated with various symbols.

From the *Manufacture Nationale de Beauvais:* One picture consisting of several pieces of tapestry, the work of the first exercises of the scholars. One piece of tapestry, prize study on a flat block of marble.

Ministère de l'Instruction Publique et des Beaux-Arts. (Through M. E. Tourquet.) 17922. '86. (i)

Bird-skins, 24 specimens, 20 species, including:

Icterus spurius.	*Chlorophonia occipitalis.*
Hyphanthornis sp.	*Buteo albicaudatus.*
Podiceps californicus.	*Fulica americana.*
Scops sp.	*Planesticus migratorius.*
Butorides virescens.	*Centurus aurifrons.*
Colaptes auratus mexicanus.	*Spizella pallida.*
Harporhynchus curvirostris.	*Collurio excubitorides.*
Charadrius vociferus.	*Molothrus ater.*
Anthus ludovicianus.	*Sayornis nigricans.*
Sialia azurea.	*Empidonax obscurus.*

Prof. Alfred Dugès, Guanajuato, Mexico. 17923. '86. (v, a)

Shells, *Tryonia* and *Valvata.*

Prof. Alfred Dugès, Guanajuato, Mexico. 17923. '86. (ix)

Fishes, *Cyprinodonts, Ammocœtes* (probably undescribed), *Characodon atripinnis, C. variatus,* and *Limnurgus variegatus.*

Prof. Alfred Dugès, Guanajuato, Mexico. 17923. '86. (vii)

Plants.

Alfred Dugès, Guanajuato, Mexico. 17923. '86. (xiv)

Reptiles, Carapace of *Eutœnia* sp., *Eumeces callicephalum, E. lynxe, Triton cristatus* (France), *Scaphiopus dugesi, Hyla eximia, Eutœnia flavilabris, Hyla arenicolor.*

Prof. Alfred Dugès, Guanajuato, Mexico. 17923. '86. (vi)

Insects, *Argas megnini* Dug., *Erebus odora, Libellula* rouge, *Phaneroptera* sp., Phasmids, etc.

Prof. Alfred Dugès, Guanajuato, Mexico. 17923. '86. (x)

H. Mis. 600, pt. 2——39

MAMMAL SKIN, *Heteromys longicaudatus.*
> Prof. ALFRED DUGÈS, Guanajuato, Mexico. 17923. '86. (IV)

POLISHING SLATE, from Moro Leon.
> Prof. ALFRED DUGÈS, Guanajuato, Mexico. 17923. '86. (XVIII)

INSECT, caught at Lagoon Heights.
> Dr. ROBERT WHITE, Boston, Massachusetts. 17924. '86. (X)

CLAY IMAGE, a small terra-cotta figure found in earthworks. (Returned.)
> D. F. SAYRE, Marietta, Ohio. 17925. '86. (III)

POLISHED DUFRENITE, limonite pseudomorph after pyrite, showing oscillatory combination between the octahedron and a tetragonal tris-octahedron, and limonite pseudomorph after pyrite (cubes).
> Prof. J. H. MORRISON, Lexington, Virginia. 17926. '86. (XVI)

FOSSILS.
> Prof. J. H. MORRISON, Lexington, Virginia. 17926. '86. (XIII, A)

BRACHIOPOD, *Rhynchonella ;* for examination.
> Mrs. MARGARET TRUMBLE, Wakeman, Ohio. 17927. '86. (XIII, A)

ARCHÆOLOGICAL OBJECT.
> BUREAU OF ETHNOLOGY, Washington, District of Columbia. (Through Major J. W. Powell, Director.) 17928. '86. (III)

GLASS SPONGE, from Enoshima, Japan. Collected by Mr. S. Kneeland.
> BUREAU OF ETHNOLOGY, Washington, District of Columbia. 17928. '86. (XI)

ETHNOLOGICAL OBJECTS: Cloth pictures, clay vases and bowls, reindeer lichen, straw shoes, prepared betel, Chinese anatomical plates, shell bracelet, stone idol (?), hand mirror, "pulu" used for stuffing pillows, and photograph of Japanese worshiping at the tombs of deceased persons. Presented by Mr. S. Kneeland.
> BUREAU OF ETHNOLOGY, Washington, District of Columbia. 17928. '86. (II, A)

FISH-SOUNDS.
> C. J. HERING, Colony of Surinam, Dutch Guiana, South America. 17929. '86. (I)

LEPIDOPTERA,* destroyed by *Anthreni.*
> C. J. HERING, Colony of Surinam, Dutch Guiana, South America. 17929. '86. (X)

POTTERY.
> C. J. HERING, Colony of Surinam, Dutch Guiana, South America. 17929. '86. (II, B)

FROGS, snake, snake's egg, etc. (Nine specimens).
> C. J. HERING, Colony of Surinam, Dutch Guiana, South America. 17929. '86. (VI)

BIRD (skeleton), *Lophornis ornatus.*
> C. J. HERING, Colony of Surinam, Dutch Guiana, South America. 17929. '86. (XII)

BIRD-SKIN, *Phaëthornis* sp.
> C. J. HERING, Colony of Surinam, Dutch Guiana, South America. 17929. '86. (V, A)

ETHNOLOGICAL OBJECTS: Two Indian fans made of the Auara palm leaf, Carib Indian rattle, water goblet, earthen dish, two necklaces of the Arecuna Indians, one of the "Japoo papoo" seed and the other made of shells; string of Bamfro seed, and Bush negro calabashes, plates, and spoons.
> C. J. HERING, Colony of Surinam, Dutch Guiana, South America. 17929. '86. (II, A)

BLUE CRAB, *Callinectes hastatus,* with small oyster growing on the back of carapax.
> W. DE C. REVENEL, St. Jerome, Maryland. 17930. '86. (XI)

HIND FEET of the ass "Sara Bernhardt," showing an extraordinary abnormal development, with photograph of the same. (Noticed in *Science* Oct. 1, No. 191, p. 304.)
> J. C. BALDWIN, Houston, Texas. 17931. '86. (IV)

---

* See Report on Department of Insects, Section II.

VEGETABLE FIBRES, from Brazil.

Dr. J. CARLOS BERRINI, Guissaman, Brazil. 17932. '86. (I)

DIVER (OR LOON), *Colymbus torquatus* (skeleton); for identification.

G. H. HICKS, Grayling, Michigan. 17933. '86. (XII)

PRICEITE (ten specimens), from Curry County, Oregon, and twelve specimens of colemanite, from San Bernardino County, California.

CALIFORNIA STATE MINING BUREAU, San Francisco, California. 17934. '86. (XVI)

DENDRITES (one slab) from the lower Silurian; from Smith's Ferry, Rockbridge County, Virginia.

Prof. J. H. MORRISON, Virginia Military Institute, Lexington, Virginia. 17935. '86. (XVII)

CRYSTALLIZED BARITE; for examination.

R. W. STEFFEN, Payson, Yavapai County, Arizona. 17936. '86. (XVIII)

TETRADYMITE, in quartz; halite, natrolite, and apophyllite.

Dr. F. W. TAYLOR, Washington, District of Columbia. 17937. '86. (XVI)

SHELLS.

CHARLES R. KEYES, Des Moines, Iowa. 17938. '86. (IX)

ARROW-HEAD, found on Padre Island, Texas.

L. C. LEITH, Corpus Christi, Texas. 17939. '86. (III)

FLINT IMPLEMENTS (5 specimens). (Exchange.)

G. L. FAUCHER, West Winsted, Connecticut. 17940. '86. (III)

CRICKET, with intestinal worm; a medium-sized species of *Mermis*; for examination.

H. G. HODGE, York, Clark County, Illinois. 17941. '86. (X)

UNIFORM of a private soldier of the First Maryland Artillery, C. S. A. Also cross-cannons captured at battle of Winchester from the Federal artillery. (Deposited.)

GEORGE W. WILSON, Upper Marlboro, Prince George County, Maryland. 17942. '86. (I)

ENAMEL BEAD (Venetian) from an Indian mound in Florida; for examination.

JOHN E. YOUNGLOVE, Bowling Green, Kentucky. 17943. '86. (III)

ARROW-HEAD, from near Crockett's Mill, Virginia.

H. Shriver, Wytheville, Virginia. 17944. '86. (III)

LEAD BUCKLES.

HARRISON BROS. & Co., Philadelphia, Pennsylvania. 17945. '86. (XVIII)

CLAY mixed with sand, ejected in liquid form during the earthquake at Charleston, South Carolina, August 31, 1886.

GEORGE H. INGRAHAM, Washington, District of Columbia. 17946. '86. (XVII)

HEMATITE, containing a very small amount of titanium; for examination.

M. KENNEDY, Stanardsville, Virginia. 17947. '86. (XVIII)

BIRD-SKINS,* from the Tokyo Educational Museum.

Name.	Locality.	Japanese names.	No. of specimens.
FALCONIDÆ.			
Pandion haliœtus, Linn	Kachiyama, Awa	Misako	1
Milvus melanotis, Tem. & Schleg	Tokyo	Tobi	1
Haliœtus albicilla, L	Kadzusa	Ojirowashi	1
Buteo japonicus, Schleg	Kachiyama, Awa	Nosuri	1
STRIGIDÆ.			
Syrnium rufescens, Tem	Iwaki	Fukoro	1
Scops semitorgues Schleg	Tokyo	Okonohazuka	2
CYPSELIDÆ.			
Chœtura caudacuta, Lath	Nikko	Amatsubame	1

* See Report on Department of Birds, Section II.

BIRD-SKINS, from the Tokyo Educational Museum—Continued.

Name.	Locality.	Japanese names.	No. of specimens.
ALCEDINIDÆ.			
Halcyon coromondeliana, Scop	Sagami	Miyamajobin	1
Alcedo bengalensis, Gm	Tokyo	Kawasemi	1
Ceryle guttata, Vig	Chichibu	Kanokodori	1
ANABATIDÆ.			
Sitta europæa, Linn	Subashiri	Kimawari	2
CERTHIIDÆ.			
Certhia familiaris, Linn	Iwaki	Kibashiri	2
TROGLODYTIDÆ.			
Troglodytes fumigatus, Tem	Iwashiro	Misosasi	1
LUSCINIDÆ.			
Calamoherpe orientalis, T. & S	Tokyo	Oyoshkiri	2
Cettia cantans, T. & S	do	Uguisu	1
Regulus japonicus, Bp	do	Kikuitadaki	1
Ruticilla aurora, Pall	Iwaki	Jobitaki	2
Larvivora cyanea, Hodge	Amagisau	Koruri	11
Erythacus komadori, T. & S	Linkin	Akahige	1
Ianthia cyanura, Pall	Chichibu, Linkin	Ruribitaki	2
Accentor rubidus, T. & S	Chichibu	Kayakuguri	1
PARIDÆ.			
Parus varius, T. & S	Chichibu, Linkin	Yamagara	2
Parus palustris, Linn	Chichibu	Kogara	1
Parus minor, T. & S	Tokyo	Ahijiukara	1
Acredula trivirgatus, Tem	Iwaki	Yenaga	2
MOTACILLIDÆ.			
Motacilla lugens, T. & S	Chichibu	Segurosekirei	
Anthus maculatus, Bl	Sagami	Binzui	1
Anthus japonicus, T. & S	Tokyo	Tahibari	1
TURDIDÆ.			
Turdus fuscatus, Pall	do	Chomathugumi	2
Turdus chrysolaus, Tem	do	Akahara	2
Turdus pallidus, Gm	do	Shirohara	1
Oreocincla varia, Pall		Nayethuga	1
Cinclus pallasii, Tem	Iwaki	Kawagarasu	1
Monticola solitaria, Müll	Linkin	Isohiyo	1
PYCONOTIDÆ.			
Hypsipetes amaurotis, Tem	Sagami	Hiyodori	2
MUSCICAPIDÆ.			
Xanthopygia narcissina, Tem	Amagisau	Kibitaki	2
Cyanoptilla cyanomelana, Tem	Amagi	Reifuri Osuri	
Pericrocotus cinereus, Lafr	do	Reifuri	2
Pericrocotus, sp	Linkin	do	1
AMPELIDÆ.			
Ampelis phanicoptera, Tem	Linkin	Hirenjaku	1
Ampelis garrulus, Linn	Iwaki	Kirenjaku	2
LANIIDÆ.			
Lanius bucephalus, T. & S	Amagisau, Suruga	Moza	2
CORNIDÆ.			
Garrulus japonicus, Schleg	Subashiri	Kakesu	2
Cyanopica cyana, Pall	Tokyo	Onagadori	2
Sturnus cinerscens, Tem	do	Mukudori	2

BIRD-SKINS, from the Tokyo Educational Museum—Continued.

Name.	Locality.	Japanese names.	No. of speci- mens.
FRINGILLIDÆ.			
Fringilla montifringilla, Linn	Tokyo	Atori	1
Chrysomitris spinus, Linn	Linkin	Mahiwa	2
Passer rutilans, Tem	Magebashi, Joshiu	Niunaisuzume	3
Coccothraustes japonicus, Schleg	Subashiri	Shime	1
Coccothraustes personata, Schleg	do	Ikaru	1
Uragus sanguinollentus, Tem	do	Mahiko	1
Carpodacus roseus, Pall	Iwaki	Omahik	2
Loxia albiventris, Swinhoe	do	Isuka	2
Leucosticte brunneoncha, Brandt	Shimotsuke	Hakimahiko	2
EMBERIZIDÆ.			
Emberiza rustica, Pall	Tokyo	Kashiradaka	2
Emberiza ciopsis, Bp	Sagami	Hojiro	2
Emberiza personata, Tem	Tokyo	Awoji	1
Emberiza yessoensis, Swinhoe	Shimosa	Nabekaburi	1

TEKANUMA.

ALAUDIDÆ.			
Alauda japonica, Tem	Tokyo	Hibari	2
PICIDÆ.			
Picus major, Linn	do	Akagera	2
Picus kisuki, Tem	Subashiri	Kogera	2

SURUGA.

Gecinus awakera, Tem. & Schleg	Iwaki	Awagera	2
CUCULIDÆ.			
Cuculus poliocephalus, Lath	Tokyo	Hotogisu	1
COLUMBIDÆ.			
Turtur risorius, Linn	do	Shirakobato	1
Turtur gelastes, Tem	Sagami	Kijibato	1
PHASIANIDÆ.			
Phasianus versicolor, Vieillot	Chichibu	Kiji	1
Phasianus sœmmeringii, Tem	do	Yamad ri	1
TETRAONIDÆ.			
Coturnix japonica, Schleg	Shimoso	Uzura	1
CHARADRIADÆ.			
Vanellus cristatus, Mey	Shimosa	Tag6ri	1
Lobivanellus inornatus, T. & S.	do	Keri	2
Charadrius fulvus, Gm	do	Munaguroshigi	
Squatarola helvetica, Linn	do	Deisen	
Ægialitis monglica, Pall	do	Medaichidori	1
HEMATOPOLIDÆ.			
Strepsilas interpres, Linn	Giyotoku, Shimosa	Giyojoshigi	2
ARDEIDÆ.			
Herodias russata, Wagl	Mayebashi, Joshiu	Amasagi	1
Herodias modesta, Gray	Joshiu	Daisagi	2
Herodias garzetta, Linn	do	Shirasagi	3
Ardetta sinensis, Gm	Shimosa	Yoshigosagi	1
Butoroides macrorhynchus, Gould	Sagami	Minogoi	1

BIRD-SKINS from the Tokyo Educational Museum—Continued.

Names.	Locality.	Japanese names.	No. of specimens.
PLATALEIDÆ.			
Platalea major, T. & S	Shimosa	Herasagi	1
TAULALIDÆ.			
Ibis nippon, T. & S	Shimosa	Tokio	1
SCOLOPACIDÆ.			
Totanus ochropus, Linn	Shimosa		1
Totanus glottis, Linn	do	Awoashishigi	2
Heteroscelus incanus, Gm	do	Kiashi	2
Tringa acuminata, Horsf	do	Uzurashigi	2
Tringa cinclus, Linn	do	Hashinagashigi	
Tringoides hypoleucus, Linn	do	Kawashigi	2
Limosa brevipes, G. R. Gray	do	Sorihashishigi	
Scolopax ruticola, Linn	Tokyo	Botoshigi	2
Rhynchœa bengalensis, Linn	Shimosa	Tamashigi	2
PALLIDÆ.			
Porzana erythrothorax, T. & S	Tokyo	Hikuina	2
ANATIDÆ.			
Anser hyperboreus, Pall	Tokyo	Hakugan	1
Aix galericulata, Linn	Sagami	Oshidori	2
Querquedula crecca, Linn	Tokyo	Kogamo	2
Anas zonorhyncha, Linn	do	Karugamo	1
Anas boschas, Linn	Sagami	Magamo	1
Clangula histrionica, Linn	Sendai	Shinorigamo	1
PODICEPIDÆ.			
Podiceps philippensis, Bonn	Tokyo	Keizumuria	1
ALCIDÆ.			
Mormon cirrhatus, Gm	Kuril Islands	Etaperica	1
Ceratorhyncha monocerata, Pall	Misaki	Uto	1
Phaleris camtschatica, Lepechim	Kuril Islands	Etorufumisuzme	1
URIIDÆ.			
Brachyramphus antiquus, Lath	Boshiu	Umisuzume	2
LARIDÆ.			
Larus ridibundus, Linn	Tokyo	Urikamone	1

TOKYO LIBRARY AND TOKYO EDUCATIONAL MUSEUM, Tokyo, Japan. 17948. '86. (V, A)

LARVA of *Citheronia regalis*.

Dr. E. NEAN, Richmond, Virginia. 17949. '86. (X)

UNIOS (about 350 specimens), from Coosa River, Alabama.

I. C. RUSSELL, Collinsville, Alabama. 17950. '86. (IX)

MOUSE, *Arvicola austerus*.

Dr. R. W. SHUFELDT, U. S. Army, Fort Wingate, New Mexico. 17951. '86. (IV)

CATERPILLAR, larva of *Lagoa opercularis*, from Athens, Georgia ; for examinaion.

Dr. SAMUEL C. BENEDICT, Athens, Georgia. 17952. '86. (X)

MINERAL.

Donor not known. 17953. '86. (XVI)

WHITEFISH, *Coregonus williamsoni ;* grayling, *Thymallus tricolor*, and trout, *Salmo purpuratus*, from Gallatin River, Montana.

WILLIAM C. HARRIS, New York City. 17954. '86. (VII)

SUNFISH, *Mola rotunda*.

ROBERT C. HANDY and Mrs. STURGIS, Cotuit, Massachusetts. 17955. '86. (XII)

LARVA of a bot fly from a deer, and *Hippodamia convergens;* from Shasta County, California.

    C. H. TOWNSEND, U. S. National Museum. 17956. '86. (x)

CROW, *Corvus americanus* (2 skeletons), from Washington, District of Columbia.

    F. A. LUCAS, U. S. National Museum. 17957. '86. (XII)

CAGE BIRD, *Psittacula passerina* (skeleton), from Brazil.

    GEORGE D. BIGGS, Washington, District of Columbia. 17958. '86. (XII)

BIRDS: *Chrysotis levaillantii*, and *Fringilla canariensis.* (For skeletons).

    W. C. WEEDEN, U. S. National Museum. 17959. '86. (XII)

SPOON made from pearly nautilus shell, used by Buddhist priests in Siam in eating rice.

    Dr. D. BETHUNE McCARTEE, Washington, District of Columbia. 17960. '86. (II, A)

BRASS COIN issued by the founder of the Ming Dynasty, Hung Wu, 1363–1398 A. D.

    Dr. D. BETHUNE McCARTEE, Washington, District of Columbia. 17960. '86. (I)

ETHNOLOGICAL PHOTOGRAPHS (30).

    O. T. MASON, U. S. National Museum, 17961. '86. (II, A)

BIRDS.

    U. S. FISH COMMISSION, Wood's Holl, Massachusetts. 17962. '86. (V, A)

PLANT: *Ginko biloba*, L. (leaf), a native of China and Japan; for examination.

    W. J. BROWN, Jr., Jackson, Mississippi. 17963. '86. (XV)

BIRDS' NESTS: Blue Grosbeak, *Guiraca cœrulea;* American Goldfinch, *Spinus tristis;* Field Sparrow, *Spizella pusilla;* and Yellow-breasted Chat, *Icteria virens;* from Gainesville, Virginia.

    ROBERT RIDGWAY, U. S. National Museum. 17964. '86. (V, B)

FISHES: *Trichiurus japonicus, Tetraodon, Periophthalmus, Carassius, Monocanthus, Saurida, Hoplegnathus, Murœna, Cestracion, Percis, Sillago, Platycephalus,* and *Centridermichthys fasciatus,* from China, Japan, and Corea.

    N. McP. FEREBEE, Surgeon U. S. Navy, U. S. S. *Trenton.* 17965. '86. (VII)

MARINE INVERTEBRATES: Crustacea, Star-fishes, Ophiurans, Alcyonium, etc.; from Corea and China.

    N. McP. FEREBEE, Surgeon U. S. Navy. 17965. '86. (XI)

SNAKES, 7 specimens, from Corea.

    N. McP. FEREBEE, Surgeon U. S. Navy. 17965. '86. (VI)

INSECTS (alcoholic specimens).

    N. McP. FEREBEE, Surgeon U. S. Navy. 17965. '86. (x)

CEPHALOPODS and SHELLS, from Japan and China.

    N. McP. FEREBEE, Surgeon U. S. Navy. 17965. '86. (IX)

SILVER SANDSTONE, from Storm King mine, Silver Reef, Utah.

    Dr. F. W. TAYLOR, Washington, District of Columbia. 17966. '86. (XVIII)

PHONOLITE; for examination.

    HENRY L. DE ZENG, Geneva, New York. 17967. '86. (XVII)

FRESH-WATER SHELLS, from a mound.

    Dr. J. C. McCORMICK, Strawberry Plain, Tennessee. 17968. '86. (Sent to Dr. Cyrus Thomas.)

PARROT, *Amazona levaillantii* (2).

    Mrs. George W. Albaugh, Washington, District of Columbia. 17969. '86. (V, A)

HELLBENDER, *Menopoma* (15 specimens), and eggs, from Pennsylvania.

    C. H. TOWNSEND, U. S. National Museum. 17970. '86. (VI)

SILVERY HAIR-TAIL, *Trichiurus lepturus;* head, for name.

    ALONZO D. RICKER, Brooklyn, New York. 17971. '86. (VII)

ALCOHOLIC FISHES.

    Donor not known. 17973. '86. (VII)

ORNAMENTAL STONES, cut and polished, including onyx, sardonyx, agate-jasper, plasma, amethyst charms, smoke-quartz charm, chalcedony, jasper, chalcedony (artificially colored), jasper (artificially colored), carnelian, carnelian agate, moss agate, clouded agate, banded agate, heliotrope (bloodstone), rock crystal scarf-pin, and rock crystal letter seal (154 specimens in all). (Purchased.)

 W. J. KNOWLTON, Boston, Massachusetts. 17974. '86. (XVI)

CONFEDERATE NOTES, etc., post-office draft for $21.25, four twenty-dollar notes, Nos. 25712–15, and one hundred ten-cent postage stamps.

 M. W. ROBINSON, Asheville, North Carolina. 17975. '86. (I)

DEER'S HEAD (skin and horns), used as a decoy by "Eskelteche," an Apache Indian; found in a cave on the East Fork of the Verde.

 Dr. JAMES REAGLES, U. S. Army. (Through Dr. John S. Billings, U. S. A.) 17976. '86. (II, A)

CAMPHENE CHANDELIER, illustrating a method of illumination prior to the use of gas.

 J. McNAMARA, Lynchburgh, Virginia. 17977. '86. (II, A)

"KING OF THE HERRING," Chimæra (skeleton).

 THOMAS THOMPSON, master of schooner M. A. Barton. (Through W. A. Wilcox.) 17978. '86. (XII)

FIELD MICE, Hesperomys leucopus sonoriensis and Ochetodon mexicanus.

 Dr. R. W. SHUFELDT, U. S. Army, Fort Wingate, New Mexico. 17979. '86. (IV)

MANATEE, Trichecus inunguis (?). (Casts of two skulls.) (Purchased.)

 Dr. J. W. SPENGEL, Bremen, Germany. 17980. '86. (XII)

BIRDS (skins and skeletons).

 U. S. FISH COMMISSION, Wood's Holl, Massachusetts. 17981. '86. (V, A & XII)

STONE CHAIR, found in mountain near Hillsborough, Virginia. (Model.)

 SAMUEL B. HOOPMAN, Purcellville, Virginia. 17982. '86. (I)

ARROW-HEAD.

 A. R. ROESSLER, Liberty Hill, Texas. 17983. '86. (III)

MINERALS; for examination.

 A. R. ROESSLER, Liberty Hill, Texas. 17983. '86. (XVI)

BIRDS.

 U. S. FISH COMMISSION, Wood's Holl, Massachusetts. 17984. '86. (V, A)

BIRDS, Laughing Gull, Larus atricilla (1), and Purple Sandpiper, Tringa maritima (2); from near Rockland, Maine.

 E. C. GREENWOOD, Ipswich, Maine. 17985. '86. (V, A)

ETHNOLOGICAL OBJECTS, knives, spears, shields, war-horns, etc.; from the Congo River region, near Stanley Falls.

 Lieut. E. H. TAUNT, U. S. Navy. 17986. '86. (II, A)

SUCKING-FISH (Remora), Echeneis naucratus.

 E. R. NORNY, Odessa, Delaware. 17987. '86. (VII)

OLD IRON FLUE in south tower of Smithsonian Institution (piece).

 SMITHSONIAN INSTITUTION, Washington, District of Columbia. 17988. '86. (I)

MINERALS.

 Dr. O. J. SHEPARDSON, Chester, Massachusetts. 17989. '86. (XVI)

CRYSTALLIZED DIASPORE (one specimen). (Exchange.)

 H. H. MACIA, Chester, Massachusetts. 17990. '86. (XVI)

MINERALS. (Exchange.)

 AMHERST COLLEGE, Amherst, Massachusetts. 17991. '86. (XVI)

MINERALS.

 E. M. BAILEY, Andover, Maine. 17992. '86. (XVI)

MINERALS, from Maine, Massachusetts, and Maryland.

 U. S. GEOLOGICAL SURVEY (through Prof. F. W. Clarke). 17993. '86. (XVII)

CERARGYRITE, from Lake Valley, New Mexico, and a polished agate.

 Dr. F. W. TAYLOR, Washington, District of Columbia. 17994. '86. (XVI)

QUARTZ GEODES, containing calcite (16 specimens), from Keokuk, Iowa. (Exchange.)

W. T. HORNADAY, U. S. National Museum. 17995. '86. (XVI)

ARROW-HEADS (10) and a rude chipped ax.

JAMES MORTIMER, jr., Lawyers, Virginia. 17996. '86. (III)

ARROW-HEADS (7 specimens).

Miss GRACIE CLARK, Lawyers, Virginia. 17997. '86. (III)

SHOES (one pair), manufactured in 1864 by Sylvester Budford, of Budford, Virginia, such as were worn by soldiers and citizens. (Deposited.)

M. C. KULP, Lynchburgh, Virginia. 17998. '86. (I)

SABER AND BELT drawn from the army stores at Richmond, Virginia, and carried by the donor from 1862 to 1865.

Lieut. PATRICK McDEVITT, Lynchburgh, Virginia. 17999. '86. (I)

QUARTZ CRYSTAL, from Crystal Mountain, near Hot Springs, Arkansas.

Prof. SPENCER F. BAIRD, Secretary Smithsonian Institution. 18000. '86. (XVI)

CATFISH, *Amiurus albidus;* Mullet, *Moxostoma macrolepidotum;* and Chub, *Micropterus salmoides.*

W. E. CUTSHAW, City Engineer's Office, Richmond, Virginia. 18001. '86. (VII)

MOOSE, *Alces machlis,* young and adult (92 hides).

Col. CECIL CLAY, Chief Clerk, Department of Justice. (Through R. A. Klock, Klock's Mill, Ontario, Canada.) 18002. '86. (IV)

MINERALS. (Exchange.)

N. H. PERRY, South Paris, Maine. 18003. '86. (XVI)

PIPE-FISH, *Siphostoma;* for examination.

W. ST. J. MAZYCK, Waverly Mills, Georgetown County, South Carolina. 18004. '86. (VII)

ROCKS stained by decomposition; for examination.

JOSEPH COX, Phœnix, Arizona. 18005. '86. (XVIII)

VIREO, *Vireo alticola* (skin): new to the collection.

Dr. F. W. LANGDON, 65 West Seventh street, Cincinnati, Ohio. 18006. '86. (V, A)

COCOON of *Attacus cecropia,* from Washington, District of Columbia; for name.

M. A. TOLSON, Smithsonian Institution. 18007. '86. (X)

OBSIDIAN (4 specimens), from the Yellowstone Park, Wyoming.

U. S. GEOLOGICAL SURVEY, Washington, District of Columbia. 18008. '86. (XVI)

ORES, from Arkansas.

DEPARTMENT OF THE INTERIOR. (Through Hon. H. L. Muldrow, Acting Secretary.) 18009. '86. (XVIII)

MINERALS, etc., from Arkansas.

DEPARTMENT OF THE INTERIOR. (Through Hon. H. L. Muldrow, Acting Secretary.) 18009. '86. (XVI)

PETRIFIED WOOD, from Yellowstone Park.

DEPARTMENT OF THE INTERIOR, Washington. (Through Hon. H. L. Muldrow, Acting Secretary.) 18009. '86. (XIV)

QUARTZ CRYSTALS, chalcedony, silicified wood-twigs, onyx, agate, jasper and amethyst (34 specimens), from Yellowstone Park; also a quartz crystal from Crystal Mountains, near Hot Springs, Arkansas.

DEPARTMENT OF THE INTERIOR. (Through Hon. H. L. Muldrow, Acting Secretary.) 18009. '86.(XVI)

COPPERHEAD SNAKE, *Ansistrodon contortrix;* for identification.

HENRY L. BARKER, Oakley, South Carolina. 18010. '86. (VI)

ROCK CRYSTAL (2 specimens), from Ozark Mountains, Saline County, Arkansas. (Exchange.)

Mrs. W. S. YEATES, Washington, District of Columbia. 18011. '86. (XVI)

FOSSIL CORAL, *Lithostrotion mamillare.*

    J. W. BOWMAN, Prairie du Rocher, Illinois. 18012. '86. (XIII, A)

HOG-NOSED SNAKE (or Spreading Adder), *Heterodon platyrhinus*, from Mount Vernon, Virginia.

    J. H. KUEHLING, Washington, District of Columbia. 18013. '86. (VI)

HAIR-WORMS, *Gordius* sp.; for identification.

    Dr. M. N. VAN FLEET, Weed, Lincoln County, New Mexico. 18014. '86. (XI)

FRESH-WATER MUSSELS (1 box) and *Goniobasis virginica*, from Potomac River.

    FRANK BURNS, U. S. Geological Survey. 18015. '86. (IX)

SHELLS, *Helix Downicana* and *Zonites cuspidotus* (2 specimens each).

    Miss A. E. LAW, Concord, Tennessee. 18016. '86. (IX)

METEORIC IRON, from Jefferson County, Tennessee.

    IRA SAYLES, U. S. Geological Survey. 18017. '86. (XVI)

ALMANDITE, coated with chlorite (2 crystals); from Salida, Colorado. (Exchange.)

    WARD and HOWELL, Rochester, New York. 18018. '86. (XVI)

MINERALS. (24 specimens).

    W. C. POTEAT, Wake Forest, North Carolina. 18019. '86. (XVI)

SHELLS, *Physa heterotropha* (2 specimens).

    W. C. POTEAT, Wake Forest, North Carolina. 18019. '86. (IX)

FISH, *Potamocottus gulosus* (3 specimens); San Geronimo Creek, California.

    CHARLES A. ALLEN, Nicasio, California, 18020. '86. (VII)

BIRDS.

    U. S. FISH COMMISSION, Wood's Holl, Massachusetts. 18021. '86. (V, A)

STALACTITES and STALAGMITES; for examination.

    C. A. WHITTEMORE, Grand Rapids, Michigan. 18022. '86. (XVII)

BOT-FLY, *Œstrus* sp.

    W. W. ANDERSON, Stateburgh, South Carolina. 18023. '86. (X)

EUROPEAN BULLFINCH, *Pyrrhula vulgaris*, and Weaver Bird, or "African Finch," *Munia undulata.*

    W. C. WEEDEN, U. S. National Museum. 18024. '86. (XII)

CONFEDERATE BOND CERTIFICATE for one hundred dollars, and a copy of the last wall-paper edition of the *Daily Citizen* of Vicksburg, printed two days before the capture of the city.

    WALTER HOUGH, U. S. National Museum. 18025. '86. (I)

FASHION PLATES and Confederate invoices. Almanac printed at Philadelphia in 1796.

    WILLIAM L. PAGE, Lynchburgh, Virginia. 18026. '86. (I)

WILD-CAT SKIN (black).

    F. L. TAPPAN, Minneapolis, Minnesota. 18027. '86. (I)

HARPOON-HEAD; native hammered copper and whalebone; from Takoo Indians, Takoo River, southeastern Alaska.

    EDWIN B. WEBSTER, paymaster, U. S. Navy. 18028. '86. (II, A)

CUTTING TOOL, remarkable for an unusual notch.

    Dr. H. H. THORP, Liberty Hill, Texas. 18029. '86. (III)

VOTIVE OFFERING (silver amalgam), made by miners near Cuzco, to place in cathedral. Made by pressing the pasty metal into shape and then roasting out the mercury.

    S. L. M. BARLOW, Madison avenue, New York. 18030. '86. (II, A)

TOAD-FISH, *Batrachus tau.*

    H. P. HOARE, Soldiers' Home, Hampton, Virginia. 18031. '86. (VII)

MINERALS; for examination.

    STEPHEN D. LACY, Franklin, Robertson County, Texas. 18032. '86. (XVI)

TANGAI NUTS; for examination.

    IGNACIO PALAN & CO., Bahia, Ecuador. (Through S. Samper & Co., New York.) 18033. '86. (I)

    The result of the examination is published in the report of the curator of the Section of Materia Medica.

WOOD; for identification.

    M. A. KEACH, Providence, Rhode Island. 18034. '86. (XV)

OCTOBER.

WHITE-TAILED HAWK, *Buteo albicaudatus:* new to the collection.

    GEORGE B. SENNETT, American Museum of Natural History, New York. 18035. '86. (V, A)

ETHNOLOGICAL OBJECTS,* from the following localities:

    Kassianamute, Togiak River (108 specimens); Tuniakput, Togiak River (25 specimens); Ikaliuk, Togiak River (24 specimens); Togiagamute, Togiak River (51 specimens); Agivigiak, Agivigiak River (5 specimens); Iguswek, Iguswek River (16 specimens); total, 229 specimens.

    I. APPLEGATE, Sergeant Signal Corps, U. S. Army, Unalashka, Alaska. 18036. '86. (II, A)

CRUSTACEA: echinodermata and 1 annelid.

    I. APPLEGATE, Sergeant Signal Corps, U. S. Army, Unalashka, Alaska. 18036. '86. (XI)

STONE AX.

    I. APPLEGATE, Unalashka, Alaska. 18036. '86. (III)

INSECTS, *Carabus truncaticollis.*

    I. APPLEGATE, Unalashka, Alaska. 18036. '86. (X)

FISHES: *Podothecus acipenserinus, Blepsias cirrhosus, Trichodon stelleri, Artedius notospilotus, Murænoides ornatus, Siphagonus barbatus, Ammocœtes aureus.*

    I. APPLEGATE, Unalashka, Alaska. 18036. '86. (VII)

GRASSES. This collection, though small, is very valuable and contains several species new to the Museum herbarium, and one (*Carex decidua* Boott), collected for the third time in North America.

    I. APPLEGATE, Unalashka, Alaska. 18036. '86. (XV)

Clypeaster rotundus; for examination.

    C. C. NUTTING, State University of Iowa. 18037. '86. (XI)

FOSSIL FERN, *Callipteridium;* a good specimen.

    T. E. S. GRIFFIN, McKeesport, Pennsylvania. 18038. '86. (XIV)

MOLE CRICKET, *Gryllotalpa* sp.

    HART VANCE, assistant engineer in charge of Red River survey. 18039. '86. (X)

ORES, from Tennessee.

    Dr. J. C. McCORMICK, Strawberry Plains, Tennessee. 18040. '86. (XVIII)

RED WORMS, taken from the Richmond Reservoir Lake.

    W. E. CUTSHAW, Richmond, Virginia. 18041. '86. (XI)

INSECTS.

    D. MACRAE, Wilmington, Delaware. 18042. '86. (X)

FLOWER-FLY, *Eristalis* (larva); for examination.

    W. G. BLISH, Niles, Michigan. 18043. '86. (X)

LARVA of a species of Moth, *Logoa;* for examination.

    Dr. H. P. BRISBANE, Vicksburg, Mississippi. 18044. '86. (X)

AMERICAN HERCULES BEETLE, *Dynastes tityus;* for examination.

    W. J. HUYBURN, Wakeup post-office, Athens County, Ohio. 18045. '86. (X)

DROP-BLOCK: a game played among the Chinese.

    HENRY HORAN, U. S. National Museum. 18046. '86. (II, A)

---

* See Report on Department of Ethnology, Section II.

BOOKS: "Illustrations of Tillage and Weaving," a Japanese work in two volumes; also Serrurier's Japanese Cyclopædia in French-Japanese. Pt. I. Quadrupeds and birds.

> Dr. D. B. McCARTEE, Washington, District of Columbia. 18047. '86. (II, A)

NAVAJO CRADLE (model,) and a string of silver beads, from Arizona.

> COSMOS MINDELEFF, U. S. Geological Survey. 18048. '86. (II, A)

CONFEDERATE UNIFORM, private of artillery. (Deposited.)

> JOSEPH THOMPSON, Lynchburgh, Virginia. (Through William F. Page.) 18049. '86. (I)

TAPE PISTOL, old.

> WILLIAM SILVERTHORN, Lynchburgh, Virginia. (Through William F. Page.) 18050. '86. (II, A)

BRANDING IRON, used by an old Virginian family.

> Capt. J. J. DILLARD, Lynchburgh, Virginia. (Through William F. Page.) 18051. '86. (II, A)

BOOKS: "Songs of Zion," "Questions on the Gospels" (1839), "Young Lady's Equestrian Manual" (1839).

> D. B. PAYNE, Lynchburgh, Virginia. (Through William F. Page.) 18052. '86. (II, A)

HYMN-BOOK. (Deposited.)

> Rev. P. PATERSON, Lynchburgh, Virginia. (Through William F. Page), 18053. '86. (II, A)

STOCK worn by an old gentleman, and two fashion plates.

> WILLIAM L. PAGE, Lynchburgh, Virginia. 18054. '86. (II, A)

CHINESE ROBIN, *Leiothrix luteus.* (Skeleton.)

> LOUIS SCHMID & SONS, Washington, District of Columbia. 18055. '86. (XII)

PYRITE IN LIMESTONE; for examination.

> AMBROSE CONANT, Big Run, Athens County, Ohio. 18056. '86. ·(XVI)

JAPANESE IDOL, "Amida," worshiped by the most intelligent Japanese. (Exchange.)

> G. L. FAUCHER, West Winsted, Connecticut. 18057. '86. (II, A)

BIRDS: *Merganser serrator* (skull), and *Oceanodroma leachii* (skeleton), from Waterville, Maine.

> Dr. C. HART MERRIAM, Department of Agriculture, Washington, District of Columbia. 18058. '86. (XII)

ROCKS, from lake beds about 5 miles west of Orleans, Nebraska.

> GEORGE P. MERRILL, U. S. National Museum. 18059. '86. (XVII)

CANDLE MOULD, and three broiling irons, smith-made.

> Mrs. E. HUNTER, Lynchburgh, Virginia. (Through William F. Page.) 18060. '86. (II, A)

SPHEROID OF GRANITE, from Fonni, Sardinia. (Exchange.)

> B. STÜRTZ, Bonn, Prussia. 18061. '86. (XVII)

HOG-NOSED SNAKE (or Spreading Adder), *Heterodon platyrhinus* (young), from Virginia.

> J. H. KUEHLING, Washington, District of Columbia. 18062. '86. (VI)

IVORY FAN in embroidered case, Chinese traveler's knife, chopsticks in case, and specimen of silk. (Deposited.)

> Dr. D. B. McCARTEE, Washington, District of Columbia. 18063. '86. (II, A)

SHELLS; for examination.

> Dr. W. H. RUSH, Hyannis, Massachusetts. 18064. ·86. (IX)

DRUM captured at Yorktown by Capt. D. K. Wardell, of the Twenty-second Massachusetts Volunteers.

> JOSEPH SESSFORD, Smithsonian Institution. 18065. '86. (I)

DOUBLE YELLOW-HEAD PARROT, *Chrysotis levaillanti* (skeleton).

> Mrs. WOOD, Washington, District of Columbia. 18066. '86. (XII)

ARCHÆOLOGICAL OBJECTS : Rude cutting tool, 14 arrow-heads, 3 rude implements, 13 fragments of pot-stone bowls, 3 pieces of pottery, grooved ax, unfinished pot-stone bowl; from the District of Columbia; 7 arrow-heads, from Montgomery County, Maryland; grooved ax, from Annapolis, Maryland, and 3 arrow-heads, from Hampshire County, West Virginia.

Dr. LEWIS KENGLA, Kansas City, Missouri. 18067. '86. (III)

FUNGUS, probably a species of *Coprinus*.

Commander L. A. BEARDSLEE, U. S. Navy, Little Falls, New York. 18068. '86. (XV)

SALAMANDER, *Amblystoma* (larva); for examination.

H. J. SHAW, New Berlin, Chenango County, New York. 18069. '86. (VI)

UNDULATED GRASS PARAKEET, *Melapsittacus undulatus* (skeleton).

W. C. WEEDEN, U. S. National Museum. 18070. '86. (XII)

ANTIQUITIES, from France.

THOMAS WILSON, Munich, Bavaria. 18071. '86. (III)

SQUIRREL, *Sciurus aureogaster;* locality not known.

ZOOLOGICAL SOCIETY OF PHILADELPHIA. (Through Arthur E. Brown, esq.) 18072. '86. (IV)

PAPER MONEY of the General Government, and of the states, counties, and cities of the Confederate States of America, bond certificates, tax bills, postage-stamps, merchandise invoices, etc.

W. F. PAGE, U. S. Fish Commission. 18073. '86. (I)

SHELL, probably *Helix septemvolva* Say; for examination.

W. E. HUDSON, Orlando, Florida. 18074. '86. (IX)

LITTLE BROWN CRANE, *Grus canadensis.*

G. F. MORCOM, Chicago, Illinois. 18075. '86. (V, A)

AMERICAN GROUND SQUIRREL, *Tamias striatus.*

F. C. HOUGH, Morgantown, West Virginia. 18076. '86. (IV)

LEPIDOPTERA, 26 species, 31 specimens.

GEORGE H. HUDSON, Plattsburgh, New York. 18077. '86. (X)

JUMPING MICE, *Zapus hudsonius* (seven specimens), from Chatham, New Jersey.

J. M. C. EATON, Irvington, New Jersey. 18078. '86. (IV)

BONES from a burial cave in Grainger County, Tennessee.

Dr. J. C. McCORMICK, Strawberry Plains, Tennessee. 18079. '86. (III)

GILA MONSTER, *Heloderma suspectum.*

Dr. GEORGE H. MITCHELL, Sacaton, Pinal County, Arizona. 18080. '86. (VI)

NEST OF *Vespa maculata*, containing a large number of specimens; from Mount Vernon, Virginia.

J. H. KUEHLING, Washington, District of Columbia. 18081. '86. (X)

BIRD-SKINS;* a collection including 11 specimens, 6 species, including 6 adults and young of *Sialia azurea, Trogon ambiguus,* juv., in the first plumage, from Arizona; the head of a female Imperial Woodpecker, *Campephilus imperialis,* from Sonora, Mexico, a species of which the Museum as yet possesses no complete specimen, the above head being the first fragment of this magnificent bird received.

Lieut. HARRY C. BENSON, U. S. Army, Fort Huachuca, Arizona. 18082. '86. (V, A)

ALBINO WESTERN ROBIN, *Merula migratoria propinqua* (skin).

JOHN J. SNYDER, Murphys, Calaveras County, California. 18083. '86. (V, A)

BIRDS (19 specimens, 8 species), mostly vireos and flycatchers.

WILLIAM LLOYD, Paint Creek, Concho County, Texas. 18084. '86. (V, A)

FLAX, from France. Also Consular Report 87, containing a statement concerning the same.

Hon. CHAS. P. WILLIAMS, U. S. consul at Rouen, France. (Through Department of State.) 18085. '86. (I)

---

* See Proceedings U. S. National Museum, vol. 10, p. 147.

MINERALS (17 specimens), from New Jersey. (Exchange.)

AMERICAN MUSEUM OF NATURAL HISTORY, New York City, New York. 18086. '86. (XVI)

SHELLS, *Cocculina spinigera*, Jefferys, and *Allopora norvegica*, Sars; from Northern Europe.

Rev. A. M. NORMAN, Fence Houses, Durham, England. 18087. '86. (IX)

FOSSIL SCALARIA (32 specimens); from France. (Exchange.)

E. DE BOURY, Thémérlcourt par Vigny, France. (Through W. H. Dall.) 18088. '86. (IX)

FRESH-WATER SHELLS, *Amnicola limosa*, Lag.; for examination.

CHARLES E. BEECHER, Albany, New York. 18089. '86. (IX)

WESTERN PORCUPINE, *Erethrizon epixanthus* (2), and Mink, *Putorius vison* · from Alaska.

Ensign A. P. NIBLACK, U. S. Navy. 18090. '86. (IV)

BIRD-SKINS, from Africa and Polynesia. (Exchange.)

OBERLIN COLLEGE, Oberlin, Ohio. 18091. '86. (V, A)

STONE PERFORATOR. Lent for casting. (Returned.)

Col. CHARLES C. JONES, Augusta, Georgia. 18092. '86. (III)

STONE PESTLE, from Montgomery County, Maryland.

C. B. BOYLE, U. S. Geological Survey. 18093. '86. (III)

APPLE, of unusual growth; for examination.

GEORGE McDOWELL, Fresno City, California. 18094. '86. (XV)

MUSK OX AND WOLF SKINS.

Captain CHURCH. 18095. '86.

MOLLUSKS, *Mytilus hamatus*, from lower Potomac River, Virginia.

FRANK BURNS, U. S. Geological Survey. 18096. '86. (IX)

WATER BIRDS; a collection of 108 specimens, 10 species, from the coasts of Massachusetts and from the Newfoundland Bank, collected by the naturalists at Wood's Holl, and on board the steamer *Albatross* and the schooner *Grampus*. The collection is very valuable and interesting, containing a series of 44 specimens of *Puffinus borealis* (which was described only a few years ago and was, up to that time, a very rare species); also a very large series of two species of Jaegers, *Stercorarius parasiticus* and *S. pomarinus*, illustrating the enormous individual variation of color in these birds.

U. S. FISH COMMISSION. 18097. '86. (V, A)

FISH; *Ophiognathus leei* (type), Ryder.

U. S. FISH COMMISSION, Wood's Holl, Massachusetts. 18098. '86. (VII)

SHAD, *Alosa sapidissima;* about 40 specimens.

SHELL-FISHERY COMMISSION, New Haven, Connecticut. 18099. '86. (VII)

WOOD RAT, *Neotoma* sp. (skull and bones).

Dr. WILLIS E. EVERETTE, Wallula Junction, Washington Territory. 18100. '86. (XII)

BIRD'S NEST; for examination.

Dr. WILLIS E. EVERETTE, Wallula Junction, Washington Territory. 18100. '86. (V, B)

POTTERY (large specimen).

Mrs. FANNIE B. EWING, Lynchburgh, Virginia. 18101. '86. (I)

FISHES: *Prionotus roseus, Scarus evermanni, Steinegeria rubescens, Anthias vivanus, Scarus bollmani, Zygonectes escambiœ, Callechelys murœna, Serranus ocyurus, Phycis floridanus.*

Prof. D. S. JORDAN, Indiana University, Bloomington, Indiana. 18102. '86. (VII)

JAPANESE WORKS OF ART: Pair of bronze vases made by the first Tokyo manufacturing company, Japan; pair of Japanese cloisonné enameled vases; pair of Kaga porcelain vases; pair of Satsuma faience vases; Tokugawa or lacquer ink box from the Shogun's palace; Japanese sword and scabbard. Also a Chinese inlaid box. (Deposited.)

Dr. D. BETHUNE McCARTEE, Washington, District of Columbia. 18103. '86. (I)

CHINESE PORCELAIN DISH and antique Japanese bronze vase. (Gift.)

Dr. D. BETHUNE McCARTEE, Washington, District of Columbia. 18103. '86. (I)

BERMUDA SPONGES (collected by Dr. G. Brown Goode in 1876–1879): *Tuba vaginalis,* varieties *bursaria, papyracea, nuda, crispa ; Hircinia campana,* varieties *marginalis, amorphous, dendritica, turrita; Spongia tublifera,* varieties *disciformis, turrita; Spongia punctata,* var. *bermudensis,* and *Verongia fistularis* (?) (484 specimens).

WESLEYAN UNIVERSITY, Middletown, Connecticut. 18104. '86. (XI)

SHARK, *Carcharias glaucus* (?), and two heads of specimens of the same species; *Somniosus microcephalus, Raia ocellata,* and *R. lævis.*

U. S. FISH COMMISSION, Wood's Holl, Massachusetts. 18105. '86. (VII)

MOOSE (skull and bones), from Canada.

Col. CECIL CLAY, Department of Justice. 18106. '86. (XII)

ADZE-HEAD, or celt, and sample of wood; for examination. (Returned.)

Capt. G. R. MANN, Sturtevant House, New York City. 18107. '86. (II, A)

MINERALS. (Exchange.)

N. H. PERRY, South Paris, Maine. 18108. '86. (XVI)

CHUB MACKEREL, *Scomber pneumatophorus.*

R. A. GOLDEN, Washington, District of Columbia. 18109. '86. (VII)

MINERALS.

CHARLES D. MERWIN. 18110. '86. (XVI)

"WALKING-STICK," *Diapheromera femorata ;* for examination.

W. T. LANDER, Williamston, South Carolina. 18111. '86. (X)

CHUB MACKEREL, *Scomber pneumatophorus.*

R. EDWARD EARLL, Tiverton, Rhode Island. 18112. '86. (VII)

PALÆOZOIC FOSSILS, from England.

H. B. FABIANI, New York City, New York. 18113. '86. (XIII, A)

VERTEBRATE FOSSILS, from England.

H. B. FABIANI, New York City, New York. 18113. '86. (VIII)

SALAMANDER, *Amblystoma mavortium* (about 250 specimens).

Dr. R. W. SHUFELDT, U. S. Army, Fort Wingate, New Mexico. 18114. '86. (VI)

RED-THROATED LOON, *Colymbus septentrionalis ;* Red-breasted Merganser, *Merganser serrator;* Crested Grebe, *Podiceps holbollii;* Surf Ducks (2), *Melanetta velvetina* and *Pelionetta perspicillata;* Scoters (2), *Oidemia americana.* (Skeletons.)

ISAAC M. JACKSON, Plymouth, Massachusetts. 18115. '86. (XII)

GREATER SHEARWATER, *Puffinus major;* Fulmar Petrel, *Fulmarus glacialis ;* Petrels, *Oceanites oceanica* and *O. leucorhoa ;* Gulls, *Larus argentatus* and *Rissa tridactyla;* Surf Duck, *Pelionetta perspicillata,* and Pomarine Jaeger, *Stercorarius pomarhinus.* (Skeletons.)

U. S. FISH COMMISSION. 18116. '86. (XII)

CATFISH, *Amiurus marmoratus,* with lernæan parasites.

B. B. WHITE, Thomaston, Georgia. 18117. '86. (VII)

IMPURE GRAPHITE, and rocks stained by decomposition; for examination.

C. W. HITCHCOCK, Custer City, Dakota. 18118. '86. (XVIII)

CASSINITE, from Blue Hill, near Media, Pennsylvania.

ISAAC LEA, LL. D., Philadelphia, Pennsylvania. 18119. '86. (XVI)

FISHES: *Coregonus williamsoni, Salvelinus malma, Ptychochilus oregonensis.*

W. C. HARRIS, Broadway, New York City. 18120. '86. (VII)

IRON ORES, fuel and fluxes; from Rusk, Texas.

L. C. JOHNSON, U. S. Geological Survey. 18121. '86. (XVIII)

IRON PYRITES; for examination.

URIAH J. CULP, Adamsville, Bradley County, Arkansas. 18122. '86. (XVIII)

MUSICAL INSTRUMENTS: zither and case, inlaid; guitar and case, Russian model; and instruction book for zither. (Deposited.)

RUDOLPH HEINRICHS, Washington, District of Columbia. 18123. '86. (I)

LIMESTONE containing iron pyrites; for examination.

AMBROSE CONANT, Big Run, Athens County, Ohio. 18124. '86. (XVI)

MAGNESIAN LIMESTONE; for examination.

WILLIAM WATTS, Caldwell, Sumner County, Kansas. 18125. '86. (XVI)

LONG-HAIRED ARMADILLO, *Dasypus vellerosus* Gray.

ZOOLOGICAL SOCIETY OF PHILADELPHIA. (Through A. E. Brown, Esq.) 18126. '86. (IV)

FOSSIL FISH HEAD, found imbedded in blue slate rock 20 feet below the surface.

Dr. R. W. NOBLE, Barclay, Falls County, Texas. 18127. '86. (VII)

TOKENS AND COINS (6), United States and Canada.

H. E. HUBER, Baltimore, Maryland. 18128. '86. (I)

BADGE and cards of Columbian Commandery, Knights Templar, of Norwich, Connecticut.

JOHN ECCLES, Taftville, Connecticut. 18129. '86. (I)

COPPER AND SILVER COINS of Canada, United States, Great Britain, France, and Sweden.

W. PALMER, U. S. National Museum. 18130. '86. (I)

BRONZE MEDAL of Louis Kossuth, "the Washington of Hungary." Found in a field at Christiansburgh, Floyd County, Virginia, in 1885. (Deposited.)

Miss S. E. LATHAM, U. S. National Museum. 18131. '86. (I)

TRUMPET-FISH (Tobacco-Pipe-fish), *Fistularia tabaccaria;* for examination.

JAMES T. HAVENS, Point Pleasant, New Jersey. 18132. '86. (VII)

ENAMEL BEAD, Venetian origin, found in a mound near New Smyrna; for examination.

J. T. DETWILER, New Smyrna, Florida. 18133. '86. (III)

BAT-FISH, *Malthe vespertilio.*

J. Y. DETWILER, New Smyrna, Florida. 18133. '86. (VII)

CHIMERA, *Chimæra affinis* (2 specimens), and Blue Hake, *Haloporphyrus viola.*

THOMAS THOMPSON, captain of sc ooner *M. A. Barton.* (Through W. A. Wilcox, Gloucester, Massachusetts.) 18134. '86. (VII)

GALENA.

J. H. BUTTON, Knoxville, Knox County, Tennessee. 18135. '86. (XVIII)

OXIDES of Iron and Asbestos.

Dr. C. HART MERRIAM, Washington, D. C. 18136. '86. (XVIII)

HOG-NOSE SNAKE, *Heterodon platyrhinus* (1 specimen).

J. H. KUEHLING, Washington, District of Columbia. 18137. '86. (VI)

ETHNOLOGICAL OBJECTS. A stone spoon used by Buddhist priest in eating rice; 10 photographs; odd numbers of the "Pekin Gazette;" and paintings on silk.

Dr. D. BETHUNE McCARTEE, Washington, D. C. 18138. '86. (II, A)

PAINTING ON SILK, "The Metal Worker." (Deposited.)

Dr. D. BETHUNE McCARTEE, Washington, District of Columbia. 18139. '86. (II, A)

BIRDS' NESTS AND EGGS: Nest and four eggs of *Spinus pinus;* nest and four eggs of *Helminthophila pinus,* and four eggs of *Empidonax flaviventris* (very rare).

Dr. A. K. FISHER, Sing Sing, New York. 18140. '86. (V, B)

EGG of *Crypturus pileatus.*

ZOOLOGICAL SOCIETY OF PHILADELPHIA. (Through Arthur E. Brown, esq.) 18141. '86. (V, B)

SHELLS, 76 species (324 specimens) of land, fresh-water, and marine shells.

MEXICAN GEOGRAPHICAL EXPLORING COMMISS:ON, City of Mexico. 18142. '86. (IX)

VOLCANIC DUST, taken from a piece of board at Nuga Island.

Capt. C. A. ABBEY, U. S. Revenue Marine steamer *Corwin.* 18143. '86. (XVII)

CHINESE ENVELOPE, Japanese postal card, and ten Chinese visiting cards.

Dr. D. BETHUNE McCARTEE, Washington, D. C. 18144. '86. (II, A)

SLAG CRYSTALS.

ALFRED SHARPLESS, West Chester, Chester County, Pennsylvania. 18145. '86. (XVIII)

GOLD in quartz, from Sky High mine, Plumas County, California.

J. S. DILLER, U. S. Geological Survey. 18146. '86. (XVI)

INSECTS: *Argynnis eurynome, Colias chrysomelas, C. eytheme, Phyciodes morpheus, Satyrus charon, Lycæna acmon, L. Scudderi, L. melissa, Thymelicus garita, Pyrgus tessellata, Pamphila pawnee, P. napa, Pieris protodice, P. Beckeri, Chrysophanus sirius, C. dione, C. zeroe;* for examination.

Dr. J. C. MERRILL, U. S. Army, Klamath, Oregon. 18147. '86. (x)

INSECTS: *Anticarsia gemmatilis, Tolype velleda, Asopia costalis, Aletia argillacea, Nematocampa filamentaria, Heliothis armiger, Limacodes rectilinea* (?), *Xanthia togata, Oligostigma albalis, Pterophura (Cidaria) diversilineata, Zerene catenaria, Mesograpta stramentalis, Euphanessa mendica, Gortyna Harrissi, G. purpurifascia, G. nitela, Xylina antennata, Catocala relicta, C. unijuga, C. briseis, Smerinthus myops, Criocephalus agrestis, Margarodes 4-stigmalis, Ligyrus relictus, Semiothisa ocellinata,* and *Copris anaglypticus.*

GEORGE H. HUDSON, Plattsburgh, New York. 18148. '86. (x)

SNUFF-DIPPING APPARATUS.

J. ROGERS, Mount Union, Alabama. 18149. '86. (II, A)

PIGEON TREMEX, *Tremex columba* (3 specimens); also Ichneumon fly, *Rhyssa lunator;* for examination.

H. R. STRONG, Wilson, North Carolina. 18150. '86. (x)

BEETLE, *Adalia bipunctata.*

Rev. J. W. GUERNSEY, Rutland, Vermont. 18151. '86. (x)

SNAKES, *Eutænia vagrans* (3 specimens).

Dr. R. W. SHUFELDT, U. S. Army, Fort Wingate, New Mexico. 18152. '86. (VI)

STEAM-ENGINE, built about the year 1829.

Capt. C. M. BLACKFORD, Lynchburgh, Virginia. 18153. '86. (I)

ORES.

Dr. W. B. ROBERTSON, Lynchburgh, Virginia. (Through W. F. Page.) 18154. '86. (XVIII)

TOBACCO, and sample boxes for packing same.

HANCOCK BROS. & CO., Lynchburgh, Virginia. 18155. '86. (I)

WATER-BUG, *Belostoma americanum;* for examination.

C. W. DARLING, Utica, New York. 18156. '86. (x)

SNAKE, *Ophiosaurus ventralis* (1 specimen).

HENRY L. BARKER, Oakley, South Carolina. 18157. '86. (VI)

PYROLUSITE (1 specimen), from the manganese mining district, Polk County, Arkansas. J. T. WARD, Lamar, Missouri. (Through U. S. Geological Survey.) 18158. '86. (XVI)

RAMIE FIBER, in different stages of manufacture.

Hon. CHARLES P. WILLIAMS, United States consul, Rouen, France. (Through Department of State.) 18159. '86. (I)

SCOURED WOOLS.

Hon. JACOB SCHOENHOF, United States consul, Tunstall, England. (Through Department of State.) 18160. '86. (I)

RECENT PLANTS, *Pteris aquilina,* L. (Exchange.)

JAMES RODERICK, Strawberry Plains, Tennessee. 18161. '86. (XV)

OIL from the liver of *Chimæra plumbea;* for examination.

JAMES P. GREASON, Gloucester, Massachusetts. 18162. '86. (I)

BIRD-SKINS.

U. S. FISH COMMISSION, Washington, District of Columbia. 18163. '86. (V, A)

BIRDS' NESTS (23 specimens); from Arizona, Colorado, Massachusetts, and Ohio.

H. W. HENSHAW, U. S. Geological Survey. 18164. '86. (V, B)

MARINE INVERTEBRATES, mainly crustacean fish parasites; from Iceland.

JOHN MARSHALL, captain, schooner *Landseer.* (Through W. A. Wilcox, Gloucester, Massachusetts.) 18165. '86. (XI)

DRIED FISH, *Potamocottus*, sp., *Coregonus williamsoni*, *Thymallus tricolor*, var. *montanus* (3 specimens); from Gallatin River, Gallatin County, Montana.

Dr. A. C. PEALE, U. S. Geological Survey. 18166. '86. (VII)

ERMINE, *Putorius erminea;* Mink, *Putorius vison*, and Spermophile, *Spermophilus richardsoni* (three skins and three stomachs); from Gallatin Valley, Montana.

Dr. A. C. PEALE, U. S. Geological Survey. 18166. '86. (IV)

SILVER ORE, from Lexington Mine, Butte, Montana.

Dr. A. C. PEALE, U. S. Geological Survey. 18166. '86. (XVIII)

ROCKS, from Montana.

Dr. A. C. PEALE, U. S. Geological Survey. 18166. '86. (XVII)

WOOD OPAL, from near Gallatin City, Montana.

Dr. A. C. PEALE, U. S. Geological Survey. 18166. '86. (XV)

MINERALS: Wood opal (18 specimens).

Dr. A. C. PEALE, U. S. Geological Survey. 18166. '86. (XVI)

DUCK, *Erismatura rubida* (skin), from Gallatin County, Montana.

Dr. A. C. PEALE, U. S. Geological Survey. 18166. '86. (V, A)

RATTLESNAKE, *Crotalus scutulatus*, and Horned Toads (2), *Phrynosoma modestum;* from Gallatin County, Montana.

Dr. A. C. PEALE, U. S. Geological Survey. 18166. '86. (VI)

SPIDER CRAB, *Lithodes maia*, from Marblehead, Massachusetts.

SCHOONER "*Dixie*," Gloucester, Massachusetts. (Through W. A. Wilcox.) 18167. '86. (XI)

SILVER MEDAL struck in 1757 to commemorate the victories of Frederick the Great of Prussia over the French, Austrians, Russians, and Swedes during that year.

JOHN H. OWEN, Hallowell, Maine. 18168. '86. (I)

SET TYPE melted together by heat, fished from the ocean in 1885, 500 feet off Virginia Beach.

PAUL BECKWITH, Washington, District of Columbia. 18169. '86. (I)

LAKE CARP, *Carpiodes thompsoni ;* for examination.

GEORGE DECKER, Bay City, Michigan. 18170. '86. (VII)

BASKET made by Choctaw Indians.

A. S. GATSCHET, Alexandria, Louisiana. 18171. '86. (II, A)

BUNCH OF LEAVES left by a freshet.

Mrs. LISLE LESTER, Stamford, Connecticut. 18172. '86. (X)

LITTLE GREBE, *Podiceps nigricans* (1 specimen), from Japan.

Dr. L. STEJNEGER, U. S. National Museum. 18173. '86. (V, A)

BONE FISH-HOOKS and six stone instruments, from the Trenton gravels. Collected by Dr. C. C. Abbott.

PEABODY MUSEUM, Cambridge, Massachusetts. (Through Prof. F. W. Putnam). 18174. '86. (III)

SNAKE, *Eutœnia sirtalis ornatus*.

Dr. H. J. BIGELOW, Boston, Massachusetts. 18175. '86. (VI)

BARN OWL, *Strix pratincola;* for examination.

Dr. FREDERICK TAYLOR, Hillsborough, Loudoun County, Virginia. 18176. '86. (V, A)

NEST and five eggs of *Perisoreus obscurus*, from Beaverton, Oregon; and one egg of *Scops asio maxwellœ*, from Colorado.

A. W. ANTHONY, North Denver, Colorado. 18177. '86. (V, B)

DRIED FISH, *Argyropelecus olfersi*.

W. A. WILCOX, Gloucester, Massachusette. 18178. '86. (VII)

COPPER COIN, Hebrew quadrans or "widow's mite"—value, about ¼ cent. (Cast.) For examination.

W. D. ROBERTSON, Lincoln, Nebraska. 18179. '86. (I)

OLD SQUAW DUCK, *Harelda glacialis ;* Eider Duck, *Somateria mollissima ;* Loon, *Colymbus torquatus ;* Red-Necked Loon, *Colymbus septentrionalis*. (Seven skeletons.)

I. M. JACKSON, Plymouth, Massachusetts. 18180. '86. (XII)

MARINE SHELLS, 20 species, 27 specimens, from the Gulf of Mexico; and 5 species, 20 specimens of land shells, from Honduras.

CHARLES T. SIMPSON, Ogallala, Nebraska. 18181. '86. (IX)

MARINE SHELLS, foreign (7 specimens).

Miss CORA MASON, Washington, District of Columbia. 18182. '86. (IX)

COW-MOOSE, photographs of side and front view of head.

General CECIL CLAY, Washington, District of Columbia. 18183. '86. (IV)

BINDING, ancient vellum, Bremen, 1735.

G. BROWN GOODE, U. S. National Museum. 18184. '86. (I)

CONFEDERATE GUN-BARRELS (2), and a ramrod.

WILLIAM L. PAGE, Lynchburgh, Virginia. (Through William F. Page.) 18185. '86. (I)

STEATITE.

A. WEIRMAN, Lynchburgh, Virginia. (Through William F. Page.) 18186. '86. (I)

ARCHÆOLOGICAL OBJECTS : Arrow-heads, a discoidal stone, pottery, human skull, jaw-bones and teeth, from a mound in Amherst County, Virginia; a notched ax and five arrow-heads, from Bedford County, Virginia.

Dr. THOMAS H. NELSON, Coffee, Virginia. 18187. '86. (I)

HYMN BOOKS (2).

Miss DEBORAH DAVIS, Lynchburgh, Virginia. (Through W. F. Page.) 18188. '86. (I)

CANDLE-SNUFFERS (one pair).

Miss DEBORAH DAVIS, Lynchburgh, Virginia. (Through W. F. Page.) 18188. '86. (II, A)

BUTTONS from Confederate Army uniforms (40).

Mrs. NANNIE LITCHFORD, Daniel's Hill, Lynchburgh, Virginia. (Through William F. Page.) 18189. '86. (I)

INDIAN PIPE and tomahawk given to General Leftwitch at Fort Meigs, Texas, 1812.

JOHN S. LEFTWITCH, Bedford Springs, Virginia. (Through William F. Page.) 18190. '86. (I)

OLD RELIGIOUS BOOKS (4).

CHARLES MORTIMER, Lynchburgh, Virginia. (Through W. F. Page.) 18191. '86. (I)

"SEWING BIRD" made by hand fifty years ago.

Mrs. H. W. JONES, Liberty, Virginia. (Through W. F. Page.) 18192. '86. (II, A)

FOSSIL WOOD.

MAX KELLEY, Lovely Mount, Virginia. (Through W. F. Page.) 18193. '86. (XIV)

CONFEDERATE BRASS EPAULETTE.

Capt. J. J. DILLARD, Lynchburgh, Virginia. (Through William F. Page.) 18194. '86. (I)

PERSONAL ACCOUNT BOOK of the war period in the Confederate States.

D. B. BAYNE, Jr., Lynchburgh, Virginia. (Through William F. Page.) 18195. '86. (I)

HYMN BOOKS (2).

D. B. BAYNE, Sr., Lynchburgh, Virginia. (Through William F. Page.) 18196. '86. (I)

CANDLE-MOULDS (one set, known to have been used seventy-five years).

W. L. PAGE, Lynchburgh, Virginia. 18197. '86. (II, A)

OLD PISTOL and cylinder.

S. O. FISHER, Lynchburgh, Virginia. (Through W. F. Page.) 18198. '86. (II, A)

BIRDS' NESTS and two eggs, *Chondestes grammacus.*

W. H. ADAMS, Elmore, Illinois. 18199. '86. (V, B)

GASTEROPOD, *Haliotis splendens.*

> MRS. MARY H. BENNETT, San Bernardino, California. 18200. '86. (IX)

PARASITES (*Cryptolepas rhachianecti*) from California Gray Whale, *Rhachianectes glaucus.*

> C. H. TOWNSEND, U. S. National Museum. 18201. '86. (XI)

PIPE, said to have been smoked in many Indian councils presided over by Black Hawk, a noted chief of the Sac and Fox tribe.

> JAMES C. CLARK. (Through Department of the Interior.) 18202. '86. (I)

HERBARIUM containing about 600 species, and a large duplicate set.

> A. G. PEARCE, North Hannibal, New York. 18203. '86. (XV)

ARCHÆOLOGICAL OBJECTS. More than 20,000 specimens.

> BUREAU OF ETHNOLOGY, Washington, District of Columbia. 18204. '86. (III)

ARCHÆOLOGICAL OBJECTS: 39 arrow-heads, spear-head, two scrapers, and a leaf-shaped implement.

> ARCHER L. PAYNE, Lynchburgh, Virginia. (Through William F. Page.) 18205. '86. (III)

TOBACCO-PRESSER and crimper.

> HANCOCK BROTHERS & Co., Lynchburgh, Virginia. 18206. '86. (I)

LOWER JAW of Ground Shark, *Somniosus microcephalus,* taken on the Grand Bank in August, 1886; also eggs of the Slime Eel, *Myxina glutinosa.* Collected by Nathaniel Day of the schooner *M. A. Barton,* Gloucester, Massachusetts.

> Capt. J. W. COLLINS, schooner *Grampus,* U. S. Fish Commission. 18207. '86. (VII)

LOGGERHEAD TURTLE, *Thalassochelys caretta* (skull), from Swan Island, Caribbean Sea.

> JOHN HOWSON, Boston, Massachusetts. 18208. '86. (XII)

RED-BELLIED SQUIRREL, *Sciurus aureigaster,* and Moor Monkey, *Macacus maurus.*

> ZOOLOGICAL SOCIETY OF PHILADELPHIA. (Through Arthur E. Brown, Esq.) 18209. '86. (IV)

SNAKE, *Tropidonotus bisectus,* type, new species, Cope; caught at Central Station, Washington.

> U. S. FISH COMMISSION. 18210. '86. (VI)

CARVED PIPE of a green serpentine, found near Santa Fé, New Mexico. (Cast.)

> Major W. S. BEEBE, U. S. Army, Brooklyn, New York. 18211. '86. (III)

OXIDE OF IRON, with a little quartz; for examination.

> JOHN C. WHITE, Bisbee, Cochise County, Arizona. 18212. '86. (XVIII)

CARVED STONE PIPE, and a small copper ax. (Deposited).

> J. B. NICKLIN, Chattanooga, Tennessee. 18213. '86. (III)

FOSSIL TEETH: Molar Fragments of upper and of lower molar teeth of Horse, *Equus* sp.; fragments of molar of a mastodon and two fragments of molars of a large ruminant.

> U. S. GEOLOGICAL SURVEY, Washington, District of Columbia. (Through Mr. W. H. Dall.) 18214. '86. (XII)

FOSSIL FISH, apparently *Uranidea* or an allied genus of fresh-water *Cottoids;* found in the tunnel of the Monte Cristo Mine on the summit of Spanish Peak, in the auriferous gravel of California.

> JOHN G. PHELPS, San Francisco, California. 18215. '86. (VII)

OLD LAMP, hymn-book, and clay cup.

> E. L. STOUT, New Hope, Virginia. (Through W. F. Page.) 18216. '86. (II, A)

SHELLS: *Helix spinosa* Lea, *H. alternata* Say, *H. appressa* Say, *H. elevata* Say, *Campeloma ponderosa* Lea, *C. decisa* Say, *Io spinosa* Lea, *Angitrema verrucosa* Raf., *Pleurocera filum* Lea, *P. anthonyi* Lea, *Unio verrucosus* Barnes, and *U. bullatus* Raf. ? var.; for examination.

> Dr. J. C. McCORMICK, Strawberry Plains, Tennessee. 18217. '86. (IX)

STONE IMPLEMENTS from the "Trenton Gravel;" also a worked piece of jasper from Trenton.

> Dr. C. C. ABBOTT, Trenton, New Jersey. 18218. '86. (III)

MOURNING DOVE, *Zenaidura macroura.*

HENRY MARSHALL, Laurel, Maryland. 18219. '86. (V, A)

WHIP-POOR-WILL, *Antrostomus vociferus.*

GEORGE MARSHALL, Laurel, Maryland. 18220. '86. (V, A)

BIRD-SKINS.

ANASTASIO ALFARO, San José, Costa Rica. 18221. '86. (V, A)

ANTIQUITIES (photographs).

ANASTASIO ALFARO, San José, Costa Rica. 18221. '86. (III)

GEOLOGIC SPECIMENS collected by I. C. Russell, in the field, in 1885.

U. S. GEOLOGICAL SURVEY, Washington, District of Columbia. 18222. '86. (XVII)

ETHNOLOGICAL OBJECTS: Hat worn by Ecuador Indians at carnival time; leggings worn by natives of Ecuador, Peru, Bolivia, and Chili; knife carried by natives of Chili; Patagonian harpoon-head; horn vessels made by Guachos of Buenos Ayres; bone carving; pair of sandals of Inca mummy; tip of a wand, from the grave of an Inca mummy.

W. E. CURTIS, Chicago, Illinois. 18223. '86. (II, A)

MOSS, from near the pass of Chicta, Peru, Andes Mountains, 15,000 feet in height.

W. E. CURTIS, Chicago, Illinois. 18223. '86. (XV)

ORE; specimen from the Cerro del Pasco Mine, Peru.

W. E. CURTIS, Chicago, Illinois. 18223. '86. (XVIII)

LADIES' COMPANION, used in the Confederate States during the war.

Mrs. H. W. JONES, Liberty, Virginia. (Through William F. Page.) 18224. '86. (I)

BIRD-SKINS; a collection from various parts of the world. (Exchange.)

H. K. COALE, Chicago, Illinois. 18226. '86. (V, A)

LIGNITE (2 specimens), from the new reservoir, north of Washington, District of Columbia.

GEORGE H. BOEHMER, Smithsonian Institution. 18227. '86. (XIV)

PHARHYNGEALS of the fresh-water Drum, *Aplodinotus grunniens;* for examination.

Dr. M. M. ADAMS, Greenfield, Indiana. 18228. '86. (VII)

MODEL of the ruin named Peñasco Blanco, New Mexico.

BUREAU OF ETHNOLOGY, Washington, District of Columbia. 18229. '86. (II, A)

CHUB MACKEREL, *Scomber pneumatophorus.*

WILLARD NYE, Jr., New Bedford, Massachusetts. 18230. '86. (VII)

FISHES (6 species).

GEORGE A. LEWIS, Wickford, Rhode Island. 18231. '86. (VII)

FISH, *Blepharis crinitus.*

THOMAS W. LEWIS, Wickford, Rhode Island. 18232. '86. (VII)

SALAMANDER, *Amblystoma* sp.

Dr. R. W. SHUFELDT, U. S. Army, Fort Wingate, New Mexico. 18233. '86. (VI)

COOPER'S HAWK, *Accipiter cooperi;* from Picowaxen Creek, Charles County, Maryland.

E. R. TODD, U. S. National Museum. 18234. '86. (V, A)

ARCHÆOLOGICAL OBJECTS: Spear-head, a grooved ax, and a cup-shaped natural formation.

Dr. THOMAS H. NELSON, Boonesborough, Virginia. (Through William F. Page.) 18235. '86. (III)

CHIPMUNK, *Tamias striatus* (5 skins).

GEORGE F. ATKINSON, Chapel Hill, North Carolina. 18236. '86. (IV)

GRAPHITE; for examination.

W. PATTON, Llano, Llano County, Texas. 18237. '86. (XVI)

COCOON of *Telea polyphemus* (so-called Electric Worm); for examination.

C. F. SHUEY, Maclenny, Florida. 18238. '86. (X)

BLACK GRUNT, *Hæmulon elegans*, and Stickle-back, *Gasterosteus aculeatus*.
R. A. GOLDEN, Washington, District of Columbia. 18239. '86. (VII)

SAUCER-EYE PORGY, *Calamus calamus*.
WALTER MORELAND, Washington, District of Columbia. 18240. '86. (VII)

SHORE LARKS, *Otocoris alpestris*, *Chrysotæma* (2), from Santa Cruz Island, California.
E. W. BLAKE, Jr., Providence, Rhode Island. 18241. '86. (V, A)

MARINE INVERTEBRATES. A collection made by the U. S. Fish Commission steamer *Albatross* during the summer of 1886.
U. S. FISH COMMISSION, Washington, District of Columbia. 18242. '86. (XI)

FUNGUS, and a Night Blooming Cereus, from Wood's Holl, Massachusetts.
U. S. FISH COMMISSION, Wood's Holl, Massachusetts. 18242. '86. (XV)

SHELLS, collected by the U. S. Fish Commission steamers *Albatross* and *Fish Hawk* and the U. S. Fish Commission schooner *Grampus*, during the summer of 1886 (194 lots).
U. S. FISH COMMISSION, Washington, District of Columbia. 18242. '86. (IX)

FISHES. A large and valuable collection, including *Chalinura simula*, *Bathygadus*, *Bathysaurus agassizii*, *Psenes* sp., *Onos rufus*, *Harriotta*, *Caulolepis*, *Histiobranchus*, *Gastrostomus*, etc.
U. S. FISH COMMISSION, Wood's Holl, Massachusetts. 18242. '86. (VII)

BIRDS: *Spinus tristis*, *Dendroica striata*, and *Puffinus borealis*.
U. S. FISH COMMISSION, Wood's Holl, Massachusetts. 17242. '86. (V, A)

ARCHÆOLOGICAL OBJECTS: scraper, leaf-shaped implement, 3 arrow-heads, and 6 fragments of chipped implements.
THOMAS LEE, U. S. Fish Commission, Wood's Holl, Massachusetts. 18242. '86. (III)

INSECT, probably an immature *Spectrum bivittatum*.
U. S. FISH COMMISSION. 18242. '86. (X)

TURTLE and Hyla, from Nassau, Bahamas.
U. S. FISH COMMISSION. Wood's Holl, Massachusetts. 18242. '86. (VI)

MINERALS: Megabasite in quartz (6 specimens).
F. MENTZEL, Durango, Colorado. 18243. '86. (XVI)

INDIA-INK DRAWINGS (2) of Totem posts and Indian chief's grave at Fort Wrangel, Alaska.
Mrs. E. B. WEBSTER, Washington, District of Columbia. 18244. '86. (II, A)

MARINE INVERTEBRATES. Collection of alcoholic specimens made by the steamer *Albatross* during a cruise from Wood's Holl to Washington, October 23–26, 1886.
U. S. FISH COMMISSION, Washington, District of Columbia. 18245. '86. (XI)

NEST and eight eggs of *Regulus satrapa*.
Capt. B. F. GOSS, Pewaukee, Wisconsin. 18246. '86. (V, A)

ROSEATE SPOON-BILLS, *Ajaja ajaja* (3 specimens).
L. C. LEITH, Corpus Christi, Texas. 18247. '86. (V, A)

BIRDS: Cassin's Purple Finch, *Carpodacus cassini* (6 specimens); Pink-sided Junco, *Junco annectens;* Oregon Junco, *Junco oregonus*.
A. W. ANTHONY, North Denver, Colorado. 18248. '86. (V, A)

CHROMIUM ORE (2 specimens).
General D. E. COOMBS, Baracoa, Cuba. 18249. '86. (XVIII)

BIRDS.
D. RIDGWAY, Wheatland, Illinois. 18250. '86. (V, A)

MAMMALS, *Putorius vison*, *Mus musculus*, *Hesperomys leucopus*, *Arvicola riparius*, *Vespertilio lucifugus*, and *Vesperugo georgianus*.
R. RIDGWAY, Wheatland, Illinois. 18250. '86. (IV)

REPTILES:
    Farancia abacura.   *Eutænia saurita.*
    Ophibolus getulus.   *Storeria dekayi.*
    Ophibolus sp.   *Coluber emoryi.*
    Tripodonotus sipedon.   *Rana halecina* (3 specimens).
    T. rhombifer.   *Hyla versicolor.*
    (27 specimens).
        D. RIDGWAY, Wheatland, Illinois. 18250. '86. (VI)

SNAKE, *Storeria dekayi.*
    "WACO CHIEF," Waco, Texas. 18251. '86. (VI)
QUARTZ and mica, and quartz; for examination.
    ANDREW OLESON, Doylestown, Wisconsin. 18252. '86. (XVIII)
COPPER ORE; f r analysis.
    JAMES BRACKETT, Stockton, Tooele County, Utah. 18253. '86. (XVI)
*COTIGNA, a new species, *Cotigna ridgwayi* Zeledon, and a female of *Carpodectes antoniæ*
    Zel., both hitherto undescribed; for examination.
    JOSÉ C. ZELEDON, San José, Costa Rica. 18254. '86. (V, A)
SILVER AND COPPER COINS of Japan, China, Straits Settlements, and India (26 speci-
    mens); paper money of Japan (3 specimens), and American colonial paper cur-
    rency (2 specimens).
        Dr. D. B. McCARTEE, Washington, District of Columbia. 18255. '86. (I)
BIRD-SKINS (5 specimens), from Newfoundland and Key West, Florida.
    U. S. FISH COMMISSION. 18256. '86. (V, A)
ALBINO FIELD SPARROW, *Spizella pusilla.*
    GEORGE MARSHALL, Laurel, Maryland. 18257. '86. (V, A)
METEORIC IRON (6 specimens) and Meteoric Stone (3 specimens).
    Prof. J. P. COOKE, Harvard College, Cambridge, Massachusetts. 18258. '86.
    (XVI) (Exchange.)
METEORIC IRON (4 specimens) and Meteoric Stone (2 specimens). (Exchange.)
    B. STURTZ, Bonn, Germany. 18259. '86. (XVI)

FISHES:
    Ictalurus punctatus.   *Pimephales promelas.*
    Minnilus umbratilis.   *Chrosomus erythrogaster.*
    M. megalops.   *Catostomus teres.*
    Squalius elongatus.   *Hyodon alosoides.*
    Campostoma anomalum.   *Amiurus melas.*
    Hybognathus argyrites.
    From Kansas.
        O. P. HAY, Irving, Indiana. 18260. '86. (VII)

INSECTS, four type species.
    C. H. BOLLMAN, Bloomington, Indiana. 18261. '86. (X)

FOSSILS:
    Cythere carbonaria.   *Bellerophon sublævis.*
    Euomphalus planistria.   *Endothyra baileyi.*
    Murchisonia vermicula.
    (34 specimens.)
        E. PLEAS, Dunreith, Indiana. 18262. '86. (XIII, A)

SHELLS.
    E. PLEAS, Dunreith, Indiana. 18262. '86. (IX)
MARBLE (2 specimens), from Loudoun County, Virginia.
    U. S. GEOLOGICAL SURVEY, Washington, District of Columbia. (Through Col.
    George W. Shutt.) 18263. '86. (XVII)

---

* See Proceedings U. S. National Museum, vol. 10, pp. 1 and 20.

INSECTS:

Catocala briseis.
Pyrrhia exprimens.
Lathomia germana.
Homoptera woodii.
Trigonophora brunneum.
Lithophane disposita.
Hadena finitima.
H. fractilinea.
Lithophane petulca.
Mamestra rosea.
M. meditata.
Agrotis badinodes.
Acronycta occidentalis.
A. sperta.
A. hasta.
Plemyria fluviata.
Agrotis messoria.
A. sextalis.
A. muranala.

Caradrina sp.
Ingura delineata.
Orthodes infirma.
Leptina dormitans.
Nephelodes violans.
Anytus sculptus.
Croeigrapha normani.
Agrotis mimallonis.
A. cupida.
A. baja.
Luceria Burgessi.
Tæniocampa incerta.
Agrotis fennica.
Perigea luxa.
Arctia rectilinea.
A. nais.
Lithophana cinerola.
L. laticinerea.
L. antennata.

For examination.

HOWARD L. CLARKE, Providence, Rhode Island. 18264. '86. (x)

HORNED TOAD, *Phrynosoma cornutum*, from El Paso, Texas.

R. T. HILL, U. S. Geological Survey. 18265. '86. (VI)

SANDSTONE and bitumen on a fragment of calcite geode; for examination.

KEMPER BENNETT, Wyandotte, Kansas. 18266. '86. (XVI)

ORE, for analysis.

C. W. HITCHCOCK, Custer City, Dakota Territory. 18267. '86. (XVI)

SEA GULLS.

U. S. FISH COMMISSION. 18268. '86. (V, A)

BIRD-SKINS: Types (3) of *Pyranga bivittata* Lafr.; for examination.

BOSTON SOCIETY OF NATURAL HISTORY, Boston, Massachusetts. 18269. '86. (V, A)

HAZEL-NUT SHELL (fossil), from Prince George's County, Maryland.

J. F. HICKEY, Washington, District of Columbia. 18270. '86. (XIV)

FRAGMENT OF SUPPOSED METEORIC ROCK; for examination.

F. E. SHELDON, St. Paul, Minnesota. 18271. '86. (XVI)

RUFFED GROUSE, *Bonasa umbellus*, wings, tail-feathers, etc., of two specimens; for examination.

Rev. T. M. THORPE, McDonough, Chenango County, New York. 18272. '86. (V, A)

CALIFORNIA TROUT, *Salmo irideus*, from Wytheville, Virginia.

U. S. FISH COMMISSION, Washington, District of Columbia. 18273. '86. (VII)

ROCKS: Dacite, from Lassen's Peak, California; peridatite, from Elliott County, Kentucky, and quartz basalt, from northeast of Lassen's Peak.

J. S. DILLER, U. S. Geological Survey. 18274. '86. (XVII)

SEA LAMPREY, *Petromyzon marinus* L.; for examination.

A. F. CLAPP, Sunbury, Pennsylvania. 18275. '86. (VII)

ALBINO DEER, *Cariacus virginianus*, from Clover Creek, Highland County, Virginia.

R. A. GOLDEN, Washington, District of Columbia. 18276. '86. (IV)

SOUTH AMERICAN DEER, *Cariacus gymnotis* (2 specimens).

ZOOLOGICAL SOCIETY OF PHILADELPHIA. (Through Arthur E. Brown, Esq.) 18277. '86. (XII)

CHIMÆRAS, *Chimæra affinis* (2 specimens).

W. A. WILCOX, Gloucester, Massachusetts. 18278. '86. (VII)

HOG-NOSE SNAKE, *Heterodon platyrhinus.*
> ARTHUR E. WILSON, Portsmouth, Virginia. 18279. '86. (VI)

BIRDS' EGGS: Five species, seventy-nine specimens, and three nests; from North Carolina, Connecticut, and Labrador. (Exchange.)
> M. ABBOTT FRAZAR, Boston, Massachusetts. 18280. '86. (V, B)

INSECT: *Lasioderma serricorne;* for examination.
> THOMAS C. WILLIAMS & CO., Richmond, Virginia. 18281. '86. (X)

SHARP-SHINNED HAWK.
> JOHN MURDOCH, U. S. National Museum. 18282. '86. (V, A)

STILETTO (Japanese), from Tokio. (Deposited.)
> Dr. D. B. MCCARTEE, Washington, District of Columbia. 18283. '86. (II, A)

BAVARIAN HELMET and cuirass, used in Franco-Prussian war 1870–1871.
> ROBERT F. ROCHE, hospital steward, Washington Barracks, District of Columbia. 18284. '86. (II, A)

FLUORITE ASH-TRAYS (two specimens.) (Purchased.)
> W. J. KNOWLTON, Boston, Massachusetts. 18285. '86. (XVI)

YELLOWSTONE TROUT, *Salmo purpuratus* (two specimens); and Rocky Mountain White-fish, *Coregonus williamsoni,* from Montana.
> W. C. HARRIS, New York City. 18286. '86. (VII)

OBSIDIAN (1 specimens), from Yellowstone National Park.
> U. S. GEOLOGICAL SURVEY, Washington, District of Columbia. 18287. '86. (XVI)

ARGULUS, taken from a specimen of *Esox nobilior* at Clayton, New York.
> FRED. MATHER, Cold Spring Harbor, New York. 18288. '86. (XI)

NEST, also three eggs of Robins, and sixteen eggs of English Sparrows; taken at Flushing, Long Island.
> L. PARMLY BROWN, Flushing, Long Island. 18289. '86. (V, B)

CROWS, *Corvus ossifragus* and *C. americanus;* also a Turkey-Buzzard, *Cathartes aura;* from Alexandria County, Virginia.
> Dr. A. K. FISHER, Department of Agriculture. 18290. '86. (XII)

INSECTS:

Smerinthus ophthalmicus, var. *pallidulus.*	*Scopelosoma vinnulenta.*
	Chrytolita petrealis.
Pamphila metea.	*Lithopana Bethunei.*
Thecla pœas.	*Priocyela bilinearia.*
Acronycta rubricoma.	*Endropia amœnaria.*
Nolaphana Zelleri.	*Lithophana unimoda.*
Serricoris corrusca.	*Coelodasys unicornis.*
Heterophleps 3-guttata.	*Heterocampa unicolor.*
Pensia laticlava.	*Coelodasys biguttatus.*
Lythria chœnœchrysaria.	*Gluphisia 3-lineata.*
Epiritta perlineata.	*Acronycta luteicoma.*
Therina seminudaria.	*Chamupis cerinthe.*
Metanema quercivoraria.	*Heterocampa subalbicans.*
Endeopia effectaria var.	*Charada deridens.*
Scopelosoma vinnulenta.	*Euclea bifida.*
Pityolita pedipilalis.	*Cerura cinerea.*

For identification.
> W. N. TALLANT, Columbus, Ohio. 18291. '86. (X)

BIRD-SKINS, from different parts of the world, chiefly from Europe.
> EDWARD HARGITT, Broadwater Lodge, Broadwater, Worthing, Sussex, England. 18292. '86. (V, A)

MAMMAL-SKINS:

Erinaceus europæus. *Hesperomys* sp.
Mus rattus. *Lepus cuniculus.*
M. decumanus. *Rhinolophus ferrum-equinum.*
Putorius erminea. *R. hipposideros.*
Felis catus. *Vespertilio daubentoni.*
Meles taxus. *V. mystacinus.*
Lutra vulgaris. *Plecotus auritus.*

EDWARD HARGITT, Broadwater Lodge, Broadwater, Worthing, Sussex, England. 18292. '86. (IV)

FROG, *Rana esculenta* (?); from France (?).

EDWARD HARGITT, Sussex, England. 18292. '86. (VI)

MINERALS: Nosite; from Sweden, Austria, Norway, Switzerland, and Germany.

B. STURTZ, Bonn, Germany. 18293. '86. (XVI)

JASPER PEBBLE, perforated.

WILLIAM P. SEAL, Philadelphia, Pennsylvania. 18294. '86. (III)

ARCHÆOLOGICAL OBJECTS: 3 hammer-stones, 6 sinkers, polishing tool, 5 fragments of pottery, part of brass kettle, box of berry seeds found in kettle, and box of shells from an Indian grave.

W. W. ADAMS, Mapleton, Cayuga County, New York. 18295. '86. (III)

HUMAN SKULLS, *Homo sapiens* (5 specimens).

W. W. ADAMS, Mapleton, New York. 18295. '86. (XII)

LAND AND FRESH-WATER SHELLS. (Exchange.)

GEORGE J. STREATOR, Garrettsville, Ohio. 18296. '86. (IX)

MINERALS: Celestite.

Dr. H. H. THORPE, Liberty Hill, Texas. 18297. '86. (XVI)

LIMESTONE (2 specimens); for examination.

Dr. H. H. THORPE, Liberty Hill, Texas. 18297. '86. (XVII)

INDIAN COSTUMES, baskets, arrows, pots, etc.; for examination. (Returned.)

A. FRANK RANDALL, San Bernardino, California. (Through F. P. Blair, St. Louis, Missouri.) 18298. '86. (II, A)

RAILROAD IRON.

J. E. WATKINS, Camden, New Jersey. 18299. '86. (I)

DIASPORE, and Corundophilite in emery (2 specimens.)

N. A. HARWOOD, Chester, Massachusetts. 18300. '86. (XVI)

RICHARDSON'S MERLIN, *Falco richardsonii* (2 specimens); from Loveland, Larimer County, Colorado.

Dr. ELLIOTT COUES, Smithsonian Institution. 18301. '86. (V, A)

BIRDS, 10 specimens, 9 species.

Dr. W. H. FOX, Hollis, New Hampshire. 18302. '86. (V, A)

EGGS of Purple Gallinule (13); from Jefferson County, Texas. (Exchange.)

M. ABBOTT FRAZAR, Boston, Massachusetts. 18303. '86. (V, B)

MAMMALS: From Asia, Africa, Madagascar, New Holland, and France.

MUSÉE D'HISTOIRE NATURELLE (Bureau of Arts), Paris, France. 18304. '86. (IV)

INSECTS: *Epicauta verticalis, Mylabris melanura, Sitaris humeralis, Stenoria apicalis,* from France; *Lyduo algiricus* and *Œnas afer,* from Algeria.

MUSÉE D'HISTOIRE NATURELLE, Paris, France. 18304. '86. (X)

OLD ENGLISH PISTOL and gun-lock.

WILLIAM DEEDS MILLER, Lynchburgh, Virginia. (Through S. O. Fisher.) 18305. '86. (II, A)

ROCKS. (Exchange.)

W. O. CROSBY, Boston, Massachusetts. 18306. '86. (XVII)

ORES.

E. WILLIS, Vesuvius, Virginia. 18307. '86. (XVII)

ELÆOLITE(1 specimen) ; from Brevig, Norway. (Exchange.)

H. C. HALLOWELL, Sandy Spring, Maryland. 18308. '86. (XVI)

ROCKS collected by L. C. Johnson in Louisiana and Texas. 1885–1886.

U. S. GEOLOGICAL SURVEY. 18309. '86. (XVII)

ORES collected in Louisiana and Texas, 1885–1886.

L. C. JOHNSON, U. S. Geological Survey. 18309. '86. (XVIII)

TURKISH CAIQUE, with oars, dresser, etc.

Hon. S. S. COX, ex-U. S. minister to Turkey. 18310. '86. (I)

ALLIGATOR, *Alligator mississippiensis.*

U. S. FISH COMMISSION, Washington, District of Columbia. 18311. '86. (VI)

FOSSIL SHELLS : *Rhynchonella tetrahedra* (6 specimens) ; *Terebratula punctata* (6 specimens) ; *Inoceramus sulcatus* (2 specimens).

EDWARD CRANE, Brighton, England. 18312. '86. (XIII, B)

RED-TAILED HAWK, *Buteo borealis.*

JAMES P. STABLER, Sandy Spring, Maryland. 18313. '86. (V, A)

POTTERY : Clay head, 30 miniature clay heads, 2 clay toys, 6 obsidian arrow-heads, and serpent in two parts; from Mexico. (Purchased.)

WARD BATCHELOR, Clark's Summit, Pennsylvania. 18314. '86. (II, B)

JAPANESE PIPE.

W. H. CHANDLEE, Washington, District of Columbia. 18315. '86. (II, A)

SWORD from a sword-fish which killed Capt. Franklin D. Armstrong, Lanesville, Massachusetts.

W. A. WILCOX, Gloucester, Massachusetts. 18316. '86. (I)

WOOD, 20 thin sections.

Dr. F. B. HOUGH, Lowville, New York. 18317. '86. (XV)

RED-TAILED HAWK, *Buteo borealis,* adult, from Mount Vernon, Virginia.

Master HAROLD CUSHMAN, Washington, District of Columbia. 18318. '86. (V, A)

KAOLIN; for examination.

W. H. ADAMS, Tolersville, Virginia. 18319. '86. (XVIII)

HYALITE, from Gallatin County, Montana.

U. S. GEOLOGICAL SURVEY, Washington, District of Columbia. (Through Frank Tweedy.) 18320. '86. (XVI)

YELLOW-GREEN VIREO, *Vireo flavoviridis,* from Godbout, Canada.

Dr. C. HART MERRIAM, Department of Agriculture. 18321. '86. (V, A)

BIRDS' SKINS, from the West Indies.

CHARLES B. CORY, Boston, Massachusetts. 18322. '86. (V, A)

"THE 31 PUZZLE," 1883.

G. BROWN GOODE, U. S. National Museum. 18323. '86. (II, A)

BIRDS, 10 specimens, 6 species, from Colorado.

C. W. BECKHAM, Bardstown, Kentucky. 18324. '86. (V, A)

COPPER COIN, a Brazilian 20-reis piece of Pedro I, date 1823 (?); for examination. (Returned.)

J. L. FORBES, Roanoke, Alabama. 18325. '86. (I)

EGGS of *Trichoglossus rubritorquis* (2), and 5 eggs of *Spermestes castanotus ;* habitat, Australia ; eggs laid in captivity.

H. K. COALE, Chicago, Illinois. 18326. '86. (V, B)

EGG of Belding's Marsh Sparrow, *Ammodramus beldingi,* from Santa Barbara, California.

H. W. HENSHAW, U. S. Geological Survey. 18327. '86. (V, B)

FISH PARASITES.

S. E. MEEK, Fulton Market, New York City. 18328. '86. (XI)

BUILDING STONE, from Bedford, Lawrence County, Indiana.

HOOSIER STONE COMPANY, Chicago, Illinois. 18329. '86. (XVI)

FISHES: *Alepocephalus bairdii*, aud *Pteraclis carolinus*, the second specimen in American collections.

ALFRED JOHNSON, Gloucester, Massachusetts. (Through W. A. Wilcox.) 18330. '86. (VII)

CLARK'S TROUT, *Salmo purpuratus*.

W. C. HARRIS, New York City. 18331. '86. (VII)

INTERNATIONAL POSTAGE-STAMP ALBUM, by J. W. Scott; quarto, bound in full morocco; seventh edition.

SCOTT STAMP AND COIN COMPANY, New York City. 18332. '86. (I)

SNAILS: *Helix* (*Mesodon*) *thyroides*, Say; *H.* (*Mesodon*) *thyroides*, toothed variety; *H.* (*Polygyra*) *Texasiana*, Mor.; *H.* (*Dorcasia*) *Berlandieriana* Mor.; *Physa gyrina*, Say; *Bulimus dealbatus*, Say, and *Helicina tropica*, Pfr.; for examination.

W. W. WESTGATE, Houston, Texas. 18333. '86. (IX)

SHORT-EARED OWLS, *Asio accipitrinus* (3).

JAMES P. STABLER, Sandy Spring, Maryland. 18334. '86. (V, A)

BROWN IRON ORE (Limonite); for examination.

W. P. CANADAY, Sergeant-at-Arms, U. S. Senate. 18335. '86. (XVI)

MARINE INVERTEBRATES (small collection).

U. S. FISH COMMISSION. 18336. '86. (XI)

EGGS and MILT of *Gadus morrhua* and *Pollachius virens;* eggs of *Brosmius* and of *Phycis.* One specimen of *Maurolicus* and two of *Sebastophus.*

U. S. FISH COMMISSION. 18336. '86. (VII)

COPPER ORE.

T. O. TAYLOR, Hickory Grove, Prince William County, Virginia. 18337. '86. (XVIII)

POSTAGE-STAMPS, a sheet of 15 Confederate States 10-cent stamps.

W. F. PAGE, U. S. Fish Commission. 18338. '86. (I)

ROMAN COPPER COINS (4).

COPELAND JONES, Washington, District of Columbia. 18339. '86. (I)

CARBONIFEROUS FOSSILS.

J. B. STOCKTON, Toronto, Kansas. 18340. '86. (XIII, A)

LEPERDITIA (small bivalve crustacea). Cincinnati formation (Ordovician).

T. C CHAMBERLIN, Beloit, Wisconsin. 18341. '86. (XIII, A)

BATTLE FLAG, surgeon's uniform coat, fatigue and dress vest, flannel shirt, sash cord, sword, belt, camp pillow, bayonet, camp kettle, with blade of knife, box of cartridges, surgeon's bandages.

Dr. I. E. NAGLE, Mount Joy, Pennsylvania. 18342. '86. (I)

CANARY-BIRDS.

LOUIS SCHMID & SONS, Washington, District of Columbia. 18343. '86. (V, A)

RABBIT, *Lepus cuniculus*, albino.

LOUIS SCHMID & SONS, Washington, District of Columbia. 18343. '86. (IV)

SWALLOW, *Chelidon gutturalis*, from Hong-Kong.

P. L. JOUY, Washington, District of Columbia. 18344. '86. (V, A)

LIMESTONE containing iron pyrites; for examination.

B. C. YATES, Weatherford, Texas. 18345. '86. (XVI)

PHOTOGRAPHIC NEGATIVES (23), taken in Alaska and elsewhere.

A. P. NIBLACK, Ensign, U. S. Navy, Mare Island, California. 18346. '86. (I)

CONTENTS of the stomach of a cod.

B. McGRATH, Gloucester, Massachusetts. 18347. '86. (—)

BASKET made of bark and twigs of Wisteria vine; from province of Shin-shin, Japan. Also photograph of a Phallic temple, Japan.

P. L. JOUY, Washington, District of Columbia. 18348. '86. (II, A)

CARDINAL, *Cardinalis cardinalis*, in remarkable abnormal (yellow) plumage; from Riverview, Maryland.

FRED. ZELLER, Washington, District of Columbia. 18349. '86. (V, A)

BLOODHOUND, *Canis familiaris;* the father came from Russia and was a Siberian bloodhound; the mother was an "Ulmer Dogge," a fine specimen of the so-called Ulmer bull-dog.

PHILIP HUNCKEL, Washington, District of Columbia. 18350. '86. (IV)

INDIAN HEAD, dried, with war paint still adhering to the skin.

E. B. WEBSTER, paymaster, U. S. Navy. 18351. '86. (II, A)

ROCKS.

L. J. IGELSTRÖM, Sunnemo, Wermland, Sweden. 18352. '86. (XVII)

MINERALS.

L. J. IGELSTRÖM, Sunnemo, Wermland, Sweden. 18352. '86. (XVI)

LAND SHELLS; 46 species.

A. G. WETHERBY, Wilders, Mitchell County, North Carolina. 18353. '86. (IX)

MUSICAL INSTRUMENT (bamboo neck, cocoanut body, membrane head, two small wire strings).

Mrs. M. E. BROWN, Orange, New Jersey. 18354. '86. (I)

FULVOUS TREE-DUCK, *Dendrocygna fulva;* from North Carolina.

SWAN ISLAND CLUB. (Through William Sohier, Norfolk, Virginia.) 18355. '86. (V, A)

INTERNAL PARASITES of fishes.

S. E. MEEK, Fulton Market, New York City. 18356. '86. (XI)

CONTRIBUTION BOX, donated to the Washington National Monument Society by Great Barrington, Massachusetts.

NATIONAL MONUMENT SOCIETY, Washington. (Through Hon. Horatio King.) 18357. '86. (I)

ARCHÆOLOGICAL OBJECTS: One bearing resemblance to the so-called "boat-shaped" objects, and another, probably an ornament; for examination.

J. W. A. WRIGHT, Livingston, Alabama. 18358. '86. (III)

BIRDS; 12 specimens, 6 species.

WILLIAM LLOYD, Paint Rock, Concho County, Texas. 18359. '86. (V, A)

CUBAN PARROT, *Chrysotis leucocephala.*

WILLIAM C. WEEDEN, U. S. National Museum. 18360. (V, A)

BIRDS' EGGS, for identification:

Cooper's hawk, *Accipiter cooperi.*
Mourning dove, *Zanaidura carolinensis.*
Passenger pigeon, *Ectopistes migratoria.*
"Bobwhite" or American quail, *Ortyx virginiana.*
Roseate tern, *Sterna dougalli.*
Common crow, *Corvus frugivorus.*
Sparrow-hawk, *Tinnunculus sparverius.*
Killdeer, *Oxyechus vociferus.*
Little blue heron, *Florida cærulea.*
Bobolink, *Dolichonyx oryzivorus.*
Scarlet tanager, *Pyranga rubra.*
Small hen's egg, *Gallus domesticus.*
Ruffed grouse, *Bonasa umbellus.*
Purple finch, *Carpodacus purpureus.*
American goldfinch, *Astragalinus tristis.*
Turkey or hen's egg, abnormal.
Guinea fowl.
Robin, *Merula migratoria.*
Black-billed cuckoo, *Coccyzus erythrophthalmus.*
Yellow-shafted flicker, *Colaptes auratus.*
Cardinal grosbeak, *Cardinalis virginianus.*

Belted kingfisher, *Ceryle alcyon.*
English sparrow, *Passer domesticus.*
Cow blackbird, *Molothrus ater.*
Cedar waxwing, *Ampelis cedrorum.*
Barn swallow, *Hirundo erythrogastra.*
Great crested flycatcher, *Myiarchus crinitus.*
Sharp-shinned hawk, *Accipiter fuscus.*
Night heron, *Nyctiardea grisea nævia.*
Wood thrush, *Hylocichla mustelina.*
Turkey buzzard, *Carthartes aura.*
Small hen's egg, *Gallus domesticus.*
Brown thrasher, *Harporhynchus rufus.*
Red and buff shouldered blackbird, *Agelæus phœniceus.*
Yellow-breasted chat, *Icteria virens.*
Blue jay, *Cyanocitta cristata.*
Yellow-bellied woodpecker, *Sphyrapicus varius.*
Carolina wren, *Thryothorus ludovicianus.*
Meadow-lark, *Sturnella magna.*
American herring gull, *Larus argentatus Smithsonianus.*

BIRDS' EGGS, for identification—Continued.

Catbird, *Galeoscoptes carolinensis*.

Song sparrow, *Melospiza fasciata*.

Field sparrow, *Spizella pusilla*.

Red-eyed vireo, *Vireosylvia olivacea*.

Scarlet tanager, *Pyranga rubra*.

Pewee bird, *Sayornis fuscus*.

Golden-crowned thrush, *Siurus auricapillus*.

King-bird, *Tyrannus carolinensis*.

Bank swallow, *Cotile riparia*.

Worm-eating warbler, *Helminthotherus vermivorus*.

Mocking-bird, *Mimus polyglottus*.

Baltimore oriole, *Icterus galbula*.

Downy woodpecker, *Picus pubescens*.

Orchard oriole, *Icterus spurius*.

White-bellied nut-hatch, *Sitta carolinensis*.

Bluebird, *Sialia sialis*.

Hairy woodpecker, *Picus villosus*.

Redstart, *Setophaga ruticilla*.

Blue-gray gnat-catcher, *Polioptila cærulea*.

Wilson's thrush, *Turdus fuscescens*.

Whip-poor-will, *Caprimulgus vociferus*.

Acadian fly-catcher, *Empidonax acadicus*.

Indigo bunting, *Passerina cyanea*.

Wood pewee, *Contopus virens*.

Night hawk, *Chordeiles popetue*.

Chipping sparrow, *Spizella domestica*.

Blue grosbeak, *Guiraca cærulea*.

Summer yellow bird, *Dendrœca œstiva*.

Black-capped chickadee, *Parus atricapillus*.

Prof. GEORGE F. ATKINSON, Chapel Hill, North Carolina. 18361. '86. (V, B)

LLAMA, *Auchenia llama*.

ZOOLOGICAL SOCIETY OF PHILADELPHIA. (Through Arthur E. Brown, Esq.) 18362. '86. (IV)

COMMON SEA HERRING, "White bait,". *Clupea harengus* L.; for examination.

JOHN W. TALLMAN, Portsmouth, Rhode Island. 18363. '86. (VII)

FISHING CATAMARAN, full-rigged, native made, from Pernambuco, Brazil, 1883. (Exchange.)

E. B. WEBSTER, paymaster, U. S. Navy. 18364. '86. (II, A)

BIRDS: *Pyrrhula vulgaris, Accentor modularis, Erithacus rubecula, Parus ater, P. cœruleus, P. caudatus, P. major, Linaria chloris, Fringilla montifringilla, Emberiza citrinella, Sturnus vulgaris, Garru'us glandarius, Luscinia philomela, Sylvia cinerea, Muscicapa griseola, Corvus monedula*. (Exchange.)

Dr. W. K. PARKER, London, England. 18365. '86. (XII)

FOSSILS, probably from the latest Cretaceous or Laramie Group.

C. R. BEIDERMAN, Fort Stanton, New Mexico. 18366. '86. (XIII, B)

SILICEOUS LIMESTONE, fine grained, resembling lithographic stone, from waters of Fall Creek, San Saba County, Texas; for examination.

A. R. ROESSLER, Liberty Hill, Texas. 18367. '86. (XVII)

MINERALS (16 specimens). (Exchange.)

THEO. A. KENDALL, Reading, Pennsylvania. 18368. '86. (XVI)

FISHES: *Phycis regius, Decapterus macarellus, Clupea œstivalis, Anguilla rostrata, Fundulus pisculentus, Gadus tomcod, Brevoortia tyrannus, Stolephorus perfasciatus*.

U. S. FISH COMMISSION. (Through Vinal N. Edwards.) 18369. '86. (VII)

MARINE INVERTEBRATES, mostly parasitic copepods and worms.

U. S. FISH COMMISSION. (Through Vinal N. Edwards.) 18369. '86. (XI)

CARDINAL, *Cardinalis cardinalis*.

LOUIS SCHMID & SONS, Washington, District of Columbia. 18370. '86. (V, A)

YOUNG DEER, 3½ months old; fawn of deer; also *Hystrix cristata*.

ZOOLOGICAL SOCIETY OF PHILADELPHIA. (Through Arthur E. Brown, Esq.) 18371. '86. (IV)

CALCITE; for examination.

AMBROSE CONANT, Big Run, Athens County, Ohio. 18372. '86. (XVI)

ANNELID JAWS, found in Cincinnati rock, Lower Silurian, 6 species: *Arabellites quadratus, A. spicatus, A. cornutus, A. lunatus, A. fastigiatus, A. cervicornus*. (Exchange.)

CHARLES SCHUCHERT, Newport, Kentucky. 18373. '86. (XIII, A)

WOOD OPAL, asbestus, and manganese-oxide dendrite.

Miss MARY H. BENNETT, San Bernardino, California. 18374. '86. (XVI)

GRANITE, from Yosemite Valley.

Miss MARY H. BENNETT, San Bernardino, California. 18374. '86. (XVII)

SILVER ORE, chloride, Temescal tin ore, etc.

Miss MARY H. BENNETT, San Bernardino, California. 18374. '86. (XVIII)

FOSSIL.

Miss MARY H. BENNETT, San Bernardino, California. 18374. '86. (XIII, A)

SHELLS, *Vitrina limpida* (53 specimens).

T. F. MORGAN, Garden Cove, St. George Island, Alaska. (Through H. W. Elliott.) 18375. '86. (IX)

TERNS, *Sterna forsteri;* from the Potomac River.

THOMAS MARRON, U. S. National Museum. 18376. '86. (XII)

OWL, *Syrnium nebulosum.*

J. SCHNECK, Mount Carmel, Illinois. 18377. '86. (V, A)

PIKE, *Esox lucius;* pickerel, *Esox americanus.*

FRED. MATHER, Cold Spring Harbor, New York. 18378. '86. (VII)

BIRDS: *Buteo borealis* and *B. lineatus.*

JAMES P. STABLER, Sandy Spring, Maryland. 18379. '86. (V, A)

TURKEY BUZZARD.

JAMES P. STABLER, Sandy Spring, Maryland. 18379. '86. (XII)

KNIVES (2) forged from the first crucible cast-steel made in America by Dr. William Garrard; also wood-cut of the first steel works in America.

JAMES E. EMERSON, Beaver Falls, Pennsylvania. 18380. '86. (XVIII)

CERARGYRITE (2 specimens), from Lake Valley, New Mexico.

Dr. W. P. LAWVER, Washington, District of Columbia. 18381. '86. (XVI)

PHOTOGRAPH of *Tetradon setosus.*

Miss ROSA SMITH, San Diego, California. 18382. '86. (VII)

QUARTZ CRYSTAL; for examination.

CYRIL N. NEWALL, National City, California. 18383. '86. (XVI)

DARTERS: *Etheostoma nianguæ spilotum,* from Kentucky; and *E. cragini,* from Kansas.

C. H. GILBERT, Cincinnati, Ohio. 18384. '86. (VII)

"AMERICAN SOLE," *Achirus mollis;* for examination.

ISAAC C. NORTON, Cottage City, Massachusetts. 18385. '86. (VII)

FOSSIL LAND TORTOISE, *Testudo* sp.; for examination.

S. F. FLEHARTY, Kimball, Cheyenne County, Nebraska. 18386. '86. (VI)

SUNAPEE TROUT,* *Salvelinus agassizii* (8 specimens).

E. B. HODGE, Plymouth, New Hampshire. 18387. '86. (VII)

GARNET FRAGMENT, from Cape Colony, South Africa. (Exchange.)

Dr. C. A. HARVEY, Washington, District of Columbia. 18388. '86. (XVI)

CLAY, and a quartz rock containing pyrite; for examination.

HICKS AND SITGREAVES, Bristol, Tennessee. 18389. '86. (XVIII)

ZINC BLENDE, or sulphide of zinc; for examination.

E. B. HOWARD, Potter, Polk County, Arkansas. 18390. '86. (XVI)

ANCIENT COPPER COINS (78).

General M. C. MEIGS, U. S. Army. 18391. '86. (I)

NAVAJO BABY CRADLE. (Purchased.)

Dr. R. W. SHUFELDT, U. S. Army, Fort Wingate, New Mexico. 18392. '86. (II, A)

FOSSILS, from Greenland.

Lieut. R. E. PEARY, U. S. Navy. 18393. '86. (XIII)

ANTIQUITIES, from France.

THOMAS WILSON, Nice, France. 18394. '86. (III)

RED-TAILED HAWK, *Buteo borealis.*

JAMES P. STABLER, Sandy Spring, Maryland. 18395. '86. (V, A)

---

* See Proceedings U. S. National Museum, vol. 10, p. 628.

ALBINO OPOSSUM, *Didelphys virginiana*. (Purchased.)

GEORGE F. ATKINSON, Chapel Hill, North Carolina. 18396. '86. (IV)

STONE IMAGE OF SEAL, used as a head-scratcher.

E. B. WEBSTER, U. S. Navy. 18397. '86, (II, A)

CLAY, for examination.

C. J. BROWN, Elmira, New York. 18398. '86. (XVI)

OAK LEAVES, sugar-bearing; from California.

LIVINGSTON STONE, Charlestown, New Hampshire. 18399. '86. (I)

AMADREVADE FINCH, *Estrilda amandava* (2 skeletons).

LOUIS SCHMID & SONS, Washington, District of Columbia. 18400. '86. (XII)

BITUMEN; for examination.

W. A. ELLIS, Bailey Springs, Alabama. 18401. '86. (XVIII)

MOUSE, *Arvicola pinetorum*.

Hon. JOHN S. WISE, Richmond, Virginia. 18402. '86. (IV)

LAND AND FRESH-WATER SHELLS (38 specimens) in fine condition; many rare ones. Supplementary to Acc. 18353.

A. G. WETHERBY, Wilders, Mitchell County, North Carolina. 18403. '86. (IX)

COINS, copper, nickel, billon coins and tokens. Ancient Roman (4), Turkey (1), Russia (1), Tunis (1), Switzerland (4), Hindostan (3), Brazil (3), Belgium (1), Portugal (2), German (20), China (1), Great Britain and colonies (66), Spain (2), United States (33), Sardinia (1), France (11).

JOHN MURDOCH, U. S. National Museum. 18404. '86. (I)

INSECTS, *Lepisma domestica;* for examination.

General M. C. MEIGS, U. S. Army, Washington, District of Columbia. 18405. '86. (X)

FRAGMENT OF POTTERY, rim-piece, bearing the marks of the woven basket in which the vessel was moulded.

HENRY P. HAMILTON, Two Rivers, Wisconsin. 18406. '86. (III)

FOSSILIFEROUS LIMESTONE, probably of the Lower Silurian formation.

HENRY P. HAMILTON, Two Rivers, Wisconsin. 18406. '86. (XIII, A)

INSECTS.

JOHN DEAN CATON, Chicago, Illinois. 18407. '86. (X)

SHELLS, *Physa gyrina* Say.; from the Del Monte Lake at Monterey, California. Collected by R. Ulrich.

JOHN DEAN CATON, Chicago, Illinois. 18407. '86. (IX)

CRUSTACEANS, mostly amphipods.

JOHN DEAN CATON, Chicago, Illinois. 18407. '86. (XI)

STONE AX, cast (original returned).

W. H. ABBOTT, Washington, District of Columbia. 18408. '86. (III)

CHILKAHT DRUM and Tinné Indian Snow-shoes. (Exchange.)

E. B. WEBSTER, U. S. Navy. 18409. '86. (II, A)

FISHES: *Tylosurus notatus, Harengula pensacolæ, Acanthurus cœruleus, Pomacanthus aureus, Chilomycterus geometricus, Tetrodon spengleri, Hœmulon arcuatum, Alutera scripta, Arius felis,* and *Ostracion quadricornis;* from Key West, Florida.

L. A. BEARDSLEE, Commander, U. S. Navy. 18410. '86. (VII)

LIMONITE, calcite, and selenite crystals; from Louisiana.

U. S. GEOLOGICAL SURVEY, Washington, District of Columbia. (Through W. H. Dall.) 18411. '86. (XVI)

MORTAR, from the auriferous gravels on the north side of the American River at Folsom, California.

U. S. GEOLOGICAL SURVEY. (Through H. W. Turner.) 18412. '86. (III)

BIRD SKINS. A collection of 40 specimens, 17 species; a valuable addition, adding several new species not hitherto possessed by the Museum, among which is the type of *Picoides albidior* Stejneger; from Kamtschatka.

Dr. L. STEJNEGER, U. S. National Museum. 18413. '86. (V, A)

JAPANESE DOMESTIC ARTICLES:
I. Fire implements. II. Tools and implements. III. Clothing: (1) Articles of clothing; (2) Foot-covering; (3) Head-gear. IV. Ornaments: (1) Articles of ornamentation; (2) Head ornament; (3) Toilet articles. V. Household utensils: (1) Vessels, plates, etc.; implements for cleaning, etc.; (2) Lamps; (3) Personal articles. VI. Writing implements. VII. Powdered-tea service. VIII. Articles in common use by natives of Loo-Choo.

TOKYO LIBRARY AND TOKYO EDUCATIONAL MUSEUM, Tokyo, Japan. 18415. '86. (II, A)

JAPANESE MINERALS:

Calcite.	Galena.	Obsidian.
Native gold.	Cinnabar.	Anthracite.
Semiopal.	Rhodonite.	Brown coal.
Diallage.	Hylite.	Lignite.
Stalactite.	Chromite.	Jasper.
Chrysocolla.	Sphalerite.	Vermiculite.
Garnet.	Arsenopyrite.	Orthoclase.
Cassiterite.	Anhydrite.	Aventurine.
Chrysolite.	Wood opal.	Graphite.
Asbestus.	Tourmaline.	Quartz schist.
Amber.	Wollastonite.	Molybdenite.
Aragonite.	Argenti-bornite.	Fluorite.
Rock crystal.	Stephanite.	Argentite.
Amethyst quartz.	Chalcopyrite.	Pyrolusite.
Smoky quartz.	Pyrrhotite.	Magnetite.
Stibnite.	Actinolite.	Agate.
Agalmatolite.	Marble.	Realgar.
Analcite.	Smithsonite.	Topaz.
Serpentine.	Auriferous quartz.	Calamine.
Asbolite.	Petroleum.	

TOKYO LIBRARY AND TOKYO EDUCATIONAL MUSEUM, Tokyo, Japan. 18415. '86. (XVII)

JAPANESE FISHES:

Synaptura zebra, Bleek. Shimazarei. Tokio Market. (1)

Plagusia japonica, Schleg. (?) Ushinoshita. Tomo. Bingo. (1)

Dactylopterus orientalis, C. and V. Semihoto. T. M. (1)

Priacanthus japonicus, C. and V. Kintarodai. T. M. (1)

Chrysophrys hasta, Bleek. Kurodai. T. M. (2)

Serranus brunneus, Bloch. Fuko. T.M. (1)

Serranus tsirimenara, Schleg. Akahata. T. M. (1)

Anthias japonicus, Doderl. Alkahata. T. M. (1)

Prionurus scalprum, Langsd. Nissadai. T. M. (1)

Lepidotrigla microptera, Gthr. Kanagashira. T. M. (1)

Anoplus banjos, Richards. T. M. (1)

Pelor aurantiacum, Schleg. Akaokoze. T. M. (1)

Tetrodon lunaris, Bleek. Ginfugu. T. M. (1)

Sebastes ventricosus, Schleg. Kurowaka. T. M. (1)

Anthias margaritacus, Hilgd. Sakuradai. T. M. (1)

Dictyosoma Temminckii, Bleek. Dainanzimpo. T. M. (1)

Parophrys cornuta, Schleg. Meitakarei. T. M. (1)

Polymixia japonica, Gthr. Gimme. T. M. (1)

Upeneoides bensasi, Bleek. Benisashi. T. M. (2)

Platyglossus pœcilopterus, Schleg. Awobera. T. M. (1)

P. pynogrammus, Schleg. A k a b e r a. Boshiu. (2)

Centronotus nebulosis, Schleg. Gimpo. Boshiu. (1)

Monacanthus setifer, Benn. M a h a g i. Boshiu. (1)

JAPANESE FISHES—Continued.

Pseudorhombus cinnamoneus, Schleg. Gan-zōhirame. Boshiu. (2)

Platycephalus rudis, Gthr. Kochi. Boshiu. (2)

Serranus mystacinus, Poey. Uata. Boshiu. (1)

Ostracion cubicus, Linn. H a k o f u g u. Boshiu. (1)

Beryx splendens, Lowe. Kimmedia. T. M. (1)

Chilomycterus tigrinus, Cuv. Hishifugu. T. M. (1)

Sillago japonica, Schleg. Kisu. T.M. (2)

Gobius flavimanus, Schleg. Haze. T. M. (2)

Clupea zunasi, Bleek. Zunashi. T. M. (2)

Ditrema Temminckii, Bleek. Umitanago. T. M. (1)

Chatœssus punctatus, Schleg. Konoshiro. T. M. (1)

Barus Schlegelii, Gthr. Sai. T. M. (I)

Percalabrax japonicus, C. and V. Suzuki. T. M. (1)

Caranx muroadsi, Schleg. Muroaji. T. M. (2)

Sphyrœna obtusata, C. and V. Kamasu. T. M. (1)

Cestracion philippii, Bleek. Nekosame. T. M. (1)

Seriola Dumerilii, Risso. Shio or Gam-pachi. T. M. (1)

Magaperca ischinagi, Hilza. Ishinagi. T. M. (1)

Girella punctata, Gray. Mejinadi. T. M. (1)

Sebastes marmoratus, Cuv. and Val. Ka-sago. T. M. (1)

Echeneis naucrates, Linn. Kobanitadaki. T. M. (1)

Tetrodon rubripes, Schleg. Mafugu. T. M. (1)

Platycephalus insidiator, Forok. Kochi. T. M. (1)

Congromurœna anago, Schleg. Anago. T. M. (2)

Misgurnus anguillcaudatus, Canton. Dojo. T. M. (2)

Uranoscopus asper, Schleg. Temmondaio-koze. T. M. (1)

Centropristis hirundinaceus, C. and V. Ki-toji. Ajiral. (2)

Zeus nebulosus, Schleg. Kagamidai. Ajiro. (1)

Peristethus orientalis, Schleg. Kihōbō. Ajira. (1)

Halieutœa stellata, Wahl. Iroankō. Ajiro. (1)

Leuciscus hakuensis, Charl. A k a h a r a. Ajiro. (1)

Opsariichthys Temminckii, Schleg. Iwana. Chicibu. Musashi. (2)

Opsariichthys platypus, Schleg. Oikawa. Chichibu. Musashi. (2)

Gasterosteus noveboracensis, C. and V. Ito-riwo. Niigata. Echigo. (2)

Monocentris japonicus, Houtt. Matsuga-sauwo. T. M. (1)

Pagrus cardinalis, C. and V. Casukodai. T. M. (1)

Caranx hippos, Linn. Kishimaji. T. M. (1)

Cybium niphonium, C. and V. Sawara. Niigata. Echigo. (1)

TOKYO LIBRARY AND TOKYO EDUCATIONAL MUSEUM, Tokyo, Japan. 18415. '86. (VII)

MARBLE (16 specimens).

TOKYO LIBRARY AND TOKYO EDUCATIONAL MUSEUM, Tokyo, Japan. 18415. '86? (XVII)

BIRDS-KINS.

J. W. JOHNSON, Port Huron, Alaska. 18416. '86. (V, A)

ETHNOLOGICAL OBJECTS.*

J. W. JOHNSON, Port Huron, Alaska. 18416. '86. (II, A)

PLANTS, a finely preserved and interesting collection.

J. W. JOHNSON, Port Huron, Alaska. 18416, '86. (XV)

BIRDS' EGGS, *Calcarius lapponicus.* (Destroyed.)

J. W. JOHNSON, Port Huron, Alaska. 18416. '86. (V, B)

MUSICAL INSTRUMENTS (3).

J. W. JOHNSON, Port Huron, Alaska. 18416. '86. (I)

BIRD-SKINS.

HENRY D. WOOLFE, Cape Lisburne, Alaska. 18417. '86. (V, A)

* See Report on Department of Ethnology, Section II.

FISHES, *Ammodytes personatus.*
    HENRY D. WOOLFE, Cape Lisburne, Alaska. 18417. '86. (VII)
SHELLS: *Acmæa testudinalis* L. (2 specimens), *Velutina coriacea* Pall. (6 specimens).
    HENRY D. WOOLFE, Cape Lisburne, Alaska. 18417. '86. (IX)
INSECTS.
    HENRY D. WOOLFE, Cape Lisburne, Alaska. 18417. '86. (X)
JASPER PEBBLE (2 fragments).
    HENRY D. WOOLFE, Cape Lisburne, Alaska. 18417. '86. (XVI)
BONES.
    HENRY D. WOOLFE, Cape Lisburne, Alaska. 18417. '86. (XII)
COAL.
    HENRY D. WOOLFE, Cape Lisburne, Alaska. 18417. '86. (XVIII)
BIRDS' EGGS: *Grus canadensis, Branta canadensis hutchinsii, Uria lomvia arra, Dafila acuta, Lagopus lagopus, Oidemia americana, Larus brachyrynchus, Rissa tridactyla pollicaris, Stercorarius pomarhinus* (40 specimens, 9 species).
    HENRY D. WOOLFE, Cape Lisburne, Alaska. 18417. '86. (V, B)
MARINE INVERTEBRATES: Miscellaneous collection of crustaceans, echinoderms, actinians, ascidians, etc.
    HENRY D. WOOLFE, Cape Lisburne, Alaska. 18417. '86. (XI)
WHITE EARTH used as food by natives, and bark used as a dye.
    HENRY D. WOOLFE, Cape Lisburne, Alaska. 18417. '86. (I)
GRAY WHALE, *Rhachianectes glaucus* (skull).
    ALASKA COMMERCIAL COMPANY, San Francisco, California. 18418. '86. (XII)
VEGETABLE OF ABNORMAL GROWTH.
J. W. C. SMITH, Benton, Mississippi, 18419. '86. (I)
HAWAIIAN BATS (2), *Atalapha cinereus* (variety).
    VALDEMAR KNUDSEN, Kekaha, Waiawa Kawai, Hawaiian Islands. 18420. '86. (IV)
BIRD-SKINS, 37 specimens, 16 species, most of which are new to the collection, while no less than five are new to science, and will be described as *Himantopus knudseni, Chasiempis dolei, Phæornis myadestina, Himatione parva,* and *Oreomyza bairdi,* the latter being the type of a new genus.
    VALDEMAR KNUDSEN, Kekaha, Hawaiian Islands, 18420. '86. (V, A)
CRUSTACEA, small alcoholic collection; also one species of *Echini.*
    VALDEMAR KNUDSEN, Kekaha, Hawaiian Islands. 18420. '86. (XI)
SHELLS, dry and alcoholic.
    VALDEMAR KNUDSEN, Kekaha, Hawaiian Islands. 18420. '86. (IX)
HAWAIIAN BAT, *Atalapha cinerea* (variety).
    CHARLES N. SPENCER, Kau, Hawaii. (Through F. P. Hastings, vice and deputy consul-general, Honolulu, Hawaiian Islands.) 18421. '86. (IV)
BANDED SEA SNAKE, *Platurus fasciatus* (skeleton).
    J. W. SCOLLICK, U. S. National Museum. 18422. '86. (XII)
INTESTINAL WORMS, from viscera of *Gymnotus amazon.*
    S. E. MEEK, Fulton Market, New York City. 18423. '86. (XII)
CLAMS or Quahaugs, *Venus mercenaria* (shells).
    HENRY G. FITZ, Peconic, Long Island, New York. 18424. '86. (XI)
BIRD-SKINS, 5 specimens, 5 species; from San Angelo, Texas.
    WILLIAM LLOYD, Paint Rock, Concho County, Texas. 18425. '86. (V, A)
APATITE; for examination.
    GEORGE W. WATKINS, Moriah, New York. 18426. '86. (XVI)
INSECTS: *Dynastes tityus, Prionotus cristatus,* and pupa of *Sphinx carolina.*
    JOHN M. DAVIS, president Eastern Mississippi College, Sylvarena, Smith County, Mississippi. 18427. '86. (X)
WAX IMPRESSION of the seal of the Foreign Office, Vienna, Austria; original copy of No. 1 of the Dresden Weekly Anzeiger, in September, 1730.
    GEORGE H. BOEHMER, Smithsonian Institution. 18428. '86. (I)

REDBREAST, *Erythacus rubecula* (skeleton).

LOUIS SCHMID & SONS, Washington, District of Columbia. 18429. '86. (XII)

BILL OF EXCHANGE, first and second, for £100 sterling, dated Norfolk, February 6, 1819, drawn on bankers at Liverpool, England, and protest of same.

THOMAS MARRON, U. S. National Museum. 18430. '86. (I)

SHELLS: *Helix subrupicola*, from Clinton's Cave, Utah.

Dr. A. S. PACKARD, Jr., Brown University, Providence, Rhode Island. 18431. '86. (IX)

REPTILE, from British Guiana.

OTTO LUGGER, Baltimore, Maryland. 18432. '86. (VI)

FLINT FISH-HOOK (fragment); for examination.

W. W. ADAMS, Mapleton, New York. 18433. '86. (III)

METEORIC IRON: Slab weighing 850 grammes; from Toluca, Mexico. (Exchange.)

WARD AND HOWELL, Rochester, New York. 18434. '86. (XVI)

BLACK GUILLEMOT, *Cepphus grylle*, downy young; from Green Isle, Maine.

E. C. GREENWOOD, Ipswich, Massachusetts. 18435. '86. (V, A)

FOSSIL BONES of *Zeuglodon cetoides;* from Shubuta, Clark County, Mississippi.

U. S. GEOLOGICAL SURVEY. (Through W. H. Dall.) 18436. '86. (XII)

FOSSIL WOOD, from California and South Carolina.

U. S. GEOLOGICAL SURVEY. (Through W. H. Dall.) 18436. '86. (XIV)

HAWAIIAN BAT, *Atalapha cinerea* (variety); from Sandwich Islands.

VALDEMAR KNUDSEN, Hotel Bellevue, Boston, Massachusetts. 18437. '86. (IV)

CATLINITE PIPE, Kansas War Hatchet, and Pawnee War Club. (Deposited.)

Rev. J. O. DORSEY, Washington, District of Columbia. 18438. '86. (II, A)

ETHNOLOGICAL OBJECTS: Winnebago dolls, Omaha moccasins. (Deposited.) Toy cradle, Nattuetunne Indians, Oregon. (Exchange.)

Mrs. J. O. DORSEY, Washington, District of Columbia. 18439. '86. (II, A)

FOSSILS: 31 specimens of *Nothozoa Vermontana,* 3 specimens of *Olenellus,* from the Middle Cambrian, Salisbury, Vermont. This collection is of special interest, owing to the specimens being from the quartz rock re-referred to the base of the Taconic system of Emmons.

Prof. HENRY M. SEELEY, Middlebury, Vermont. (Through C. D. Walcott.) 18440. '86. (XIII, A)

LEGAL PAPERS relating to claims on U. S. mineral lands; power of attorney (*de facto*) given in Germany to be used in the United States; Canadian, South American, and European revenue and postage stamps (38).

PAUL BECKWITH, U. S. National Museum. 18441. '86. (I)

COINS in silver, nickel, and copper; from Germany, France, Switzerland, Ceylon, etc. (Deposited.)

FREDERICK W. TRUE, U. S. National Museum. 18442. '86. (I)

PIG-SKIN TRUNKS (3), from Fuchow, China.

(Donor Unknown.) 18443. '86. (II, A)

KANGAROO RAT, *Dipodomys deserti* (type), from Mohave River, California.

F. STEPHENS, San Bernardino, California. 18444. '86. (IV)

ARCHÆOLOGICAL OBJECTS: eighteen flakes of flint, jasper, etc., a scraper, a hammer-stone, four polished celts, an unfinished celt, a broken celt, fourteen shell beads, twenty-one fragments of pottery, and eleven fragments of human bones.

J. I. LENGSFIELD, Greenville, Mississippi. 18445. '86. (III)

BIRDS, from Japan.

Prof. R. COLLETT, Christiania, Norway. 18446. '86. (V, A)

SEEDS of *Victoria regia.*

Prof. W. T. THISELTON-DYER, Kew Gardens, London, England. 18447. '86. (Carp pond.)

COPPER "CROWN," found in a grave; for examination. (Returned.)

Miss HELEN HOBBS, Little Rock, Arkansas. 18448. '86. (III)

WORK of *Calotermes* sp.; for examination.

JOHN C. WHITE, Bisbee, Arizona. 18449. '86. (X)

CARVED STONE IMAGE. (Returned.)

JOHN M. PARK, Dallas, Texas. 18450. '86. (II, A)

FIBROUS SERPENTINE in matrix; for examination.

JOHN COLE, Cedar Point, Page County, Virginia. 18451. '86. (XVIII)

BIRDS, twelve species, nineteen specimens, from District of Columbia.

H. W. HENSHAW, Washington, District of Columbia. 18452. '86. (V, A)

SILVER AND COPPER COINS of Great Britain, and of Switzerland.

W. V. COX, U. S. National Museum. 18453. '86. (I)

QUARTZ and chloritic material; for examination.

Dr. A. W. LAKIN, Boonesborough, Washington County, Maryland. 18454. '86. (XVIII)

COINS: A collection of four hundred and fifteen varieties of United States cents dating from 1793 to 1886. Also twelve specimens of metallic store cards, political medals, mint tokens, and continental state coins, Cape diamonds, explosive bullet, and musket-flints.

Dr. I. E. NAGLE, Mount Joy, Pennsylvania. 18455. '86. (I)

FOSSIL SHELLS.

Dr. I. E. NAGLE, Mount Joy, Pennsylvania. 18455. '86. (XIII, B)

STONE IMPLEMENT, found in an ancient camp of Indians, near Round Head, Hardin County, Ohio; also four arrow-heads from various localities.

Dr. I. E. NAGLE, Mount Joy, Pennsylvania. 18455. '86. (III)

PAPER CURRENCY: Ten centavos of the Bank of Spain, Havana, Cuba.

Miss C. C. CURRY, care of Paul Beckwith, U. S. National Museum. 18456. '86. (I)

SHELLS, from Upper Tennessee River.

Dr. J. C. McCORMICK, Strawberry Plains, Tennessee. 18457. '86. (IX)

HARBOR SEAL, *Phoca vitulina*.

U. S. FISH COMMISSION. 18458. '86. (IV)

SKULLS of *Sorex Haydeni* (10), *Arivicola riparius* (3).

Dr. J. C. MERRILL, U. S. Army, Fort Klamath, Oregon. 18459. '86. (XII)

SKINS of *Arivicola riparius* (1), and *Hesperomys leucopus* (1).

Dr. J. C. MERRILL, U. S. Army, Fort Klamath, Oregon. 18459. '86. (IV)

METEORIC IRON (three specimens); troilite from the "Cranbourne meteorite," meteoric stone (three fragments), and a slice of iron and stone meteorite. (Exchange.)

BRITISH MUSEUM, London, England. 18460. '86. (XVI)

LONG PRIMER TYPE (20 pounds), and iron chase, 12 by 19.

H. L. PELOUZE & SON, Washington, District of Columbia. 18461. '86. (I)

"FASTEN PRETZELN," from St. Petersburg, Russia.

GEORGE H. BOEHMER, Smithsonian Institution. 18462. '86. (I)

MINERALS, for analysis.

E. REMUS, Ravenna, Los Angeles County, California. 18463. '86. (XVI)

VENETIAN BEADS, of glass and enamel, for examination. (Returned.)

Mrs. W. B. POWELL, Natchitoches, Louisiana. 18464. '86. (III)

QUARTZ (33 specimens). (Exchange.)

F. P. GREAVES, Bonne Terre, Missouri. 18465. '86. (XVI)

DENTIGEROUS BONE (? pharyngeal) of fossil fish, probably Ganoid.

Dr. H. H. THORPE, Liberty Hill, Texas. 18466. '86. (VII)

DEPOSIT of impure carbonate of lime, from a spring or stream.

Dr. H. H. THORPE, Liberty Hill, Texas. 18466. '86. (XVII)

ARROW-HEADS, 2 spear-heads, and 2 fragments of spear-heads.

Dr. H. H. THORPE, Liberty Hill, Texas. 18466. '86. (III)

APATITE, from Bedford, Canada, and pyrophyllite from Chesterfield County, South Carolina.

W. S. YEATES, U. S. National Museum. 18467. '86. (XVI)

LAND SHELLS; for examination.

> Dr. V. STERKI, New Philadelphia, Ohio. 18468. '86. (IX)

HALF-PENNY of George II, Great Britain, 1740.

> WILLIAM MERO, Alexandria, Virginia. 18469. '86. (I)

COIN, silver three-cent piece of 1853, United States.

> SAMUEL BOND, U. S. National Museum. 18470. '86. (I)

IRON ORE, from Cranberry Lake, New York.

> Hon. JOHN S. NEGLEY, Washington, District of Columbia. 18471. '86. (XVIII)

CUBAN BOA, *Epicrates angulifer;* for identification.

> E. P. ALEXANDER, Savannah, Georgia. 18472. '86. (VI)

COMPOUND NEST of *Agelæus phœniceus* and *Cistothorus palustris,* both occupied at the same time. Also double nest of *Dendroica æstiva,* from Flushing, Long Island.

> DANIEL C. BEARD, New York City. 18473. '86. (V, B)

LOG of the steamship *Savannah,* the first steam-vessel to cross the Atlantic, Moses Rogers, master.

> Mrs. SARAH A. WARD. (Through Col. F. A. Seely, U. S. Patent Office.) 18474. '86. (II, A)

ROCKS, from Missouri. (Exchange.)

> Prof. E. HAWORTH, Oskaloosa, Iowa. 18475. '86. (XVII)

CALCITE, millerite in quartz, micaceous hematite, wolframite (?), and mica in quartz.

> Prof. E. HAWORTH, Oskaloosa, Iowa. 18475. '86. (XVI)

JANUARY, 1887.

HARBOR SEAL, *Phoca vitulina,* taken at Wood's Holl, Massachusetts.

> U. S. FISH COMMISSION. (Through Vinal N. Edwards.) 18476. '87. (IV)

PORPOISE, *Delphinus delphis* (skull), from Cobb's Island, Virginia.

> GEORGE H. BOEHMER, Smithsonian Institution. 18477. '87. (XII)

ARACHNIDES and myriapods, from the sources of the Usumasinta River, Mexico.

> RICHARD W. WALKER, Guatemala City, Central America. 18478. '87. (X)

POLISHED CROCIDOLITE, in quartz. (Exchange.)

> AMERICAN MUSEUM OF NATURAL HISTORY, New York City. 18479. '87. (XVI)

BOOK: "The elements of the common lawes of England containing some principal rules and maxims of the common lawes of England," by Francis Bacon, 1630.

> GEORGE B. HARDY, St. Charles Hotel, District of Columbia. 18480 '87. (I)

QUARTZ CRYSTAL, found at the base of the Sierra Madre, Mexico; for examination.

> A. S. WERTHEIM, Comfort, Kendall County, Texas. 18481. '87. (XVI)

QUARTZ CRYSTAL, supposed to be diamond. (Returned.)

> S. J. WATTS, Corbin, Kentucky. 18482. '87. (XVIII)

OIL PAINTING of four horses drawing a wagon, by De Pratére, of Brussels. (Deposited.)

> Mrs. MARY F. HENDERSON, 3010 Pine street, St. Louis, Missouri. 18483 '87. (II, A)

FISHES, from Ozark regions in southern Missouri.

> R. ELLSWORTH CALL, Columbia, Missouri. 18484. '87. (VII)

CAMCARUS (five specimens), from Bear Creek, Missouri.

> R. ELLSWORTH CALL, Columbia, Missouri. 18484. '87. (XI)

REPTILES, *Sceloporus undulatus* and *Tropidonotus sipidon* (7 specimens).

> R. ELLSWORTH CALL, Columbia, Missouri. 18484. '87. (XI)

KYAK (complete), from Godhaven, Greenland.

> Lieut. R. E. PEARY, U. S. Navy. 18485. '87. (II, A)

ETRUSCAN POTTERY, arrow-head, and Indian pipe; for examination. (Pottery and pipe returned.)

> F. T. BESSAC, Natchez, Mississippi. 18486. '87. (II, B)

BIRD-SKIN, *Accipiter fuscus,* juv.

> JAMES E. BENEDICT, St. Paul, Minnesota. 18487. '87. (V, A)

GOPHER, *Geomys bursarius*, and 13-lined Sphermophile, *Sphermophilus* 13-*lineatus* (skins).

> JAMES E. BENEDICT, St. Paul, Minnesota. 18487. '87. (IV)

GOPHER, *Geomys bursarius*, and 13-lined Sphermophile, *Sphermophilus* 13-*lineatus* (skulls).

> JAMES E. BENEDICT, St. Paul, Minnesota. 18487. '87. (XII)

CORALS; 28 lots of specimens. (Exchange.)

> OBERLIN COLLEGE, Oberlin, Ohio. 18488. '87. (XI)

WATER BUG, *Belostoma americana;* for examination.

> C. R. MOORE, Bias, West Virginia. 18489. '87. (X)

ETHNOLOGICAL OBJECTS:* Stone axes, stone scrapers, stone knives, stone pigulkis, spear-heads, bone spear, 2 spokeshaves, 1 polisher, fire-making implement, wooden mask, bone wand, rattle, shaman's cap, shaman's whistle, bone fish-hooks, tobacco-box, snow knives, ivory carvings, stone ear-ring, comb, mortars and pestles, etc. (175 specimens.)

> WILLIAM J. FISHER, Kodiak, Alaska. 18490. '87. (II, A)

BIRD-SKINS, from Alaska.

> Lieut. G. M. STONEY, U. S. Navy. 18491. '87. (V, A)

FISHES: *Cottus quadricornis, Lota maculosa, Oncorhynchus keta, O. gorbuscha, Coregonus kennicotti, C. tullibee, C. quadrilateralis, C. nelsoni,* and *merki* subsp., *Salvelinus namaycush, S. malma, Thymallus signifer, Stenodus mackenzii, Hypomesus olidus, Esox lucius,* and *Dallia pectoralis;* from Kowak River, Alaska.

> Lieut. G. M. STONEY, U. S. Navy. 18491. '87. (VII)

ETHNOLOGICAL OBJECTS,† from Alaska.

> Lieut. G. M. STONEY, U. S. Navy. 18491. '87. (II, A)

FROG, *Rana cantabrigensis* (3 specimens); from Fort Cosmos, Alaska.

> Lieut. G. M. STONEY, U. S. Navy. 18491. '87. (VI)

MAMMALS, from Alaska.

> Lieut. G. M. STONEY, U. S. Navy. 18491. '87. (IV)

INSECTS,‡ from Alaska.

> Lieut. G. M. STONEY, U. S. Navy. 18491. '87. (X)

PLANTS; a good collection of common northern species.

> Lieut. G. M. STONEY, U. S. Navy. 18491. '87. (XV)

BIRDS' EGGS:

Hesperocichla nævia.	*Clangula hyemalis.*
Turdus aliciæ.	*Larus brachyrhynchus.*
Dendroica striata.	*Branta canadensis minima.*
Seiurus noveboracensis notabilis.	*Dafila acuta.*
Grus canadensis.	*Olor columbianus.*
Sterna paradisea.	*Urinator pacificus.*

From Alaska.

> Lieut. G. M. STONEY, U. S. Navy. 18491. '87. (V, B)

ROCKS, from Alaska.

> Lieut. G. M. STONEY, U. S. Navy. 18491. '87. (XVII)

PHOTOGRAPHS (5) of antiquities in the Museum at Cartago, Costa Rica.

> ANASTASIO ALFARO, Cartago, Costa Rica. 18492. '87. (III)

LAND SHELLS, 5 species; from Atilla, Honduras. (Supplementary to accession 18181.) Named by C. F. Ancey, and used as types in one of his publications.

> CHARLES T. SIMPSON, Ogallala, Nebraska. 18493. '87. (IX)

MONKEY, *Brachyurus rubicundus,* from South America.

> ZOOLOGICAL SOCIETY OF PHILADELPHIA. (Through Arthur E. Brown, Esq.) 18494. '87. (IV)

---

* See Report on Department of Ethnology, Section II.
† See Report on Department of Ethnology, Section II.
‡ See Report on Department of Insects, Section II.

MYRIAPODS.

L. M. UNDERWOOD, Syracuse, New York. 18495. '87. (x)

COPPER ORNAMENT, crescent shape; for examination.` (Returned.)

J. D. McGUIRE, Ellicott City, Maryland, 18496. '87. (III)

HAIR BALL, found in the stomach of a Texas steer slaughtered at Laredo, on the Rio Grande, 1878.

DANIEL RUGGLES, Fredericksburgh, Virginia. 18497. '87. (IV)

CONTINENTAL PAPER CURRENCY; Confederate States Government and State notes and fractional currency; local postage-stamps; Virginia State tax return, dated 1788; sheriff's warrants dated 1813; Poughkeepsie Bank paper currency 1862; piece of Fort Sumter flag-staff at time of surrender, 1861.

JAMES D. MARTIN, Willard's Hotel, District of Columbia. 18498. '87. (I)

COINS and tokens in copper, bronze, etc., from England, Canada, Switzerland, France, Connecticut, colonial Mexico, Venezuela, Peru, Jamaica, India, British Guiana, Austria, Spain, Prussia, Buenos Ayres, Caracas, Chili, Brazil, Baden, Holland, Saxony, Hayti, Hanover, Bremen, Denmark, German States, United States Mint token, and 53 metallic store cards. (116 specimens.)

HENRY E. HUBER, Baltimore, Maryland. 18499. '87. (I)

MODEL of restoration of Pueblo Bonito by W. H. Jackson. Modelled by W. H. Hoffman.

BUREAU OF ETHNOLOGY, Washington, District of Columbia. 18500. '87. (II, A)

JAPANESE HERALDIC DEVICES (one volume) and five volumes of Japanese designs.

Dr. D. Bethune McCARTEE, Washington. 18501. '87. (II, A)

DEWEYLITE, from Ashe County, North Carolina.

Dr. C. A. HARVEY, Washington, District of Columbia. 18502. '87. (XVI)

GROUSE and Pheasant (skins).

W. B. MALLEIS, Portland, Oregon. 18503. '87. (V, A)

LIVE SEAL, from Wood's Holl, Massachusetts. Sent to Zoological Garden, Philadelphia.

U. S. FISH COMMISSION. (Through Vinal N. Edwards.) 18504. '87.

INSECTS; for examination. (Returned.)

Prof. G. F. ATKINSON, Chapel Hill, North Carolina. 18505. '87. (x)

LEPIDOPTERA, from Adirondack Mountains, New York, part for determination and 78 specimens for the Museum collection; for examination.

Dr. C. S. McKNIGHT, Saratoga, New York. 18506. '87. (x)

INSECTS: *Smerinthus paddidulus*, *Pamphila* sp., *Geometer* sp.

W. N. TALLANT, Columbus, Ohio. 18507. '87. (x)

MINERALS (99 specimens); from Norway, France, Italy, Germany, and Switzerland. (Exchange.)

Dr. T. SCHUCHARDT, Gorlitz, Germany. 18508. '87. (XVI)

PILEATED WOODPECKER, *Hylotomus pileatus* (skeletons); from Buck Valley, Pennsylvania.

WILLARD NYE, Jr., New Bedford, Massachusetts. 18509. '87. (XII)

INSECTS, 40 specimens, 27 species, largely new to the collections, and containing two types.

JAMES FLETCHER, Ottawa, Canada. 18510. '87. (x)

SILVER COIN, five-franc, Emperor Napoleon, 1811.

HARRY P. GODWIN, "Evening Star" Office, Washington, District of Columbia. 18511. '87. (I)

COIN, Irish half-penny of George III, 1805.

HENRY HORAN, U. S. National Museum. 18512. '87. (I)

COINS: Copper cent, 1827, United States; copper half-penny, 1843, New Brunswick, and metallic store card of the Joint Stock Company, New York. Also canceled coupon of bond, Republic of Peru.

AUGUSTUS W. MARRON, Washington, District of Columbia. 18513. '87. (I)

MEDALS: Silver mortuary medal of Nicolas, Czar of Russia, 1855, and a miniature copy in silver of the royal Prussian life-saving medal.

GEORGE H. BOEHMER, Smithsonian Institution. 18514. '87. (I)

MINERALS: Cut moonstone, from Virginia; cut sapphire, from Montana; cut sapphire, from North Carolina; two cut sapphires, from Ceylon; and two cut zircons, from Ceylon.

C. S. BEMENT, Philadelphia, Pennsylvania. 18515. '87. (XVI)

SOUTH AMERICAN DEER, *Cariacus gymnotis*.

ZOOLOGICAL SOCIETY OF PHILADELPHIA. (Through Arthur E. Brown, Esq.) 18516. '87. (IV)

GLAUCOPHAN SCHIST, from near Hermopolis, Isle of Syra.

J. S. DILLER, U. S. Geological Survey. 18517. '87. (XVII)

BIRD, *Jynx torquilla*, from Japan.

P. L. JOUY, Washington, District of Columbia. 18518. '87. (V, A)

FRESH-WATER SHELLS (5 species), from Texas, Iowa, and Illinois.

HARRY E. PILSBRY, Davenport, Iowa. 18519. '87. (IX)

BERYL (silicate of glucina), from a mica mine near New Milford, Connecticut; for examination.

Mrs. MARION B. SPOONER, New York City. 18520. '87. (XVIII)

GRASS PAROQUET, *Melopsittacus undulatus*.

LOUIS SCHMID & SONS, Washington, District of Columbia. 18521. '87. (V, A)

BREWER'S BLACKBIRD, *Scolecophagus cyanocephalus*.

LEVERETT M. LOOMIS, Chester, South Carolina. 18522. '87. (V, A)

COMMON GRAY SQUIRREL, *Sciurus carolinensis*, from Arlington, Virginia.

WILLIAM PALMER, U. S. National Museum. 18523. '87. (XII)

EUROPEAN FERRET, *Putorius fœtidus* (2 specimens).

C. CURTICE, Department of Agriculture. 18524. '87. (IV)

BIRDS, 14 species, 14 specimens, from various localities.

HENRY K. COALE, Chicago, Illinois. 18525. '87. (V, A)

BIRDS, 4 species, 5 specimens, from Europe.

Dr. L. STEJNEGER, U. S. National Museum. 18526. '87. (V, A)

STONE RELICS: Rude chipped implement, 2 spear-heads, 2 arrow-heads, a chisel, polished celt, discoidal stone, grooved hematite sinker, fragment of a pierced tablet, small clay pipe, fragment of pottery, and necklace of bone and shell beads, animal teeth, etc. (13 specimens).

L. W. BROWN, Redstone, Pennsylvania. 18527. '87. (III)

GRANT RELICS: A collection of objects presented to General U. S. Grant by various Governments.

Aerolite, part of which passed over Mexico in 1871.

Arabian Bible.

Silver menu and card, farewell dinner at San Francisco, California.

Silver menu of Paris dinner.

Horn and silver snuff-box.

Gold table, modeled after the table in Mr. McLean's house on which General R. E. Lee signed the articles of surrender. This was presented to General Grant by ex-Confederate soldiers.

Gold cigar-case (plain), presented by the Second King of Siam.

Silver trowel used by General Grant in laying the corner-stone of the American Museum of Natural History, New York.

Field-glasses used by General Grant during the war.

Medal from the United States Congress (gold) for opening the Mississippi.

Forty-five medals (gold, silver, and bronze), badges of armies and corps.

Silk paper (Louisville Commercial) printed for General Grant.

Silk paper (Daily Chronicle) printed for General Grant.

Silk paper (Burlington Hawkeye) printed for General Grant.

GRANT RELICS—Continued.

Collection of Japanese coins.*

Commission, brevet first lieutenant.

Commission as first lieutenant, U. S. Army.

Commission of brevet captain, U. S. Army.

Commission of captain, U. S. Army.

Commission as colonel of volunteers.

Commission as brigadier-general.

Commission as major-general.

Commission as major-general, U. S. Army.

Commission as lieutenant-general, U. S. Army.

Commission as general, U. S. Army.

Commission as member of Sacramento Society of Pioneers.

Commission as honorary member Royal Historical Society.

Commission as member of military order of Loyal Legion.

Commission as member of the Aztec Club.

Certificate of election President of the United States.

Certificate of honorary membership Territorial Pioneers of California.

Certificate of honorary membership St. Andrew's Society.

Certificate of election to the degree of Doctor of Laws by Harvard College.

Certificate of election honorary membership of the Sacramento Society.

Certificate of election honorary member Mercantile Library, San Francisco.

Freedom of the city of Dublin, Ireland.

Freedom of the city of Stratford-on-Avon.

Freedom of the city of London, England.

Freedom of the city of Glasgow, Scotland.

Freedom of the city of Edinburgh, Scotland.

Freedom of the city of Ayr, Scotland.

Freedom of the burg of Inverness, Scotland.

Freedom of the city of Oakland, California.

Freedom of the city of Londonderry, Ireland.

Address to General Grant from the Chamber of Commerce, Newcastle-upon-Tyne, 1877.

Address to General Grant from the mayor, aldermen, and citizens of the city of Manchester, England, May 13, 1877.

Address to General Grant by the workingmen of Birmingham, England, October 16, 1877.

Address to General Grant from the Chamber of Commerce and Board of Trade, San Francisco, California, September, 1879.

Address to General Grant by the mayor, aldermen, and burgesses of the borough of Gateshead, England.

Address to General Grant by the mayor, aldermen, magistrates, and councilors of the borough of Leicester, England.

Address to General Grant by the Americans of Shanghai, China, May 19, 1879.

Address to General Grant by the Calumet Club of Chicago, Illinois.

Address to General Grant by the Society of Friends in Great Britain.

Address to General Grant from Chamber of Commerce of Penang.

Address to General Grant by the mayor, aldermen, and burgesses of the borough of Southampton, England.

Address to General Grant by the provost, magistrates, and town council of the royal borough of Stirling.

Address to General Grant by the mayor, aldermen, and burgesses of Tynemouth, England.

---

* This is the only complete set except that which is in the Japanese treasury. Seven of these pieces cost $5,000. This set was presented by the Government of Japan.

GRANT RELICS—Continued.

Address to General Grant by the mayor and town council of Sunderland.

Address to General Grant by the trade and friendly societies of Sunderland.

Address to General Grant by the public schools of Louisville, Kentucky.

Address to General Grant by the colored men of Louisville, Kentucky.

Address to General Grant by ex-Confederate soldiers.

Address to General Grant by the State of Louisiana.

Address to General Grant by the British workmen of London, England.

Address to General Grant by the North Shields Ship-Owners' Society, England.

Address to General Grant by the Chamber of Commerce, Sheffield, England.

Address to General Grant from the mayor, aldermen, and burgesses of the borough of Leamington Spa, England.

Address to General Grant by the mayor, aldermen, and burgesses of Sheffield, England.

Address to General Grant by the wardens, etc., and commonalty of the town of Sheffield, England.

Address to General Grant from the provost, magistrates, and town council of the city and royal burg of Elgin, Scotland.

Address to General Grant from the mayor, aldermen, and burgesses of the borough of Folkestone, England.

Address to General Grant by the mayor, aldermen, and burgesses of the borough of Jarrow, England.

Resolutions of the Territorial Pioneers admitting General Grant to membership.

Resolutions of the citizens of Jo Daviess County, Illinois, presenting a sword to General Grant (sword of Chattanooga).

First resolution of thanks of the Congress of the United States.

First resolutions inviting General Grant to visit the house of representatives of the Commonwealth of Pennsylvania.

Second resolution of thanks from the Congress of the United States.

Letter from citizens of Jersey City, thanking General Grant for his Des Moines, Iowa, speech on the question of public schools.

Presentation of a silver medal, by the Union League Club of Philadelphia, for gallantry and distinguished services.

Address, Chinese, on silk.

Resolution, Chamber of Commerce, New York City.

Two large elephant tusks, presented by the King of Siam.

Coptic Bible, presented by Lord Napier, who captured it with King Theodore of Abyssinia.

Sporting rifle.

Sword of Donelson, presented to General Grant after the fall of Fort Donelson, by officers of the Army, and used by him until the end of the war.

New York sword, voted to General Grant by the citizens of New York, at the fair held in New York.

Sword of Chattanooga, presented to General Grant by the citizens of Jo Daviess County, Illinois (Galena), after the battle of Chattanooga.

Roman mug and pitcher.

Silver match-box (used by General Grant).

Gold cigar-case (enameled), presented by the Celestial King of Siam.

Gold-handled knife, presented by the miners of Idaho Territory.

Six pieces of jade-stone, presented by Prince Koon, of China.

Knife made at Sheffield for General Grant.

Gold pen, General Grant's.

Iron-headed cane, made from the rebel ram *Merrimac.*

Silver-headed cane, made from wood used in the defense of Fort Sumter.

Gold-headed cane, made of wood from old Fort Duquesne, Pennsylvania.

GRANT RELICS—Continued.

Gold-headed cane, presented to General Grant as a tribute of regard for his humane treatment of the soldiers and kind consideration of those who ministered to the sick and wounded during the war.

Gold-headed cane used by General La Fayette, and presented to General Grant by the ladies of Baltimore, Maryland.

Carved-wood cane from the estate of Sir Walter Scott.

Fifteen buttons, cut from the coats worn by General Grant during the war, by Mrs. Grant, after different battles.

Hat ornament worn at Belmont.

Hat ornament worn at Fort Donelson.

Shoulder-straps (brigadier-general) worn by General Grant at Belmont, Fort Donelson, and Shiloh.

Shoulder-straps (lieutenant-general) cut from the coat worn by General Grant in the campaigns against Richmond and Petersburg and Lee's army.

Pair of shoulder-straps (general) cut from a coat General Grant worn after the war.

Freedom of the city of San Francisco, California.

Address to General Grant by the Chamber of Commerce and Board of Trade of San Francisco, California.

Address, Chinese, in tin case.

Resolution of the Caledonian Club of San Francisco, enrolling General Grant as an honorary member.

Two bronze vases, presented to General Grant by the Japanese citizens of Yokohama, Japan.

Two small elephant tusks from the Maharajah of Johore.

Two cloisonné jars (old), presented by Li Hung Chang.

Mexican onyx cabinet. (Two columns in box No. 7.)

Two Chinese porcelain jars (old). (Bases in box No. 7.)

Two crackleware bowls (very old).

One arm of idol (1,000 years old).

Two columns of the cabinet which is packed in Nos. 4 and 5.

Two bases belonging to the jars packed in box No. 6.

Address to General Grant from the Carpenter's Company.

Address to General Grant from the citizens of Cincinnati.

Address to General Grant from the citizens of Nagasaki, Japan.

Embroidered picture (cock and hen).

Vote of thanks of Congress to General U. S. Grant, etc.

Picture of General Scott, by Page.

Marble bust and pedestal of General Grant.

Painting of General Grant and family.

Uniform of General Grant (coat and epaulettes). (These articles were received from Colonel Grant by the Adjutant-General and turned over to the War Department in connection with the Grant relics.)

Articles belonging to General U. S. Grant, now in the War Department safe, disbursing clerk's office:

Received October 7, 1885:

Address from citizens of New York, asking acceptance of the portrait of Lieutenant-General Scott.

Address from workingmen of Northumberland.

Received October 9, 1885:

Freedom of the city of Elizabeth, North Carolina.

Received October 19, 1885:

Address from the Midland International Arbitration Union, Birmingham.

GRANT RELICS—Continued.

Address from clerks and work-people of Cambridge Street Works and Rolling Mills, Birmingham.

Received October 19, 1885:

Description of the Hundred of Salford assize courts.

WILLIAM H. VANDERBILT and JULIA DENT GRANT. (Through the United States Government.) 18528. '87. (I)

INSECTS:* *Lithobius minnesotæ* sp. nov., *L. bilabiatus*, *L. tuber* sp. nov., *L. providens* sp. nov., *L. pullus* sp. nov., *L. trilobus* sp. nov., *L. cardinalis* sp. nov., *L. howei* sp. nov., *L. politus*, *L. mordax*, and *L. juventus* sp. nov.; from Indiana, Minnesota, and Michigan.

G. H. BOLLMAN, Bloomington, Indiana. 18529. '87. (X)

COPPER COIN, Roman-Semitic, issued in 266 A. D., for use in the Roman Syriac provinces; for examination. (Returned.)

F. TIPTON, Selma, Alabama. 18530. '87. (I)

WURDEMANN'S HERON,† *Ardea wuerdemanni* (two specimens). (Purchased.)

R. C. STUART, Tampa, Florida. 18531. '87. (V, A)

FOSSILS.‡

Cincinnati formation: *Buthotrephis succulens*, Hall; *Beatricea nodulosa*, Billings; *Stromatopora* sp.?; *Columnaria stellata*, Hall; *Zaphrentis spinulosa*, E. and H.; *Palæophyllum divaricans*, Nicholson; *Palæophyllum divaricans*, Nicholson, and *Ptilodictya emacerata*, Nicholson (on same block); *Tetradium fibratum*, Safford; *Helopora emacerata*, Nicholson; *Chætetes* sp.; *Monticulipora frondosa*, D'Orbigny; *Monticulipora*; *Fenestella oxfordensis*, Ulrich; *Streptorhynchus crassus*, Nicholson; *Strophomena alternata*, Conrad; *S. rhomboidalis*, and *S. rhomboidalis* var. *tenuistriata* (on same block); *Leptæna sericea*, Sowerby; *Orthis occidentalis*, Hall; *O. biforata* var. *acutilirata*; *O. sinuata*, Hall; *Pterinea demissa*, Conrad; *Megaptera alata*?, Meek; *Cyclonema bilix*, Conrad; *Gomphoceras eos*, Hall; *Orthoceras* sp.?; *Asaphus megistos*, Locke; 22 genera, 24 species, cies, 2 varieties, and 75 specimens.

Niagara formation: *Pentamerus oblongus*, Sowerby; *Orthoceras annulatum*, Sowerby; 2 genera, 2 species, and 5 specimens.

Lower Carboniferous formation: *Fenestella* and undetermined *Bryozoa*; *Fenestella delicata*, Meek; *Retzia verneuiliana*, Hall; 3 genera, 2 species, and 5 specimens.

Total, 27 genera, 29 species, 2 varieties, and 98 specimens.

A. C. BENEDICT, Indianapolis, Indiana. 18532. '87. (XIII, A)

MOLLUSKS, a small collection of dry and marine shells from Japan and Corea.

P. L. JOUY, Washington, District of Columbia. 18533. '87. (IX)

MARINE INVERTEBRATES, sponges, corals, echinoderms, and crustacea, from Japan and Corea.

P. L. JOUY, Washington, District of Columbia. 18533. '87. (XI)

QUARTZ; for examination. (Returned.)

Hon. W. C. WHITTHORNE, U. S. Senate. 18534. '87. (XVI)

JAPANESE PHEASANT, *Phasianus versicolor* ♀ (skeleton).

ZOOLOGICAL SOCIETY OF PHILADELPHIA. (Through Arthur E. Brown, Esq.). 18535. '87. (XII)

METEORIC IRON, from Johnson County, Arkansas.

J. C. BETTEN, Eureka Springs, Arkansas. 18536. '87. (XVI)

ARSENICAL PYRITES; for examination.

D. G. McLEAN, San Bernardino, California. 18537. '87. (XVI)

FLINT KNIFE.

W. W. ADAMS, Mapleton, New York. 18538. '87. (III)

---

* See Proceedings U. S. National Museum, Vol. 10, p. 254.

† See Proceedings U. S. National Museum, Vol. 10, p. 112.

‡ See Report on Department of Paleozoic Fossils, Section II.

ARROW-HEAD of white quartz; for examination.

HENRY P. HAMILTON, Two Rivers, Wisconsin. 18539. '87. (III)

PEBBLES of thomsonite, and piece of limestone containing iron pyrites; for examination.

HENRY P. HAMILTON, Two Rivers, Wisconsin. 18539. '87. (XVI)

CYATHAPHYLLOID CORAL, *Zaphrentis* sp., Lower Devonian; for examination.

HENRY P. HAMILTON, Two Rivers, Wisconsin. 18539. '87. (XIII)

RED POLLS (4), mounted by Dr. J. P. Kirkland.

Dr. E. STERLING, Cleveland, Ohio. 18540. '87. (V, A)

PARROT, *Chrysotis panamensis* (skeleton).

W. C. WEEDEN, U. S. National Museum. 18541. '87. (XII)

LIMESTONE and rock containing iron pyrites; for examination.

AMBROSE CONANT, Big Run, Athens County, Ohio. 18542. '87. (XVI)

ARROW-HEADS (27) and 6 grooved axes. (Exchange.)

JOHN H. LEMON, New Albany, Floyd County, Indiana. 18543. '87. (III)

FOSSILS:

Niagara formation: *Stromatopora concentrica*, Goldfuss; *Stromatopora* sp.; *Heliolites megastoma*, McCoy; *H. interstinctus*, Linné; *Plasmopora follis*, E. and H.; *Favosites favosus*, Goldfuss; *F. Niagarensis*, Hall; *Alveolites fibrosus*, Davis; *Cladopora reticulata*, Hall; *Thecia major*, Rominger; *T. minor*, Rominger; *Halysites catenulatus*, Linnæus; *Omphyma verrucosa*, E. & H.; *Strombodes pentagonus*, Goldfuss; 10 genera, 13 species, and 65 specimens.

Corniferous formation: *Stromatopora substriatella*, Nicholson; *Favosites amplissimus*, Davis; *F. arbor*, Davis; *F. cariosus*, Davis; *F. convexus*, Davis; *F. cymosus*, Davis; *F. Emmonsii*, Rominger; *F. hemisphericus*, Troost, *F. pirum*, Davis; *F. spiculatus*, Davis; *F. tuberosus*, Rominger; *F.* sp. ?; *Alveolites mordax*, Davis; *Michelinia clappii*, E. and H.; *Syringopora tabulata*, E. and H.?; *Cyathophyllum davidsoni*, E. and H.; *C. greenei*; *C. validum*, Hall; *C.* sp. ?; *Heliophyllum annulatum*, Hall; *H. corniculum*; *H. invaginatum*, Hall; *H.* sp. ?; *Clisiophyllum oneidaensis*, Billings; *Clisiophyllum*, sp. ?; *Blothrophyllum decorticatum*, Billings; *B. louisvillensis*, Davis; *B. prolificum*; *B. promissum*, Hall; *B.* sp. ?; *Diphyphyllum archiaci*, Billings; *D. cruciforme*; *D. sentium*; *Cystiphyllum vesiculosum*, Goldfuss; *Cystiphyllum*, sp. ?; *Zaphrentis gigantea*, Baf. ; *Z. greeneana*; *Z. nitida*, Hall; *Z. rafinesquei*, E. and H.; *Z.* sp. ?; *Amplexus yandelli*, E. and H.; *Amplexus.* sp. ?; *Spirifera gregaria*, Clapp (?); 14 genera; 45 species, and 283 specimens.

Hamilton formation: *Favosites placenta*, Rominger; *Heliophyllum halli*, E. and H.; *Cystiphyllum americanum*, E. and H.; 2 genera, 3 species, and 3 specimens.

JOHN H. LEMON, New Albany, Indiana. 18543. '87. (XIII, A)

SIGNAL FLAG of the *Huron* which was lost near Nag's Head, on the North Carolina coast. (Fragment.)

ROBERT LODER, Captain, steam-tug *Virginia*, Duke, Florida. 18544. '87. (I)

SANDSTONE QUARTZ; for examination.

A. B. ROSS & CO., Cherokee, Iowa. 18545. '87. (XVI)

POLISHED SLATE SPEAR-HEADS; for examination.

W. W. ADAMS, Mapleton, New York. 18546. '87. (III)

FOSSIL; for examination.

A. W. ALLEN, Aurora, Cayuga County, New York. 18547. '87. (XIII, A)

CHINESE COPPER COIN, One-cash of Kang-Hsi Dynasty, 1661–1722.

DANIEL LEECH, Smithsonian Institution. 18548. '87. (I)

BIRDS, mounted by Dr. Jared P. Kirtland.

Dr. E. STERLING, Cleveland, Ohio. 18549. '87. (V, A)

HEMIPTERA, 39 species, 58 specimens, mostly new to Museum collection. (Exchange.)

W. H. ASHMEAD, Jacksonville, Florida. 18550. '87. (X)

SEAL, *Monachus tropicalis* (skeleton), from Los Triangulos, Yucatan. (Purchased.)

HENRY A. WARD, Rochester, New York. 18551. '87. (XII)

STONE AX.

J. H. WALKER, Homer, Louisiana. 18552. '87. (III)

MAGNETITE, stained by decomposition; for examination.

L. ATCHISON, Panaca, Nevada. 18553. '87. (XVIII)

POLISHED CELT.

Dr. J. F. JOHNSTON, Homer, Louisiana. 18554. '87. (III)

IRON BALL, supposed to have been made either by the Indians or De Soto; plowed up in a field near Homer, Louisiana.

Capt. J. M. WALKER, Homer, Louisiana. 18555. '87. (I)

SHELLS: *Cardium magnum, Lucina Jamaicensis, Unio* sp., *Tagelus gibbus, Raeta canaliculata, Planorbis trivolvis, Melanian* sp., *Columbella mercatoria, Petricola pholadiformis, Nerita tesselata, Chione cingenda, Mactra ovalis, Arca pexata, Pinna seminuda, Tellina alternata, T. constricta;* for identification.

W. W. WESTGATE, Houston, Texas. 18556. '87. (IX)

MEDALS in white metal (2): Yorktown surrender centennial, and Oriole celebration in Baltimore, October, 1881. Also, silver franc, Emperor Napoleon, 1812.

F. W. TRUE, U. S. National Museum. 18557. '87. (I)

CARBONIFEROUS FOSSILS: *Syringopora* sp.?, *Zaphrentis* sp., *Productus nevadensis*, Meek, *Pleurotomaria* sp., *Straparollus* sp., *Euomphalus* sp., concretionary limestone (15 specimens).

ARTHUR LAKES, Golden City, Colorado. 18558. '87. (XIII, A)

BIRDS' EGGS: *Junco hyemalis carolinensis* (4), from Highland, North Carolina; *Pipilo erythrophthalmus alleni* (2), from Charleston, South Carolina; and *Helinaia swainsoni* (3), from Charleston, South Carolina.

WILLIAM BREWSTER, Cambridge, Massachusetts. 18559. '87. (V, B)

BADGE and Pin of the U. S. Veteran Signal Corps Association.

E. H. HAWLEY, U. S. National Museum. 18560. '87. (I)

LOGAN FUNERAL BADGE, U. S. Pension Office. (Deposited)

J. L. JOHNSON, U. S. Pension Office. 18561. '87. (I)

CARD OF ADMISSION to the Memorial Service of J. A. Garfield in the United States House of Representatives, February 27, 1882.

Miss C. C. CURRY, Washington, District of Columbia. (Through Paul Beckwith.) 18562. '87. (I)

EAR-RING, with paste gem; an artificial silicate of lead colored by protoxide of iron; for examination.

JAMES YOUNG, Washington, District of Columbia. 18563. '87. (XVI)

BADGE of the New York Retail Grocers' Union.

CHARLES BRICKWEDEL, New York City. 18564. '87. (I)

BADGE of Retail Merchants' Central Association of New York and vicinity.

C. F. BASSING, New York City. 18565. '87. (I)

BADGE of Union Veteran's Union, First National Encampment, January 19, 1887, at Washington, District of Columbia.

Maj. M. A. DILLON, Washington, District of Columbia. 18566. '87. (I)

PIECE OF POTTERY; for examination.

A. A. PELING, Wrights, Pennsylvania. 18567. '87. (II, B)

HORNBLENDE containing garnet; for examination.

A. A. PELING, Wrights, Pennsylvania. 18567. '87. (XVI)

FOSSIL PLANT, *Lepidodendron* sp.; for examination.

A. A. PELING, Wrights, Pennsylvania. 18567. '87. (XV)

FOSSILS: Coral, *Favosites hemisphericus* (?); coral, *Diphyphllum simcoense,* and a large specimen covered with intertwining casts of worm trails and borings; for examination.

A. A. PELING, Wrights, Pennsylvania. 18567. '86. (XIII, A)

STONE IMPLEMENTS: 5 cutting tools, a perforator, 25 arrow-heads, 2 rude chipped celts, a chipped celt with grooved edge for cutting, 3 polished celts, a fragment of leaf-shaped implement, a celt gouge, a pestle, 2 pierced tab ets, a grooved sinker, a pierced ceremonial object; 46 specimens presented, and 24 arrow-heads and 5 celts in exchange.

A. A. PELING, Wrights, Pennsylvania. 18567. '87. (III)

AMERICAN RED-NECKED GREBE, *Podiceps cornutus* (skeleton).

W. B. BARROWS, Department of Agriculture. 18568. '87. (XII)

BUZZARD, *Cathartes aura* (skeleton); from Virginia.

H. W. HENSHAW, Bureau of Ethnology, District of Columbia. 18569. '87. (XII)

CROW, *Corvus americanus* (skeleton); from Maryland.

E. R. TODD, U. S. National Museum. 18570. '87. (XII)

MOCKING-BIRD, *Mimus polyglottos* (skeleton).

LOUIS SCHMID & SONS, Washington, District of Columbia. 18571. '87. (XII)

FISHES: *Querimana gyrans* (3 specimens), *Gambusia puncticulata* (2 specimens), *Sphyræna picuda*, juv. (1 specimen); retained from a collection sent for identification.

JOHNS HOPKINS UNIVERSITY, Baltimore, Maryland. (Through C. F. Hodge.) 18572. '87. (VII)

GRUB, highly esteemed by the natives of Venezuela as an article of food; found in the heart of palm trees on the Orinoco River.

Dr. H. C. YARROW, Washington, District of Columbia. 18573. '87. (I)

SNAKE-HEADS: Macapie, *Xephosoma ruschenborgeis*, and Capabella, *Orynbopus plumbeus*; from the Island of Trinidad. Collected by W. Hallett Phillips.

Dr. H. C. YARROW, U. S. Army, Washington, District of Columbia. 18573. '87. (VI)

COINS: A Connecticut colonial copper coin and a "Knickerbocker currency" war token of 1863.

Mrs. SARAH ECKELS, Carlisle, Pennsylvania. 18574. '87. (I)

FOOD of Ixtatan Indians: Totoposte, piñol, birrin, frijol, chile, and café.

Prof. MILES ROCK, Guatemala, Central America. 18575. '87. (I)

BLACK WOOLEN COAT worn by the Ixtatan Indians.

Prof. MILES ROCK, Guatemala, Central America. 18575. '87. (II, A)

ORE, from Piedras Negras Mine, Mexico; for examination.

J. G. WELCH. (Through Hon. W. G. Allen, United States consul, Piedras Negras, Mexico.) 18576. '87. (XVIII)

ARROW-HEAD, cutting tools (2), and fragments of chipped implements (3); from Nebraska.

U. S. GEOLOGICAL Survey. 18577. '87. (III)

BIRD-SKINS (9 specimens, 6 species), from New Hampshire, New Brunswick, and Florida. (Exchange.)

ARTHUR P. CHADBOURNE, Cambridge, Massachusetts. 18578. '87. (V, A)

OPOSSUM, *Didelphys cinereus*; from Nicaragua.

ZOOLOGICAL SOCIETY OF PHILADELPHIA. (Through Arthur E. Brown, Esq.) 18579. '87. (IV)

ROSE HILL PARAKEET, *Platycercus eximius*. (Skeleton.)

ZOOLOGICAL SOCIETY OF PHILADELPHIA. (Through Arthur E. Brown, Esq.) 18579. '87. (XII)

CANARY BIRD, *Serinus canariensis* var. in flesh.

W. C. WEEDEN, U. S. National Museum. 18580. '87. (V, A)

SHELLS: *Unio ozarkensis* Call. and *U. brevicolas, Triodopsis craigeni*, and *Helix* sp.; from Missouri and Indian Territory. Author's types of species.

R. ELLSWORTH CALL, University of Missouri, Columbia, Missouri. 18581. '87. (IX)

TOURMALINE CRYSTAL; for examination.

W. S. H.CKEY, Bakersville, North Carolina. 18582. '87. (XVI)

MOLYBDENITE; for examination.

WILLIAM ZEEKENDORF, Tucson, Arizona. 18583. '87. (XVI)

ENGRAVING, head of Christ on Veronica's handkerchief, 1649.

G. BROWN GOODE, Washington, District of Columbia. 18584. '86. (I)

HARBOR SEAL, *Phoca vitulina*, from Wood's Holl, Massachusetts.

U. S. FISH COMMISSION, Washington. 18585. '87. (IV)

ETCHING TOOLS: Hand-vise, cake of etching ground, dabber, bottle of transparent etching paste, etching needle, cake of banking wax, bottle of acid, roller, bottle of "stopping out" varnish, scraper, 2 burnishers, charcoal, piece of crocus paper, 2 dry-point needles, 2 pens, and 2 gravers.

PETER MORAN, Philadelphia, Pennsylvania. 18586. '87. (I)

ENGLISH CRESTED CANARY, *Serinus canariensis*, var.

W. C. WEEDEN, U. S. National Museum. 18587. '87. (V, A)

TOOTH, left post upper molar of domestic pig, *Sus scrofa;* for examination.

ELGIN SCIENTIFIC SOCIETY, Elgin, Illinois. (Through S. F. Perry.) 18588. '87. (XII)

LOWER PHARYNGEAL BONE of Big-jawed Sucker, *Placopharynx* sp.; for examination.

ELGIN SCIENTIFIC SOCIETY, Elgin, Illinois. 18588. '87. (VII)

PLANT, *Cassia* sp.; for examination.

ELGIN SCIENTIFIC SOCIETY, Elgin, Illinois. 18588. '87. (XV)

CRETACEOUS FOSSIL, *Belemnitella;* for examination.

ELGIN SCIENTIFIC SOCIETY, Elgin, Illinois. 18588. '87. (XIII, B)

GYPSUM, and fluorite; for examination.

ELGIN SCIENTIFIC SOCIETY, Elgin, Illinois. 18588. '87. (XVI)

FOSSIL, *Illœnus coxus* (?), cast of *Euomphalus*, of the type *E. decewi*, of the Upper Helderberg.

ELGIN SCIENTIFIC SOCIETY, Elgin, Illinois. 18588. '87. (XIII, A)

FOSSIL, *Conularia pappilata;* for examination.

JAMES W. ROGAN, Rogersville, Tennessee. 18589. '87. (XIII, A)

ROCK, consisting of a hydrous silicate of magnesia with free iron oxides and carbonate of lime; for examination.

Hon. M. C. BUTLER, U. S. Senate. 18590. '87. (XVII)

LARVÆ of a May fly, *Palegenia* sp.; for examination.

A. R. REED, Pleasant Hill, Missouri. 18591. '87. (X)

MANGANESE ORE; for examination.

THOMAS J. CYPERT, Cypress Inn, Wayne County, Tennessee. (Through Hon. W. C. Whitthorne.) 18592. '87. (XVIII)

SWAINSON'S HAWK, *Buteo swainsoni.*

J. A. LOOMIS, Paint Rock, Concho County, Texas. 18593. '87. (V, A)

PLANTS (9,269 specimens). (Purchased.)

Dr. J. P. F. BRUNNER, Krumsville, Pennsylvania. 18594. '87. (XV)

SHREW, *Sorex vagrans.*

Dr. J. C. MERRILL, U. S. Army, Fort Klamath, Oregon. 18595. '87. (IV)

CALIFORNIA QUAIL, *Lophortyx californicus.* (Deposited.)

R. RIDGWAY, U. S. National Museum. 18596. '87. (V, A)

BIRD-SKINS (4 specimens) (3 species).

WILLIAM LLOYD, Paint Creek, Concho County, Texas. 18597. '87. (V, A)

NUDIBRANCH MOLLUSK, probably *Dendronotus.*

JAMES G. SWAN, Port Townsend, Washington Territory. 18598. '87. (IX)

BIRD-SKINS; for examination. (Returned.)

CHARLES B. CORY, Boston, Massachusetts. 18599. '87. (V, A)

CHINESE BRASS COIN, one-cash of Shim-Chih, 1644–1661.

Dr. D. BETHUNE MCCARTEE, Washington, District of Columbia. 18600. '87. (I)

HARBOR SEAL, *Phoca vitulina*, from Wood's Holl, Massachusetts.

U. S. FISH COMMISSION. 18601. '87. (IV)

FISH; for examination

GWYNN HARRIS Washington, District of Columbia. 18602. '87. (VII)

CANARY, *Serinus canariensis* (2 skeletons).

ROBERT F. MCMILLAN, Washington, District of Columbia. 18603. '87. (XII)

MENHADEN, from Pawley Island.

W. ST. J. MAZYCK, Waverly Mills, South Carolina. 18604. '87. (VII)

ARROW-HEAD and wedge-shaped implement.

J. F. KUMMERFELD, Minden, Pottawattamie County, Iowa. 18605. '87. (III)

POLITICAL MEDALS, coins, tokens, etc.: Six Jacksonian tokens; General Jackson campaign token; Zachary Taylor campaign medal, 1848; Lewis Cass campaign medal, 1848; Winfield Scott campaign medal; Abraham Lincoln campaign medal, 1860; Abraham Lincoln campaign medal; Abolition of Slavery token, 1838; Washington Calendar medal; Nova constellatio, New York colonial cent, 1783; Washington "Liberty and Security" cent; Mount Vernon medal, "General George Washington," 1776; "Franklin cent," 1787; English half-penny, George II, 1753; Irish half-penny, George I, 1723; two Russian copper coins, two-kopek, 1810; four Turkish copper coins; medal, "Liberty enlightening the World."

B. H. COLLINS, Washington, District of Columbia. 18606. '87. (I)

BIRD-SKINS. (Exchange.)

OBERLIN COLLEGE, Oberlin, Ohio. 18607. '87. (V, A)

FISHES, *Potamocottus gulosus.*

LOREN W. GREEN, Baird, Shasta County, California. 18608. '87. (VII)

INDIAN BASKETS (4 specimens), and material from which made. (Purchased.) Also a stone pestle.

LOREN W. GREEN, Baird, Shasta County, California. 18608. '87. (II, A)

FROG, *Hyla regilla.*

LOREN W. GREEN, Baird, Shasta County, California. 18608. '87. (VI)

OCHERS; for examination, from Virginia.

Hon. J. S. NEGLEY, House of Representatives. 18609. '87. (XVIII)

CLAY; for examination.

N. BAYARD CLINCH, Green Cove Springs, Florida. 18610. '87. (XVIII)

POTSDAM QUARTZITE with peculiar markings, from Chateaugay, Franklin County, New York, and 39 pieces "Au Sable Granite" (Norite), from Keeseville, New York.

U. S. GEOLOGICAL SURVEY. (Through C. D. Walcott.) 18611. '87. (XVII)

GOPHER, *Thomomys talpoides bulbivorus* (3 specimens), and common mouse, *Mus musculus* (2 specimens).

Dr. J. C. MERRILL, U. S. Army, Fort Klamath, Oregon. 18612. '87. (IV)

BANDED SEAL, *Phoca fasciata.*

Capt. M. A. HEALY, U. S. Revenue Marine steamer *Bear*, San Francisco, California. 18613. '87. (IV)

REPTILES: *Bufo columbiensis, Rana cantabrigensis,* and *Diemyctylus torosus* (4 specimens).

HENRY E. NICHOLS, lieutenant-commander, U. S. Navy, Sitka, Alaska. 18614. '87. (VI)

PORPOISE, *Phocœna communis* (skeleton), and *P. dalli* (skull); from Glacier Bay.

HENRY E. NICHOLS, lieutenant-commander, U. S. Navy, Sitka, Alaska. 18614. '87. (XII)

CRUSTACEA,* worms, and echinoderms, from Alaska; and crustacea, from Brazil.

HENRY E. NICHOLS, lieutenant-commander, U. S. Navy, Sitka, Alaska. 18614. '87. (XI)

---

* See Proceedings U. S. National Museum, Vol. 9, p. 256,

FISHES: *Hexagrammus asper, H. decagrammus, Anoplopoma fimbria, Bathymaster signatus, Ophiodon elongatus, Pollachius chalcogrammus, Salvelinus malma, Microgadus proximus, Hemilepidotus hemilepidotus, Lumpenus anguillaris, Raia stellulata, Ammodytes, Liparis,* etc.; from Alaska. Also *Myxine australis,* from Straits of Magellan.

> HENRY E. NICHOLS, lieutenant-commander, U. S. Navy, Sitka, Alaska. 18614. '87. (VII)

ETHNOLOGICAL OBJECTS.*

> CHARLES WILLOUGHBY, Indian agent, Quinaielt Agency, Washington Territory. 18615. '87. (II, A)

ETHNOLOGICAL OBJECTS,* from Alaska.

> Lieut. GEORGE M. STONEY, U. S. Navy. 18616. '87. (II, A)

SUIT, worn in Alaska by the donor. (Deposited.)

> Lieut. G. M. STONEY, U. S. Navy. 18616. '87. (II, A)

MAMMALS: *Bison americanus, Canis latrans, Antilocapra americana, Cariacus macrotis, C. virginianus, Vulpes velox,* and *Taxidea americana* (skins and skeletons); collected by W. T. Hornaday in Montana.

> SMITHSONIAN INSTITUTION. 18617. '87. (IV)

SPANISH GOLD COIN, two-scudo, 1776; copy of "Dunlap's Pennsylvania Packet," July 8, 1776, containing Declaration of Independence; religious book printed at Madrid in 1792, found at city of Mexico in November, 1847; one-peso bill on Bank of Spain, Havana, Cuba; and a miniature copy of Cincinnati Enquirer, May, 1878.

> WALTER S. PHELPS, Santa Catalina, Cuba. 18618. '87. (I)

YELLOW-WINGED SUGAR BIRD, *Cœreba cyanea* (2 skeletons).

> ZOOLOGICAL SOCIETY OF PHILADELPHIA. (Through Arthur E. Brown, Esq.) 18619. '87. (XII)

CONFEDERATE MONEY and stamps and North Carolina currency; for examination. (Returned.)

> GEORGE S. KEEHLN, Salem, North Carolina. 18620. '87. (I)

CENTENNIAL MEDAL of the Batavian Society of Arts and Sciences, Rotterdam, 1878.

> GEORGE H. BOEHMER, Smithsonian Institution. 18621. '87. (I)

BIRD-SKINS, from Santarem, Brazil (3 specimens.) (Exchange.)

> C. J. MAYNARD & CO., Boston, Massachusetts. 18622. '87. (V, A)

IRON AND MANGANESE ORE, from Buckingham County, Virginia.

> W. D. HILLS, Cleveland, Ohio. 18623. '87. (XVIII)

SILVER ORE, from White Pine County, Nevada.

> JOHN IVEY, Treasure City, Nevada. 18624. '87. (XVIII)

PIGMY SPERM WHALE, *Kogia breviceps;* Common dolphin, *Delphinus delphis;* and Southern blackfish, *Globiocephalus brachypterus.*

> BAILEY T. BARCO, Keeper of Dam Neck Mills Life-Saving Station, Sand Bridge, Virginia. 18625. '87. (XII)

STEATITE, volcanic rock, mineral dust, etc.

> Lieut. R. E. PEARY, U. S. Navy. 18626. '87. (XVII)

SHELLS, *Littorina gronlandica.*

> Lieut. R. E. PEARY, U. S. Navy. 18626. '87. (IX).

SAND LAUNCE, *Ammodytes tobianus* L.

> Lieut. R. E. PEARY, U. S. Navy. 18626. '87. (VII)

ROSE QUARTZ, pyrite, iron, muscovite, and tourmaline in quartz

> Lieut. R. E. PEARY, U. S. Navy. 18626. '87. (XVI)

GRAPHITE.

> Lieut. R. E. PEARY, U. S. Navy. 18626. '87. (XVIII)

HARBOR SEAL, *Phoca vitulina.*

> U. S. FISH COMMISSION. (Through Vinal N. Edwards, Wood's Holl, Massachusetts.) 18627. '87. (XII)

---

* See Report on Department of Ethnology, Section II, pp. 66–67.

MOCKING-BIRD, *Mimus polyglottos.* (Skeleton.)

LOUIS SCHMID & SONS, Washington, District of Columbia. 18628. '87. (XII)

IRON ORE (6 specimens), representing some important New England localities.

Prof. R. PUMPELLY, Newport, Rhode Island. 18629. '87. (XVIII)

WINGS OF INSECTS: *Junonia lavininia, Eacles impenalis, Agraulis vanillæ, Pipilio ajax,* and *Sphinx carolina;* for examination.

F. C. GRUGAN, Warrington, Florida. 18630. '87. (X)

FOSSIL SHARK'S TOOTH. (Returned.)

A. M. DAWSON, Rhome, Wise County, Texas. 18631. '87. (IV)

YELLOW-SHAFTED FLICKER, *Colaptes auratus;* Red-headed woodpecker, *Melanerpes erythrocephalus;* Cedar Bird, *Ampelis cedrorum;* Red and buff shouldered Blackbird, *Agelæus phœniceus.*

L. O. PINDAR, Hickman, Kentucky. 18632. '87. (XII)

IRISH SETTER, "Glenclaire," with pedigree.

JAMES T. WALKER, Palmyra, New York. 18633. '87. (IV)

SHELL, *Voluta junonia;* for examination. (Returned.)

B. F. BLACKBURN, Osprey, Manatee County, Florida. 18634. '87. (IX)

BONES, from a cavern in Florida.

U. S. GEOLOGICAL SURVEY, Washington, District of Columbia. 18635. '87. (XII)

ROCKS containing phosphoric acid; for examination.

C. L. BUSH, Lake City, Florida. 18636. '87. (XVIII)

COOPER'S SHREW, *Sorex cooperi;* for identification.

F. C. JESSUP, West Hampton, New York. 18637. '87. (IV)

"SIXTEEN PUZZLE."

HENRY HORAN, Washington, District of Columbia. 18638. '87. (II,A)

CANARY, *Serinus canariensis.* (Skeleton.)

LOUIS SCHMID & SONS, Washington, District of Columbia. 18639. '87. (XII)

SHELLS.

EARL FLINT, Rivas, Nicaragua. 18640. '87. (IX)

TUFA, bearing print of human foot, and sand.

EARL FLINT, Rivas, Nicaragua. 18640. '87. (XVII)

CARBONIFEROUS FOSSILS:

Fenestella sp. ?; *Spirifera camerata,* Morton; *Productus cora,* D'Orbigny; *P. nebraskensis,* Owen; *P. semireticulatus,* Martin; *Allorisma* sp. ?; *Athyris* sp. ?; *Streptorhynchus crenistria,* Phil.; *Chonetes granulifera,* Owen; *Nuculana* sp. ?; *Bellerophon* sp. ?.

AUGUSTUS D. SELBY, Ironton, Ohio. 18641. '87. (XIII, A)

CLINTON FOSSILS: *

Clinton formation: *Chætetes lycoperdon,* Say; *Zaphrentis bilateralis,* Hall; *Streptelasma* sp. ?; *Leptocœlia hemispherica,* Sowerby; *Rhynchonella* sp. ?; *R. bidentata,* Sowerby; *Stricklandia salteri,* Billings; *Pentamerus oblongus,* Sowerby; *Orthis biloba,* Linnæus; *O. flabellum,* Hall; *O. hybrida,* Sowerby; *O. reversa,* Salter (type); *Strophomena rhomboidalis,* Wahl; *Streptorhynchus subplanus,* Conrad; *Leptæna transversalis,* Dalman; *Crania* (?); *Tentaculites distans,* Hall; *Cyclonema* sp.; *Murchisonia* sp.; *Metoptoma* sp.; *Avicula,* sp.; *Dalmanites* sp. ?; *Calymene* sp.; *Proetus* sp.

Trenton formation: *Stictopora elegantula,* Hall (?); *Leperditia fabulites,* Conrad. (190 specimens).

U. S. GEOLOGICAL SURVEY. (Collected by I. C. Russell.) 18642. '87. (XIII, A)

WAX IMPRESSION of the seal of the town of Columbia, South Carolina, which was found in the street after the burning of the town, February 17, 1865.

ST. JULIAN FILLETTE, Washington, District of Columbia. 18643. '87. (I)

---

* See Report on Department of Paleozoic Fossils, Section II.

BLACK-TAILED PARAKEET, *Polytelis melanurus;* and Brush-Turkey, *Talegallus lathami* (skins).
> ZOOLOGICAL SOCIETY OF PHILADELPHIA. (Through Arthur E. Brown, Esq.) 18644. '87. (V, A)

MARKSMAN'S CERTIFICATE and two button badges issued by command of General Hancock.
> JAMES BURK, Soldiers' Home, District of Columbia. 18645. '87. (I)

BIRD-SKINS (5 species, 6 specimens). (Exchange.)
> P. L. JOUY, Washington, District of Columbia. 18646. '87. (V, A)

ELECTROTYPES of foreign and American coins and medals (361 specimens).
> Mr. —— BROOKS, Washington, District of Columbia. 18647. '87. (I)

IMPURE LIMONITE, water-worn fragment; for examination.
> I. E. WELCH, Alpine, Talladega County, Alabama. 18648. '87. (XVIII)

IMPURE LIMESTONE and a decomposed volcanic rock; for examination.
> W. H. GERMAIN, Centro, Los Angeles County, California. 18649. '87. (XVIII)

ALMANDITE in mica schist (2 specimens), from near Fort Wrangel, Alaska; and one slice of meteoric iron, and model of meteorite; from Allen County, Kentucky. (Exchange.)
> WARD & HOWELL, Rochester, New York. 18650. '87. (XVI)

TURKEY-BUZZARD, *Cathartes aura,* in the flesh.
> GEORGE MARSHALL, Laurel, Maryland. 18651. '87. (V, A)

FOSSILS; from Kealagvik Bay, Alaska.
> EDWIN E. HOWELL, Rochester, New York. 18652. '87. (XIII, C)

BADGES; from World's Exposition at New Orleans.
> HENRY HORAN, U. S. National Museum. 18653. '87. (I)

YELLOW-TAIL FISH, *Ochyurus chrysurus.*
> SILAS STEARNS, Pensacola, Florida. 18654. '87. (VII)

MIXTURE of limestone and slate; for examination.
> W. C. HALE, Austin's Springs, Tennessee. 18655. '87. (XVIII)

QUARTO VOLUME of "Regulations for the Uniform and Dress of the Navy and Marine Corps of the United States." Printed for the Navy, 1852.
> F. W. TRUE, U. S. National Museum. 18656. '87. (I)

RED ARTILLERY BLANKET. (Purchased.)
> ORDNANCE DEPARTMENT, U. S. Army. 18657. '87. (II, A)

RED-TAILED HAWK, *Buteo borealis,* juv.
> JAMES P. STABLER, Laurel, Maryland. 18658. '87. (XII)

POINTER DOG, *Canis familiaris.*
> THOMAS MARRON, U. S. National Museum. 18659. '87. (XII)

WESTERN FIELD SPARROW, *Spizella pusilla arenacea* (2 specimens).
> WILLIAM LOYD, Paint Rock, Concho County, Texas. 18660. '87. (V, A)

CINCINNATI FOSSILS:
> Cincinnati formation: *Dystactospongia insolens,* Miller; *Pasceolus claudii,* Miller; *P. darwini,* Miller; *Pattersonia difficilis,* Miller; *Monticulipora dawsoni,* Nicholson; *M. parvonia,* D'Orbigny; *M. parvonia* (photograph); *Stromatocerium richmondense,* Miller; *Lichenocrinus affinis,* Miller; *Glyptocrinus angularis,* M. and D.; *Lepadocrinus moorii,* Meek; *Helopora harrisi; Orthis Ella,* Hall; *O. insculpta,* Hall; *Cyclonema cincinnatense,* Miller; *Bellerophon mohri,* Miller; *Cypricardites Hainesi,* Miller; *Orthcesma nicholboroughi,* Whit.; *Crania socialis,* Ulrich; *Lingula norwoodi,* James; *Spirorbis cincinnatiensis,* M. and D.; Annelid jaws; Trilobite tracks; *Plumulites jamesi,* H. and W., and photographs; 84 specimens.
> CHARLES L. FABER, Cincinnati, Ohio. 18661. '87. (XIII, A)

BLUE-SPOTTED SUNFISH; for examination.
> Capt. H. CATLEY, Second Infantry, U. S. Army, Fort Omaha, Nebraska. 18662. '87. (VII)

NEST of *Pipilo erythrophthalmus alleni*, from St. Helena Island, South Carolina. New to Museum collection.

WILLIAM BREWSTER, Cambridge, Massachusetts. 18663. '87. (V, B)

PIG IRON; for examination.

Dr. G. A. SWANN, Decatur, Texas. 18664. '87. (XVIII)

CRAB, *Callianassa Stimpsoni*; for examination.

GEORGE A. LEWIS, Wickford, Rhode Island. 18665. '87. (XI)

BIRDS: Towhee, *Pipilo erythrophthalmus;* Rusty Blackbird, *Scolecophagus carolinus;* Tufted Titmouse, *Parus bicolor;* Fox-colored Sparrow, *Paserella iliaca;* and Song Sparrow, *Melospiza fasciata;* for examination.

L. O. PINDAR, Hickman, Kentucky. 18666. '87. (XII)

VESUVIANITE with calcite and quartz; altered meteoric iron (returned), and sodalite (9 specimens); for examination.

GEORGE F. KUNZ, Hoboken, New Jersey. 18667. '87. (XVI)

MINERAL; for examination.

Mrs. JOHN GILES, Lowell, Michigan. 18668. '87. (XVI)

"ARCTIC COTTON" used by Eskimo for making lamp-wicks.

Capt. J. O. SPICER, Groton, Connecticut. 18669. '87. (II, A)

COPPER COINS, copper one-mill, 1866; copper one-cent, 1880; brass one-cash (2) Emperor Kang Hsi, 1661–1722; brass one-cash, Emperor Shun Chih, 1644–1661.

J. V. LEECH, U. S. National Museum. 18670. '87. (I)

COMMON SEAL, *Phoca vitulina.*

U. S. FISH COMMISSION, Wood's Holl, Massachusetts. (Through Vinal N. Edwards.) 18671. '87. (IV)

WHITEFISH, *Coregonus clupeiformis.*

FRANK N. CLARK, Northville, Michigan. 18672. '87. (VII)

GRAY EAGLE, *Haliœtus leucocephalus*, from Fauquier County, Virginia.

P. ORD, Washington, District of Columbia. 18673. '87. (XII)

EVENING GROSBEAK, *Hesperiphona vespertina.*

EDWARD A. COLBY, Chicago, Illinois. 18674. '87. (V, A)

MANGANESE ORE and iron ore (hematite).

B. A. HELTON, Hazel Spring, Virginia. 18675. '87. (XVI)

DAMOURITE pseudomorph after chiastolite, from Rochester, New Hampshire.

JOHN I. LEGRO, New Britain, Connecticut. 18676. '87. (XVI)

FISH, *Ophichthys retropinnis;* from Pensacola, Florida.

C. H. EIGENMANN, Indiana University, Bloomington, Indiana. 18677. '87. (VII)

INSECTS: *Pachylomerus carabivorus* Atk., nest and specimen; *Myrmekiaphila foliata* Atk., and *Nidivalvata marxii* Atk.

Prof. GEORGE F. ATKINSON, Chapel Hill, North Carolina. 18678. '87. (X)

MEDAL MOLDS (42), plaster casts of medals (5), metal casts of medals (71), metal coin molds (300), original medals (3), and 2 certificates of membership of Joseph Saxton in Franklin Institute and American Philosophical Society of Philadelphia. (Deposited.)

J. S. PENDLETON, Washington, District of Columbia. 18679. '87. (I)

PARASITES, *Limothrips* sp., found on *Richardia œthiopica;* for examination.

JAMES N. BISHOP, Plainville, Connecticut. 18680. '87. (X)

GARNET PEBBLES (8), and garnet in quartzose schist; from Atlantic City, Wyoming.

Col. J. STEVENSON, Bureau of Ethnology. 18681. '87. (XVI)

BUG, *Convilinus*, probably an immature *sanguisirga;* for examination.

Dr. JOHN H. LACY, Clifton, Arizona. 18682. '87. (X)

RED SQUIRREL, from Africa (?).

CHARLES B. CORY, Boston, Massachusetts. 18683. '87. (IV)

BLACK-FOOTED PENGUIN, *Spheniscus demersus* (skeleton).

Dr. J. W. SPENGEL, Bremen, Germany. (Purchased.) 18684. '87. (XII)

RUFFED GROUSE, *Bonasa umbellus* (mounted). (Exchange.)

HENRY MARSHALL, Laurel, Maryland. 18685. '87. (V, A)

HARBOR SEAL, *Phoca vitulina.*

U. S. FISH COMMISSION, Wood's Holl, Massachusetts. 18686. '87. (IV)

FIBER; for examination.

Dr. G. P. SARGEANT, Bryn Mawr, Pennsylvania. 18687. '87. (I)

BRICK, from the house in which Washington was born.

HARRY C. GIVEN, Washington, District of Columbia. 18688. '87. (I,

ENGRAVINGS, "The Battle near Bergen," and "The Siege of Groningen," 1664.
(Deposited.)

J. S. PENDLETON, Washington, District of Columbia. 18689. '87. (II, A)

CANARY, *Serinus canariensis.*

LOUIS SCHMID & SONS, Washington, District of Columbia. 18690. '87. (XII)

CODFISH, *Gadus ogac,* freak; with one anal fin of 38 rays instead of two separate
anals; for examination.

Capt. J. W. COLLINS, U. S. National Museum. 18691. '87. (VII)

IMPURE KAOLIN; for examination.

C. M. WEYMAN, Daggett, California. 18692. '87. (XVI)

CASTS of African and other typical heads (26). (Purchased.)

MUSÉE DU TROCADÉRO, Paris, France. (Through Dr. E. Hamy.) 18693. '87.
(II, A)

ETHNOLOGICAL OBJECTS, from Africa, Oceania, Asia, and America (151.)

MUSÉE DU TROCADÉRO, Paris, France. (Through Dr. E. Hamy.) 18694. '87.
(II, A)

CAT SQUIRREL, *Bassaris astuta.*

CHARLES RUBY, Fort Apache, Arizona. 18695. '87. (IV)

FOSSILS: Crinoid stem (Carboniferous ?), *Spirifera camerata,* and *Streptorhynchus crenistria* (3 specimens).

CHARLES RUBY, Fort Apache, Arizona. 18695. '87. (XIII, A)

ZINC BLENDE; for examination.

HENRY ROSS, Elm Valley, Rush County, Kansas. 18696. '87. (XVI)

GRAVEL cemented by a ferruginous substance; for examination.

ALEXANDER KUHN & CO., Vicksburg, Mississippi. 18697. '87. (XVI)

SHELL CONGLOMERATE, found 5 feet under water in Chesapeake Bay, near Fortress
Monroe.

F. J. GIACCHETTI, Fortress Monroe, Virginia. 18698. '87. (XVII)

QUARTZ CRYSTAL with flattened termination; quartz crystals interpenetrated; and
quartz crystals with implanted crystal.

CHARLES F. BROWN, Hot Springs, Arkansas. 18699. '87. (XVI)

METALLIC IRON, found 150 feet below the surface; for examination.

Dr. G. A. SWANN, Decatur, Texas. 18700. '87. (XVI)

SHORT-EARED OWL, *Asio accipitrinus.*

T. E. SKINNER, Smithsonian Institution. 18701. '87. (XII)

SHELLS, *Helix Cumberlandiana;* for examination.

E. E. JONES, Sewanee, Tennessee. 18702. '87. (IX)

BARNACLES, found attached to a wreck at Payta, Peru, 1886.

W. C. BABCOCK, lieutenant, U. S. Navy, U. S. Flagship *Hartford.* 18703. '87.
(XI)

"RED-FISH" or "FAT-HEAD", *Pimelometopon pulcher* Ayres.

Lieut. W. C. BABCOCK, U. S. Navy. 18703. '87. (VII)

ARIZONA JUNCO, *Junco cinereus palliatus* (skin).

F. STEPHENS, San Bernardino, California. 18704. '87. (V, A)

MINERALS

JOHN W. LANGDALE, Tacoma Station, District of Columbia. 18705. '87. (XVI)

MINERALS; for examination.

J. A. FITE, Resaca, Georgia. (Hon. J. C. Clements.) 18706. '87. (XVIII)

KAOLIN; for examination.

> Dr. WILLIS E. EVERETTE, Portland, Oregon. 18707. '87. (XVIII)

METEORIC IRON, from Orange River, Africa. (Exchange.)

> AMHERST COLLEGE, Amherst, Massachusetts. 18708. '87. (XVI)

SELENITE ; for examination.

> C. J. PERKINS, Daggett, San Bernardino County, California. 18709. '87. (XVI)

SPELTER, or metallic zinc.

> A. J. ROWLAND, Falkner, Mississippi. (Through Hon. J. B. Morgan.) 18710. '87. (XVIII)

GREY SQUIRREL, *Sciurus carolinensis* (albino).

> H. J. GIFFORD, Washington, District of Columbia. 18711. '87. (IV)

CANARY, "half cinnamon" variety.

> W. C. WEEDEN, U. S. National Museum. 18712. '87. (V, A)

BIRDS' EGGS: *Buteo latissimus* (3), *Anas obscura* (6), *Aix sponsa* (8).

> G. A. BOARDMAN, Calais, Maine. 18713. '87. (V, B)

SMALL-MOUTHED BLACK BASS, *Micropterus dolemiei;* for examination.

> H. H. ROTTAKEN, State Fish Commission, Little Rock, Arkansas. 18714. '87. (VII)

BIRD-SKINS.

> HENRY K. COALE, Chicago, Illinois. 18715. '87. (V, A)

FOSSILS.

> Prof. I. CONDON, Eugene, Oregon. 18716. '87. (XIII, B)

STURGEON HOOKS, Chinese; found in San Pablo Bay, 20 miles north of San Francisco.

> R. H. BUCKINGHAM, Fish Commissioner of the State of California, Sacramento, California. 18717. '87. (I)

INDIAN POTTERY (three specimens).

> J. K. WATSON, Shorter's Depot, Mason County, Alabama. 18718. '87. (II, B)

TOMAHAWK, clay pipe, three arrow-heads, and four stone implements. All of the specimens of this accession were washed up by the floods on the Tallapoosa River. (Purchased).

> J. K. WATSON, Shorter's Depot, Mason County, Alabama. 18718. '87. (III)

FELDSPAR.

> G. M. EDMONSTON, Milton, Iowa. 18719. '87. (XVI)

WOODEN SHOES, similar to those worn in Minnesota by the Swedes and Norwegians.

> REUBEN WRIGHT, Clifton Station, Virginia. 18720. '87. (II, A)

VIRGINIA DEER, *Cariacus virginianus;* from Titus County, Texas.

> REUBEN WRIGHT, Clifton Station, Virginia. 18720. '87. (XII)

ROCKS.

> JOHN N. ATWOOD, Keeseville, New York. 18721. '87. (XVII)

CORALS: *Diploria, Meandrina, Porites clavaria, Madracis, Mycedium fragile, Isophyllia dipsacea, Millepora olicornis, Occulina diffusa, O. varicosa, O. valenciennesii,* and *Gorgonidæ* (266 specimens); from Bermuda.

> WESLEYAN UNIVERSITY, Middletown, Connecticut. 18722. '87. (XI)

INDIAN FOODS; from Mexico.

> Dr. E. PALMER, Washington, District of Columbia. 18723. '87. (I)

ETHNOLOGICAL OBJECTS (9); from Jalisco and Guadalajara, Mexico. Also terra-cotta figures.

> Dr. E. PALMER, Washington, District of Columbia. 18723. '87. (II, A)

POTTERY, ancient and modern; from Mexico.

> Dr. E. PALMER, Washington, District of Columbia. 18723. '87. (II, B)

MATERIA MEDICA ; from Mexico.

> Dr. EDWARD PALMER, Washington, District of Columbia. 18723. '87. (I)

ROCKS; from Mexico.

> Dr. EDWARD PALMER, Washington, District of Columbia. 18723. '87. (XVII)

PLANTS; from Mexico. A very valuable collection.

Dr. EDWARD PALMER, Washington, District of Columbia. 18723. '87. (XV)

ARCHÆOLOGICAL OBJECTS: 3 obsidian nuclei, 4 obsidian chips, 2 very large obsidian knives, 6 worked obsidian flakes, 20 obsidian arrow-heads, 7 flint arrow-heads, 2 obsidian ornaments, stone chisel, 2 stone axes, metate, small mortar, rubbing or grinding stone, 2 stone carvings, and ornamented clay bead. (47 specimens.)

Dr. EDWARD PALMER, Washington, District of Columbia. 18723. '87. (III)

CONGLOMERATE of siliceous pebbles with ferrugineous cement; for examination.

FRANCIS B. PERRY, Greenfield Hill, Connecticut. 18724. '87. (XVII)

MEXICAN PLANTS.

C. G. PRINGLE, Charlotte, Vermont. 18725. '87. (XV)

FRACTIONAL PAPER CURRENCY, three-cents, 1863.

T. B. HOWE, Pataskola, Licking County, Ohio. 18726. '87. (I)

IRON PYRITES, and Brown Iron Ore; for examination.

B. A. HELTON, Hazel Spring, Virginia. 18727. '87. (XVI)

ROCK, apparently from a decomposed granite vein, containing a feldspar, mica, and obscure constituent; for examination.

Hon. T. D. JOHNSTON, House of Representatives. 18728. '87. (XVI)

MANGANESE ORE containing 0.365 per cent. phosphorus; for examination.

Hon. A. H. PETTIBONE, House of Representatives. 18729. '87. (XVIII)

BIRD-SKINS,* from Sonora, Mexico.

Lieut. H. C. BENSON, U. S. Army, Fort Huachuca, Arizona. 18730. '87. (V, V)

EGGS (3), of *Melospiza fasciata fallax*, from Arizona.

R. G. WHEELER, Alameda, California. 18731. '87. (V, B)

CANARY, *Serinus canariensis*.

WILLIAM C. WEEDEN, U. S. National Museum. 18732. '87. (XII)

BIRD-SKINS, 7 specimens in exchange, and 28 specimens presented.

ERNEST E. THOMPSON, Toronto, Ontario, Canada. 18733. '87. (V, A)

BRONZED GRACKLE, *Quiscalus quiscula æneus*, from Prince George's County, Maryland.

FRED. ZELLER, Washington, District of Columbia. 18734. '87. (V, A)

CLINTON AND ORISKANY FOSSILS: *Scolithus* sp.; *Spirifera arenosa*, Conrad; *S. arrecta*, Hall; *Orthis* sp. (?); *Platyceras magnificum*, Hall; *Pterinea* sp, (?). (22 specimens.)

U. S. GEOLOGICAL SURVEY, Washington, District of Columbia. (Through C. D. Walcott.) 18735. '87. (I)

KNIFE found embedded in the flesh of a cod-fish.

Capt. JOHN Q. GETCHELL, Gloucester, Massachusetts. 18736. '87. (I)

MATERIAL taken from flesh of cod-fish.

Capt. DONALD BEATON, Gloucester, Massachusetts. 18737. '87. (I)

CANARY, *Serinus canariensis*.

LOUIS SCHMID & SONS, Washington, District of Columbia. 18738. '87. (XII)

IRON PYRITES; for examination

H. J. GRAM, Moline, Texas. 18739. '87. (XVIII)

PHOTOGRAPHS of the Nushegak River scenery, and lakes of Alaskan Peninsula (64.) (Purchased.)

HENRY D. WOOLFE, San Francisco. 18740. '87. (II, A)

SHREW, *Blarina talpoides*, in the flesh; for examination.

AMBROSE PAGE, Salem, Roanoke County, Virginia. 18741. '87. (IV)

QUARTZ, with sulphide of iron (pyrites) and sulphide of lead (galena); for examination.

A. BARKLEY, Eastman, Mississippi. 18742. '87. (XVIII)

GUN FLINT, illustrating its manufacture at Brandon, England. (Exchange.)

EDWARD LOVETT, Outram Road, Croydon, England. 18743. '87. (II, A)

VOLCANIC DUST.

HENRY ZAHN, Denver, Colorado. 18744. '87. (XVII)

---

* See Proceedings, U. S. National Museum, Vol. 10, p. 148.

DORY (model), used in the vicinity of Martha's Vineyard for setting drag seines; built in 1875.

CHARLES GIFFORD, Vineyard Haven, Massachusetts. (Through Capt. J. W. Collins.) 18745. '87. (I)

GALVANIZED FISH HOOKS (4).

Capt. J. W. COLLINS, Washington, District of Columbia. 18746. '87. (I)

FRAGMENT of *Somerset*, British man-of-war, wrecked on Peaked Hill Bar in 1778.

Capt. JOHN Q. GETCHELL, Gloucester, Massachusetts. (Through Capt. J. W. Collins.) 18747. '87. (I)

GRIVET MONKEY, *Cercopithecus sabœus*.

ZOOLOGICAL SOCIETY OF PHILADELPHIA. (Through Arthur E. Brown, Esq.) 18748. '87. (IV)

BRICK from wall of China.

General A. C. JONES, U. S. consul, Chin-Kiang, China. 18749. '87. (I)

"NAPE BONE HOOK," used in the preparation of boneless cod.

Capt. GEORGE MERCHANT, Gloucester, Massachusetts. 18750. '87. (I)

GUINEA PIG, *Cavia aperea*.

LOUIS SCHMID & SONS, Washington, District of Columbia. 18751. '87. (XV)

MOLE CRICKET, belonging to the order Orthoptera; for examination.

Dr. D. M. BUTE, Burgaw, North Carolina. 18752. '87. (X)

FOSSIL OYSTER, *Ostrea sellæformis*.

JOHN D. BARTLETT, Washington, District of Columbia. 18753. '87. (IX)

MAHOGANY CASE, containing three guns. (Lent.)

JOSEPH S. PENDLETON, Washington, District of Columbia. 18754. '87. (II, A)

TERTIARY FOSSILS. (Exchange.)

S. H. DREW, Wanganui, New Zealand. 18755. '87. (X)

OBSIDIAN FLAKES (43), chert flakes (32), bone and shell-fish hook, cast of jade ornament, and eleven fragments of Moa bones. (Exchange.)

S. H. DREW, Wanganui, New Zealand. 18755. '87. (III)

GLOBE-FISH, *Tetrodon richei*. (Exchange.)

S. H. DREW, Wanganui, New Zealand. 18755. '87. (VII)

COPPER SPEAR-HEAD. (Purchased.)

W. W. ADAMS, Mapleton, Cayuga County, New York. 18756. '87. (III)

YOUNG DEER, *Cariacus* sp.; from British Honduras (?).

W. A. CONKLIN, Central Park Menagerie, New York. 18757. '87. (IV)

TASMANIAN WOLF, *Thylacinus cynocephalus*; Wombat, *Phascolomys wombat* (two specimens), and "Tasmanian Devil," *Dasyurus ursinus* (two specimens).

BALLARAT FISH ACCLIMATIZATION SOCIETY, Victoria, Tasmania. (Through New South Wales Zoological Society.) 18758. '87. (IV)

BIRDS' EGGS,* *Sitta pygmœa* (4 sets, 25 eggs); *Corvus cryptoleucus* (2 sets, 8 eggs); *Columba fasciata* (3 sets, 5 eggs); *Aphelocoma sieberii arizonœ* (1 set, 5 eggs); *Tyrannus vociferans* (1 set, 3 eggs); *Urubitinga anthracina* (1 egg).

Lieut. HARRY C. BENSON, U. S. Army, Fort Huachuca, Arizona. 18759. '87 (V, B)

ORE; for examination.

C. J. BROWN, Elmira, New York. 18760. '87. (XVI)

FLAKE CORE, from Montgomery County, North Carolina.

WILLIAM H. SMEATON, New York City. 18761. '87. (III)

HEMATITE IRON ORE; for examination.

L. H. LEZEOST, Evanston, Wyoming. 18762. '87. (XVI)

METALLIC PARTICLES containing iron, silica, and carbon, strongly magnetic; for examination.

Dr. G. A. SWANN, Decatur, Texas. 18763. '87. (XVI)

BIRDS (five specimens).

Dr. L. STEJNEGER, U. S. National Museum. 18764. '87. (V, A)

---

* See Proceedings U. S. National Museum, Vol. 10, p. 551.

BIRDS from India and western Africa (34 specimens).

H. K. COALE, Chicago, Illinois. 18765. '87. (V, A)

"SPINNER," *Attacus cercropia;* for examination.

GEORGE T. BARTLETT, Wilmington, Delaware. 18766. '87. (X)

WAX IMPRESSIONS of a coin.

Miss MARY COLLINS, Dorchester, Massachusetts. 18767. '87. (I)

HUMAN SKULLS (6), lower jaws (6), upper jaw; from mound and graves in Schuyler and Kane Counties, Illinois.

Mrs. ABNER FOSTER, Bardstown, Illinois. 18768. '87. (III)

BOX made of a portion of the heart of the "Signal Tree" on Allatoona Mountain, Georgia.

JOSEPH M. BROWN, Atlanta, Georgia. 18769. '87. (I)

ROCK; for examination.

RICHARD BENNETT, Whitcomb, Arkansas. 18770. '87. (XVIII)

ENGLISH ENGRAVINGS (1742–'50): "Voyage to Siam performed by six Jesuits," London, 1688; and "Vegetable Statics," S. Hales, London, 1731. (Deposited.)

J. S. PENDLETON, Washington, District of Columbia. 18771. '87. (II, A)

RED-TAILED HAWK, *Buteo borealis* (4 specimens).

Dr. A. K. FISHER, Washington, District of Columbia. 18772. '87. (XII)

STONE resembling a calf's head. (Returned.)

W. G. MCADOO, Knoxville, Tennessee. 18773. '87.

FOSSILS (small collection).

MUSEUM OF COMPARATIVE ZOOLOGY, Cambridge, Massachusetts. 18774. '87. (XIII, A)

FOX SPARROW, *Passerella iliaca*, and a goldfinch, *Carduelis carduelis.*

W. C. WEEDEN, U. S. National Museum. 18775. '87. (V, A)

PIG IRON.

C. COFFIN, Muirkirk, Prince George's County, Maryland. 18776. '87. (XVIII)

ORE, from Beaver Head County, Montana.

HENRY GARRETT, Dillon, Montana. 18777. '87. (XVIII)

LIGNITE and clay; for examination.

J. H. MEAD, Palestine, Texas. 18778. '87. (XVIII)

BIRDS (12 specimens).

DENIS GALE, Gold Hill, Colorado. 18779. '87. (V, B)

BIRDS' EGGS: *Megascops asio maxwelliæ* (4), *Dryobates villosus harrisii* (4), *Mimus polyglottos* (4), *Sitta carolinensis aculeata* (5), and *Harporhynchus rufus* (5).

DENIS GALE, Gold Hill, Colorado. 18779. '87. (V, B)

BIRD-SKINS; for examination. (Returned.)

GEORGE B. SENNETT, New York City. 18780. '87. (V, A)

QUARTZ CRYSTAL; for examination.

JAMES A. MULLIN, Ruston, Lincoln Parish, Louisiana. 18781. '87. (XVI)

POTSDAM QUARTZITE, with ripple marks (2 slabs); from Keeseville, New York.

CHARLES D. WALCOTT, U. S. Geological Survey. 18782. '87. (XVII)

FOX SPARROW, *Passerella iliaca.*

R. C. STEUART, U. S. National Museum. 18783. '87. (V, A)

PUPA of *Sphinx carolina*, and pupa of a noctuid, dried and broken.

Dr. D. M. BUIE, Burgaw, North Carolina. 18784. '87. (X)

SHELLS, *Patula cumberlandiana* Lea (2 specimens).

W. P. RYDER, Upper Marlborough, Maryland. (Through W. H. Dall.) 18785. '87. (IX)

"AXOLOTL", *Amblystoma mavortium* (larva); for examination.

S. D. KARUS, Deuel, Colorado. 18786. '87. (VI)

PHYLLOPOD CRUSTACEAN, *Opus* sp.; for examination.

S. D. KARUS, Deuel, Colorado. 18786. '87. (XI)

SOIL; for examination.

Dr. D. M. BUIE, Burgaw, North Carolina. 18787. '87. (XVII)

LARVA of an *Anthrenus* or *Dermestes* (broken skin); for examination.

A. E. THOMAS, Bellmore, Indiana. 18788. '87. (X)

LIMB of spruce tree, the outer surface covered with a limy substance; for examination.

JOHN FANNIN, Victoria, British Columbia. 18789. '87. (XV)

PLANT, *Malva* (?) sp.; for examination.

Mrs. C. V. S. HACHENBERG, Austin, Texas. 18790. '87. (XV)

GALENA; for examination.

WILLIAM H. BADGER, Hickman, Kentucky. 18791. '87. (XVII)

MINERALS (20 specimens); from Sterling Iron Mine. (Exchange.)

R. S. HODGE, Antwerp, New York. 18792. '87. (XVI)

CRYSTALLIZED MUSCOVITE (2 specimens), and crystallized muscovite, rutile, and calcite, (2 specimens); from Alexander County, North Carolina.

W. E. HIDDEN, Newark, New Jersey. 18793. '87. (XVI)

BLACK-FISH (2 specimens.) (Skeletons.)

A. J. AUSTIN, Keeper, Poyner's Hill Life-Saving Station, North Carolina. 18794. '87. (XII)

FOSSIL TEETH, tusk, and bones.

JAMES W. ROGAN, Rogersville, Tennessee. 18795. '87. (XII)

CALIFORNIA WOODPECKER, *Melanerpes formicivorus bairdi;* from Camp Lowell, Arizona.

F. STEPHENS, San Bernardino, California. 18796. '87. (V, A)

GAY-LUSSITE, from Ragtown, Nevada.

I. C. RUSSEL, U. S. Geological Survey. 18797. '87. (XVI)

AUDUBON'S SHEARWATER, *Puffinus auduboni;* from the Bahamas (2 specimens). (Exchange.)

C. J. MAYNARD & Co., Boston, Massachusetts. 18798. '87. (V, A)

BAT, *Atalapha cinerea,* var. *grayi;* from Buenos Ayres.

BRITISH MUSEUM, London, England. 18799. '87. (IV)

CALIFORNIA VALLEY QUAIL.

GUSTAV EISEN, Fresno, California. 18800. '87. (V, A)

MEDALS and badges of societies, expositions, and historical events (190 specimens).

W. H. WARNER & BRO., Philadelphia, Pennsylvania. 18801. '87. (I)

BIRDS' NESTS AND EGGS: Blue Yellow-back Warbler (4 eggs and 2 nests); Redstart (3 eggs and 2 nests); Maryland Yellow-throat (3 eggs and 1 nest); Golden-crowned Thrush (2 eggs and 1 nest); Hermit Thrush (7 eggs and 1 nest); Barn Swallow (3 eggs); Cow Bunting (1 egg); Song Sparrow (4 eggs and 2 nests); Screech Owl (5 eggs); Belted Kingfisher (7 eggs); Red-wing Blackbird (4 eggs and 1 nest); Purple Grackle (5 eggs and 2 nests); Yellow-shafted Flicker (13 eggs); Catbird (3 eggs and 1 nest); King-bird (1 nest); Mandarin Duck (2 eggs).

VINAL N. EDWARDS, Wood's Holl, Massachusetts. 18802. '87. (V, B)

BLACK SWAN, *Chen pis atrata.*

W. A. CONKLIN, Central Park Menagerie, New York City. 18803. '87. (V, A)

EGGS of *Larus franklinii* (1 set of 3 eggs), from Heron Lake, Minnesota.

J. PARKER NORRIS, Philadelphia, Pennsylvania. 18804. '87. (V, B)

RED-TAILED HAWK, *Buteo borealis,* and Red shouldered Hawk, *B. lineatus* (2 specimens each), from Montgomery County, Maryland.

A. K. FISHER, Department of Agriculture. 18805. '87. (XII)

SHREWS, *Sorex vagrans* (4 specimens).

Dr. J. C. MERRILL, U. S. Army, Fort Klamath, Oregon. 18806. '87. (IV)

COPPER COIN issued by Austria for use in Flanders, 1684.

CHARLES F. BILLOPP, Washington, District of Columbia. 18807. '87. (I)

INDIAN ARROW-HEADS and spear-heads (206).

CHARLES A. HARRINGTON, Vinitaville, Virginia. 18808. '87 (III)

WORMS FROM THE INTESTINE OF A SEAL.

U. S. FISH COMMISSION, Washington, District of Columbia. (Through Vinal N. Edwards.) 18809. '87. (XI)

LICE, from seals.

U. S. FISH COMMISSION, Washington, District of Columbia. 18809. '87. (X)

GREEN TURQUOISE, from Los Cerillos, New Mexico.

W. C. GREGORY, Cincinnati, Ohio. 18810. '87. (XVI)

"TIGER EYE," from Orange River, South Africa.

HENRY HORAN, U. S. National Museum. 18811. '87. (XVI)

SHOEMAKING MATERIALS, such as are used by the Navajo Indian shoemakers.

W. M. STEPHEN, Keam's Cañon, Arizona. 18812. '87. (II, A)

SILVER COIN, di-drachma, of Syracuse, Sicily, about 410 to 450 B. C.

H. WEIDENBACH, Washington, District of Columbia. 18813. '87. (I)

TWO-DOLLAR BILL of Farmers' Exchange Bank, Gloucester, Rhode Island, November 4, 1800; and two silver coins, 5 cents and 10 cents, of Danish West Indies.

W. C. GREGORY, Cincinnati, Ohio. 18814. '87. (I)

DIAMOND BRILLIANTS (106), weight 4.23 grams, and 27 diamond chips, not weighed, total about 21 carats; 148 perforated pearls, weight 35.88 grams, and 2 large pear-shaped pearls, weight 2.98 grams. (Presented to the United States Government by the Imaum of Muscat in 1840.)

TREASURY DEPARTMENT, Washington, District of Columbia. 18815. '87. (XVI)

GOLD PLATE, inside lining of snuff-box; silk cord and tassel; gold ornament. and two lumps of gold. (Presented to the United States Government by the Imaum of Muscat in 1840.)

TREASURY DEPARTMENT, Washington, District of Columbia. 18815. '87. (XVIII)

ATTAR OF ROSES (1 bottle, sealed). (Presented to the United States Government, in 1840, by the Imaum of Muscat.)

TREASURY DEPARTMENT, Washington, District of Columbia. 18815. '87. (I)

BALD EAGLE, *Haliœtus leucocephalus* (skeleton).

T. J. POYNER, Poplar Branch, North Carolina. 18816. '87. (XII)

GOLDFINCH, *Carduelis carduelis* (skeleton).

LOUIS SCHMID & SONS, Washington, District of Columbia. 18817. '87. (XII)

FOSSILS, *Bolboporites americanus*, from the Chazy formation, Terrebonne, Canada.

EDWARD ARDLEY, Peter Redpath Museum, Montreal, Canada. 18818. '87. (XIII, A)

COPPER ORE and black quartz; for analysis.

B. A. HELTON, Hazel Spring, Virginia. 18819. '87. (XVI)

COLEOPTERA.

Rev. F. GARDNER, Jr., Sioux Falls, Dakota. 18820. '87. (X)

ORIGINAL PLATE of "Ariadne," engraved by A. B. Durand; a very fine specimen of line engraving.

JOHN DURAND, South Orange, New Jersey. 18821. '87. (I)

PIERCED TABLET and a broken boat-shaped implement; for examination.

LAFAYETTE FARRIS, Princetown, Highland County, Ohio. 18822. '87. (III)

BARITE; for examination.

Dr. J. W. PEARSON, Colorado, Texas. 18823. '87. (XVI)

JET of inferior quality; for examination.

Dr. J. W. PEARSON, Colorado, Texas. 18823. '87. (XVIII)

SELENITE; for examination.

Hon. THOMAS C. MCRAE, Prescott, Arkansas. 18824. '87. (XVI)

HERONS,* *Ardea wuerdemanni*, from Cape Sable, Florida; for examination. (Returned.)

R. C. STUART, Tampa, Florida. 18825. '87. (V, A)

COBALT and nickel ore.

GEORGE LOVELOCK, Lovelock, Nevada. 18826. '87. (XVIII)

ORE.

W. H. BECK, Washington, District of Columbia. 18827. '87. (XVIII)

INSECTS; for study and comparison.

E. L. GRAEF, Brooklyn, New York. 18828. '87. (X)

*See Proceedings U. S. National Museum, Vol. 10, p. 112.

BEECH WOOD, a curious malformation, resembling human head; for examination (Returned.)

Dr. H. A. TINGLEY, Susquehanna, Pennsylvania. 18829. '87. (XV)

LIMONITE, from near Village Springs, Jefferson County, Alabama.

FRANK BURNS, U. S. Geological Survey. 18830. '87. (XVI)

MARINE SHELLS, 6 species, from Florida; for examination.

Mrs. J. A. HENSHALL, Cynthiana, Kentucky. (Through W. H. Dall.) 18831. '87. (IX)

LAND AND FRESH-WATER SHELLS, 6 varieties; from Texas and Louisiana.

HARRY E. PILSBRY, Davenport, Iowa. (Through W. H. Dall.) 18832. '87. (IX)

LIGNITE; for examination.

L. V. MARYE, Alexandria, Louisiana. 18833. '87. (XVIII)

MANDARIN DUCKS, *Aix galericulata*; from Wood's Holl, Massachusetts.

FRED. MATHER, Cold Spring Harbor, New York. 18834. '87. (V, A)

LIMONITE (probably pseudomorph after pyrite) in quartz; for examination.

W. TERTSH LANDER, Williamston, South Carolina. 18835. '87. (XVIII)

COINS: Medal struck by French Government to commemorate the victories of the French army under Napoleon in Italy; Spanish silver coins; Grecian, Austrian, English and Danish West Indies, East Indian, and Japanese coins; for examination. (Returned.)

F. T. BESSAC, Natchez, Mississippi. 18836. '87. (I)

WILD-TURKEY, *Meleagris gallopavo*, male.

JAMES BELL, Gainesville, Florida. 18837. '87. (V, A)

MODEL of Pueblo Shamopavi, ancient province of Tusayan, Moki, Arizona; in exchange for old model.

BUREAU OF ETHNOLOGY, Washington. 18838. '87. (II, A)

PLANT, *Malva* (?) sp.; for examination.

Dr. O. EASTLAND, Wichita Falls, Texas. 18839. '87. (XV)

MICROSCOPIC SLIDE, containing what was supposed to be volcanic dust; for examination.

GEORGE H. CURTIS, Cincinnati, Ohio. 18840. '87. (XVII)

QUARTZ with particles of mica, and rock crystal and amethyst; for examination.

S. B. HENSHAW, Stanardsville, Virginia. 18841. '87. (XVI)

PORTION OF MANDIBLE of a fossil horse with three molar teeth in position; for examination.

TRAVIS MORSE, Scott City, Kansas. 18842. '87. (XII)

UNITED STATES POSTAGE STAMPS, newspaper stamps, and wrappers, and stamped envelopes (170 specimens).

POST-OFFICE DEPARTMENT, Washington, District of Columbia. (Through A. D. Hazen, Third Assistant Postmaster-General.) 18843. '87. (I)

SPARROW HAWK, *Tinnunculus sparverius*; from Maryland.

Dr. A. K. FISHER, Department of Agriculture, District of Columbia. 18844. '87. (XII)

QUARTZ, apparently from a talcose schist; for examination.

LEONARD CONRAD, Stoutsville, Ohio. 18845. '87. (XVI)

RABBIT, *Lepus callotis*.

Dr. R. W. SHUFELDT, U. S. Army, Fort Wingate, New Mexico. 18846. '87. (XII)

BLACK-FISH, *Globiocephalus* sp. (skeletons and cranium).

JOHN G. WEBB, Osprey, Florida. (Through Joseph Willcox.) 18847. '87. (XII)

INSECTS, *Cis* nov. sp. (10 specimens).

WILLIAM H. CRANE, Cincinnati, Ohio. 18848. '87. (X)

MUD-FISH or Bowfin, *Amia calva* L. (head); for examination.

H. V. NORZKY, Rosetta, Florida. 18849. '87. (VII)

ORES; for assay.

Lieut. H. E. NICHOLS, U. S. Navy. 18850. '87. (XVI)

VIOLIN supposed to be a genuine "Stradivarius." (Returned.)

H. M. ELLINGTON, Mineral Bluff, Georgia. 18851. '87. (I)

BOX OF TOY FURNITURE.

(Donor not known.) 18852. '87. (II)

SPONGES, hydroids, etc.; from Florida.

U. S. GEOLOGICAL SURVEY, Washington, District of Columbia. (Through W. H. Dall.) 18853. '87. (XI)

FOSSILS and rocks; from Florida.

U. S. GEOLOGICAL SURVEY, Washington, District of Columbia. (Through W. H. Dall.) 18853. '87. (XI)

METEORIC IRON (1 specimen); from Allen County, Kentucky. (Deposited.)

CHARLES U. SHEPARD, Jr., Charleston, South Carolina. 18854. '87. (XVI)

YELLOW-QUARTZ SEAL; from Germany. (Deposited.)

THOMAS WILSON, Washington, District of Columbia. 18855. '87. (XVI)

ORE; for examination.

Hon. J. T. MORGAN, U. S. Senate. 18856. '87. (XVIII)

FISHES: *Lepomis pallidus*, *Malthe cubifrons*, *Batrachus tau*, and *Paralichthys albigutta* (5 specimens); also fish skull; from Florida.

W. H. DALL, U. S. National Museum. 18857. '87. (VII)

MOLLUSKS and dry shells; from Charlotte Harbor, Florida.

W. H. DALL, U. S. National Museum. 18857. '87. (IX)

POST-PLIOCENE ROCK containing Indian pottery; from Sarasota Bay, near Osprey, Florida.

W. H. DALL, U. S. National Museum. 18857. '87. (II, A)

CRUSTACEA, radiates, ascidians, and sponges.

W. H. DALL, U. S. National Museum. 18857. '87. (XI)

SPIDERS: *Gasteracantha rufospinosa* and *Dioclus chryosorrhocus* Fabr.

W. H. DALL, U. S. National Museum. 18857. '87. (X)

CALCITE and iron pyrites; for examination.

Capt. JACK SCOTT, Dallas, Texas. 18858. '87. (XVI)

BITUMINOUS COAL; for examination.

S. D. EDWARDS, Era, Idaho Territory. 18859. '87. (XVIII)

FOSSIL CORAL: *Striatopora*, *Cladopora*, and *Diphyphyllum*; also *Spirifera pinonensis* and *Dalmanites meeki* of the Devonian age; for examination.

E. H. ROSE, Eureka, Nevada. 18860. '87. (XIII, A)

FERRUGINOUS CONCRETION OF SANDSTONE; for examination.

PETER CAMERON, Sandy Hook, New Jersey. 18861. '87. (XVIII)

MAMMAL SKINS. (Purchased.)

F. STEPHENS, San Bernardino, California. 18862. '87. (IV)

BIRD-SKINS (33 specimens). (Purchased.)

F. STEPHENS, San Bernardino, California. 18862. '87. (V, A)

CASTS (6) of depressions produced by grinding stone implements from the rock on which the depressions occur, at Middletown, Rhode Island.

EDWARD L. HYDE, Middleborough, Massachusetts. 18863. '87. (III)

LEGAL PARCHMENTS (34) and other papers in the Flemish language, fourteenth to eighteenth century; piece of amber; signet; 564 ancient Grecian and Roman coins; 179 modern coins; and 22 casts of portrait-medals. (Deposited.)

THOMAS WILSON, Washington, District of Columbia. 18864. '87. (I)

WOOLEN BLANKET, worn by Navajo women. (Exchange.)

Dr. WASHINGTON MATTHEWS, U. S. A., Bureau of Ethnology. 18865. '87. (II, A)

BRASS WARMING-PAN.

JOSEPH PALMER, U. S. National Museum. 18866. '87. (II, A)

REALGAR; for examination.

C. G. TALCOTT, assistant engineer, U. S. Navy. 18867. '87. (II, A)

ARABIAN HARP, "kanoon." (Exchange.)
> Mrs. M. E. BROWN, South Orange, New Jersey. 18868. '87. (I)

SULPHIDES in quartz; for examination.
> SIMON K. WORSTELL, Coronado, Wichita County, Kansas. 18869. 'o7. (XVIII)

ROCK, apparently serpentine; for examination.
> CHARLES F. HAYWARD, Los Angeles, California. 18870. '87. (XVI)

IRON PYRITES in quartz; for examination.
> A. H. WEBB, Hazel Spring, Virginia. 18871. '87. (XVI)

CALCITE PAPER-WEIGHTS (2), from near Upper Soda Springs, Siskiyou County, California.
> J. S. DILLER, U. S. Geological Survey. 18872. '87. (XVI)

CRYSTALS, found in gray limestone.
> Dr. H. H. THORPE, Liberty Hill, Texas. 18873. '87. (XVI)

HALIBUT, *Hippoglossus hippoglossus* L., having in its stomach a partly digested freshwater catfish, *Amiurus albidus;* from Colonial Beach. (Purchased.)
> R. A. GOLDEN, Washington, District of Columbia. 18874. '87. (XII)

RIBBON BADGE of the "Nullifiers," or advocates of state rights, Charleston, South Carolina, 1832.
> ST. JULIAN FILLETTE, Washington, District of Columbia. 18875. '87. (I)

GARNETS; for examination. (Purchased.)
> S. G. MAXWELL, Bluffton, Texas. 18876. '87. (XVI)

FLANGED PLATE, showing the effect upon cast-iron of long-continued action of the products of combustion of anthracite coal.
> General M. C. MEIGS, U. S. Army, Washington, District of Columbia. 18877. '87. (XVII)

BAHAMA CUCKOO, *Saurothera bahamensis;* for examination.
> W. T. MCLEOD, Nassau, Bahamas. 18878. '87. (V, A)

BIRD SKINS, 3 species, one (*Accipiter fringilloides*) new to the collection; 9 specimens.
> Dr. JOHN GUNDLACH, Fermina, Cuba. 18879. '87. (V, A)

CONCRETIONS.
> CHARLES RUBY, Fort Apache, Arizona. 18880. '87. (XIII, A)

FOSSILS: *Arthrophycus harlani* Conrad, *Calamites, Graptolites, Sponge, Euomphalus, Ophileta compacta* Salter, *Chœtetes, Orthoceras annulatum* Sowerby, Knox dolomite, *Maclurea* (20 specimens).
> W. C. BAYLESS, Mossy Creek, Tennessee. 18881. '87. (XIII, A)

FOSSILS: *Orthis* sp. (4 specimens); from Trenton formation, Minneapolis, Minnesota.
> C. W. HALL, University of Minnesota, Minneapolis, Minnesota. 18882. '87. (XIII, A)

AFRICAN PARAKEET.
> Dr. W. W. GODDING, Washington, District of Columbia. 18883. '87. (V, A)

PHOTOGRAPHS representing Lapland and Hungarian customs (3). (Deposited.)
> Mrs. E. S. BRINTON, Washington, District of Columbia. 18884. '87. (II, A)

SILVER MEDALS (2) made for ornaments; for examination.
> CHARLES KOHLER, Brick Church, New Jersey. 18885. '87. (I)

HORNET'S NEST, *Vespa maculata* L.
> Hon. WADE HAMPTON, United States Senate. 18886. '87. (X)

FOSSIL CORALS; from Florida.
> Col. W. G. BARTHOLOMEW, Tampa, Florida. 18887. '87. (XI)

LIMONITE or brown hematite of good quality; for examination.
> A. R. JOHNSON, Burnet, Texas. 18888. '87. (XVIII)

MARBLES AND GRANITE; for examination.
> A. R. JOHNSON, Burnet, Texas. 18888. '87. (XVII)

PHOTOGRAPHS of Es-ta-yesht, sister of Mariana, chief of the Navajos, and Choli, nephew of Mariana.
> Dr. R. W. SHUFELDT, U. S. Army, Fort Wingate, New Mexico. 18889. '87. (II, A)

FISHES: Sea-herring, *Clupea harengus* (larval)?; Rockling, *Onos cimbrius;* Stickleback, *Gasterosteus gymnurus;* Hake, *Phycis* sp.; and Pollock, *Pollachius virens*, taken from the mouth of a mackerel; for examination.

Capt. WILLIAM HERRICK, Swan's Island, Hancock County, Maine. 18890. '87. (VII)

COPEPODA; taken from the throat of a mackerel.

Capt. WILLIAM HERRICK, Swan's Island, Hancock County, Maine. 18890. '87. (XI)

CASTS OF BONE IMPLEMENTS AND CARVINGS. The originals were found in caves at La Madeleine, Laugerie (Haute et Basse), and Brumiquel.

MUSÉE DE SAINT GERMAIN, Paris, France. 18891. '87. (III)

HEMATITE IRON ORE; for examination.

I. E. WELCH, Alpine, Alabama. 18892. '87. (XVIII)

ORES.

FRED E. LINES, Albany, Oregon. 18893. '87. (XVIII)

WEATHERED ROCK.

Donor not known. 18894. '87. (XVII)

BIRD SKELETON, *Penelope superciliosa.*

ZOOLOGICAL SOCIETY OF PHILADELPHIA. (Through Arthur E. Brown, Esq.) 18895. '87. (XII)

SULPHIDE OF IRON; for examination.

Hon. H. S. VAN EATON, Washington, District of Columbia. 18896. '87. (XVIII)

WROUGHT IRON (5 specimens), containing aluminum; for examination.

Capt. A. A. THOMAS, Washington, District of Columbia. 18897. '87. (XVIII)

ETHNOLOGICAL OBJECTS: Shirt of chain mail, pair of gauntlets (plate and chain), pair of elaborately carved pattens, musical instrument with sounding-board of gourd, native fiddle and bow, brass drum with drumstick (?) of hide, two whistling arrows, stock of cross-bow, pair of elaborately ornamented and inlaid pattens, drum hollowed out of one piece of wood and covered with snake-skin, club and sagobeater of black wood (slightly damaged at the point), two long arrows without notches or feathers, paddle-shaped black-wood club, paddle with short and broad blade, two arrows, two poisoned arrows (human-bone points and hard-wood foreshafts), two not poisoned, ¡ ouch of leather (ornamented), pair of leather leggings, tomtom or drum of hammered copper, two assegais (one short for stabbing), two arrows, two iron-pointed arrows and two bone-pointed arrows used by Bushmen, fluted club of ebony, chief's staff, two gourd bowls, two gourd spoons, wooden spoon used by peasants, and a cap of woven grass; from Persia, India, Japan, New Guinea, Solomon Islands, New Hebrides, New Zealand, Africa, Nubia, Russia, Italy, and Central and South America. (Exchange.)

CHARLES HEAPE, Manchester, England. 18898. '87. (II, A)

BOMBYCID, *Attacus cecropia* Linn.; for examination.

JOHN S. WEBB, Disputanta, Virginia. 18899. '87. (X)

CHINESE SUN-AND-MOON DIAL.

Dr. D. BETHUNE MCCARTEE, Washington, D. C. 18900. '87. (II, A)

ROCKS, from Europe. (Exchanged.)

B. STÜRTZ, Bonn, Prussia. 18901. '87. (XVI)

HAWK, *Accipiter cooperi* (2 specimens).

H. MARSHALL, Laurel, Maryland. 18902. '87. (V, A)

RIBBON BADGE of Young Men's Democratic Club of the District of Columbia.

JOHN H. DOYLE, Washington, D. C. (Through P. L. Jouy.) 18903. '87. (I)

IMPURE HEMATITE, from North Carolina.

Col. W. A. NIXON, Washington, District of Columbia. 18904. '87. (XVIII)

SEED of the Blue and Salt Brush. Collected in Australia by H. C. Mais.

JOSEPH S. SPINNEY, New York City. 18905. '87. (XV)

EGGS (2) of *Syrnium nebulosum alleni*, from Lee County, Texas.

J. PARKER NORRIS, Philadelphia, Pennsylvania. 18906. '87. (V, B)

H. Mis. 600, pt. 2——43

INDIAN RELICS.   (Purchased.)
    J. W. EMMERT, Bristol, Tennessee.   18907.   '87.   (III)
FOSSIL PLANT, *Stigmaria fucoides* (?).
    J. W. EMMERT, Bristol, Tennessee.   18907.   '87.   (XIV)
OBJECTS OF ART: Pair of antique bronze vases, modern bronze bowl, bronze candle-
    stick, pair of shoes, and pair of slippers, from Damascus; peasant's traveling
    box, stolkjearee village cart (model), cariole (model), portrait (Christian IV,
    reigned from 1596 to 1648), peasant's jackknife, carved wooden spoon, carved
    wooden jewel case, pair of white cotton knit gloves, pair of embroidered woolen
    gloves, peasant's scarlet belt (five silver ornaments), forty-five photographs of
    costumes, doll (costume complete) from Norway; Swedish vase, from Sweden;
    blue shoe, russet slippers, two-stringed musical instrument, straw basket, brass
    tray, pair earthen pitchers, vase, and plate, from Tunis; glass jugs and goblets,
    from Bohemia; Hungarian porcelain jug, plate, cup and saucer, earthen pitcher,
    porcelain plate, blue porcelain cup and plate, gravy dish, from Hungary; plate,
    representation of ancient ware and jug, from Switzerland; majolica pitcher and
    plate, figures of peasants coming to market eating, fisherman, fisherman seated,
    Capo de Monti vase, earthen lamp (Bacchus), copy of Etruscan lamp, from
    Italy; earthen antique lamp, from excavated palace of Cæsar; antique lamp,
    from Roman columbaria; antique lamp, modern Roman brass lamp, copy of
    Pompeian lamp, copy of two Pompeian bronze lamps, reproduction of catacomb
    lamp, copy of antique inkstand, Roman bronze; statuettes: Mercury of John
    of Bologna; marble base from tomb of Augustus; Remus and Romulus and the
    wolf; Roman chariot and horses; copy of antique biga in Vatican; pair of child-
    ren's plaited rag shoes, from Northern Italy; earthen lamp, from Joseph's tomb,
    Syria; pair of wooden sandals, from the island of Rhodes; pair of red shoes,
    from Athens, Greece; set of Pan's pipes, inkstand and pen-holder, from Cairo,
    Egypt; lace cap, straw bonnets, from Antwerp; German beer jug and bottle, from
    Vienna Exhibition; German and Italian peasants' slippers; pair of Holland shoes;
    reproduction of old French coffee-pot (two hundred years ago); double bottle;
    small nappy faience de Gien; enameled brass Byzantine prayer tablet; tenth cen-
    tury; silver prayer amulet, in constant use by members of the Greek church; small
    piece insertion, Russian peasant's, from Moscow market, set Hungarian jewelry,
    one brooch and two ear-rings, copied from originals two hundred years old (in a
    case); silver brooch, design being the bow they place above a horse in harness,
    from Russia; silver filigree cup-holder and earthen cup, from silver bazar, Dam-
    ascus; silver bracelet, six coins set in filigree, from silver bazar, Damascas,
    Syria; silver filigree cross, from Genoa, Italy; silver amulet, from the mountains
    of Lebanon, supposed to be two hundred years old; silver bracelet and neck-
    lace, from Roumania; silver chain with pendants of coins of Christian IV, 1617;
    and Christian V, 1654, pair gilt silver bangle rings, supposed to be two hundred
    years old, ancient silver brooch, silver filigree buttons, peasant's coat, from Nor-
    way; silver ear-rings, from Cairo; silver necklace (chain work with forty-eight
    bangles), modern Egyptian, silver purse with sliding cover, from Egypt; pam-
    phlet: Funereal Discourse, Samuel Mather, D. D., of Boston, Massachusetts,
    printed 1738; books: "Psalms and Hymns," "Discourse Concerning the Nature
    of Man," 1694, "De Pace Regis," Pulton; 1609, "Exercitations on the Epistle to
    the Hebrews," J. Owen, D. D., 1663, "Controversy upon the Catechism," Andrew
    Willet, 1634; reproduction of a catacomb lamp of the fourth and fifth centuries;
    antique bronze Pompeian lamp; small unmounted photograph of the catacombs;
    Russian tea cloth; Russian toilet towel (legend, "A man can have gray hair but
    the devil in his heart"); toilet towel, bought at Smyrna; and ancient oriental
    embroidery, part of a mantel cloth, from Constantinople; pina sash (fiber of
    the pine apple); part of a Turkish costume, embroidered; and one photograph.
    (Deposited.)
    Mrs. E. S. BRINTON, Washington, District of Columbia.   18908.   '87.   (I)

BIRDS.

U. S. FISH COMMISSION, Washington, District of Columbia. (Through Vinal N. Edwards.) 18909. '87. (V, A)

ROCK containing particles of mica; for examination.

JOHN COLE, Cedar Point, Virginia. 18910. '87. (XVI)

ALLIGATOR, *Alligator mississippiensis;* from St. Augustine, Florida.

Dr. I. E. NAGLE, West Winsted, Connecticut. 18911. '87. (VI)

FLOWER; for examination.

CHARLES BATTEY, Buffalo, New York. 18912. '87. (XV)

MINERALS: polyadelphite, fowlerite, tephroite, and calcite (1 specimen), from Franklin, New York. (Exchange.)

JOHN W. LANGDALE, Tacoma, District of Columbia. 18913. '87. (XVI)

LITHOGRAPHIC LIMESTONE, from Tennessee; for examination.

JOHN M. BISHOP, Washington, District of Columbia. 18914. '87. (XVII)

SLATE and ore; for examination.

J. H. BORDWINE, Greendale, Virginia. 18915. '87. (XVIII)

FERRUGINOUS SANDSTONE, fragments; for examination.

F. T. BESSAC, Natchez, Mississippi. 18916. '87. (XVI)

GUANO.

W. NATION, Lima, Peru. 18917. '87. (I)

WALL-EYED PIKE, *Stizostedium vitreum,* Mitchill, from the Connecticut River; for examination.

Prof. WILLIAM NORTH RICE, Wesleyan University, Middletown, Connecticut. 18918. '87. (VII)

MOLLUSK; large specimen in alcohol; from near Cedar Keys.

Lieut. J. F. MOSER, U. S. Navy, commanding Coast Survey steamer *A. D. Bache.* 18919. '87. (IX)

MARINE INVERTEBRATES, from the vicinity of Cedar Keys, Florida.

Lieut. J. F. MOSER, U. S. Navy, commanding Coast Survey steamer *A. D. Bache.* 18919. '87. (XI)

MUHLENBURG'S TERRAPIN, *Chelopus muhlenbergii.*

F. C. HILL, College of New Jersey, Princeton, New Jersey. 18920. '87. (VI)

ORE containing small quantity of oxide and carbonate of iron; for examination.

J. T. PAXTON, Lick Run, Virginia. 18921. '87. (XVIII)

IRON ORE, slag, and quicklime (8 specimens); for examination.

Hon. M. C. BUTLER, Edgefield Court-House, South Carolina. 18922. '87. (XVIII)

CHERT CONCRETIONS from limestone, cellular and crystallized quartz, dolomite, etc.; for examination.

RICHARD GRAHAM and J. ROGERS & Co., Knoxville, Tennessee. 18923. '87. (XVIII)

ORE resembling zinc; for examination.

GEORGE W. KUHNEST, Bristol, Tennessee. 18924. '87. (XVIII)

FRESH-WATER SHELLS,* *Goniobasis* sp., from San Marco Springs, Hays County, Texas.

ROBERT T. HILL, U. S. Geological Survey, Washington. 18925. '87. (IX)

MINERALS.

Dr. H. H. THORPE, Liberty Hill, Texas. 18926. '87. (XVI)

ARROW-HEADS (7).

HOWARD SHRIVER, Wytheville, Virginia. 18927. '87. (III)

DECOMPOSED MAGNETITE of good quality, and white ore supposed by sender to contain zinc; for examination.

S. L. KING, Bristol, Tennessee. 18928. '87. (XVIII)

MUHLENBERG'S TERRAPIN (2).

F. C. HILL, Princeton, New Jersey. 18929. '87. (VI)

---

* See Proceedings U. S. National Museum, Vol. 9, p. 253.

LUMP FISH, *Cyclopterus lumpus* L.
> JOSEPH F. REED, Keeper, Island Beech Life-Saving Station, Tom's River, New Jersey. 18930. '87. (VII)

GREAT WHITE HERON, *Ardea occidentalis* Aud.; from Florida. (Purchased.)
> R. C. STUART, Tampa, Florida. 18931. '87. (V, A)

KINGFISHER, *Ceryle alcyon*, in the flesh.
> COPELAND JONES, Washington, District of Columbia. (Through A. Howard Clark.) 18932. '87. (V, A)

MARINE INVERTEBRATES: Small collection taken by *Albatross* off Fort Monroe.
> U. S. FISH COMMISSION. 18933. '87. (XI)

FISHES: *Clupea vernalis, Micropogon undulatus, Phycis regius, Bothus maculatus*, and *Achirus mollis.*
> U. S. FISH COMMISSION. 18933. '87. (VII)

BRONZE MEDAL struck December, 1886, in commemoration of the three hundredth anniversary of the University of Grätz.
> UNIVERSITY OF GRÄTZ, Austria. 18934. '87. (I)

CHROME ORES; from Oxford, Chester County, Pennsylvania; Del Norte, Placer, and San Luis Obispo Counties, California, and Alexandretta, Syria.
> BALTIMORE CHROME WORKS, Baltimore, Maryland. 18935. '87. (XVIII)

BIRDS.
> U. S. FISH COMMISSION. (Through Vinal N. Edwards, Wood's Holl, Massachusetts.) 18936. '87. (V, A)

FROGS (3), *Rana catesbiana*; for examination.
> A. C. WIGHTMAN, Baltimore, Maryland. 18937. '87. (VI)

ORE.
> L. H. JEROME, Tucson, Arizona. 18938. '87. (XVIII)

HERMIT THRUSH, *Turdus pallasi*, Cab.; for examination.
> Dr. C. S. THORNTON, Moorestown, New Jersey. 18939. '87. (XII)

CRAY FISHES (5).
> H. G. HODGE, York, Clark County, Illinois. 18940. '87. (XI)

BIRD SKINS (102 specimens). (Purchased.)
> E. W. NELSON, Springerville, Arizona. 18941. '87. (V, A)

ORIENTAL AND EUROPEAN COINS, silver, copper, etc. (99 specimens).
> Lieut. T. DIX BOLLES, U. S. Navy. 18942. '87. (I)

PETRIFIED WOOD.
> W. G. ROBINSON, Rosston, Cooke County, Texas. 18943. '87. (XV)

LARVA of *Trogosita* sp.; for examination.
> HENRY M. RAND, Hanover, Pennsylvania. 18944. '87. (X)

BIRD-SKINS. (Returned.)
> GEORGE N. LAWRENCE, New York City. 18945. '87. (V, A)

CETACEAN VERTEBRA, *Zeuglodon* sp.
> GEORGE DUFFY, Alexandria, Virginia. 18946. '87. (XII)

GRAY PARROT, *Psittacus erythacus*, in the flesh.
> LOUIS SCHMID & SONS, Washington, District of Columbia. 18947. '87. (XII)

BIRD-SKINS, *Molothrus æneus* (6 specimens); also specimens for examination.
> GEORGE B. SENNETT, American Museum Natural History, New York Ci y. 18948. '87. (V, A)

WORM-EATEN PLANKS (3) taken out of schooner *Melissa S. Robbins*, of Portland, Maine.
> U. S. FISH COMMISSION. (Through W. A. Wilcox.) 18949. '87. (IX)

KAMTSCHATKAN SEA EAGLE, *Thalassodetes pelagicus*, in transition plumage.
> Dr. L. STEJNEGER, U. S. National Museum. 18950. '87. (V, A)

GROUSE: *Bonasa* sp. (3 specimens) and *Pediocætes* sp. (2 specimens).
> ERNEST E. THOMPSON, Toronto, Canada. (Through Dr. C. Hart Merriam.) 18951. '87. (V, A)

CARP, *Cyprinus carpio.*

S. R. FRED, Middleburgh, Virginia. 18952. '87. (VII)

CALCITE; for examination.

E. R. FERRIS, Beelerville, Kansas. 18953. '87. (XVI)

INSECTS:* *Penthetria* sp. and cocoon, *Forficula* sp. and eggs, *Anisomorpha buprestoides* (4 specimens), *Pityophthorus manzanita* (2 specimens) and samples of work, *Thysanoes ficus,* samples of work; also, parasites of this species.

E. A. SCHWARZ, Washington, District of Columbia. 18954. '87. (X)

TEETH of *Sus scrofa* (?), from silex bearing mark at Ballast Point, Hillsborough Bay, near Tampa, Florida.

W. H. DALL, U. S. National Museum. 18955. '87. (XII)

METEORIC IRON (14.8 grams), from a mound near Madisonville, Ohio. (Exchange.) PEABODY MUSEUM OF ARCHÆOLOGY, Cambridge, Massachusetts. (Through F. W. Putnam.) 18956. '87. (XVI)

LARGE-MOUTHED BLACK BASS, *Micropterus salmoides;* for examination.

Col. M. MCDONALD, U. S. Fish Commission. 18957. '87. (VII)

VIOLIN; for examination.

CHARLES HARRIS, Washington, District of Columbia. 18958. '87. (I)

PAPER MONEY (3 specimens) of the East Florida Steam Saw-Mill, Panama, East Florida, 1825.

Dr. T. H. BEAN, U. S. National Museum. 18959. '87. (I)

PAPER MONEY: $5, Confederate States of America; 10 cents and 25 cents, South Carolina; 10 cents, Tennessee; $1, Balston Spa Bank, New York; one peso, Buenos Ayres, and $1, Hungarian fund.

JOHN MURDOCH, U. S. National Museum. 18960. '87. (I)

MOTH, *Actias luna,* Leach; for examination.

JOHN S. WEBB, Disputanta, Virginia. 18961. '87. (X)

INSECTS, *Artia* sps. (Returned.)

GEORGE D. HULST, Brooklyn, New York. 18962. '87. (X)

RUTILE.

WILLIAM GESNER (post-office not known), Randolph County, Alabama. 18963. '87. (XVIII)

GOLD AND SILVER ORES, from Oaxaca, Mexico.

Hon. J. T. MORGAN, United States Senate. 18964. '87. (XVIII)

ROCKY MOUNTAIN BROOK TROUT, *Salmo purpuratus,* from Colorado.

U. S. FISH COMMISSION. 18965. '87. (VII)

MODEL OF TURKISH CAIQUE, from Constantinople.

JOHN MURDOCH, U. S. National Museum. 18966. '87. (I)

BIRDS (8 specimens).

U. S. FISH COMMISSION. (Through Vinal N. Edwards, Wood's Holl, Massachusetts.) 18967. '87. (V, A)

ORE; for examination.

THOMAS SMITH, Pactola, Dakota. 18968. '87. (XVIII)

CANARY, *Serinus canariensis* (skeleton).

LOUIS SCHMID & SONS, Washington, District of Columbia. 18969. '87. (IV)

DECOMPOSED ROCK; for examination.

SCIPLE SONS, Atlanta, Georgia. 18970. '87. (XVI)

SURFACE TOWINGS, designated as mackerel food, found off coasts of Virginia and North Carolina.

U. S. FISH COMMISSION, Washington, District of Columbia. 18971. '87. (XI)

COKE; for examination.

A. A. ARTHUR, Knoxville, Tennessee. 18972. '87. (XVIII)

SALAMANDER, *Amblystoma mavortium.*

Dr. R. W. SHUFELDT, U. S. Army, Fort Wingate, New Mexico. 18973. '87. (VI)

---

* See Report on Department of Insects, Section II.

HORNED TOAD, *Phrynosoma cornutum* (2 specimens), from Piney Point, Texas.

    Mrs. FANNIE MALONE, Washington, District of Columbia. 18974. '87. (VI)

PUEBLO POTTERY.

    Mrs. LANDON, Lawrence, Kansas. 18975. '87. (II, B)

RED CROSSBILL, *Loxia curvirostra minor.*

    GEORGE MARSHALL, Laurel, Maryland. 18976. '87. (V, A)

FRENCH COPPER COINS: One décime, 1815; one sol, 1796, and one double, 1638.

    PAUL BECKWITH, U. S. National Museum. 18977. '87. (I)

MILITARY PASSES and permits (7) issued in 1863–'65.

    DOMINIC DEALDI, Washington, District of Columbia. (Through A. Zeno Shindler.) 18978. '87. (I)

PAPER MONEY, 37½ cents, Southern Exchange Bank, Richmond, Virginia. 1861.

    H. M. SMITH, U. S. National Museum. 18979. '87. (I)

"GOOD-LUCK PENNY."

    WALTER HOUGH, U. S. National Museum. 18980. '87. (II, A)

BIRDS' EGGS:* *Aphelocoma sieberii arizonœ, Geococcyx californianus, Pipilo fuscus mesoleucus, Psaltriparus plumbeus;* new to the collection. (10 sets, 46 specimens.)

    Lieut. HARRY C. BENSON, U. S. Army, Fort Huachuca, Arizona. 18981. '87. (V, B)

ORES, fossils, hematites, limestones, etc., from Pennsylvania.

    ROBERT HARE POWEL'S SONS & CO., Philadelphia, Pennsylvania. 18982. '87. (XVIII)

BIRD SKINS (170 specimens).

    Lieut. HARRY C. BENSON, U. S. Army, Fort Huachuca, Arizona. 18983. '87. (V, A)

INDIAN TEA-SEED.

    THOMAS CHRISTY & CO., London, England. 18984. '87. (I)

OXIDE OF IRON, coarse-grained and fine-grained granite containing a little copper; for examination.

    I. TURNBAUGH, Panaca, Lincoln County, Nevada. 18985. '87. (XVIII)

POWDERED MATERIAL; for examination.

    L. EWELL, Egypt, Washington Territory. 18986. '87. (XVIII)

SILICEOUS LIMONITE, containing a small amount of manganese, from Tennessee; for examination.

    JAMES N. BISHOP, Washington, District of Columbia. (Through John M. Bishop.) 18987. '87. (XVIII)

CONCRETION.

    PETER CAMERON, Spermaceti Cove life-saving station, Sandy Hook, New Jersey. 18988. '-7. (XVII)

SELENITE, a variety of gypsum; for examination.

    R. GREATHOUSE, Otta, Cottle County, Texas. 18989. '87. (XVI)

OFFICIAL POSTAGE STAMP of Uruguay, one of Argentine Republic, and two of Mexico.

    PAUL BROCKETT, U. S. National Museum. 18990. '87. (I)

FOSSILS,† Lower Helderberg formation: *Astylospongia inornata,* Hall; *Favosites helderbergiœ,* Hall; *Zaphrentis (strehtelasma) stricta,* Hall; *Fenestella althea,* Hall (?); *Cœlospira concava,* Hall;* *Spirifera perlamellosa,* Hall; *S. macropleura,* Conrad; *Merista arcuata,* Hall; *Nucleospira ventricosa,* Hall; *Trematospira globosa,* Hall; *Eatonia medialis,* Vanuxem; *Rhynchonella abrupta,* Hall; *Strophomena rhomboidalis,* Wilck.; *Streptorhynchus woolworthianus,* Hall; *Strophonella headleyana,* Hall; *Strophodonta becki,* Hall; *Orthis oblata,* Hall; *Discina discus,* Hall; *Platyceras platyostoma,* Hall; *P. retrorsum,* Hall. (113 specimens.) Collected by W. H. Darton.

    U. S. GEOLOGICAL SURVEY. 18991. '87. (XIII, A)

---

    * See Proceedings U. S. National Museum, Vol. 10, p. 551.

    † See Report on Department of Paleozoic Fossils, Section II.

DECOMPOSED ROCK; for examination.

    HENRY C. MOYER, Hilltown, Pennsylvania. 18992. '87. (XVIII)

BREASTPIN, of polished graphic granite, set in silver, and a polished blood-stone.

    Mrs. S. F. BAIRD, Washington, District of Columbia. 18993. '87. (XVI)

"ACTOR'S MAKE-UP BOX" and Chinese scroll pictures.

    G. BROWN GOODE, U. S. National Museum. 18994. '87. (IV)

GUINEA PIG, *Cavia aperes.*

    LOUIS SCHMID & SONS, Washington. 18995. '87. (IV)

GRAINS OF SAND, cemented by manganese di-oxide; for examination.

    R. C. COOK, Richmond, Virginia. 18996. '87. (XVI)

FOSSIL, *Illænus,* from the Trenton formation, near Knoxville, Tennessee.

    CHARLES WACHSMUTH, Burlington, Iowa. (Through C. D. Walcott.) 18997. '87. (XIII, A)

TRENTON FOSSILS: *Zaphrentis* sp.; *Streptelasma* sp. (?); Cystidean plates; *Chætetes* sp. undescr.; *Bryozoa* sp.; *Rhynchonella capax,* Conrad; *Streptorhynchus filitextus,* Hall; *Leptæna sericea,* Sowerby; *Orthis subquadrata,* Hall; *O. testudinaria,* Dalman; *Murchisonia* sp.; *Crytoceras* sp.; *Pterinea* sp.; *Ceraurus* sp.; *Trinucleus concentricus,* Eaton; *Dalmanites* sp.; *Bathyurus* sp. (?); *Illænus* sp. (?); *Asaphus* sp.; *Trilobita* sp. (142 specimens.)

    U. S. GEOLOGICAL SURVEY, Washington, District of Columbia. 18998. '87. (XIII, A)

KAOLIN; for examination.

    F. T. BESSAC, Natchez, Mississippi. 18999. '87. (XVI)

METEORIC IRON. (Deposited.)

    C. U. SHEPARD, Jr., Charleston, South Carolina. 19000. '87. (XVI)

BUSTS, collection of, illustrating the human races. (Exchange.)

    MUSEUM OF NATURAL HISTORY, Paris, France. 19001. '87. (II, A)

BARN OWLS, living specimens; from South Carolina.

    Maj. T. B. FERGUSON, Washington, District of Columbia. (Lent to Zoological Garden, Philadelphia.) 19002. '87.

MOLYBDENITE (gift); pyrrhotite containing chalcopyrite; for examination.

    WILLIAM ZEEKENDORF, Tucson, Arizona. 19003. '87. (XVI)

CONFEDERATE RELICS: Tripod, revolving gridiron, officer's sword, long cavalry sword, stirrups, bits, and one spherical bomb.

    WILLIAM WHEELER HUBBELL, Concord Depot, Virginia. 19004. '87. (I)

IRON PYRITES, quartz, and limonite.

    AMBROSE CONANT, Big Run, Ohio. 19005. '87. (XVIII)

ANTIQUITIES, from Italy, France, England, and Switzerland.

    THOMAS WILSON, Washington, District of Columbia. 19006. '87. (III)

MAGNETITE; for examination.

    M. KENNEDY, Standardsville, Virginia. 19007. '87. (XVIII)

SPALERITE, containing a little lead and copper; for examination.

    Dr. J. M. SPAINHOUR, Lenoir, North Carolina. 19008. '87. (XVI)

PAINT MULLER, and pot-stone gaming disc.

    Dr. J. M. SPAINHOUR, Lenoir, North Carolina. 19008. '87. (XII)

DUNITE, from near Webster, North Carolina.

    H. J. BIDDLE, Washington, District of Columbia. 19009. '87. (XVII)

MAY.

ANCIENT COREAN ARMOR. (Deposited.)

    G. BROWN GOODE, U. S. National Museum. 19010. '87. (II, A)

RUBY-CROWNED KINGLET, *Regulus calendula.*

    P. L. JOUY, Washington, District of Columbia. 19011. '87. (XII)

ALBINO ROBIN, *Merula migratoria.*

    GEORGE MARSHALL, Laurel, Maryland. 19012. '87. (V, A)

SEEDS.

JOHN H. LEMON, New Albany, Floyd County, Indiana. 19013. '87. (XV)

FOSSILS: *Favosites emmonsii* Rominger, *F. hemispherica* Troost, and *Michelina favositoidea* Billings (107 specimens).

JOHN H. LEMON, New Albany, Indiana. 19013. '87. (XIII, A)

EGGS (3) of *Megascops asio.*

Dr. R. W. SHUFELDT, U. S. Army, Fort Wingate, New Mexico. 19014. '87. (V, B)

SHELLS: *Helix fidelis, H. conspecta, H. vancouverensis, H. columbiana, Bulinus fabricius* (2), *Melania* sp. (9 specimens).

AURELIUS TODD, Elk Head, Oregon. 19015. '87. (IX)

MAMMALS: *Haplodon rufus, Neotoma fuscipes, Sciuropterus volucella, Scapanus townsendi,* and *Arvicola townsendi* (skins).

AURELIUS TODD, Elk Head, Oregon. 19015. '87. (IV)

COLEOPTERA.

AURELIUS TODD, Elk Head, Oregon. 19015. '87. (X)

BURBOT, *Lota lota maculosa;* for examination.

Capt. HENRY ROMEYN, U. S. Army, Fort Keogh, Montana. 19016. '87. (VII)

RED-BREASTED MERGANSER, *Merganser serrator.*

Dr. A. K. FISHER, Department of Agriculture. 19017. '87. (V, A)

PAWNEE HEAD-DRESS; said to be the last in the Pawnee tribe.

NELSON RICE, Pawnee Indian Agency, Indian Territory. 19018. '87. (II, A)

EGGS of *Aphelocoma sieberii arizonœ* and 6 eggs of *Psaltriparus plumbeus.*

Lieut. HARRY C. BENSON, U. S. Army, Fort Huachuca, Arizona. 19019. '87. (V, B)

BIRD-SKINS.

WILLIAM LLOYD, Paint Rock, Texas. 19020. '87. (V, A)

ORE, for analysis.

M. L. CRAWFORD, Salado, Bell County, Texas. 19021. '87. (XVIII)

LIMONITE, rich in iron; for examination.

LEWIS McKENZIE, Alexandria, Virginia. 19022. '87. (XVIII)

QUARTZ and chloritic material, quartzose conglomerate containing iron; for examination.

WILLIAM F. CARLISLE, Washington, District of Columbia. 19023. '87. (XVIII)

ANCHOR-STONE; for examination. (Returned.)

R. H. DAY, Philadelphia, Pennsylvania. 19024. '87. (III)

ARCHÆOLOGICAL OBJECTS brought from Easter Island (Rapa Nui) by U. S. S. *Mohican* and U. S. S. *Galena:*

No. 1. Stone image, weighing about 3 tons, and about 8 feet in height by 4 in width, showing head, shoulders, and bust, but only outlines of arms, the latter not distinct from the body, but a slightly raised surface carved straight down the side, with the forearms placed across the stomach at right angles, fingers touching and slightly interlaced. Below this point the general shape of the monolit ı is square.

No. 2. Block of red tufa or calcareous rock, porous and brittle, slightly oval-shaped, square on top, with slightly convex base. Supposed to be a crown for image.

No. 3. Image (head and shoulders) composed of or cut from substance resembling sandstone, measuring about 26 inches across shoulders and about 40 in height. Mouth small, lips very thin, nose and ears well defined and abnormally large. Eyes are simply deep recesses.

Nos. 4 and 5. Stone slabs, with hieroglyphics in reddish-brown and white color traced upon them. Average thickness, about 3 inches; length and width, about 4 feet by 2.

Nos. 6, 7, and 8. Stone slabs similar to but smaller than the above, and hieroglyphics more indistinct.

ARCHÆOLOGICAL OBJECTS—Continued.

No. 9. Stone slab slightly larger and heavier than Nos. 4 or 5, with diagonal and horizontal lines of reddish-brown and white color traced upon it. Two black circular spots are painted on the horizontal lines.

No. 10. Small, irregularly shaped porous stone, with an indistinct hieroglyphic cut into it. Weight, about 25 pounds.

No. 11. Stone about three times as large as No. 10, having numerous hieroglyphics cut into it. Weight, about 60 pounds.

No. 12. Small stone of about the same size and weight as No. 10, on which is a rude carving representing a human head and features.

Nos. 13, 14, 15, and 16. Small slabs, seemingly of iron ore, very brittle. No tracings, carvings, or hieroglyphics anywhere visible. Small pieces of Nos. 15 and 16 have been broken off, the fragments being placed upon the slabs from which they were detached.

Commander BENJAMIN F. DAY, U. S. Navy, commanding U. S. S. *Mohican.* 19025. '87. (II, A)

BIRD-SKINS.

Ensign W. E. SAFFORD, U. S. S. *Mohican.* 19026. '87. (V, A)

BIRDS' EGGS (14 species, 38 specimens, and 1 nest), from Montevideo, Uruguay, the Falkland Islands, Easter Island, and the Straits of Magellan.

Ensign W. E. SAFFORD, U. S. S. *Mohican.* 19026. '87. (V, B)

ARCHÆOLOGICAL OBJECTS: 8 flint arrow-heads, grooved-stone sinker, ladle, small box, copper knife with wooden handle, 4 copper fish-hooks, bone fish with stone sinker attached, 3 cactus spines, spindle with whorl and cord attached, 2 combs, 2 miniature mattresses made of splints, Pan pipe of small reeds, fragments of pottery, etc.; from graves on the beach at Arica, Peru.

Ensign W. E. SAFFORD, U. S. S. *Mohican.* 19026. '87. (III)

ETHNOLOGICAL OBJECTS, from graves at Arica, Peru.

Ensign W. E. SAFFORD, U. S. S. *Mohican.* 19026. '87. (II, A)

WATER PEBBLE and fulgurite, from South America.

Ensign W. E. SAFFORD, U. S. S. *Mohican.* 19026. '87. (XVII)

MARINE SHELLS, from Magellan Straits, and Pteropods, fresh-water and land shells, from Montevideo, Argentine Confederation, South America.

Ensign W. E. SAFFORD, U. S. S. *Mohican.* 19026. '87. (IX)

TARANTULOID SPIDER, from Montevideo.

Ensign W. E. SAFFORD, U. S. S. *Mohican.* 19026. '87. (X)

MAMMALS, from South America.

Ensign W. E. SAFFORD, U. S. S. *Mohican.* 19026. '87. (IV)

MARINE INVERTEBRATES: Miscellaneous collection, consisting mainly of surface towings, from off the Rio de la Plata, the South Pacific Ocean, west coast of South America, and of North America as far north as San Francisco, California.

Ensign W. E. SAFFORD, U. S. S. *Mohican.* 19026. '87. (XI)

REPTILES: *Bufo, Hyla, Gerrhonotus, Cnemidophorus* (6 specimens); from Montevideo.

Ensign W. E. SAFFORD, U. S. S. *Mohican.* 19026. '87. (VI)

COPPER PLATE. (Deposited.)

M. F. FORCE, Cincinnati, Ohio. 19027. '87. (III)

METEORIC IRON (3 specimens) and meteoric stone (2), from various localities. (Exchange.)

Dr. E. S. DANA, Yale University, New Haven, Connecticut. 19028. '87. (XVI)

BIRD-SKINS (3), from Demerara. (Exchange.)

C. J. MAYNARD & CO., Boston, Massachusetts. 19029. '87. (V, A)

BIRD-SKINS (seven fragments), from Colorado.

Col. JAMES STEVENSON, Washington, District of Columbia. 19030. '87. (V, A)

BIRD'S NEST used by an American White-footed Mouse as a sleeping apartment and store-house.

D. C. BEARD, New York City. 19031. '87. (IV)

POTTERY from Peru. Collected by W. E. Curtis.

    BUREAU OF ETHNOLOGY, Washington, District of Columbia. 19032. '87. (II, B)

SHELLS from Peru. Collected by W. E. Curtis.

    BUREAU OF ETHNOLOGY, Washington, District of Columbia. 19032. '87. (IX)

SEA-URCHINS, star-fish, Gorgonian and hydroid corals, decapod crustaceans, barnacles, etc.; from Peru. W. E. Curtis, collector.

    BUREAU OF ETHNOLOGY, Washington, District of Columbia. 19032. '87. (XI)

MINERALS.

    BUREAU OF ETHNOLOGY, Washington, District of Columbia. 19032. '87. (XVI)

FRAGMENT of the great wall of China.

    Lieut. SETH M. ACKLEY, U. S. Navy. 19033. '87. (I)

BADGE, G. A. R.

    Maj. WALTER THOMAS (address unknown). 19034. '87. (I)

MACHINE invented by Joseph Saxton for engraving on copper plate. (Deposited.)

    JOSEPH S. PENDLETON, New York City. 19035. '87. (L)

EGG-SHAPED STONE, found in a mound near Macon, Georgia. (Returned.)

    I. C. PLANT, Macon, Georgia. 19036. '87. (III)

CROW BLACK-BIRDS (12 specimens).

    U. S. FISH COMMISSION. (Through Vinal N. Edwards, Wood's Holl, Massachusetts.) 19037. '87. (V, A)

CRYSTALS of cuprite altering to malachite (four specimens); from Crécy, France. (Exchange.)

    S. C. H. BAILEY, Oscawana, New York. 19038. '87. (XVI)

STEM of *Fonguiera splendens.*

    Miss H. C. DeS. ABBOTT, Philadelphia, Pennsylvania. 19039. '87. (I)

LEPIDOPTERA, myriapods, and specimens of *Pityophthorus ficus*, with twigs showing "work" of same.

    E. A. SCHWARZ, Washington, District of Columbia. 19040. '87. (X)

GUINEA PIG, *Cavia aperea.*

    LOUIS SCHMID & SONS, Washington, District of Columbia. 19041. '87. (IV)

HYLA, *Hyla versicolor.*

    G. M. RHEES, Mount Pleasant, District of Columbia. 19042. '87. (VI)

FOSSILS (Pogonip formation): *Leptœna melita*, Hall and Whitfield; *Strophomena fontinalis*, White; *S. nemea*, H. and W. (types); *Orthis electra*, Billings (?); *O. eurekensis*, Walcott; *O. hamburgensis*, Walcott; *O. lonensis*, Walcott; *O. perveta*, Conrad; *O. pogonipensis*, H. and W. ; *O. testudinaria*, Dalman; *O. tricenaria*, Conrad; *Orthisina* sp.; *Streptorhynchus minor*, Walcott; *Porambonites obscurus*, H. and W.; *Triplesia* sp.; *Tellinomya contracta*, Salter (?); *T. hamburgensis* (?), Walcott; *Modiolopsis occidens*, Walcott; *M. pogonipensis*, Walcott; *Nucula*, sp.?; *Bellerophon (Bucania) bicordata*, Hall; *Straparollus* sp.; *Euomphalus* sp.?; *Raphistoma scutum*, H. and W.; *R. nasoni*, Hall (?); *R.* (?) *trochiscum*, Meek; *R.* (?) *rotuliformis*, Meek; *Murchisonia milleri*, Hall sp.?; *Pleurotomaria lonensis*, Walcott sp.?; *Helicotoma* sp.?; *Maclurea annulata*, Walcott; *M. carinata*, Walcott; *M. subannulata*, Walcott; *M. depressa*, Walcott; *M. minima*, H. and W.; *Metoptoma analoga*, Walcott; *M. phillipsi*, Walcott (2 types); *Cyrtolites sinuatus*, H. and W. (1 type); *Fusispira compacta*, H. and W. (type); *Subulites* sp.?; *Ecculiomphalus* sp.; *Ophileta* sp.; *Coleoprion minutus*, Walcott; *Hyolithes vanuxemi*, Walcott; *Orthoceras multicameratum*, Hall; *Endoceras multitubulatum* (?); *E. proteiforme*, Hall; *Serpulites*, sp.; *Leperditia bivia*, White; *Beyrichia* sp. (31 genera, 68 species, and 1,202 specimens.) (Collected by Charles D. Walcott.)

    U. S. GEOLOGICAL SURVEY. 1904?. '87. (XIII, A)

"CHRISTIAN BANNER," Vol. I, No. 2, published at Fredericksburgh, Virginia, May 17, 1862.

    J. S. TAYLOR, Washington, District of Columbia. 19044. '87. (I)

Owl, *Bubo virginianus.* (Exchange.)

C. A. Steuart, Washington, District of Columbia. 19045. '87. (v, a)

Bird-skins, from Chihuahua, Mexico. (Returned.)

William Brewster, Cambridge, Massachusetts. 19046. '87.° (v, a)

Letter written by General Santa Anna to Dr. M. M. De Meza, his private secretary, dated at Nassau, February 23, 1874.

Dr. M. M. De Meza, Washington, District of Columbia. 19047. '87. (i)

Preliminary Studies and sketches by the Japanese artists Rinsai, Tenshin, Shimkiyo, and others.

G. Goward, Washington, District of Columbia. 19048. '87. (ii, a)

Tusk of Mammoth, *Elephas primigenius;* for examination.

J. W. Posey, Sweet Water, Texas. 19049. '87. (iv)

Rocks collected by E. E. Howell in 1874.

U. S. Geological Survey, Washington, District of Columbia. 19050. '87. (xvii)

Rag Rug, made of pieces, some of which are one hundred years old.

Mrs. May E. Hughes, Washington, District of Columbia. 19051. '87. (ii, a)

Indian Blanket, worn by the Indians of southeast Alaska; made from the hair of the mountain-goat and worked up with cedar bark. It is usually hung up in the chief's house as a badge of wealth and rank, and is generally burned with him on his funeral pyre unless his body is buried, when it is hung on his tomb. (Deposited.)

Mrs. George M. Robeson, Washington, District of Columbia. 19052. '87. (ii, a)

Rabbit.

Louis Schmid & Sons, Washington, District of Columbia. 19053. '87. (iv)

Copper Coin, one centavo of Chili, 1835.

N. Burnham, Washington, District of Columbia. 19054. '87. (1)

Silver Coin, two annas, India.

T. R. B. Edwards, Boston, Massachusetts. 19055. '87. (i)

Micaceous Specular Iron Ore; for examination.

M. M. Moore, Mount Jackson, Virginia. 19056. '87. (xviii)

Manganese Ore; for examination.

James W. Rogan, Rogersville, Tennessee. 19057. '87. (xviii)

Stone Relics. (Returned.)

G. W. Clemens, Midway, Boone County, Missouri. 19058. '87. (iii)

Fowl, *Gallus ferrugineus domesticus.*

Dr. R. H. Evans, Washington, District of Columbia. 19059. '87. (v, a)

Fowl, *Gallus ferrugineus domesticus* (skeleton).

Dr. R. H. Evans, Washington, District of Columbia. 19059. '87. (xii)

Quartz and Calcite, containing the red oxide of iron (hematite); for examination.

J. Meigs, Washington, District of Columbia. 19060. '87. (xviii)

Broad-winged Hawk, *Buteo latissimus;* for examination.

G. Curtis Bishop, New London, Connecticut. 19061 '87. (v, a)

Rabbit, *Lepus cuniculus.*

Louis Schmid & Sons, Washington, District of Columbia. 19062. '87. (iv)

Minerals: Chlorastrolite and thomsonite pebbles, from Lake Superior.

Mrs. S. B. Conger, Detroit, Michigan. 19063. '87. (xvi)

Chalcedony found around a rope in a salt and gas well.

J. R. Proctor, Brandenburgh, Kentucky. 19064. '87. (xvi)

Ancient Pottery Lamp and Polynesian cocoanut drinking vessel.

William Green, Washington, District of Columbia. 19065. '87. (ii, a)

Ore; for analysis.

A. H. Webb, Hazel Springs, Virginia. 19066. '87. (xviii)

Hornblende Rock; for examination.

John Duke, Ophir, Tooele County, Utah. 19067. '87. (xvi)

DIPTERA and Myriapoda, from Dade County, Florida.
    E. A. SCHWARZ, Washington, District of Columbia. 19068. '87. (X)
DRESSED MARBLES. (Exchange.)
    E. FRITSCH, New York, New York. 19069. '87. (XVII)
BRONZE MEDAL, struck by Americans in 1782.
    W. R. GIBBES, New Orleans, Louisiana. 19070. '87. (I)
GOLD WATCH-PENDANT, with quartz setting, with coat of arms and the words "Vincit amor patriæ."
    W. R. GIBBES, New Orleans, Louisiana. 19070. '87. (XVI)
FOSSIL SKULL of Batrachian.
    CHARLES RUBY, U. S. Army, Fort Apache, Arizona. 19071. '87. (VIII)
*BIRD-SKINS; part for identification and part as a gift.
    TOKYO LIBRARY AND TOKYO EDUCATIONAL MUSEUM, Tokyo, Japan. 19072. '87. (V, A)
BATS, Natalus micropus, Dobson. Very rare. (58 specimens.)
    C. B. CORY, Boston, Massachusetts. 19073. '37. (IV)
SKULL (piece) of horse, Equus caballus; for examination.
    C. N. VAN PELT, Craig, Missouri. 19074. '87. (XII)
COPPER TOMAHAWK, found in Sunnidale, near the Georgian Bay, Lake Huron. (Purchased.)
    WILLIAM CUPPAGE, Winfield, Kansas. 19075. '87. (III)
MAMMAL-SKIN, Herpestes widdringtoni.
    ZOOLOGICAL SOCIETY OF PHILADELPHIA. (Through Arthur E. Brown, Esq.) 19076. '87. (XII)
BIRDS' NESTS and eggs.
    U. S. FISH COMMISSION. (Through Vinal N. Edwards, Wood's Holl, Massachusetts.) 19077. '87. (V, B)
BIRDS.
    U. S. FISH COMMISSION. (Through Vinal N. Edwards, Wood's Holl, Massachusetts.) 19077. '87. (V, A)
EEL POUT, Zoarces anguillaris.
    J. M. C. EATON, Irvington, New Jersey. 19078. '87. (VII)
CHARCOAL BIRDS in palm-leaf basket.
    Mrs. WILLIE MANGUM, Washington, District of Columbia. 19079. '87. (II, A)
CARVED ELEPHANT'S TUSK, from the Loangos of Congo River; and garment of native cotton cloth dyed and embroidered, from the Upper Niger River (Haousas).
    Lieut. E. H. TAUNT, U. S. Navy, Washington, District of Columbia. 19080. '87. (II, A)
PHOTOGRAPHS (10) of Easter Island tablets, now in possession of the Bishop of Tahiti.
    Commander BENJAMIN F. DAY, U. S. Navy. 19081. '87. (II, A)
MINERAL WATER; for analysis.
    Dr. S. BOWERS, San Buenaventura, California. 19082. '87. (XVI)
BIRDS; for examination.
    HARRY V. HENSON, Hakodote, Japan. 19083. '87. (II, A)
TERTIARY FOSSILS (52 species) of the Coralline Crag and St. Erth tertiary beds, partly typical specimens used by S. V. Wood, jr., in his supplement to the "Crag Mollusca", published by the Ray Society of London; from Britain.
    ROBERT BELL, London, England. (Through W. H. Dall.) 19084. '87. (IX)
GUINEA PIG, Cavia aperea; Cardinal bird, Cardinalis virginianus. (Skeleton.)
    LOUIS SCHMID & SONS, Washington, District of Columbia. 19085. '87. (XII)
FLATFISH, Limanda ferruginea; Eel, Anguilla rostrata.
    U. S. FISH COMMISSION, Washington, District of Columbia. (Through Vinal N. Edwards.) 19086. '87. (VII)
MICROSCOPIC SLIDE of pine pollen which fell at Princeton, Indiana, March 6, 1887.
    GEORGE H. CURTIS, Cincinnati, Ohio. 19087. '87. (XV)

COTTON; supposed wild species taken from a tree in Acapulco, Mexico.

C. M. MOORE, New York City. 19088. '87. (I)

SUNFISH, *Lepomis auritus;* and Rock Bass, *Ambloplites rupestris.*

Dr. WILLIAM OVERTON, Stony Creek, Virginia. 19089. '87. (XII)

GUINEA PIG, *Cavia aperea.*

LOUIS SCHMID & SONS, Washington, District of Columbia. 19090. '87. (IV)

CHIPMUNK, *Tamias asiaticus dorsalis* (3).

Dr. R. W. SHUFELDT, U. S. Army, Fort Wingate, New Mexico. 19091. '87. (IV)

RUBY-CROWNED KINGLET, *Regulus calendula.*

Dr. R. W. SHUFELDT, U. S. Army, Fort Wingate, New Mexico. 19091. '87. (V, A)

ROCKS, from North Carolina.

THOMAS C. HARRIS, Raleigh, North Carolina. 19092. '87. (XVII)

ZINC-BLENDE with iron pyrites, probably a little galena; for examination.

Hon. JAMES H. BERRY, Bentonville, Arkansas. 19093. '87. (XVI)

QUARTZ CRYSTALS; for examination.

I. A. HEAD, Cane Ridge, Van Buren County, Tennessee. 19094. '87. (XVI)

IRON ORE; for analysis.

A. P. JACKSON, Lindell, Virginia. 19095. '87. (XVIII)

ORE; for analysis.

JAMES HANE, Ohio, Herkimer County, New York. 19096. '87. (XVIII)

CRINOID COLUMNS (sections), *Pentremites,* etc.; for examination.

I. A. HEAD, Cane Ridge, Tennessee. 19097. '87. (XIII, A)

VELVET SCOTER, *Oidemia deglandii* (one pair).

JOHN CASEY, Newport, Rhode Island. (Through John Hare Powel). 19098. '87. (XII)

BIRD-SKINS.

From Swan Island, 31 species, 22 of which are land birds. This number includes 17 migrants from eastern North America; *Coccyzus seniculus,* from Central America and West Indies; *Columba leucocephala,* from the coast of Honduras and some of the Greater Antilles; *Mimocichla rubripes,* identical with the Cuban species, and not the same as that found on Grand Cayman (*M. ravida* Cory); *Contopus albicollis* Lawr. ?, probably identical with a Yucatan species; and *Dendroica vitellina* Cory, identical with a species found elsewhere only on Grand Cayman.

The only new form is a *Butorides,* allied to *B. virescens,* but altogether darker in coloration, and perhaps different enough to be considered specifically distinct.

The water-birds include specimens of the following species: *Tringa maculata, Ereunetes pusillus, Totanus flavipes, Porzana carolina, Sula piscator, S. sula, Fregata aquila.*

From Grand Cayman,* 12 species: *Certhiola sharpei, Dendroica vitellina, Centurus caymanensis, Quiscalus caymanensis,* and *Myiarchus denigratus.* A fine specimen of *Vireo caymanensis* was also secured, and also a good series of the *Dendroica,* which Mr. Cory identified (from very poor specimens) as *D. petectria gundlachi,* which proves to be a very strongly characterized new race not specially near to anything else.

C. H. TOWNSEND, Smithsonian Institution. 19099. '87. (V, A)

MARINE INVERTEBRATES, corals, and sponges, from Swan Island, Caribbean Sea.

C. H. TOWNSEND, Smithsonian Institution. 19099. '87. (XI)

PLANTS, about 25 species.

C. H. TOWNSEND, Smithsonian Institution. 19099. '87. (XV)

REPTILES: 3 lizards, 11 iguanas; from the West Indies.

C. H. TOWNSEND, Smithsonian Institution. 19099. '87. (VI)

FISHES: *Ostracion trigonum, Gobius soporator, Platyglossus radiatus, Acanthurus tractus* and *hepatus, Glyphidodon saxatilis, Lutjanus caxis, Gerres lefroyi, Albula vulpes, Sphyræna picuda, Tylosurus gladius, Trachynotus glaucus, Mugil trichodon, Trachurops crumenophthalmus, Hemirhamphus pleei, Atherina velieana,* and *Caranx latus.*

C. H. TOWNSEND, Smithsonian Institution. 19099. '87. (VII)

---

* See Proceedings U. S. National Museum, Vol. 10, p. 572.

SHELLS, 25 species, several of which are quite rare, from Swan Island, Caribbean Sea.

C. H. TOWNSEND, Smithsonian Institution. 19099. '87. (IX)

INSECTS, *Lepidoptera*, from Swan Island, Caribbean Sea.

C. H. TOWNSEND, Smithsonian Institution. 19099. '87. (X)

BIRDS' SKELETONS : *Tachypetes aquila, Sula leucogaster,* and *Sula piscator ;* from Swan Island, Caribbean Sea.

C. H. TOWNSEND, Smithsonian Institution. 19099. '87. (XII)

GUANO, from Swan Island, Caribbean Sea.

C. H. TOWNSEND, Smithsonian Institution. 19099. '87. (I)

MAMMALS : *Capromys brachyurus* and *Mus* sp., from Swan Island, Caribbean Sea.

· C. H. TOWNSEND, Smithsonian Institution. 19099. '87. (IV)

BIRD'S NEST AND EGGS: 4 eggs of *Tachypetes aquila,* 6 of *Sula piscator,* 8 of *Sula leucogaster,* and nest of *Dendroica vitellina.*

C. H. TOWNSEND, Smithsonian Institution. 19099. '87. (V, B)

MOSS AGATE, banded agate, onyx, sardonyx, chalcedony, blood-stones, and phenacite crystals (22 specimens).

GEORGE F. KUNZ, Hoboken, New Jersey. 19100. '87. (XVI)

BROWN TOURMALINE ; from Orford, New Hampshire.

C. H. HITCHCOCK, Hanover, New Hampshire. 19101. '87. (XVI)

CHALCEDONY ; from Tampa Bay, Florida.

W. H. DALL, Smithsonian Institution. 19102. '87. (XVI)

* BIRD-SKINS.

TOKYO LIBRARY AND TOKYO EDUCATIONAL MUSEUM, Tokyo, Japan. 19103. '87. (V, A)

ORE ; for analysis.

RIVES WALKER, Bristol, Tennessee. 19104. '87. (XVIII)

† EGGS of *Falco fusco-cœrulescens* (3), *Buteo swainsoni* (2), *Accipiter cooperi* (4), *Psaltriparus plumbeus* (6), *Pyrocephalus ruber mexicanus* (6), *Aphelocoma siberii arizonœ* (26).

Lieut. H. C. BENSON, U. S. Army, Fort Huachuca, Arizona. 19105. '87. (V, B)

GALENA lead ore, quite pure ; for examination.

W. W. WINTERS, Oliver Springs, Anderson County, Tennessee. 19106. '87. (XVI)

REPTILES : Crowned horned lizard, *Phrynosoma coronatum* (3 specimens), and Worm Snake, *Aniella pulchra* (2 specimens) ; for examination.

F. STEPHENS, San Bernardino, California. 19107. '87. (VI)

BIRD SKINS.

F. STEPHENS, San Bernardino, California. 19107. '87. (V, A)

TURTLE, *Chelopus insculptus* (skeleton).

FRANKLIN C. HILL, Princeton, New Jersey. 19108. '87. (XII)

IDOLS and other antiquities (38 specimens).

WARD BATCHELOR, Mexico, Mexico. 19109. '87. (III)

ESKIMO CLOTHING ;‡ from Point Barrow, Alaska.

Capt. E. P. HERENDEEN, San Francisco, California. 19110. '87. (II, A)

TURTLES, *Pseudemys elegans* (4 specimens) ; from Edisto Island, South Carolina.

Misses MABEL and MARGARET JOHNSON, Washington, District of Columbia. 19111. '87. (VI)

BIRD-SKINS ; from United States of Colombia.

Hon. V. O. KING, U. S. Consul-General, Bogota. 19112. '87. (V, A)

---

* See Proceedings U. S. National Museum, Vol. 9, pp. 634, 416.

† *Ibid.,* Vol. 10, p. 551.

‡ See Report on Department of Ethnology, Section II.

ETHNOLOGICAL OBJECTS; from United States of Colombia.

Hon. V. O. KING, U. S. Consul-General, Bogota, United States of Colombia. 19112. '87. (II, A)

SANDSTONE and limestone (4 specimens); from United States of Colombia.

Hon. V. O. KING, U. S. Consul-General, Bogota, United States of Colombia. 19112. '87. (XVII)

CALCITE (2 specimens), pyrite native sulphur and fibrous gypsum.

Hon. V. O. KING, U. S. Consul-General, Bogota, United States of Colombia. 19112. '87. (XVI)

SEA URCHINS, *Echinometra subangularis.*

Hon. V. O. King, U. S. Consul-General, Bogota, United States of Colombia. 19112. '87. (XI)

COAL.

Hon. V. O. KING, U. S. Consul-General, Bogota, United States of Colombia. 19112. '87. (XVIII)

INSECTS.

Hon. V. O. KING, U. S. Consul-General, Bogota, United States of Colombia. 19112. '87. (X)

REPTILES: 4 snakes and 1 toad.

Hon. V. O. KING, U. S. Consul-General, Bogota, United States of Colombia. 19112. '87. (VI)

INSECTS (miscellaneous collection); from Florida.

E. A. SCHWARZ, Washington, District of Columbia. 19113. '87. (X)

EGGS of *Falco fusco-cærulescens* (specimens) and *Buteo swainsoni* (15 specimens).

Lieut. H. C. BENSON, U. S. Army, Fort Huachuca, Arizona. 19114. '87. (V, B)

FOSSILS, Taconic series: *Protospongia* sp. undt.; *ethmophyllum*; *Lingulella cœlata*, Hall; *L. granvillensis*, Walcott; *Linnarssonia taconica*, Walcott; *Kutorgina pannula*, White; *Obolella*, sp.; *Orthis salemensis*, Walcott; *Camarella*, sp.; *Fordilla troyensis*, Barrande; *Modiolopsis prisca*, Walcott; *Platyceras primævum*, Billings; *Hyolithes americanus*, Billings; *H. communis*, Billings; *H. impar*, Ford; *Hyolithellus micans*, Billings; *H. micans* var. *rugosa*, Walcott; *Stenotheca elongata*, Walcott; *S. rugosa*, Hall; *Aristozoe rotundata*, Walcott; *A. troyensis*, Ford; *Leperditia dermatoides*, Walcott; *Microdiscus connexus*, Walcott; *M. lobatus*, Hall; *M. speciosus*; *Olenellus asaphoides*, Emmons; *Olenoides fordi*, Walcott; *Solenopleura nana*, Ford; *S.* (?) *tumida*, Walcott; *Conocoryphe trilineata*, Emmons; *Ptychoparia clavata*, Walcott; *P.* (?) *fitchi*, Walcott; *Trilobite* sp.; 23 genera, 35 species, 2 varieties, and 1,152 specimens. (Collected by C. D. Walcott.)

U. S. GEOLOGICAL SURVEY. 19115. '87. (XIII, A)

FEATHER CAPE, obtained fifty years ago from the Hawaiian Islands. (Deposited.)

Mrs. J. C. WELLING, Washington, District of Columbia, and Miss DIXON, Hartford, Connecticut. 19116. '87. (II, A)

BADGE of Company A, Louisville Legion, Kentucky State Guard.

J. M. SOHAN, lieutenant, Company A, Louisville Legion, Camp George Washington, District of Columbia. 19117. '87. (I)

BADGE, of Battery A, Louisville Legion.

FRANK HAGER, Battery A, Louisville Legion, Kentucky State Guard, Camp George Washington, District of Columbia. 19118. '87. (I)

BADGE of Company D, Louisville Legion, Kentucky State Guard.

GEORGE F. SAUNDERS, Company D, Louisville Legion, Kentucky State Guard, Camp George Washington, District of Columbia. 19119. '87. (I)

BADGE of Company D, Louisville Legion, Kentucky State Guard.

Capt. D. W. GRAY, Camp George Washington, District of Columbia. 19120. '87. (I)

FOSSILIFEROUS SAND, from Caloosahatchie beds, Florida.

JOSEPH WILCOX, Philadelphia, Pennsylvania. 19121. '87. (IX)

PRESSED PLANTS and a medicine case.

Mrs. LILLA MAY PAVY, New York City. 19122. '87 (II, A)

BIRD-SKINS (4 specimens).

L. BELDING, Stockton, California. 19123. '87. (V, A)

BADGE of Custer Guard, Company I, Michigan State Troops.

H. F. DEGRAFF, Custer Guard, Camp Washington, District of Columbia. 19124. '87. (I)

JERSEY CLOTH.

F. P. ROBINSON & COMPANY. 19125. '87. (1)

SKETCHES of fishes found in Congo River.

Lieut. E. H. TAUNT, U. S. Navy. 19126. '87. (VII)

ESKIMO SLIPPERS (one pair).

Mrs. L. M. PAVY, Omaha, Nebraska. (Through Dr. R. M. Stone.) 19127. '87. (II, A)

CIRCULARS, tickets, and programmes, and two badges of the eighteenth reunion of the Army of the Cumberland and unveiling of the Garfield statue; also a Garfield funeral badge worn by the Army of the Cumberland at Cleveland, Ohio, September 26, 1881.

General R. D. MUSSEY, Washington, District of Columbia. 19128. '87. (I)

BADGE of the Indianapolis Light Infantry.

J. R. ROSS, Indianapolis Rifles, Camp George Washington, District of Columbia. 19129. '87. (I)

BADGE of the Bloomdale Rifles.

JAMES P. LEAF, Bloomdale Rifles, Company H, Second Regiment, Ohio National Guard, Camp George Washington. 19130. '87. (I)

BADGE of the Jackson Rifles, Company D, First Regiment, Michigan State troops.

A. STRAUB, Jackson Rifles, Company D, First Regiment, Michigan State troops, Camp George Washington. 19131. '87. (I)

BADGE of the Grand Rapids Guard used at reunion of the Army of the Cumberland.

J. SCHRONDER, Sergeant, Company B, Second Michigan National Guard, Camp George Washington. 19132. '87. (I)

BADGE of the Chicago Zouaves, Company E, Fourth Illinois National Guard.

FRANK E. NAVAK, Camp George Washington, District of Columbia. 19133. '87. (I)

CASTS OF HAILSTONES (3) which fell in Wurzburg, Bavaria, in May, 1882.

WILLIAM HALLOCK, U. S. Geological Survey. 19134. '87. (XVIII)

PHOTOGRAPHS of Apaches (30) and Sacs and Foxes (10).

BUREAU OF ETHNOLOGY, Washington, District of Columbia. 19135. '87. (II, A)

EGYPTIAN CAT, *Felis caligata.* (Purchased.)

Dr. E. REY, Leipzig, Germany. 19136. '87. (IV)

BADGE of Company D, Third Regiment, Virginia Volunteers.

T. J. WILK, Company D, Third Regiment, Virginia Volunteers, Camp Washington, District of Columbia. 19137. '87. (I)

BADGE of the Belknap Rifles.

H. A. VIOLLAND, Washington, District of Columbia. 19138. '87. (I)

BADGE of the "Saratoga citizens," Saratoga, New York.

F. E. ISBELL, Saratoga, New York. 19139. '87. (I)

BADGE of Bullene Guards of Missouri.

W. P. HOWARD, Company B, Third Regiment, Camp George Washington. 19140. '87. (I)

BADGE of the Lee Light Infantry.

A. J. CANTHEN, Jr., Camp George Washington, District of Columbia. 19141. '87. (I)

BIRD-SKINS. (Exchange.)

Prof. R. COLLETT, Christiania, Norway. 19142. '87. (V, A)

BADGE of Company D, First Regiment M. N. G.

F. H. HAUPT, Company D, First Regiment M. N. G., Camp George Washington, District of Columbia. 19143. '87. (I)

BADGE of Keck Zouaves, of Chicago, Illinois.

LYMAN ARGERSINGER, Camp George Washington, District of Columbia. 19144. '87. (I)

SHELLS: *Sphærium cubense* Prime and *S. stamineum* Cour., not before known from the North American continent; also *Planorbis* sp., young.

I. GREEGOR, Jacksonville, Florida. 19145. '87. (IX)

MINERALS; for examination.

Dr. HERSCHEL FISHER, Des Moines, Iowa. 19146. '87. (XVI)

ORE; for analysis.

GEORGE H. STOKES, Kingston, New Mexico. 19147. '87. (XVIII)

BONES collected in Tennessee.

Dr. J. C. McCORMICK, Strawberry Plains, Tennessee. 19148. '87. (III)

MEDAL, in white metal, of Camp George Washington.

FRED. A. OLDS, Raleigh, North Carolina. 19149. '87. (I)

BADGE of National Rifles, of Washington, District of Columbia.

HENRY HORAN, Washington, District of Columbia. 19150. '87. (I)

BADGE of the Monmouth Guard, Company H, Sixth Regiment, Illinois National Guard.

E. J. CLARKE, Monmouth, Illinois. 19151. '87. (I)

BADGE of First Light Battery, Wisconsin National Guard.

Lieut. H. W. THOMPSON, Camp George Washington, District of Columbia. 19152. '87. (I)

BADGE of First Light Battery of Wisconsin National Guard.

FRANK J. BIRKEL, Milwaukee, Wisconsin. 19153. '78. (I)

BADGE of the Fort Wayne Rifles.

CHARLES B. FOLGER, Camp George Washington. 19154. '87. (I)

BADGE of the Michigan Cadets.

Capt. E. B. WINANS, Jr., Camp George Washington. 19155. '87. (I)

BADGE of the Memphis Merchant Zouaves, Company K, First Tennessee National Guard.

JOSEPH SHELLY, Camp George Washington. 19156. '87. (I)

BADGE of the Memphis Merchant Zouaves.

GEORGE LANGBEN, Camp George Washington. 19157. '87. (I)

BADGE of Knights Templar.

W. A. SEILING, Allegheny City, Pennsylvania. 19158. '87. (I)

BADGE of the Danville Blues, Company H, Third Regiment, Virginia Volunteers.

Lieut. SAMUEL SCOTT, Camp George Washington. 19159. '87. (I)

SILVER COIN, 50 cents, United States, 1821.

S. A. JEWETT, Cleveland, Ohio. 19160. '87. (I)

BADGE of Louisiana Rifles.

CHARLES AUTH, Camp George Washington. 19161. '87. (I)

BADGE of Company D, First Regiment M. N. G.

E. S. BEEM, Camp George Washington. 19162. '87. (I)

BADGE of Company A, First Regiment, National Guard, Minnesota.

JOHN A. AMES, Minneapolis, Minnesota. 19163. '87. (I)

BADGE of the Governor's Guard, Company C, First Regiment, North Carolina.

L. WILDER, Camp George Washington. 19164. '87. (I)

BADGE of Chicago Zouaves.

JOHN BEEM, Camp George Washington. 19165. '87. (I)

"HISTORY OF THE RED CROSS," "Daughters of America" (one copy each), and one arm-badge of Red Cross Society.

Miss CLARA BARTON, president of the American Red Cross Society, Camp George Washington, District of Columbia. 19166. '87. (I)

BADGE of the Bloomdale Rifles.

C. S. SCHAFER, Bloomdale Rifles, Camp George Washington, District of Columbia. 19167. '87. (I)

ALLIGATORS (?).

LOUIS SCHMID & SONS, Washington, District of Columbia. 19168. '87. (XII)

RABBIT, *Lepus cuniculus.*

LOUIS SCHMID & SONS, Washington, District of Columbia. 19168. '87. (IV)

NESTS of *Spizella pusilla, Compsothlypis americana,* and set of 5 eggs of *Corvus ossifragus.*

R. RIDGWAY, U. S. National Museum. 19169. '87. (V, B)

BIRD SKINS, 16 species (46 specimens); Gainesville, Virginia.

R. RIDGWAY, U. S. National Museum. 19169. '87. (V, A)

LARVA of bot-fly, *Cuterebra* sp.

ROBERT A. MILLS, Chuluota, Orange County, Florida. 19170. '87. (X)

BADGE of the Nealy Rifles.

W. A. GOSS, Lewiston, Maine. 19171. '87. (I)

BADGE of the Molineaux Rifles, Company D, Thirty-second Regiment, New York.

JAMES T. PUSEY, Brooklyn, New York. 19172. '87. (I)

BADGE of the Pennsylvania Guard.

G. W. DEMOTT, Chatham, Virginia. 19173. '87. (I)

BADGE of the Fort Wayne Rifles.

Lieut. I. W. LEONARD, Fort Wayne, Indiana. 19174. '87. (I)

BADGE of the Indianapolis Light Artillery.

SAMUEL B. ROBINSON, Indianapolis, Indiana. 19175. '87. (I)

BADGE of the Cayuga Military Academy.

W. VERBECK, Aurora, New York. 19176. '87. (I)

BADGE of Monmouth Guards, Company H, Sixth Regiment, Illinois National Guard.

GEORGE C. RANKIN, Monmouth, Illinois. 19177. '87. (I)

CORALS: five species of *Stylaster,* from the Gulf of Mexico.

MUSEUM OF COMPARATIVE ZOOLOGY, Cambridge, Massachusetts. 19178. '87. (XI)

MAGNETIC IRON ORE; for analysis.

MOORE, HOBSON & CONWAY, Bristol, Tennessee. 19179. '87. (XVIII)

MEDAL, commemorating dedication of the Washington Monument.

JAY K. B. VOSE, Washington, District of Columbia. 19180. '87. (I)

METEORIC STONE.

(Donor not known.) 19181. '87. (XVI)

GROUND SQUIRREL, *Tamias striatus,* from Gainesville, Virginia.

ROBERT RIDGWAY, U. S. National Museum. 19182. '87. (IV)

YELLOW-BREASTED CHAT, *Icteria virens.*

CONRAD ZELLER, Washington, District of Columbia. 19183. '87. (V, A)

JUNE.

BEETLE, *Prionus laticollis;* Grasshopper, *Acridium americanum.*

ROBERT A. MILLS, Chuluota, Florida. 19184. '87. (X)

SHELLS (100) from dredgings made off the east coast of the southern states and the West Indies.

Dr. W. H. RUSH, U. S. Navy, Philadelphia, Pennsylvania. 19185. '87. (IX)

CLUB with stone head, from New Britain; war ax, from Savage Island; spear with obsidian blade, from Admiralty Island; club, from Tonga Island; double-bladed paddle and ceremonial ax, carved bird's head and carved paddle, from New Ireland; paddle, from Navigator's Islands; pillow, from Fiji Islands; and 2 wigs. (Exchange.)

APPLETON STURGIS, New York City. 19186. '87. (II, A)

IDOLS AND HEADS, 22 specimens, from Mexico.

WARD BATCHELOR, city of Mexico, Mexico. 19187. '87. (II, B)

MINERALS: Aglaite, muscovite, and tourmaline (23 specimens).

COLUMBIA COLLEGE (School of Mines), New York City. 19188. '87. (XVI)

MINERALS.

Dr. H. H. THORPE, Liberty Hill, Texas. 19189. '87. (XVI)

AMERICAN GOLDFINCH, *Astragalinus tristis.*

CONRAD ZELLER, Washington, District of Columbia. 19190. '87. (XII)

SYRIAN COAT. (Purchased.)

FARES A. FERZAN, Mount Lebanon, Syria. 19191. '87. (I)

PHOTOGRAPHS of a Turkish woman and of an Egyptian peasant.

FARES A. FERZAN, Mount Lebanon, Syria. 19191. '87. (II, A)

CASSITERITE (2 specimens), from King's Mountain, North Carolina.

Dr. C. W. DABNEY, Raleigh, North Carolina. 19192. '87. (XVI)

BADGE of the Lomax Rifles.

E. J. DAINES, Mobile, Alabama. 19193. '87. (I)

BADGE of Bowling Green Guards.

ALLIE COLBURN, Bowling Green, Kentucky. 19194. '87. (I)

BADGE of the Bullene Guards.

S. H. POTTER, Kansas City, Missouri. 19195. '87. (I)

GOLD DOLLAR, coined at Rutherfordton, North Carolina, and issued in 1842-'49; or North Carolina gold.

CHARLES H. BETTS, Raleigh, North Carolina. 19196. '87. (I)

RIBBON AND METAL BADGE of the American Society of Mechanical Engineers.

THOMAS W. CAPEN, Stamford, Connecticut. 19197. '87. (I)

PYRITE in calcite; for examination.

S. HEYMANN, Fayetteville, Tennessee. 19198. '87. (XVIII)

PHOTOGRAPHS of base bullion.

PAUL BECKWITH, U. S. National Museum. 19199. '87. (XVIII)

CONCRETIONS.

S. R. HARRISON, Clarksburgh, West Virginia. 19200. '87. (XVII)

NATIVE CLOTH, from the Baluba country, headwaters of the Kassai River, Central Africa.

Lieut. E. H. TAUNT, U. S. Navy. 19201. '87. (II, A)

EGGS of *Lophophanes bicolor.*

AUDUBON RIDGWAY, U. S. National Museum. 19202. '87. (V, B)

EGGS (3) of *Peucæa æstivalis.*

I. M. CHAPMAN, Englewood, New Jersey. 19203. '87. (V, B)

EGGS of *Sitta pusilla,* and three nests; eggs of *Stelgidopteryx serripennis.*

CHARLES W. RICHMOND, Washington, District of Columbia. 19204. '87. (V, B)

BIRDS' NESTS,* *Psaltriparus plumbeus* (6); *Amphispiza bilineata* (1); *Pyrocephalus ruber mexicanus* (3); *Aphelocoma sieberii arizonæ* (1), and *Pipilo fuscus mesoleucus* (1).

Lieut. HARRY C. BENSON, U. S. Army, Fort Huachuca, Arizona. 19205. '87. (V, B)

PALEOZOIC FOSSILS, 893 specimens (44 genera, 77 species, 5 varieties):

Endothyra baileyi, Hall.	*Heliophyllum halli,* E. and H.
Favosites goldfussi, D'Orbigny.	*Heliophyllum annulatum,* Hall.
Favosites polymorphus, Goldfuss.	*Heliophyllum infundibulum.*
Favosites invaginatus, Nicholson.	*Heliophyllum pravum,* Hall.
*Favosites forbesi,*var.*occidentalis,* Hall.	*Phillipsastræa,* sp. undet.
Favosites spinigerus, Hall.	*Hadrophyllum orbignyi,* E. and H.
Favosites sp. ?	*Zaphrentis conica* ?
Halysites catenulatus, Linn.	*Zaphrentis concava,* Hall.
Cyathophyllum rugosum, E. and H.	*Streptelasma* (D.) *borealis,* Hall.

---

* See Proceedings U. S. National Museum, Vol. 10, p. 551.

PALEOZOIC FOSSILS—Continued.

Aulacophyllum convergens, Hall.
Aulacophyllum sulcatum, D'Orbigny.
Pentremites conoideus, Hall.
Pentremites koninckianus, Hall.
Ancyrocrinus bulbosus, Hall.
Trematopora ?
Trematopora osculum, Hall.
Trematopora infrequens, Hall.
Trematopora echinata, Hall.
Lichenalia concentrica, Hall.
Paleschara maculata, Hall.
Chonetes yandelliana, Hall.
Orthis vanuxemi, Hall.
Orthis elegantula, Hall.
Orthis hybrida, Sowerby.
Orthis dubia, Hall.
Spirifera euruteines, Owen.
Spirifera euruteines, Owen (showing spires).
Spirifera crispa, Hisinger.
Spirifera crispa, var. *simplex*, Hall.
Spirifera radiata, Sowerby.
Spirifera sulcata, Hisinger.
Spirifera oweni, Hall.
Spirifera oweni, Hall (showing spires).
Cyrtina hamiltonensis, var. *recta*, Hall.
Nucleospira pisiformis, Hall.
Meristella rectirostra, Hall.
Meristina nitida, Hall.
Meristina maria, Hall.
Retzia evax, Hall.
Atrypa nodostriata, Hall.
Atrypa reticularis, Linn.
Atrypa reticularis, Linn. (showing spires).
Rhynchonella grosvenori, Hall.
Rhynchonella stricklandi, Sowerby.

Rhynchonella neglecta, Hall.
Rhynchonella acinus, Hall.
Rhynchonella whitii, Winchell.
Rhynchonella indianensis, Hall.
Rhynchonella cuneata,var. *americanus*, Hall.
Anastrophia internascens, Hall.
Athyris hirsuta, Hall.
Athyris spiriferoides, Eaton.
Athyris spiriferoides, Eaton (showing spires).
Terebratula formosa, Hall.
Eumetria verneuiliana, Hall.
Eichwaldia reticulata, Hall.
Conularia (?) *subulata* (?).
Naticopsis carleyana, Hall.
Holopea proutana, Hall.
Platystoma niagarensis, Hall.
Straparollus spergenensis, Hall.
Straparollus spergenensis, var. *planorbiformis*.
Straparollus planispira, Hall.
Straparollus quadrivolvis, Hall.
Pleurotomaria subglobosus, Hall.
Murchisonia turritella, Hall.
Murchisonia vermicula, Hall.
Murchisonia insculpta, Hall.
Cyclonema leavenworthianum, Hall.
Bellerophon sublœvis, Hall.
Polyphemopsis bulimiformis, Hall.
Bulimorpha elongata, Hall.
Bulimorpha canaliculata, Hall.
Orthoceras epigrus, Hall.
Nucula shumardana, Hall.
Leperditia carbonaria, Hall.
Fossiliferous strata (sample).

E. PLEAS, Dunreith, Indiana. 19206. '87. (XIII, A)

SILVER COIN, 960-reis of Brazil, 1817.

J. A DUNNING, Aulander, North Carolina. 19207. '87. (I)

ZINC-BLENDE, and rock fragments; for examination.

B. A. HELTON, Hazel Spring, Virginia. 19208. '87. (XVI)

IBIS, *Bubulus ibis*, from Egypt.

C. B. CORY, Boston, Massachusetts. 19209. '87. (V, A)

MARINE INVERTEBRATES.

U. S. FISH COMMISSION, Washington, District of Columbia. 19210. '87. (XI)

INSECTS (9 specimens), collected by schooner *Grampus*.

U. S. FISH COMMISSION, Washington, District of Columbia. 19210. '87. (X)

FISHES.

U. S. FISH COMMISSION, Washington, District of Columbia. 19210. '87. (VII)

BIRD-SKINS; for examination.

BOSTON SOCIETY OF NATURAL HISTORY, Boston, Massachusetts. 19211. '87. (V, A)

BOWS AND ARROWS (5) made specially as insignia of authority and office of chief of the tribe, for presentation to McGill, as successor to Pasqual, chief of the Yumas, in the event of the death of the latter, which, however, did not then occur.

Hon. A. B. UPSHAW, Assistant Commissioner of Indian Affairs. 19212. '87. (II. A)

INSECT, *Actias luna.*

Dr. N. M. BURKHOLDER, Harrisonburgh, Virginia. 19213. '87. (X)

MINERALS; for assay.

W. PATTON, Colfax, Grant Parish, Louisiana. 19214. '87. (XVI)

ITALIAN EXECUTIONER'S SWORD.

THOMAS WILSON, Washington, District of Columbia. 19215. '87. (II, A)

GREAT HORNED OWL, *Bubo virginianus;* from Virginia.

G. A. STEUART, Smithsonian Institution. 19216. '87. (V, A)

FOSSILS, *Bryozoa,* from the Trenton limestone.

JAMES E. BENEDICT, St. Paul, Minnesota. 19217. '87. (XIII, A)

CHINESE BRONZE KETTLE.

Mrs. WILLIE MANGUM, Washington, District of Columbia. 19218. '87. (II, A)

BADGE of the Toledo Cadets.

Capt. W. V. McMAKIN, Toledo, Ohio. 19219. '87. (I)

CAMPAIGN BADGES (two) of General Harrison, 1840; funeral badge of General Harrison, 1841; badge of Bunker Hill Celebration, 1843. Also eight specimens paper money and Confederate bond, and three unsigned bank notes of the old Bank of South Carolina, Charleston, etc.

NATHAN RITTER, Washington, District of Columbia. 19220. '87. (I)

FLINT; for examination.

WILL S. HAZLETT, Alpine, Alabama. 19221. '87. (XVI)

SANDSTONE containing oxides of manganese and iron; for examination.

I. COMBS, Hawk's Nest, West Virginia. 19222. '87. (XVI)

BIRD-SKINS. Lent for comparison and study. (Returned.)

BOSTON SOCIETY OF NATURAL HISTORY, Boston, Massachusetts. 19223. '87. (V, A)

ARROW HEADS.

Dr. WILLIAM OVERTON, Stony Creek, Virginia. 19224. '87. (III)

STONE SLAB.

GEORGE H. BOEHMER, Smithsonian Institution. 19225. '87. (XVII)

MEDALS of John Tillotson, Archbishop of Canterbury, who died in 1694, and James Oglethorpe, founder of the colony of Georgia, 1733. (2 sulphur casts.)

HENRY WEIDENBACH, Washington, District of Columbia. 19226. '87. (I)

BEETLES; miscellaneous collection.

LEWIS L. KENNEDY, Blackford, Custer County, Montana. 19227. '87. (X)

WHETSTONES.

A. F. PIKE MANUFACTURING COMPANY, Pike Station, New Hampshire. 19228. '87. (XVII)

OVEN BIRD, *Seiurus aurocapillus* (nestling).

GEORGE MARSHALL, Laurel, Maryland. 19229. '87. (V, A)

FISH, *Thalassophryne dowi.*

D. S. JORDAN, Bloomington, Indiana. 19230. '87. (VII)

BIRDS' EGGS:* *Corvus cryptoleucus* (46), *Geococcyx californianus* (10), *Amphispiza bilineata* (3), and *Buteo swainsoni* (3).

Lieut. H. C. BENSON, U. S. Army, Fort Huachuca, Arizona. 19231. '87. (V, B)

---

* See Proceedings U. S. National Museum, vol. 10, p. 551.

BADGES: Thirtieth Anniversary, 1884, Independent Order of Good Templars; Union Veteran Corps, Old Guard, Washington, 1886; Logan Tribe No. 8, Improved Order of Red Men, District of Columbia; Associated Veterans, District of Columbia Volunteers, Twenty-fifth Anniversary, 1886; Badge of Webster Lodge, No. 7, Knights of Pythias, 1886; Badge of floor committee at the Garfield Ball of Ohio Club, Washington, January 24, 1881; Badge of honorary members of Emmet Guard, Washington, 1884; Badge worn at the fair held by the Washington Continentals, January, 1887; and five United States bronze coins.

> PAUL BECKWITH, U. S. National Museum. 19232. '87. (I)

CHIPMUNK, *Tamias asiaticus 4-vittatus*.

> Dr. J. C. MERRILL, U. S. Army, Fort Klamath, Oregon. 19233. '87. (IV)

INSECTS from Dade County, Florida.

> E. S. SCHWARZ, Washington, District of Columbia. 19234. '87. (X)

SNAPPING-TURTLE, *Chelydon serpentina*.

> ANTON SCHOTT. (Through A. L. Schott, U. S. National Museum.) 19235. '87. (VII)

PYRITES.

> H. J. DAVIS, Davis, Massachusetts. 19236. '87. (XVI)

PLANT; for examination.

> Dr. J. L. GREENE, Denver, Colorado. 19237. '87. (XV)

MINERAL; for examination.

> JACOB P. SNYDER, Murphys, California. 19238. '87. (XVI)

MICA; for examination.

> R. J. S. THOMPSON, Denver, Colorado. 19239. '87. (XVIII)

CRYSTALS of rutile. (Deposited.)

> C. U. SHEPARD, Charleston, South Carolina. 19240. '87. (XVI)

MEDAL of National Prize Drill at Camp George Washington, District of Columbia, May, 1887.

> J. H. BARRY, Washington, District of Columbia. 19241. '87. (I)

BADGE of the Washington Light Infantry Corps.

> JOHN G. COWIE, first lieutenant, Company A, Washington Light Infantry Corps, District of Columbia. 19242. '87. (I)

NAIL from the door of a dungeon cell under the Doge's palace in Venice. In this cell the Doge Marino Falieri was confined prior to his execution, which occurred in the year 1355.

> JAMES M. STEWART, War Department, Washington, District of Columbia. 19243. '87. (I)

BIRD-SKINS, *Auriparus flaviceps*,* *Polioptila californica* ad., *P. cærulea* (new subspecies ?) ad., *Spizella atrigularis* (3), *Chætura vauxii* (very rare) ad., *Harporhynchus lecontei* adult and nestling, and hybrid *Lophortyx californicus* x *L. gambeli* ad. (Purchased.)

> F. STEPHENS, San Bernardino, California. 19244. '87. (V, A)

SKELETON OF A SEAL. (Purchased.)

> Rev. Mr. HARVEY, St. John's, Newfoundland. 19245. '85. (XII)

SEAL-SKINS: *Cystophora cristata*, young specimen of same, and young specimen of *Erignathus barbatus*; for examination.

> Rev. Mr. HARVEY, St. John's, Newfoundland. 19245. '87. (IV)

FOSSILS, *Corbula perangulata*, Whiteaves; from the Laramie Group of Canada.

> J. F. WHITEAVES, Canada Geological Survey. (Through Dr. C. A. White.) 19246. '87. (XIII, B)

FOSSIL WOOD, from Stony Creek, Virginia.

> JOHN E. BROWN, U. S. Fish Commission. 19247. '87. (XV)

---

* See Proceedings U. S. National Museum, Vol. 10, p. 549.

ETHNOLOGICAL OBJECTS: Spears, throwing-stick, arrows, articles of dress, baskets, knives, bows, carvings, needles and needle-cases, etc., from Alaska. (147 specimens.) (Purchased.)

LUCIEN M. TURNER, Washington, District of Columbia. 19248. '87. (II, A)

IRISH ANTIQUITIES.

JAMES F. JOHNSON, Holywood, Ireland. 19249. '87. (III)

MANGANESE GARNET, spessartite; for examination.

F. F. ORON, Villa Rica, Carroll County, Georgia. 19250. '87. (XVIII)

BADGE of the Lee Light Infantry of Chester, South Carolina.

FRANK BURNS, U. S. Geological Survey. 19251. '87. (I)

EGGS of *Corvus cryptoleucus* (13 sets, 69 eggs).

Lieut. H. C. BENSON, U. S. Army, Fort Huachuca, Arizona. 19252. '87. (V, B)

GOOSE, *Anser cærulescens* (2 skins).

LUDWIG KUMLEIN, Public Museum, Milwaukee, Wisconsin. 19253. '87. (V, A)

SMALL STALACTITE; for examination.

Dr. H. H. THORPE, Liberty Hill, Texas. 19254. '87. (XVI)

FOSSIL, fragment of *Ammonites feruvianus;* for examination.

Dr. H. H. THORPE, Liberty Hill, Texas. 19254. '87. (XIII, B)

"TWO-SPOTTED TREE HOPPER," *Thelia bimaculata* Fabr.; for examination.

WILLIAM J. C. GOODE, Gilliamsville, Buckingham County, Virginia. 19255. '87. (X)

LAMPREY EEL, *Petromyzon marinus,* and Kingfish, *Menticirrus nebulosus.*

W. A. WILCOX, Gloucester, Massachusetts. 19256. '87. (VII)

SHELL found at mouth of Potomac Creek, Virginia.

Captain ELLIS. (Through N. King, Bureau of Engraving and Printing, Washington, District of Columbia.) 19257. '87. (IX)

CONCRETION found in the Hudson River tunnel.

Dr. F. R. HORNBLOWER, Jersey City, New Jersey. 19258. '87. (XVII)

"ANT LION," larva of *Myrmeleon* sp.

B. RUSH RHEES, Washington, District of Columbia. 19259. '87. (X)

LARVÆ of *Sphinx (Daremma) catalpa* Bd.; for examination.

Maj. WILLIAM A. KOBBÉ, Third Artillery, U. S. Army, Fort Monroe, Virginia. 19260. '87. (X)

MINERALS; for examination.

JAMES M. BARKER, Bristol, Tennessee. 19261. '87. (XVI)

ORCHIDS, from the island of Grand Cayman, Caribbean Sea.

C. H. TOWNSEND, U. S. Fish Commission. 19262. '87. (XV)

BIRD-SKINS, from the island of Grand Cayman, Caribbean Sea.

C. H. TOWNSEND, U. S. Fish Commission. 19262. '87. (V, A)

PHOTOGRAPHS of Easter Island (39) taken by Passed Assistant Surgeon H. W. Whittaker, U. S. Navy.

Commander BENJAMIN F. DAY, U. S. Navy, commanding U. S. S. *Mohican.* 19263. '87. (II, A)

DRINKING WATER; for analysis.

G. P. GALLOWAY, Redrock, Montrose County, Colorado. 19264. '87. (XVI)

KEY found in the sand near the fort at Sandy Hook.

P. CAMERON, New Brunswick, New Jersey. 19265. '87. (II, A)

FOSSILS, type specimens: *Corbicula willisi,* White; *C. pugetensis,* White; *Cerithium?* sp.; *Cardium (Adœna?); Psammobia obscura,* White; *Neritina* sp.; *Cyrena brevidens* White; *Teredo pugetensis,* White; *Batissa dubia,* White; *B. Newberryi,* White; *Sanguinolaria (?) caudata,* White; *Anatina sulcatina,* White; *Clisocolus dubius* (Gabb), White; *C. cordatus* (Whiteaves), White; *Crassatella tuscana,* White; *Vanikoropsis suciensis,* White; *Rhynchonella,* sp.; *Perna excavata,* White; and *Ammonites maclurei,* White.

Dr. J. S. NEWBERRY, Columbia College, New York City. Through Dr. C. A. White. 19266. '87. (XIII, B

SELENITE CRYSTALS (2); for examination.

    A. T. SHERWOOD, Bismarck, Dakota. 19267. '87. (XVI)

GREEN-TAILED TOWHEE, *Pipilo chlorurus*, from Zuñi, New Mexico.

    Dr. H. C. YARROW, Washington, District of Columbia. 19268. '87. (V, A)

DOUBLED-BRAINED CHICKENS (5).

    Dr. R. H. EVANS, Washington, District of Columbia. 19269. '87. (V, A)

BIRD-SKINS, from various localities. (Returned.)

    LUDWIG KUMLEIN, Public Museum, Milwaukee, Wisconsin. 19270. '87. (V, A)

ROCKS, collection from water-works tunnel, District of Columbia.

    I. ROBINSON, Howard University, District of Columbia. 19271. '87. (XVII)

ARROWHEADS (10); from Wateree River, South Carolina.

    E. M. KIRKLEY, Camden, South Carolina. 19272. '87. (III)

POTTERY (fragments).

    E. M. KIRKLEY, Camden, South Carolina. 19272. '87. (II, B)

NEST AND EGG OF *Dendroica dominica*.

    R. B. McLAUGHLIN, Statesville, North Carolina. 19273. '87. (V, B)

"TORTOISE" BEETLES, *Coptocycla (Cassida) aurichalcea;* for examination.

    Mrs. E. S. WARNER, Palma Sola, Florida. 19274. '87. (X)

BIRD-SKINS, from Europe.

    C. W. WARD, New York City. 19275. '87. (V, A)

DINING TABLE, from Corea.

    P. L. JOUY, Smithsonian Institution. 19276. '87. (II, A)

GRAYHOUND, *Canis familiaris*.

    Mrs. THEODORE WASSERBACH, Hillman House, Washington, District of Columbia. 19277. '87. (XII)

EGGS of *Buteo latissimus* (?), from Sandy Spring, Montgomery County, Maryland.

    Dr. A. K. FISHER, Washington, District of Columbia. 19278. '87. (V, B)

BIRD, type of *Myioturdus fuscatus*, Leop.; for examination. (Returned.)

    BOSTON SOCIETY OF NATURAL HISTORY, Boston, Massachusetts. 19279. '87. (V, A)

PHOTOGRAPH of Passamaquoddy Indians and their priest, Father Vermilyea.

    SAMUEL SHACKFORD, Chicago, Illinois. 19280. '87. (II, A)

LEAD, copper, and zinc ores.

    G. H. HOLDEN, Deer Isle, Maine. 19281. '87. (XVIII)

STIBNITE, quartz, and calcite stained by copper, perlite, quartz and sulphide of copper and iron, galena and pyrite, and quartz; for examination.

    H. C. DURKEE, Baker City, Oregon. 19282. '87. (XVIII)

KILLIFISHES: *Fundulus similis* (1 specimen), *Mollienesia latipinna* (2 specimens).

    E. A. SCHWARZ, Washington, District of Columbia. 19283. '87. (VII)

STONE VESSEL, ladle-shaped.

    Dr. H. F. WILLIAMS, Fairbank, Cochise County, Arizona. 19284. '87. (III)

COINS (65), American and foreign.

    G. A. B. WALKER, Augusta, Georgia. 19285. '87. (I)

MAGNETIC IRON ORE; for examination.

    Hon. J. T. MORGAN, Selma, Alabama. 19286. '87. (XVIII)

MOLLUSCA, *Octopus* sp.

    Lieut. W. M. WOOD, U. S. Navy. 19287. '87. (IX)

FISH: *Haplochiton zebra* Jenyns. Also mould and cast of same.

    Lieut. W. M. WOOD, U. S. Navy. 19287. '87. (VII)

TURTLE.

    Lieut. W. M. WOOD, U. S. Navy, U. S. S. *Juniata*. 19287. '87. (VI)

COPPER COINS of ancient Rome. (Returned.)

    General M. C. MEIGS, U. S. Army, Washington, District of Columbia. 19288. '87. (I)

BADGE of Cadets of St. John's Academy worn at Camp Washington, 1887.

R. L. CARNES, Alexandria, Virginia. 19289. '87. (I)

ANCIENT ROMAN COIN: Æs of L. Peso Fruji, 89 B. C. (Deposited.)

FRANK REYNOLDS, U. S. National Museum. 19290. '87. (I)

TEREDO TUBE, lining; from Quoddy Bay, Maine; for examination.

PETER GODFREY, South Lubec, Maine. 19291. '87. (IX)

TYPES OF FOSSILS (39).

U. S. GEOLOGICAL SURVEY, Washington, District of Columbia. 19292. '87. (XIII, B)

FOSSILS:

Dr. J. S. NEWBERRY, Columbia College, New York. 19293. '87. (XIII, B)

ETHNOLOGICAL* AND ARCHÆOLOGICAL OBJECTS: From Wolpi-si-chom-i-vi, Tewa Shong-oh-pa-vi, Mu-shong-o-nu-bi and Shu-pa-la-bi, and Oraibe, Arizona Territory.

BUREAU OF ETHNOLOGY, Washington, District of Columbia. (Through Col. and Mrs. James Stevenson.) 19294. '87. (II, A & B)

ETHNOLOGICAL OBJECTS;* a large collection.

Mrs. JAMES STEVENSON, Washington, District of Columbia. 19294. '87. (II, A)

POTTERY.

Mrs. JAMES STEVENSON, Washington, District of Columbia. 19294. '87. (II, B)

MINERALS (21 specimens); for examination. (Returned.)

W. A. H. SHREIBER, Webster, North Carolina. 19295. '87. (XVI)

INSECTS; for examination.

A. E. THOMAS, Bellmore, Park County, Indiana. 19296. '87. (X)

BIRD-SKINS (25); from Isthmus of Panama.

Ensign W. E. SAFFORD, U. S. Navy, U. S. S. *Mohican.* 19297. '87. (V, A)

BIRD-SKINS. (Returned.)

H. K. COALE, Chicago, Illinois. 19298. '87. (V, A)

EGG of *Buteo latissimus.*

G. CURTIS BISHOP, New London, Connecticut. 19299. '87. (V, B)

HORNED TOAD, *Phrynosoma cornutum:* from Arizona.

THOMAS FLYNN, Soldiers' Home, Washington, District of Columbia. 19300. '87. (VI)

SANDSTONE containing pyrite, and pig-iron; for examination.

S. HEYMANN, Fayetteville, Tennessee. 19301. '87. (XVIII)

SHELLS, *Helix* and *Purpura.*

R. HITCHCOCK, Osaka, Japan. 19302. '87. (IX)

WINGED TERMITES.

R. HITCHCOCK, Osaka, Japan. 19302. '87. (X)

MINERALS; for examination.

FRANK PRICE, Rapid City, Dakota. 19303. '87. (XVI)

LOWER CARBONIFEROUS CHERT, containing sponge spicules (4 specimens).

Dr. GEORGE J. HINDE, Croydon, England. (Through Dr. C. A. White.) 19304. '87. (XIII, A)

INDIGO BIRDS, *Passerina cyanea* (4 specimens); also *Coccyge samericanus* and *Vireosylvia olivacea.*

H. M. SMITH, U. S. Fish Commission. 19305. '87. (XII)

APPARATUS used by Professor Henry.

SMITHSONIAN INSTITUTION, Washington, District of Columbia. 19306. '87. (I)

GERMAN CARP, *Cyprinus carpio* (2 specimens).

NATHAN KEITH, Campbell, Massachusetts. 19307. '87. (VII)

---

* See Report on Department of Ethnology; Section II.

PIECE OF MORTAR from the old reservoir which supplied the city of Rome with water.

Mrs. SARAH D. DAVIS, Springfield, Massachusetts. 19308. '87. (I)

MEDALLION of Benjamin Franklin, 1777; foreign coins (176); two cuneiform inscriptions in baked clay, from Babylon; volume, "Mémoires de la République Romaine," and plaster cast of ancient Roman gold plate.

THOMAS WILSON, Washington, District of Columbia. 19309. '87. (I)

UNITED STATES MARINE DRUM, found on battle-field at Manassas Junction in 1861. (Returned.)

GILBERT B. WALDEN, Washington, District of Columbia. 19310. '87. (I)

BADGES: Sherman Cadets, of Sherman, Massachusetts; Gate City Guard, Atlanta, Georgia, and "Welcome to Atlanta" Gate City Guard.

J. H. CONGER, Washington, District of Columbia. 19311. '87. (I)

HAIR-WORM, *Gordius* sp. ; for examination.

Dr. E. G. SHORTLIDGE, Wilmington, Delaware. 19312. '87. (XI)

BIRDS' EGGS: *Corvus cryptoleucus* (160), *Buteo swainsoni* (44), *B. borealis calurus* (2), *Geococcyx californianus* (4), *Tyrannus verticalis* (8), *Lanius excubitorides* (8), *Amphispiza bilineata* (3), *Empidonax* sp. (4).

Lieut. H. C. BENSON, U. S. Army, Fort Huachuca, Arizona. 19313. '87. (V, B)

EGGS of *Ictinia mississippiensis*.

N. S. GOSS, Neosho Falls, Kansas. 19314. '87. (V, B)

BIRD-SKINS; for examination. (Returned.)

CHARLES B. CORY, Boston, Massachusetts. 19315. '87. (V, A)

PIÑON JAY, *Cyanocephalus cyanocephalus*.

Dr. R. W. SHUFELDT, U. S. Army, Fort Wingate, New Mexico. 19316. '87. (V, A)

CARD OF INVITATION to ceremonies, and order of proceedings at dedication of Washington Monument, February 21, 1885. (Deposited.)

Prof. S. F. BAIRD, Washington, District of Columbia. 19317. '87. (I)

SILVER AND COPPER COINS of United States, Canada, Nova Scotia, France, Prussia, Denmark, Great Britain, and one Vermont continental.

W. PALMER, Washington, District of Columbia. 19318. '87. (I)

COINS, American and foreign (318); two specimens postage-stamp money; gold badge of the Eclectic College fraternity (Phi Nu Theta), and subscriber's card to Vice-President Hendricks's monument fund. (Deposited.)

G. BROWN GOODE, U. S. National Museum. 19319. '87. (I)

INSECT, *Sphinx 5-maculata*, in fragments.

C. E. RUTHERFORD, Peru, Indiana. 19320. '87. (X)

"RHINOCEROS" BEETLE, *Dynastes tityus*, female; for examination.

Mrs. T. D. PEARSON, Saratoga, Tennessee. 19321. '87. (X)

FOSSIL FISH, *Clupeoid;* from the Green River Falls, Wyoming.

W. H. DALL, U. S. National Museum. 19322. '87. (VII)

BLUE GOOSE, *Chen cœrulescens* (2 specimens).

LUDWIG KUMLEIN, Public Museum, Milwaukee, Wisconsin. 19323. '87. (V, A)

BRANCH ALEWIFE, *Clupea vernalis;* from Penobscot River; for examination.

J. FRANK ELLIS, U. S. Fish Commission. 19324. '87. (VII)

BIRD-SKINS; from Hawaiian Islands.

VALDEMAR KNUDSEN, Marion, Massachusetts. 19325. '87. (V, A)

DECOMPOSED DIABASE; for examination.

R. W. PAGE, Salem, Virginia. 19326. '87. (XVII)

CHAIR once belonging to Thomas Jefferson and made by a carpenter on his plantation. (Deposited.)

Mrs. ELLEN DOUGLASS, St. Louis, Missouri. 19327. '87. (I)

RAINBOW TROUT, *Salmo irideus*.

SOUTH SIDE SPORTSMAN CLUB, Oakdale, New York. 19328. '87. (VII)

SHELLS, *Limnœa elodes* Say; taken from stomach of a fish.

    SOUTH SIDE SPORTSMAN CLUB, Oakdale, New York. 19328. '87. (IX)

COREAN SCREEN.

    GUSTAV GOWARD, Washington, District of Columbia. 19329. '87. (II, A)

BIRD-SKINS.

    S. ALBERT SHAW, Hampton, New Hampshire. 19330. '87. (V, A)

DECOMPOSED SLATE; for examination.

    J. Y. BRADFORD, Daingerfield, Texas. 19331. '87. (XVIII)

FOSSIL LAMELLIBRANCHIATA of the Upper Helderberg, Hamilton, Portage, and Chemung Groups:

Mytilarca (P.) arenacea, Hall.
Conocardium cuneus, Conrad.
Cypricardinia planulata, Conrad.
Paracyclas elliptica, Hall.
Actinoptera muricata, Hall.
Leiopteria lœvis, Hall.
Panenka lincklœni, Hall.
Aviculopecten princeps, Conrad.
A. scabridus, Hall.
A. exactus, Hall.
A. fasciculatus, Hall.
A. idas, Hall.
A. lautus, Hall.
A. bellus, Conrad.
Pterinopecten conspectus, Hall.
P. intermedius, Hall.
P. vertumnus, Hall.
P. undosus, Hall.
Pterinea flabella, Conrad.
Actinoptera subdecussata, Hall.
A. decussata, Hall.
A. boydi, Conrad.
Glyptodesma erectum, Conrad.
Leiopteria conradi, Hall.
L. greeni, Hall.
L. rafinesqui, Hall.
L. sayi, Hall.
L. bigsbyi, Hall.
L. dekayi, Hall.
Leptodesma rogersi, Hall.
Limoptera macroptera, Conrad.
Mytilarca (P.) oviformis, Conrad.
Gosseletia triqueter, Conrad.
Modiomorpha concentrica, Conrad.
M. mytiloides, Conrad.
M. alta, Conrad.
M. macilenta, Hall.
M. subalata, Conrad.
Goniophora hamiltonensis, Hall.
Microdon bellistriatus, Conrad.
M. gregarius, Hall.
M. tenuistriatus, Hall.
Nucula randalli, Hall.
N. lirata, Conrad.
N. bellistriata, Conrad.

N. varicosa, Hall.
N. corbuliformis, Hall.
N. lamellata, Hall.
Nuculites oblongatus, Conrad.
N. triqueter, Conrad.
Leda diversa, Hall.
L. rostellata, Conrad.
Palœoneilo constricta, Conrad.
P. plana, Hall.
P. tenuistriata, Hall.
P. fecunda, Hall.
P. muta, Hall.
P. emarginata, Conrad.
P. perplana, Hall.
P. brevis, Hall.
Microdon complanatus, Hall.
Macrodon hamiltoniœ, Hall.
Nyassa arguta, Hall.
Grammysia bisulcata, Conrad.
G. nodocostata, Hall.
G. circularis, Hall.
G. obsoleta, Hall.
G. alveata, Conrad.
G. globosa, Hall.
G. arcuata, Conrad.
G. constricta, Hall.
G. (Sphenomya) cuneata, Hall.
Sphenotus arcœformis, Hall.
S. cuneatus, Conrad.
Paracyclas lirata, Conrad.
P. tenuis, Hall.
Schizodus appressus, Conrad.
Prothryris lanceolata, Hall.
Tellinopsis subemarginata, Conrad.
Cimitaria corrugata, Conrad.
C. elongata, Conrad.
C. recurva, Conrad.
Pholadella radiata, Conrad.
Phthonia cylindrica, Hall.
P. sectifrons, Conrad.
Orthonota undulata, Conrad.
O. carinata, Conrad.
O. parvula, Hall.
Cypricardinia indenta, Conrad
Modiella pygmœa, Conrad.

FOSSIL LAMELLIBRANCHIATA—Continued.

Glyptocardia speciosa, Hall.
Lunulicardium fragile, Hall.
Ccnocardium cuneus, var. trigonale, Hall.
Lunulicardium marcellense, Vanuxem.
Ammigenia catskillensis, Vanuxem.
Aviculopecten rugœstriatus, Hall.
A. duplicatus, Hall.
Lyriopecten priamus, Hall.
Pterinopecten neptuni, Hall.
P. suborbicularis, Hall.
Crenipecten amplus, Hall.
C. crenulatus, Hall.
Pterinea chemungensis, Conrad.
P. consimilis, Hall.
Ptychopteria salamanca, Hall.
P. sao, Hall.
P. thetis, Hall.
P. falcata, Hall.
P. elongata, Hall.
Leptodesma spinigerum, Conrad.
L. longispinum, Hall.
L. agassizi, Hall.
L. protextum, Conrad.
L. sociale, Hall.
L. potens, Hall.
L. mortoni, Hall.
L. billingsi, Hall.
L. stephani, Hall.
L. medon, Hall.
L. cadmus, Hall.
L. creon, Hall.
L. demus, Hall.
L. extenuatum, Hall.
L. hector, Hall.
L. corydon, Hall.
L. jason, Hall.

L. nereus, Hall.
L. orus, Hall.
L. flaccidum, Hall.
L. patulum, Hall.
L. arciforme, Hall.
L. phaon, Hall.
L. propinquum, Hall.
L. lichas, Hall.
L. quadrula, Hall.
Byssopteria radiata, Hall.
Mytilarca chemungensis, Conrad.
M. carinata, Hall.
Modiola (Mytilops) prœcedens, Hall.
Modiomorpha subalata, var. chemungensis, H.
M. subangulata, Hall.
M. quadrata, Hall.
Macrodon chemungensis, Hall.
Grammysia elliptica, Hall.
G. communis, Hall.
G. undulata, Hall.
Edmondia phillipi.
E. tumidula, Hall.
E. subovata, Hall.
Sphenotus contractus, Hall.
S. clavulus, Hall.
Spathella typica, Hall.
Schizodus rhombeus, Hall.
S. chemungensis, Conrad.
S. chemungensis, var. quadrangularis, Hall.
Prothyris exuta, Hall.
Palœanatina typa, Hall.
P. angusta, Hall.
Glossites lingualis, Hall.
G. patulus, Hall.
Stylonurus excelsior, Hall (cast).

(47 genera, 146 species, 3 varieties, and 236 specimens.)

NEW YORK STATE MUSEUM OF NATURAL HISTORY, Albany, New York. (Through Prof. James Hall.) 19332. '88. (XIII)

ROSE-CRESTED COCKATOO, Cacatua moluccensis.

W. A. CONKLIN, Central Park Menagerie, New York City. 19333. '87. (V, A)

IRON PYRITE, magnetic iron ore, galena, chalcopyrite, metallic copper, etc.; for examination.

SHAH OF PERSIA, Teheran, Persia. (Through Department of State.) 19334. '87. (XVIII)

QUARTZ containing a small amount of crystallized pyrite.

F. GLASER, Germania, Alabama. 19335. '87. (XVI)

PLANT, Cortilleia (one specimen); for examination.

Lieut. F. P. FREMONT, U. S. Army, Fort Missoula, Montana. 19336. '87. (XV)

PLANT; for examination.

Lieut. F. P. FREMONT, U. S. Army, Fort Missoula, Montana. 19336. '87. (XV)

STONE PIPE with human faces carved on opposite sides, an unfinished ceremonial object, a natural formation, small round stone with groove, and two fragments of celts. (Exchange.)

R. W. MERCER, Cincinnati, Ohio. 19337. '87. (III)

SALMON-SKINS, four dried specimens, and three specimens tanned by Indian method. As the Indians tan them, they possess an extraordinary elasticity, when they are fastened onto the backs of their yew-tree bows, which seem to resist without injury a constant strain of many years.

ROBERT RADCLIFFE, Baird, California. 19338. '87. (I)

BABYLONIAN AND ASSYRIAN SEALS.

R. S. WILLIAMS, Utica, New York. 19339. '87. (II, A)

U. S. COPPER ONE-HALF CENT, dated 1809.

A. L. WOODWORTH, Norfolk, Virginia. 19340. '87. (I)

MEALY AMAZON, *Chrysotis farinosa.*

ZOOLOGICAL SOCIETY OF PHILADELPHIA, (Through A. E. Brown). 19341. '87. (XII)

COINS, silver and copper, and paper money of Mexico.

Dr. E. PALMER, Smithsonian Institution. 19342. '87. (I)

NORWICH CANARY.

CONRAD ZELLER, Washington, District of Columbia. 19343. '87. (V, A)

FOSSIL CORAL (100 specimens) and *Petremites* sp. (65 specimens), Lower Carboniferous.

JOHN H. LEMON, New Albany, Indiana. 19344. '87. (XIII, A)

BIRD, type of *Porzana alfaro,* from Costa Rica.

ANASTASIO ALFARO, secretary Costa Rica National Museum. (Through J. C. Zeledon.) 19345. '87. (V, A)

CHAMELEON (scorpion or green lizard), *Anolis principalis* (two specimens from Cape Romano, Florida).

Lieut. J. F. MOSER, U. S. Navy, U. S. Coast Survey steamer *A. D. Bache,* Newport, Rhode Island. 19346. '87. (VI)

FISHES: *Ictalurus, Lagocephalus, Elacate, Prionotus, Vomer, Hemirhamphus, Echeneis, Parephippus, Chilomycterus, Achirus, Dactyloscopus, Ophidium, Callionymus, Liphostoma, Chasmodes,* etc.; from the west coast of Florida.

Lieut. J. F. MOSER, U. S. Navy, U. S. Coast Survey steamer *A. D. Bache,* Newport, Rhode Island. 19346. '87. (VII)

MOLLUSKS, from Florida Reefs; in alcohol.

Lieut. J. F. MOSER, U. S. Navy, U. S. Coast Survey steamer *A. D. Bache,* Newport, Rhode Island. 19346. '87. (IX)

INSECTS; from Florida.

Lieut. J. F. MOSER, U. S. Navy, U. S. Coast Survey steamer *A. D. Bache,* Newport, Rhode Island. 19346. '86. (X)

MARINE INVERTEBATES: Echinoderms, Crustaceans, Sponges, Ascidians, etc.; from the west coast of Florida.

Lieut. J. F. MOSER, U. S. Navy, U. S. Coast Survey steamer *A. D. Bache,* Newport, Rhode Island. 19346. '87. (XI)

BIRD, type of *Porzana alfaro,* from Costa Rica.

ANASTASIO ALFARO, secretary Costa Rica National Museum. (Through J. C. Zeledon.) 19345. '87. (V, A)

AMERICAN HERCULES BEETLE, *Belostoma americana*; for examination.

H. C. MOSLEY, Charleston, South Carolina. 19347. '87. (X)

FALSE TOPAZ (8 specimens). (Purchased.)

Miss LAURA E. SCOTT, Washington, District of Columbia. 19348. '87. (XVI)

METEORIC IRON from Tennessee and Virginia; meteoric stones from Italy and from India. (Exchange.)

WARD AND HOWELL, Rochester, New York. 19349. '87. (XVI)

CHINESE CERAMICS.

Case 1: Blue and white pilgrim bottle; red vase; red gourd-shaped vase; Celadon vase; vase, flambé; 10 snuff bottles; 2 vases, Kü züeh hsuan, blue ground, medallions; Chien white teapot; bottle, green Kinkiang; 2 vases, gold on blue ground; 2 rose back plates; 2 Kaughsi plates, ornamentation on body; 2 Chienlung plates, perforated edges; 3 bowls.

Case 2: 4 cups; 6 eggshell cups, Yung lo; 2 porcelain screens (?); vase, purple ground, white flowers; cup, plum blossoms; Shenté t'ang cup; cup; 2 cups, purple ground; Celadon cup; wine cup, peach ornamentation; small flambé vase; small vase; 2 Kü züeh hsüan wine cups; 2 Kü züeh hsüan pen-holders; green vase (figures of flowers); large snuff bottle, flowers; small blue and white vase 6 blue and gold wine cups; 2 plates, flowers; Yüan plate; vase (flowers and figures); 2 cups, flowers over edge; 2 cups, white bamboo on red ground; 2 cups, enamel on metal; 2 cups, flowers on white ground; 2 cups, flowers; 2 plates, lotus flower; vase, green ground.

Case 3: Small flambé vase; 2 small vases, blue and white; snuff bottle, glass; gold-colored teapot; vase, blue, flowers white; small vase, sang de bœuf ;wall vase, purple ground with flowers; 6 snuff bottles; 2 bowls, eggshell porcelain, decoration in porcelain; teapot, colored, gourd-shaped vase; blue and white vase; deep red vase; 2 bowls and covers (?), flowers, etc.; small vase (? red lizard); 2 small bowls, flowers and fruit; small bowl; small bowl, flowers; 2 small yellow plates; 2 small plates, flowers, etc.; plate; small plate, black ground; 2 small bowls, flowers on red ground; 2 red bowls and covers; bowl and cover, figures; 2 bowls, white flowers on red ground; 2 purple ground vases; 2 blue and white vases (pa kwa); large plate, flower crossing edge to back; 4 bowls; 2 blue and white plates; plate, flowers in un ts'ai; 2 gourd-shaped vases, flowers; small glass vase; small blue vase; pencil holder, enamel on metal; biscuit pen-holder; Kü züeh hsüan cup; Kü züeh hsüan small teapot; 2 porcelain bamboo pen-holders; eggshell (?) flower pot; 2 seals.

Case 4: Vase, white dragon in relief; water cruet, with lizard; small vase, Celadon; 6 wine cups, various colors; small blue vase, ciselé; pencil-holder, white porcelain; pencil-holder, yellow; vase, gold flowers on tea dark ground; vase, green sang de bœuf; 2 plates, crab-apple blossoms; 2 yellow bowls; vase, blue and white?; 2 Kü yüeh hsüan bowls; Kaughsi vase; porcelain snuff bottle; enamel on metal bottle; small red vase; water cruet, 8 fairies; small vase, Celadon; small vase, flambé; green porcelain box; vase, chi hung; yellow bowl; small vase, black and white; 11 plates, various colors.

Case 5: 4 bronze pots; vase, green; vase, blue and white; vase, white with purple dragons; 2 bowls and covers; water cruet, red; plate, blue and white; 4 bowls, blue and white; 19 snuff bottles; vase, flambé; 2 small water bowls; vase, Kaughsi, figures, etc.; vase, Kü züeh hsüan; water cruet, famille verte; vase, black and white; water cruet; vase, yellow ground, deep brown dragon: vase, wu ts'ai, figures, etc.; 3 wine cups; small vase.

Case 6: 3 small plates; 3 seals, chien tzu; 8 snuff bottles, porcelain; vase, peacock green; vase, black and white; 10 medallion bowls; vase, Kaughsi, square; 8 bowls, Celadon; water cruet, peacock green; bowl, Celadon with landscape medallions; large Celadon, black and white; bowl, eggshell porcelain; 9 bowls; 12 plates, eggshell porcelain; water cruet, cucumber skin.

Case 7: 4 cups, black ts'ai; 2 vases, pair of stags; vase, chi hnng; 2 small bowls, white bamboos; bowl, black and white; water cruet, coral red; 2 bowls, colors on yellow ground; 2 bowls, cucumber skin; 2 flower bowls, iron rust; bowl, colors on red ground; snuff bottle, glass; 8 wine cups, painted; bowl, black and white; porcelain plate; 2 bowls; 4 panels, porcelain screen; small bowl, 100 flowers; small bronze pot; 2 bowls, coral red, ven chih hung; 6 wine cups (?) Kaughsi ts'ai; vase, dragon, black and white; 2 vases, black and white; 4 plates, Kaughsi ts'ai.

CHINESE CERAMICS—Continued.

Case 8 : Porcelain brick ; vase, flambé ; 20 panels from porcelain brick ; 2 plates, enamel on metal ; 2 bowls, black and white ; bowl, small ; 4 bowls, red characters ; vase, Celadon with lizard ; vase, Kaughsi ; vase, Celadon, with ornamentation in relief ; vase, tea dust.

Case 9 : Teapot ; fish bowl, black and white ; plates ; bowl ; bowl, Ning szuasty ; 4 or 5 pieces ivory ware ; teapot, Kü züeh hsüan ; 2 cups, Kü züeh hsüan ; 2 saucers ; small bowl ; 3 bowls, pictures in medallions ; vase ; pencil-holder, black and white ; 4 small bowls, various ; box, red dragon ; vase ; snuff bottle ; bronze ; 2 vases, frogs ; 2 candlesticks ; vase, with silver damascene ; pot with Arabic inscription ; Buddah's finger ; 2 snuff bottles ; small pot.

ALFRED E. HIPPISLEY, London, England. 19350. '87. (I)

INDEXES TO ACCESSION LIST.

INDEX A.

AFRICA.

17718, 17986, 18091, 18304, 18388, 18404, 18694, 18708, 18765, 18811, 18815, 18898, 19029, 19080, 19126, 19201, 19209.

AMERICA.

NORTH AMERICA.

BRITISH AMERICA: 17707, 17736, 17759, 17884, 18002, 18097, 18106, 18128, 18130, 18207, 18256, 18280, 18321, 18467, 18499, 18510, 18513, 18578, 18733, 18789, 18818, 18878, 18898, 18951, 19245, 19246.
GREENLAND: 17800, 17854, 18393, 18485.

UNITED STATES.

ALABAMA: 17740, 17821, 17908, 17950, 18149, 18358, 18401, 18530, 18642, 18648, 18718, 18830, 18892, 18963, 19193, 19286, 19335.
ALASKA: 18028, 18036, 18090, 18143, 18244, 18346, 18375, 18409, 18412, 18416, 18490, 18491, 18614, 18616, 18650, 18652, 18669, 18740, 18892, 19052, 19110, 19127, 19248.
ARIZONA: 17756, 17790, 17814, 17904, 17936, 17976, 18005, 18048, 18080, 18082, 18164, 18212, 18300, 18449, 18583, 18682, 18695, 18731, 18759, 18796, 18812, 18880, 18938, 18941, 18981, 18983, 19003, 19019, 19071, 19105, 19114, 19205, 19231, 19252, 19284, 19313.
ARKANSAS: 17756, 17813, 17835, 17861, 17877, 17898, 18000, 18008, 18009, 18011, 18122, 18158, 18390, 18448, 18536, 18699, 18714, 18770, 18824, 19093.
CALIFORNIA: 17760, 17767, 17795, 17801, 17818, 17863, 17883, 17907, 17934, 17956, 18020, 18083, 18094, 18146, 18200, 18201, 18215, 18241, 18298, 18327, 18374, 18382, 18383, 18399, 18407, 18412, 18418, 18436, 18444, 18463, 18537, 18608, 18613, 18649, 18650, 18692, 18704, 18709, 18717, 18734, 18796, 18800, 18862, 18870, 18872, 18935, 19026, 19082, 19107, 19110, 19123, 19238, 19244, 19264, 19338.
COLORADO: 17766, 17784, 17789, 17899, 17991, 18008, 18009, 18018, 18164, 18177, 18243, 18248, 18287, 18301, 18324, 18558, 18744, 18779, 18786, 18965, 19030, 19237, 19239, 19264.
CONNECTICUT: 17724, 17729, 17775, 17940, 18099, 18104, 18129, 18172, 18280, 18499, 18520, 18680, 18722, 18724, 18918, 19028, 19061, 19197, 19299.
DAKOTA: 17819, 17851, 18118, 18267, 18820, 18968, 19267, 19303.
DELAWARE: 17987, 18042, 18766, 19312.
DISTRICT OF COLUMBIA: 17710, 17712, 17715, 17738, 17744, 17746, 17748, 17751, 17763, 17783, 17788, 17800, 17803, 17815, 17828, 17839, 17846, 17852, 17853, 17882, 17885, 17892, 17906, 17913, 17918, 17928, 17937, 17957, 17959, 17961,

District of Columbia—Continued.

17969, 17988, 18007, 18024, 18046, 18055, 18066, 18067, 18070, 18073, 18096, 18109, 18123, 18136, 18137, 18163, 18166, 18182, 18183, 18204, 18210, 18214, 18222, 18227, 18239, 18240, 18242, 18282, 18311, 18323, 18335, 1833~, 18339, 18343, 18350, 18351, 18360, 18370, 18376, 18391, 18397, 18460, 18404, 18405, 18408, 18422, 18429, 18452, 18461, 18470, 18474, 18490, 18498, 18500, 18513, 18514, 18521, 18524, 18534, 18541, 18557, 18560, 18561, 18562, 18563, 1~566, 18568, 18571, 18580, 18584, 18587, 18590, 18596, 18602, 18603, 18606, 18626, 18628, 18638, 18639, 18642, 18645, 18646, 18647, 18656, 18657, 18659, 18679, 18688, 18690, 18691, 18701, 18705, 18711, 18712, 18723, 18728, 18729, 18732, 18735, 18738, 18746, 18751, 18753, 18754, 18764, 18771, 18772, 18775, 18783, 18807, 18813, 18815, 18817, 18827, 18838, 18843, 18856, 18864, 18865, 18866, 18867, 18875, 18877, 18883, 18884, 18886, 18896, 18~97, 18903, 18908, 18932, 18942, 18947, 18954, 18957, 18958, 18959, 18960, 18969, 18978, 18980, 18990, 18991, 18993, 18995, 18998, 19011, 19017, 19023, 19040, 19041, 19042, 19043, 19045, 19047, 19050, 19051, 19053, 19059, 19060, 19062, 19079, 19085, 19115, 19128, 19129, 19135, 19138, 19150, 19166, · 19168, 19180, 19183, 19190, 19199, 19202, 19204, 19210, 19212, 19220, 19221, 19225, 18232, 19234, 19235, 19241, 19242, 19259, 19269, 19271, 19277, 19283, 19288, 19290, 19292, 19294, 19297, 19300, 19305, 19306, 19309, 19310, 19311, 19317, 19318, 19319, 19322, 19324, 19343, 19348.

Florida : 17709, 17716, 17905, 17943, 18074, 18133, 18238, 18256, 18410, 18531, 18544, 18550, 18578, 18610, 18630, 18634, 18635, 18636, 18654, 18677, 18763, 18825, 18831, 18837, 18847, 18849, 18853, 18857, 18887, 18911, 18919, 18931, 18955, 19068, 19102, 19113, 19121, 19145, 19170, 19184, 19234, 19274, 19283, 19346.

Georgia : 17952, 18092, 18117, 18472, 18706, 18769, 18851, 18957, 18970, 19036, 19250, 19285.

Idaho : 18859.

Illinois: 17776, 17786, 17940, 17941, 18012, 18075, 18199, 18226, 18250, 18326, 18377, 18407, 18519, 18525, 18588, 18674, 18715, 18768, 18940, 19133, 19144, 19151, 19165, 19177, 19280, 19298.

Indiana: 17728, 17887, 17891, 17905, 18102, 18228, 18261, 18262, 18329, 18529, 18532, 18543, 18788, 19013, 19087, 19154, 19175, 19206, 19230, 19296, 19320, 19344, 19349.

Indian Territory: 18581, 19018.

Iowa: 17793, 17873, 17938, 17995, 18037, 18475, 18519, 18545, 18605, 18719, 19146.

Kansas: 17742, 17917, 18125, 18260, 18266, 18340, 18384, 18438, 18696, 18842, 18869, 18953, 18975, 19314.

Kentucky: 17780, 17864, 18274, 18373, 18384, 18482, 18632, 18650, 18666, 18791, 18854, 19064, 19117, 19118, 19119, 19120.

Louisiana : 17892, 18171, 18309, 18411, 18464, 18552, 18554, 18555, 18653, 18781, 18832, 18833, 19070, 19161, 19214.

Maine: 17896, 17985, 17992, 17993, 18003, 18058, 18108, 18435, 18713, 18890, 18949, 19171, 19281, 19291, 19324.

Maryland: 17755, 17762, 17771, 17802, 17807, 17880, 17930, 17912, 17993, 18067, 18093, 18128, 18219, 18220, 18234, 18257, 18270, 18298, 18313, 18334, 18349, 18375, 18379, 18395, 18454, 18496, 18499, 18570, 18572, 18651, 18658, 18685, 18734, 18772, 18776, 18785, 18805, 18844, 18874, 18902, 18937, 18976, 19012, 19229, 19278.

Massachusetts: 17737, 17777, 17782, 17797, 17808, 17825, 17836, 17868, 17874, 17909, 17924, 17955, 17962, 17974, 17978, 17981, 17984, 17989, 17990, 17991, 17993, 18021, 18064, 18097, 18098, 18105, 18115, 18134, 18162, 18164, 18167, 18174, 18175, 18178, 18180, 18230, 18242, 18245, 18258, 18269, 18278, 18285, 18300, 18306, 18316, 18330, 18347, 18354, 18357, 18369, 18385, 18476, 18504, 18585, 18599, 18601, 18627, 18671, 18683, 18686, 18736, 18737, 18745, 18747, 18750, 18767, 18774, 18802, 18809, 18834, 18863, 18909, 18936, 18967, 19037, 19073, 19077, 19086, 19211, 19236, 19256, 19279, 19286, 19307, 19308, 19315.

Utah : 17966, 18253, 18431, 19067.

Vermont : 18151, 18440, 18820.

Virginia : 17730, 17735, 17752, 17758, 17770, 17796, 17810, 17858, 17860, 17881, 17889, 17897, 17912, 17914, 17916, 17926, 17935, 17944, 17947, 17949, 17964, 17977, 17982, 17996, 17997, 17998, 17999, 18001, 18013, 18015, 18026, 18031, 18041, 18049, 18050, 18051, 18052, 18053, 18054, 18060, 18062, 18065, 18081, 18096, 18101, 18131, 18153, 18154, 18155, 18169, 18176, 18185, 18186, 18187, 18188, 18189, 18191, 18192, 18193, 18194, 18195, 18196, 18197, 18198, 18205, 18206, 18216, 18224, 18235, 18257, 18263, 18273, 18276, 18279, 18281, 18290, 18305, 18307, 18318, 18319, 18337, 18355, 18402, 18451, 18477, 18489, 18515, 18523, 18569, 18609, 18623, 18625, 18648, 18673, 18675, 18688, 18698, 18720, 18727, 18741, 18808, 18813, 18819, 18841, 18871, 18874, 18899, 18910, 18915, 18921, 18927, 18933, 18946, 18952, 18961, 18971, 18979, 18996, 19004, 19007, 19022, 19044, 19056, 19066, 19089, 19095, 19137, 19141, 19159, 19169, 19182, 19200, 19208, 19213, 19216, 19224, 19247, 19255, 19257, 19260, 19289, 19326, 19340, 19349.

Washington : 17741, 18100, 18598, 18615, 18986.

West Virginia : 17758, 17890, 18067, 18076, 18489, 18641.

Wisconsin : 17915, 18246, 18252, 18341, 18406, 18539, 19152, 19253, 19270, 19323.

Wyoming : 18008, 18287, 18681, 18762.

MEXICO.

17794, 17857, 17895, 17923, 18082, 18142, 18181, 18314, 18434, 18478, 18481, 18499, 18576, 18723, 18725, 18730, 18964, 18990, 19046, 19088, 19109, 19178, 19187, 19342.

WEST INDIES.

17777, 17920, 18104, 18208, 18242, 18249, 18322, 18456, 18499, 18573, 18618, 18722, 18798, 18836, 18878, 18879, 19099, 19185, 19262.

Central America.

17733, 17820, 17849, 18181, 18221, 18254, 18492, 18493, 18551, 18575, 18579, 18640, 18757, 18849, 18898, 19099, 19262, 19345.

South America.

17761, 17806, 17809, 17929, 17932, 17958, 18030, 18033, 18223, 18277, 18325, 18364, 18404, 18432, 18494, 18499, 18513, 18516, 18573, 18614, 18622, 18703, 18757, 18799, 18898, 18917, 18990, 19026, 19029, 19032, 19054, 19112, 19207.

ASIA.

Arabia : 18815.

Burmah : 17855.

Ceylon : 18442, 18515.

China : 17727, 17781, 17798, 17838, 17960, 17963, 17965, 18063, 18103, 18138, 18144, 18255, 18344, 18404, 18443, 18548, 18600, 18670, 18749, 18900, 18994, 19033, 19218, 19276, 19329, 19350.

Cochin China : 18304.

Corea : 17965, 18533, 19010, 19276.

India : 17855, 17866, 17960, 18255, 18304, 18404, 18499, 18765, 18836, 18898, 19055, 19349.

Japan : 17822, 17928, 17948, 17963, 17965, 18047, 18057, 18103, 18139, 18173, 18255, 18283, 18302, 18315, 18348, 18415, 18446, 18501, 18518, 18533, 18836, 18898, 19048, 19072, 19083, 19103, 19302.

Kamtschatka : 18413, 18950.

Persia : 18898, 19334.

Siam : 17960.

Syria ; 18935, 19191.

EUROPE.

AUSTRIA: 17791, 18293, 18428, 18499, 18836, 18934.

BELGIUM: 18404, 18483.

DENMARK: 18499.

FRANCE: 17922, 18071, 18085, 18088, 18130, 18159, 18292, 18293, 18304, 18394, 18404, 18442, 18499, 18508, 18511, 18693, 18694, 18836, 18891, 18977, 19001, 19006, 19038.

GERMANY: 17753, 17764, 17765, 17792, 17980, 18168, 18259, 18284, 18293, 18404, 18428, 18442, 18499, 18508, 18684, 18855, 18901, 19134, 19136.

GREAT BRITAIN: 17799, 17837, 17865, 18113, 18130, 18160, 18292, 18312, 10365, 18404, 18430, 18447, 18453, 18460, 18469, 18499, 18512, 18743, 18984, 19006, 19084, 19249, 19304.

GREECE: 18517, 18836.

HOLLAND: 18499, 18621.

ICELAND: 18165.

ITALY: 18404, 18508, 18898, 19006, 19215, 18243, 19349.

NORWAY: 18293, 18308, 18508, 19142.

NORTHERN EUROPE: 18087.

PORTUGAL: 18404.

RUSSIA: 17817, 17867, 18404, 18462, 18898.

SARDINIA: 18061, 18404.

SPAIN: 18404, 18499, 18836.

SWEDEN: 17812, 18130, 18293, 18352.

SWITZERLAND: 18293, 18404, 18442, 18453, 18499, 18508, 19006.

SYRIA: 18517.

TURKEY: 18310, 18404, 18966.

MISCELLANEOUS: 18526.

OCEANICA.

AUSTRALASIA.

17845, 18304, 18326, 18755, 18758, 18898, 18905.

POLYNESIA.

17779, 17826, 18091, 18420, 18421, 18437, 18694, 18898, 19025, 19026, 19065, 19081, 19116, 19186, 19263, 19325.

Index B.

Department I.

Arts and Industries (260 accessions): 17705, 17715, 17725, 17744, 17753, 17760, 17770, 17775, 17782, 17783, 17794, 17797, 17831, 17847, 17849, 17865, 17868, 17869, 17883, 17886, 17889, 17894, 17907, 17913, 17922, 17929, 17932, 17942, 17960, 17975, 17982, 17988, 17998, 17999, 18025, 18026, 18027, 18033, 18049, 18065, 18073, 18085, 18101, 18103, 18107, 18123, 18128, 18129, 18130, 18131, 18153, 18155, 18159, 18160, 18162, 18168, 18169, 18179, 18184, 18185, 18186, 18187–18191, inclusive, 18194, 18195, 18196, 18202, 18205, 18206, 18224, 18255, 18299, 18310, 18316, 18325, 18332, 18338, 18339, 18342, 18346, 18354, 18357, 18391, 18399, 18404, 18415, 18416, 18417, 18428, 18430, 18441, 18442, 13453, 18455, 18456, 18461, 18462, 18469, 18470, 18480, 18498, 18499, 18511, 18512, 18513, 18514, 18528, 18530, 18544, 18548, 18550, 18555, 18557, 18560, 18561, 18562, 18564, 18565, 18566, 18573, 18574, 18575, 18584, 18586, 18600, 18606, 18618, 18620, 18621, 18643, 18645, 18647, 18653, 18656, 18670, 18679, 18687, 18688, 18717, 18723, 18726, 18735, 18736, 18737, 18745, 18746, 18747, 18749, 18750, 18767, 18769, 18801, 18807, 18813, 18814, 18815, 18821, 18836, 18843, 18851, 18864, 18868, 18875, 18885, 18903, 18908, 18917, 18934, 18942, 18958, 18959, 18960, 18966, 18977, 18978, 18979, 18984, 18990, 19004, 19033, 19034, 19035, 19039, 19044, 19047, 19054, 19055, 19070, 19088, 19099, 19117, 19118, 19119, 19120, 19124, 19125, 19128, 19129, 19130, 19131, 19132, 19133, 19137, 19138, 19139, 19140, 19141, 19143, 19144, 19149–19167 inclusive, 19171–19177 inclusive, 19180, 19191, 19193, 19194, 19195, 19196, 19197, 19207, 19219, 19220, 19226, 19232, 19241, 19242, 19243, 19251, 19285, 19288, 19289, 19290, 19306, 19308, 19309, 19310, 19311, 19317, 19318, 19319, 19327, 19338, 19340, 19342, 19350.

Department II.

(A.) Ethnology (142 accessions): 17727, 17746, 17781, 17798, 17800, 17801, 17811, 17822, 17826, 17838, 17854, 17855, 17866, 17867, 17900, 17928, 17929, 17960, 17961, 17968, 17972, 17976, 17977, 17986, 18028, 18030, 18036, 18046, 18047, 18048, 18050–18054 inclusive, 18057, 18060, 18063, 18103, 18107, 18138, 18139, 18144, 18149, 18171, 18188, 18192, 18197, 18198, 18214, 18216, 18223, 18229, 18244, 18283, 18284, 18298, 18305, 18315, 18323, 18348, 18351, 18364, 18392, 18397, 18409, 18415, 18416, 18438, 18439, 18443, 18448, 18450, 18474, 18483, 18485, 18490, 18491, 18500, 18501, 18575, 18608, 18615, 18616, 18638, 18657, 18669, 18689, 18693, 18694, 18711, 18720, 18723, 18740, 18745, 18754, 18771, 18812, 18838, 18852, 18857, 18865, 18866, 18867, 18884, 18889, 18898, 18900, 18980, 19001, 19010, 19018, 19025, 19026, 19048, 19051, 19052, 19065, 19079, 19080, 19081, 19109, 19110, 19112, 19116, 19122, 19127, 19135, 19186, 19191, 19201, 19212, 19215, 19218, 19248, 19263, 19265, 19276, 19280, 19294, 19329, 19339.

(B.) American Prehistoric Pottery (13 accessions): 17929, 18314, 18486, 18567, 18718, 18723, 18975, 18998, 19032, 19187, 19272, 19294, 19339.

Department III.

Antiquities (93 accessions): 17716, 17717, 17721, 17722, 17733, 17749, 17762, 17816, 17829, 17830, 17860, 17894, 17908, 17921, 17925, 17928, 17939, 17940, 17943, 17944, 17983, 17996, 17907, 18029, 18036, 18067, 18071, 18079, 18092, 18093, 18107, 18133, 18174, 18204, 18205, 18211, 18213, 18218, 18221, 18235, 18239, 18242, 18294, 18295, 18358, 18394, 18406, 18408, 18412, 18433, 18445, 18448, 18455, 18464, 18466, 18492, 18496, 18527, 18538, 18539, 18543, 18546, 18552, 18554, 18567, 18577, 18605, 18718, 18723, 18755, 18756, 18761, 18768, 18808, 18822, 18863, 18891, 18907, 18927, 18998, 19006, 19024, 19026, 19027, 19036, 19058, 19075, 19148, 19224, 19249, 19272, 19284, 19337

DEPARTMENT IV.

MAMMALS (94 accessions): 17706, 17708, 17711, 17712, 17729, 17736, 17750, 17754, 17774, 17801, 17812, 17832, 17876, 17884, 17919, 17920, 17923, 17931, 17951, 17979, 18002, 18072, 18076, 18078, 18090, 18126, 18166, 18183, 18209, 18236, 18250, 18276, 18292, 18304, 18343, 18350, 18362, 18371, 18396, 18402, 18420, 18421, 18437, 18444, 18458, 18459, 18476, 18487, 18491, 18494, 18497, 18516, 18524, 18579, 18585, 18595, 18601, 18612, 18613, 18617, 18631, 18633, 18637, 18671, 18683, 18686, 18695, 18711, 18741, 18748, 18757, 18758, 18799, 18806, 18862, 18969, 18994, 18995, 19015, 19026, 19031, 19041, 19049, 19053, 19062, 19073, 19090, 19091, 19099, 19136, 19168, 19182, 19233, 19245.

DEPARTMENT V.

(A.) BIRDS (202 accessions): 17733, 17735, 17736, 17738, 17750, 17755, 17779, 17781, 17802, 17803, 17806, 17807, 17809, 17815, 17837, 17839, 17853, 17862, 17863, 17881, 17882, 17884, 17885, 17899, 17923, 17929, 17948, 17962, 17969, 17981, 17984, 17985, 18006, 18021, 18035, 18075, 18076, 18082, 18083, 18084, 18087, 18091, 18097, 18163, 18166, 18173, 18176, 18219, 18220, 18221, 18226, 18234, 18241, 18242, 18246, 18247, 18248, 18250, 18254, 18256, 18257, 18268, 18269, 18272, 18282, 18292, 18301, 18302, 18313, 18318, 18321, 18322, 18324, 18334, 18338, 18339, 18343, 18344, 18349, 18355, 18359, 18360, 18370, 18377, 18379, 18395, 18402, 18413, 18415, 18416, 18417, 18420, 18425, 18435, 18446, 18452, 18487, 18491, 18503, 18518, 18521, 18522, 18525, 18526, 18531, 18540, 18549, 18578, 18580, 18587, 18593, 18596, 18597, 18599, 18607, 18622, 18644, 18646, 18651, 18660, 18674, 18685, 18704, 18712, 18715, 18730, 18733, 18734, 18764, 18765, 18775, 18780, 18783, 18796, 18798, 18800, 18803, 18825, 18834, 18837, 18862, 18878, 18879, 18883, 18902, 18909, 18931, 18932, 18936, 18941, 18945, 18948, 18950, 18951, 18967, 18976, 18983, 19012, 19017, 19020, 19026, 19029, 19030, 19037, 19045, 19046, 19059, 19061, 19072, 19077, 19083, 19091, 19099, 19103, 19107, 19112, 19123, 19142, 19169, 19183, 19209, 19211, 19216, 19223, 19229, 19244, 19253, 19262, 19268, 19269, 19270, 19275, 19279, 19297, 19298, 19315, 19316, 19323, 19325, 19330, 19333, 19343, 19345.

(B.) BIRDS' EGGS (51 accessions): 17750, 17864, 17884, 17906, 17929, 17964, 18100, 18140, 18141, 18164, 18177, 18199, 18280, 18289, 18303, 18326, 18327, 18361, 18416, 18417, 18473, 18491, 18559, 18663, 18713, 18731, 18759, 18779, 18802, 18804, 18906, 18981, 19014, 19019, 19026, 19077, 19099, 19105, 19114, 19169, 19202, 19203, 19204, 19205, 19231, 19252, 19273, 19278, 10299, 19313, 19314.

DEPARTMENT VI.

REPTILES AND BATRACHIANS (58 accessions): 17710, 17720, 17752, 17805, 17816, 17820, 17874, 17890, 17923 17929, 17965, 17970, 18010, 18013, 18062, 18069, 18080, 18114, 18137, 18152, 18157, 18166, 18175, 18210, 18233, 18242, 18250, 18251, 18265, 18279, 18292, 18300, 18311, 18386, 18432, 18472, 18484, 18491, 18573, 18608, 18614, 18786, 18911, 18920, 18929, 18937, 18973, 18974, 19026, 19042, 19099, 19107, 19111, 19112, 19235, 19287, 19300, 19346.

DEPARTMENT VII.

FISHES (125 accessions): 17726, 17731, 17732, 17734, 17748, 17778, 17799, 17804, 17808, 17817, 17821, 17823, 17836, 17842, 17846, 17854, 17872, 17873, 17875, 17878, 17891, 17903, 17909, 17923, 17954, 17955, 17965, 17971, 17973, 17987, 18001, 18004, 18020, 18031, 18036, 18098, 18099, 18102, 18104, 18105, 18109, 18112, 18117, 18120, 18127, 18132, 18133, 18134, 18166, 18170, 18178, 18207, 18215, 18228, 18230, 18231, 18232, 18236, 18239, 18240, 18242, 18260, 18273, 18275, 18278, 18286, 18330, 18331, 18336, 18363, 18369, 18378, 18382, 18384, 18385, 18387, 18410, 18415, 18417, 18427, 18466, 18484, 18491, 18572, 18588, 18602, 18604, 18608, 18614, 18616, 18654, 18662, 18672, 18677, 18691, 18703, 18714, 18755, 18849, 18857, 18890, 18912, 18918, 18930, 18933, 18938, 18952, 18957, 18965, 19016, 19078, 19086, 19099, 19126, 19210, 19228, 19230, 19256, 19283, 19287, 19307, 19322, 19324, 19328, 19346.

DEPARTMENT VIII.

VERTEBRATE FOSSILS (4 accessions): 17726, 17923, 18113, 19071.

DEPARTMENT IX.

MOLLUSKS (76 accessions): 17707, 17733, 17736, 17737, 17742, 17776, 17777, 17795, 17858, 17878, 17923, 17938, 17950, 17965, 18015, 18016, 18019, 18064, 18074, 18087–18089 inclusive, 18096, 18142, 18147, 18181, 18182, 18200, 18217, 18242, 18262, 18296, 18333, 18353, 18375, 18403, 18407, 18417, 18419, 18420, 18431, 18457, 18468, 18493, 18519, 18533, 18556, 18581, 18598, 18626, 18634, 18640, 18702, 18753, 18755, 18785, 18831, 18832, 18853, 18857, 18919, 18925, 18949, 19015, 19026, 19032, 19084, 19099, 19121, 19145, 19185, 19257, 19291, 19302, 19328, 19346.

DEPARTMENT X.

INSECTS (108 accessions): 17709, 17719, 17728, 17740, 17743, 17767, 17833, 17834, 17848, 17850, 17888, 17897, 17905, 17912, 17914, 17917, 17923, 17924, 17929, 17941, 17949, 17952, 17956, 17965, 18007, 18023, 18036, 18039, 18042, 18043, 18044, 18045, 18077, 18081, 18111, 18147, 18148, 18150, 18151, 18156, 18172, 18238, 18242, 18261, 18264, 18281, 18291, 18304, 18405, 18407, 18417, 18427, 18449, 18478, 18489, 18491, 18495, 18505, 18506, 18507, 18510, 18529, 18550, 18591, 18630, 18678, 18680, 18682, 18752, 18755, 18766, 18784, 18788, 18809, 18820, 18828, 18848, 18857, 18861, 18886, 18899, 18944, 18954, 18961, 18962, 19015, 19026, 19040, 19068, 19099, 19112, 19113, 19170, 19184, 19210, 19213, 19227, 19234, 19255, 19259, 19260, 19274, 19296, 19302, 19320, 19321, 19346, 19347.

DEPARTMENT XI.

MARINE INVERTEBRATES (52 accessions): 17707, 17736, 17893, 17895, 17915, 17928, 17930, 17965, 18014, 18036, 18037, 18041, 18104, 18165, 18167, 18201, 18242, 18245, 18271, 18288, 18328, 18336, 18356, 18369, 18407, 18417, 18420, 18424, 18484, 18488, 18533, 18614, 18665, 18703, 18722, 18786, 18809, 18853, 18857, 18887, 18890, 18919, 19933, 18940, 18971, 19026, 19032, 19099, 19112, 19178, 19312, 19346.

DEPARTMENT XII.

COMPARATIVE ANATOMY (112 accessions): 17750, 17796, 17811, 17814, 17825, 17828, 17845, 17852, 17870, 17880, 17884, 17918, 17929, 17933, 17955, 17957, 17958, 17959, 17978, 17980, 17981, 18024, 18055, 18058, 18066, 18070, 18100, 18106, 18115, 18116, 18180, 18208, 18214, 18260, 18277, 18290, 18295, 18365, 18376, 18379, 18400, 18417, 18418, 18422, 18423, 18429, 18436, 18459, 18477, 18487, 18509, 18523, 18535, 18541, 18551, 18568, 18569, 18570, 18571, 18579, 18588, 18603, 18614, 18619, 18625, 18627, 18628, 18632, 18639, 18658, 18659, 18666, 18673, 18684, 18690, 18701, 18720, 18732, 18738, 18772, 18794, 18795, 18805, 18816, 18817, 18842, 18844, 18846, 18847, 18874, 18895, 18920, 18939, 18946, 18947, 18955, 19008, 19011, 19059, 19074, 19076, 19085, 19089, 19098, 19099, 19108, 19168, 19190, 19245, 19277, 19305, 19341.

DEPARTMENT XIII.

(A.) INVERTEBRATE FOSSILS (Palæozoic) (44 accessions): 17713, 17793, 17926, 17927, 18012, 18113, 18262, 18340, 18341, 18373, 18374, 18393, 18406, 18440, 18532, 18539, 18543, 18547, 18558, 18567, 18588, 18589, 18641, 18642, 18661, 18695, 18735, 18774, 18818, 18860, 18880, 18881, 18882, 18991, 18997, 18998, 19013, 19043, 19097, 19115, 19206, 19217, 19304, 19344.

(B.) INVERTEBRATE FOSSILS (Mesozoic) (16 accessions): 17714, 17761, 17764, 17765, 17791, 18312, 18340, 18366, 18455, 18588, 18716, 19246, 19254, 19266, 19292, 19293.

(C.) INVERTEBRATE FOSSILS (Cenozoic) (1 accession): 18652.

DEPARTMENT XIV.

FOSSIL PLANTS (13 accessions): 17860, 17878, 17892, 17915, 18009, 18038, 18193, 18227, 18270, 18436, 18789, 18907, 18247.

DEPARTMENT XV.

RECENT PLANTS (44 accessions): 17739, 17759, 17768, 17773, 17776, 17786, 17849, 17851, 17857, 17894, 17963, 18034, 18036, 18068, 18094, 18161, 18166, 18203, 18223, 18242, 18317, 18416, 18491, 18567, 18588, 18594, 18723, 18725, 18751, 18789, 18790, 18823, 18829, 18839, 18905, 18912, 18943, 19013, 19087, 19099, 19237, 19247, 19262, 19336.

DEPARTMENT XVI.

MINERALS (219 accessions): 17708, 17723, 17730, 17747, 17756, 17757, 17758, 17784, 17785, 17818, 17827, 17841, 17843, 17857, 17859, 17860, 17861, 17869, 17892, 17896, 17898, 17916, 17926, 17934, 17937, 17953, 17974, 17983, 17989–17995 inclusive, 18000, 18003, 18008, 18009, 18011, 18017, 18018, 18019, 18032, 18056, 18086, 18108, 18110, 18119, 18124, 18125, 18146, 18158, 18166, 18237, 18243, 18253, 18258, 18259, 18266, 18267, 18271, 18285, 18287, 18293, 18297, 18300, 18308, 18320, 18329, 18335, 18345, 18352, 18368, 18372, 18374, 18381, 18383, 18388, 18390, 18398, 18411, 18415, 18417, 18426, 18434, 18460, 18463, 18465, 18467, 18475, 18479, 18481, 18502, 18508, 18515, 18534, 18536, 18537, 18539, 18542, 18545, 18563, 18567, 18582, 18583, 18588, 18626, 18650, 18667, 18668, 18675, 18676, 18681, 18692, 18696, 18697, 18699, 18700, 18705, 18708, 18709, 18719, 18727, 18728, 18747, 18760, 18762, 18763, 18781, 18792, 18793, 18797, 18810, 18811, 18815, 18819, 18823, 18824, 18830, 18833, 18841, 18845, 18850, 18854, 18855, 18858, 18870, 18871, 18872, 18873, 18876, 18901, 18910, 18913, 18916, 18926, 18953, 18956, 18970, 18989, 18993, 18996, 18999, 19000, 19003, 19008, 19028, 19032, 19038, 19063, 19064, 19067, 19070, 19082, 19093, 19094, 19100, 19101, 19102, 19106, 19112, 19146, 19181, 19188, 19189, 19192, 19208, 19214, 19221, 19222, 19236, 19238, 19240, 19254, 19261, 19264, 19267, 19295, 19303, 19335, 19348, 19349.

DEPARTMENT XVII.

LITHOLOGY AND PHYSICAL GEOLOGY (72 accessions): 17745, 17771, 17840, 17844, 17856, 17877, 17879, 17887, 17935, 17946, 17967, 18022, 18059, 18061, 18143, 18163, 18166, 18222, 18263, 18274, 18297, 18306, 18307, 18309, 18329, 18352, 18367, 18374, 18388, 18397, 18415, 18466, 18475, 18491, 18517, 18590, 18611, 18626, 18640, 18649, 18698, 18721, 18723, 18724, 18744, 18782, 18787, 18791, 18840, 18861, 18877, 18888, 18894, 18914, 18988, 19009, 19026, 19050, 19069, 19092, 19112, 19200, 19225, 19228, 19258, 19271, 19326.

DEPARTMENT XVIII.

METALLURGY AND ECONOMIC GEOLOGY (145 accessions): 17724, 17741, 17751, 17763, 17766, 17769, 17772, 17776, 17780, 17787–17790 inclusive, 17810, 17813, 17819, 17824, 17835, 17871, 17877, 17901, 17902, 17904, 17911, 17923, 17936, 17945, 17947, 17966, 18005, 18009, 18040, 18118, 18121, 18122, 18135, 18136, 18145, 18154, 18166, 18212, 18223, 18249, 18252, 18263, 18309, 18319, 18337, 18374, 18380, 18389, 18401, 18417, 18451, 18454, 18471, 18482, 18520, 18553, 18576, 18592, 18609, 18610, 18623, 18624, 18626, 18627, 18629, 18636, 18648, 18649, 18653, 18655, 18664, 18706, 18707, 18710, 18729, 18739, 18742, 18776, 18777, 18778, 18806, 18815, 18823, 18826, 18827, 18833, 18835, 18845, 18850, 18856, 18859, 18861, 18864, 18869, 18892, 18893, 18896, 18897, 18904, 18915, 18921–18924 inclusive, 18928, 18935, 18938, 18963, 18964, 18968, 18972, 18982, 18985, 18986, 18987, 18992, 19005, 19007, 19021, 19022, 19023, 19056, 19057, 19060, 19066, 19095, 19096, 19104, 19112, 19134, 19147, 19179, 19198, 19199, 19239, 19250, 19281, 19282, 19286, 19301, 19331, 19334.

INDEX C.

Accession numbers.

Clapp, A. F.	18275
Clark, A. Howard	(18932)
Clark, Frank N	18672
Clark, Miss Gracie	17997
Clark, Howard L	18264
Clark, James C	18202
Clarke, E. J	19151
Clarke, F. W.	(17993)
Clay, Cecil	18002, 18106, 18183
Clemens, G. W	19058
Clements, J. C	(18706)
Clinch, N. Bayard	18610
Coale, H. K	18226, 18326, 18525, 18715, 18765, 19298
Coffin, C	18776
Colburn, Allie	19194
Colby, Edward A	18674
Cole, John	18451, 18910
Collett, R	18446, 19142
Collins, B. H	18606
Collins, J. W	18207, 18691, (18745), 18746, (18747)
Collins, Miss Mary	18767
Colorado Smelting Company	17789
Conant, Ambrose	18056, 18124, 18372, 18542, 19005
Condon, I	18716
Cone, W. C	17829
Conger, J. H	19311
Conger, Mrs. S. B	19063
Conklin, W. A	(17919), (18803), (18757), (19333)
Conrad, Leonard	18845
Cook, R. C	18996
Cooke, J. P	18258
Coombs, D. E	18249
Cooper, C. S	17916
Cory, C. B	18322, 18599, 18683, 19073, 19209, 19315
Coues, Elliott	18301
Cowie, John G	19242
Cox, Joseph	18005
Cox, S. S	18310
Cox, W. V	18453
Crane, Edward	18312
Crane, William H	18848
Crawford, M. L	19021
Crowkhite, A. H	17784
Crosby, W. O	18306
Culp, Uriah J	18122
Culver, C. P	17904
Cuppage, William	19075
Curry, Miss C. C	18456, 18562
Curtice, C	18524

Accession numbers.

Curtis, George H	18840, 19087
Curtis, W. E	18223
Cushman, Harold	18318
Cutshaw, W. E	18001, 18041
Cypert, Thomas J	18592
Dabney, C. W	19192
Daboll, G. L	17775
Daines, E. J	19193
Dall, Rev. C. H. A	17855
Dall, W. H	(17777), (18214), (18411), (18436), (18785), (18831), (18832), 18857, 18955, 19084, 19102, 19322
Dana, E. S	19028
Darling, C. W	18156
Darton, N. H	18991
Davis, Miss Deborah	18188
Davis, H. J	19236
Davis, John M	18427
Davis, Mrs. Sarah D	19308
Dawson, A. M	18631
Day, Benjamin F., U. S. Navy	19025, 19081, 19263
Day, Francis	17799
Day, R. H	19024
Dealdi, Dominic	18978
Decker, George	18170
Degraff, H. F	19124
DeMott, G. W	19173
Department of the Interior	18009
Department of State	18085, (18159), (18160)
Detweiler, J. T	18133
Dick, F. N	17711
Dillard, J. J	18051, 18194
Diller, J. S	18146, 18274, 18517, 18872
Dillon, M. A	18566
Dixie, Schooner	18167
Dixon, Miss	19116
Dorsey, Rev. J. Owen	18438
Dorsey, Mrs. J. Owen	18439
Dougherty, James M	17879
Douglass, Mrs. Ellen	19327
Dow, I. C	(18398)
Doyle, Bernard	17778
Doyle, John H	18903
Drew, S. H	18755
Duffy, George	18946
Dugès, A	17895, 17923
Duke, John	19067
Dunning, J. A	19207
Dupuy, P. E	17770
Durand, John	18821
Durden, H. S	17818
Durkee, H. C	19282

	Accession numbers.
McCormick, J. C	17894, 17968, 18040, 18079, 18217, 18457, 19148
McDevitt, Patrick	17999
McDonald, M	18957
McDowell, George	18094
McGaha, J. C	17773
McGee, W. J	(17771)
McGrath, B	18347
McGuire, J. D	18496
McKenzie, Lewis	19022
McKnight, C. S	18506
McLaughlin, R. B	19273
McLean, D. G	18537
McLeod, W. T	18878
McMaken, W. V	19219
McMillan, Robert F	18603
McNamara, J	17977
McRae, Thomas C	18824
Macia, H. H	17990
MacRae, D	18042
Mais, H. C	(18905)
Malleis, W. B	18503
Malone, Mrs. Fannie	18974
Maugum, Mrs. Willie	19079
Mann, G. R	18107
Marrou, Augustus W	18513
Marron, Thomas	18376, 18430, 18659
Marshall, George	17755, 17802, 17807, 18220, 18257, 18651, 18976, 19012, 19229
Marshall, Henry	18219, 18685, 18902
Marshall, John	18165
Martin, James D	18498
Marye, L. V	18833
Mason, Charles	17810
Mason, Miss Cora	18182
Mason, O. T	17961
Mather, Fred	18288, 18378, 18834
Mathers, J. R	17890
Matthews, Washington, U. S. Army	18865
Maxwell, S. G	18876
May, W. L	17734
Maynard, C. J., & Co.	18622, 18798, 19029
Mazyck, W. St. J	18004, 18604
Mead, J. H	18778
Medford, Harvey C	17768
Meek, S. E	18328, 18356, 18423
Meigs, J	19060
Meigs, M. C., U. S. Army	18391, 18405, 18877, 19288
Memphis Avalanche	17719
Mengel, Levi W	17811
Menzel, F	18243
Mercer, R. W	19337
Merchant, Capt. George	18750

	Accession numbers.
Merchant, P. A	17797
Merica, F. M. & C. O	17887
Mero, William	18469
Merriam, C. Hart	(17713), 18058, 18136, 18321, (18951)
Merrill, George P	18059
Merrill, J. C., U. S. Army	18147, 18459, 18595, 18612, 18806, 19233
Merwin, Charles D	18110
Mexican Geographical Exploring Commission	18142
Meza, M. M. de	19047
Middletown, George	17717
Miller, Benjamin	17712
Milles, William Deeds	18305
Mills, R. A	19170, 19184
Mindeleff, Cosmos	18048
Miner, H. H	17774
Ministère de l'Instruction Publique et des Beaux-Arts	17922, (18304), (18693), (18694), (19001)
Mitchell, George H	18080
Moore, C. M	19088
Moore, C. R	18489
Moore, Hobson & Conway	19179
Moore, M. M	19056
Moran, Peter	18586
Morcom, G. F	18075
Moreland, Walter	18240
Morgan, J. B	(18710)
Morgan, J. T	18856, 18964, 19286
Morgan, T. F	18375
Morrison, J. H	17730, 17926, 17935
Morse, Travis	18842
Mortimer, Charles	18191
Mortimer, James, jr	17996
Mosely, H. C	19347
Moser, J. F., U. S. Navy	19346
Moyer, Henry C	18992
Muldrow, H. L	18009
Mullin, James A	18781
Murdoch, John	18282, 18404, 18960, 18966
Murtfeldt, Miss Mary E	17848
Musée de St. Germain	18891
Musée d'Histoire Naturelle, Paris	18304, 19001
Musée du Trocadéro	18693, 18694
Museum of Comparative Zoology	18774, 19178
Musser, Harry D	17902
Mussey, R. D	19128
Nagle, I. E	18342, 18455, 18911
Nation, W	18917
National Monument Society	18357

	Accession numbers.
Ransom, C. S., & Co	17831
Rathbone, J. S	17722
Rau, Charles	17857
Raw, Henry M	18944
Rawe, William	17861
Reagles, James, U. S. Army	17976
Rector, H. M	17813
Reed, A. R	18591
Reed, Joseph F	18930
Remus, E	18463
Revenel, William de C	17930
Rey, E	19136
Reynolds, Frank	17744, 19290
Rhees, B. Rush	19259
Rhees, G. M	19042
Rice, Nelson	19018
Rice, William North	18918
Rich, Thomas A	17782
Richmond, C. W	19204
Ricker, Alonzo D	17971
Ricksecker, L. E	(17767)
Ridgway, Audubon	19202
Ridgway, D	18250
Ridgway, Robert	17735, 17881, 17885, 17899, 17918, 17964, 18596, 19169, 19182
Riker, C. B	17809
Ritter, Nathan	19220
Robeson, Mrs. George M	19052
Robertson, William B	18154
Robertson, W. D	18179
Robinson, M. W	17975
Robinson, S. A	17716
Robinson, Samuel B	19175
Robinson, F. P., & Co	19125
Robinson, T	19271
Robinson, W. G	18943
Roche, Robert F	18284
Rock, Miles	18575
Roderick, James	18161
Roessler, A. R	17983, 18367
Rogan, James W	18589, 18795, 19057
Rogers, J	18149
Rogers, J. & Co	18923
Romeyn, Henry, U. S. Army	17743, 19016
Rose, E. H	18860
Ross, A. B., & Co	18545
Ross, Henry	18696
Ross, J. R	19129
Rottaken, H. H	18714
Rowland, A. J	18710
Ruby, Charles, U. S. Army	18695, 18880, 19071
Ruggles Daniel	18497
Runge, C	17843

	Accession numbers.
Rush, W. H., U. S. Navy	18064, 19185
Russell, I. C	17908, 17950, (18642), 18797
Rutherford, C. E	19320
Ryder, W. P	18785
Safford, W. E., U. S. Navy	19026, 19297
Samper & Company	18033
Sandberger, F	17765
Sargeant, G. P	18687
Saunders, George F	19119
Sayles, Ira	18017
Sayre, D. F	17925
Schafer, C. S	19167
Schluter, C	17764
Schmid, Louis, & Sons	17738, 17815, 17852, 18055, 18343, 18370, 18400, 18429, 18521, 18571, 18628, 18639, 18690, 18738, 18751, 18817, 18947, 18969, 18995, 19041, 19053, 19062, 19085, 19090, 19168
Schneck, J	18377
Schoenhof, Jacob	18160
School of Mines, Columbia College	19188
Schott, Anton	19235
Schott, A. L	(19235)
Schronder, J	19132
Schuchardt, T	18508
Schuchert, Charles	18373
Schwaner, John W	17886
Schwarz, E. A	18954, 19040, 19068, 19113, 19234, 19283
Sciple Sons	18970
Scollick, J. W	18422
Scott, Captain Jack	18858
Scott, Mrs. Laura E	19348
Scott, Samuel	19159
Scott Stamp and Coin Company	18332
Seal, W. P	18294
Seeley, Henry M	18440
Seely, F. A	(18474)
Seiling, W. A	19159
Selby, Aug. D	18641
Sellers, John, & Sons	17705
Sennett, George B	18035, 18780, 18948
Sessford, Joseph	18065
Seton, Ernest E. T	17884
Sèvres, Manufacture Nationale de.	17922
Sewell, J. A	17911
Shackford, Samuel	19280
Shah of Persia	19334
Sharpe, R. Bowdler	17837
Sharpless, Alfred	18145
Shaw, H. J	18069
Shaw, S. Albert	19330
Sheldon, F. E	18271
Shell Fishery Commission	18099

Accession numbers.

Shelley, Joseph 19156
Shepard, Charles U............. 17747,
              18854, 19000, 19240
Shepardson, O. J 17989
Sherwood, A. T................. 19267
Shindler, A. Zeno............... (18978)
Shuey, C. F 18238
Shortledge, E. G............... 19312
Shreiber, W. A. H 19295
Shriver, H 17860, 17944, 18927
Shufeldt, R. W., U. S. Army..17951, 17979,
    18114, 18152, 18233, 18392, 18846,
      18889, 18973, 19014, 19091, 19316
Shutt, George W .... (18263)
Siler, James W.................. 17718
Silverthorn, William 18050
Simpson, Charles T.......... 18181, 18493
Skinner, T. E................... 18701
Slayton, C. H 17915
Smeaton, W. H.................. 18761
Smith, H. M................18979, 19305
Smith, J. B..................... 17767
Smith, K. Q 17830
Smith, L. H 17759
Smith, Miss Rosa................ 18382
Smithsonian Institution 17750,
        17988, 18617, 19306
Smith, Thomas 18968
Snyder, Jacob P................. 19238
Snyder, John J.................. 18083
Sohan, J. M.................... 19117
Sohier, William................. (18355)
Southside Sportsman Club........ 19328
Southwick, James M............. 17875
Spainhour, J. M 19008
Spears, P. H.................... 17756
Spencer, Charles N 18421
Spengel, J. W 17980, 18684
Spicer, Capt. J. O 18669
Spinney, Joseph S............... 18905
Spooner, Mrs. Marion B 18520
Spurlock, Charles 17877
Stabler, James P 18313,
    18334, 18379, 18395, 18658
Stadtmuller, L 17724
Stalker, B. F 17728
State Department .... (19334)
State Mining Bureau of Califor-
nia 17818
Stearns, Silas 18654
Steffen, R. W 17936
Stejneger, L.................... 17882,
   18173, 18413, 18526, 18764, 18950
Stephen, W. M 18812

Accession numbers.

Stephens, F 18444,
   18704, 18796, 18862, 19107, 19244
Sterki, V 18468
Sterling, E............. 17737, 18540, 18549
Steuart, C. A.............. 19045, 19216
Steuart, R. C.............. 18783, 18931
Stevenson, J 18681, 19030
Stevenson, Mrs. James 19294
Stewart, James M 19243
Stockton, J. B 18340
Stokes, George H................ 19147
Stone, E. S.................... 17820
Stone, Livingston 18399
Stone, R. M.................... (19127)
Stoney, G. M., U. S. Navy....18491, 18616
Stout, E. L.................... 18216
Straub, A 19131
Streator, George J.............. 18296
Strong, H. R 18150
Stuart, C. A 19045
Stuart, R. C.....18531, 18783, 18825, 18931
Sturgis, Appleton 19186
Sturgis, Mrs................... 17955
Stürtz, B 18061, 18259, 18293, 18901
Sutter, John A 17794
Swan Island Club 18355
Swan, T. G.................... 18598
Swann, G. A 18664, 18763
Talcott, C. G., U. S. Navy......... 18867
Tallant, W. N 18291, 18507
Tallman, John W 18363
Tappan, F. L 18027
Taunt, E. H., U. S. Navy......... 17986,
      19080, 19126, 19201
Taylor, Frederick 18176
Taylor, F. W 17937, 17966, 17994
Taylor, J. S 19044
Taylor, T. O.................. 18337
Thiselton-Dyer, W. T........... 18147
Thomas, A. A 18897
Thomas, A. D 17721
Thomas, A. E 18788, 19296
Thomas, Walter 19034
Thompson, E. E 18733, 18951
Thompson, H. W 19152
Thompson, Joseph............... 18049
Thompson, R. J. S 19239
Thompson, Thomas..........17978, 18134
Thorne, Walter 19034
Thornton, C. S 18939
Thorpe, H. H 18029,
  18297, 18466, 18873, 18926, 19189, 19254
Thorpe, Rev. T. M.............. 18272
Tingley, H. A 18849

INDEX.